INDUSTRY	TRANSPORT	
		1700
1727. Board of Trustees for Manufacturers	1726–40. Wade in Highlands	
1729. Charcoal furnace at Invergarry		
1746. British Linen Company	1741–60. Caulfield in Highlands	
1749. Vitriol works at Prestonpans		
1752. Charcoal furnace at Taynuilt	1751. Turnpike Act for Edinburgh and District	1750
1759. Carron Ironworks	1754. Edinburgh–London by stage-coach (10–12 days)	
1765. Watt's separate condenser		
1778. Cotton spinning-mill at Penicuik		
1780. Monteith's all-cotton web		
1786. New Lanark cotton-mill	1788. Steamboat trial at Dalswinton	
1789. Linen spinning-mill at Bervie	1790. Forth and Clyde Canal completed	
1793. Cotton power-loom at Glasgow	1792. Monkland Canal completed	1800
	1801. Crinan Canal opened	
1810. Linen power-loom	1807. Aberdeen–Inverurie Canal opened	
	1812. Bell's Comet	
	1822. Caledonian Canal opened	
1823. Jute imported to Dundee	1831. Glasgow–Garnkirk Railway	
1825. Jacquard loom introduced	1839. MacMillan's bicycle	
	1840. Cunard Company	
	1840. Penny Post	
	1846. "Railway Mania"	
		1850
1851. Shale oil production started		
1863. Linoleum invented	1869. Cutty Sark built	
	1883. Road-tolls abolished	
	1885. Dunlop's pneumatic tyre	
1895–6. Hydro-electric scheme at Foyers	1895. Railway "race to the north"	
		1900
	1901. King Edward – first turbine passenger ship	
1909. Hydro-electric scheme at Kinlochleven	1902. Electric tramways in Glasgow	
1926. Clyde Valley electricity scheme	c.1922. Motor omnibuses	
1938. Industrial Estates		
1947–8. Nationalization of coal, gas, electricity	1948. Nationalization of railways	
		1950

A HISTORY
OF SCOTLAND
FOR SCHOOLS

BY

I. M. M. MACPHAIL, M.A., Ph.Dr.
Principal Teacher of History, Clydebank High School

BOOK II
From 1702 to the present day

LONDON
EDWARD ARNOLD (PUBLISHERS) LTD.

Copyright in all countries signatory to the Berne Convention
First published 1956
Reprinted 1958

A HISTORY OF
SCOTLAND
FOR SCHOOLS

BOOK I
From the earliest times
to 1747

BOOK II
From 1702 to the
present day

Printed in Great Britain by
ROBERT CUNNINGHAM & SONS LTD.,
Longbank Works, Alva

PREFACE

THIS is the second volume of a history of Scotland intended for the language classes of senior secondary schools and should be found suitable for pupils of the third year and upwards. This volume overlaps with the first in that the last two chapters of Book I, "The Union of Parliaments" and "The Jacobite Rebellions", give the political background of the early part of the period covered here (1702 to the present day). There are certain features common to both volumes—the emphasis in the exercises on individual work, the encouragement to further study, particularly of local history, in the questions and source extracts, the greater prominence given to the history of Celtic Scotland, and the increased space devoted to social and economic affairs. In this volume there is comparatively little political history, mainly because it is assumed that the pupil will be familiar with some textbook of British history.

The changed attitude to history in recent times is perhaps best illustrated by the fact that the whole of this volume is necessary for the treatment of a period which in the textbooks of a past generation was dismissed in one chapter. Indeed, there is much here that could be used to advantage by pupils in senior geography classes, and the book would probably fit conveniently into most schemes of social studies. It is hoped that the young people who use it will not merely acquire a knowledge of their Scottish heritage but will be enabled to understand more intelligently the background of the many problems that confront us in Scotland today.

It is perhaps necessary to add that although brief outlines of literature, art and music have been given in Chapters VII, IX and XVIII, they are in no sense intended as substitutes for the more serious study which is possible in the English, Art and Music classes of the senior secondary school.

Acknowledgements of the assistance generously offered and

gratefully received are again due to many friends, too numerous to mention, and in particular to the librarian and staff of Dumbarton Public Library, to Mr R. R. Sellman for permission to make use here of his diagrams and notes on Newcomen's Steam Pump and on Watt's Single Acting Engine, appearing on pages 92 and 93 respectively, and to Mr Douglas Young for permission to publish his poem *For Alasdair* on pages 303-4.

I. M. M. MacPhail

CONTENTS

Time Charts:

ILLUSTRATIONS AND MAPS

CHAPTER I

LOWLAND FARMING—OLD STYLE

Dearth and Famine.—Scottish agriculture at the beginning of the eighteenth century was very backward in almost every respect. In those days little, if any, food was imported except for the rich man's table, and a bad harvest in one year could cause extreme want and suffering in the spring and early summer of the next. At the end of William III's reign, Scotland had experienced the "seven ill years" and, although such a continuous spell did not recur, there were many other years of bad harvests caused by wet, stormy weather—1709, 1740 and 1756 being long remembered for the dearth and famine which followed. Visitors from England, where agriculture was more highly developed than in any other country of Europe except the Netherlands, were much impressed by the backwardness of the farming and the poverty of the people. As late as 1753, when Lieutenant-Colonel (later General) James Wolfe was returning from a long stay in Scotland, he was struck by the difference to be observed as soon as he crossed the Border. "The soil is much the same for some space either north or south, but the fences, enclosures and agriculture are not at all alike. The English are clean and laborious, and the Scottish excessively lazy and dirty, though far short, indeed, of what we found at a greater distance from the border." Even allowing for the prejudice of a soldier returning home after being compelled to spend some years in the Highlands, it is obvious that farming in eighteenth-century Scotland stood much in need of improvement.

The Land.—The mountains and moors of Scotland, which seemed so desolate and wild to the traveller, forced to move slowly by foot or on horseback, have not changed much since that time, but the landscape of the Lowlands was very different indeed. If we were whisked back in time to the Scotland of 1700, we would notice immediately the absence of trees, hedges, fences or dykes. There were some forests in the glens of the north and west Highlands, but in the south and east, as an English knight remarked in 1617, when he accompanied James VI on his visit to Scotland, "Judas had sooner found the grace of repentance than a tree to hang himself on". Although many of the lairds went in for extensive schemes of tree-planting, Dr Johnson after his famous tour of 1773 could still write, "A tree might be a show in Scotland as a horse in Venice." The cultivated fields presented a very different appearance from those of today. Much good land in the valleys was left untilled for lack of proper drainage, while the more difficult slopes of the hills were ploughed. Throughout Scotland the arable land was generally divided into the INFIELD or croft-land near the farm, permanently under cultivation, and the OUTFIELD—patches of land which carried crops for four or five years, without receiving any manure, and were then allowed to lie for as many years again until they had regained some fertility. Like the English open fields, the infield and outfield were divided into long strips or ridges, called "rigs", each man's rigs being separated by his neighbours'—a system which the Scots called RUNRIG or RUNDALE. The rigs might be from 18 to 20 feet wide (sometimes double that width in the middle) and from 200 to 500 yards long, often curving like a giant S. The soil was usually heaped up from the sides towards the centre of the rig, for fear lest some should find its way on to the neighbouring rig. Between the rigs lay the uncultivated BALKS, overgrown with grass, weeds, brambles and briars, and in some places broad enough to be used as pasture for a tethered animal. In both the Highlands and the Lowlands there prevailed, at this time and for long after, the practice of re-allotting the rigs at regular intervals to the different people in the village—it may be every year or every two or three years. There was thus little encouragement for a man to improve his rig, when it was such a short time in his possession. It can be seen that the old agrarian or field system of Scotland was not at all conducive to good farming.

Crops.—The two chief grain crops at that time in Scotland were barley and oats, but a little wheat and rye were also to be

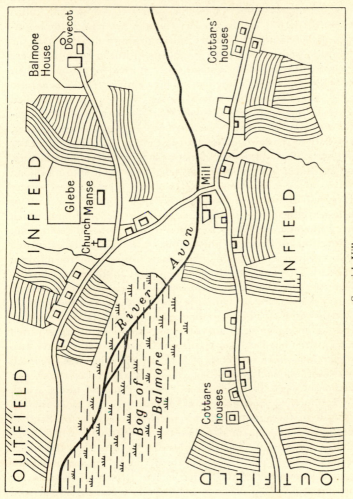

Scottish Village, 1700

found in certain districts. The varieties of oats and barley were poor and unproductive. The thin grey OATS (sometimes called the "small corn"), common everywhere in Scotland at the beginning of the eighteenth century and still grown for fodder in the Hebrides, were probably the worst oats in Europe, but they were considered better fitted to stand up to stormy, wet weather than the taller and heavier white oats. The common BERE or bear (also called "bigg") was a four-rowed barley, which was also reckoned better for the wet Scottish climate than the more productive two-rowed variety. Peas and beans were widely grown, often together, especially in the lowlands of the south and east. FLAX (or LINT as it was called) was grown in many places for linen manufacture, and also small patches of hemp, which was made into ropes and harness in the winter-time. Near the larger houses a great variety of vegetables was to be found; the most popular was kail, or curly-leaved cabbage, which was used for the broth and which gave its name to the kitchen-garden of the Scots—the KAILYARD.

Rotations of Crops.—The fertility of the soil can be exhausted by successive crops of grain, which draw from the soil the nitrogen necessary for plant life. In England and in Europe generally, where the three-field system prevailed, it was usual to leave one of the fields FALLOW or without a crop each year and the common rotation was wheat, barley, fallow. In Scotland, fallowing of this kind was unknown until almost 1700. Rotations of crops varied from district to district. A common rotation was to have two crops of oats, then one crop of bere, which alone was preceded by manuring. In East Lothian, however, there was a four-year rotation of wheat, barley, oats and peas. Peas and beans, which are leguminous plants like clover, improve the soil by storing up nitrogen in their roots. At this period there were no Scottish field crops of turnips or potatoes, the cultivation of which helps to clean the ground. The corn-rigs of 1700 often had thus more weeds than corn. Wild mustard, thistles and corn-marigold grew apace despite medieval acts of parliament passed against allowing corn-marigold or "gool" as it was called. Generally, if the seed produced four-fold (compared with ten- or twelve-fold today) it was reckoned "a noble return"; but a three-fold return was more common. Of the grain crop, one-third would go for rent, one-third for food and one-third would have to be kept as seed for the next year's crop. As the country saying had it:

> Ane tae saw, ane tae gnaw
> An' ane tae pay the laird witha'.

Naturally enough years of dearth and famine occurred frequently.

Livestock.—The animals on the farms of the early eighteenth century were as poor and miserable as the crops. The important CATTLE-TRADE with England was not confined to the small, black cattle from the Highlands, over 30,000 of which were sold at Crieff market in 1723, mainly for fattening in England. Galloway cattle—polled, black beasts, larger than the Highland cattle—were also greatly prized by the English dealers. It was for their cattle that the Galloway farmers made the first enclosures and provoked the rising of the "Levellers" in 1724-25.[1] Generally, throughout Scotland, the cattle were small and thin; only in the summer months did they receive proper feeding. As there was little winter fodder in those days before turnips, clover and rye-grass were introduced, many of the cattle were sold in the autumn markets or killed off at Martinmas (11th November), the salted "marts" providing meat for the family for a few months. The remaining beasts, fed on boiled chaff, mashed whins and poor hay, cut from the marshy meadow-lands, scarcely survived the winter. Sometimes they were so weak from lack of nourishment that they had to be lifted bodily out of the byre in springtime and allowed to stagger about the croft-land till the crops were sown. In the parish of Dunlop, in the Cunningham district of Ayrshire, where cheese-making had been a cottage industry from the late seventeenth century, a breed of cattle was developed which was first named after the parish, then after the district and later after the county. Some cattle were kept neither for milk nor beef. These were the oxen, huge, lumbering beasts, strong and slow, used for the heavy work of the farm like ploughing. They were stronger than the under-sized horses, more like ponies, which were used as pack-horses or for riding. Sometimes, however, oxen and

[1] See Bk. I, p. 240

horses were yoked together in a ploughteam. The SHEEP were not so numerous in Scotland then as today. They were mostly to be found in the valleys of the Southern Uplands, where they had been reared since the days of the Cistercian monks. In the south-western counties a black-faced breed, called the Linton, was common; it was a small, hardy sheep which produced a very coarse wool. Among the Cheviot hills near the Tweed was to be found the white-faced breed, later called Cheviot, the fine wool of which was in great demand for cloth-making. Further north, in the Highlands and Islands, the sheep were much smaller but their wool, especially in Shetland, was of very fine quality. Pigs were not common anywhere and in the remoter Highlands almost unknown because of the prejudice of the people there against pork. Poultry were plentiful on every steading, picking up what scraps they could round the doors and wandering in and out of the houses at will. Kain fowls ("kain" was the old word for a payment in kind) usually formed part of the rent till well on in the century, and most farms had more poultry than they could properly feed. Indeed, many writers considered that the land from which such yields were obtained was overstocked with cattle, sheep, horses and poultry.

Implements.—The implements used in Scottish farming in the early eighteenth century differed little from those of pre-historic times. The huge, cumbersome plough was not unlike that introduced by the Romans into Britain. Except for the coulter and the share, it was made entirely of wood. At least two men and sometimes four men were needed to control the plough and ploughteam of oxen or horses. The harrows were made entirely of wood and, according to Lord Kames, were "more fit to raise laughter than to raise soil". A small harrow was sometimes attached to the tail of a young horse which was being broken in. Behind the harrow went a man with a bag of whin roots, hardened in the fire, as spares to replace the broken teeth. Carts were seldom used because of the lack of good roads. As late as 1753, when Lord Cathcart offered carts to his tenants in Ayrshire, few accepted them as the roads were so bad. Heavy loads were taken on "slides" or sledges, and smaller loads, in sacks or creels, were carried by horses or people. At harvest-time the sickle or "hook" was used until the scythe replaced it later in the century. For threshing the corn, the flail was still the implement as in Biblical times; the winnowing of the chaff was done sometimes on breezy hill-tops ("shilling-laws" or shelling-hills) or in barns with doors opposite one another to provide a good, through-going draught. After this, it was usual, in the damp, western districts, to dry the grain in kilns before it was ground. Although the oats were generally sent to the laird's mill, barley was ground at home in a small mortar or "knockin'-stane". The barley used for broth was this "knockit bere". Almost all the work of the farm was thus performed by primitive methods, both inefficient and laborious; but in this respect, Scotland was little worse than other countries at that time.

The People.—In the Lowlands, the LAIRDS were the most important people. They had been the leaders in the religious and political troubles of the sixteenth and seventeenth centuries; but at the beginning of the eighteenth century the great majority of the lairds seemed to be interested mainly in squeezing rents out of their TENANTS. Unlike the descendant of the English villein, the copy-holder who could be deprived of his land or his rights only with great difficulty, the Scottish peasant was usually a tenant-at-will. But the practice of granting leases for two or three years or longer periods had already begun, and a life-renter was con-sidered the equal of a land-owner or HERITOR. Besides the tenants, there was a numerous class of COTTARS, who worked for the laird or the tenants. From tenants and cottars the laird received rent, paid both in money and in kind, and also certain dues and services. The rents due in 1734 from a Galloway farm (which in 1862 paid a rent of £165 per year) amounted to £5 11s. 11d. (sterling), 2 bolls of oatmeal, 2 bolls of bere, 1 lamb, 12 fowls and 2 quarters of butter. Services rendered by the tenants varied from one estate to another. Nearly all were "thirled to the laird's mill" and not only had to pay a proportion to the miller but also a "multure" (usually a tenth) to the laird. Repairs to the mill-dam, the mill-lade and the mill itself had to be carried out by the tenants' labour. In addition, the tenants had to give so many days of "carriage" (carrying of peats, coal, lime or timber), "arrage" (tilling), "bonnage" (harvesting), and even on occasions go on errands for the laird. Lest we should think that the Scottish lairds of that time were nothing but wealthy exploiters of miser-

By courtesy of the Elgin Literary and Scientific Association

Coxton Tower, Moray

An excellent example of a laird's tower-house still in use

able, servile peasants, we should remember that most of the lairds were themselves very poor, burdened with debt, incurred perhaps by raising money for a daughter's "tocher" (or dowry) or perhaps by some litigation which dragged on for years in the law-courts.

Even the poorest "bonnet laird" liked a "guid-gangin' plea", and of many it could be said as was once remarked of the Fife lairds: "A pickle land, a mickle debt, a doocot and a lawsuit." Of the peasants themselves, Burns's words might be quoted:

> But how it comes, I never kent yet,
> They're maistly wonderfu' contented.

Country Houses.—Scattered throughout the countryside were the castles or towers of the nobility and lairds. Many of these castellated mansions were gloomy without and gloomier still within, cold and damp in winter. The smaller lairds and more substantial tenants generally had houses of only two rooms, "but" and "ben". The first was the living-room, where meals were taken and the servants and some of the family slept; the second was the better furnished "spence", the room of the "gudeman" and his wife. Many of the houses wore a look of decay. Ramsay of Ochtertyre wrote of them: "On approaching a laird's dwelling, the stable, byre and dunghill at the very door presented themselves to view; and all around was a plentiful crop of nettles, dock and hemlock." The cottars' houses were mere hovels, generally made of thick stone walls, and the roofs covered not with thatch but with turfs, a poor protection in wet weather. Every few years the roofs were stripped and renewed, the decayed and sooty turfs providing much-needed manure for the croft-land. Such huts or "biggins" the family shared with their livestock, only a wooden partition or "hallan" dividing their living-quarters from the stall where the only cow was kept. There was no proper chimney and the smoke from the fire of peat or wood curled round the walls and rafters before finding its way out through a hole in the roof. Such conditions help to explain why in the middle of the century a traveller could say of the Scottish cottars: "The nastiness of the common people is really greater than can be reported; their faces are coloured with smoke, their mouths are wide, and their eyes are sunk."

The Farming Calendar.—The drudgery and monotony of farmwork from dawn to dusk had increased since the Reformation, through the Scots losing the many religious holidays of the

Roman Catholic Church. The Presbyterian Church of Scotland frowned upon the celebration of the old church holidays. Even Christmas was ignored in those days and for long afterwards, but they made up for it in one way by the festivities at Hogmanay and New Year's Day. Some important days in the Christian calendar continued to be observed for other than religious reasons. CANDLEMAS (2nd February) was the first of the quarterly terms, the others being WHITSUNDAY (which in Scotland was a fixed date, 15th May), LAMMAS (2nd August) and MARTINMAS (11th November). Candlemas was the earliest date for starting ploughing, although in some districts that was delayed till the 10th or 20th of March, with the result that sowing and harvesting were likewise late. It must be remembered that up to 1752, when the calendar was reformed, the people of Britain were eleven days behind the Catholic countries of Europe. For long after that time, country people continued to prefer the Old Style to the New Style, and even in the twentieth century there were some districts in the Highlands where they kept the Old New Year on the 12th or 13th of January. Shrove Tuesday or FASTERN'S E'EN was not only the occasion of merry-making in the burghs but the day when in Aberdeenshire the lairds invited the tenants to a dinner of beef and brose as a sign that he was willing to renew the tenancy for another year. HALLOWE'EN or All Hallows' Eve was the traditional occasion of feasting and superstitious rites, not connected with the church at all. Robert Burns in his poem, *Hallowe'en*, describes the customs observed in Ayrshire in his day, many of them being still common there and in other parts of Scotland. The end of harvest was naturally an important event. The cutting of the last sheaf on the cornfield was itself surrounded with ceremony. It was known by different names throughout the country—the "Maiden", the "clyack" and others. The sheaf was generally decorated with ribbons and set in a prominent place for the harvest-supper and merry-making. In some districts it was kept till New Year's Day and then divided among the cattle. Despite the strict control of the Kirk, many pagan customs survived. In some villages, at BELTANE (May Day) or Midsummer, all the fires in the village were put out and the men gathered on a

hill, where by the rubbing together of two pieces of wood fire
was produced. From this "need-fire" a bonfire was lit and when
it was big enough it was divided so that the cattle and young
people would be made to pass through. From the bonfires also
those of the village were re-lit. Superstitions, drudgery, occasional festivities, the weekly visits to the Kirk on the Sabbath
Day—these made up to a great extent the old Scottish rural
calendar.

SOURCE EXTRACT

"'Tis almost incredible how much of the Mountains they plough,
where the Declensions, I had almost said the Precipices, are such
that to our thinking, it puts them to greater difficulty and charge
to carry on their work than they need be at in draining the Valleys.
Their Harvest is very great of Oats and Barly, which is the more
common and flourishing Grain of the Country; the Straw whereof
is very serviceable to them for the support of their cattle. Not but
they have Beans, Pease and some Wheat likewise."

Thomas Morer: *A Short Account of Scotland* (1702)

EXERCISES

1. Describe briefly the arable land of a typical Scottish estate about
   1700.

2. State the difference between Scottish and English farming in
   1700 and between Scottish farming then and now.

3. Give at least four reasons for the poor yield of Scottish crops
   about 1700.

4. What events in the rural calendar of the eighteenth century do
   you associate with 2nd February, 15th May, 2nd August, 11th
   November, Fastern's E'en and Hallowe'en? Explain "Old New
   Year's Day".

5. Explain the following words: Infield, outfield, runrig, balk,
   kailyard, kain fowls, shilling-laws, knockin'-stane, tocher, spence,
   multure, heritor, biggin, hallan, clyack.

6. Explain the following passages:
   (a) A rosebud by my early walk
       Adown a corn-enclosèd bawk.
   (b) A bonnet-laird wi' a small kailyard
       Is naethin' but a mockery.
   (c) The sowpe their only hawkie does afford
       That 'yont the hallan snugly chows her cood.
   (d) There lanely by the ingle-cheek
       I sat and eyed the spewing reek
       That filled, wi' hoast-provoking smeek,
       The auld, clay biggin.
   (e) Kyle for a man,
       Carrick for a coo,
       Cunningham for butter and cheese,
       And Galloway for 'oo'.

CHAPTER II

THE IMPROVERS

The Beginnings.—Early in the eighteenth century some Scotsmen were beginning to advocate changes in farming. It is not surprising that at first they looked to England for examples to follow, as English farmers were among the best in Europe, only those of the Netherlands and Flanders being considered superior. Fallowing, in imitation of the English system, was first practised in Scotland in 1690 by an East Lothian farmer, John Walker of Beanston near Haddington, who also kept an inn and heard of the benefits of fallowing from English travellers. During the "seven ill years" (1696-1702), enclosures, manuring of land and the introduction of vegetable crops were advocated by James Donaldson, an old soldier turned journalist, in a book on *Husbandry* (1697), which was the first of its kind in Scotland. We learn of the introduction of English methods to the north-east of Scotland from the Jacobite leader MACKINTOSH OF BORLUM, who had escaped from Newgate Prison in 1716 only to be recaptured in 1719 and kept in Edinburgh Castle for the rest of his life. In one of the two books on farming which he wrote in prison he gave credit to an English lady for bringing English ploughs and ploughmen to Moray. She was Henrietta Mordaunt, daughter of the Earl of Peterborough, the great general of the Spanish Succession War, and in 1707 she married the Duke of Gordon's heir, to become later the DUCHESS OF GORDON. About the same time as she came to Scotland, the EARL OF HADDINGTON, with the help of English farmers, began to practise on his estate of Tyninghame in East Lothian fallowing, enclosing, tree-planting and the sowing of clover and grasses. It should be noticed that Haddington copied not only the methods which had been used in England from time immemorial, like fallowing, but also those which had recently arrived from the Low Countries, such as sowing of clover and grasses. Soon Scotsmen were vying with Englishmen in experimenting with new ideas.

Cockburn of Ormiston.—John Cockburn of Ormiston (1679-1758), who was M.P. first in the Scottish Parliament and after 1707 in the British Parliament, had a great influence in spreading a knowledge of English methods and has been called "the father of Scottish husbandry". His father ADAM COCKBURN, Lord Chief Justice of Scotland, was among the first to encourage tenant-farmers by giving them longer leases, and when John Cockburn took charge of the estate of ORMISTON in East Lothian in 1714, he continued and extended the practice. Instead of the old runrig system, his tenants were given compact, enclosed farms with new steadings. Even although Cockburn spent much of his time at Westminster, his thoughts were constantly on his lands at Ormiston. His letters to his gardener, Charles Bell, are full of detailed instructions about everything connected with the estate. For hedges which no cattle would break through, he recommended planting mixed hawthorn, wild rose, privet, elder, honeysuckle and bramble with a ditch beside them, and, at intervals in the hedgerow, ash or elm trees, for preference the English elm. In his plantations he grew not only oak, elm, ash and beech, but also walnut, silver fir, spruce, hornbeam and cherry trees, and even mulberries and quinces. Englishmen were brought north to help with the cultivation of new crops—turnips, clover, rape and "artificial" grasses, while the sons of his tenants he sent to England for experience. Cockburn thought the turnip of first importance as cattle-feed for the winter. It was one of his tenants, Alexander Wight, who is reckoned to have been the first Scotsman to sow turnips in drills. Due to Cockburn's enthusiasm, an agricultural society was formed at Ormiston, where some of the neighbouring lairds met regularly from 1736 to 1747 for discussions. In addition to his agricultural improvements, he encouraged linen manufacture, bringing in Irish and Dutch workers to instruct his tenants. Cockburn never managed to clear off the debt of £10,000 he inherited and in 1744 he was compelled to sell his estate, but he had left behind him an example which was readily followed in East Lothian and elsewhere.

Tree-Planting.—The vast improvements in Scottish agriculture in the eighteenth century were due almost entirely to the Scottish lairds like Cockburn. It was they who, in a spirit of enlightened self-interest, carried out the changes which made the Scottish countryside what it is today. Although the revolution in agriculture started in Moray and East Lothian, "improving" lairds were soon to be found in most other parts of Scotland. In Aberdeenshire, Sir ARCHIBALD GRANT (1696-1778) took over in 1716 the direction of what was then the impoverished estate of Monymusk on Donside and in the next fifty years improved and developed it until his rents were quadrupled. Grant's programme included draining of the land and enclosing for plantations, abolition of runrig, granting of long leases of fifteen to twenty years, the introduction of turnips, potatoes and "artificial" grasses, and the building of two villages with schools, lint-mills and saw-mills. In the year 1722 there were planted at Monymusk 35,000 firs and 5,000 alders and by 1731 over a million trees had been grown in the nurseries. Other great tree-planters were Sir JOHN CLERK of Penicuik (1677-1755), who in thirty years planted more than 300,000 trees, and the DUKE OF ATHOLL, "the planting Duke", who from 1727 on covered 16,000 acres with 27 million trees, mainly conifers. Scott in his *Heart of Midlothian* made the

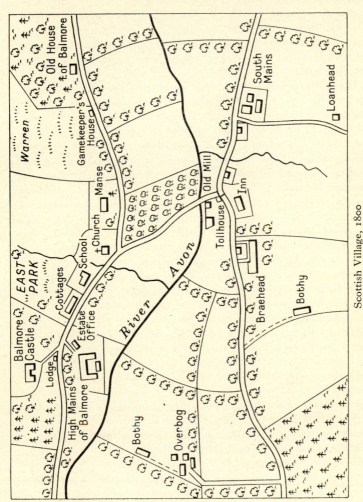

Scottish Village, 1800

Explain the changes in the appearance of the village between 1700 and 1800,
as shown by the two maps

laird of Dumbiedykes say in 1736 to his son: "Jock, when ye hae naething else to do, ye may be aye sticking in a tree; it will be growing, Jock, when ye're sleeping." So many Scottish lairds went in for extensive plantations that Dr Johnson must have seen many trees on his tour of 1773 despite his remark, quoted in the last chapter.

The Improvers.—By that time there were hundreds of "improving" lairds, for it had become fashionable as well as profitable to be an "improver". It was in the south-east of Scotland that the greatest changes were to be seen. In Berwickshire the EARL OF MARCHMONT (1718-94) had great success in improving his lands of Polwarth. In addition to the normal work of the "improver" he is credited with introducing on his Ayrshire estates some cattle from which the famous Ayrshire breed of dairy cattle derives the brown and white markings. Another Berwickshire "improver" was LORD KAMES (1696-1782), who helped greatly to spread a knowledge of the new methods by his writings, of which the best known was *The Gentleman Farmer* (1776). He and his son, George Drummond, carried through one of the greatest schemes of reclamation of the century on their estate of Blair Drummond in Perthshire, where about one-third of the Moss of Kincardine was cleared by being shovelled into water-channels and washed into the Forth. Sir JOHN SINCLAIR (1754-1835) of Ulbster, Caithness, not only made extensive improvements on his own lands but helped to establish the Board of Agriculture in 1793 and organized a national investigation into methods of agriculture. First of all, he induced the parish ministers of Scotland to give descriptions of their parishes (population, natural history, antiquities, industry and agriculture), which were published in twenty-one volumes between 1791 and 1799, under the title of *The Statistical Account of Scotland*. These volumes, now known as the *Old Statistical Account* as a new series was published about fifty years later, give a wealth of information about the 839 parishes of Scotland. In addition, Sinclair arranged for separate books on the agriculture of each county, from which we can obtain a detailed picture of the changes of the eighteenth century.

Agricultural Societies.—As far back as 1723 there had been formed in Edinburgh the SOCIETY FOR IMPROVING IN THE KNOWLEDGE OF AGRICULTURE. It included over 300 of the

Photo: James G. Gair

Statue of Blackface Sheep, Moffat

leading Scottish landowners, who received advice on methods of improving their lands. The Chairman of the Society, THOMAS HOPE of Rankeillor, and the Secretary, ROBERT MAXWELL of Arbigland in Galloway, were indefatigable in their efforts. Hope, who travelled in England, Holland and France to learn new methods, drained a marsh in Edinburgh, sowed it with grass and clover, planted a border of lime-trees and presented the land to the citizens of Edinburgh, who still enjoy it as a public park, known as the Meadows. Maxwell spent much time giving advice to correspondents how to sow turnips by drills instead of broadcast, how to fatten sheep and cattle, how to fallow, plough and manure the ground, how to grow flax and prepare it for linen manufacture, how to improve pastures with red clover and ryegrass. The society collapsed after the "Forty-five" but others were started, the most notable being the HIGHLAND SOCIETY of Edinburgh, which was founded in 1784 and survives today under a slightly different name. It was originally intended to promote the improvement of the Highlands and Islands in all respects, including language, poetry and music, but in time the main interest became agriculture, not merely in the Highlands but all over Scotland. Under its auspices there were staged ploughing-matches and cattle-shows (the first in 1822) and today the show of the ROYAL HIGHLAND AND AGRICULTURAL SOCIETY OF SCOTLAND is one of the most important events of the farming year.

Root Crops.—The introduction of TURNIPS or the "neeps" as a field-crop was one of the greatest benefits which Scottish farmers owed to England. They had been grown in gardens since the beginning of the century. By 1725 John Cockburn of Ormiston was instructing one of his tenants, ALEXANDER WIGHT, on their cultivation and the necessity for hoeing. Grant of Monymusk, who bought a copy of Jethro Tull's *Horse-hoeing Husbandry* in 1736 (five years after its publication), soon arranged for growing turnips in drills for easy hoeing. After the middle of the century the cultivation of turnips increased, but even at the end of the century they were still being sown broadcast in some places, both in England and Scotland. By the hoeing which was carried on in the turnip-field in the summer, the ground was cleared of weeds and thereby improved for the next crop. The turnips were grown mainly as cattle-feed and enabled the farmers to fatten their livestock instead of selling them off at the autumn fairs or killing them off at Martinmas. As a result of the increased number of livestock, there was more manure available for ferti-

lizing the ground. POTATOES, like turnips, were first grown in
gardens and were also useful as a cleaning crop. In 1729 they
were first grown in Scotland as a field-crop by THOMAS PRENTICE,
a day-labourer of Kilsyth. His example was copied by a neighbour, Robert Graham, whose success with potatoes soon induced
many others to follow his example. The potato was not so important in the diet of the eighteenth-century Lowlanders as it
was in Ireland or the Highlands, but with the growth of large
industrial towns it later became more popular as a cheap, wholesome food, especially when corn became dear during the Napoleonic War.

New Rotations.—Turnips and potatoes, which cleaned the
ground, and clover, which improved the fertility of the soil by
storing nitrogen in its roots, made it possible to have bumper
following crops of wheat, oats and barley. New and better
varieties of grain were sown and the old Scottish grey oats and
bere gradually disappeared. The NORFOLK ROTATION of crops,
started by Viscount Townshend in his Norfolk estates (turnips,
barley, clover sown in the barley, wheat) was introduced into
south Scotland, but the Scottish farmers changed it and improved
on it. In East Lothian, and later in most other counties, a six-year
rotation became common—wheat or oats, turnips, barley, clover
and sown grasses for three years. Between 1785 and 1832 the
Highland and Agricultural Society gave premiums to farmers in
order to encourage the production of these temporary LEYS of
clover and grass. The result was a great increase in the fertility
of the arable land, so that the yields of Scottish crops could compare with any in Europe. What a change from the dearth and
famine of the "seven ill years"!

New Methods.—The abolition of the runrig system, by which
the farmer's rigs were widely separated and remained in his
possession for only a few years at a time, was one of the first improvements carried out and enabled lairds and tenants to try out
new methods as well as new crops. Long leases usually followed.
No longer was the go-ahead farmer held back by the laziness or
obstinacy of his neighbours. Enclosing of fields (with hedges or
dry-stone dykes) came as a result of cultivating turnips, which

had to be protected from cattle. The application of lime to the soil, sour and acid in many parts of Scotland, gradually became general in districts where limestone was to be found. We may still see the remains of limekilns where the limestone was burned. The carting of the lime was at first a difficulty; but, after the Turnpike Act of 1751,[1] new roads were constructed which helped the farmer as well as the traveller. Shellmarl, which also contains lime, was obtained by draining lochs, as the Earl of Strathmore did with the Loch of Forfar. The great craze for artificial fertilizers did not come till after the German chemist, LIEBIG, published his epoch-making works on organic and agricultural chemistry in the middle of the nineteenth century. Draining made it possible for the farmer to raise bumper crops in what had formerly been the marshy land in the valleys. The method introduced by the Englishman, WALTER BLIGH, had been to dig trenches 4 feet deep in the lower parts of the field, with smaller branches, about 20 feet apart, running into them, all filled with broken stones and covered with about $1\frac{1}{2}$ to 2 feet of soil. JAMES SMITH of Deanston in Perthshire, who took over his uncle's farm in 1823, was able to achieve wonderful results on what had formerly been marshy wasteland by combining Bligh's system of drainage with deep ploughing, for which he invented a special sub-soil plough. Later, tile drains, invented by a Warwickshire manufacturer, replaced the broken stones, and thousands of acres of fertile ground were thereby improved.

New Machines.—All the time, new machines were being introduced. Some of the first inventions were for a long time ignored by the conservative Scottish farmers. In 1710, Andrew Fletcher of Saltoun, who was living in Holland, sent for his clever millwright, JAMES MEIKLE, to study Dutch machines. On his return, Meikle introduced a barley-mill which ground barley much superior to that of the "knockin'-stane" but for about fifty years the Saltoun barley-mill was the only one of its kind in Scotland. Another machine, invented by James Meikle after his visit to Holland, was the "fanners" for winnowing corn, but it was many years before Scotsmen would consent to use it. Some religious people declared it was "making the Devil's wind, and

[1] See p. 144

(a)

(b)

Scottish Champions: (a) Aberdeen-Angus, (b) Ayrshire

Photos: Farmer and Stockbreeder

taking power out of the hands of the Almighty". A later invention, that of the light swing-plough by JAMES SMALL, a Berwickshire farmer and implement-maker, was rapidly taken up in the
1760's. Improved harrows, with teeth of iron, horse-hoeing
machines, wheeled carts, all became common after the middle of
the century. The scythe took the place of the sickle in the
harvest-field and it in turn was replaced by the reaping-machine,
invented in 1827 by PATRICK BELL, who later became minister of
Carmyllie near Arbroath. Till well on in the nineteenth century,
however, bands of harvesters used to come from the Highlands
and Ireland for cutting the grain. Long before this time, the most
laborious stage of farmwork—threshing the corn—had been made
easy by another member of the Meikle family of Saltoun, ANDREW
MEIKLE, who about 1775 produced the first practical threshing-
machine. It soon became popular throughout the country and
in other lands. All these inventions helped to make the land more
productive and the labour of farming much easier.

Stock-breeding.—The new crops of clover and turnips and
the Scottish system of ley-farming (three-year periods of sown
grasses) made it possible for Scottish farmers to fatten their
cattle themselves. Later on, the by-products of the textile industry, linseed and cotton-cakes, provided nutritious additions to
the winter fodder. The trade with England did not die off, however, but rather increased. At the autumn fairs, like Falkirk
Tryst, or the "Paldy" Fair at Fordoun in Kincardineshire, or
Aikey Fair at Old Deer in Buchan, or Kelton Hill and Dumfries
in the south, there were plenty of English dealers to bargain with
the drovers. By 1800, about 100,000 cattle were being exported
annually to England, where "prime Scotch beef" was a favourite,
the most popular cattle being the small black or dun-coloured
West Highland KYLOES. The black, polled, GALLOWAY breed,
which produced excellent beef, was the first to be recognized as
a definite breed in the Lowlands. Other breeds were later developed by careful selection of stock along the lines of the great
pioneer of English stock-breeding, Robert Bakewell. HUGH
WATSON (1789-1865), of Keillor near Coupar-Angus, was the
man mainly responsible for developing the world-famous

ABERDEEN-ANGUS breed of black cattle, and after him an Aberdeenshire farmer, WILLIAM MACCOMBIE of Tillyfourie. These three breeds were "beef" cattle, but Scotland was not lacking in an excellent milking breed, the AYRSHIRE. Dunlop, in the Cunningham district of Ayrshire, was known for its milk and cheeses long before 1750 when the Earl of Marchmont introduced on his estates in Kyle, the middle district of Ayrshire, brown-and-white cattle which are said to have given the distinctive markings to the

Photo: B. H. Humble
Highland Cattle near Tyndrum

breed. The neighbouring county of Lanarkshire was early on famous for its strong draught horses, the CLYDESDALES, almost certainly bred originally from the old English or Flemish warhorses. In the Border counties the most important animal was the sheep. Both the CHEVIOT and the LINTON or BLACKFACE breeds were improved during the eighteenth century. The wool of the first breed was much sought after for the mills of Galashiels and the English textile towns, while the Blackface, whose wool was too coarse for ordinary cloth-manufacture, was highly prized for its excellent mutton. It is estimated that even before 1760, when these two breeds were introduced to the Highlands, about 150,000 sheep were sold each year across the Border. But Low-

B

land farmers were also interested in the autumn markets and bought the sheep for fattening in their fields of clover, rape and turnips. By the early nineteenth century, Scottish farmers had won a stock-breeding reputation fully maintained at the present day.[1]

The People.—Nearly all the parish ministers who wrote for Sir John Sinclair's *Statistical Account* (1791-99) remark on the increased prosperity of the countryside since the middle of the century. The lairds had certainly become wealthier, not only through the sale of the produce of their land, such as grain, live-stock, timber, but also through the much higher rents they received from their tenant-farmers. Farm-buildings were greatly improved and on nearly every large estate there was a "home farm" with a vast collection of stables, byres, barns and outhouses. Some lairds rebuilt old villages, which were erected into small burghs of barony, while others set themselves to plan new towns, feuing the land to prospective inhabitants. There are many such towns in Scotland dating from this time—Fochabers, Helens-burgh, Castle Douglas and others. But what of the tenants and cottars? The tenant-farmers, with their longer leases, became a prosperous, substantial class, although the struggle to pay the laird's rents and reclaim poor land proved too much for some, like William Burnes, the poet's father. For the cottar or farm labourer there was still much drudgery in his everyday life. By the end of the eighteenth century he was free from the various services and dues formerly rendered to the laird, and for his work was paid wages in money and in kind, with the keep of a cow and a piece of ground for potatoes and vegetables. In many districts the unmarried men who worked on a farm lived together in a "bothy" or hut and were fed at the expense of the farmer—a common food allowance being $1\frac{1}{4}$ stones of oatmeal a week, 4 pints of milk a day (for breakfast and supper porridge) and plenty of potatoes, meat, fish and broth for the midday meal. We must not forget that until well into the nineteenth century the linen industry and later the cotton industry, before the factory system developed, provided a part-time occupation for many of those who lived on the land. In some of Burns's poems like *The Twa Dogs* and *The*

[1] For later farming developments see pp. 180-1.

Cotter's Saturday Night, we have pictures of both the unpleasant and the pleasant aspects of rural life and in John Galt's *Annals of the Parish* there is an excellent account, in the form of a novel, of the changes in an Ayrshire parish between 1760 and 1810. In dress, in food and in housing, all classes of the Lowland country people had certainly improved since the beginning of the eighteenth century.

SOURCE EXTRACT

Comparative Statement of the parish of Mains of Fintry
(Forfarshire) in 1760 and 1790

"In 1760, Land was rented at 6s. an acre, on an average only 2 small farms were inclosed. In 1790, Land is rented at 30s. an acre, all inclosed with stone dikes and thorn hedges. In 1760, No wheat was sown in the parish except one half acre by the minister, no grass nor turnip seed was sown, and no kail nor potatoes in the open fields. In 1790, Above 100 acres are sown with wheat; about three fifths of the ground are under grass, turnips, kail and potatoes. In 1760, The wages of men servants that followed the plough were £3 a-year: of maid servants, £1 10s. In 1790, Men servant's wages are £8, some £10: maid servant's ditto £4. In 1760, Day-labourers were got at 6d. a-day; tailors at 3d; wrights at 6d; and masons at 10d a-day. In 1790, Day-labourers receive 1s; tailors 8d; wrights 1s 2d and masons 2s a-day. In 1760, No English cloth was worn but by the minister and a quaker. In 1790, There are few who do not wear English cloth; several the best super-fine; cotton vests are common. In 1760, There were only two hats in the parish; the men wore cloth bonnets. In 1790, Few bonnets are worn; the bonnet-maker trade in the next parish is given up. In 1760, There was only one eight day clock in the parish, six watches and one tea kettle. In 1790, There are 30 clocks, above 100 watches, and at least 160 tea-kettles, there being scarce a family but hath one, and many that have two."

Sir John Sinclair: *Statistical Account of Scotland*

EXERCISES

1. What were the crops introduced into Scotland in the eighteenth century? Why were they so important for Scottish agriculture?

2. Write a paragraph on trees in eighteenth-century Scotland, commenting on Dr Johnson's remark quoted in the last chapter.

3. Write short notes on the following "Improvers": Duchess of Gordon, Earl of Haddington, John Cockburn of Ormiston, Robert Maxwell, Sir Archibald Grant, Earl of Marchmont, Lord Kames, Sir John Sinclair.

4. What inventions do you associate with the names of James Meikle, Andrew Meikle, James Small, Patrick Bell, James Smith?

5. Give five reasons for the great improvement in agriculture in eighteenth-century Scotland. Which, in your opinion, was the most important?

6. Write an account of eighteenth-century farming in your district, using Sir John Sinclair's *Statistical Account* for your parish (or a neighbouring parish if you live in a town). What are the main differences from today?

CHAPTER III

A CENTURY IN THE HIGHLANDS AND ISLANDS

After the "Forty-five".—The century following the "Forty-five" was to bring many changes for the people of the Highlands and Islands.[1] No more than half of the able-bodied men in the north and west had been "out" in 1745-46 but the failure of the rebellion affected almost all of them. The system of military roads, started by Wade, was maintained and developed by his successor, Caulfield, and others, so that the roads lay across the Highlands like great chains binding them. The kilt and the bagpipe disappeared from most of the glens until they were made respectable by Highland soldiers serving in the British Army. In 1782, the act against the wearing of the tartan was repealed and when Sir Walter Scott's novels had made Jacobitism romantic and fashionable, the Hanoverian George IV actually appeared in

[1] See Bk. I, pp. 248-9

Highland dress on his visit to Edinburgh in 1822. The old powers of the chiefs had been removed by the Heritable Jurisdiction Act of 1747 and gradually their influence declined. By the end of the century, they had become mere landlords, although traces of the old clan loyalty remained. The tacksmen, usually relatives of the chief from whom they held tacks or leases of land, which they sub-let to the poorer tenants, were gradually forced out as the chiefs became less interested in the number of fighting men they could raise and more interested in the value of rents from their lands. The disappearance of the tacksmen and the rise in rents helped to bring about clearances later; they were, however, only two of the changes which the century brought to the clansmen.

Forfeited Estates.—Where the estates of the Jacobite chiefs had been forfeited to the Crown, the tenants often strove to pay two rents, one to the absent chief living perhaps in exile in Paris, and another to the COMMISSIONERS FOR THE FORFEITED ESTATES. The story of the Appin Murder of 1752, so well known through Stevenson's *Kidnapped*, is apt to arouse our sympathies for James Stewart, who was hanged for the crime, rather than for the victim, Colin Campbell of Glenure, who had been factor for the Stewart estates in Appin. But, on the whole, the Commissioners for the Forfeited Estates could not be called oppressive, and they at least put some of the rents they collected from the estates to good use. From an annual income of less than £12,000, the Commissioners, in addition to maintaining the estates and paying pensions to widows and relatives of the owners, built new roads and bridges, including the Tay Bridge at Perth, erected new schools, subsidized the linen industry, and gave financial assistance to the construction of the Register House in Edinburgh, the Forth and Clyde Canal and the Crinan Canal, the harbours of Peterhead and Fraserburgh, and a less important but still useful building, the gaol at Inverness. In 1784, when the forfeited estates were handed back to their owners, the work of the Commissioners was carried on by the HIGHLAND SOCIETY, founded in that year not merely for agriculture but for the general improvement of the Highlands.[1]

Farming.—Throughout most of the eighteenth century and

[1] See p. 28

early nineteenth century, farming in the Highlands and Islands resembled very closely conditions in southern Scotland about 1700. There was the same system of runrig, the same periodic reallotment of strips or rigs, the same division into infield and outfield, the same poor crops and the same payment of rent in kind and in services. Similarly, bad harvests brought the people to near starvation, as in 1763 and 1764 and again in 1782 and 1783. There were, however, many differences from Lowland agriculture and many differences also between the glens of the mainland and the islands of the Hebrides, Orkney and Shetland. Cattle-raising played a much more prominent part in the agriculture of the north, long before the cultivation of turnips made it popular and profitable in the south. An interesting feature of Highland farming was the removal of the cattle every summer from the village to the hill pastures, where those who herded the cattle lived in shielings (small, rude huts) for a few months—a happy holiday time often referred to in Gaelic songs. Instead of the cumbersome plough, pulled by horses or oxen, the ground was often tilled by a man with a foot-plough, the *cas chrom*, which has lingered on in some places even to the twentieth century. The *cas chrom*, although it seems primitive to us, was an efficient implement which enabled a man to cultivate the soil of a rocky countryside much more thoroughly than he could with a plough. In the districts which had once been under Norse rule—the Hebrides, Orkney and Shetland—instead of only one large water-mill belonging to the laird, there were to be found numerous small water-mills, different from those in the south in that the water-wheels worked horizontally instead of vertically. In addition, querns or hand-mills were still used, and in many places, instead of threshing and milling in the ordinary way, a sheaf of corn was placed on the fire and burned for a moment until the slightly charred grains could be shaken off and then ground in a hand-mill or "knockin'-stane". This method, called *gradan* in Gaelic, was wasteful, as they thereby lost the straw which could have been used for many purposes. Although the agriculture of the Highlands and Islands was very backward and the climate unfavourable because of heavy rain, hard winters and strong winds,

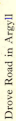

Photo: The Scotsman

Drove Road in Argyll

there were some districts, especially the fertile coastal strips or *machair* land of the Hebrides, where a crop yielding less than a ten-fold return was considered a failure. For example, in South Uist, where cultivation was by the *cas chrom* and plentiful sea-weed, containing valuable potash, was available as a manure, the yield was sometimes even as much as twenty-fold—a contrast to the "noble return" of a four-fold harvest in the Lowlands. In still another respect the Highlands differed from the Hebrides and the Lowlands—in the abundant supply of timber available from the pine forests in the glens of the mainland. Finally, we should remember that fishing on the coast provided, if not a whole-time occupation, at least plentiful food, fresh or cured.

Drovers and Drove Roads.—Across the moors of Scotland run grassy tracks, some of which are slowly disappearing in the heather but still provide wonderful walking for those who care to seek them out. These are the drove roads along which for well over a hundred years the drovers brought their droves of cattle from the far west and north to the markets of the Lowlands and over the Border to England. The great advantages of the drove roads over the ordinary highway were that the cattle could be kept in much better condition on their way to market and that the tolls on the turnpike roads were avoided. When the drovers reached the south and crossed the Border, they were forced to keep to the highroad and the cattle were actually shod. The cattle trade, it has already been shown, was of first importance in Scotland, both in the Highlands and Lowlands. The Highland KYLOE, black in those days but today almost invariably dun or reddish-brown in colour, was a small, thin beast but when fat-tened in the Lowlands or in England provided excellent beef. Thousands of these "store" cattle were ferried over from the Hebrides or (as in the crossing from Skye at Kylerhea) made to swim to the mainland. Droves might consist of two or three hundred beasts, occasionally even a thousand, with one drover, perhaps mounted on a pony, to each hundred. Ten or twelve miles were covered in a day on an average, and at the drove stances in the Highlands, such as Bridge of Orchy, Dalwhinnie, Dalnaspidal, the drover would spend the night outside, wrapped in his plaid and watching the beasts. There were bad years also in the cattle trade; the cattle plague or rinderpest which lasted from 1745 to 1757 was a terrible blow to the Highlands, as many as ninety per cent of affected herds dying or having to be destroyed.

Fairs and Trysts.—In the early eighteenth century the chief market in Scotland was CRIEFF, where in 1723 about 30,000 cattle were sold. Many cattle were taken direct into England; even in 1745, a drover from Ross-shire took a drove of cattle as far south as Craven in Yorkshire. Many other towns developed markets or fairs, as has already been mentioned in the last chapter, but by the end of the eighteenth century they were all far outstripped in importance by the FALKIRK TRYST. This fair, first held on the moor just south of Falkirk, was moved to Rough Castle, near the old Antonine Wall fort, and finally in 1785 to Stenhousemuir, where it remained till almost 1900. When Crieff declined, Falkirk Tryst became the gathering-place for drovers and dealers from all over Scotland and England on the second Tuesday of August, September and October. There were no auctioneers and the cattle were sold only after a bargain had been struck between the Highland drover and the English dealer and the bargain sealed by drinking a "dram" of whisky. By 1792 the price of the Highland kyloe at Falkirk was £4 per head, while some of the larger turnip-fed cattle sold for as much as £25 each. The scene on the Tryst ground, on which there were congregated perhaps 50,000 cattle and even more sheep, with their drovers and dogs, with the tents for the banks and for "refreshments" (as they called the whisky-drinking), must have been a lively one. Cattle and sheep droving increased in the nineteenth century, but in the second half of the century the development of railway and steamboat transport and the importation of cheap meat from overseas brought about a decline.

The Coming of the Sheep.—The old Highland sheep was a small, tan-faced animal, usually housed at night and carefully herded during the day from the eagle, the wild cat and the fox. Wolves were still to be found in Scotland in the early eighteenth century, the last being killed in 1743 on the lands of Mackintosh of Mackintosh near Inverness; but foxes were very common and the Disarming Acts were blamed for their great increase. In many places, the sheep were not so numerous as the goats, which were much hardier and were kept for their milk. The wool of the old Highland sheep was fine but very short and, instead of being shorn, was plucked by hand as it is today in Shetland, where the process is called "rooin". Descendants of the old breed were to be found in the twentieth century not only in Shetland, which is famous for its fine wool, but also in some of the remoter islands like St. Kilda, evacuated in 1930, and Soay near Skye. It was about 1760 that Lowland sheep of the LINTON or BLACK-FACE breed and the CHEVIOT breed were introduced into the glens of the Highlands, first near Callander and later in Cowal, in Glen Falloch and Glen Dochart. Gradually, sheep-farming was extended throughout the Highlands until by 1800 only in the far north-west and in the Hebrides was cattle-raising still more important. The south-country farmers who undertook this experiment at first hoped that the Cheviots, whose wool was much better than that of the Lintons, could winter on the high ground. But the hardier Linton or Blackface remained the commonest sheep in the Highlands until, mainly through the influence of Sir John Sinclair of Ulbster, the Cheviot was introduced about 1800 into Sutherland and Caithness, being wintered on the low ground in the straths. By 1827, at Falkirk Tryst, where over 200,000 sheep were sold (in addition to 150,000 cattle), the Cheviot was the most popular breed.

A Silent Revolution.—The coming of the sheep, it has been said, brought about a silent revolution which radically affected both the land and the people. The pine forests, although many had been burned through carelessness or sometimes deliberately because they harboured wolves or thieves, were still very extensive in the north and west in the eighteenth century. Much timber was cut down to meet the demands of the iron-smelting industry, furnaces being set up at Glengarry, Loch Fyne and elsewhere; at the end of the century it was estimated that the annual profits from Rothiemurchus Forest in Strathspey were as much as £20,000. When the pine forests went, they were succeeded by birch scrub, which was cleared by the sheep-farmers to provide grazing for their sheep. The sheep have been held responsible for the spread of bracken, which covers some of the best land in the Highlands to such an extent that it is officially described as the BRACKEN PEST. The sheep is a selective feeder and it lacks the heavy hoofs of the cattle which would tread and kill the young fronds of the bracken. But by far the greatest effect of the introduction of sheep-farming was on the people. To provide winter-grazing for the sheep, especially the Cheviots, the lower, fertile lands of the straths were "cleared" of their inhabitants, and a couple of Lowland shepherds would take the place of perhaps forty Highland families. These CLEARANCES contributed greatly to the depopulation and decay of the Highlands, as we shall read later.

Potatoes.—The agricultural revolution cannot be said to have reached the north until the nineteenth century (in some places not before the twentieth century) but the countryside saw certain changes in the old way of farming. Even before the "Forty-five" the potato had made its appearance. In 1743, at a time of great scarcity, CLANRANALD, chief of the MacDonalds in South Uist and Benbecula, with difficulty persuaded his clansmen to sow them. Clanranald had lived in Ireland with his relatives in Antrim, and knew what wholesome food the potato provided. The Islesmen were sceptical and, it is said, after they had harvested the crop, left it at their chief's door, saying they would never eat them. But in time they did and, with the steady growth of the population, the potato became almost as important in the diet of the people in the Highlands and Islands as it was in Ireland, more especially after 1800, when the crofter's life was very hard indeed. As the turnip had helped to transform Lowland agriculture, so the potato helped to improve the farming in the north and west, especially in the Hebrides. There the cultivation of potatoes in ridges or *feannagan* (called "lazy-beds" by the Lowlanders) meant constant attention and hard work in the spring— first in the collection of the sea-ware, then in the digging and sowing, and later in the hoeing. The result was a fine crop of potatoes, to be followed in the next year by a bumper crop of barley. The potato, which had saved people from famine, was to cause one of the worst famines of all. But when the POTATO BLIGHT of 1846-47 came to Scotland only a few died of starvation, in comparison with over a million in Ireland, where potatoes in one form or another formerly appeared at every meal.

Kelp Industry.—Seaweed has been used for many purposes, notably the manufacture of glass and the production of iodine. The great natural harvest of seaweed round the northern and western coasts of Scotland was for over a century gathered and burned; the ash or kelp, containing sodium carbonate, was then sold to the manufacturers of glass and soap. The kelp industry was introduced to Orkney from Ireland by JAMES FEA of Stronsay in 1722; the people at first opposed it, thinking the smoke from the kelp fires would spoil the crops and the cattle. A few years later the kelp industry was established in many parts of the Western Isles—in North and South Uist, Barra, Coll and Tiree. It was a seasonal occupation, involving laborious and monotonous work, usually for about two months in summer but in some places in winter also. It took eighty carts or twenty tons of seaweed to make one ton of kelp, the final product being a hard, solid cake of ash about three to six feet high. In the eighteenth century the price averaged between £2 and £5 per ton, but in the French wars, when foreign supplies of soda were cut off, the price went up as high as £22 per ton in 1808-9. At that time it was estimated that 3,000 (or most of the adult population) were employed in Orkney alone. On an average, a family might make £3 a year and at the height of the boom as much as £7, but the kelp industry brought great wealth to the landowners. The shores of North Uist for many years were let for an annual rent of £7,000 and Clanranald is said to have made £30,000 a year when prices were high. A plentiful labour supply was important and landowners at this time encouraged the sub-division of crofts to allow as many families as possible to live on the land. The cultivation of the potato made it easier to feed this increased population. But the kelp boom ended when barilla could be imported from Spain after the start of the Peninsular War and potash salts from Germany after 1815; when the import tax on barilla was removed in

1823 the kelp trade collapsed. By the middle of the century the native proprietors in the Hebrides were ruined and forced to sell their estates; thus the MacLeods sold Harris in 1834, the Mac-Neills Barra in 1838, the Clanranald family South Uist in 1839 and the Seaforths Lewis in 1844. Orkney continued to produce kelp for iodine until after the middle of the century when the trade was killed by the import of Chilean nitrates.

Fishing.—Despite the many attempts made by the Stewart kings to encourage British fisheries, the Dutch continued to monopolize the herring fishing on our coasts till well into the eighteenth century. Every year about midsummer as many as 2,000 of their "busses", low barge-like vessels of about 75 feet in length, would congregate in Bressay Sound off Lerwick in Shetland and fish for the herring along the British coast as far south as East Anglia, making three voyages back home each season. In the eighteenth century the Dutch fishing industry began to decline and at the same time the British government began to encourage home fishermen by the BOUNTY SYSTEM. After two unsuccessful attempts, an act was passed in 1750 making bounties or bonuses payable to the owners of decked fishing vessels built and used according to the regulations laid down in the act. This bounty system, which had been copied from the Dutch, was criticized by many, especially by the inshore fishermen on the west of Scotland, for example in Loch Fyne and in the Firth of Clyde, where herring were caught by nets from small, open boats, operated by only four of a crew. In those days the herring visited many sea-lochs on the west coast which never see them today and they were caught in the Clyde well above Greenock. In 1787 the bounty system was extended to cover inshore fishermen as well. The merchants of Glasgow and Greenock, who controlled the herring fishing in west and north-west Scotland, complained of the salt laws which hampered the fishing industry. They managed, however, not merely to satisfy a great demand in the towns (where "tatties an' saut herrin" were a regular meal, seven herrings being considered the portion for one man) but also to send over 40,000 barrels of herrings a year to the West Indies. In the Outer Hebrides and in the Orkney and Shetland Isles, white fishing mainly for cod, ling and haddock had gone on from time immemorial. The Shetlanders carried on deep-sea white fishing (which they called "haaf" fishing) in open boats, "sixerns" or "fourareens" for crews of six or four, until late in the nineteenth century.

North-east Coast.—The native Scottish large-scale herring fishing on the north-east coast had its beginnings in 1767 when three Caithness merchants fitted out two large sloops with which they were very successful in the Moray Firth. By the end of the eighteenth century WICK had become the chief herring-port in Scotland, a position it held for long after.[1] The tremendous development of the herring fisheries in the early nineteenth century was due partly to the bounty system, which was revised in 1808 and finally abolished in 1829, and partly to the encouragement given by the formation of the "British Society to extend the Fisheries and improve the Sea Coast of the Kingdom". This BRITISH FISHERIES SOCIETY, founded in 1786 by wealthy and influential Scotsmen, raised £40,000 by private subscription and set out to build curing-stations, wharves and houses in fishing-ports like Wick, Ullapool and Tobermory. The suburb of Pulteneytown, the chief centre of the fishing industry in Wick, was erected by the British Fisheries Society in 1808 and named after their president, William Pulteney. Within the next twenty years, mainly through the efforts of the Society, gutting and curing-stations were established at many places in the Moray Firth—at Fraserburgh, Helmsdale, MacDuff, Banff, Cullen, Lossiemouth, Burghead and Peterhead. In the Western Isles, large-scale herring fishing did not develop till some time later; there, however, in addition to inshore fishing, the people profited from the periodic visits of schools of whales which often resulted in wholesale slaughter on the shores where they had been driven.

Growth of Population.—In 1755 DR WEBSTER, minister of the Tolbooth Church in Edinburgh, published the results of his census of Scotland, which gives us the only reliable statistics of the population before Sir John Sinclair's *Statistical Account* of 1791-99 and the first official census of 1801. According to Dr Webster's figures, the population of the counties of Argyll, Inver-

[1] See pp. 185-7

ness, Ross and Cromarty in 1755 was 173,933 out of a total population of 1,265,380; in 1801 it had grown to 210,267 and in 1821, 256,039. These figures show a remarkable increase in the population, to which a number of factors contributed—an improved standard of living due to the cultivation of the potato, the expansion of fisheries, the kelp industry and the cattle trade; the end of clan warfare and the Jacobite rebellions; and the lower mortality from smallpox as a result of the practice of inoculation carried out by the parish ministers long before Dr Jenner started vaccination. What is not obvious from these figures is that at the same time there was a steady loss of population through people going overseas never to return. During the wars of the period— the Seven Years' War (1759-63), the American War (1775-83), the French wars (1793-1815)—there were raised in the Highlands many regiments of soldiers, who fought in Europe, America and India, until the complaint was made that the Highlands were being bled white. Nor was it only for the Army that the Government looked north for recruits: the press-gangs of the Navy made regular visits to the fishing-ports of the north. Of these soldiers and sailors, many never returned, and others, veterans of campaigns in America, would tell tales of their adventures that made their young listeners restless to leave the homeland. The increase in population meant that there were young brothers for whom the crofts had no room. As the cattle trade began to improve, after the cattle plague years in the middle of the century, some landlords set up large grazing farms and many tenants were made to quit. In most districts, the former chiefs were more interested in raising rents than in helping the tenants by improvements to pay them; the Highland landlords were not "improvers". Bad harvests, such as those of 1763 and 1764, and the resulting high prices, coupled with high rents, also led many to decide to seek their fortune elsewhere.

Emigration.—From 1770 to 1774 there was a steady stream of emigrants to America especially to North Carolina, which had some Scottish settlements, mainly of people from Argyll, dating back to before the "Forty-five". Among those who left for North Carolina in 1773 was Flora MacDonald, with many more of her

kindred from Skye. Two Catholic groups of settlers, one composed of MacDonalds from South Uist and the other led by
MacDonells of Glengarry, Glenmoriston, Urquhart and Strath-
glass, found homes at this time in Albany near New York and in
Prince Edward Island respectively. Canada became more popular
after the American War; surprisingly enough, most of the Highlanders in North Carolina were Loyalists during the war and
emigrated from the United States to Canada after 1783.[1] Just
about this time the rage for sheep-farming led first to big increases
in rents, then to evictions of tenants to make room for Lowland
sheep-farmers. One of these is said to have offered a rent of £300
for a grazing in Kintail which previously had been let to several
crofters for a total rent of £15. When the kelp industry at last
collapsed, the lot of many people in the Hebrides and in the north
islands of Orkney and Shetland was indeed miserable. During
the boom, landlords had encouraged the sub-division of crofts
for the sake of a plentiful supply of labour until the crofts had
become too small and uneconomic. In the first half of the nineteenth century the stream of emigration became a flood. Some
Highlanders and Islesmen left to find an occupation in the growing industrial towns of the Lowlands but many others settled in
the backwoods or prairies of Canada or on the shores of the St.
Lawrence.

Clearances.—In the early period of emigration, evictions or
clearances for sheep-farming did not play a large part. But in
1783, just after the American War, fifty-five tenants in Glengarry
were evicted, and others left later when rents were raised and
their rights of grazing their cattle were restricted in favour of
sheep-farmers. The Highlanders saw in the poor sheep dangerous
enemies; in 1792 the people of Ross-shire took part in a great
"sheep drive" to clear sheep from off their lands and were stopped
only by the intervention of the Black Watch.[2] Evictions for
sheep-farming became more frequent after 1800 and went on
till after 1850. The Sutherland clearances, on the estate of the
Countess of Sutherland who had married the Marquis of Stafford,
were the most thorough of all clearances and caused great distress;
over 15,000, it is estimated, were forcibly removed between 1809

[1] See p. 108   [2] See p. 115

and 1821 to make room for sheep. Many of the tenants had their homes and belongings burned before their eyes and for months afterwards eked out a living on the coast, where some land had been offered to them. There was little active resistance to the evictions; most of the people regarded it as a punishment from God, and of the seventeen parish ministers, only one took the side of those evicted. Although many blamed the Marchioness of Stafford's English husband and English factors for the ruthless clearances, it was mainly Highland landlords who were responsible elsewhere. Generally, the clearances were worse on the mainland but in Rum several hundred families had to make way for one farmer with 8,000 sheep. Clearances were made for deer forests later in the nineteenth century when, mainly as a result of Queen Victoria's enthusiasm for Balmoral, Scottish landowners found it profitable to let their estates for deer-stalking and grouse-shooting. In many glens the deserted "larachs" or ruins stand today as silent relics of a vanished race.

Bibles and Bards.—The century after Culloden may seem to have been mainly one of toil and trouble, but it is wrong to think of history (to use Gibbon's words) as "nothing but the register of the crimes, follies and misfortunes of mankind". During this period the people of the Highlands and Islands came to live more peaceful lives, not merely because of the Disarming Acts but also through the spread of Christian preaching and education.[1] Over 180 schools were founded in the Highlands in the first eighty years after the formation of the Society for Propagating Christian Knowledge in 1709, and the same society was responsible for a Scottish-Gaelic translation of the New Testament, published in 1767. Before that date there were available only Irish-Gaelic and English versions of the Bible; it was not until 1826 that the whole of the Bible was translated into Scottish-Gaelic. Gaelic poetry also showed the change which came over the Highlands. In the seventeenth century there had been plenty of bards to sing the praises of clan chiefs and some fine heroic poems date from that time. One of them, the *Elegy for Sir Roderick MacLeod*, was composed in 1664 by a woman, Mary MacLeod, who is said to have died about 1720 at the advanced age of 105 years. Other

[1] See pp. 234-5

famous bards before the "Forty-five" were Iain Lom MacDonald of Keppoch, who composed poems about Montrose's battles; Roderick Morrison, the "blind harper" to MacLeod of Harris, whose *Oran Mor Mhic Leoid* ("The Great Song of MacLeod") is a poem of wonderful beauty; and ALEXANDER MACDONALD, the Jacobite bard, the first edition of whose poems was burned at the Market Cross of Edinburgh in 1751 and whose *Birlinn Chla nn Raghnaill* ("Clanranald's Galley") contains passages descript[1]ve of the sea probably unequalled in any language. After the "Forty-five" there was no decline in the number or quality of the bards—Dugald Buchanan, Ian MacCodrum, Rob Donn MacKay and DUNCAN BAN MACINTYRE (1724-1812), whose poems, *Moladh Beinn Dorain* ("Praise of Ben Doran") and *Mairi Bhan Og* ("Fair Young Mary"), are among the best known in the Gaelic language. DUGALD BUCHANAN (1716-60) was a religious poet whose hymns were very popular; his influence was such that he has been called "the greatest blessing bestowed on the Highlands in the eighteenth century". In addition to the poems of these bards, hundreds of folk-songs existed, to be sung, as Dr Johnson, Wordsworth and other travellers noted, during the hours of labour as well as on the shieling or at an evening's *ceilidh*. Some of the anonymous composers have produced melodies which have been acclaimed by a musical critic of the twentieth century, Ernest Newman, as "without their superior, whether in folk-song or in art-song". Fortunately, a great number of these songs of the Hebrides have been noted down or recorded, to become a permanent part of our Scottish heritage.

SOURCE EXTRACT

"During these proceedings, I was resident at my father's house, but I had occasion on the week immediately ensuing to visit the manse of Tongue. On my way thither, I passed through the scene of the campaign of burning. The spectacle presented was hideous and ghastly. The banks of the lake and river, formerly studded with cottages, now met the eye as a scene of desolation. Of all the houses, the thatched roofs were gone, but the walls, built of alternate layers of turf and stone, remained. The flames of the preceding week still slumbered in their ruins, and sent up into the air spiral columns of smoke . . . ."

Rev. Donald Sage on Strathnaver Clearances (1819)
in Memorabilia Domestica

EXERCISES

1. Locate Strathnaver, to which the above extract refers.
2. What were the main differences between farming in the Lowlands and farming in the Highlands and Islands?
3. What were the main differences between farming in the Highlands and farming in the Islands?
4. Find out any old drove road or drove stance in your district and the site of the nearest fair or tryst.
5. Distinguish between the three main breeds of sheep in Scotland in the eighteenth century.
6. What were the chief consequences to the Hebrides of the kelp industry and its final collapse?
7. Account for the expansion of the herring fishery in the early nineteenth century.
8. What were the main causes of emigration from the Highlands and Islands from 1760 to 1840?
9. Explain the following words: kyloe, quern, tryst, dram, buss, rooin', larach, "haaf" fishing, *machair, gradan, cas chrom.*
10. If you live in the Highlands or Islands, find out from Sir John Sinclair's *Statistical Account* and the *New Statistical Account* about the agriculture and industries of your district before 1800 and about 1840.
11. Write short notes on the following: Alexander MacDonald, Duncan Ban Macintyre, Dugald Buchanan, the Gaelic Bible.

CHAPTER IV

THE RISE OF GLASGOW

Before the Union.—The story of Glasgow's rise to the position of the "second city" of Great Britain is one of interest to all Scottish people for it is more or less the story of Scottish trade and industry after the Union of Parliaments. Even before 1707, Glasgow merchants had shown great enterprise in the face of many difficulties. Chief among these was the shallowness of the river Clyde, which prevented ships of more than a few tons from coming within fourteen miles of the town; between Glasgow and Dumbarton there were seven fords on the river where it could be crossed at low water. In addition, other towns on the Clyde, like Rutherglen, Renfrew and Dumbarton, which had received charters with trading privileges, were jealous of Glasgow merchants and many quarrels ensued. In 1656, when Scotland was ruled by Cromwell, Glasgow was reckoned by Thomas Tucker, the English Commissioner who reported on Scottish trade, as "one of the most considerablest burghs of Scotland" but had only twelve small vessels, in which they traded with France, Ireland, Norway and the Hebrides. The principal exports then were herring, coals and plaiding (coarse woollen cloth); the herring cured at Glasgow, Greenock and Gourock had a high reputation, comparable with Dutch-cured herring. After the Restoration of 1660, the Glasgow merchants bestirred themselves to improve their trade. A small quay was built at the Broomielaw in 1662 to help unloading, the Town Council giving permission for oak timber to be taken from the Cathedral. In 1668, land was acquired down the Clyde at Newark to build a harbour, which became known as Port Glasgow. Some time after, the Glasgow merchants began to import tobacco, at first not direct from Virginia but from the Delaware, then part of Pennsylvania. A few of them, like Walter Gibson, appointed Provost by the Catholic James VII in 1688, were not above selling as slaves to the American colonies Covenanters captured by Government troops. The

Photo: Picture Post

View of Glasgow about 1720

The Molendinar burn can be seen in front and the Bishop's Castle and part
of the Cathedral on the right

failure of the Darien Scheme was a great disappointment to Glasgow, but the Union of Parliaments, despite the outcry raised by the Glasgow mob in 1707, gave the merchants an opportunity which they were ready to seize with both hands.

Old Glasgow.—The appearance of old Glasgow never failed to arouse the admiration of visitors. Daniel Defoe, writing in 1727, called it "one of the cleanliest, most beautiful, and best built cities of Great Britain". If we could visit it as it was in the early eighteenth century, we would find it a small town of nearly 14,000 inhabitants, living in houses strung out between the Clyde and the Cathedral on the hill. By 1707 the Glasgow people, who had once been called the "bishop's men", used the Cathedral for three Presbyterian churches—the Inner High Kirk, meeting in the choir; the Outer High Kirk occupying the nave; and the Laigh Kirk or Barony Kirk meeting in the crypt. The Bishop's Castle was gradually falling into ruins; it was used as a prison for Jacobites in 1715 but soon after became a kind of quarry for Glasgow builders, and by the middle of the century the Town Council gave permission for its stones to be taken away for the building of the Saracen's Head Inn. Passing down the High Street, with its side-streets, Rottenrow and Drygait, we would view the College or University and through the handsome gateway we might catch a glimpse of the two courts and the tower within. At the foot of the High Street, where the Mercat Cross stood until 1659, could be seen the Tolbooth or Town House, the centre of the town's activities, at the junction of the High Street, Trongait, Gallowgait and Saltmarket. Every visitor to Glasgow praised the wide streets at the Cross, especially the Trongait, with the colonnaded buildings, called "piazzas", under the arches of which shopkeepers displayed their goods. From the Saltmarket we might walk over to the Green, where the burgesses' cattle are grazing, or pass down by the Bridgegait to the fourteenth-century, high-backed bridge, which led over to the pleasant gardens of Gorbells. At the Broomielaw, the small quay of 1662 had been extended in 1688 to accommodate the gabbarts or lighters which brought the merchandise from Port Glasgow or Greenock. Of the beautiful town of 1707, traces still remain—

the Cathedral, altered by nineteenth-century "improvements"; the towers of the Tolbooth at the Cross, the old Merchants' House isolated in the Fishmarket, and the Tron Kirk jutting out into the modern Trongate; and Provand's Lordship in Castle Street, the only pre-Reformation house left in Glasgow. But the centre of the city has gradually been moved westwards and the boundaries extended for miles around.

Plantation Trade.—The Union, which left the Fife ports "heaps of decay", as an English traveller described them in 1733, was soon used by Glasgow merchants to their advantage. At first, they chartered ships from Whitehaven in Cumberland to sail for cargoes of tobacco to the American plantations, as the colonies were then called. The first Glasgow-owned vessel to sail to Virginia was one of 60 tons, built at Crawfordsdyke, Greenock, in 1718. By that time the Glasgow people had made it quite clear during the Jacobite Rebellion of 1715-16 that they were for the Hanoverian Succession and the Union; later, in the "Forty-five" they suffered for their Hanoverian zeal by having to provide supplies for Prince Charles Edward's Jacobite army on his visit to the city.[1] By 1720 the tobacco merchants of Whitehaven, Liverpool, Bristol and London had become jealous of the success of the Glasgow merchants, who were able to undersell their rivals in their own towns. The English complaints that the men of Glasgow were evading the import duties were proved without foundation but the Glasgow trade began to suffer from constant interference by customs officers. In the Malt Tax riots of 1725, when several were killed, the people showed their resentment at government officials and taxes.[2] With the French wars in the middle of the century, however, Glasgow trade grew rapidly, as the route from Scotland to the American plantations became much the safest and speediest. By 1772, when the total imports of tobacco into Britain amounted to 90,000 hogsheads, Glasgow alone accounted for 49,000, the bulk of which was later re-exported, mainly to France. It was not only to Virginia and Maryland for cargoes of tobacco but also to the West Indies for sugar, rum and cotton that the Glasgow merchants traded. Sugar refineries had been set up in Glasgow in the seventeenth century

[1] See Bk. I, p. 246   [2] See Bk. I, p. 240

but up till about 1730 the molasses were imported through Bristol. This West Indian trade continued for some time after the American War of Independence had brought about the collapse of the tobacco trade. When the trade with the new American states revived after 1783, it was cotton which was to be the most important commodity imported, but there are still to be found tobacco-manufacturing firms in or around Glasgow, although the centre of the sugar-refining industry is now Greenock.

Glasgow's Exports.—What was Glasgow able to offer to the colonists in exchange for the tobacco, sugar and cotton which they bought? Linen, woollen and even cotton goods, made in or near Glasgow, were their principal exports in 1726, according to Daniel Defoe, but twenty years later they were forced to buy goods in Manchester to make up sufficient cargoes for the colonies. By the time of the outbreak of the American War (1775), the linen industry was well established in Paisley and in the village of Anderston near Glasgow, where they had advanced from making the coarse harn to finer cloths, cambrics, lawns and gauzes, the quality of which could be compared with the French. Later, by the end of the century, the manufacture of cotton goods for export became the main industry of Clydeside. But there were other manufactures for which Glasgow was noted. The first inkle-factory in Britain (inkle was the old name for linen tape) was started in Glasgow in 1732 by Alexander Harvey, who brought two looms from Holland and a Dutchman to work them. Glasgow inkles became so popular in America that even today in the United States adhesive tape is known as "Scotch tape". About the same time, the brothers Dinwiddie, one of whom later became Governor of Virginia, set up a glass-works for bottle-making on the Old Green near the Broomielaw; in old pictures of Glasgow the "Bottle-house Lum" stands out as a conspicuous landmark near the river. The largest leather-works in Europe was located in Glasgow, and other specialities connected with the city were soap and candle manufacture, hat-making, ropeworks, type-founding for printing, delft pottery, and, of course, salt herring, the trade in which was monopolized by Glasgow and Greenock merchants. It must be remembered that, although the American trade was most important, European countries also received these goods in addition to the tobacco which passed through Glasgow. And with all these industries, Glasgow itself was growing.

POPULATION OF GLASGOW
1708 - 91

67,000

23,546

12,766

1708   1755   1791

The really big expansion was to come after 1800.

Tobacco Lords.—The profits from the American trade were such that Glasgow became a very wealthy city, with its "merchant princes" like the medieval cities of Venice and Florence. These "tobacco lords", as they were called, were wont to parade on the pavements of the Trongait, dressed in scarlet cloaks, curled wigs, cocked hats, and bearing canes. One of them, John Glassford, was described by Smollett, the novelist, as one of the greatest merchants in Europe; in the Seven Years' War (1756-63) he possessed 25 ships, carrying his own goods, and had a business with an annual turnover of £500,000. During his sojourn in Glasgow in 1745-46, Prince Charles had resided in Glassford's mansion, Shawfield House, then the property of a wealthy West Indian merchant, Colonel MacDowall. The house of another "tobacco lord", William Cunningham, who alone managed to avoid bankruptcy in the American War, was later converted into the Royal Exchange and still stands in Buchanan Street. The "tobacco lords" were a very wealthy but a very small group of men, who would not mix with ordinary merchants and tradesmen, and Burns's lines have been applied to them:

Ye see yon birkie ca'd a lord
Wha struts an' stares an' a' that.

They certainly helped, however, to make possible the tremendous expansion of Glasgow.

Science and the Arts.—But Glasgow had notables of another kind, who were not interested only in money matters. The small University was fortunate in having as professors during this period

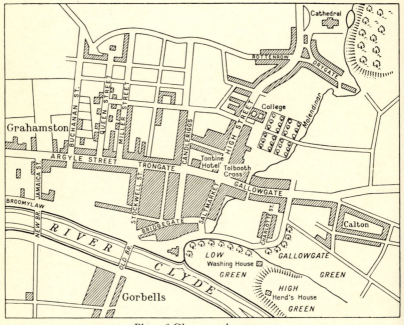

Plan of Glasgow, about 1790

some remarkable men. There were the philosophers, Francis Hutcheson (1694-1746) and Thomas Reid (1710-96), and the scientists, William Cullen (1710-90) and Joseph Black (1728-99), the discoverer of latent heat. Professor John Anderson (1726-96), who encouraged James Watt in his experiments, is regarded as having started adult education with his twice-weekly classes for mechanics and in his "Andersonian" University founded the first technical college in Europe.[1] Adam Smith (1723-90), "the father of economics", who was professor at Glasgow University from 1751 to 1763, is said to have owed much of the knowledge of commerce displayed in his famous *Wealth of Nations*[2] to discussions with Glasgow merchants, especially Andrew Cochrane, who had been Provost at the time of the "Forty-five". Glasgow was interested in more than science and economics; the people were also beginning to dabble in literature and the arts. Their old motto had been "Let Glasgow flourish by the preaching of the Word", and in the early part of the century they had interpreted this very strictly, sending out "seizers" or church elders on the Sunday mornings to check up on any absentees from the church services. But gradually theatres were established, despite occasional riots stirred by fiery preachers. In 1753, the brothers Foulis, who were held to be the best printers of their time, set up an Academy to encourage painting and sculpture. Glasgow had several social and literary clubs, where men of different occupations could meet over a bowl of punch to discuss the topics of the day or argue the merits of the latest book. Newspapers began to appear with some regularity; the *Glasgow Herald* was first published in 1783 under the name of *The Advertiser* and by the end of the century Glasgow had two newspapers, the *Herald* and the *Courier*, appearing thrice weekly.

Clyde Navigation.—It has often been said that "the Clyde made Glasgow and Glasgow made the Clyde". Few realize that for most of the eighteenth century Glasgow, although such an important commercial centre, was not a port in the real sense of the word; indeed, as a port it could not compare with Greenock at that time. Greenock, which had been a mere burgh of barony belonging to the family of Shaw, had at first a struggle for trade against the opposition of the older royal burghs on the Clyde, but with the building of its harbour (1707-10) and the growth of the American trade, it made a bid to outdo its up-river rival. Although Port Glasgow was so vital to Glasgow, it was too far from the city when trade began to expand, and by the middle of the century Glasgow merchants began to seek means to improve Clyde navigation. In 1755, John Smeaton, the builder of Eddystone

[1] See p. 258   [2] See p. 132

Lighthouse, made a survey of the river and reported that he had found between Glasgow Bridge and Renfrew, a stretch of five miles, twelve shoals, three of which had only eighteen inches at low water. In those days, the river, without a regular channel or proper banks, had spread itself wide over the countryside, as can be seen from names of places inland like Whiteinch and Abbots-inch, the suffix "inch" meaning island. Smeaton suggested a lock or dam on the river four miles down from Glasgow, to ensure a uniform depth of four feet six inches up to the Broomielaw. Happily his advice was not taken. In 1768, JOHN GOLBORNE of Chester again surveyed the Clyde and suggested that the river should be deepened by dredging and narrowed by the construc-tion of over a hundred jetties. Thereafter, he argued, the water in its narrow channel would scour out its own bed. James Watt in 1769 confirmed Golborne's survey and Golborne was told to carry out his plan. The result was a triumph for Golborne, who by 1773 provided for Glasgow ships a depth of at least seven feet at low water, and by 1781 a depth of fourteen feet. The land between the jetties was reclaimed and the ends of the jetties later joined by quays, making the river scour all the deeper. Another similar venture, which took a long time to complete, was that of the Forth and Clyde Canal between Grangemouth on the Forth and Bowling on the Clyde.[1] After it was opened in 1790, many ships used it instead of the Clyde and went by the branch canal to Port Dundas in Glasgow, which was sometimes as busy as the Broomielaw. In the nineteenth century, the Clyde was further deepened and more quays built. Today the river is controlled by the Clyde Navigation Trust and ocean liners can now proceed up to Glasgow. At the same time Port Glasgow and Greenock have become less important as ports, although they for a long time surpassed Glasgow in shipbuilding.

Cotton.—The American War of Independence (1775-83) was a grave blow to Glasgow and most of the "tobacco lords" went bankrupt. But by the end of the war the Glasgow merchants were seeking new worlds to conquer. The leading man in Glasgow at that time was Patrick Colquhoun, who became Provost in 1782.[2] It was mainly due to him that in 1783 there was set up the Glasgow

[1] See p. 148   [2] See also pp. 206-7

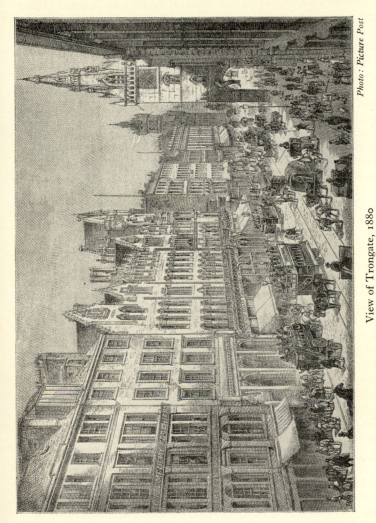

Photo: Picture Post

View of Trongate, 1880

The Tron Kirk steeple can be seen on the right, the Tolbooth steeple behind it and,
on the left of the Tolbooth steeple, the old Tontine Hotel

Chamber of Commerce, the first of its kind in Britain. The previous year he had been chairman of the committee responsible for the erection beside the Tolbooth of one of the finest hotels in Europe, the Tontine, the coffee-room of which was to serve as Glasgow's Exchange for many years. Other Glasgow business-men continued what he had begun. You will read later of mill-owners such as James Monteith of Anderston (see page 71) and David Dale (see page 73). By the end of the century, Eli Whitney's cotton gin, which separated the seeds from the fibre quickly instead of by the old, slow, hand process, caused a great expansion of the cotton industry in the United States. Hitherto British cotton had come from India, the Levant and the West Indies; by 1800 Georgia, Carolina and other southern states of the United States had swung over to cotton production on a large scale. Glasgow and the Clyde were as favourably situated for cotton manufacture as Liverpool and Lancashire: their port was convenient for the north American trade, their climate favourable because of its dampness, there were plenty of streams to provide water-power for the mills and many workmen skilled in the making of fine linen fabrics who could easily change over to the cotton yarn. As we shall see, Glasgow men, such as James Watt, George Macintosh, David Dale, Charles Tennant and Charles Macintosh, played a leading part in introducing bleaching and dyeing processes and in the new chemical industry which developed out of these.[1] From 1790 to 1820 cotton-manufacture was the main industry of Clydeside and Glasgow the natural centre, although it was carried on in every valley in the countryside around.

New Trade and Industries.—The French Revolutionary and Napoleonic Wars (1793-1815) brought trouble to Glasgow just as the American War had done. By the "Continental System", which he started in 1806, Napoleon tried to kill British trade and by 1810 there was a depression in the cotton industry which became worse when Britain went to war with the United States in 1812. But Napoleon's blockade was broken by Glasgow and Greenock merchants, who used the newly-acquired island of Heligoland near Germany as a base for their contraband trade.

[1] See pp. 75-6

It was said that in 1810 and 1811 Heligoland was nearly covered with the San Domingo coffee of Walter Ritchie of Greenock, and chief among the cotton importers who defied Napoleon's embargo was Kirkman Finlay, head of the great firm of James Finlay and Company and later Provost and M.P. for Glasgow. It was Kirkman Finlay, Walter Ritchie and Hugh Crawford, also of Greenock, who helped to bring to an end in 1813 the East India Company's monopoly of trade between Britain and India, and it was Finlay who in 1816 sent the *Earl of Buckingham* to India, the

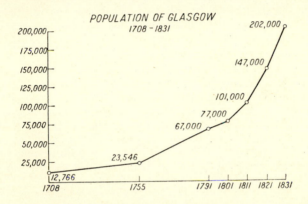

first ship to sail there from the Clyde. Later, the Glasgow merchants were the first in Britain to extend their trade to China and Burma. In addition to the new trade, there were new, fast-expanding industries. Coal, mined all round Glasgow, had been for many years one of the city's exports; by the new methods of deep-mining, the output was greatly increased and the Monkland Canal was cut in 1790 to bring the coals more easily into the city. When the iron industry began to boom in Lanarkshire in the 1820's and 1830's, partly as a result of the invention of the hot-blast furnace by James Neilson, manager of Glasgow gasworks, the natural centre for the industry was Glasgow.[1] The building of steamboats was started down the Clyde at Port Glasgow (where

[1] See p. 96

the *Comet* was launched in 1812), Greenock and Dumbarton, but Glasgow was not slow to follow, and the typical Clydeside workman was no longer a cotton operative but a shipwright or engineer.[1] For the new industries workers swarmed into the city and neighbouring towns from the Highlands, and also from Ireland from about 1820 onwards. The statistics in the diagram on the preceding page show the tremendous growth of the population from the date of the first official census onwards.

By the end of the century the figure was to rise to nearly a million, and Glasgow had become the "second city in the Empire". We shall read later of the problems which Glasgow and other industrial towns had to face because of this tremendous expansion.[2]

SOURCE EXTRACT

"Glasgow is the most handsome city in Scotland, all the buildings being of fine freestone. . . . The air of this place is so clear that a mountain called Ben Lomond, 25 miles distant, may be seen from the head of King Street. . . . The inhabitants have been remarkable for their strictness in attending to the public and private worship of God; so that, in going past their doors in an evening, you may hear so many singing psalms, that strangers are apt to think themselves in a church. The hour of dinner is 3 o'clock; but it is customary also to take what is called a meridian, or a pint of ale and a salt herring about one. A salt herring they call 'a Glasgow Magistrate'. The students at the College, about 400 in number, wear scarlet gowns. . . . Many of the merchants acquire vast fortunes and they have such an inclination to business that little besides it ever engages their attention. Those that trade to Virginia are decked out in great wigs and scarlet cloaks and strut about on the Exchange [the pavement in front of the later Tontine] like so many actors on a stage. They carry on an extensive trade to Holland by means of the Forth; and when the new canal is cut the advantages will be considerable. . . . They have a great share of the herring fishery; and many of them are proprietors of plantations in America. The linen manufactures are carried on to a more extensive degree than in any other town or city in Scotland; and almost everything taken in hand by them prospers. . . ."

Spencer: *English Traveller* (1771)

[1] See pp. 152-5   [2] See Chap. XIII

EXERCISES

1. What parts of the above passage show a contrast with the Glasgow of today?
2. What were the main difficulties which Glasgow merchants had to overcome in the eighteenth century?
3. Give the names and dates of the wars fought by Britain between 1740 and 1815. What effect did they have on Glasgow's trade?
4. Write short notes on the following: Walter Gibson, Andrew Cochrane, John Glassford, William Cunningham, John Anderson, Patrick Colquhoun, Kirkman Finlay.
5. Explain the following: Laigh Kirk, piazzas, gabbarts, Tolbooth, Tron, plantations, harn, inkle, plainstanes, seizers, meridian, "Glasgow Magistrates".
6. If you live in or near Glasgow, find out more about the traces of Old Glasgow mentioned in the second paragraph.
7. If you live on the Clyde, find out more about your town or district in the eighteenth century—the size of population, the kind of trade and industry most common, etc.
(You will find details in Sir John Sinclair's *Statistical Account* for your parish.)

CHAPTER V

THE INDUSTRIAL REVOLUTION—I

LINEN AND COTTON

Domestic System.—The eighteenth century saw great changes in industry, so great that they have been summed up in the word "Revolution". Hitherto, industry had been carried on mainly on a small scale in the home—hence the name, "Domestic System". There were some exceptions in the seventeenth century which we have already noticed,[1] such as coalmining, salt-manu-facture and the woollen factory at NEW MILLS, HADDINGTON, which kept going only for a quarter of a century after its founda-

c   [1] See Bk. I, p. 178, p. 223

tion in 1681. But generally the domestic system prevailed and in
almost every home there was some spinning of flax, wool and
sometimes a little hemp. In the eighteenth century, when linen
became the main export of Scotland, it was still mainly a cottage
industry and, so far as the weaving process was concerned, remained so even into the middle of the nineteenth century. The
linen industry was almost universal in Scotland during that time
but there were some other cottage industries peculiar to certain
localities. For example, DOUNE in Perthshire was famous for the
craftsmanship and beauty of the pistols made by one or two
families, the Caddells, Campbells, Murdochs and Christies, until
the cheap, mass-produced weapons of Birmingham and London
ended the old craft; CULROSS in Fife was famous for its girdles,
KILMARNOCK for its woollen bonnets, Aberdeenshire and Shetland
for their knitted stockings. The changeover from the domestic
to the factory system, from small-scale individual craftsmanship
to large-scale mass-production, was first marked in the linen and
cotton industries, which provided the bulk of Scotland's exports
in the eighteenth and early nineteenth centuries.

Linen Industry.—The main processes of the textile industries
(wool, linen, cotton, etc.) are fairly similar but it is as well for us
to study more particularly those of the linen industry, which was
so important in Scottish life after the Union of 1707. Flax was
grown in most parts of Scotland at the beginning of the eighteenth
century but, as the industry expanded, it became necessary to
import it from Holland, the Baltic countries and elsewhere. The
"Improvers" did not like to grow flax, as it was known as a
"scourging" crop, which reduced the fertility of the soil. The
first stage after the reaping or plucking was RETTING—rotting of
the flax by steeping it in water. Then followed the SCUTCHING—
separating the fibre by beating the flax, after which came the
HECKLING or dressing the flax with a heckle or steel comb. The
SPINNING of the yarn was a part-time occupation for the women
and an unmarried woman naturally became a "spinster". Before
the spinning-wheel was introduced about the middle of the century (it had been in use in England since Tudor times), women
used the primitive method of distaff and spindle, called by them

"rock" and "reel". In the winter-time they would make the spinning a sociable affair, having a "rocking" in one another's house in rotation (like a modern "sewing-bee"); even after spinning-wheels were introduced, it was usual to refer to a pleasant social evening as a "rocking". The dressed flax was generally sent out by merchants to be spun and the yarn was later collected by their agents or "intakers". The WEAVING of the linen cloth was a highly-skilled craft, which provided a full-time occupation for a man. His work tended to be solitary, as the clatter of the loom made conversation impossible, and the "wabster" had the reputation of being a clever, deep-thinking person. Last came the finishing processes of BLEACHING, DYEING and PRINTING. At one time, all the processes of linen manufacture might be performed by the members of one family, but gradually it became easier and more profitable to have specialization for each process. In every process, too, the domestic system was replaced by large-scale factory production, although it lingered on well after 1850 in the weaving section of the industry.

State Control.—People sometimes talk as if state control of industry and government subsidies are of twentieth-century origin, but there was probably as much regulation of industry in Tudor England as there is today. The linen industry in Scotland owed a great deal to government control and financial encouragement. One of the unforeseen effects of the Union of 1707, by which Scottish merchants hoped to compete with English merchants in colonial markets, was to open the Scottish market to the superior English cloth and thereby help to ruin the Scottish woollen industry. For a long time after this it continued only as a cottage industry for home consumption and the Scots concentrated on linen as their main export to the colonies and to Europe. In 1727, a Board of Trustees for Manufactures was set up by the Government to encourage the manufacture of linen, hempen and other goods. This BOARD OF TRUSTEES gave premiums for growing "lint" (flax), started spinning-schools, gave subsidies for bleachfields, brought in French weavers to Edinburgh (Picardy Place, off Leith Walk, is called after their small settlement), Irish weavers to Galloway, and skilled flax-dressers or hecklers from Flanders.

It was now that the linen industry began to see some specialization and large-scale enterprise. In 1729 there was set up at Bonnington, Edinburgh, a lint-mill for scutching with machines driven by water-power; by 1772, there were 252 such lint-mills in Scotland. Heckling also became a specialized job, done sometimes at lint-mills and sometimes at "heckleries" or private workshops, such as Robert Burns worked at in Irvine for a time. Several bleachfields were laid out by 1729, a subsidy of £50 an acre being given; the largest, 12 acres in extent, was at Dalquhurn in the Vale of Leven, which later became the main centre in Scotland for bleaching, dyeing and printing of cotton.

Private Enterprise.—The Board of Trustees, which continued its efforts for almost a century, was not alone in its encouragement of linen manufacture. We have already noticed how "improving" lairds like Cockburn of Ormiston and Grant of Monymusk tried to promote the industry on their estates.[1] We shall see later how thread-making was started in Renfrewshire by a clever woman, Mrs Christian Millar, who managed to get hold of the Dutch method.[2] In 1746, just after the rebellion had collapsed, the BRITISH LINEN COMPANY was started in Edinburgh by the Duke of Argyll and others; in the following year they began a banking business, which helped tradesmen or merchants by giving them credit. The British Linen Bank still exists, although its connection with the linen industry has long since ceased. Scottish linen was at first mainly the coarse "harn", but the production of finer fabrics, lawns and cambrics, was given a fillip in Glasgow in 1765, when forty skilled French workers were brought over to settle in the village of Anderston nearby. The effect of all this encouragement and enterprise was the great expansion of the linen industry throughout Scotland, as is shown by the annual totals of yards of linen approved and stamped by the Board of Trustees (see diagram opposite).

Almost every county produced some linen by the end of the century, the highest totals being those of Forfarshire, Fife, Aberdeenshire and Perthshire while Renfrewshire and Lanarkshire were not far behind. The main processes, spinning and

[1] See pp. 23-4   [2] See p. 70

weaving, were almost entirely still domestic. In some towns like Cullen, where Lord Deskford had laid out a bleaching field in 1752, nearly every householder was a weaver. In Dundee, as in Glasgow, there lived the merchants who supplied the yarn to the weavers of nearby towns such as Forfar, Brechin, Blairgowrie and Kirriemuir (which is the "Thrums" of J. M. Barrie's novels). Dundee not only supplied the American colonies with coarse

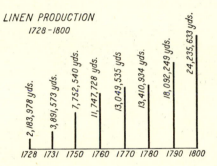

LINEN PRODUCTION
1728 - 1800

linens but also produced the best canvas in Britain for sail-cloth, the sails of Nelson's *Victory* being made of Dundee canvas. Perth, like Glasgow, was famous for its cambric and lawn printed handkerchiefs, and Dunfermline for its damask table linen. Yet, although the linen industry went on expanding, by the end of the century the output of linen was surpassed by that of cotton.

Paisley.—For two centuries the name of Paisley has been prominent as a centre of the textile industry; the names of some of its old streets recall the variety of its industries—Lawn, Gauze, Incle, Silk, Cotton, Thread and Shuttle Streets. Paisley had grown up under the protection of the wealthy Abbey (in the church of which Marjory Bruce lies buried) and at the end of the seventeenth century had a population of over 2,000, of whom about a hundred were weavers. In 1710, they were said to be busy weaving "Bengals", striped cloths of mixed linen and cotton, in imitation of Indian muslins. The manufacture of fine linen thread was introduced to Paisley not long after it had been started in Johnstone, a neighbouring village, by a MRS CHRISTIAN

Millar, a minister's widow, whose life story may be said to bridge medieval and modern times. Before her marriage she had been Christian Shaw, daughter of the Laird of Bargarran in Renfrewshire; as a girl of eleven, she had suffered from fits which were blamed on witchcraft and, after a lengthy trial, six people were burnt to death for the "crime" in 1697. Mrs Millar started in 1721 to make by hand fine thread for lacemaking, bleaching the flax on slates at her window, but soon she obtained

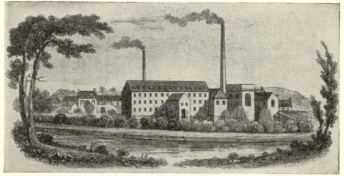

By courtesy of J. and P. Coats, Ltd.

Ferguslie Thread Works, Paisley, 1835

from Holland a thread-twisting mill with which she could produce a finer thread. The Bargarran thread was copied and by 1744 there were 93 thread-twisting mills in Paisley; the thread-manufacture started then has never since died out. Linen-weaving still continued to be the chief occupation in the town and, like Glasgow, Paisley produced fine lawn and cambric piece goods for export to America. A new industry started just after the middle of the century. Humphrey Fulton of Beith had settled in Paisley in 1749 as a linen-weaver and after a few years he began the weaving of silk gauze. Others followed him so that by 1766 there were 702 silk looms. Edinburgh and other towns had silk-making on a small scale but nothing to compare with Paisley, which was the outstanding success in Scotland in this branch of textiles; Paisley silk gauze was considered even better than that of Spitalfields in London, where the industry had been started by some Huguenot refugees from France after 1685. By the end of the century, cotton, to which the skilled Paisley worker could easily turn his hand, was ousting both silk and linen. Cotton thread manufacture was taken up by James and Patrick Clark in 1812 and in time became Paisley's main industry; today the firm of J. P. COATS AND CO., formed by an amalgamation of the two large firms, Coats and Clark, is the world's greatest thread-making concern. The other great Paisley specialty was the Paisley or harness shawl, made from about 1806 in imitation of the Indian cashmere shawl. These shawls, woven with spun silk and the finest wool in elaborate patterns and beautiful colours, at one time cost as much as £20 and were very fashionable in Britain and America; Queen Victoria wore one at the christening of her eldest child and once gave an order for seventeen shawls. By 1870 the Paisley shawl went out of fashion and the trade died out. The manufacture of ordinary, everyday thread has provided more continuous employment than the silk gauzes of the eighteenth century or the shawls of the nineteenth century.

Cotton Spinning-Mills.—We have seen already that the Scottish cotton industry had its origins on Clydeside, in Paisley and Glasgow. Some of the weavers there had been for long making muslins, fine cotton fabrics, and like the English cotton-weavers at that time used linen for the warp, the threads that ran lengthwise, and cotton for the weft, the threads that were carried by the shuttle across the warp. In 1780, JAMES MONTEITH of Anderston, Glasgow, using "bird's-nest" Indian yarn, produced the first all-cotton web in Scotland. It was about this time that the spinning-machines invented by the Englishmen, Hargreaves, Arkwright and Crompton, were introduced to Scotland. Cotton yarn, spun on Hargreaves's jenny, was not strong enough for the warp and it was not until 1775, when Arkwright's water-frame produced a stronger thread, that cotton yarn, suitable for both warp and weft, was produced on the one machine. Arkwright's water-frame was such a heavy machine that it needed water-power to work it (hence the name), and the result was the building of mills beside rivers and the beginning of the factory system in the cotton industry, which in this case took the lead over the linen industry. The first spinning-mills in Scotland were started at Penicuik (1778), Rothesay (1779), Neilston (1780), Johnstone (1782), East Kilbride, and North Woodside, Glasgow (1783). Arkwright himself helped to start large-scale cotton-spinning in Scotland by entering into negotiations in 1783 with David Dale of Glasgow, who opened the New Lanark cotton-mill in 1786. Up to this time the yarn spun in Scotland had been suitable only for the coarser calicoes and fustians. It was not until about 1785, when Crompton's mule was introduced, that weavers could obtain fine, strong yarn suitable for making muslins which could rival those of the East. In 1790, water-power was first applied in Scotland to Crompton's mule by William Kelly, the manager of the New Lanark mill, and cotton-spinning on the domestic system gradually died out.

King Cotton.—From the end of the American War (1783) to the end of the century, the cotton industry boomed. We have already seen how the new plantations in the southern states of

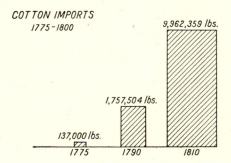

COTTON IMPORTS
1775-1800

9,962,359 lbs.

1,757,504 lbs.

137,000 lbs.

1775   1790   1810

the U.S.A. and the invention of Whitney's cotton-gin (1793) caused this expansion and how Glasgow profited from it. As Lancashire became the "cotton county" of England, so Clydeside became the cotton area of Scotland—and for similar reasons, which have been explained in the last chapter. The collapse of the tobacco trade helped rather than hindered this new industry, for men who had accumulated wealth invested it in cotton-mills instead of tobacco plantations. The tremendous expansion is best shown by statistics of raw cotton imported into the Clyde (see diagram opposite).

Even before 1800, cotton manufacture had become the premier industry of Scotland. The demand for cotton goods came not only from overseas, America and the continent of Europe, but also from the home market. Cotton proved a cheap and attractive substitute for silk and linen, and has remained the standard material for women's wear until the twentieth century, when new fabrics like rayon are in turn supplanting it.

David Dale.—The story of David Dale (1737-1806), who has been called "the father of the Scottish cotton industry", gives us some idea of the way in which capitalists like him helped to develop the new industry. Dale had started his career as a "herd laddie", looking after the cattle at his native Stewarton in Ayrshire. He learnt linen-weaving in Paisley and worked at it in Hamilton and Cambuslang before he started up in the linen yarn trade in Glasgow. At first he travelled about the countryside buying yarn from farmers' wives but he later began to import fine French yarn which brought him great profit. Like most importers of yarn, he employed a large number of weavers, and he also engaged in the manufacture of inkles (linen tapes) in Glasgow. In 1783, when he was Bailie of the city, vice-president of the newly-founded Chamber of Commerce, and first agent of the Glasgow branch of the Royal Bank of Scotland, he built, at a cost of £6,000, a house in Charlotte Street which was demolished only in 1954. In the same year, along with Richard Arkwright, he visited the Falls of Clyde and discussed with the English inventor a project to use the water-power for the new spinning-machine, the water-frame. The two men entered into a partnership which did not last, but Dale himself succeeded in 1786 in opening the NEW LANARK cotton mill, which, when it was extended in 1793, was the largest in Europe. In 1787, he joined with James Monteith of Anderston in setting up a cotton-mill at Blantyre (where David Livingstone was later to work) and along with the laird of Balloch-

Agricultural and Industrial Revolutions

Find out why these places are mentioned in Chapters I, II, V and VI

myle also started a mill at Catrine in Ayrshire, which is still in existence. He was a friend of the Highland dyer, George Macintosh, and combined with him to open the first turkey-red dye-works in Britain at Barrowfield, Glasgow, and a model cotton-mill and village, Spinningdale, on the Dornoch Firth, which proved a failure. He is also said to have lost over £20,000 in sinking a coal-mine. Dale was a deeply religious man, who from the age of thirty had been a lay preacher in an Independent church in Glasgow, learning Greek and Hebrew the better to study the Bible. At New Lanark he gave better wages and better working conditions than any employer of his time; he built good houses and provided sanitation for his workers, for whom he gave opportunities for education. In spite of that, the conditions were such as would appal people today: the 500 orphans, whom he collected from Edinburgh and Glasgow poorhouses, worked 11½ hours a day (with sometimes 2 hours of schooling in addition) and received no holidays except Sundays, which their employer gave them because of his religious objections to Sunday work. Dale's philanthropic work was continued and developed by his son-in-law, ROBERT OWEN, who made New Lanark one of the showplaces of Europe. New Lanark mills have passed into the possession of a ropework company but cotton manufacture is still carried on at Catrine mills, now the property of James Finlay and Company, the oldest cotton company in Scotland.

Industrial Chemistry.—It was mainly in connection with the finishing processes of the linen and cotton industry—bleaching, dyeing and printing—that industrial chemistry developed, and Scotland played a leading part in this field. Bleaching was one of the first textile processes to be specialized and performed by large-scale concerns. As we have seen, the Board of Trustees gave subsidies as large as £600 for starting bleachfields in 1728. The bleaching process was at first a very slow one and might take eight months; the linen was "soured" with butter-milk, laid out on grass or beech hedges, and regularly soaked for months with water ladled from small channels until the sun and the air had bleached it white. Bleachfields might be as large as 12 acres and were owned by well-to-do men like Sandeman of Perth or Stirling of Dalquhurn in the Vale of Leven, who had several employees working for them. It was a nephew of the bleacher, Stirling, who laid out the first large-scale printfield in Scotland at Dawsholm, on the banks of the Kelvin near Glasgow, about 1750, moving later to the Vale of Leven also. The bleaching process was hastened by the use of very dilute sulphuric acid, which became available after 1749 when DR JOHN ROEBUCK started his vitriol works at Prestonpans, where he used the large supplies of local salt to make soda. The next improvement came in 1787 when James Watt brought back from Paris the secret of Berthollet's process of bleaching with chlorine for his father-in-law, who had a large bleachfield in Glasgow. In 1799, CHARLES TENNANT and CHARLES MACINTOSH of Glasgow combined chlorine with slaked lime to produce a bleaching powder, which gradually became almost universal in the cotton industry. Tennant founded the St. Rollox chemical works, the tall chimney of which was known as "Tennant's Stalk", a landmark for miles round Glasgow. Dyeing in Glasgow at this period was ahead of the rest of the country. GEORGE MACINTOSH, who founded the Gaelic Club of Glasgow and whose son, Charles, gave his name to the waterproof, started a factory in Glasgow for the manufacture of cudbear, a purple dye prepared from lichen. In 1785 he brought to Glasgow a Frenchman, Papillon, to introduce turkey-red dyeing to Britain. This colour had an enormous vogue in the nineteenth century and the United Turkey Red Company of the Vale of Leven, one of the few old firms still in the cotton industry in Scotland, was at one time the largest organization of its kind in the world. It was another Scottish firm, Pullars of Perth, which in the middle of the nineteenth century encouraged the experiments in aniline dyes and opened up a new range of colours. The Vale of Leven, with its fine supply of pure water from Loch Lomond, was well suited for dyeing and bleaching; it also became the main centre for calico-printing, a process which was greatly improved in 1783 by the invention of cylinder printing, at Preston, Lancashire, by a Scotsman, Thomas Bell. By the nineteenth century all these finishing processes were conducted in large-scale undertakings, so far as the cotton and linen industries were concerned, but in the manufacture of wool, which remained a rural industry for a long time after, home-dyeing still went on.

Handloom Weavers.—By 1790, there were 15,000 cotton-weavers between Girvan in the south and Stirling in the north, employed by Glasgow manufacturers who supplied the weavers with yarn and later collected the webs of cotton. In the next twenty years, their numbers increased but not fast enough to cope with the demand for their products. They were then able to make from 30s. to 40s. for a four-day week, high wages when an average wage was 10s. for a six-day week, and the weavers were reckoned "the aristocrats of labour". But the coming of the power-loom spelt their doom. It had been patented by Edmund Cartwright in 1787 and was first used in Scotland in 1793 by James Robertson who installed a pair of looms in a cellar in Argyle Street, Glasgow, using Newfoundland dogs to drive them. In 1794, power-looms were introduced in a bleaching and printing works at Milton, near Dumbarton, where the owners were unable to obtain sufficient supplies of calico from the handloom weavers. Not much headway in factory-weaving was made till after 1807 when an improved power-loom was set up at the Catrine mill of James Finlay and Company. By 1812, when the Luddite riots had started in England, the weavers were attempting to smash the power-looms both at Catrine and at Deanston, near Doune, where the Finlays had another mill. In the same year, they staged a strike in the Glasgow district when the employers tried to reduce their wages. Although steam-power was used in a Glasgow spinning-mill as early as 1792, it was not generally applied for a long time either to spinning or weaving machines, mainly because mill-owners found water-power cheap and plentiful. The disappearance of the handloom weaver was slow and in most cases painful. He could perform fine work for which the power-loom was unsuitable and in 1840 there were still over 50,000 hand-looms in Scotland; but the high wages were no longer obtainable. Few, if any, weavers earned more than 10s. a week, and many only half of that amount, so that they needed some other source of income as well and often lived in appalling poverty. Most of these weavers were to be found in Glasgow, Renfrewshire and

Ayrshire, but north of Glasgow there were also many "weaving towns" such as Kilsyth, Kirkintilloch, Balfron, Dunblane, Auchterarder, Kinross and Perth. By 1850, the cotton power-loom had triumphed, except for special lines like the Paisley shawl, which was being produced finally in a cotton imitation. Not long after this, the whole cotton industry suffered a crippling blow when supplies of raw cotton were cut off during the American Civil War (1861-65). Lancashire recovered but in Scotland it gradually declined, although there are still over 50 firms spinning and weaving cotton, and many others engaged in various other processes.

Linen Machinery.—The story of the advent of machinery and factories in the linen industry is similar to those of cotton, except that they came later. The first linen spinning-mill was started in 1787 by Sim and Thorn at Bervie in Kincardineshire but machine-spinning proved unsatisfactory because of the stickiness of the fibres. In 1826 the machine process was improved by Kay (almost a hundred years after his namesake had invented the flying-shuttle); he suggested steeping the fibres for six hours previous to spinning to make it easier. The power-loom was first used in the linen industry by Wilson of Brechin in 1810 but it was not generally adopted till well after the middle of the century. The eastern counties, north of the Forth, were the linen counties of the nineteenth century, and Dunfermline, Kirkcaldy, Brechin, Dundee, Arbroath, Forfar, Montrose and Aberdeen the principal centres, although weaving went on in nearly every village. The introduction of the Jacquard loom in 1825 proved of great benefit to Dunfermline in its manufacture of fine damask table linen, and generally linen production went on increasing till the middle of the century, as can be seen from the figures of average annual output for each decade in diagram opposite.

The cotton shortage during the American Civil War (1861-65) gave linen goods a temporary boost but thereafter the trade gradually declined. By 1865, handlooms were still in use for linen weaving; J. M. Barrie's father did not give up the handloom weaving until 1870, when he left Kirriemuir for a clerical job in Forfar. Long before this, many weavers had given up the

struggle involved in working 14 hours a day (and sometimes one
night a week) to make only four or five shillings a week. Among
those who emigrated was Andrew Carnegie's father, who left

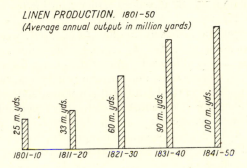

LINEN PRODUCTION. 1801-50
(Average annual output in million yards)

25 m. yds. 33 m. yds. 60 m. yds. 90 m. yds. 100 m. yds.

1801-10   1811-20   1821-30   1831-40   1841-50

Dunfermline for Pennsylvania in 1848.[1] As we shall see later the
advent of the jute industry to Dundee and the linoleum industry
to Kirkcaldy saved these places, while Dunfermline still produces
table linen of the highest quality.[2]

Factory System.—The changes we have been considering
took place over a period of more than a century. What effects
did they have on Scotland? The most obvious was the disappearance of the domestic system in the linen and cotton industries,
although it lingered on in weaving for a long time, and in the
woollen industry continues today. In its place came the factory
system, in which the factory-owners, a small class of "capitalists",
owning and controlling the factories, employed great numbers of
workers. Many of the people were henceforth no longer self-
employed but were wage-earners, working regular hours, the start
and finish of which were signalled by the works whistle or siren.
Although the plight of the handloom weaver in his cottage might
be miserable enough and his hours at the loom long and weary,
he felt at any rate that he was not just a wage-slave like the factory
worker. Since the time of the Industrial Revolution, the working
hours of most people have been regulated for them, the number
of hours being gradually reduced by successive Factory Acts.

[1] See p. 264   [2] See pp. 187-8

Another result of the coming of the factory system was a marked decline in the health standards of the working-classes in the towns. Factories and cotton-mills were originally built for the efficient running of the machines rather than for the health and comfort of the workers. Further, in the towns overcrowding and insanitary conditions, hardly credible to us today, were normal; when epidemics, like cholera, came to Scotland, they swept through the slums, killing off many of the poorer people.[1] Child labour, made possible by the introduction of machinery, also helped to undermine the health of the workers, and many found themselves deformed or afflicted with some incurable disease before they were twenty-one. Still another result of the changes in the textile industry was the mushroom growth of the towns, with all the evil consequences inevitable from such a rapid expansion. But here we must remember that some of the textile workers still lived in country villages. Cotton-mills were at first situated in valleys, where the rivers or streams provided the necessary water-power and the three or four hundred workers lived in pleasant country surroundings. The weavers, as we have seen, also maintained their cottage industry in the villages. We are apt to think of the Industrial Revolution as bringing only gloom and misery to the people but there is another side to the picture, as we can see in the extract from the *Statistical Account* given at the end of Chapter II, which shows how the country-dwellers benefited. Finally, the factory system allowed Britain to build up the trade and the wealth which were later to give her workers the highest standards of living in Europe. When times were good, a factory job was an attraction. But good times were succeeded by slumps and depressions, when there was little or nothing to relieve the misery and sufferings of the workless. For this reason, as we shall see, the period, 1815-50, was one of unparalleled distress and discontent in the towns.[2]

SOURCE EXTRACT

"The 1727 is as far back as I can remember. At that time there was little bread in Scotland, Manefactorys brought to no perfection

[1] See p. 197   [2] See p. 161

either in linnen or woolen. Every woman made her web of wove linnen and bleched it herself; it never rose higher than 2 shillings the yeard, and with this cloth was every body cloathed. The young gentlemen, who at this time were growing more delicat, got their cloth from Holland for shirts; but the old was satisfied with necks and sleeves of the fine, which were put on loose above the country cloth. I remember in the 30 or 31 of a ball where it was agreed that the company should be dress'd in nothing but what was manufactur'd in the country. My sisters were as well dressed as any, and their gowns were strip'd linen at 2s and 6d per yard. Their heads and ruffles were of Paisly muslings, at 4 and sixpence, with four peny edging from Hamilton; all of them the finest that could be had. A few years after this, wevers were brought over from Holland, and manefactorys for linen established in the West. The dress of the ladys were nearly as expencive as at present, tho' not so often renewed. At the time I mention houps were worn constantly 4 yards and a half wide, which required much silk to cover them, and gould and silver was much used for trimming, never less than three rows round the peticot, so that tho' the silk was slight the price was increased by the triming. Then the heads were all dress'd in laces from Flanders; no blonds nor courss-edging used; the price of those was high but two sute would serve for life; they were not renewed but at marriage or some great event. Who could not afoard those wore fringes of thread."

Elizabeth Mure: *Some Observations of the Change of Manners in My Own Time*, 1700-1790

EXERCISES

1. Try to find out something about Elizabeth Mure of Caldwell, who wrote the above passage.
2. On a blank map of Scotland, headed INDUSTRIAL REVOLUTION, insert the places mentioned in this chapter, putting the letter (C) or (L) after the name, to show its connection with the cotton or linen industries.
3. Explain the following lines and try to find their sources:
    (a) "On Fasten-e'en we had a rockin";
    (b) "Her cutty sark of Paisley harn".
4. Find the derivation of the following words: Damask, lawn, cambric, calico, fustian, muslin.

5. Write short notes on the following: Board of Trustees for Manufactures, British Linen Company, Mrs Christian Millar, Humphrey Fulton, James Monteith, Charles Tennant, Charles Macintosh, David Dale, J. P. Coats & Co., James Finlay & Co. Ltd., U.T.R. Co., Ltd.
6. Write a short paragraph on the "Domestic System".
7. Why did Clydeside become the "cotton area" of Scotland?
8. Why did the linen industry continue so long in north-east Scotland?
9. Make a list of improvements in agriculture or industry introduced from Holland in the eighteenth century.
10. From the old and new Statistical Accounts, find out as many facts as you can about the linen or cotton industries in your districts—names of mills, wages paid, etc.

CHAPTER VI

THE INDUSTRIAL REVOLUTION—II

COAL, IRON AND ENGINEERING

Heavy Industries.—Between the Highlands and the Southern Uplands of Scotland lie the Central Lowlands, the industrial belt of Scotland. As you know from your study of geography, one of the main reasons why this area is so much industrialized is that in it are located all the main Scottish coalfields. Associated with coalmining are to be found today the other heavy industries—iron and steel, engineering and shipbuilding. The coalfields have been there long before our era and were worked from at least the Middle Ages but the other industries, with the exception of a little shipbuilding, can hardly be said to have existed till modern times. In this chapter, we shall see how the growth of these industries in the eighteenth and nineteenth centuries was so tremendous that, like that of the textile industries, it is also considered a "revolution". In this case, it was not a change from the domestic to the factory system. Coalmining had for long been conducted as a large-scale, capitalist enterprise. In the seventeenth century, as we have seen in Book I, some of the Scottish lairds had become industrialists, like the Earl of Wemyss, who during the Commonwealth period took up the development of the coal-heughs on his lands, building the harbour of Methil for exporting coal. The Scottish mine-owning lairds were greatly helped by acts of Parliament passed by their fellow-landowners and burgesses, acts which left the colliers and salters little better than the serfs of the Middle Ages. Many of the seventeenth-century coal-heughs or coal-pits, e.g., at Wemyss, Saltcoats and Prestonpans, were connected with the manufacture of salt from sea-water, since much coal was used as fuel in the salt-pans. In 1700, coal-mining was thus being conducted on quite a large scale for that period, partly for salt manufacture and partly also to satisfy the growing demand for it as a household fuel in the towns. In addition, there were the leadmines at Leadhills, which had been worked for centuries, and silver was also mined in the same district and elsewhere. Earlier, in the sixteenth and seventeenth centuries, when a keen interest was taken in the search for precious metals, there had been found at Crawford, Lanarkshire, gold which was used for the beautiful Scottish coin, the "bonnet-piece", and also for part of the Scottish regalia. In the seventeenth century, also, iron had been smelted at two places on the remote Loch Maree, the woods on the lochside being felled for charcoal for the *ceardach ruadh* (the "red smithy"), but no iron ore was being smelted at all in Scotland in 1700. Engineering, if the work of a millwright could be given such a name, was in its infancy. We shall see how all these industries developed and, as they expanded, reacted upon one another to cause further expansion, until they became the key industries of our country.

Collier Serfs.—The condition of the Scottish colliers and salters was a standing disgrace to Scotland in the seventeenth century and was little better than slavery, which indeed was the term used to describe it in the act of Parliament of 1774, the first to afford them relief. Their low status was due partly to their

dirty and dangerous occupation and partly to the fact that mine-
owners were permitted by acts of Parliament to apprehend
vagrants and to receive convicted criminals for the work. It was
probably a Highland cateran, who in 1701 thus became a collier-
serf of Sir John Erskine of Alva; on the iron collar, which he
wore and which was dragged up from the bed of the Forth years
later, was the inscription—"Alexander Steuart, found guilty of
death for theft at Perth, the 5th of December, 1701, and gifted
as a perpetual servant to Sir John Aresken of Alva". The Scottish

Photo : National Museum of Antiquities of Scotland

Serf's Iron Collar

Habeas Corpus Act, passed in the same year, 1701, protecting
the subject against "wrongous imprisonment", did not apply to
colliers and salters, who were expressly excluded. Although in
strict law the child of a collier was free, in practice he was regarded as bound to be a collier also, through the lairds' custom
of making a gift to the parents at the time of the christening. This
gift was considered as an "arles", binding the parents to bring
up the child as a collier. Invariably the father did so, for in
Scotland the winning of coal was a family business. The father
(and his sons, if they were old enough) were the colliers, the

'hewers" of coal, while his wife and daughters were the "bearers", employed and paid by the collier, not the mine-owner. In most pits, where there was no winding-gear, all the coal was carried in creels on the women's backs, not only along the underground ways but by ladders up pits, as deep as 100 feet. The creel, which had a strap to pass round the forehead, might contain as much as 170 lb. of coal and required two men to lift it on to a woman's shoulders. Hugh Miller, the geologist, remarked on the peculiar type of mouth found in collier women, no doubt due to their constant drudgery—"wide, open, thick-lipped, projecting equally above and below, accompanied with traits of almost infantine weakness". Many women had worked in the mines since childhood; in Alloa colliery there were 103 boys and girls under 7 years of age at work in 1780. An old collier, giving evidence in 1841 before a government commission on mines, said that, in his youth at Preston Grange, colliers guilty of disobedience were "placed by the neck in iron collars, called 'jougs', and fastened to the wall", or "made to go the 'rown'", that is, "tied in front of the horse at the gin" (winding-gear) "and made run backwards all day". The colliers of the eighteenth century gradually improved their condition, however, and as the growing demand for their labour could not be met from collier families, their wages were increased in order to attract recruits and to hold the others in their jobs. In 1771, according to Adam Smith, the economist, their weekly wage was 13s. or 12s. while ordinary day-labourers received only 4s. or 6s. a week. High wages could not entice sufficient men to become colliers, despised by their fellow-men even to the extent of being denied burial in consecrated ground. Finally, the masters, who could not get enough coal to satisfy the demands of the iron-furnaces, glass-works, salt-pans and the domestic fires in the growing towns, themselves sought to remove the stigma. First, an act was passed in 1774, making emancipation possible only with great difficulty, and later, in 1799, another act made the colliers finally free. For many years, however, the shortage of labour in the mines continued because of the memories of the collier's servile lot.

Early Iron Industry.—In the eighteenth century, the English iron industry was facing a crisis. For centuries, charcoal had been the fuel used for almost all the processes, and the forests that had formerly provided the wood for the charcoal were gradually disappearing, partly because of the demands for fuel and partly to build the "wooden walls" of England. The iron industry which had been so prosperous in the Weald in southern England declined there for lack of fuel supplies, and moved to more isolated parts of the country where timber could be more readily obtained. It was for this reason that in the early eighteenth century iron-smelting started in Scotland, not in the Central Lowlands, where it is located today, but in the West Highlands where there were abundant, natural forests of pine and birch. At four places, iron-furnaces were set up by English companies, using mainly English iron-ore brought by sea and charcoal made from the Scottish forests. The first, which operated from 1729 to 1736, was erected at Invergarry, near Fort Augustus, by a company from Cumberland; the English manager, Rawlinson, it is claimed, was responsible for introducing the short pleated kilt for the local people employed as labourers in the roadmaking there. Another furnace which was short-lived was that at Abernethy, Strathspey, which operated from 1730 to 1739 and which used iron-ore brought by ponies from the Lecht mines fourteen miles away. But a more successful venture was Bonawe furnace, started by a Lancashire company near Taynuilt on the shores of Loch Etive, where iron-ore, brought from Lancashire, was smelted from 1753 to 1864. Six miles from Inveraray, Loch Fyne, another Lancashire firm in 1775 started an ironworks, which continued to operate till 1813, the village nearby being called Furnace to this day. The Scottish iron industry, which was started by Englishmen, was to owe much to English ideas and methods for most of the eighteenth century.

New Methods.—Another way of overcoming the shortage of charcoal was to find some other fuel. In 1709, a Quaker iron-master, Abraham Darby of Coalbrookdale, Shropshire, managed to use coal for his blast-furnaces—not coal in its ordinary state but as coke, formed by partly burning coal as charcoal is formed by partly burning the wood. This invention did not become widely known for a long time for various reasons. Darby tried to keep the secret to himself and his friends; the Shropshire "clod" coal produced a coke much more suitable for smelting than that from other coal, but even his pig-iron was inferior to what was obtained from charcoal-furnaces and was considered fit only for making "cast" iron. It should be understood that after the iron-ore has been smelted (with coke or charcoal) in a BLAST-FURNACE, the pig-iron could be re-melted in a FOUNDRY and shaped or cast in moulds to form CAST IRON, which is hard but brittle, or the pig-iron could be frequently re-heated and hammered in a FORGE until it was WROUGHT IRON. Cast iron was used for farm implements, stoves, grates, pans, cannon; wrought iron was used where greater strains were likely, e.g., pumps, bolts, nails. Pig-iron produced by Darby's process of coke-smelting was not used for making wrought iron until about 1750, when his son introduced improvements. After this, furnaces, foundries and forges came to be located no longer in forests but in or near coalfields. Coal thus became more important and much more was mined, especially since Newcomen's steam-pump, invented in 1708, made it possible to reach seams hitherto inaccessible because of being flooded. In the eighteenth century, Britain was engaged in a series of wars with France and munitions were manufactured on an increasing scale with each war. When the Seven Years' War (1756-63) cut off the supply of iron-ore from Sweden, which even then was considered of high quality, there was a great incentive for the erection of new ironworks to use native ores. At the same time, the improvements in agriculture and the changes in industry called for the manufacture of more iron implements and machines. It is only with a knowledge of this background that we can properly understand the origin of the modern native iron industry of Scotland at Carron near Falkirk.

Anglo-Scottish Enterprise.—Three men were responsible for the founding of the CARRON IRONWORKS in 1759. They were WILLIAM CADELL of Cockenzie, near Prestonpans, an importer of iron and timber; SAMUEL GARBETT, a manufacturer of Birmingham, already noted for its light metal industries; and DR JOHN

ROEBUCK, an Englishman, who had studied medicine at Edinburgh and Leyden and who had started sulphuric acid works at Prestonpans some years before. Garbett and Roebuck had been in partnership at Prestonpans and had there made the acquaintance of Cadell. After much careful preliminary investigation, a site

Photo: National Maritime Museum

A Carronade

beside the river Carron near Falkirk was selected for what was to be an undertaking of the largest size, with a capital of £121,000. Carron possessed many of the prerequisites for success in the iron industry—plenty of coal, iron-ore and wood at hand, water-power for working the giant bellows in the blast-furnaces and for heavy machinery, and proximity to a port, Borrowstounness (as Bo'ness was then called), convenient for London and the Continent. Skilled English workmen were brought from Birmingham, Coalbrookdale and elsewhere to teach the Scottish workmen, and after a year of preparation and building the first Scottish blast-furnace, using Scottish iron-ore and Scottish coal, was lighted in 1760. The partners had many obstacles to overcome. Because of the lack of skill of their workers, the guns they cast in their foundry were several times rejected by the War Office and Admiralty. Dr Roebuck had seen the importance of Darby's method of smelting the ore with coke and he himself in 1762 took out a patent for converting cast iron into wrought iron or malleable iron by the action of a hollow coal fire in conjunction with a powerful blast. Through his sinking coal-mines which he was unable to develop because of water flooding the workings, he got into financial difficulties. It was in order to obtain a better engine for pumping water in the coal-pits that Roebuck came in contact with James Watt, of whose invention he had heard from a mutual friend, Professor Black. Watt spent some years in unsuccessful attempts to make his steam-engine work the water-pump at the Carron Company's coal-pit at Kinneil, which is almost at the eastern terminus of the Antonine Wall of the Romans. But in time, although Roebuck had to sell his share in Watt's invention to pay off part of his debts, the ironworks prospered.

Success of Carron.—By the end of the American War of Independence (1783), the Carron Company had the largest foundry in the world and enjoyed the highest reputation for the cannon they cast. Their short, large-calibre cannon, which was known as the "carronade", was used by the navies on both sides in the French Revolutionary and Napoleonic Wars. In addition, there were manufactured at Carron domestic utensils and agricultural implements, which were exported to the American colonies and Europe. (Carron oil, which was formerly much used as a dressing for burns, is so called because of its becoming well-known first in the ironworks, where burns were frequent.) The cutting of the Forth and Clyde Canal helped them considerably in the transport of iron-ore and coal to Carron and manufactured goods from Carron, and a new port, Grangemouth, developed near Carron at the eastern end of the canal. Other

Scottish ironworks, using Scottish iron-ore and Scottish coal, were set up near coalfields, and by 1796, apart from the two charcoal furnaces on Loch Etive and Loch Fyne, there were eighteen blast-furnaces in Scotland, five of them at Carron. In addition, after 1784, when Henry Cort, an iron-forger working for the Navy, by his two inventions of puddling and rolling, made it possible to use coke as a fuel for producing wrought iron, forges as well as foundries were located in the coalfields. But, although nearly all prospered greatly, none had the success or the reputation of the Carron Company, which still continues to operate after almost two hundred years.

Watt's Early Career.—James Watt's connection with the Carron ironworks has already been mentioned but his career and achievements are of such importance that they deserve a fuller

account. He was born at Greenock in 1736, the son of a master-wright and merchant, who later became a bailie of the burgh, and the grandson of a teacher of mathematics and navigation. James Watt was delicate in his youth and was taught at first at home by his mother, and later in the local school, where he showed his ability at mathematics. He early made acquaintance with instruments and mechanical contrivances in his father's workshop, where the first Greenock crane was made. Desiring to become an instrument-maker, he tried without

Crown Copyright. From an exhibit in the Science Museum, South Kensington

James Watt

success to find someone in Glasgow to teach him the trade and then decided to go to London. In 1755, therefore, after sending his box by sea from Leith, he set off on horseback with a friend, taking twelve days on the road. He had difficulty in finding a master, as he had served no apprenticeship and was at nineteen too old for one, but finally paid an instrument-maker twenty guineas to allow him to work in his shop for a year. There, by his diligence and perseverance, he made great progress, although his health was affected by his close confinement, due partly to his keenness on his work and partly to his fear of the press-gang. When on his return to Scotland he tried to open a workshop in Glasgow, he found it difficult at first because of the opposition of local tradesmen. He was fortunate in having friends at the University, who managed to procure for him the title of "mathematical instrument maker to the University" and a small room at the College. This he used as his workshop for two years until he removed to premises in the Saltmarket. His connection with the University brought him into close contact with some brilliant men. One of them, Dr Joseph Black, professor of Anatomy and Chemistry, discovered in 1761 the principle of latent heat, later to be of importance to Watt in his experiments. In 1763, when he moved again, this time to the busy thoroughfare of the Trongate, he claimed in an advertisement to sell "all sorts of mathematical and musical instruments". His business expanded until in time he was employing as many as seventeen journeymen. It was in the session of 1763-64 that Professor John Anderson gave Watt the task of repairing the model of Newcomen's engine for the Natural Philosophy class and set him on the course which was to bring him such fame.

Watt and the Steam-Engine.—There had been steam-engines before Thomas Newcomen invented his steam-pump in 1708, but his was the first of real practical value because of its use in pumping the water out of mines. It was clumsy and inefficient, however, and Watt's mind gradually turned to ways of improving it. One Sunday afternoon in May, 1765, when he was taking a walk across Glasgow Green, he hit upon the idea of a separate condenser for the engine. He continued with his experiments

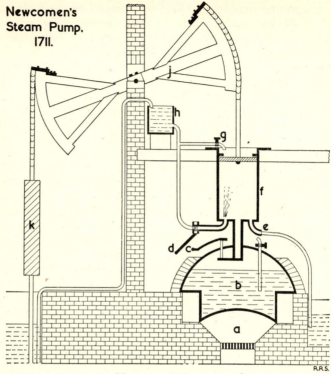

Newcomen's Steam Pump. 1711.

NEWCOMEN'S ENGINE

a—Furnace   b—Boiler
c—Steam Cock, admitting steam to cylinder
d—Injection Cock, admitting cold water to cylinder to condense steam
e—Escape valve through which water in cylinder is expelled by next
      blast of steam
f—Cylinder
g—Tap admitting water on to piston, to keep it airtight
h—Cold-water tank
j—Balance Beam
k—Counterweight on pump gear, pulling piston up between strokes
    Working: (i) c opened to admit steam to cylinder as counter-weight
raises piston, then closed
    (ii) d opened to let cold water into cylinder, condensing steam and
producing a vacuum, whereupon atmospheric pressure pushes piston
down

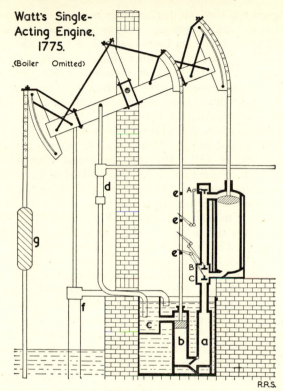

Watt's Single-Acting Engine, 1775.

(Boiler Omitted)

R.R.S.

WATT'S ENGINE

a—Separate Condenser
b—Exhaust pump of condenser, discharging into—
c—Hot water tank, from which—
d—Feed Pump fills boiler
e—Tappets working valves **A, B,** and **C**
f—Pump supplying cold water to condenser
g—Counterweight
A—Steam Valve, admitting steam above piston
B—Equilibrium Valve, equalizing pressure above and below piston
C—Condenser Valve

Working: (i) Valves **C** and **A** opened, creating vacuum below piston and admitting steam above—downstroke follows

(ii) At end of downstroke **C** and **A** are shut and **B** opened, allowing counterweight to pull piston up while steam flows from above piston to beneath it; **B** then shut and (i) repeated

but progress was slow, so that, in order to make some money, he engaged in surveys in 1766 and 1767 for a projected canal from the Forth to the Clyde via Loch Lomond, as he did later for the Monkland Canal and many other similar projects. Dr Black, who helped him with loans of money, became professor of Chemistry at Edinburgh in 1766 and gave Watt an introduction to Dr Roebuck, then having difficulties with water flooding the new pit he was sinking at Kinneil. In 1769, they took out a patent for the separate condenser engine, at first only for England, Berwick-on-Tweed and the Plantations but extended in 1775 to cover Scotland as well. Although the model Watt made had worked well, there were not skilled enough craftsmen in Scotland to construct the engine, and both Roebuck and Watt found themselves running further into debt. In 1774, when things seemed at their blackest to Watt, who had just lost his wife, Roebuck sold his share in the patent to MATTHEW BOULTON, a Birmingham manufacturer. The Kinneil engine was removed to the Soho ironworks, which Boulton had recently set up near Birmingham. When the engine was reconstructed it was provided for the first time with a well-made cylinder by John Wilkinson of Bersham, near Chester, who had just patented a new method of boring a cylinder which could really be called cylindrical. Accurate, careful measurements were necessary for his engine to be a success, and the Birmingham craftsmen were much superior to those Watt had to work with in Scotland. The first two engines constructed were for a water-pump at a colliery and for a blast-furnace belonging to Wilkinson. Soon the Cornish mine-owners were keen to have the Boulton and Watt pump instead of Newcomen's which had proved inadequate in many cases. It was in connection with the Cornish mines that WILLIAM MURDOCH,[1] the young Ayrshire engineer and inventor of the steam-locomotive and gas-lighting, first made his name. Many other improvements were made by Watt on the steam-engine. A rotative engine was made possible by the sun-and-planet motion or epicyclic gear, the crank having been patented by another man after Watt had thought of it. Instead of working with only the up-and-down reciprocating motion, the steam-engine could now be used to turn wheels,

[1] See p. 97

which meant it could be applied to various machines in industry. The double-acting engine, the parallel motion, the governor were all due to the fertile brain of Watt and by the end of the century, when the patent expired, the engines of Boulton and Watt were famous throughout the world. Watt had many other inventions to his credit—a letter-copying press, which became almost universal until it was superseded by carbon paper, a furnace designed to burn with little smoke, and even a machine for copying sculptures. He it was, also, who, for his own convenience, worked out a method of calculating the power of engines in terms of what a horse could be said to perform, and, independently of Cavendish and Lavoisier, he discovered the composition of water. His own name has been used for the main unit of electrical power, which has almost taken the place of steam power in most spheres. A shy, retiring type of man, he declined many high honours but was spared, after the hardships and worries of his youth and middle age, to live to a ripe old age, dying at Birmingham in 1819 a very wealthy man. Although most of his work was carried out in England, probably no Scotsman of the eighteenth century had such an influence on the world as James Watt. Not only was he chiefly responsible for the development of the steam-engine which came to be applied to so many branches of industry but he was the first of the race of great engineers, so necessary and so important in our modern civilization.

Scotland's Black Country.—Up till 1800 the Scottish iron industry lagged behind that of England with one or two exceptions like Carron, which had been started mainly by Englishmen. Scotland had been handicapped by her late start and also by the fact that although coal was plentiful and fairly easily mined, it was not so suitable for coking as most English coal. At the very beginning of the nineteenth century, the first steps were taken to put Scotland in the forefront so far as iron was concerned. In 1801, DAVID MUSHET (1772-1847), a young metallurgist, discovered the existence of the valuable BLACKBAND IRONSTONE, an ore which also contained coal and which stretched from the north of Glasgow eastwards across the Central Lowlands. It was especially abundant in the parishes of Old and New MONK-

LAND, which had produced coal from the Middle Ages, when coal-mining was started by the monks of Newbattle Abbey near Dalkeith (the birthplace, incidentally, of David Mushet). The Monkland Canal had been opened in 1790 in order to bring the coal more easily from this area to Glasgow.[1] At first, ironmasters regarded the blackband ore as useless but by 1825 it was being smelted by the Monkland Company alone without any coal. Its great value was not appreciated until after the invention of the HOT-BLAST FURNACE by JAMES B. NEILSON (1792-1865), who patented the process in 1828. Neilson was the first manager of Glasgow Gasworks, to which he was appointed in 1817. His suggestion that a hot blast would work better than a cold blast was also received at first with scepticism by the ironmasters. When it was found, however, that the blast, if heated to 600° Fahrenheit, produced three times as much iron as the cold blast with the same quantity of coal, the ironmasters were impressed. Further, it was possible to use raw coal instead of coke with the hot blast and at last the despised blackband ironstone could be utilized. It was also found that the iron obtained from it was superior to that from supposedly better ones. Within a short time ironworks and coal-pits multiplied themselves in the Monkland area, which has been called the "Black Country" (as it seemed by day) and the "Land of Fire" (as it seemed by night). Coal-mining also developed, especially after steam-engines had been installed not only for pumping water but also for the winding machinery at the pit, and it became safer when Humphry Davy and George Stephenson produced the safety lamp. In one year, 1840, the profits of a single ironworks, the partners of which had twenty years previously been mere farmers, amounted to nearly £60,000. Most of the iron towns of Lanarkshire—Airdrie, Coatbridge, Motherwell and Wishaw—grew up like mushrooms at this time. In addition to blast-furnaces, there were set up foundries and forges where the pig-iron could be made into cast iron or wrought iron. Before cheap steel became available, malleable or wrought iron was used a great deal more than today and the forges became more and more important as engineering developed. JAMES NASMYTH (1808-90), son of the portrait-painter, Alexander

[1] See p. 147

Nasmyth, invented in 1839 a steam-hammer which made possible heavy forgings such as were needed in shipbuilding and other industries. By the middle of the century, the Scottish iron industry was booming, as can be seen from the figures of pig iron produced:

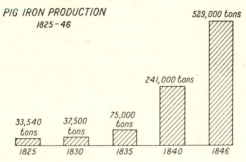

PIG IRON PRODUCTION
1825-46

33,540 tons — 1825
37,500 tons — 1830
75,000 tons — 1835
241,000 tons — 1840
529,000 tons — 1846

In 1846 (which marks the peak of railway construction), Scotland accounted for more than a quarter of Britain's production, and Britain was producing more than all the other countries in the world together.

Engineering.—Unlike the coal and iron industries, which had been known in Scotland for centuries before 1800, engineering had its origin in the Industrial Revolution. Not only coal-pits, which first used the steam-engine, but boats which used steam-power for paddles or screws, cotton-mills which applied steam-power to their new machines, railways on which steam locomotives pulled trains—all of these called for engines. The earliest engineers were usually called mill-wrights or engine-wrights, and were employed in cotton-mills or mines. Richard Trevithick, William Hedley and George Stephenson, the railway pioneers, were at first colliery engine-wrights. These early engineers were men who could turn their hands to very many different tasks. Watt's life-story shows the diversity of his work and interests. His assistant, WILLIAM MURDOCH (or Murdock, as he was known in England) had almost as varied a career. Born in 1754 at Lugar in Ayrshire, he walked all the way to Birmingham

D

to work with Boulton and Watt. Boulton was so impressed by Murdoch's hat, a wooden one which he had made on a lathe of his own construction, that he offered him a job. Murdoch was the right-hand man of the firm in Cornwall, where he supervised the erection of the new steam-engines, and it was he who worked out the details of the sun-and-planet device for Watt. In 1784, at Redruth, Cornwall, he invented a steam-locomotive, with which he frightened the wits out of some of the villagers on his evening excursions. He first used compressed air for power and invented pneumatic bells and pneumatic lifts. He is most famous for his invention of gas-lighting, which he himself used in 1792, and which before his death at Birmingham in 1839 had become the main kind of lighting in most towns. Watt and Murdoch worked in the days when there were no machine tools and a man's faulty measurements or craftmanship often ruined a job of work. The invention of machine tools became a necessity. John Wilkinson's boring-mill, which made the cylinder for Watt's first successful engine, was one of the early machine tools. In the period, 1820-50, lathes, planing and drilling machines were invented, which made accurate work much easier; most of these came from Leeds, Manchester and London engineers. Scottish engineers, as we shall see later, pioneered the development of the marine engine.[1]

Inventions.—What we have been studying in this chapter is the history of the tremendous changes in the coal and iron industries and the origin of a new industry, engineering. These changes, which formed an important part of the Industrial Revolution, were brought about mainly by the enterprise, the skill and the inventiveness of many individuals. But it would be a mistake to imagine that, if Roebuck, Watt, Murdoch and others mentioned in this chapter had not lived, the changes would not have come about at all. They might have happened a little later or slightly differently but they were brought about because the circumstances of the time called for them and rendered them inevitable. A better pump was needed for the deeper mines which were being dug because of the increased demand for coal, and Watt worked away at his experiments until he produced it; but

[1] See pp. 152-5

there were others trying to solve the same problem. He was, of course, in the long run successful only because he had the assistance and co-operation of men like Dr Black, Dr Roebuck, Matthew Boulton, John Wilkinson and William Murdoch. Thus, an invention, like that of the separate condenser engine, did not just happen in 1765 or 1783 because a genius had been born at Greenock in 1736. It was the end-product of a long series of experiments, of trials and errors and was the result of the co-operation of many people and the combination of circumstances. But it would equally be wrong to discount or belittle the achievements of the great inventors. Watt stands out among them all because he pioneered a new industry, the key industry of the modern world—engineering. Not only did he improve the steam-engine until it could be of practical everyday use, but he laid down the principles of methodical observation and regular maintenance, which are so necessary to the good engineer. If great men are those who shape events and who alter the course of history, then Watt may be held to deserve the name.

SOURCE EXTRACT

"I had gone to take a walk on a fine Sabbath afternoon, early in 1765. I had entered the Green by the gate at the foot of Charlotte Street, and had passed the old washing-house. I was thinking upon the engine at the time, and had gone as far as the herd's house, when the idea came into my mind that, as steam was an elastic body, it would rush into a vacuum, and if a communication were made between the cylinder and an exhausted vessel, it would rush into it, and might be condensed without cooling the cylinder. . . . I had not walked further than the golf-house when the whole thing was arranged in my mind."

> James Watt's Invention of the Separate Condenser
> (from an account given by him in 1813 or 1814 to
> Robert Hart of Glasgow)

EXERCISES

1. Where were gold and silver formerly found in Scotland? Mention any other places you know in addition to those mentioned in the text.

2. Write notes on the following: Emancipation of Scottish colliers, Scottish charcoal-furnaces, Carron Ironworks, Dr Roebuck, William Murdoch, David Mushet, James Neilson, James Nasmyth.

3. On a blank map of Scotland, headed INDUSTRIAL REVOLUTION, insert the following places: Methil, Invergarry, Abernethy, Bonawe, Furnace, Carron, Grangemouth, Prestonpans, Airdrie, Coatbridge, Wishaw, Motherwell (adding the letters (I) or (C) to show the connection with coal or iron).

4. Explain the following: coal-heugh, arles, jougs, pig-iron, cast iron, wrought iron, carronade, blackband ironstone.

5. Write a short biography of James Watt.

6. Find out details of the oldest ironworks or coal-mines in your district. (You will find some information in the Old Statistical Account of the late eighteenth century and the New Statistical Account of the mid-nineteenth century.)

7. Write a short essay or make a speech on one of these subjects:
   (a) "Necessity is the mother of invention";
   (b) "Genius is 10% inspiration and 90% perspiration".

CHAPTER VII

NORTH AND SOUTH BRITAIN

Scottish M.P.s.—For a long time after the Union of Parliaments, it seemed as if the Scots had been absorbed into England instead of being equal partners in a United Kingdom of Great Britain. Some people indeed began to call Scotland North Britain, but England was always England—never South Britain. The forty-five Scottish members of the House of Commons and the sixteen Scottish peers of the House of Lords at first played an inconspicuous part in the proceedings at Westminster. Only on occasions such as when Edinburgh was harshly treated after the Porteous Riot of 1736 or when the vindictive measures were taken against the Jacobites in 1746 did the Scottish representatives make any vocal protest. Generally, they were content to vote with the Government as directed by the second Duke of Argyll or his brother, the Earl of Islay, who succeeded to the title in 1743. Although there was no regular Secretary for Scotland, the post being abolished in 1746, these two noblemen and their successors were regarded as "Managers" for Scottish affairs, not so much governing Scotland as controlling the patronage of Scottish offices, which were awarded to subservient M.P.s and their friends. These sinecures, "the jobs for the boys" of the eighteenth century, multiplied as time went on until they became a scandal. For example, Sir Gilbert Elliott, father of the first Lord Minto and brother of the lady who wrote "The Flowers o' the Forest", was Treasurer of the Navy (a post which afforded ample opportunity for lining his pockets), Treasurer of the Chamber and Keeper of the Scottish Signet (a sinecure worth £4,000 a year), while his son was made a Captain on half-pay when a mere lad of ten years—all in return for faithful service to the Government in the division lobbies. Few people at the time saw any disgrace in this "racket" or "jobbery", as it was then called, and a political career was regarded as the natural way of obtaining preferment and picking up a few plums of office for a man and his friends.

Anglo-Scottish Writers.—As London was the centre of patronage, it became a common practice for young men of literary and political ambition to make for the Capital and thus inspire Dr Johnson's jibe—"But, Sir, let me tell you, the noblest prospect which a Scotsman ever sees is the high road that leads him to England!" The first Scottish writer to make his mark in London after the Union was JAMES THOMSON (1700-45), born in the manse of Ednam, near Kelso. His *Seasons* (1726-30), a long poem in blank verse, showed a feeling for nature which was not uncommon in Scottish poetry but which made a break with the sophisticated English fashion of the time; it may be said to have heralded a new era in English poetry. The patriotic song, "Rule Britannia", was written in 1740 by Thomson and another London Scot, David Malloch or Mallet. Although Englishmen continued for long to regard the Navy as their own peculiar possession, it gradually came to be known as the British Navy and "Rule

Britannia" is pre-eminently the song which shows the nation's pride in their naval power. One of the earliest novelists in Britain was TOBIAS SMOLLETT (1721-71), who left his home in the Vale of Leven in 1739 to seek a career for himself in England. He was for a time a surgeon's mate in the navy but he made more money with his pen than with his lancet. His picaresque novels, *Roderick Random* and *Peregrine Pickle*, proved very popular; but he did all kinds of literary work—journalism,[1] pamphleteering, drama and even a history of England. His last and best novel, *Humphry Clinker*, written in the form of a series of letters, gives a vivid picture of an eighteenth-century family party touring through England and Scotland. A more sensational success than Smollett's or Thomson's was that obtained by the Highlander, JAMES MACPHERSON of Badenoch (1736-96), with the publication between 1760 and 1763 of what he claimed to be a translation from Ossian, a Gaelic poet of the third century A.D. MacPherson, when challenged by critics, produced forgeries which only served to discredit him in the eyes of most people. Today it is recognized that MacPherson translated and freely adapted Gaelic poems which, if not as old as the third century, were very ancient indeed. Despite the controversy about their authenticity, MacPherson's Ossianic poems had an extraordinary influence and helped to bring about the Romantic Revival in Britain and on the Continent; Napoleon was one of those deeply impressed by MacPherson's "Ossian" and always carried a copy of the poems on his campaigns.

French Wars.—When England had been fighting in the War of the Spanish Succession (1702-13), Scotland had at first been a neutral; later wars with France, which went on long enough to be called "The Second Hundred Years' War", helped to make the two countries feel more like a "United Kingdom". The "Forty-five", which takes its place in European history merely as an episode in the WAR OF THE AUSTRIAN SUCCESSION (1740-48), had however the opposite effect of arousing hatred of the Scots; and, as we have seen, *God Save the King* became popular because of the threat of the Jacobite invasion.[2] Some Scots regiments actually fought on the Continent during that time, although a

[1] See p. 105   [2] See Bk. I, pp. 245-6

number of the Black Watch mutinied in 1743 when they heard they were to be sent overseas and reached Oundle in Northamptonshire on their way home from London before being overtaken and captured. The Commander-in-Chief of the British forces at Dettingen (1743) was a veteran Scotsman, the second Earl of Stair, but he resigned in disgust at the interference of George II, who was the last British king to take part in an actual battle. The War of the Austrian Succession was not merely a dynastic conflict between the German states but also a struggle for colonies and sea-power between Britain and France. The SEVEN YEARS' WAR (1756-63) saw this struggle develop, and out of it Britain emerged victorious and possessed of one of the greatest empires the world had seen. William Pitt, who was mainly responsible for the British success, was the first minister to organize the national defences of Britain, both on sea and land. One of his earliest actions in 1757 was to send hired Hessian and Hanoverian troops back to Germany and raise new British regiments, including two from the Highlanders who had so recently been in rebellion. The command of one regiment was actually given to Lord Lovat's son, Simon Fraser, whose lands were under the Commissioners for the Forfeited Estates. Fraser's Highlanders and Montgomerie's Highlanders (under Archibald Montgomerie, who later became Earl of Eglinton) both served in America. At the assault on Quebec under General James Wolfe, the British troops were challenged in the darkness by a French sentry and it was the quick-wittedness of a Highland officer who knew French that saved the British from immediate detection. Some feeling was aroused in Scotland in 1757 when a bill was passed to raise a militia or national defence force for England only. Scotland, it seemed, was not yet fit to be trusted with troops of its own; the memory of December, 1745, was still too fresh in the minds of London people. Later, however, in 1760, when a French squadron landed 600 men at Carrickfergus in Northern Ireland and threatened to invade Scotland, a Militia Bill for Scotland was proposed but this time there was plenty of opposition to it from Scottish farmers and merchants, who complained that a militia would take away their workers. A similar proposal was later

made during the American War of Independence without being
carried into effect; it was not until 1797, when invasion again
threatened, that the Scots were entrusted with militia of their own.[1]

Anglo-Scottish Politicians.—It was not only for a literary
career that young Scots took the road to England. By the time
of the Seven Years' War, some Scotsmen were occupying the
highest positions in the land. William Murray, EARL OF MANS-
FIELD (1705-93), who was appointed Lord Chief Justice of the
King's Bench in 1756, was born in Perthshire but educated at
Westminster School and Christ Church College, Oxford, so that
he lost the Scottish accent which handicapped so many of his
countrymen in their London careers. It was of him that Dr
Johnson remarked, "Much may be made of a Scotchman if he
be caught young." His brother, John Murray of Broughton, was
Prince Charles Edward's secretary during the "Forty-five", and
saved his skin by turning informer on his fellow-Jacobites after
the Rebellion. Mansfield, who sat as M.P. for an English borough
before he became a peer, was renowned for his eloquence in an
age of Parliamentary orators and later was regarded as an outstanding judge. At the end of the Seven Years' War there was
actually a Scottish Prime Minister. John Stuart, EARL OF BUTE
(1713-92) had entered Parliament at an early age through the
influence of his uncle, the Earl of Islay (later Duke of Argyll).
His advancement to the office of Prime Minister came through
his being the tutor and friend of the young king, George III, who
came to the throne in 1760. George was the first Hanoverian
king to be brought up in Britain and it may be through Bute's
influence that he added these words to the King's Speech given
him to read out to his first Parliament: "Born and educated in
this country, I glory in the name of Britain." George's determination "to be a king" led him to get rid of the Whig aristocrats who
had for so long ruled the country and replace them with men
likely to be complaisant. When he appointed his favourite, Bute,
to be Prime Minister in 1762, he aroused the bitterest opposition
that any British Prime Minister ever had to face.

"The North Briton".—Bute was not merely chief of the
"King's Friends"; he was also a Scotsman and the minister who

[1] See p. 118

bungled the peace negotiations at the end of the war in 1763. As the King had taken upon himself the patronage previously exercised by the Whig ministers and had even increased the number of sinecures in order to secure more supporters, the Whigs raised a howl against what they called "corruption more rampant than ever". Scotsmen in office were attacked as "a plague of locusts" which had settled in England. In addition to Bute himself there was the Lord Chief Justice, the Earl of Mansfield, the highest judge in England; the Archbishop of York was Hay Drummond, whose brother, the Earl of Kinnoul, had just retired from the Cabinet; Allan Ramsay (the younger) was court painter and Robert Adam, another Edinburgh man, was the King's architect, while many other Scots occupied minor posts. A weekly paper, "THE BRITON", had been started in 1762 with Tobias Smollett[1] as editor, and in reply there appeared "THE NORTH BRITON", in which John Wilkes poured out a stream of virulent abuse against Bute and Scotsmen. Wilkes pretended to be greatly grieved over the death of Mr John Bull, "a very worthy plain, honest, old Gentleman of Saxon descent; he was choked by inadvertently swallowing a thistle". The bitterness of these diatribes against the Scots (which Wilkes himself did not believe in) was due to the fact that the King seemed determined not merely to reign but to govern. Bute, overwhelmed by the opposition, resigned after less than a year in office. *The North Briton* continued to attack him as the power behind the throne, and at last, in No. 45, Wilkes went so far that he was clapped in gaol. The Wilkes case became famous as one involving the principle of the freedom of the subject, but it also left strained relations between North and South Britain.

American War.—The American War of Independence, which broke out in 1775, became another war with France in 1778, when that country lent its aid to the colonists; later Spain, Holland and other European powers joined in against Britain, which was forced to grant the Americans their independence in 1783. Although the celebrated Scottish writers, Adam Smith and David Hume, had joined Chatham, Burke and Fox in criticizing the Government's treatment of the colonies, there was not much

[1] See p. 102

sympathy for the Americans once the war had started, and even less after it became a European war. One of the first effects of the war was the crippling of Glasgow's lucrative American trade; after the war, however, Glasgow managed to win back and increase its trade with the newly-created United States, which became an exporter of raw cotton as well as tobacco. The war was brought near to the Scots by an American invasion threat from one of their own sons, John Paul, better known as PAUL JONES (1747-92), often called "the founder of the American Navy". In 1778, with a brig of eighteen guns, he sailed into the Solway Firth and actually landed on St. Mary's Isle near Kirkcudbright, not far from his birthplace, Arbigland. In the following year, in command of a small French squadron, he appeared in the Firth of Forth but was driven off by bad weather. The alarm in Edinburgh was very great, and the Government shortly afterwards introduced its press-gang system into Scotland in order to strengthen the Navy. Later in 1779, Paul Jones captured two English men-o'-war off the Yorkshire coast. After the War of Independence he entered the Russian service and became Admiral of the Black Sea Fleet in the war against the Turks. Another Scotsman who played a notable part on the opposite side from Paul Jones was the vegetarian GENERAL GEORGE ELIOTT of Stobs in Roxburghshire; his heroic defence of Gibraltar from 1779 to 1783 was one of the outstanding British military achievements of the eighteenth century. During the war, the people at home were for a time far less excited about the Americans than about the possibilities of relief for Catholics from the restrictions on the education of their children and the ownership of the land. Riots broke out in Glasgow and Edinburgh in February, 1779, a Catholic chapel being burnt down. The following year, under the influence of the fanatical Lord George Gordon, a son of the Duke of Gordon, "No Popery" agitation in London led to riots, in which the mob got completely out of hand, burning and plundering for three days.

Highland Regiments.—As in the Seven Years' War, the Government again turned to the Highlanders for recruits for the Army. In the earlier war, General Wolfe had advocated their use "as hardy, intrepid, accustomed to a rough country, and no great mischief if they fall". But it was more from a desire to obtain good fighting material than to get rid of possible rebels that thirteen new battalions were raised in Scotland. Lord Lovat, who as Simon Fraser, Master of Lovat, had raised the regiment known as Fraser's Highlanders in 1757, mustered over 2,000 men in 1775. As a colonel received £3 a head for new recruits, Highland lairds, especially those whose families had been connected with the Jacobite Rebellions, were not unwilling to call upon their tenants and tenants' sons to serve in the army. Among the other Highland battalions of this time was the 73rd, Lord MacLeod's Highlanders, raised by the Earl of Seaforth's son, who had served in the Swedish Army since the "Forty-five". Later on, when it was re-numbered as the 71st Highland Regiment of Foot, it became famous for its deeds in the Peninsular War and today as the 1st Battalion of the Highland Light Infantry it can claim as long a list of battle honours as any battalion in the British Army. The Earl of Seaforth himself raised another regiment, which bore his name, the 72nd or Seaforth High-

Photo : *Scottish United Services Museum*
Soldier, 42nd Regiemnt, 1742

landers, the only regiment in the British Army today with a Gaelic motto in its badge—*Cuidich 'n Righ* ("Help the King"). At first, the Seaforth Highlanders were not too keen to help the King, at least not to the length of going overseas to fight in India. In 1778, some of them mutinied at Edinburgh when informed that they were to be embarked for India; they took up a position on Arthur's Seat, where the trenches they dug are still to be seen. When they finally came to terms, they were sent not to India first but to Jersey, where they were drafted to various countries. This "affair of the wild MacRaes", as it was called, was only one of several small mutinies which occurred during the American War, when the soldiers found that they were being sent abroad, contrary to the terms of their enlistment. Once overseas, however, they played their parts courageously—in India, in America and elsewhere. In the American colonies, some of the Jacobite emigrants in North Carolina fought as Loyalists and were defeated in 1776 at the battle of Moore's Creek Bridge. Their action seems strange for people many of whom had formerly been rebels themselves; but it was caused not so much by a feeling of loyalty to the house of Hanover as by their quarrel with the gentry of North and South Carolina, who had declared for independence. Partly as a result of the valiant service rendered by the Highlanders, the act against the kilt and the bagpipe was repealed in 1782 and most of the forfeited estates were returned to their owners in 1784.

Henry Dundas.—The British failure in the American War brought about the fall of George III's minister, Lord North, and the return of the Whigs to power in 1782. But their triumph did not last long. In 1783, after two short-lived governments, the young William Pitt became Prime Minister, a post he held till 1801 and again from 1804 to 1806. Although the Whigs were thus kept out of power, the disastrous outcome of the King's American policy and his recurrent bouts of insanity prevented him from ever again controlling the Government as he had done at the beginning of his reign. Pitt, who was just twenty-four years old when called to office, had at first only one debater of skill on his side to match the galaxy of Whig talent—Fox, Burke, Sheridan and others; this was HENRY DUNDAS, M.P. for Midlothian since 1774. During the rest of Pitt's long tenure of power, Dundas was his able lieutenant and intimate friend. The Dundas family of Arniston in Midlothian had produced many able lawyers and judges, and Henry Dundas himself, after training for the law, became Solicitor-General and later Lord Advocate for Scotland.

His gifts as a debater and as a politician soon gained him notice at Westminster. He was not afraid to make a show of independence but was usually astute enough to be on the winning side. After being a strong supporter of North in the American War, he swung over to the Whig side in 1782, and in the following year joined Pitt. From 1783 to 1801, he was not merely "the uncrowned King of Scotland" (he was nicknamed "King Harry the Ninth", according to James Boswell, the Scottish biographer of Dr Johnson) but also one of the most important men in Pitt's cabinet —Treasurer of the Navy, a leading member of the India Board, and Home Secretary from 1791. During the long period when he maintained a control of Scotland so complete that it has been called the "Dundas Despotism", he was the person to whom all Scotsmen, keen on a career, looked for help and promotion. English critics complained that the fellow-countrymen of Dundas or Viscount Melville (his title after 1802) received places in

Photo: The Mansell Collection

Henry Dundas, 1st Viscount Melville

the East India Company, the Navy and elsewhere out of all proportion to the number of Scotsmen. He was in 1806 impeached in Westminster Hall for embezzling public funds while Treasurer of the Navy but was acquitted on all charges. He took little part in affairs thereafter but till his death in 1811 he still remained the most important man in Scotland. His son, Robert Dundas, who succeeded him as Viscount Melville, was First Lord of the Admiralty from 1812 to 1830 apart from a short interval and like his father he was "Manager" for Scotland for most of the time.[1] No other family—not even the Dukes of Argyll—can compare

[1] See p. 165

with the Dundases for the power which they wielded in modern
Scotland

Eighteenth-Century Burgh Elections.—Henry Dundas was
able to sit secure as "uncrowned King of Scotland", partly because the corrupt electoral system favoured the Government,
which could control so much patronage. Elections were then far
removed from those of today. Of the towns, only the royal
burghs had seats, so that small, decayed towns like Anstruther
Easter, Anstruther Wester and Kilrenny in Fife were represented,
while large, thriving, industrial towns like Greenock or Paisley
were unrepresented. Only Edinburgh, of all the 66 royal burghs
in Scotland at the Union, had the right to a member; for the
other 65 only 14 seats were available, one member representing
a group of 4 or 5 burghs. At elections, the town council of each
burgh chose a delegate to vote for one or other of the candidates,
and the 4 or 5 delegates then met and elected the member of
Parliament. The election was held in each burgh in rotation and
in the case of a group of four burghs such as that of the Clyde
District—Glasgow, Rutherglen, Renfrew and Dumbarton—an
extra vote was given to the returning burgh to prevent a deadlock.
A candidate thus only required to make sure of the votes of two
town councils in order to be returned. Nor was there anything
democratic about the election of the town councils. From the
fifteenth century the retiring councillors each year elected the
new councillors, often returning themselves from one year to
another, except that in about half of the burghs part of the council
was elected by the Merchant Guilds and the Trades Incorporations. In Glasgow and Edinburgh these bodies still elect a Deacon
Convener of the Crafts and a Dean of Guild to the Town Council,
while in other Scottish towns the Dean of Guild is a member of
the council elected in the ordinary way.[1] The members of the
guilds and incorporations were not ordinary workmen but
masters or merchants in business for themselves; and in many
Scottish royal burghs, where the population might be less than
a thousand, the number was very small. The total number of
electors in the 66 burghs at the end of the eighteenth century was
little more than 1,000, in comparison with 17,000 in the borough

[1] See pp. 218-19

of Westminster, 6,000 in Bristol and 12,000 in the City of London. Small numbers made it easier for neighbouring landowners to influence elections: thus the Earl of Bute controlled Rothesay, the Duke of Argyll Dumbarton, the Earl of Eglinton Irvine and the Earl of Galloway Whithorn and Wigtown. The Scottish M.P.s formed a docile group in Parliament, with only occasional exceptions like GEORGE DEMPSTER, the "improving" laird of Dunnichen and M.P. for the Fife and Forfar District of Burghs. He once complained that Scottish elections were dominated by "the great lord, the drunken laird, and the drunkener bailie". It cost the independent Dempster over £10,000 to win his first election in 1761, as he had to counter the influence of the county lairds.

Eighteenth-Century County Elections.—Only 30 seats were allotted to the Scottish counties in the united Parliament; most of the counties had the right to one member each, but the six smallest counties—Bute, Caithness, Clackmannan, Cromarty, Kinross and Nairn—were represented only in every other Parliament, while Shetland was not represented at all until 1832. The franchise seemed at first similar to that in the English shires, where there were usually large polls at the elections: in each case it was restricted only to freeholders of land of 40s. annual value. But, whereas the English franchise had become widened with the fall in the value of money since 1430, when the county franchise act was passed, the Scottish franchise was based on "a 40s. land of old extent holden of the King", the "Old Extent" being a valuation made in the reign of Alexander III in the thirteenth century, since when the 40s. had become worth very much more. A freeholder in Scotland could also claim a vote, if his land was valued at £400 Scots a year for the land tax. There were few people in any county who owned as much land as would enable them to qualify for the vote. But by a legal quibble, it was possible for a wealthy landowner to divide up his land into portions worth at least £400 Scots per annum, which he gave to friends. They did not become owners of the land but only had the "superiority" of the lands (a legal term which was a relic of feudalism), voting at elections as the real owner required them.

These fictitious votes were so common that in 1790 they amounted to nearly one-half of the 2,655 votes in the Scottish counties. In some counties, they were comparatively few: e.g., in Perthshire there were only 19 out of 147, and in Midlothian only 10 out of 93. But in other counties they were predominant, as in Banffshire where there were 104 fictitious votes out of a total of 123, Renfrewshire where there were 82 out of 114, and Bute where there were 9 out of 12. What made the scandal worse in the public mind was the fact that many of these "PARCHMENT BARONS" did not even live in the county where they held a vote. As the elections were not all held on the same day it was possible for the same group of "parchment barons", usually Edinburgh lawyers, to appear in turn among the county lairds at the elections in Ayrshire, Lanarkshire, Dunbartonshire, Stirlingshire, etc., and cast their votes for the Government nominees. No wonder the "Dundas Despotism" had so firm a grip on the country and no wonder that English observers called Scotland "one vast rotten borough"! Attempts were made to change the electoral system by appeals to the Court of Session and by bills in the House of Commons, but they failed because the M.P.s and the judges were themselves dependent on the very system they were being asked to alter or abolish. To any Scotsman of independent mind, the conditions at the end of the eighteenth century must have seemed to cry aloud for reform; but, despite the agitation following the French Revolution, it was a long time before reform came.[1]

SOURCE EXTRACT

"I am above all local prejudices, and care not whether a man has been rocked in a cradle on this or the other side of the Tweed: I sought only for merit, and I found it in the mountains of the North. I found there a hardy race of men, able to do the country service but labouring under a proscription. I called them forth to her aid and sent them forth to fight her battles. They did not disappoint my expectations, for their fidelity was equal to their valour."

Earl of Chatham (William Pitt) on Highland soldiers

[1] See p. 168

EXERCISES

1. What period is referred to in the above extract?
2. Write notes on the following: James Thomson, Tobias Smollett, James MacPherson, Earl of Mansfield, Earl of Bute, Paul Jones, General George Eliott, Lord George Gordon, George Dempster.
3. Explain the following words or phrases: sinecures, patronage, militia, "King Harry the Ninth", Old Extent, parchment barons.
4. Make a list of the Scottish regiments mentioned in this chapter and any other regiments with battle honours dating from before 1789.
5. Write a short biography of Henry Dundas, first Viscount Melville.
6. What differences existed between Scottish and English elections in the eighteenth century?
7. Find out the names of any notable M.P.s for your burgh or county in the eighteenth century. If you live in a royal burgh, find out the names of the other burghs with which your burgh formed a group.

CHAPTER VIII

FRENCH REVOLUTION AND NAPOLEON

Scotland in 1789.—The political apathy which had prevailed in Scotland throughout the eighteenth century was rudely shattered by the news of the French Revolution in 1789. What kind of country was Scotland at that time? In the Highlands, the Jacobite Rebellions had become a distant memory; more important to most people were the questions of sheep-farming and emigration. All over Scotland, the linen industry was well established, but in the south, especially near Glasgow, it was already being challenged by a rival, the cotton industry, in which the factory system was being introduced. The iron industry had also gained a footing, the Carron ironworks being the largest of its kind; and Watt's steam-engine had just recently been put to practical use in coal-mines, blast-furnaces and elsewhere. With the growth of material wealth, there had also been an advance in the arts, in literature and in science. Schools were more numerous everywhere and newspapers common in the large cities. In general, although there were riots by Glasgow weavers for higher rates of pay in 1787, when six people were killed, there was a feeling of satisfaction with the improved conditions of living, more plentiful food, better and cheaper clothes, higher wages, and people thought little about politics. The system of government which seems to us today to have been full of corruption was greatly admired by many at the time, both in Britain and abroad. In 1788, the centenary of the "Glorious Revolution", the General Assembly of the Church of Scotland, in an address to the King, described the British constitution as "the wonder and envy of the world". Before the end of the century, however, there was plenty of criticism of this "wonderful" constitution.

Scotland and the French Revolution.—The first reaction in Britain to the French Revolution was one of enthusiasm. Most people felt that France was just following the British example in establishing a constitutional monarchy. The storming of the Bastille on 14th July 1789 was regarded as a victory of liberty over despotism; and Charles James Fox, the Whig statesman, was not alone in thinking: "How much the greatest event it is that ever happened in this world and how much the best!" In 1790, the Whig Club of Dundee sent an address of congratulation to the National Assembly in Paris. Edmund Burke made a sneering reference to this Dundee club in his *Reflections on the French Revolution* (1790), in which he strongly criticized the changes in France. Burke's book evoked many replies, the most notable being Tom Paine's *The Rights of Man*, a pamphlet which became one of the best-sellers of the time, although the Government tried to suppress it as seditious. In Scotland, Principal Robertson, an enthusiastic supporter of the French Revolution, spoke of "the ravings of Burke". Two London Scots defended the French against Burke's attack—James Christie, son of a provost of Montrose, and JAMES MACKINTOSH, who came from near Inverness. Mackintosh's *Vindiciae Gallicae*, although it was intended as a reply to Burke, went on to discuss the British constitution, and denounced the prevailing political system as completely un-representative. He reminded his fellow-Scotsmen of the Declaration of Arbroath, and he hoped that the Revolution in France would inspire them to revive their old ideas of freedom. The works of Paine and Mackintosh gained widespread popularity among the middle and lower classes in Scotland. Societies were formed to agitate for the abolition of the slave trade in the colonies and the reform of burgh and parliamentary elections. Pitt's government, of which Henry Dundas was a prominent member, was much concerned about all this agitation, which to them seemed to amount to sedition.

Political Agitation.—Sympathy with the French, who were now threatened with invasion by the Austrians and other powers, became common in Scotland. Subscriptions were raised for the French National Assembly, and Robert Burns tried to send to France four carronades he had bought at an auction of goods confiscated from a smuggler ship.[1] In the summer of 1792 there were demonstrations in many Scottish towns against the Government. In the north of Scotland the effigy of Dundas was burned in towns and villages, while riots broke out in the south, in Lanark and in Edinburgh. Ross-shire tenants, who saw how sheep-farming led to clearances, started to drive the sheep out of the county, and were stopped only by a large force of soldiers. The Government was now genuinely alarmed. Two new societies became very active in this year—the LONDON CORRESPONDING SOCIETY founded by Thomas Hardy, a native of Falkirk, and the SOCIETY OF THE FRIENDS OF THE PEOPLE, founded by some Whig M.P.s. Branches of the latter society were formed in many parts of Scotland, and in December a convention of delegates from over eighty branches was held in Edinburgh. The convention declared itself against any kind of violence and passed proposals for equal representation of the people and more frequent elections. Demonstrations and riots continued in many of the large towns. In Perth and Dundee fir trees were planted as "Trees of Liberty" in imitation of the French, and "Liberty and Equality" became a popular slogan. To many people it looked as if the Scottish

[1] See p. 118

people were rushing down the slippery slope to revolution.

Thomas Muir.—In the beginning of 1793 the Government began to prosecute some of the leaders of reform agitation on charges of sedition. THOMAS MUIR (1765-98), a young advocate from Huntershill, near Kirkintilloch, who had taken a prominent part in the convention of the Societies of the Friends of the People, was arrested on a charge of circulating Tom Paine's *The Rights of Man* and other works. He was released on bail and, after visits to France and Ireland, which made the Government more suspicious of him than ever, he was tried in Edinburgh. Muir's trial by judges and a jury, convinced of his guilt before the start, was a travesty of justice. In a three-hour speech in defence, Muir pleaded guilty to one "offence" only, that of advocating parliamentary reform. For years afterwards, New England schoolboys used to learn by heart the last part of his speech, concluding with these words:

My mind tells me that I have acted agreeably to my conscience and that I have engaged in a good, a just and a glorious cause—a cause which, sooner or later, must and will prevail, and by timely reform save this country from destruction.

LORD BRAXFIELD, the presiding judge, was a coarse, bullying type of individual, who made no secret of his opposition to the reformers. "Let them bring me prisoners and I'll find them law," he was fond of saying; during Muir's case he remarked to one of the jurors, "Come awa' and help us to hang ane of they damned scoondrels." To another prisoner, who had made an eloquent speech in defence, Braxfield once said: "Ye're a verra clever chiel, man, but ye wad be nane the waur o' a hanging" ("hanging" being his word for all kinds of punishment). The vicious sentence which Muir received, one of transportation to New South Wales for fourteen years, aroused much sympathy for him in France and in the United States. In 1796 he was rescued from the convict settlement by an American ship and, after many adventures, died in France in 1798.

Political Martyrs.—After Muir's trial, others followed. An English Unitarian clergyman, Rev. Thomas Palmer of Dundee, was tried on similar charges and received a sentence of transportation for seven years. Another convention of the Societies of the Friends of the People was held in Edinburgh in the autumn of 1793. The delegates passed resolutions, demanding annual parliaments and votes for all men; some of them, in imitation of the French, began to call each other "Citizen". Two of the English delegates, Joseph Gerrald and Maurice Margarot, were tried along with William Skirving, a Kinross-shire laird who was secretary of the convention, and all received sentences of fourteen years' transportation. During Gerrald's trial the prisoner made an impassioned oration, in the course of which he claimed that all great men had been reformers, "even our Saviour Himself". Lord Braxfield's comment was typical of him: "Muckle He made o' that: He was hanget!" The trials caused some men to turn to talk of rebellion and begin to manufacture arms—pikes which could be made in a village smithy. The Government, in May 1794, speedily suspended the Scottish Act against Wrongous Imprisonment and the English Habeas Corpus Act, to enable them to deal with the emergency. Some of the leading agitators were tried for high treason; in England they were acquitted but in Scotland two men, Robert Watt and David Downie, were convicted. Watt, who had at first acted for the Government as a spy, was executed. The Whigs tried to have the sentences reconsidered in Parliament but without effect. Fox's comment on the Scottish trials was a biting one: "God help the people who have such judges!" It must be remembered, of course, that the outbreak of war between Britain and France and the massacres in Paris which culminated in the "Reign of Terror" (1793-94) made it difficult for the Government to view the reformers as other than dangerous people. A man had only to advocate parliamentary reform to be called a "Jacobin". But the difference between English and Scottish justice was very marked and was not creditable to the Scottish ruling classes. The effect of the vicious sentences was to damp down the ardour of the reformers, although the memory of the political martyrs was kept green. A tall obelisk, the "Martyrs' Monument", was erected in 1844 in Edinburgh to commemorate them.[1]

[1] See p. 170

Invasion Threats.—The possibility of a French invasion made many people think again about the French Revolution. Burns's loyalty had been suspect because of various remarks he made, and there was little doubt where his sympathies lay, as can be seen from *A Man's a Man for a' That, Scots Wha Hae* and other poems.[1] But in 1795, he published his poem, *Does Haughty Gaul Invasion Threat?* and, shortly before his untimely death, he joined the Dumfries Volunteers.[2] The success of the French, for whom the young general, Bonaparte, won brilliant victories against the Austrians in Italy, was such that by 1797 Britain stood alone, faced with a threat of invasion. France had secured the fleets of Spain and the Netherlands but, fortunately, the Spanish fleet was defeated off Cape St. Vincent in February 1797 by Admiral Sir John Jervis, whose second-in-command was Horatio Nelson. The danger of invasion was still present and, to make things worse, mutinies broke out among the sailors in the British fleets at Spithead, the Nore and Yarmouth. Conditions of food and pay were disgraceful and the horrible floggings often imposed (on men who had perhaps been impressed into the Navy) were almost bound to lead to mutiny sooner or later. The Scottish ADMIRAL ADAM DUNCAN, in command at Yarmouth, had only his own ship and one other still loyal, while the Dutch fleet was expected to arrive at any time. Duncan's situation was desperate but he boldly advanced with his two ships into Dutch waters, and by making false signals induced the Dutch to believe that the whole British fleet was lying off the coast so that their ships stayed in harbour. Later in the year, when the mutinies were over, Duncan trounced the Dutch fleet off Camperdown (a name he took for the house near his native Dundee to which he retired). Among the civil population there was also great discontent. A MILITIA ACT, which at last was passed for Scotland in 1797, enforced conscription by ballot for men between eighteen and twenty-three and was most unpopular with the working classes. The bitterness of the people arose from the fact that militia-men might be drafted overseas and that most of the middle and upper classes were either Volunteers (and thus exempt from the militia) or could afford to buy themselves out by paying £20 or more to

[1] See also p. 115   [2] See pp. 123-4

a substitute. Riots broke out in many places; schoolmasters, who had to draw up the lists of men for the militia "ballot", had their houses sacked and parish registers were destroyed. The most serious disturbance took place at Tranent, near Prestonpans, where eleven people were killed and several wounded when soldiers were brought in. In the same year, a secret society, that of the UNITED SCOTSMEN, was formed on the model of the United Irishmen; its aim was revolution but after the transportation of one of the leaders, George Mealmaker, a Dundee weaver, the movement collapsed in 1798. By that time the danger of invasion was over for a time at least.

Napoleon.—Unable to break through the "wooden walls" of the British Navy, the French turned to the east to strike a blow at British power there. Bonaparte first made a dash from Toulon to Alexandria but although he was successful in conquering Egypt, which he hoped to use as a base for an attack on India, his fleet was destroyed by Nelson at Aboukir Bay (1798) and he was compelled to return to France without his soldiers. Bonaparte's army was finally defeated in the battle of Alexandria (1801) by the veteran Scottish general, SIR RALPH ABERCROMBY, who died of wounds soon after his victory, the first achieved by the British over the French since the start of the war in 1793. Another Scottish general, John Moore, who was also wounded in the battle, recovered in time to witness the surrender of the French at Cairo. In India, the French had stirred up against the British an old enemy, Tipoo Sahib, who with his father, Hyder Ali, had given much trouble during the American War. In 1799, his capital, Seringapatam, was taken after a fierce assault, led by SIR DAVID BAIRD, and Tipoo himself was killed. Baird, who came from Newbyth in East Lothian, had been a prisoner at Seringapatam for four years after 1780 when Hyder Ali had almost annihilated a British force. He was a man of great courage but a fiery temper, and when his mother heard that Hyder Ali had ordered the prisoners to be chained together, she remarked: "The Lord help the man that's chained to oor Davie!" Baird was in charge of the expedition which re-conquered Cape of Good Hope in 1806 and he was with Moore at Corunna, where Moore was

Lord Braxfield   Thomas Muir
Admiral Duncan   Sir John Moore

Acknowledgements: Top Left, Picture Post; Top Right, Picture Post; Bottom Left, National Galleries of Scotland; Bottom Right, The Mansell Collection

killed and Baird himself seriously wounded. After a short period of peace, war broke out again between Britain and France, and in 1804 there was again a serious threat of invasion. But Napoleon (as Bonaparte had now become) lacked the sea-power to enable him to transport his huge army from Boulogne to England. All over Britain, Volunteers were training. In August 1805, when the beacon fires had been lit by mistake, Walter Scott, an enthusiastic Volunteer, rode a hundred miles from Cumberland to the muster at Dalkeith. Napoleon's hopes of winning control of the Channel were finally destroyed by Nelson's victory at Trafalgar on 21st October 1805. Thereafter, he tried by throttling British trade to bring "the nation of shopkeepers" to submission, but instead he wrought his own downfall through the wars which ensued from this attempt to enforce his "Continental System".

Peninsular War.—It was during the twenty years of the French war that Scotland won fame as a producer of fighting men for the British Army. Many new regiments were embodied and Scots were to be found almost all over the world in the many campaigns which the British government started. At first there was little success, except in India. The major expedition, the largest hitherto sent abroad, was one against the Netherlands in 1809 but it proved a colossal failure, thousands of men dying of malaria on the island of Walcheren, once the base of Scottish merchants on the Continent. What began as a side-show in Portugal turned out to be in time a decisive campaign; this was the Peninsular War, which Napoleon later described as the "Spanish ulcer". The Portuguese and Spanish, especially the latter, were constantly harassing the French troops by their guerrilla tactics; and the small British Army, based on Lisbon and ably commanded by Sir Arthur Wellesley, later Duke of Wellington, was the first to register victories in Europe against the all-conquering French. In the winter of 1808-9, following French defeats at the hands of the British and Spanish, Napoleon himself took command of 200,000 men, and proceeded to wipe out one Spanish army after another, when SIR JOHN MOORE, in charge of a small army of 27,000 men, made a bold attack to the rear of the French, threatening their communications. Moore (1761-1809) was the son of a Glasgow surgeon and man of letters, and by his new training methods at Shorncliffe, near Folkestone, without the usual brutal military discipline (500 or more lashes were some-times given in a single flogging) he had built up a force of light infantry, able to move with speed across the country, to live on it, and to use the new rifle with accuracy. Moore's system was introduced at a time when the British Army was at its lowest ebb, and it made possible the later successes of the Peninsular War. To deal with Moore's threat, Napoleon turned from his Spanish foes but had to hand over command to one of his marshals, Soult, in order to hasten away to Austria. Moore's retreat in midwinter over mountainous country, almost impassable because of torrents swollen by heavy rains, was an epic performance and was crowned by a victory over Soult at Corunna (1809) in which Moore was mortally wounded by grape-shot. Among the right-hand men of Wellington, who held command after Corunna until the triumphant victory at Toulouse in France and the abdication of Napoleon in 1814, were two Scotsmen, GENERAL ROBERT CRAW-FURD of Kilburnie in Stirlingshire and GENERAL SIR THOMAS GRAHAM (later Lord Lynedoch) of Balgowan in Perthshire. "Black Bob" Crawfurd once marched his men 62 miles in 26 hours, each man carrying a pack of over 50 lb.—a wonderful feat and a tribute both to Moore's system and Crawfurd's leadership. Sir Thomas Graham became a soldier at the age of forty-three as a way of getting over his wife's death; he was a man who loved action and he saw plenty of it in the next twenty years, becoming Wellington's second-in-command by the end of the war.

Home Front.—The number of Scotsmen in the ranks of the Army was very high in proportion to the population. All through the war, the Highlands were combed by the recruiting sergeants for the Army as well as by the press-gangs for the Navy; and the Lowlands also furnished their quota of fighting men. New regi-ments were raised—the 79th or Cameron Highlanders, the 91st or Argyllshire Highlanders, the 92nd or Gordon Highlanders, and the 93rd or Sutherland Highlanders. In forty years, over 11,000 men from the Seaforth and Cromartie estates in the Isle of Lewis and on the mainland were enlisted in the 71st, 72nd and

78th Regiments; and probably thousands also were pressed into service in the Navy. Even before 1800, complaints were made that the Highlands were being "bled white" and by the end of the war most of the Highland regiments contained a fair proportion of Lowlanders, Englishmen, and Irishmen. In the Lowlands, a young man might join the Fencibles (as the volunteers for home defence were usually called) if he could afford to buy his own uniform at a cost of at least £7; or he might be chosen for the Militia, although he could escape such service (which could mean going overseas) if he had enough money to pay for a substitute. It is obvious that war in Napoleon's time was not the "total war" of the twentieth century. More important to Scottish people at home (except to those whose relatives were serving abroad) were the great changes taking place in trade, industry, agriculture and transport, which are mentioned in other chapters. It was during this time that Glasgow grew into one of the great industrial cities of the world while Edinburgh became established as a centre of literature and the arts. At first the war did not interfere much with trade and the new cotton industry boomed. But a depression came when Napoleon imposed his Continental System and it worsened when Britain and the United States went to war in 1812. In that year the cotton-spinners on Clydeside were on strike after a dispute with their employers about wages and the ringleaders suffered imprisonment for forming a "Combination" or association of employees.[1] By 1815, the year of Waterloo, the agitation for reform had long since died down. But the end of the French war was to bring about social distress and economic upheavals which caused a revival of reform agitation. For a whole generation afterwards political reform was the burning question in Britain.[2]

Does Haughty Gaul Invasion Threat?

Does haughty Gaul invasion threat?
    Then let the loons beware, Sir;
There's WOODEN WALLS upon our seas,
    And VOLUNTEERS on shore, Sir:

[1] See p. 225   [2] See Chap. XI

> The NITH shall run to CORSINCON,
>   And CRIFFEL sink in SOLWAY,
> Ere we permit a Foreign Foe
>   On British ground to rally!
> We'll ne'er permit a Foreign Foe
>   On British ground to rally!
>
> The wretch that would a TYRANT own,
>   And the wretch, his true-born brother,
> Who would set the MOB above the THRONE,
>   May they be damn'd together!
> Who will not sing "God save the King"
>   Shall hang as high's the steeple;
> But while we sing "God save the King",
>   We'll ne'er forget THE PEOPLE!
> But while we sing "God save the King",
>   We'll ne'er forget THE PEOPLE!

Robert Burns

EXERCISES

1. When was the above poem written? In what way does it reveal Burns's attitude to reform?
2. Write short notes on the following: Sir James Mackintosh, Tom Paine, Society of Friends of the People, United Scotsmen, Admiral Duncan, Sir Ralph Abercromby, Sir David Baird, Sir John Moore.
3. Write a short biography of Thomas Muir. (Find out what you can about his adventures after his rescue from Botany Bay.)
4. Explain: Tree of Liberty, Fencibles, Militia, Jacobin, Continental System, Total War, Spanish Ulcer.
5. Explain the following quotations:
   (a) "How much the greatest event it is that ever happened in the world and how much the best!"
   (b) "Come awa' and help us to hang ane of they damned scoondrels!"
   (c) "The Lord help the man that's chained to oor Davie!"
6. Make a list of the battle honours of any Scottish regiment in the wars between 1793 and 1815.

7. Find out the names of any regiments, regular or volunteer, raised in your district in the period, 1793-1815.
8. Give an account of any disturbances in your district over political reform in 1793-94 or over the Militia Act in 1797.

CHAPTER IX

THE ATHENS OF THE NORTH

After the Union.—The first half of the eighteenth century has been called the "dark age" of Edinburgh's history. The immediate effect of the Union of Parliaments had been to leave Scotsmen embittered. Glasgow early began to exploit the commercial advantages of the Union, although its progress was at first slow. But to Edinburgh it seemed as if it had lost everything and gained nothing. No longer a capital, it harboured against the Government a feeling of resentment which flared up on various occasions as in 1736, when sympathy with the smugglers in their conflicts with the customs officials led to the Porteous Riot. The disappearance of the old Scottish Parliament and the absence of the 45 M.P.s and 16 representative peers, who could not often face the 12 day' journey from and to London, made a difference to the social life of Edinburgh. Edinburgh from the time of the Union had always to face the loss of brilliant Scotsmen who were attracted by the greater possibilities of a career in London. But the dullness of Edinburgh life has been exaggerated by later generations, conscious of the splendours of the end of the century, when it was called "the Athens of the North".

Old Edinburgh.—In the early part of the eighteenth century, Edinburgh was shockingly overcrowded. At that time, the population of over 40,000 lived in tall houses, some of them as high as 12 storeys, flanking the "royal mile" between the Castle and Holyroodhouse, with the Cowgate running parallel on the south side, and the closes and wynds running off these streets. In one

building or "land", the occupants might include nobility, ministers or professors in the middle flats, shopkeepers or clerks in
the upper flats, and the very poorest down at street level or in the
cellars. Jostling one another on the narrow stairs leading from
the mouth of the "close", ladies with their hooped petticoats, four

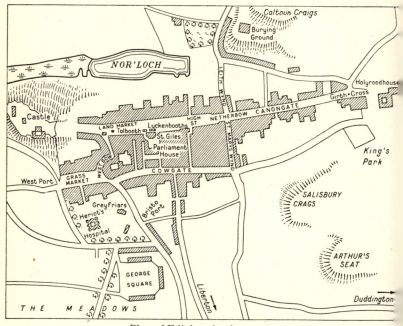

Plan of Edinburgh, about 1765

feet wide and tilted to permit them to pass, would meet "caddies"
on their way from one notable to another with a message or an
invitation, or servant lasses in their "duffle" coats bringing back
water from the well. The cobbled streets were so filthy that
ladies invariably were carried in sedan-chairs by "chairmen",
often sturdy Highlanders with only a few words of English.
Because of the lack of any proper sanitation it was the practice of

Edinburgh householders to dispose of their filth by throwing it on the streets after ten o'clock in the evening. The opening of shutters or windows and the cry of "Gardyloo!" (from the French *Gardez l'eau*) was a warning to the passer-by, who if he could not reach the shelter of a building quickly enough would shout, "Haud yer haun'!" Until the scavengers cleaned the streets in the morning, the stench of these "flowers of Edinburgh" was almost insufferable.

Royal Mile.—The "royal mile", although it still retains much that is older even than the eighteenth century, would have looked strange to modern eyes. At the foot of the Castle Hill in the middle of the High Street stood the public weigh-house, the Butter Tron, and nearby, the stalls of the Lawnmarket (originally the "Landmarket", where people from the land or country brought their goods for sale). Not much further down the High Street was another obstruction, "THE HEART OF MIDLOTHIAN", the Old Tolbooth or town-house, in which the Council had once held their meetings but which was in the eighteenth century used as a prison. Today, stones in the roadway, arranged in the form of a heart, mark the position of the Old Tolbooth. Beyond the Tolbooth, in the middle of the High Street stood the Luckenbooths, a tall building consisting mainly of shops, and between the Lucken-booths and St. Giles' was a collection of booths or stalls, called the "Krames". St. Giles' Church before the Reformation could accommodate as many as 3,000 persons, but, like Glasgow Cathedral, it had been divided up by stone walls into separate churches for four Presbyterian congregations. Behind St. Giles' stood Parliament House, which for a time after the Union was used as a market before it became the meeting-place for Edinburgh lawyers, as it is today. The High Street led down past the old Mercat Cross and the Salt Tron, the main public weigh-house of the city, to the NETHERBOW PORT, the eastern gateway through which Lochiel with his Camerons had made their daring rush in 1745. Beyond the Netherbow Port, the Canongate presented an appearance in the main not unlike that of today. At the foot, near the Water Port, stood the Girth Cross, marking the limits of the Abbey Sanctuary, which sheltered the "Abbey Lairds", debtors who had gone there to escape imprisonment. But the most noticeable difference from today was in the northern aspect of the town. Immediately below the Castle was a loch with marshy

Photo : Scottish Tourist Board
Canongate Tolbooth, Edinburgh
The town-house of the burgh of Canongate (built 1591)

surroundings, the Nor' Loch, and beyond it were green fields where today runs Princes Street with its background of Georgian mansions. A dirty, overcrowded town by modern standards,

Edinburgh was still a pleasant place to live in according to visitors, and compared favourably in that respect with London of that time, which, with its squalor, gin-drinking and crime, had the reputation of being "the wickedest and most disorderly city in the world".

The Awakening. Even in the so-called "dark age", Edinburgh was showing signs of revival from the gloom into which the ending of Scottish political independence had thrown it. Although Parliament no longer met there, it was still regarded as the capital of Scotland by the lairds, the merchants, the lawyers and the ministers. Most lairds who could afford it had a town house in Edinburgh. For the burgesses of other towns it was the meeting-place once a year of the CONVENTION OF ROYAL BURGHS, which became all the more important after the Union. The fountain-head of Scots law, which had been preserved separate from that of England in 1707, was the COURT OF SESSION in Edinburgh. Scotland was fortunate in having its law systematized by two great jurists, the first VISCOUNT STAIR (1619-95) in the late seventeenth century and JOHN ERSKINE (1695-1768), professor of Scots Law at Edinburgh University, in the eighteenth century. Scottish judges were held in high repute until the political trials at the end of the century. Not only was Edinburgh the meeting-place of the GENERAL ASSEMBLY but there was a tendency for the brilliant "divine" to be sought after by the congregations of the city churches. The influence of the Church was such as to make visitors think of Edinburgh as a very dull place. On Sundays, during the time of the services, the city seemed dead except for the "seizers", elders who patrolled the streets on the look-out for anyone "stravaiging". Oddly enough, the magistrates allowed cock-fighting, which was carried on by the boys of almost every Scottish school on Fastern's E'en,[1] and encouraged horse-racing on Leith sands by presenting prizes. There were several bowling-greens in the city and its environs, and golf was played on Leith Links and Bruntsfield Links, the Edinburgh Burgess Club being founded in 1735.[2] The theatre, however, was frowned upon by both ministers and magistrates. ALLAN RAMSAY (1686-1758), who had once been a wigmaker and who started the first British

E   [1] See p. 247   [2] See p. 288

circulating library at the Luckenbooths in 1725, also tried to set up a theatre and failed. But, under the pretence of holding a musical concert beforehand, plays from the English stage were presented in the Tailors' Hall in the Cowgate from as early as 1727. Allan Ramsay contributed in many ways to the literary life of Edinburgh. In 1725 he published *The Gentle Shepherd*, a Scottish pastoral comedy of refreshing simplicity. As an example of the language and style, here is Patie addressing his lass, Peggy:

> When corn grew yellow and the hether-bells
> Bloom'd bonny on the moor and rising fells,
> Nae birns or briers or whins e'r troubled me
> If I could find blae berries ripe for thee.

Ramsay was not a great poet but by publishing a collection of old Scottish poems, *The Evergreen*, and four volumes of Scottish songs, *The Tea-Table Miscellany*, he helped to save many songs from oblivion and paved the way for Fergusson and Burns.

The "Moderates".—By the middle of the eighteenth century, Edinburgh was becoming known as a centre of literary activities. The entire Church no longer regarded novels, plays and poetry as sinful. Some of the younger set of ministers in Edinburgh and district angered their older, stricter colleagues by their worldly interests. Prominent among these "Moderates" was ALEXANDER CARLYLE (called "Jupiter" Carlyle because of his handsome appearance), son of the minister of Prestonpans and himself minister of Inveresk from 1748 to 1805. He played a leading part in church affairs for half a century and earned the gratitude of the clergy by obtaining for them exemption from payment of the window tax, first levied in 1697 and not abolished till 1851. Carlyle helped his friend JOHN HOME, minister of Athelstaneford in East Lothian, to have his tragedy, *Douglas*, presented on the stage. Home as a young minister had fought in the "Forty-five" on the Hanoverian side and, after being taken prisoner at Falkirk, had made a daring escape from Doune Castle by using bed-clothes tied together as a rope. In 1755 he failed to persuade Garrick to produce his play in London and it was accordingly staged the following year in Edinburgh, much to the indignation of the "high-fliers", as the stricter Presbyterian ministers were called. "Jupiter" Carlyle was even censured in the General Assembly for attending the theatre. Home himself resigned his charge as a result of the outcry raised against him and later became tutor to the Prince of Wales. *Douglas* is a historical

tragedy which to us to-day seems stilted, but its first performance aroused wild enthusiasm, and one excited Scotsman called out in the interval, "Whaur's your Wullie Shakepeare noo?" DR ALEXANDER WEBSTER was another of the moderate clergy of this time, more like an Anglican bishop than a Presbyterian minister in his tastes. Although minister of the Tolbooth Kirk in St. Giles', whose congregation of stern Calvinists esteemed him highly for his pulpit eloquence, he was known in Edinburgh mainly for his

Photo: National Galleries of Scotland

The Rev. Alexander ("Jupiter") Carlyle

convivial habits. Through a marriage with a lady of means, he was able to mix with the best company; and his nickname of "Doctor Bonum Magnum" was earned by his ability to finish off five bottles of claret at a sitting and drink most of his companions under the table. To us today the conduct of Carlyle, Webster and Home seems hardly to be that befitting a minister. It was, however, a kind of reaction against the strictness of the older type of Presbyterian minister, and the conviviality should be related to the hard-drinking habits of the time. The changed attitude of

the clergy in the latter half of the century was most strikingly
shown in 1784, when Mrs Siddons, the famous actress, first
appeared during the week of the General Assembly, which
arranged its business so that the members could attend the
theatre.

The "Literati".—Among other Edinburgh clergymen of the
period who became celebrated outside the Church were the Rev.
Hugh Blair, who in 1762 was appointed Professor of Rhetoric
and Belles Lettres at the University, and Dr William Robertson,
who in the same year was appointed Principal of the University.
Robertson was considered one of the leading historians of the
eighteenth century, his *History of Charles V* receiving high praise
from Voltaire and Gibbon. Carlyle and Robertson belonged to
the Select Society founded in 1754 by the younger Allan
Ramsay the painter, George Dempster of Dunnichen and others
for the improvement of the members "in reasoning and eloquence" and the encouragement of arts, science, manufacture and
agriculture. David Hume (1711-76), the philosopher, was probably the most outstanding of this circle of "literati" (men of
letters). Although he was known to some as "Atheist Hume", he
was on the most friendly terms with Carlyle and Robertson, and
was reckoned "the best-natured man in the world". His first
work, *The Treatise of Human Nature*, published in 1739, "fell
dead-born from the press" (to use his own words) but is still read
today; and his scepticism was to have an important influence on
European philosophy of the eighteenth century. His *History of
England* was the first work of its kind; it was continued and completed by Smollett, and, although Hume's sympathy with certain
historical figures like Charles I brought him much criticism,
versions of it were used in schools until well on in the nineteenth
century. A close friend of Hume was Adam Smith (1723-90),
"the father of economics", who lived in Edinburgh from 1748 to
1751, when he was appointed professor at Glasgow University,[1]
and again from 1778 to his death. His great work, *Wealth of
Nations* (1776), which he wrote at Kirkcaldy, attacked the prevalent theories of commerce, and it found in the younger Pitt an
admirer who tried to put Smith's ideas into practice. Both Hume

[1] See p. 59

and Smith, who travelled widely on the Continent, had European reputations and their contributions to philosophy and economics entitle them to rank among the greatest Scotsmen in history. By the second half of the eighteenth century, Edinburgh had become a fashionable literary centre, attracting not only Scotsmen and Scotswomen, both rich and poor, but also visitors from England and other lands. Its University, which unlike those of Oxford and Cambridge was open to Dissenters, was attended by students from many parts of Britain.[1] In the study of medicine, it achieved a high reputation through its professors, WILLIAM CULLEN and JOSEPH BLACK,[2] both of whom left Glasgow University for chairs in Edinburgh University. Although Edinburgh was no longer the seat of government, there was little doubt that it was the intellectual capital of Scotland.

Poets.—It may be thought that the eighteenth century Scottish contributions to culture were all of a serious nature—philosophical, historical or scientific. But much poetry was produced, some of it, however, also severe and now seldom read. *The Grave* (1743), a long, gloomy poem by Rev. ROBERT BLAIR, minister of Athelstaneford before John Home, was nevertheless once popular and could be found in almost every cottage in Scotland in the eighteenth century. Another poet who took himself seriously and published in 1759 an enormously long epic poem of over 6,000 lines dealing with the siege of Thebes was WILLIAM WILKIE, the minister of Ratho, the "Scottish Homer" or "Potato Wilkie", as he was nicknamed because of his fondness for what was then a novelty. JAMES BEATTIE, professor of Moral Philosophy at Aberdeen University, also produced a lengthy poem, *The Minstrel* (1771-74), which earned him much praise. Today, however, we are not attracted by the imposing bulk of these poems but rather by the charming simplicity of the ballads, songs and lyrics of the period, like *The Braes of Yarrow* by WILLIAM HAMILTON or *Ode to the Cuckoo*, claimed for both MICHAEL BRUCE and JOHN LOGAN. Allan Ramsay's mantle as poet of Edinburgh was worn for a short time by ROBERT FERGUSSON (1750-74), author of *Leith Races*, *Auld Reekie* and other poems about the Scottish capital. He unfortunately ended his brief, dissipated life in the city

[1] See p. 257   [2] See p. 91

asylum. Burns credited him with being the inspiration of his best works, and in his use of Scots he gave Burns an example which the Ayrshire poet was not slow to copy and improve upon. One of the first things that Burns did when he came to Edinburgh was to have a tombstone placed on Fergusson's grave, which he was shocked to find quite neglected. The following verse from *The Farmer's Ingle* can be compared with Burns's *Cotter's Saturday Night.*

> Weel kens the gudewife that the pleughs require
> A heartsome meltith, and refreshing synd
> O' nappy liquor, o'er a bleezing fire:
> Sair wark and poortith douna weel be joined.
> Wi' buttered bannocks now the girdle reeks,
> I'the far nook the bowie briskly reams;
> The readied kail stand by the chimley cheeks,
> And had the riggin het wi' welcome steams,
> Whilk than the daintiest kitchen nicer seems.

Many Scottish songs were written at this time by ladies who would listen to their recital in Edinburgh drawing-rooms without admitting the authorship. Lady Anne Lindsay's *Auld Robin Gray* and Miss Alison Rutherford's *Flowers o' the Forest* (1765) were both at first thought to be of ancient origin. Another version of *Flowers o' the Forest* (1756) by Miss Jean Elliott was even finer than Alison Rutherford's.

> I've heard them lilting at the ewe-milking,
> Lasses a-lilting before the dawn of day;
> But now there is moaning in ilka green loaning,
> The flowers o' the forest are a' wede away.

Robert Burns.—The interest in Scottish poetry and the Scottish language had been increasing steadily throughout the century; it reached full flood with the visit of Robert Burns to Edinburgh in 1786. Born on 25th January 1759, at Alloway near Ayr in the "auld clay biggin" his father had built, Robert Burns had seen his father's health broken by the struggles and worries of a tenant-farmer, and he himself had been doing a man's work on the farm from the age of fifteen. He was not unlettered and, after receiving a good grounding from a young schoolmaster,

John Murdoch, he had read widely and deeply, among his favourites being Blind Harry's *Wallace*, Pope, Shakespeare, Allan
Ramsay, Robert Fergusson, Henry MacKenzie and more serious

Photo: National Galleries of Scotland
Robert Burns
From Reid's miniature (considered by the poet his best likeness)

works, such as Locke's *Essay concerning the Human Understanding*
and Hervey's *Meditations among the Tombs*. He became entangled
in two love affairs, one with Jean Armour of Mauchline (whom
he later married) and one with Mary Campbell, "Highland
Mary"; and he was planning to emigrate to Jamaica when, in an

attempt to raise money, he managed to have some of his poems published at Kilmarnock in 1786. The 612 copies of this Kilmarnock edition made a stir in Scotland. It was not merely that Burns presented something new but that his was the hand of a master. Here in his poems were Scotland and Scotsmen and Scotswomen, their joys and their sorrows, their virtues and their shortcomings, pictured in satire and song. The volume came into the possession of Dr Blacklock, a blind Edinburgh minister who was himself a poet and who immediately invited Burns to visit Edinburgh. Dr Blacklock's letter decided Burns to postpone his departure for the West Indies. The poet was assured of a warm welcome in Edinburgh by the high praise given to his poems in a magazine article by Henry MacKenzie, the lawyer whose novel, *The Man of Feeling*, had been greatly admired by Burns himself. MacKenzie referred, rather patronizingly, to "this heaven-taught ploughman", and many of the people who lionized Burns in Edinburgh drawing-rooms in the winter of 1786-87 did so mainly from a feeling of surprise that a mere rustic could write so well. But soon Burns had become a national figure. He settled down for a short time as a farmer at Ellisland, near Dumfries, on Patrick Miller's estate of Dalswinton, and finally became an exciseman or "gauger" at Dumfries. All the time he was pouring out verse of all descriptions. He helped in the production of Johnson's *Musical Museum* and Thomson's *Select Scottish Airs*, to which he contributed many songs based on older Scottish songs and airs. He could be touchingly simple and forthright in his love songs:

> O my luve is like a red, red rose
> That's newly sprung in June.
> O my luve is like the melodie
> That's sweetly played in tune.

In *Tam o' Shanter* he wrote the best poem of its kind. The story of Tam's ride home from Ayr after an evening's drinking is recited each year at hundreds of "Burns Suppers" all over the world, on the anniversary of his birth, 25th January. Although Burns's poems have been translated into many languages, his fame has nowhere been so great as in Scotland, because Scotsmen feel that he speaks to them and for them about their own land and about themselves.

New Town.—Before Burns's visit to Edinburgh, the first steps had been taken to remedy the overcrowding that had prevailed for so long. The earliest suburb was built to the south of the town near the reclaimed "Meadows"; George Square, which was laid out after 1760, became a fashionable locality for the gentry of Edinburgh and the "Meadows" a walk for the sedate philosophers and "literati". The development of the open country to the north of the town was started by Lord Provost GEORGE DRUMMOND in 1762, when the swamp at the end of the Nor' Loch was drained, and the foundation stone of the North Bridge was laid in the following year. Another access to the projected "New Town" was made further west by the mound of earth taken from the foundations of buildings, which is still called "The Mound". The planning of the New Town was put in the hands of JAMES CRAIG, a nephew of the poet James Thomson,[1] and a brave plan it was, with broad streets and squares. Lord Provost Drummond found it difficult at first to persuade people to venture out to what seemed a cold, bleak district, exposed to the north and east winds, and £20 was offered to the first man to build a house in the New Town. But soon it began to take shape, and elegant houses began to spring up. One of the first public buildings erected was the Register House at the end of the North Bridge, for the preservation of the public records of Scotland; it was begun in 1772 with the help of funds from the Forfeited Estates[2] but it was only completed in 1788. By 1800, Craig's original plan, with modifications, was almost completed. His idea had been to make George Street the main thoroughfare, terminating in two fine squares, Charlotte Square and St. Andrew Square, but Princes Street (named after George III's two eldest sons) has stolen the glory and become one of the most famous streets in the world, partly because, facing the Castle, it links the new with the old Edinburgh. The first section of the New Town contains some admirable examples of the work of ROBERT ADAM (1728-92), the architect who also designed the Register House and Edinburgh University Old Build-

[1] See p. 101   [2] See p. 37

ings, although these last were mainly the work of Playfair.[1] For the later extensions of the New Town in the early nineteenth century the main architects were WILLIAM PLAYFAIR and THOMAS HAMILTON, who were exponents of the heavy classical architecture

Photo: The Scotsman

Charlotte Square, Edinburgh

so typical of the modern part of Edinburgh. The two imposing structures on the Mound, the Royal Scottish Academy and the National Gallery, are the work of Playfair. The Royal High School, which Hamilton designed, was actually modelled on the temple of Theseus at Athens.

A Northern Athens.—Before the time of Hamilton and Playfair, Edinburgh had come to be known as "the Athens of the North", not because of its architecture but because of its philosophers and men of letters. During the long French wars, noblemen's sons, instead of making the "Grand Tour" of the

[1] See p. 256

Continent as formerly, went north to Edinburgh, attracted by its fame as a literary centre. It was as tutor to a young gentleman on such a tour that Sydney Smith, the English humorist, came to Edinburgh in 1798. Along with some young Edinburgh advocates, Francis Jeffrey, Henry Brougham and others, he founded the EDINBURGH REVIEW in 1802. It soon became famous for its outspoken criticism of literature and its scathing attacks on social abuses. A Whig journal, bound in blue and buff, the colours of Charles James Fox, it helped to bring about many reforms—the repeal of various antiquated laws, such as the Test and Corporation Acts, and the abolition of the slave trade.[1] Its contemptuous dismissal of Byron's first poem called forth from him a biting satire, *English Bards and Scotch Reviewers* (1809). In opposition to the Whigs, the Tory QUARTERLY REVIEW was founded in 1809 by John Murray, the publisher. Sir Walter Scott, a keen Tory, was a frequent contributor to it and to another Tory journal, BLACKWOOD'S MAGAZINE, started by William Blackwood, the publisher, in 1817. Sir Walter's son-in-law, J. G. Lockhart, also a lawyer, was one of a brilliant coterie which included "Christopher North" (John Wilson) and the Ettrick Shepherd (James Hogg), and which gave *Blackwood's* a reputation for trenchant criticism and sparkling wit. The young Keats, like Byron, suffered at the hands of the Edinburgh reviewers, although Jeffrey gave high praise to his poems just before his death. But Edinburgh's fame as a city of culture and letters was not due merely to its criticism of English writers. At the University DUGALD STEWART, the philosopher, was giving lectures which were thronged by students from many parts. Sir HENRY RAEBURN (1756-1823), one of the finest portrait-painters Britain has ever produced, was then at his best, painting for posterity likenesses of the famous men and women of his time. Although greatness in art is not to be measured by the price paid for an artist's pictures, it is worth noting that in 1917 Raeburn's "The Twelfth and Last of the MacNabs" fetched 24,000 guineas at an auction. In the same period, LADY NAIRNE (1766-1845) was writing the still popular songs—*Land o' the Leal, Caller Herrin, The Laird o' Cockpen*, and *The Rowan Tree*, and Sir WALTER SCOTT (1771-

[1] See p. 164

1832) "the Wizard of the North", was pouring out a stream of poems and novels.

Sir Walter Scott.—Although born in Edinburgh, Walter Scott came of Border stock and, because of an early illness which left him lame, he spent part of his youth in the Border country, where

Photo : *National Galleries of Scotland*

Sir Walter Scott

he came to know and admire the ballads he was later to do much to make famous. He went to the Royal High School and later to the University of Edinburgh but learnt as much in his leisure reading, especially during a long illness in his sixteenth year when he devoured all the old romances, plays and poems in the circulating library at the Luckenbooths founded by Allan Ramsay.[1] He entered his father's legal firm but he kept up his interest in poetry and, after translating some German poems and a play of Goethe he published in 1802 *The Minstrelsy of the Scottish Border*, which first brought him public notice. Many of the ballads included in this book he wrote himself, and he soon began to make a reputation with his long, romantic poems, *The Lay of the Last Minstrel*, *Marmion* and *Lady of the Lake*. His first novel *Waverley* he had begun to write years before it was published and it was by accident that he discovered the manuscript in an old desk in which he was looking for some fishing tackle. Doubtful about the effect on his reputation as a poet and as a man of property (he had begun to build for himself the vast, baronial mansion of Abbotsford on

[1] See p. 130

the Tweed between Melrose and Selkirk) he published it anonymously in 1814. Its success was overwhelming and the author, still keeping his identity secret, proceeded to turn out in rapid succession other novels, equally good—*Guy Mannering*, *Rob Roy*, *Heart of Midlothian*, etc. It was not until 1827 that the "Great Unknown" admitted the authorship of his novels. By that time he had become involved in the bankruptcy of the publishers, Constable and Ballantyne. Although at one time he contemplated seeking refuge in the Canongate[1] as an "Abbey Laird", he managed to raise over £50,000 in four years mainly by his literary efforts. Scott's historical romances were not the first of their kind but they gripped the imagination of the public, not only in Britain but abroad, and they produced hosts of rivals. In the "Waverley Novels", Scotsmen can find portrayed scenes from many periods of their country's history, and probably no one has done so much as Scott to create the romance of Scottish history. His *Tales of a Grandfather* have proved popular reading with boys and girls down to the present day. The Scottish tourist industry is also indebted to Scott: the main centres of attraction, Edinburgh, the Trossachs and Loch Lomond, are closely linked with his novels and poems.

A Capital City.—This chapter has been concerned almost solely with the story of Edinburgh's cultural life. But if we could speak with someone who lived at the end of the eighteenth century, he would probably pick out as the most memorable event of his time the trial in 1788 of Deacon Brodie, the respectable citizen who became a burglar by night and whose life inspired Robert Louis Stevenson to write his thrilling tale, *Dr Jekyll and Mr Hyde*; or he might mention the political trials of 1793-94, of which you read in another chapter.[2] Similarly, someone of a later generation might talk not of the architecture of the New Town but of Burke and Hare, the Irish murderers; they actually sold their victims to the brilliant anatomist, Dr Robert Knox, who could not obtain sufficient bodies for dissection from the "resurrectionists", the men who raided graveyards. These are reminders that a large city can contain the best and the worst in a nation. Despite these blots on its reputation, however, Edinburgh, since it lost its Parliament, had more than maintained its place as the nation's

[1] See Bk. I, p. 85   [2] See pp. 116-17

capital. All the time it was growing, although by 1831 Glasgow at last exceeded it in size of population (202,000 to 162,000). Industry did not obtrude at almost every corner, as in Glasgow, but there was a great variety of enterprises—printing, publishing, paper-making in the city and coalmining, fishing and quarrying nearby. No other Scottish town received so many tourists and perhaps it was for that reason that there grew up in Edinburgh by 1820 firms with a nation-wide reputation for brewing beer, making biscuits, short-bread and other confections such as "Edinburgh Rock", while the potteries of Portobello and Preston-pans produced "wally-dugs" or earthenware ornaments. Edinburgh was fortunate in being the centre of a rich agricultural land, with many kinds of industries—fairly convenient but not so near as to detract from the beauties of the town. It has changed, of course, since that time, especially with the coming of the railway through the drained Nor' Loch, but it still retains enough of the charms it possessed in its "Golden Age" to make it visited by almost every tourist to Scotland.

SOURCE EXTRACT

"I was a lad of fifteen in 1786-1787, when he came first to Edinburgh, but had sense and feeling enough to be much interested in his poetry, and would have given the world to know him.

As it was, I saw him one day at the late venerable Professor Henderson's, where there were several gentlemen of literary reputation. His person was strong and robust; his manners rustic, not clownish; a sort of dignified plainness and simplicity. There was a strong sense of shrewdness in all his lineaments; the eye alone, I think, indicated the poetical character and temperament. It was large, and of a dark cast, and glowed (I say literally *glowed*) when he spoke with feeling or interest. I never saw such another eye in a human head, though I have seen the most distinguished men of my time. . . ."

Sir Walter Scott on Robert Burns

EXERCISES

1. Write a sentence about each of the following places in old Edinburgh: Old Tolbooth, Luckenbooths, Netherbow Port, Mound, Meadows, Nor' Loch, Register House.

2. Explain the following words or phrases: Gardyloo, Heart of Midlothian, caddie, Abbey Lairds, High-fliers, Moderates, seizers, Literati.

3. Write a sentence about each of the following: *Tea-Table Miscellany, Gentle Shepherd, Douglas, Treatise of Human Nature, Wealth of Nations, The Man of Feeling, Musical Museum, Minstrelsy of the Scottish Border, Edinburgh Review.*

4. Write short notes on the following: Allan Ramsay, "Jupiter" Carlyle, John Home, David Hume, Adam Smith, Dr Alexander Webster, Robert Fergusson, Provost George Drummond, Dr Blacklock, Robert Adam, Henry Raeburn.

5. Write a short biography of Sir Walter Scott or Robert Burns.

6. If you live in Edinburgh or go to school there, find out what connections your district has with any of the people mentioned in this chapter.

CHAPTER X

TRANSPORT CHANGES

Early Travellers.—Travelling in the eighteenth century was as slow and as difficult as it had been in the Middle Ages. The record time of sixty hours from London to Edinburgh, put up by Sir Robert Carey when he brought the news of Elizabeth's death to James in 1603, was not improved upon for almost two hundred years. Roads were so poor that horseback still remained the speediest and most comfortable mode of travel for those fit to ride. An act of Parliament of 1719 had made it compulsory for every able-bodied man to give six days' labour each year on the King's highways or "statute labour roads". But, generally, nothing was achieved beyond gathering together for a few hours of conversation and a little road-making on what was called "parish road day". Wealthy people who could afford a carriage had to be prepared for broken axles and generally took a wheel-wright with them on long journeys. At some rivers where no bridges existed, the carriage was ferried over on a raft, a regular occurrence for the Duke of Argyll on his way to or from Inveraray at the river Leven, where the first bridge was built only in 1765. Carts or waggons were seldom seen outside the towns.[1] Heavy loads on farms were carried or dragged along on horse-drawn "sledges". Pack-horses were used to carry goods from one town to another; the baskets or "cadges" were slung across the horse's back, four or more horses being strung out in single file under the charge of one "cadger". Tobias Smollett, the novelist, in 1739 travelled as far as Newcastle on a pack-horse, between the two "cadges", on his way to seek fame and fortune in London.[2] A coach left for London from Edinburgh once a month, taking 12 to 16 days *en route*, but in a private chaise the journey could be done in as little as six days. These were expensive ways of travelling, however, fit only for the well-to-do; the others went on horseback like James Watt in 1755,[3] on pack-horse like Smollett in 1739, or even walking, like many a Scottish student on his journeys to University.

Turnpikes and Stage-Coaches.—The first real improvements in transport came with the passing of the Turnpike Road Act in 1751 for Edinburgh district and, later, of similar acts for other districts. By these acts, TURNPIKE TRUSTS were appointed from the owners of the land through which a road passed, with the duty of maintaining the road and the right of levying small taxes on all owners and occupiers of land in the district and tolls on the travellers at toll-bars or turnpikes. (Originally, these were bars of wood studded with pikes and swivelled on a post, but in time the pikes were omitted.) By the end of the eighteenth century, at intervals of four or five miles along almost all the main highways there were toll-houses, where the traveller had to pay his toll-dues. It was partly because of these that drovers preferred to take their droves along the hill-roads. Tolls lasted in Scotland till 1883 but some of the toll-houses can still be seen and names like Tollcross and Eglinton Toll mark the places where they stood. Our oldest milestones are also reminders of the Turnpike Trusts,

[1] See p. 16   [2] See p. 102   [3] See p. 91

which erected the first of them just after the middle of the eighteenth century. The improved surface of the turnpike roads allowed faster and more regular transport. In 1749 a stage-coach had begun to operate between Glasgow and Edinburgh, taking 12 hours for the 46 miles. Goods were carried in a waggon, called

Stage-coach Passing Tollhouse

the "Glasgow and Edinburgh Caravan", which took a day and a half, stopping at Livingston for the night. By 1766, a new fast stage-coach, the "Fly", for four passengers, driven by two postillions and four horses with a change at Whitburn, could travel from Glasgow to the capital in 9 hours. The Edinburgh-London stage-coach had been speeded up in 1754 and once a fortnight set off on its journey of over 400 miles, which it covered in 10 days in summer and 12 in winter. By 1784 there were 15 coaches a week running between Glasgow and Edinburgh, and Robert Carey's time of 60 hours from London to Edinburgh was equalled by the stage-coach. Glasgow was linked with London by a direct stage-coach service, which was scheduled to take only 65 hours, at a cost of £4 10s. for each inside passenger. In the Highlands, the work of Wade and Caulfield was continued.[1]

[1] See Bk. I, p. 239

Caulfield himself was responsible for adding, between 1741 and 1760, 700 miles of new roads to the 258 miles constructed under General Wade. On the new and improved roads inns were built and communication between town and country became common. The old coaching-inns on the stage-coach routes can still be recognized by the ample stable accommodation and coach-yard necessary for the changing of horses. Before the coming of the railway, the fastest time for the Glasgow-London journey of just under 36 hours was recorded by a journalist who brought the news of the passing of the second reading of the Reform Bill in 1831.[1] By that time the stage-coach era was in its heyday but steamboats and railways were already beginning to offer strong competition.

Road Engineers.—In connection with the road improvements of this period, three Scotsmen, Telford, Rennie and Macadam, became famous for their work as civil engineers. THOMAS TELFORD (1757-1834), the son of an Eskdale shepherd, was apprenticed to a stone-mason and went as a young man to England, where he gained a reputation as a civil engineer for the canal and bridges he constructed in Shropshire. In 1802 he was appointed by the Government to report on the public works necessary in the Highlands. Among the improvements he proposed were new roads and bridges, a canal joining Fort William to Inverness, and harbours for the fisheries on the coast. He was himself given the job of carrying out his proposals and in the next eighteen years he made almost 1000 miles of new road and over 1000 new bridges. During that time the surface of the Highland roads was as good as could be found anywhere in Britain. The Caledonian Canal, which was started in 1803 but took a long time to complete, proved a great disappointment to Telford. He is probably best known for his bridges—Bonar Bridge and Dunkeld Bridge in the Highlands, the Dean Bridge in Edinburgh, and the Menai Suspension Bridge built in connection with the London-Holyhead road, which he made the best in Britain. JOHN RENNIE (1761-1821), who was born on a farm in East Lothian, worked at first as a millwright with Andrew Meikle, the inventor of the threshing-mill, and later with Boulton and Watt. He constructed canals,

[1] See p. 166

drained marshes and made harbours but is most famous also as a bridge-builder. His beautifully-designed bridges have been much admired; two of them, which closely resembled one another, were the old Waterloo Bridge in London and the bridge over the Tweed at Kelso. JOHN LOUDON MACADAM (1750-1836) was born at Ayr of wealthy parents and only took up civil engineering as a hobby. His first road was made in 1787 from the main Ayr road through Alloway to his estate of Sauchrie, near Maybole. It was as a surveyor to the Bristol Turnpike Trust that he became famous for his cheap but effective method of road-making. He attacked the popular idea that a substantial foundation was necessary for a road. He maintained that if a road were well drained and constructed of good material (10 or 12 inches deep of small, broken stones) it needed no elaborate stone foundation such as Telford and others advocated; in time the traffic would consolidate the small stones into a hard, compact whole. As a result of his efforts, he ran into financial trouble but received £10,000 in an award made by Parliament. Later in the nineteenth century, steam-rollers were used to consolidate the material more quickly and tar was sprayed on the road to give it a smooth, hard surface, called "tarmacadam". Although much of the work of these civil engineers or surveyors was done outside Scotland, the Scottish roads also benefited so that they compared favourably with the roads of any country.

Eighteenth-Century Canals.—Heavy traffic, such as coal, iron-stone and timber could not be carried on the eighteenth century roads. It was for the purpose of carrying coals that the first English canal, the Bridgewater Canal between Worsley and Manchester, was constructed by the engineer James Brindley in 1759-61. One of the first canals opened in Scotland was made for the same purpose—the MONKLAND CANAL, which was used to bring coal cheaply from the Monkland area to Glasgow.[1] Glasgow merchants had been responsible for promoting the canal scheme in 1769, and James Watt, appointed engineer in charge at a salary of £200 *per annum*, started work soon afterwards. But delays ensued during the period of the American War, so that it was not finally completed till 1792. It proved a financial success,

[1] See p. 96

especially when the iron industry in the Monkland area was so prosperous. The FORTH AND CLYDE CANAL had also long delays in its construction, due to financial difficulties. Its main purpose, so far as Glasgow people were concerned, was to give them a quick outlet to the North Sea and the Baltic trade; and when a scheme was first mooted in 1766 and 1767 for a canal *via* Loch Lomond, there was much opposition from Glasgow. James Watt was employed in these first surveys but the construction of the canal was begun in 1768 under another famous engineer, John Smeaton, reaching the outskirts of Glasgow in 1777. When it was finally completed in 1790, it ran from Grangemouth on the Forth to Bowling on the Clyde, with a branch from Maryhill connecting with the Monkland Canal; another, the Union Canal, was later added, joining Falkirk and Edinburgh. Because of the shallowness of the Clyde, Port Dundas, the dock constructed on the Glasgow branch, proved useful as an alternative to the Broomielaw, the quay on the river. On the other side of the country, the Carron Company found the canal convenient for obtaining coal and iron and for sending their products through to the west. Like the Monkland Canal, the Forth and Clyde Canal was busiest in the 1830's and 1840's; but the width of the canal and the number of locks made it suitable only for barge-traffic. In the twentieth century, the old project of a mid-Scotland ship canal has been discussed but does not seem likely to be revived.

Inland Navigation.—The beginning of the nineteenth century saw a great enthusiasm for "Inland Navigations", as the canals were called. (The name "navigator", which was ironically given to those employed in the excavation of the canal, was shortened to "navvie" and in time was applied to all those who did similar work.) Although great hopes were entertained for the various schemes at the start, the cost of construction proved a great difficulty, and only one of the nineteenth-century Scottish canals could be called a success. This was the ABERDEEN AND INVERURIE CANAL, which was constructed between Aberdeen and Inverurie, seventeen miles away, in the years 1797-1807 and gave the inland town of Inverurie all the advantages of a port, so that it became the centre of a rich farming district. The CRINAN

Canal was started in 1793 and opened in an incomplete condition in 1801, cutting across the narrow isthmus between Loch Crinan and Loch Gilp to do away with the long and difficult voyage round the Mull of Kintyre. The Glasgow and Ardrossan Canal was never finished; only eleven miles from Glasgow to Johnstone were cut by 1811, being filled in later and used for the track of the Glasgow and South-western Railway. The Caledonian Canal, the construction of which started in 1803, was opened to traffic in 1822 but was not properly completed till 1847. It did not prove a paying concern, to Telford's great disappointment. He had hoped that it would be much used by ships carrying timber from the Baltic countries through to the west of Britain, but a high import duty, imposed in favour of Canadian timber, killed the Baltic trade. It was utilized by fishing-boats on their way to or from the herring-fishing and by tourist traffic, the lovely route through Loch Lochy, Loch Oich and Loch Ness being a popular one long before the "Loch Ness Monster" became an attraction in the 1930's. Scottish canals were not profitable for long; steamboats helped them but, in most cases, the railways put an end to their brief period of prosperity.

Steamboat Pioneers.—Who designed the first steamboat? The honour has been claimed for Frenchmen, Americans and Scotsmen. The Marquis de Jouffroy experimented with a steamboat on the river Doubs in France as early as 1776, and John Fitch built one which plied on the Delaware for two years after 1788, steaming as much as 2,000 miles altogether. There were others in these countries only a little less successful but it is usually reckoned that Scotsmen were the pioneers of practical steam navigation. William Symington (1764-1831), who was the son of the manager of the mines at Leadhills and was himself an engineer, in 1787 patented a steam-engine to work boats or ships and was fortunate in finding a patron to finance his experiments. This was Patrick Miller, a wealthy Edinburgh banker who bought the estate of Dalswinton in Dumfriesshire to settle down in as a landed proprietor. He had carried out experiments with hand-driven paddle-wheels on boats and was persuaded to try out steam-power. The first steamboat of Miller and Symington was really a double one, 25 feet long, and between the two hulls was a paddle-wheel driven by a steam-engine. It made a successful appearance on Dalswinton Loch in October, 1788, before a crowd of interested spectators, including Robert Burns, who had just recently started to farm Ellisland on the Dalswinton estate. The following year, a similar but larger steamboat was tried out on the Forth and Clyde Canal and it achieved the respectable speed of nearly 7 m.p.h. Miller unfortunately decided to withdraw his financial support and Symington was left without a patron until 1800, when Lord Thomas Dundas suggested a scheme to run steamboats for towing barges on the Forth and Clyde Canal, of which he was a chief shareholder. The outcome was the *Charlotte Dundas*, which in March 1802 towed two heavily-laden barges a distance of $19\frac{1}{2}$ miles against a strong headwind at over 3 m.p.h. Other canal shareholders, however, objected that the wash from the paddles would damage the banks of the canal, and Lord Dundas and Symington had to abandon their project. Symington's bad luck continued when the Duke of Bridgewater, the "Canal Duke", who had been responsible for the first English canal, died just after giving Symington an order for eight steamboats. The *Charlotte Dundas* differed from later steamboats in having one paddle-wheel set in the stern instead of a pair amidships, but in other respects it provided a model which steamboat engineers followed for the next twenty years. It was for a long time used for dredging the canal it was not allowed to ply on, and latterly lay in a cutting. Both Robert Fulton, the American pioneer, whose *Clermont* steamed successfully up the river Hudson from New York to Albany in 1807, and Henry Bell, whose *Comet* was the next British steamboat, used some of Symington's ideas.

Henry Bell.—The Scottish pioneer, HENRY BELL (1767-1830), was born at Torphichen Mill near Linlithgow and had a varied career as a millwright and shipwright before he and his wife took over the Baths Hotel, Helensburgh, in 1808. He was the first provost of the early seaside resort[1] and he conceived the idea of a steamboat passenger service, linking Helensburgh, Port Glasgow and Glasgow. His steamboat, the *Comet*, was built at Port

[1] See p. 287

Charlotte Dundas

Comet

Britannia
Early Steamboats

Photos : Picture Post

Glasgow by the firm of John Wood and Son, later to be one of
the leading shipbuilders in Scotland, and derived its name from
being started in 1811, the year of a famous comet. Its construction involved various other men in Glasgow, the engine being
the work of John Robertson and the boiler that of David Napier.
The first trip from Port Glasgow to the Broomielaw on 6th
August 1812 was done in 3½ hours and the *Comet* was an immediate success. The first European passenger steamboat had two
pairs of paddle-wheels, at the bow and stern, but it was later
lengthened and fitted with only one pair amidships. Its ability
to run regularly, "independent of wind and tide", as was claimed,
established steam navigation as a practical possibility, but it did
not hold its proud position for long, as faster and more commodious rival steamboats soon appeared. The Clyde for a couple
of years was unique in Europe in the steamboats that plied on its
waters, but after the Dumbarton-built *Marjory* appeared on the
Thames in 1814, London engineers at once saw the possibilities
of steam navigation.

David Napier.—The Clyde still showed the way, however.
DAVID NAPIER (1790-1869), who had cast the *Comet* boiler for
Henry Bell (without ever receiving full payment for it), was one
of a Dumbarton family of blacksmiths. His father had started
an iron foundry at Camlachie, in Glasgow, and on his father's
death in 1813 he succeeded to the business. He was one of the
few who thought that steamboats were fit for more than river
navigation and could stand up to the buffeting of the waves in the
open sea. After a few crossings to Ireland in sailing-ships to
study the force of waves in gales, he decided to have a steamboat
built for which he would provide the engines. He had serious
doubts about the merits of the traditional bluff bow for a ship
and experimented with models on the mill-dam near Camlachie
Foundry until he found that a fine bow was speedier and safer.
The result was the 90-ton *Rob Roy*, built in 1818 by William
Denny of Dumbarton with Napier's own engine of 30 horse-
power. Those who had prophesied disaster were confounded by
its running successfully between Greenock and Belfast. Soon,
old ships were being put back into dock to have their bows

sharpened and other people were becoming interested in the navigation of the open seas by steamers. Napier, who had a long career as a builder of wooden- and iron-hulled steamers in Glasgow and London, was responsible for other improvements in steam navigation, including the famous steeple-engine which jutted up through the deck. He used steam-power in two ways to open up the Clyde to tourist traffic. He bought land on the Holy Loch, built a pier at Kilmun to which his steamboats carried passengers and from which they were taken by steam-carriage along a rough road to Loch Eck. There, another of his steamboats, the *Aglaia*, the first iron-hulled steamer in Scotland and the second in Britain, took the tourists for a cruise. The Napier family produced many clever inventors. One of them, a cousin of David Napier, invented the tubular boiler in 1830, another invented a famous coffee-making apparatus, while still another, the grandfather of the motor-car manufacturer of the early 1900's, invented the news-paper rotary printing-press.

Robert Napier.—But the most celebrated of the Napier family was ROBERT NAPIER (1791-1876), who has been called "the father of marine engineering on the Clyde". He learnt the trade of blacksmith with his father in Dumbarton and was apprenticed to him in order to avoid being press-ganged. He succeeded his cousin, David, at the Camlachie Foundry, Glasgow, in 1821, choosing as his manager DAVID ELDER, whose son was later to become a prominent shipbuilder. Robert Napier soon gained the reputation of being the leading engineer on the Clyde, always insisting on the very best workmanship and materials. When two of his steamers finished first and second in the Northern Yacht Club race in the Clyde in 1827, a wealthy Englishman, Assheton Smith, gave him an order for a steam yacht costing over £20,000. Napier built for Smith several steam yachts which were the fastest vessels of their time, achieving speeds of nearly 16 knots. Through Smith, too, he began to build for the East India Company and the Admiralty, breaking the monopoly of Thames builders and engineers. Naval men gave high praise to Napier's engines, which needed only a small fraction of the expenditure on repairs neces-sary for other engines; and the East India Company was delighted with the performance of his *Berenice*, which beat its nearest rival by eighteen days on a voyage to India. It was through this East India Company connection that he became associated with SAMUEL CUNARD, the Bostonian, who asked him to build four steamships for the transatlantic passenger traffic, opened up by the voyages of the *Sirius* and *Great Western* in 1838. Napier pressed Cunard to build bigger ships than those at first suggested, and, in order to raise the necessary finance, formed a company, with Cunard the principal shareholder and various Glasgow men, including Napier, holding the other shares. This CUNARD COMPANY was to become the most famous passenger line in the world. Its first ship, the *Britannia*, built by Robert Duncan of Greenock and engined by Napier, was the first transatlantic steamship to be entrusted with mails. Her first homeward voyage in 1840 she performed in the record time of just over ten days, and she set an example for speed and reliability which Cunarders have maintained to this day. Napier was chief adviser to the Admiralty on engineering matters until his death in 1876.

Clyde-built.—It is mainly due to Napier and his successors that "Clyde-built" has come to imply high standards of craftsmanship. Many of the men who worked with him later started yards of their own or contributed to the development of marine engineering. WILLIAM DENNY, his first manager for his iron shipbuilding, left him in 1844 after two years to found the firm of William Denny and Brothers, Dumbarton. Two of his foremen, JAMES and GEORGE THOMSON, left Napier in 1846 to start the Clydebank Foundry at Finnieston, Glasgow, adding shipbuilding to their activities in 1851. It was this firm which in 1871 moved down the Clyde to a site on the farm of Barns o' Clyde, to form the nucleus of the present town of Clydebank, and which was later taken over by the Sheffield steelmakers, JOHN BROWN AND COMPANY. Another famous name in Clyde shipbuilding was that of JOHN ELDER, whose father was Napier's first engineering manager and who himself was a draughtsman with Napier. In 1852 he joined with a well-known millwright, CHARLES RANDOLPH, to form a new company, later called the FAIRFIELD SHIPBUILDING COMPANY. Elder constructed the first compound engine, by which the consumption of coal was cut by thirty per cent. There were other flourishing shipyards on the Clyde—WOOD of Port Glasgow, famous for their wooden ships; Tod and MacGregor of Partick, pioneers of the iron hull (their first iron ship being launched in 1833); Alexander Stephen, who transferred from Arbroath and Dundee to the Clyde to be nearer the ironworks of Lanarkshire; Scott of Greenock, who have been building ships for nearly two and a half centuries. These and many others contributed to making the Clyde the shipbuilding river *par excellence* in the world.

Clippers.—It was when steamships with iron hulls and screw propellers were well established that the builders of sailing-ships reached their highest peak of achievement, and again Scotland was in the forefront. The clippers, which far surpassed all previous sailing vessels in speed and beauty, were of nineteenth-century American origin, the leading builder being a Scottish-American, DONALD MACKAY of Boston. The clipper's speed came from its fineness of line towards bow and stern and the spread of sail it carried; but although it could easily outsail steamships in suitable winds, it could not carry much cargo. Donald Mackay's large clippers, which were passenger ships and not cargo ships like the British clippers, were the fastest vessels of their day; six of them succeeded in sailing more than 400 miles in a day's run, and the best recorded run was 465 miles, done by the Black Ball Line's *Champion of the Seas* in 1854. The first Scottish clippers were being built before 1840 for the coastal trade between Aberdeen and London to take the place of the smacks which had plied in competition with the stage-coach. The builders were ALEXANDER HALL AND COMPANY of Aberdeen, which before the steamboat era had been the leading shipbuilding town in Scotland. Soon clippers were being used to compete with the Yankee clippers for the opium trade in China. By 1850 the clippers were also being used in the China tea trade. Every year there was a race to London with the new season's tea from China and very high sums were paid as premiums to the ship first home, as the tea first sold fetched the highest price in the market. Not all the British clippers were built in Aberdeen. In the famous race of 1865 from Foochow to London, when five clippers came up the Channel within sight of one another, three of them had been built at Greenock, one at Glasgow and the fifth at Liverpool. The winner, the *Ariel* of Greenock, which could manage 16 knots in a favourable breeze, later put up the record time for an outward voyage, London to Hongkong, in just under 80 days. 1870 saw another memorable race, from Shanghai to London, between the *Thermopylae*, built at Aberdeen, and the *Cutty Sark*, built at Dumbarton. The *Thermopylae*, which had already on her maiden voyage put up a record time of 62 days on the wool trade run from the Lizard to Melbourne, defeated the *Cutty Sark* by four days with a time of 115 days on the longer China run. Although the *Cutty Sark* lost the race, the gallant fight of the captain and crew after the rudder had been broken in a storm won the sympathy of the public. The opening of the Suez Canal in 1869, the saving of fuel and time by the use of the compound engine and, later, the triple-expansion engine, all helped to deal the death-blow to the sailing-ship. But some of them continued to the twentieth century. The *Cutty Sark's* fastest runs were done in the 1880's as a wool-clipper from Australia and she finished up her sailing career under Portuguese owners only after the First World War. She is still preserved as an example of the beautiful sailing-ships of a past age.

Railways.—The first Scottish railways were, as in England, those laid down by mine-owners to facilitate the carriage of coals. In the eighteenth century they were used for horse-drawn waggons, the rails at first being simply iron-plates. On one of these, the railway which was constructed in 1810 to carry the Duke of Portland's coals from Kilmarnock to Troon, nine miles away, a locomotive built by George Stephenson is said to have been tried out in 1817 but proved too heavy for the light plate rails. The first railway line to be built for both locomotive and horse traction (like the Stockton-Darlington Railway, opened in 1825) was that between KIRKINTILLOCH and MONKLAND, opened in 1826 for the carriage of coal to the Forth and Clyde Canal from the Monkland area[1]; locomotives were not used on it, however, till 1832. Passengers were first carried in a train drawn by steam locomotive

[1] See p. 96

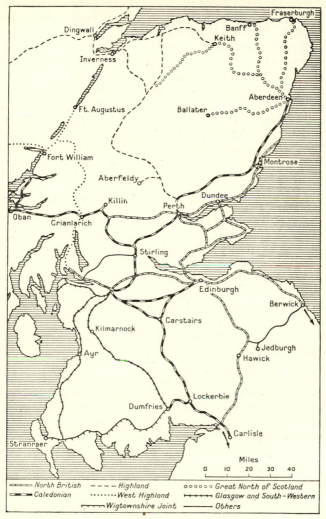

Railways Before 1921

in 1831 on the GARNKIRK-GLASGOW railway of eight miles, which led from the Kirkintilloch-Monkland railway to St. Rollox station in Glasgow. At the official opening, a locomotive, driven by George Stephenson and named after him, pulled a train of four open trucks, a couple of covered trucks, built on the model of a stage-coach, and an open carriage for ladies. The first north of Scotland railway, from DUNDEE to NEWTYLE, was opened in the same year but at first only for horse traction, locomotives being introduced in 1834. On the EDINBURGH-DALKEITH railway, opened in 1831, the waggons were drawn by horses except at the inclines, where stationary engines were used to pull the trains. At first, passengers were taken up at any point by hailing the engine-driver but in time limited stops with platforms were intro-duced. By the 1840's the Midland Plain had a network of railways used mainly for the transport of coal, iron and heavy manufac-tured goods. As a result of the "RAILWAY MANIA", which was at its peak in 1846, when railways were being built all over the coun-try, some of the smaller lines were linked up to form main lines. The opening of the EDINBURGH-BERWICK line in 1846 and, simi-larly, that between GLASGOW and CARLISLE in 1848 made possible direct connections between London and the two Scottish cities. From 1848 when it took 9 hours 36 minutes to cover the 300 miles to Carlisle, a train, now called the ROYAL SCOT, has left Euston for the north regularly at 10 o'clock each morning—the oldest scheduled train in the world; and the time taken has not become much less in the century.[1]

Improved Communications.—The benefits to industry of better roads, canals, steamboats, and railways were very great and the transport changes can be said to have been an important factor in the Industrial Revolution. Agriculture also benefited both in receiving the products of the towns—lime, manure and other fertilizers—and in sending farm produce in return. The railways made possible the development of the trade in perishable goods, like milk and vegetables, which made a great difference to the diet of the townsman. But internal trade of all kinds benefited with improved transport and communications. At the same time, people became less isolated and began to know more about the

[1] See p. 190

rest of the world. The "penny post" was introduced by the efforts of Rowland Hill in 1840, when the railways were just beginning to be established. Not only letters but newspapers were then brought quickly, and when the telegraph, invented in 1838

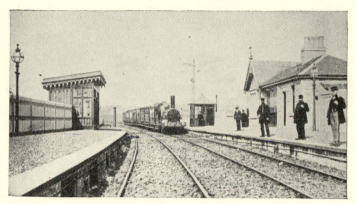

Photo: Picture Post

"Scotch Flyer", 1874

by Sir Charles Wheatstone, came into wider use, Britain began to seem a much smaller place. The result was a revolution in people's lives and a speeding-up of the tempo of living, which the twentieth century has seen in an even greater degree.

SOURCE EXTRACT

"For every horse or other beast of draught, drawing any coach, chariot, chaise, hearse or other such carriage, 6d.

For every horse, ox or other beast drawing any waggon, wain, van, caravan, each cart or other wheeled carriage, not on springs when the number not exceeding four, each 8d.

When the number shall be three, each 5d.

When the number shall be two or one, each 4d.

For every horse, mule or other beast of burden, laden or unladen and drawing, 2d.

For every drove of oxen or neat cattle, per score 10d. and in proportion for any greater or less number.

For every drove of horses or fillies, unshod, per score 1/8, and in proportion for any greater or less number.

For every drove of calves, sheep, lambs, hogs or goats, per score 5d., and in proportion for any greater or less number.

Asses shall only be charged half toll.

All carts and carriages let for hire to pay every time of passing with a new hire or load of one cwt."

List of toll rates in Ayrshire, 1870

EXERCISES

1. Make a list of the times taken at various dates for the journey from London to Edinburgh or Glasgow.
2. Write short notes on the following: Turnpike Trusts, Thomas Telford, John Rennie, John L. Macadam, Monkland Canal, Forth and Clyde Canal, David Napier, Robert Napier, Donald MacKay, Cunard Company.
3. Explain the success of some of the Scottish canals and the failure of others.
4. Write a short paragraph on "Scottish steamboat pioneers".
5. Write a sentence about each of the following: "Glasgow and Edinburgh Caravan", "The Fly", *Charlotte Dundas, Comet, Rob Roy, Aglaia, Britannia, Champion of the Seas, Ariel, Thermopylae, Cutty Sark, Royal Scot.*
6. Explain the following words or phrases: statute labour roads, parish road day, cadgers, turnpike, toll-house, tarmacadam, "navigators", steeple-engine, "railway mania".
7. Find out the date of the earliest railway in your district and the reason for its construction.
8. If you live in or near a shipbuilding town, write a brief history of one of the older shipyards, mentioning any famous ships.

CHAPTER XI

POLITICAL REFORM

Post-War Discontent.—The end of a war brings troubles to
the victors as well as to the defeated. After 1815, discontent
among the British people soon grew to such a height that the
Tory government again feared revolution. One of the main
grievances was the passing of new CORN LAWS in 1815, to protect
the home farmer by forbidding the import of foreign corn unless
the price of home corn went up to 80s. per quarter. The London
homes of Cabinet ministers were stoned and riots broke out in
many of the large industrial towns, including Perth, Dundee and
Glasgow, even although Scotsmen had little interest in the price
of wheaten bread. In Glasgow, a petition was drawn up, demanding the reform of a Parliament which could produce such laws.
In the textile and iron industries, peace brought a depression and
unemployment, as there was no longer a need for some of their
products such as uniforms and munitions. At the same time
thousands of soldiers and sailors flocked back from abroad, looking for work and thus enabling the employers to force down wages.
The COMBINATION ACTS of 1799 and 1800, forbidding associations
of employers or employees, were still in force; and the result was
that secret societies were formed among the workers. The cry
went up from all sides for a reduction of taxation, which many
had thought would be reduced when the war was over but which
still continued. The INCOME TAX which Pitt had introduced in
1798 for the duration of the war had been a small impost—2d. in
the £ on incomes of £60, rising to 2s. in the £ on incomes over
£200. This tax was reluctantly withdrawn by the Government,
mainly after agitation by the opposition, led by Henry Brougham,
one of the *Edinburgh Review* Whigs.[1] But the large NATIONAL
DEBT of over £800,000,000 made it necessary to continue the
other taxes, which, being indirect, weighed heavily upon the poor.
Almost everything was taxed—all kinds of food and drink ("the
poor man's salt and the rich man's spices") and every conceivable

F   [1] See p. 139

article—windows, wigs, roads, horses, etc. Added to all these troubles which came from the Government were the effects of the Industrial Revolution. No longer had the poor man a kailyard at his door to help him to eke out a living in hard times; the unemployed mill-hands and ironworkers now lived in crowded towns. The Scottish system of poor relief was mainly one based on charity and church-collections and could not cope with the large numbers of paupers.[1] The coming of the new machines also spelt misery for the handloom weavers, who had so recently been "the aristocrats of labour". The glorious victories of the French wars were soon forgotten in the general discontent.

Repression.—Some of the Whigs in Parliament were not slow to blame all the nation's troubles on the Tory Government, of which Lord Liverpool had been Prime Minister since 1812. Outside Parliament, agitation was whipped up by RADICALS, who wanted a more radical or thorough-going reform. Prominent among these were William Cobbett, who lambasted the Government in his newspaper, the *Political Register*, and Major Cartwright, who went about the country founding "Hampden Clubs". Both of these Englishmen had enthusiastic followings in Scotland, especially in the west. The Government could think only of repression as an answer to this agitation. Spies were paid to mix with workers in their secret societies. One of them, ALEXANDER RICHMOND, a weaver who had been outlawed as a result of his taking part in the cotton weavers' strike in 1812, was employed by the wealthy merchant, Kirkman Finlay, M.P. and Lord Provost of Glasgow.[2] Richmond the Spy and others like him at times acted as *agents provocateurs*, inciting the Radicals to consider extreme measures like rebellion, so that action could be taken against them. News of such a conspiracy among Glasgow weavers and an attempt on the Prince Regent's life in London made the Government in 1817 suspend the Habeas Corpus acts again, and introduce another bill, the GAGGING ACT, restricting the right of holding public meetings. Many reformers were clapped in gaol without a trial. Two Kilmarnock men, accused of writing and printing a violent speech, received mild sentences because of legal assistance given to the prisoners by the Whig

[1] See p. 209   [2] See p. 63

advocate, Jeffrey. Another trial in Glasgow collapsed when one of the witnesses admitted he had been bribed to give evidence. Demand for the reform of town council elections, a grievance of long standing, was revived in the burghs. 1819 saw more unemployment and more distress. Glasgow handloom weavers, who during the war had earned up to 40s. a week, could now earn only 5s., while in Maybole wages were as low as 2s. 6d. a week. In this year there occurred the "Peterloo Massacre"; an orderly crowd of 80,000 at St. Peter's Fields, Manchester, was charged by soldiers and many killed. Rumours flew around that pikes were being manufactured in village smithies and that the unemployed cotton operatives were drilling in secret. The Government was still determined to maintain order by repression, and had the Six Acts passed, forbidding ordinary public meetings, the possession of arms and unlawful drilling, and imposing a new tax of 4d. a copy on newspapers and pamphlets.

"Radical War."—The death of the old, insane King George III in January 1820 brought his son, the Prince Regent, to the throne. The proclamation of this elderly, dissipated "first gentleman of Europe" was received in silence by the London crowd, which normally hissed at him. Much of the first year of his reign was spent in a disgraceful quarrel with his wife, whom he wanted to divorce and who was actually prevented from entering Westminster Abbey for the coronation ceremony. A plot to assassinate the members of the Government, the Cato Street conspiracy, was discovered just in time. In Scotland, the Government made numerous arrests of men suspected of planning a rising; government spies were active in encouraging and also noting any seditious talk. On the night of Saturday, 1st April 1820 (an ominous date for what was to prove a tragic hoax), there were posted up in Glasgow and district hundreds of placards, calling the people to rise in rebellion for the redress of their common grievances. All over the west of Scotland people stood waiting for the spark of rebellion to be lit, and local hotheads spoke as if the day of the employers and landlords was over for ever. The Volunteers of the Napoleonic War[1] were called out in many places to deal with the impending revolt. Rumours were spread by

[1] See p. 118, p. 123

Government spies that revolution had been successful in England. A number of men, badly armed, set off for Carron Ironworks to help an English army which was said to be advancing to seize the cannon there. At BONNYMUIR, not far from Falkirk, when the *agents provocateurs* had all taken themselves away, the small force was easily scattered by a troop of Hussars. Some were killed and of the survivors, the two leaders, ANDREW HARDIE, a Glasgow weaver, and JOHN BAIRD, a smith of Condorrat, were sentenced to be hanged and beheaded (to intimidate the working classes) and eighteen were transported for life. Another body of men had been duped into marching from Strathaven to Glasgow; one of them, an old hosier, JAMES WILSON, was hanged at Glasgow Green before a silent crowd of 20,000. There seems little doubt that it was the actions of government spies or *agents provocateurs* that provoked this "Radical War", as it was called, and the Government was pleased to have the opportunity of crushing the "rebellion".

Tory Reforms.—When George IV visited Edinburgh in 1822[1] (the first visit of a reigning monarch for almost two centuries) he was fêted in the capital but took care not to visit the Radical Glasgow, where a recent riot had led to the last public whipping in Scotland. Agitation died down because of an improvement in trade which enjoyed a boom in 1825. The boom in trade was followed by a slump; the harvest also was so bad that 1826 was always referred to afterwards as "the year of the short corn". There was another outburst of industrial unrest, resulting in a few more arrests and trials. But the Government was at last beginning to introduce new reforms. In 1824, the COMBINATION ACTS were repealed after long agitation by FRANCIS PLACE, "the breeches-maker of Charing Cross", JOSEPH HUME, the wealthy Scottish Radical, and JOHN R. McCULLOCH, the editor of the *Scotsman*. Changes which the *Edinburgh Review*[2] had been advocating were carried through in Scots law, allowing jurors to be chosen by ballot and to be challenged by the accused, as in English law, and reducing the penalty for sedition. Another reform, advocated for long by two M.P.s, Sir Samuel Romilly and Sir JAMES MACKINTOSH,[3] author of *Vindiciae Gallicae*, and carried out

[1] See p. 36   [2] See p. 139   [3] See pp. 114-15

by Sir Robert Peel, was the abolition of capital punishment for many trivial offences. All during this period, the second VISCOUNT MELVILLE, son of "King Harry the Ninth", had been "Manager" of Scottish affairs.[1] When Lord Liverpool resigned in 1827, George Canning became Prime Minister; although he was a Tory, he had to rely on Whig support, and got rid of Melville as "Manager" of Scotland, thus bringing to an end the long Dundas supremacy. The last years of George IV's reign saw the repeal of the TEST ACT and CORPORATION ACT in 1828 and the passing of the ROMAN CATHOLIC RELIEF ACT in 1829 by the Tory Government, led by Wellington and Peel. The change in public opinion against Roman Catholics was evident; far from there being big riots, as in Lord George Gordon's time, large public meetings were held throughout Scotland in favour of the Relief Act. By this time there were in Scotland large numbers of immigrant Irish, most of whom were Catholics; but there was as yet little sign of the anti-Irish and anti-Catholic feeling which led to so much disorder later in the century.

Parliamentary Elections.—The Tories were still averse to parliamentary reform, which they reckoned was tampering with what Wellington called a "matchless constitution". The necessity for reform had not grown less since 1785 when Pitt's bill, proposing very moderate changes, had been rejected. The system of representation in Scotland, as we have already seen,[2] was on the whole much worse than in England; and the growth of industrial towns had made the elections seem more absurd and unfair than ever. Large industrial towns like Greenock (30,000), Paisley (46,000) and Kilmarnock (18,000) were unrepresented, while in England there were even larger towns unrepresented, such as Birmingham (over 100,000), Manchester and Salford (over 133,000). Glasgow, with a population of over 200,000, shared its single member with Renfrew, Rutherglen and Dumbarton, the combined population of which was only 11,000. In the 66 Scottish royal burghs, although none was so decayed as Gatton or Old Sarum in England, there were only about 1,300 electors, the town councillors of the burghs, for the most part self-elected. The number of county voters or freeholders, including a fairly large

[1] See p. 109   [2] See pp. 110-12

number of "parchment barons",[1] only amounted to about 3,000, and these totals, it must be remembered, were for a country with a population of nearly 2,500,000.

Reform Agitation.—When George IV died in 1830, he was succeeded by his brother, William IV, who was believed to be in favour of reform; the Tories were defeated and lost the power which they had held, except for a short interval, since 1783. The Whig Government, under Earl Grey, had only a small majority, and, when Lord John Russell introduced a bill for the reform of the franchise, it passed the second reading by only one vote. News of the narrow victory was brought to an expectant Glasgow from London in less than 36 hours (a record time)[2] and the Lord Provost's house in West George Street was illuminated by 3,000 gas-jets, with the sign, "Let Glasgow Flourish", in the middle. The Government decided on a general election in the summer of 1831, and popular enthusiasm for "the Bill, the whole Bill and nothing but the Bill" ran so high that where there were constituencies with large electorates the Whigs had sweeping majorities. In Scotland, even despite the corrupt electoral system, the burghs returned 11 Whigs and 4 Tories, while the counties returned 13 Whigs and 17 Tories, the victory of the last being due mainly to the pale-faced Edinburgh "parchment barons" who rode from one county election to another. At the elections in the manufacturing districts, large demonstrations were staged by workers. Sir Walter Scott, Sheriff of Selkirk, was stoned by the weavers at Jedburgh. Lord William Graham, son of the Duke of Montrose, was returned as Tory M.P. for Dunbartonshire with the aid of fictitious votes but narrowly escaped with his life from a mob of cotton operatives. When the House of Lords threw out a second Reform Bill in October, there was serious rioting in English towns; and a Glasgow procession, estimated at 100,000, marched through the streets with banners inscribed "Liberty or Death".

Reform Act.—The bill which at last was passed in June 1832, after the King had agreed to create new Whig peers if necessary, was a very moderate reform which enfranchised none of the working-men who had paraded so enthusiastically, but rather strengthened the position of the middle classes. In Scotland, the

[1] See p. 112   [2] See p. 146

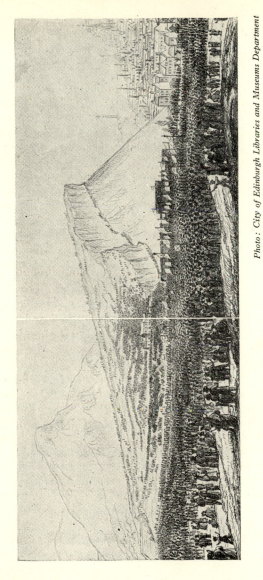

Photo: City of Edinburgh Libraries and Museums Department

The Great Reform Meeting—King's Park, Edinburgh, 1832

seats were increased and re-distributed so that 23 (an increase of 8) were allocated to the burghs, including some of the new industrial towns, all householders who paid a rent of at least £10 (a fairly high figure in those days) being entitled to vote. In 17 burghs, it was estimated, the number of electors was actually less than before 1832. The number of members for the counties remained 30 as before. The franchise of the "parchment barons" was abolished and the vote given to all freeholders of land worth £10 a year and tenants of land worth £50. The first "reformed" election was held in December, 1832, and for the first time "hustings" or platforms for public voting were erected in Scotland; hitherto, although these were common at the more popular English elections, there was little need for them in Scotland with its small polls. In Edinburgh, too, a new name for the Tories, "Conservatists", was being favoured by some who realized how unpopular the old name had become. The new Parliament contained a large Whig majority; from Scotland there were 41 Whigs and only 12 Tories, of whom all but one were county members. Although the Reform Act was limited in its scope, it marked a break with the old system and paved the way for other reforms.

Burgh Reform.—The Whigs passed three important reform acts in 1833, the abolition of slavery in the British colonies, a factory act, and the reform of municipal government in Scotland. The town councils of Scottish burghs had been denounced for years as self-interested, corrupt and responsible to no one but themselves. They were self-elected, and, as there was no supervision of accounts, there was much corruption and mismanagement. Contracts for public work were given to town councillors at high prices and most burghs were so much in debt that the town's lands were sold to pay off the debts, sometimes at low prices to councillors and their friends. *The Provost*, by JOHN GALT, the Greenock novelist, gives a good picture of "Gudetown", a small Scottish burgh, and all the "jookerie-cookerie" of public business. Committees of the House of Commons had been appointed in 1793 and 1819 and had reported on the Scottish burghs but no effective action was taken till 1833, when the Scottish MUNICIPAL REFORM ACT gave to all householders in burghs the rights of electing the town councils. A similar act for English boroughs was passed two years later. These acts, by widening the franchise to include all householders, helped to strengthen the demand by the working classes for further reforms of parliamentary elections. The Whigs' popularity did not last very long. Some of them, like Russell, who had introduced the Reform Bill in 1831, Jeffrey and Cockburn, the Edinburgh Whigs, began to talk as if the constitution was now perfect and as if it was impossible to give the franchise to "the dregs of the populace". For some time after 1832, however, the working classes were more interested in trade unions but many of these collapsed after 1834, when their strikes had failed.

Chartism.—In 1837, when William IV was succeeded by his young niece, Queen Victoria, there was a growing movement, opposed to both Whigs and Tories, among the Radicals, who advocated a complete reform of the parliamentary system. Their demands were formulated in 1838 in the PEOPLE'S CHARTER, with six points: (1) manhood suffrage, (2) vote by ballot, (3) annual elections, (4) payment of members, (5) equal electoral districts re-arranged every ten years after the census, (6) abolition of the property qualification for English and Irish M.P.s. Scottish Radicals were not slow in adopting the Charter in all its points even although the last did not affect Scotland. Monster petitions were presented to Parliament and rejected. Some Chartists considered that the best way of achieving their aims was by "moral force" or peaceful persuasion, while others spoke of "physical force" as essential. In Scotland, Rev. PATRICK BREWSTER of the Abbey Church, Paisley, and JOHN FRASER of Johnstone, editor of the Chartist paper, *The True Scotsman*, were for "moral force", while Dr JOHN TAYLOR of Irvine ("Radical Jack") was one of the leaders of the "physical force" section. Chartism spread like wildfire throughout Scotland. To many workers the People's Charter was just a preliminary to improving working conditions, shortening hours, increasing wages. To others it was the prelude to a republic and socialism. Many Chartists were also keen on "temperance" or "total abstinence" from alcoholic liquors (it was a time when the drinking of potent whisky was far too common in the industrial towns); some were interested in setting up "Chartist Churches" with a simple form of service; still other Chartists were Irishmen mostly interested in Irish independence. The progress of the movement suffered from having too many leaders with too many different ideas.

Collapse of Chartism.—Political agitation thrives on discontent: when times were bad Chartism grew stronger, and when trade improved, the movement began to lose support. The authorities tried both repression and relief. In 1842, to provide work for the unemployed, the "Radical Road" (Queen's Drive) was built on Arthur's Seat, Edinburgh, just as one had been made at the foot of the Salisbury Crags in 1819. An attempt by "physical force" Chartists of Dundee to march to Forfar fizzled out, the leaders being given mild sentences. A huge but peaceful demonstration was held in the capital in 1844 on the occasion of laying the foundation-stone of a monument in the Calton Cemetery as a memorial to Muir and the "political martyrs" of 1793-94.[1] The worst outbreak of violence of the period occurred in March 1848, just before the fiasco of the third and last petition to the House of Commons. A starving mob of Glasgow unemployed, some of them Irish immigrants who had only recently arrived after the terrible potato famine, terrorized Glasgow for a few days and looted shops in the so-called BREAD RIOTS. Soldiers and special constables were called out and the crowds in the streets and on Glasgow Green were charged, six being killed and several wounded. Many of the ringleaders were arrested and transported; but there was no evidence that the riot had been organized by Chartists. Quiet times came again with an improvement in trade and the expectation that the Whigs would soon introduce a bill to enfranchise the working classes. During this decade, known as the "HUNGRY FORTIES", there was plenty of misery in Scotland, especially in 1846-47 when the potato crop failed and the people of the Highlands and Islands were near starvation.[2] But, on the whole, industrial discontent was not so great as in England at that time. Some industries like iron and shipbuilding were booming; and many of the working classes were more concerned with the Church than with Parliament (the great "Disruption"

[1] See p. 117   [2] See p. 44, p. 183

occurred in 1843[1]), while others still were active in the Anti-Corn Law League, which through Duncan MacLaren, the able lieutenant of Cobden and Bright, became very popular. Chartism gradually died away as an organized movement but the ideas remained; today all the demands have been granted except those for annual elections and equal electoral districts, although most constituencies are fairly equal in size.

Extension of Franchise.—An extension of the franchise to some of the working classes came in 1867-68 from the Conservatives, after the Liberals had failed with a similar measure. In the Scottish Reform Act of 1868 all burgh householders received the franchise, and also lodgers paying at least £10 rent a year. In the counties, the vote was given to landowners with land worth at least £5 a year and tenants whose rent was £14 or over, which meant that the bulk of the rural population and many of the inhabitants of small industrial towns, not large enough to rank as burghs, were still excluded from the franchise. It was at this time also that the Scottish universities were placed on the same footing as the English by being given parliamentary representation, St. Andrews and Edinburgh forming one constituency and Glasgow and Aberdeen another. The enfranchisement of the artisans or town-workers did not at once bring working-class M.P.s. Only one stood at the 1868 election, Alexander MacDonald, the Scottish miners' leader, but as he could not compete with the free whisky and bribes offered by the older parties, he withdrew from the contest, eventually entering Parliament in 1874 for an English constituency as one of the first two Labour M.P.s.[2] The need for secret voting, to prevent not only bribes but also intimidation by employers and landlords, was greater than ever. In 1872, during Gladstone's first ministry, Parliament passed the Ballot Act, ensuring secret voting, and in 1883, during his second ministry, the Corrupt Practices Act, which prevented unauthorized payments at elections. A year later, the third Reform Act of 1884 gave complete manhood suffrage, with a few exceptions; but the enfranchisement of women took a long time. Women householders had been able to vote in municipal elections since 1869 and a Women's Suffrage Bill

[1] See pp. 235-8   [2] See p. 226

PARLIAMENTARY FRANCHISE

	BURGHS	COUNTIES	NUMBER OF SEATS
1831	Town councils (self-elected) of the 66 royal burghs	Freeholders of "40s. land of old extent holden of the King" or of land worth £400 (Scots) per annum; "parchment barons"—owners of superiority over land worth £400 (Scots) per annum	15—1 for Edinburgh and 14 for 65 other burghs; 30 for counties—6 small counties represented only in alternate parliaments
1832	Householders whose house was valued at £10 or more per annum	Proprietors of land or property valued at £10 or more per annum and tenants paying £50 or more in rent per annum	23 for burghs (including some new industrial towns); 30 for counties
1868	Male adult householders and lodgers paying at least £10 per annum in rent	Proprietors of land or property valued at £5 or more per annum and tenants paying £14 or more in rent per annum	60 (including 2 university seats)
1884–1885	Male adult householders and lodgers		72
1918	Male adults and females over 30, of householders or married to householders		74 (including 3 university seats)
1928	Adults		74
1948	Adults (but double franchises, such as those of university graduates, abolished)		71

was presented the following year in Parliament without success. Others followed at intervals with no better result. At last, in 1903, a SUFFRAGETTE MOVEMENT was started by Mrs Pankhurst, a doctor's widow, who with her colleagues was prepared to go to any lengths for her cause—breaking Cabinet Ministers' windows, firing pillar-boxes, etc. Many were sent to prison and there went on hunger-strikes. In 1914 the First World War came, and the work done by women in almost all spheres ended the stupid opposition to women's suffrage. The REPRESENTATION OF THE PEOPLE ACT of 1918 gave the vote at first only to women over thirty, who were also allowed in the same year to stand for Parliament; by the EQUAL FRANCHISE ACT OF 1928 the vote was given to all women over twenty-one, so that at last there was complete adult suffrage. Paradoxically enough, many men and women nowadays do not trouble to exercise the right to vote which all through the nineteenth century was so eagerly sought after.

SOURCE EXTRACT

"Francis Jeffrey—the ablest man by far in Scotland—has, we grieve to state, been beaten off at Edinburgh by a poor creature of the name of Robert A. *Dundas*—a name which stinks in every part of Scotland—excepting always, the nostrils of a few lick-spittles in, and around Edinburgh, who have fed and still feed, on the loaves and fishes which the Family of *Dundas* long ago provided for them. The 'Right Honourable' William Allan of Glen, Lord Provost of Edinburgh, on Tuesday last, the 3rd curt. 'did himself the honour to propose Mr Dundas as a *fit* and *proper* representative for the Metropolis of Scotland'—in the face of the fact that 20,000 citizens of Edinburgh, by their Petitions, earnestly entreated his Lordship to act differently, and to prefer the Lord Advocate—and not a single Petition that we are aware of, was presented in favour of the aforesaid Mr Dundas. Nothing can more completely demonstrate the necessity of a Reform in the representation of Scotland than this very election. In reward for his honourable conduct, the Lord Provost, in the course of the evening of the above day, got a blue eye and a bloody nose."

The Loyal Reformers' Gazette, 7th May 1831

EXERCISES

1. Explain the conduct of the Lord Provost in the 1831 election. In what respects does the language of the 1831 newspaper differ from that of today?
2. Why was there so much discontent in Scotland after 1815?
3. Give an account of the unreformed parliamentary elections in Scotland. (Refer also to the chapter—"North and South Britain".)
4. Write short notes on the following: Richmond the Spy, "Radical War", Municipal Reform Act, Bread Riots of 1848, Alexander MacDonald.
5. Write down in the form of a table the main provisions of the Reform Acts of 1832, 1868, 1884 as they affected Scotland.
6. Explain the following: *Agent provocateur*, Gagging Act, "the year of the short corn", hustings, Conservatists, "jookerie-cookerie", "moral force".
7. What differences were there between Scottish and English Chartism?
8. Find out details about elections in your district during this period. If you live in a royal burgh, find out in which group your burgh was before and after 1832.
9. If you live in or near a royal burgh, find out what lands belonging to the burgh were disposed of in the period, 1789-1832.

CHAPTER XII

VICTORIAN AND EDWARDIAN SCOTLAND

An Age of Expansion.—During the long reign of Queen Victoria (1837-1901) and that of her son, Edward VII (1901-10), Britain was the wealthiest country in the world, with a vast colonial empire, on which "the sun never set", and with the bulk of the world's trade, manufacturing and banking in her hands. Such a rapid expansion as the Industrial Revolution had brought about was not achieved without many troubles and complications which we shall consider in later chapters; and you have already read of the long struggle to extend the franchise to all adults. The story of the Scottish empire-builders—explorers, business-men, missionaries—contains much to make us feel proud but has also passages which do not seem so creditable to us today. But most Scotsmen of Victorian or Edwardian times, seeing the wonderful developments in industry and transport around them, believed that inventions inevitably brought about progress and felt proud to belong to a nation which had played such a leading part in these developments. To many people today who have lived through two world wars and who have seen Britain lose much of her empire and trade the reigns of Victoria and Edward VII seem to be a kind of "golden age".

Scottish Prime Ministers.—From the elections which fol-lowed the Reform Act of 1832, when 43 of the 53 Scottish seats were won by the Whigs, Scotland was invariably during this period on the side of the Whigs or the Liberals, as they later came to be called. Most of the Scottish M.P.s played humble parts at Westminster but a few of them rose to the highest positions in the Government. Some of these were Anglo-Scots, men of Scottish birth or descent but brought up or resident in England. The EARL OF ABERDEEN (1784-1860), although born in Edinburgh, was educated in England and spent most of his time there. He was Foreign Secretary in Wellington's Tory ministry of 1828-30, and again under Peel in the period 1841-46, supporting his Prime Minister over the repeal of the Corn Laws. A man of high principles and respected on all sides, he was the Prime Minister of the Coalition Government formed in 1852 just before the Crimean War and resigned office when the outcry against the muddled administration of the war became too great in 1855. Another Prime Minister of Scottish descent but of English up-bringing was WILLIAM EWART GLADSTONE (1809-98), whose grandfather had been a Leith corn-merchant and who was always very proud of his Scottish connection. He was four times Prime Minister and had a large following in Scotland, particularly after his famous election campaign in 1880, when he became M.P. for Midlothian. Gladstone was succeeded as Prime Minister in 1894

by the EARL OF ROSEBERY (1847-1929), whose estate of Dalmeny
lies near South Queensferry on the Forth. Rosebery managed to
achieve the three aims he set himself at school—to marry an
heiress, to win the Derby and to become Prime Minister, although
he only held the post for a year. A. J. BALFOUR (1848-1930) was
the laird of Whittingehame in East Lothian but was educated in
England and spent most of his life there. He entered Parliament
as a Conservative M.P. in 1874 and held various offices before he
succeeded the Marquis of Salisbury as Prime Minister in 1902.
An extremely tall man, celebrated as tennis-player and golfer,
philosopher and musician, and too clever to be popular, he held
office only till 1905, and at the elections of 1906 his party suffered
a crushing defeat at the hands of the Liberals. Again the Prime
Minister was a Scotsman, Sir HENRY CAMPBELL-BANNERMAN
(1836-1908), son of a Lord Provost of Glasgow. He played an
important part in bringing about more friendly relations with
South Africa after the Boer War but died after only two years in
office. He was succeeded by H. H. Asquith, who, though not a
Scot, sat for almost forty years for Scottish constituencies. The
Secretary for War under both these Liberal Prime Ministers was
R. B. HALDANE of Cloan, near Gleneagles, outstanding as a lawyer,
a philosopher and an administrator who remodelled the British
Army, making it fit to bear the heavy burdens which 1914 brought.

Scottish M.P.s.—Although Scotsmen held such prominent
posts in successive governments, the treatment of Scottish affairs
gave rise to much dissatisfaction. The great champion of Scottish
interests in the early part of Queen Victoria's reign was the
Radical, DUNCAN MACLAREN (1800-86). He was one of the
henchmen of Bright and Cobden in their Anti-Corn Law campaign and helped to bring almost all Scotsmen into the movement
for repeal. When Lord Provost of Edinburgh in 1852 he took an
active part in suppressing Sunday drinking, which had become
a serious problem at that time. During the Crimean War, along
with his former associates, Bright and Cobden, he opposed the
war as a Pacifist. As M.P. for Edinburgh from 1865 to 1881, he
managed to secure a better proportion of Scottish seats in Parliament in the 1868 Reform Act, and was so outspoken and know-

ledgeable on all Scottish affairs that he became known as the "Member for Scotland". MacLaren was followed in his championship of Scottish rights at Westminster by two men of the landowning class, the young Earl of Rosebery in the House of Lords and Cunninghame-Graham in the House of Commons. R. B. CUNNINGHAME-GRAHAM (1852-1936) was a Scottish laird, who had an adventurous career as a young man in South America, where he learned to be a very fine horseman. Outside politics, he gained distinction as an essayist and short story writer of the first class. As M.P. for Lanarkshire, he helped to found the Scottish Home Rule Association and the Scottish Labour Party. He was bludgeoned and arrested by the police in a demonstration in Trafalgar Square on "Bloody Sunday" in November 1887, in support of the right to hold public meetings there. The Scottish Labour movement, which also owed a great deal to ALEXANDER MACDONALD, the first Labour M.P., and J. KEIR HARDIE, of whom you will hear later,[1] had Home Rule for Scotland as one of the points in its early programmes. Cunninghame-Graham was a leader in the movement for Scottish Home Rule until his death fifty years afterwards.

Government of Scotland.—Rosebery was one of those responsible for the agitation which led to the appointment in 1885 of a SECRETARY FOR SCOTLAND, with a seat in the Cabinet, in place of the system whereby since 1827 the Home Secretary had controlled Scottish affairs, with the help of the Scottish Lord Advocate. This new post, however, did little to damp down Scottish discontent; and when an Englishman, Sir George Trevelyan, was appointed to the post, the SCOTTISH HOME RULE ASSOCIATION was formed in 1886 with Dr G. P. Clark, M.P. for Caithness, as its Chairman and Cunninghame-Graham as one of the members of committee. In 1888, when George J. Goschen was Chancellor of the Exchequer, an arrangement was made for apportioning the Scottish share of the public funds. As England and Wales contributed eighty per cent of the total revenue, Scotland eleven per cent and Ireland nine per cent, by the GOSCHEN FORMULA Scotland has received from that time $\frac{11}{80}$ of the sum granted to England and Wales, although allowance is made for certain exceptions.

[1] See pp. 227-8

The Local Government Act of 1889, which provided for COUNTY COUNCILS, elected by ratepayers, either male or female, was welcomed as a step in the devolution of government but Scottish M.P.s were still dissatisfied with the treatment of Scottish affairs at Westminster. A Standing Committee of the House of Commons was set up in 1893 to deal with Scottish bills but it also contained English members (in order to maintain the balance of the parties as Scotland was predominantly Liberal even when there was a Conservative majority in the House of Commons). There was some criticism in 1901 of the numeral VII in Edward VII's title, as to many Scots it implied the acceptance of all the previous Edwards from the time of Edward I, "The Hammer of the Scots". Between 1908 and 1914 six bills for Scottish Home Rule were introduced with a majority of Scottish members in their favour but were not allowed to proceed further than the second reading, although the Liberal Government of Asquith was supposed to be sympathetic.[1] Scottish Home Rule did not become a burning question, however, as other topics and problems engrossed the attention of ordinary Scotsmen—industrial unrest (it was a period of great strikes), Free Trade versus Protection, reform of the House of Lords, votes for women, and even (for many men) the absorbing question of how the local football team would fare in the League or Cup games.

Irish Immigration.—The treatment of the Irish after 1691 has been called "the blackest page in British history"; it is little wonder that, even before the "Potato Famine", there was already a stream of Irish emigration either to Britain or to America. Unlike their predecessors, the pre-historic strand-loopers and the Scots of the Dark Ages, who made their homes in Argyll and the Southern Hebrides, the nineteenth-century Irish immigrants (naturally mainly from the north of Ireland) settled in the Scottish Lowlands. During the French wars, before the reaping-machine was invented, bands of harvesters used to come over annually for the mowing of the corn on the Lowland farms, and after 1815 some of them became permanent settlers. The steamboats after 1818 provided a cheap crossing, and there were plenty of jobs in the coal-mines, in the ironworks, in the cotton-mills. The Irishmen

[1] See p. 321

soon had a reputation as strong, willing workers and many of the railways of Scotland were built by Irish navvies, who lived in large camps near their work. The employers welcomed them not only as good workers but also as strike-breakers, when Scottish trade unions were making their first attempts to force their masters to yield to their requests by staging strikes. The Irish were not long in taking an active part in trade unions themselves, however, and some of them were arrested as ringleaders of the "Bread Riots" in Glasgow in 1848.[1] By 1841, there were at least 125,000 Irish-born persons in Scotland, most of them in Clydeside but some also in east-coast towns as far north as Aberdeen. The "Potato Famine" almost doubled their numbers. The Irishman's dependence on the potato (in some districts a man would consume daily 7 lb. of potatoes or more) made the potato blight a disaster of the first magnitude, about one and a quarter million dying as a result and almost a million emigrating during the period, 1846-50. The "Irish Invasion", as it was termed in a Glasgow newspaper of the time, caused much bitter feeling among Scottish people. In 1849, the authorities in Glasgow, already grossly overcrowded, began to send Irish paupers back to their own country at a rate of 1,000 a month, but they did nothing to prevent their return. By 1851 about a quarter of Glasgow's 360,000 inhabitants were Irish, and in some other Clydeside towns like Greenock and Port Glasgow the proportion was not very different. Jealousy of the Irishmen as incomers and as rival competitors for the jobs available combined with a revival of the old anti-Catholic bitterness, which had almost disappeared in Scotland, to produce many scenes of violence, the Orange-and-Green riots of which you will read in another chapter.[2] Irish men and women still continued to come over, mostly for permanent work in Clyde shipyards but some of them, from Donegal, in large bands of "tattie-howkers" for the potato-harvest. By the beginning of the twentieth century, the Irish element in the population had become difficult to estimate as many of the original immigrants or their descendants, especially the Protestants, must have married into the native Scottish population; but at the 1901 census the number of Catholics in Scotland

[1] See p. 170   [2] See pp. 241-2

was 431,900, the great majority of them being of Irish origin. There can be little doubt of the importance of the Irish immigration, both to the Scots and to the Irish incomers themselves. Although gradually most of the bitterness has disappeared, there still remains an anti-Irish and anti-Catholic feeling in Scotland.

Lowland Farming.—Since the time of the "Improvers", who had introduced new crops, new rotations, new methods, new machines and stock-breeding to Scotland, Lowland farming had enjoyed a long spell of prosperity. In the Victorian period, East Lothian farming was considered the best in Europe. The credit for this was due to men like GEORGE HOPE, tenant-farmer for over thirty years of Fenton Barns, between Dirleton and Drem, where he perfected his famous six-year rotation—corn, potatoes, turnips, swedes, clover and rye-grass, not only reaping bumper crops but carrying a heavy stock of cattle and sheep in winter. Hope, whose father and grandfather had tenanted the same farm before him, was made to give up his tenancy when his lease expired in 1873, because he had opposed Lord Elcho at a parliamentary election; but he started in Peebles-shire on another farm, where he proved once again the success of his methods. In the last quarter of the century, all British farming began to suffer a depression, partly from a series of bad harvests but mainly from competition from overseas—cheap grain from the American prairies, cheap mutton from Australia and New Zealand and cheap beef from North and South America. Farmers gradually changed their methods. Stock-breeders came from overseas to buy the animals which had won prizes at the "Highland" and other shows, and stock-breeding became more important than crop-raising. Stock-breeding brought about the development of LEY-FARMING. This involves sowing mixtures of grasses and clovers to be cut for hay and also to serve as pasture. R. H. ELLIOTT, by the methods which he tried out on his farm in Roxburghshire (the CLIFTON PARK SYSTEM), established an eight-year rotation— roots, corn, roots, corn, and four years of grass, which enabled him to maintain the ground in a condition of high fertility with little need of artificial manure. His methods, which differed from those of English ley farming in sowing more elaborate mixtures

of several clovers and grasses (cocksfoot, timothy, rye-grass) were
copied by other Scottish farmers, who were able to produce crops
with heavier yields than any other farmers in Europe. Some
Scottish farmers developed potato-growing and, because the
climate of Scotland was unfavourable to certain potato pests,
Scottish seed-potatoes were sent all over the world to growers.
Two men who helped to make the Scottish potato-trade so valuable were ARCHIBALD FLEMING of Auchtermuchty, Fife, who
introduced the *Up-to-Date* and *Majestic* varieties, and DONALD
MacKELVIE of Arran, the "Potato King", most of whose varieties
bear names with "Arran" in them. By 1914, Scottish farmers
were also showing more interest in dairy produce, poultry, fruit
(raspberries and strawberries for jam-making) than in their
grain-crops.

Balmoral.—Queen Victoria was the first of the Hanoverian
dynasty to achieve popularity in Scotland. Despite the rule
previously imposed by sovereigns against marriages of royal persons with those of lower rank, she allowed one of her daughters
to marry a Scottish nobleman, the Marquis of Lorne, who later
became Duke of Argyll; and she created Scottish titles for two
sons—the Duke of Edinburgh and the Duke of Albany. From
1855 onwards, she and her husband, Prince Albert, generally
spent part of the summer and autumn at Balmoral Castle, which
was built on Deeside not far from Braemar, where the standard
of rebellion was raised in 1715. The kilt, which had once been
proscribed, was worn by the royal family, and the Prince Consort
himself designed a Balmoral tartan; Jacobitism, no longer a
political danger, had become a mere sentiment. Jacobite songs
were popular even with the royal family; and in 1936, at the
funeral of George V, Queen Victoria's grandson, pipers played
Over the Sea to Skye, which is a song about "Bonnie Prince
Charlie". Many wealthy Englishmen followed the royal example
and went north to Scotland for "The Twelfth" (12th of August),
the opening day of the grouse-shooting season, and for deer-
stalking in September. The Highlands became dotted with large
castles, built in a revived "Scots Baronial" style, with suitable
improvements. Their owners were sometimes wealthy English-

men or Americans, whose sole interest in Scotland was in the sport, deer-stalking or grouse-shooting, which the land provided. Since the time of Sir Walter Scott, who had painted such a romantic picture of Scotland in his novels and poems, tourists had visited the Highlands, admiring the scenery of the "bens and glens", despite the two great disadvantages of Highland travel—

Photo: The Mansell Collection

Queen Victoria and John Brown at Balmoral

rain and midges. Engravings of "The Monarch of the Glen" (Landseer's famous painting) were very popular with all classes, and few hotels or boarding-houses were without one. The tendency in Victorian and Edwardian times to regard the Highlands merely as a region with beautiful scenery and wonderful sport for gun and rod has been called "Balmoralism". It did not bring much benefit to the native population. Some of the men acted as stalkers, gillies or gamekeepers and a few of them found the jobs very lucrative, as "tips" from shooting-tenants and their guests could be very high. Some of the girls entered into domestic service, first in the "big house" near their homes and later in the London mansions of their wealthy employers. But deer-stalking and crofting did not mix. Unless there was a high deer-fence, the deer would cause much damage to the crofters' crops and grazings. To prevent disturbance during the shooting-season, crofters who had managed to escape the clearances for sheep were deprived of hill-pastures that had been theirs from time immemorial. As sheep-farming became less profitable, with the importation of cheap, frozen mutton from overseas, landlords not only turned their land into deer-forests but also began to raise the rents of their crofter-tenants, whose condition had gradually become worse since the beginning of the century. There had been no change or improvement in their methods of cultivation, and much of the best land had been taken from them for sheep-farms. In the "Potato Famine" of 1846-47 many were in destitution and a few deaths occurred from starvation. To those in authority it seemed that the main trouble was over-population, dating from the time of the kelp-boom and the coming of the potato, and that emigration was the only remedy. Sir James Matheson, proprietor of Lewis, himself paid the fares of over 2,000 persons from his estates to Canada between 1851 and 1863. Although many of the youngest and most vigorous did go overseas on emigrant ships, those who were left were nevertheless determined to stand up for their rights and felt encouraged by the land agitation in Ireland.

"Crofters' War".—The raising of rents, evictions for non-payment, clearances for sheep-farms or deer-forests had been going on for years but in 1882 the trouble flared up into what has been called the "Crofters' War". In many of the districts where crofters survived, they began to challenge the actions of the landlords and factors; when the latter called in the sheriff's officers to help them, the crofters defied them. Near Portree there occurred the BATTLE OF THE BRAES, when the Sheriff, accompanied by Glasgow policemen and newspaper-reporters, was met with stones from an angry crowd, and several policemen were wounded. Not far away, at Glendale, the gunboat, *Jackal*,

arrived with marines in order to intimidate crofters who refused
to answer a summons to appear in Court. A Royal Commission
under Lord Napier was set up by Parliament in 1883 and it
toured the Highland counties, collecting evidence from crofters,
ministers, factors and landlords. In 1886, a Crofters Act was
passed, guaranteeing to the crofters fixed tenure and giving
powers to a CROFTERS COMMISSION to reduce rents, cancel rent
arrears, and value improvements made. Although the crofters felt
that they had won a victory over the landlords, the agitation did
not die down as the Crofters Commission took some time to
carry out its task. It was at a meeting in Inverness during the
election of 1885 that Joseph Chamberlain quoted from the
Canadian Boat Song, which was almost unknown then, although
it had appeared in *Blackwood's Magazine* in 1829. Later, these
lines were to become famous:

> From the lone shieling of the misty island
> Mountains divide us and the waste of seas;
> Yet still the blood is strong, the heart is Highland,
> And we in dreams behold the Hebrides.
>
>   .   .   .
>
> When the bold kindred, in the time long vanished,
> Conquered the soil and fortified the keep,
> No seer foretold the children would be banished
> That a degenerate lord might boast his sheep.

A Land League, in imitation of the Irish, had already been
formed to fight the landlords by all legal means available. In 1887,
there occurred the DEER DRIVE in Lewis, where several hundred
cottars, men who had no crofts of their own and whose families
barely existed on a diet of potatoes and gruel, set out on a well-
organized raid to kill the stags and hinds in the deer-forest of
Park. After a most successful foray, they returned to their homes
just before troops arrived from the south; the ringleaders surrendered themselves and stood their trial in Edinburgh, their
acquittal leading to enthusiastic scenes in the High Street of the
capital. Raids to seize land used only for sheep or deer but
suitable for crofting were carried out in many places. Gunboats

were sent to help the Duke of Sutherland against the crofters in Assynt who evaded arrest for months in the more inaccessible parts of the hills. By the help of other Acts of Parliament, one of which set up a LAND COURT to settle difficulties, the crofters' position became more favourable by 1914. The crofter himself could supplement his meagre crops and his income from sheep and cattle by fishing with net or line; but there was a growing tendency for his younger sons or daughters to leave the croft for an occupation in the south, especially in Glasgow. An exception to the backwardness of the north and west of Scotland was Orkney, where farming improvements had been carried out since before Victoria's reign; and at Foyers near Loch Ness the British Aluminium Company established in 1895-96 the first hydro-electric scheme in the Highlands, the second being started at Kinlochleven in 1909.

Drifters and Trawlers.—Among the many suggestions made to the Crofting Commission in 1883, one of the most useful was the construction of harbours on the west coast. Since the beginning of the nineteenth century, fishing, mainly for herring, had become the livelihood of most of the men on the north-east coast from Caithness round to Aberdeenshire.[1] WICK was the leading fishing-port, over 1,000 boats gathering there for the herring-fishing in 1862; but it was closely followed by Peterhead, Fraserburgh, Rosehearty and Buckie. In the second half of the century the fishermen of Shetland and the Western Isles began to acquire larger boats to enable them to compete with the north-east coast fishermen who made annual expeditions to these. Up till about 1860 fishing-boats were open, as the nets were shot not far from the shore, but from about that time, in order to reach more distant fishing-grounds, decked or half-decked sailing-boats were introduced for the herring-fishing, the commonest types being the "Fifie", the "Baldie" (said to be called after Garibaldi, the Italian patriot), and the "Zulu" (named at the time of the first Zulu War, 1879-80). Some of these were up to 80 feet long and, starting on the north-west coast in the early summer at Castlebay or Stornoway, followed the herring shoals round the north and east coasts until they reached the English ports of Yarmouth and

See p. 45

Lowestoft. Along with the herring-fleet went the "herring-lassies", women whose job it was to clean and salt the herring for

Baldie

Zulu

Fifie

Loch Fyne Skiff

By courtesy of the B.B.C.

Scottish Fishing Boats

*The "Baldie" was introduced on the east coast after 1850;
the "Zulu" at the time of the Zulu War of 1880; the
"Fifie" was the most popular herring boat before 1900*

sending away in barrels; at that time there was a great export trade in salt herring to Russia, Germany and other lands in north-east Europe. About 1900, the steam-drifter was introduced, twenty years after the first steam-trawler had first been tried out from Aberdeen. The trawlers, based mainly on Aberdeen and

Granton, went as far off as Rockall or Iceland for their white fishing. But the trawlers were generally disliked by the inshore fishermen, who blamed them for spoiling the fishing by putting their trawls down within the territorial limit of three miles.

Linen and Cotton.—Although the linen and cotton industries declined during Victoria's reign, they did not collapse in every district. During the depression that resulted from the American Civil War (1861-65), many of the cotton operatives in Clydeside went over to shipbuilding and engineering, and the industry never revived in Scotland as it did in England. The Vale of Leven, however, enjoyed its heyday after this period, printing and dyeing cotton cloth from Lancashire. Till late on in the second half of the century, handloom weavers of linen cloth were to be found in eastern Scotland, but in most places the factories had made them superfluous.[1] Dunfermline continued to specialize in fine damask table linen, while Dundee produced heavier linen—sail-cloth, tarpaulins and railway waggon covers for all over the world. Linen thread was still produced in Renfrewshire at Johnstone where the Bargarran thread manufacture had been started, and cotton thread at Paisley, where the "Paisley Shawl" was still being woven in the 1870's and where there were the largest cotton-thread mills in the world. A greatly-improved type of sewing-machine had been invented by an American, Isaac Singer, in 1851, and thirty years later a huge factory for the manufacture of Singer sewing-machines was set up near what was later to be called Clydebank.

Other Textiles.—As early as 1823, JUTE, a plant grown in India, had been brought to Dundee, but ten years elapsed before it was found to be possible to spin the fibres into a usable thread with the help of water and whale oil. At first jute and hemp were mixed to form a coarse, heavy fabric suitable for sacks and bags, but soon jute displaced hemp almost entirely in the manufacture of sackcloth, bagging, etc., and Dundee became known as "Juteopolis". The figures of imported raw jute (in the diagram overleaf) show the great expansion of the industry.

By 1914, the Indians themselves had numerous jute-mills competing with those of Dundee. Another newcomer in the nine-

[1] See pp. 78-9

teenth century was the LINOLEUM industry. In Kirkcaldy, where floorcloths had been made of painted flax or jute canvas as from 1847, the manufacture of linoleum was started in 1877 by Michael Nairn. Linoleum, made from jute canvas covered with a thick skin of oxidized linseed oil, was invented by an Englishman, Fred Walton, in 1863, but its production is still concentrated in Kirkcaldy, the "Lang Toon". But one of the most important

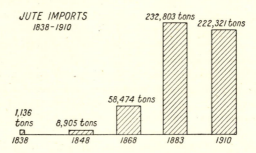

JUTE IMPORTS
1838-1910

1,136 tons — 1838
8,905 tons — 1848
58,474 tons — 1868
232,803 tons — 1883
222,321 tons — 1910

textile developments of Victorian Scotland was in the centuries-old woollen industry. Since the Union of 1707, when it had been pushed into the background because of the superior English cloth, it had been a cottage industry, producing only for home requirements. But the woollen mills of Galashiels, Jedburgh and Hawick began to manufacture a good-wearing, warm cloth which became popular outside the borders of Scotland; by the mistake of a London clerk the original trade-name, "tweel", became known as TWEED. Through tourists and sportsmen who visited the north of Scotland, homespun and handwoven tweeds from the Hebrides and kindred garments from the Shetlands became fashionable and were found both useful and attractive. Other textile industries which developed in Victorian Scotland were carpet-manufacture, the chief centres being Kilmarnock, where carpets have been woven since 1788, and Glasgow, where the firm of Templeton have made carpets for coronations, royal weddings, for the Houses of Parliament and other important places and functions; lace-making, in which the small towns of the Irvine

valley, Darvel, Newmilns and Galston, began to surpass Nottingham; the manufacture of ropes and nets which are held in the
highest regard all over the world, two of the firms engaged in it
being among the oldest in Scotland—the Edinburgh Roperie and
Sailcloth Company, which goes back to 1640, and the Gourock
Ropework Company, which can trace its history back to 1736.
The changes in the textile industry can be seen from the following
figures:

Number of Textile Workers in 1901

Total	-	175,000 (250,000 in 1851)
Jute	-	39,000
Wool	-	25,000
Linen	-	24,000
Cotton	-	15,000

Coal and Iron.—In the first ten years of Victoria's reign,
1837-47, Scotland, through the inventive genius of Mushet,
Neilson and Nasmyth, took its place as the second country in the
world in the production of iron, its total output being one-quarter
of England's.[1] Iron shipbuilding and railway construction, at
home and abroad, created a heavy demand for iron from Scotland's
"Black Country" with its rich blackband ironstone deposits.
When iron began to give way to steel in the second half of the
century, Scotland failed to keep her position. The two chief
pioneers of steelmaking on a large scale both worked and did
research in Scotland, Sir Henry Bessemer at Dixon's Ironworks,
Glasgow, and Sir William Siemens at the Cambuslang works of
the Steel Company of Scotland. But Scottish iron-ore did not
prove suitable for the Bessemer converter process or the Siemens
open hearth furnace. The lead in steel-making was actually taken
in the 1870's by a Scotsman, ANDREW CARNEGIE, a Dunfermline
weaver's son, who made an immense fortune out of his steelworks
at Pittsburg, Pennsylvania. More and more, Scottish iron and
steel works came to rely on imported ores. Coal-mining developed hand-in-hand with the iron industry and Scottish coal was
exported overseas as well as serving home industry and the
growing towns. Conditions in the mines were greatly improved

[1] See pp. 96-7

as the century went on, with the introduction of safety lamps, proper winding machinery, better pumps and ventilation, pit-props, and inspection by Government inspectors who insisted on Acts of Parliament being enforced. In West Lothian and Mid-lothian shale-mining is carried on and SHALE OIL manufactured, the centres of the industry being Broxburn, West Calder and Bathgate, where in 1851 Dr JAMES YOUNG formed the first company for distilling shale oil, from which is produced fuel oils, lubricating oils, paraffin wax, etc.

Transport.—Scotsmen had been pioneers in shipbuilding and marine engineering and they continued to lead the world in new developments. It was on the Clyde that water-tube boilers, triple-expansion engines, all-steel hulls were first tried and that the first civilian experiment tank was set up in the last quarter of the nineteenth century. Although the turbine engine was the invention of an Englishman, Charles Parsons, the *King Edward*, built by Denny, Dumbarton in 1901, was the first civilian turbine-engined ship in the world. It owed its construction to the keen competition between rival companies for the passenger tourist traffic on the Firth of Clyde. There were several yards on the Clyde producing the world's largest ships, among them that of JOHN BROWN AND CO. It had a long connection with the Cunard Company; one of the ocean greyhounds built at Clyde-bank was the *Lusitania* (1907), which was second only to its great rival, the Tyne-built Cunarder, *Mauretania* and which was tor-pedoed with terrible loss of life early in the First World War. Scottish railways were also improved: sleeping cars were intro-duced in the 1870's, heated carriages and dining-cars in the 1880's and 2nd class was abolished about the same time. The keen rivalry between the North British Railway and the Caledonian Railway culminated in the "RACE TO THE NORTH" in August 1895, when long-distance records were set up that have not been sur-passed. The N.B. express from King's Cross to Aberdeen by the east coast route covered the $523\frac{1}{2}$ miles in 8 hours 40 minutes, and the Caledonian night express from Euston to Aberdeen did the 541 miles in 8 hours 32 minutes with four stops included. One tragic railway accident, which shocked the public, was the

Tay Bridge Disaster on 28th December 1879, when the bridge, completed only the previous year, collapsed at the height of a terrible storm, the Edinburgh-Dundee express being thrown into the Tay and 79 lives lost. The present Tay Bridge was built in 1887, and three years later the Forth Bridge, a wonder of modern engineering. The public still kept their confidence in railways, on which they depended almost entirely for transport outside the cities. In Glasgow (where a subway or underground railway was opened in 1896) horse-drawn omnibuses had operated from as early as 1834, and the rough motion over the stone setts was avoided by laying iron rails or tramways. It was not until 1902 that the horse-drawn vehicle gave way in Glasgow to the electric tramcar, which soon gained the reputation of being the best of its kind. In Edinburgh, cable-hauling of tramcars was started in 1884 and continued there for many years. The Scots played little part in the development of motor-cars; they were more interested in the shipbuilding and engineering for which they had such a high reputation. There is only one survivor of the early motor-manufacturing firms in all Scotland, Albion Motors Ltd. of Scotstoun; the largest Scottish motorworks, that of the Argyll Motor Co., collapsed in 1914 just after it had erected new palatial premises at Alexandria. It was, however, a Scotsman, Kirkpatrick MacMillan, a Thornhill blacksmith, who in 1839 developed out of the dandy-horse the first bicycle, in which the rear-wheel was driven by a crankshaft worked by treadles. We owe the pneumatic tyre to two Scotsmen, R. W. Thomson, who first invented it in 1845, and J. B. Dunlop, who in 1888 patented an invention he made for his sons' bicycles. By the end of the Edwardian era, however, Scotland still continued to be dependent mainly on the older forms of transport; it led the world easily in the construction of ships, but the twentieth century was to be the age of the motor-car, the electric train and the aeroplane.

Banking.—The expansion of industry and business in nine-teenth-century Scotland would have been impossible without a well-developed banking system. Scottish banks have always borne a high reputation for reliability and, unlike ordinary English banks, they have the right to issue their own notes. The English people for a long time managed to treat these Scottish notes as if they were not proper legal tender, notes of an inferior value, and many shopkeepers would give only 19s. 6d. for a Scottish £1 note, whereas in reality the right of note issue was a mark of the higher standing of the Scottish banks. Twice in the nineteenth century that right was challenged but on both occasions the Scots managed to retain the right. What were the reasons for the high standing and reliability of the Scottish banks? Some writers have explained it as due to the strict moral training which was inculcated in eighteenth and nineteenth century schools and homes. But there were other reasons. Scotland was fortunate in the fact that its first bank, the BANK OF SCOTLAND, founded in 1695, was given a monopoly only for twenty-one years unlike the Bank of England, which, because of its service to the Government in lending money, received special privileges. As a result, although in England from 1708 no bank other than the Bank of England was allowed to have more than six partners, various joint-stock companies started banking business in Scotland; the ROYAL BANK (1727) and the BRITISH LINEN BANK (1746) were both large concerns with branches throughout Scotland long before 1826 when joint-stock banks were permitted in England at a distance of over 65 miles from London. The possession of many branch offices made banking business easier, more uniform, more stable and more fitted to weather any financial storm. There were very few failures in the history of Scottish banking, most of them in the west of Scotland, where business expansion was most rapid; the most serious was that of the CITY OF GLASGOW BANK in 1879, which ruined many Glasgow citizens. Another feature of early Scottish banking which was praised by many observers was the highly-developed system of cash-credit advances to business-men on the security of two persons. It was started by the Royal Bank as early as 1728 and copied by the other banks; by it both trade and banking business were expanded considerably. The right to issue notes also helped Scottish banks to secure more customers. When the Government threatened to abolish the issue of small notes in 1826, after a severe financial crisis, there was a national agitation, in which Sir Walter Scott took part under the *nom de*

plume of "Malachi Malagrowther". An attempt was again made
to restrict note issue to the Bank of England in 1844, when the
Bank Charter Act was passed, but again the Scottish bank-note
was saved, although no new Scottish bank was to be allowed the
privilege. Scottish banking still enjoys a high reputation, not
least for its SAVINGS BANKS, the first of which was founded by Dr
Henry Duncan, minister of Ruthwell, Dumfries-shire, in 1810.

Home Comforts.—The general standards of comfort advanced
considerably during the Victorian and Edwardian periods. Gas-
lighting which William Murdoch had invented in 1792, made a
great difference both in the home and in the streets. Glasgow
was lit by gas in 1818, Edinburgh in 1820, Aberdeen in 1824 and
other towns were not long in following their example. Although
the Victorian gas-light would have appeared very dim to us, particularly without the incandescent mantle, which was invented
by the Austrian, Welsbach, only in 1885, it seemed a wonderful
blessing to the people of the time. In the country districts, the
paraffin lamp came into general use after 1850. Some of the early
experiments in electric lighting were made in the home of LORD
KELVIN (1824-1907), professor of Physics at Glasgow University,
and in 1879 the newly-built St. Enoch Station in Glasgow was
illuminated with electric arc lamps. But only a few private
houses had the advantage of electricity before 1914. The first
practical telephone was the invention of an emigrant Scot,
ALEXANDER GRAHAM BELL (1847-1922), who patented his invention in 1875 after experiments at Boston University; but its use
before 1914 was confined to business premises and a few wealthy
homes in Scotland. An attempt to "rig up" a private telephone
service between his own home and his chums' was made by a
Helensburgh schoolboy, J. L. BAIRD (1888-1946), just after the
turn of the century, but the stormy weather of the west coast
brought his telephone lines down and the police had to inform
his father, a local minister, that the amateur telephone engineer
would have to abandon his project. A short time later he started
the experiments which were to lead in 1924 to successful television. The Victorian and Edwardian homes of the Scottish
middle class were much more comfortable than those of a cen-

G

tury earlier, not merely because of better lighting and plenty of cheap coal for the fires but also because of linoleum (made in Kirkcaldy) or carpets (made in Kilmarnock) covering the floor; net curtains (made in the Irvine valley) on the windows; uphol-stered chairs and settees, either fitted with springs or filled with horse-hair (made in Glasgow); a cooking-range (made at Carron) for the housewife to try out the elaborate recipes of Mrs Beeton's Cookery Book or the well-tried favourites of Aunt Kate's Cookery Book; a kitchen sink (often called the "jaw-box") in many houses but wash-hand-basins, baths and water-closets in only a few. By 1914, in addition to the familiar Scottish tenements, the suburbs contained many small semi-detached houses with their trim lawns, privet hedges and flower-beds in front and the vegetable-gardens behind. Houses were being built for working-men to own through the help of BUILDING SOCIETIES which advanced a loan for the purchase of a house, to be repaid over a period of twenty years or more. A period of comfort, of progress, of an advanced civilization—so it would seem to anyone old enough to remember the "Hungry Forties" early in Queen Victoria's reign. But it was also a period with many difficult problems still unsolved and with the gigantic upheavals and shocks of a world war just ahead.

SOURCE EXTRACT

First Impression of Balmoral

Balmoral,
Sept. 8, 1848.

". . . We lunched almost immediately, and at half-past four we walked out, and went up to the top of the wooded hill opposite our windows, where there is a cairn, and up which there is a pretty winding path. The view from here, looking down upon the house, is charming. To the left you look towards the beautiful hills sur-rounding Loch-na-gar, and to the right, towards Ballater, to the glen (or valley) along which the Dee winds, with beautiful wooded hills which reminded us very much of the Thüringerwald" (in

Germany). "It was so calm and so solitary, it did one good as one gazed around; and the pure mountain air was most refreshing. All seemed to breathe freedom and peace, and to make one forget the world and its sad turmoils."

Queen Victoria: *Leaves from the Journal of our Life in the Highlands*

EXERCISES

1. Write a sentence about each of the following: Earl of Aberdeen, Earl of Rosebery, A. J. Balfour, Sir Henry Campbell-Bannerman, R. B. Cunninghame-Graham, Duncan MacLaren, Dr James Young, Kirkpatrick MacMillan, J. B. Dunlop, Alexander Graham Bell, J. L. Baird.
2. On a blank map of Scotland indicate (with appropriate letters) the areas connected with these industries: coal, shale, iron, tweed, linoleum, jute, lace, carpets, fishing, shipbuilding, motor manufacture, hydro-electric schemes.
3. Explain: "Lang Toon", "Juteopolis", "tattie-howkers", "jaw-box", "Baldies", "Zulus".
4. Write brief notes on the following: Goschen Formula, Irish immigration, ley-farming, "Crofters' War", "The Twelfth", "Race to the North".
5. What steps were taken in the devolution of government so far as Scotland was concerned in the last quarter of the nineteenth century?
6. Write paragraphs on (*a*) Scottish textiles in the nineteenth century, and (*b*) Scottish banking.
7. Find out details about the industries of your own district in the period, 1837-1910, and the dates of the introduction of gas-lighting, electric lighting, horse omnibuses, electric trams, etc.

CHAPTER XIII

SOCIAL WELFARE

Social Problems.—Today we live in what is called a "welfare state", in which there are numerous public bodies, national and local, dealing with the social problems of poverty, disease, malnutrition, bad housing and working conditions. Although these have always been present in one form or another, it is only about a century ago that the public conscience was first stirred by them. Up till then, many people, including the poor themselves, felt that poverty and disease were the lot which Providence had intended for some, while wealth and comfort were the natural birthright of others.

> The rich man in his castle,
>   The poor man at his gate,
> God made them high or lowly
>   And order'd their estate.

Epidemics of cholera or smallpox, which swept the land and carried off thousands, were regarded as visitations of God's wrath, to be accepted in a spirit of Christian resignation. In the first half of the nineteenth century, as a result of the Industrial Revolution, the national complacency was severely shaken. The older methods of tackling social problems proved hopelessly inadequate. In this chapter you will read of the breakdown of the old system and the introduction of greater government control, which along with medical improvements led to higher standards of health.

Slums.—Bad housing, overcrowding, lack of sanitation were common in Scottish towns before the Industrial Revolution, as we know from the story of eighteenth-century Edinburgh; and the cottar's house was often little better than a hovel, although he and his family had the benefit of the country air. At first, the factory system did not bring much deterioration, as mills were set up in the country beside the burns and rivers which provided water-power. But in time the villages grew into small towns, with rows of badly erected houses which soon became slums. As most of the women worked long hours in the factories, there could be little or no pride in the home and little home comfort. In the large towns, conditions were worst of all. The Chief Constable of Glasgow, addressing a meeting of the British Association in the city in 1840, said: "In the centre of the City there is an accumulated mass of squalid wretchedness, which is probably unequalled in any other town in the British Dominions." In 1861, a house in the High Street of Edinburgh collapsed, killing 35 of its inmates. ("Heave-awa' House", the name of the house which replaced it, is a reminder of the lad, pinned beneath the debris, who encouraged his rescuers with the cry, "Heave awa', chaps, I'm no deid yet.") The shock this disaster created in Edinburgh led to an inquiry, which revealed that there were 1530 single-roomed houses in the city, with 6 to 15 persons living in each, and 121 of these houses were merely cellars without windows. The lack of water or sanitation in these houses rendered the inhabitants dirty and prone to disease, with the inevitable consequence—a very high death-rate. By 1861 some of the towns had made a start on the task of slum clearance, but progress was slow; and all the time more houses deteriorated into slums, the large mansions formerly occupied by wealthy merchants being subdivided into single-roomed dwellings.

Diseases.—The townsmen, huddled together in their ill-ventilated, insanitary houses were easy victims of the epidemics which occurred so frequently. During the eighteenth century there had been some improvement so far as certain diseases were concerned. There had been no major outbreak of PLAGUE after 1648, since when the black rat, which carried the plague-flea, had been almost exterminated by the brown rat. Cases of LEPROSY were reported from Shetland up to the end of the eighteenth century, but it had long since disappeared from the mainland. MALARIA, or ague as it was then called, became less common with the draining of bogs in which the malaria-carrying mosquito lived, and the yellow faces of the ague-ridden people of the north-east were no longer seen. SMALLPOX was the greatest scourge of the eighteenth century; it was sometimes called "the poor man's friend", as an epidemic meant that needy parents were left with fewer mouths to feed. Mortality in smallpox epidemics was high, and those who survived might be disfigured for life by the pock-marks left by the sores. Inoculation against smallpox had been introduced from Turkey to England by Lady Mary Wortley-Montagu as early as the reign of George I; although there was some doubt about the safety of the method, it was practised in many parts of Scotland, the ministers sometimes performing upon their parishioners' children. Vaccination (with the much less dangerous cowpox) became common in Scotland soon after the successful experiments in 1796 of Dr Edward Jenner.

EXPECTATION OF LIFE AT BIRTH
SCOTLAND, 1861-1953

	Males	Females
1861-1870	40.3 years	43.9 years
1891-1900	43.9	46.3
1920-1922	53.1	56.4
1953	65.7	70.7

Until vaccination was made compulsory in 1863, however, epidemics were still frequent; in the years 1855-64, for example, there were over 10,000 deaths from smallpox, the majority of the victims being infants. A disease which was almost confined to the poorer classes was TYPHUS, sometimes called "gaol-fever" and "camp-fever"; it was spread by the louse, which was to be found along with overcrowding, dirt and poverty. But the worst of all the nineteenth century epidemics were those of CHOLERA, a disease spread by contaminated water. 1832 was remembered by many not as the year of the Reform Act but as the year of the cholera, over 10,000 dying in the epidemic which raged in all the large cities and some of the smaller towns. Another outbreak, almost as serious, occurred in 1853-54 at the beginning of the Crimean War; but fortunately thereafter Britain had only sporadic outbreaks. In addition to all these diseases, which are fortunately little known to us today, there were others that are still familiar—measles, influenza (sometimes called the "influ-

DEATH STATISTICS, 1861-1953

Certain figures for early years may be considerably understated, e.g., those for cancer and tuberculosis

	Typhoid	Typhus	Smallpox	Measles	Scarlet Fever	Whooping Cough	Diphtheria	Pneumonia	Bronchitis	Tuberculosis	Cancer	Deaths under one year	Deaths from all causes
1861-65	3,633		992	1,377	2,423	2,193	2,549	2,071	5,768	11,171	1,207	13,166	69,265
1871-75	1,406	779	1,268	1,311	591	2,015	2,090	3,072	8,680	12,262	1,569	15,314	77,988
1881-85	1,029	162	17	1,359	1,340	2,273	1,680	4,075	7,916	11,099	2,058	14,864	74,396
1891-95	761	57	51	2,110	811	2,151	1,513	5,229	7,600	9,935	2,831	15,896	78,350
1901-05	521	25	118	1,470	403	2,222	770	6,578	5,570	9,790	3,845	15,881	77,313
1911-15	207	8	5	1,583	649	1,951	857	6,132	5,207	8,011	5,207	13,604	74,466
1921-25	61	3	5	1,237	337	1,447	517	6,402	4,507	5,678	6,329	10,299	67,652
1931-35	22	0.4	—	545	253	626	435	5,397	3,439	3,917	7,498	7,212	64,839
1941-45	10	—	5	94	21	283	269	3,057	2,679	3,974	8,688	6,202	66,302
1951-53	1	—	—	25	3	55	5	1,881	1,815	1,711	10,028	3,124	62,055

Based on material from "Annual Reports of the Registrar-General for Scotland" by permission of the Controller of H.M. Stationery Office

ence"), diphtheria, typhoid, scarlet fever, whooping cough ("kink-hoast" or "chin-cough") and, increasingly in the towns, tuberculosis.

Medical Treatment.—How did Scotsmen try to cure themselves when the causes of most of the diseases were unknown to them? Superstition still held sway even in the nineteenth century, people resorting to "holy wells" or sacrificing animals in order to cure epilepsy or insanity, as they had done in the Middle Ages. Some of the medicinal or "physick" wells, like Moffat, where there was a sulphur spring, became almost as fashionable with Scotsmen in the eighteenth century as Bath was with Englishmen. Old-fashioned remedies were still practised: blood-letting was done either by the lancet or by leeches, small sucking animals, five of them being placed behind the ear of a child with whooping-cough. In both Highlands and Lowlands whisky or toddy (made with whisky and hot water) was considered almost a panacea. In the villages, herbal cures were dispensed by "skeely" women, while in the towns apothecaries, some of them quacks, sold drugs and pills from their dispensaries. The infirmaries and dispensaries in the towns were quite inadequate to cope with cases during epidemics. During cholera epidemics, barrels of burning tar were set in the middle of the streets as disinfectants (under the impression that the disease came from the air) and the smoke and lurid glare from them made a weird impression on spectators. EDINBURGH ROYAL INFIRMARY had only six beds when it opened in 1729 in a small house in Robertson's Close, off the Cowgate. A century later, when it was moved to the site of the old High School, it had a reputation higher than that of any other infirmary in Europe, but the accommodation was still insufficient for the requirements of the Capital. The Town's Hospital of Glasgow, intended for the poor, had some beds for sick patients from 1733 when it was first opened. In 1794 GLASGOW ROYAL INFIRMARY, designed by Robert Adam, was built on a fine site near the Cathedral. Aberdeen's infirmary dates back to 1742, and Paisley and Dundee also had infirmaries in the eighteenth century. The accommodation in the infirmaries and the kind of treatment, both medical and surgical, compared

favourably with those in other parts of Britain or Europe but they
fell far below the standards of today.

Diet.—There is a close connection between food and health.
You have read in the chapter on "The Improvers" of the simple,
nutritious diet of the Scottish farm-workers at the beginning of
the nineteenth century[1]—

The halesome parritch, chief of Scotia's food,
milk, cheese, oatcakes, broth, ale, occasionally salt mutton or beef,
fish, and as the century advanced, potatoes. Such a diet was
almost meatless in comparison with that of the English countryman, who, even when his wages were being subsidized under the
"Speenhamland System", would buy 10 lb. of butcher meat a
week for a family of five. Yet the splendid physique of Highlanders who formed such a high proportion of the new police
forces was based on a diet similar to that of almost all rural
Scotland 150 years ago. For the middle and upper classes there
was a great variety of food, increased by imported novelties—tea,
coffee, cocoa, sugar. As there was a high duty on tea, it was
mostly smuggled tea that was drunk; and on the rugged coasts of
Galloway in the eighteenth and early nineteenth centuries there
was a brisk contraband trade in tea, wines, silk and other com-
modities. Over-eating and excessive drinking were normal
among Scotsmen of comfortable means. Many of the clubs
which sprang up in Glasgow, Edinburgh, Aberdeen and other
towns made a great business of eating and drinking—minced
collops of mutton, "rizart" (dried) haddock or skate, haggis,
"partan" (crab) pie, singed sheep's head, hen-broth were regular
favourites, along with punch, prepared in a huge bowl from
brandy or rum, hot water, sugar, lemons and spice. In contrast to
this was the diet of the factory-workers, who in times of depression came near to starvation level. At the end of eighteenth
century they still often made their breakfast and supper of porridge or pease-brose with milk or "swats" (ale), and their dinner
of broth or fish or, occasionally, meat. Bread and tea or coffee
with sugar became popular even although they were dearer
than oatmeal. It was reckoned in the 1820's that a meal of
porridge with milk, butter or treacle would cost $1\frac{1}{2}$d. but

[1] See p. 34

one with tea or coffee with bread or oatcakes would cost double that amount. It is difficult for us today to realize that at that time many of the people in this country scarcely consumed any sugar at all. By the "Hungry Forties", potatoes had become a stand-by for the town-dwellers as well as for the Highland crofters. In Scotland, only a few deaths occurred from starvation in the Highlands and Islands at the time of the "Potato Blight" in 1846-47 but there was much distress in the countryside and in the towns; the "Bread Riots" of Glasgow in 1848 were the result of the lack of food rather than Chartist propaganda. As the century advanced, the townsman's food deteriorated in nutritious value and his physique correspondingly declined. Scurvy (due to lack of vitamin C) was to be found in towns long after ship captains, following Cook's example, were providing lime juice, fresh fruit and vegetables for their crews; where potatoes were included in the diet, however, scurvy disappeared. Rickets (due to lack of vitamin D) had formerly been found more often among the well-to-do (Charles I had rickets as a child and was compelled to wear orthopaedic boots); but in the nineteenth century it became increasingly common among the working-classes of all the large towns.

Whisky.—Scottish and English tastes in drinking differed in the eighteenth century as they still do to some extent. Home-brewed ale or beer was universal with meals in both countries before the coming of tea or coffee. In England, during the long wars with France the consumption of vast quantities of port (the wine of England's oldest ally, Portugal) became a habit of the gentry, while in London gin-drinking proved the ruin of many of the lower classes in the first half of the eighteenth century. The Scottish lairds and wealthy townsfolk for long remained faithful to French wines, especially claret, a tribute to the "Auld Alliance"; these were supplied through the Isle of Man and the Galloway smugglers. Gradually claret gave way to port:

> Firm and erect the Caledonian stood,
> Old was his mutton and his claret good.
> "Let him drink port!" the English statesman cried.
> He drank the poison, and his spirit died.

But among the common people, whisky had become the favourite drink by the end of the eighteenth century. Whisky has been described as both a blessing and a curse to Scotland. The name itself, from the Gaelic *uisge beatha* ("water of life" or, in Latin, *aqua vitae*), denotes the high regard Scotsmen held for it. Distilled in the Highlands from barley from time immemorial, it does not seem to have become popular in the Lowlands until the eighteenth century. The family of Forbes of Culloden were in 1690 granted the privilege of distilling whisky for a very small duty, a unique privilege which the family retained till 1784; and the "Ferintosh" whisky of the Forbeses was the best-known in eighteenth-century Scotland. Smuggling from the Highlands went on from the middle of the century but it became more widespread when the Government in acts of 1787 and 1814 made it illegal for Highlanders to produce whisky except in large stills or to sell Highland whisky outside the HIGHLAND LINE or WHISKY LINE, which ran from Arrochar to Findhorn. Despite the efforts of "gaugers" (or excisemen) with soldiers to assist them, in the districts bordering the Highland line illicit distilling was almost a regular industry in which a man could make 10s. a week. In the Glenlivet-Tomintoul area there were over 200 illicit stills and it was estimated that about half of the whisky drunk in the Lowlands was contraband. Some of it was well-matured, like the Speyside whisky offered to George IV on his Edinburgh visit in 1822, but most of what came to the industrial cities was raw "fire-water". Even although an act of 1823, passed mainly at the request of the Duke of Gordon, sanctioned the distilling of whisky under licence and on payment of a small duty, illicit stills continued to operate in some districts for the best part of the century.

Liquor Control.—By the 1850's whisky-drinking in the industrial areas had become a serious social problem. In East Lothian, among the miners, it was said that "Saturday night usually begins the orgies which continue uninterrupted throughout Sunday and Monday, and often for the two next days". Toddy was given to infants if they cried or if they suffered from any illness. Boys and girls, who had acquired the taste in infancy, would occasionally become intoxicated. Weddings, christenings and funerals were all occasions for whisky-drinking. In the large cities it was no better. The Glasgow Fair, in those days before seaside holidays became popular, was often spent by the workers in intoxication until their money had gone. In 1834 it was reckoned that there was one spirit-dealer for every 14 families in Glasgow and that the average amount of spirits (mainly whisky) consumed in Scotland was 23 pints per head of population as against 7 pints in England and 13 pints in Ireland. (These figures, it should be noted, are for the whole population, men, women and children, so that the consumption for adults must have been much higher.) Temperance societies, advocating moderation or total abstinence from liquor, sprang up during the Chartist period. The Edinburgh magistrates, when Duncan MacLaren was Lord Provost, tried to curb Sunday drinking by dealing more severely in the courts with any cases of drunkenness on Sundays. Some improvement came in 1853, when Parliament passed an act known as the FORBES-MACKENZIE ACT (called after the M.P. for Peeblesshire who introduced it); it controlled the sale of alcoholic liquors, limited drinking hours to between 8 a.m. and 11 p.m. on weekdays, and prohibited Sunday drinking except in hotels for residents and *bona fide* travellers. This privilege for hotels was abused, however, by many town dwellers who travelled a few miles to a country hotel to qualify as *bona fide* travellers. The number of hours during which public-houses could be open was gradually reduced and in 1913 the Temperance (Scotland) Act made it possible for the people of a district to hold elections to decide whether they should have "No licence", "No change", or "Limitation" (a reduced number of licences). When the first poll was taken in 1920 (not long after "Prohibition" of alcoholic liquors began in the United States), 40 out of 584 areas voted for "No licence". There are still a few of these "dry" areas, and, in addition, housing estates, some of them very extensive, generally are without a public-house. Heavy drinking of whisky remained common in Scotland until the First World War when the price rose sharply through the increase in the duty. The bottle which in 1913 was 3s. then became 12s. 6d. and in 1955 cost 36s., most of it duty, while a large proportion of "Scotch" whisky is nowadays exported.

Crime and Punishment.—In 1827, a young cowherd, John Donald, thirteen years of age and 4 ft. 7¾ ins. in height, was sentenced at Glasgow to transportation for fourteen years for stealing ten sheep. Such a punishment for a young boy strikes us today as brutally harsh, and when we read also that according to the law of the time a person might be hanged for stealing an article worth 5s., we must feel glad that times have changed. But we should be careful not to exaggerate the severity of the law in those days. Although a culprit could be hanged for stealing, judges and juries were chary about convicting a guilty person; and transportation, which was considered a humane alternative to hanging, was not so terrible a punishment. The worst part of it was the voyage out, when the prisoners suffered horribly from sickness and starvation; but the life of the convict was probably better than that of many of the poor at home and, after his sentence had been served, a man might settle down to farming or some other occupation. Although there were still over 160 crimes punishable by death in Scotland in the eighteenth and early nineteenth centuries, capital punishment was thus not so common as might be expected. When John Howard, the English prison reformer, visited Scotland in 1793 he found that the average number of executions in the whole country over the previous twenty years was six. He was also impressed by the small number of offenders actually serving terms of imprisonment. Crime in the country districts was uncommon, and in the towns the councils were unwilling to pay for the guarding and upkeep of prisoners. Usually the prisoners were housed in the county gaol, not far from the Sheriff Court-house, or in "thieves' holes" or cellars in the town's house or Tolbooth, where there might be as many debtors as criminals, as imprisonment for debt was not abolished till 1880. In the largest towns there were also "bridewells" or penitentiaries, where prisoners were punished by having to perfo m some task like working a treadmill. The prisons were filthy, insanitary and overcrowded and the prisoners ill-fed, with the result that disease was rife among them, typhus being called "gaol fever". In the early nineteenth century, as a result of the efforts of English reformers, prisons were improved. Next came the abolition of the death penalty, first in the case of minor offences like pick-pocketing and stealing from a bleaching-ground, and, after 1823 when Peel became Home Secretary, for many other offences. In 1832, house-breaking, sheep-stealing and coining were also taken off the list of capital offences, the extreme penalty being reserved for murder, treason, forging a Bank of England note, and setting fire to a naval dockyard. Transportation to New South Wales ended in 1840 but continued to Van Diemen's Land (Tasmania) till 1857 and to Western Australia till 1868. Public hangings lasted till 1865, the last public execution in Scotland being that of the Glasgow doctor, Pritchard, who had poisoned his wife and mother-in-law. Execution of women has been very rare since then, and today there is a strong feeling in Britain in favour of abolishing capital punishment altogether.

Law and Order.—At the time of these penal reforms the justice administered in the law courts was being improved. Despite the Act against Wrongous Imprisonment, it was not until police forces were organized that the ordinary citizen was free from the danger of being thrown into the Tolbooth by one of the Bailies, who were responsible for the maintenance of law and order in the burghs. Thus, the following is recorded from Paisley in 1791:

Archd. Boyle incarcerated by order of Bailie Brown on suspicion of desertion; liberated after 11 days by order of Bailie Brown.

In the eighteenth century and for the early part of the nineteenth century, it was the duty of all the burgesses to support the magistrates in times of disorder, but often in cases of rioting soldiers were summoned from the nearest garrison town. In Edinburgh, the City Guard, composed mostly of veteran soldiers, was not considered fit for the prevention of crime, and many of the Guard were themselves not above suspicion. Police forces were introduced first in the large cities. The title of "the architect of the British police system" has been given to PATRICK COLQUHOUN,[1] a

[1] See pp. 60-2

Dumbarton man who became Lord Provost of Glasgow, where he founded the first Chamber of Commerce, and who started the first regular preventive police force in London in 1796. His Thames Police, he claimed, saved the West India merchants £500,000 in their first year, by their prevention of theft. Both Glasgow and Edinburgh had police forces with superintendents in charge by 1800. When Sir ROBERT PEEL introduced the Metropolitan Police Force between 1822 and 1829, he was strongly criticized by the Whigs, who feared it would be used for spying and for suppressing civil liberties. It soon earned a reputation for its effective methods of dealing with large mobs; and it was probably due to the British policemen, armed with nothing more than batons, that the stormy years of political agitation, 1830-48, passed without revolution. No longer was it necessary, except on rare occasions, to call in the military and thereby run the risk of shedding blood. Most of the burghs began to form their own police forces after 1850, and the counties at later dates.

Law Courts.—By the second half of the nineteenth century, our system of law courts had become established. The BURGH POLICE COURT, with the Bailies as magistrates and with no juries, dealt with petty offences. More serious offences went to the SHERIFF COURT, situated usually in the county town. It was not until after 1748, when heritable jurisdictions were abolished, that the Sheriff Principal or Depute had to be an advocate; but as he was not required to be resident in the county, the post became almost a sinecure. Sir Walter Scott was the non-practising Sheriff of Selkirk, an office to which he was appointed at the age of twenty-seven. The Sheriff Principal appointed a Sheriff Substitute, to whom he paid a small salary to perform his duties. After 1787 he was paid by the Crown, and from 1878 he was also appointed by the Crown. The Sheriff Substitute is still the judge before whom both criminal and civil cases in the Sheriff Court are first heard. Offences which merit heavier penalties than he can impose are considered before judges and juries in the HIGH COURT OF JUSTICIARY, which meets at intervals in the chief cities of the country. The High Court judges (who carry the title of "Lord") preside in the COURT OF SESSION at Edinburgh, the chief civil court, over appeals from the Sheriff Court and more important civil cases. There are many differences between Scottish and English law, and some of these concern trial procedure. The English jury consists of twelve and the Scottish of fifteen men and women. The verdict of a Scottish jury may be "Guilty", "Not Guilty", or "Not Proven", a verdict not found in England. Unlike England, where the jury must agree on the verdict, Scotland recognizes a majority verdict. An English murder trial is

Scottish Judges

Photo: The Scotsman

preceded by a coroner's inquest, which is not held at all in Scotland. A man can be charged with "manslaughter" in English but not in Scottish courts, while the reverse is true for "culpable homicide". In certain cases of death other than murder, the Sheriff Substitute presides over a Fatal Accidents Inquiry, particularly important if there is a question of compensation involved. The independence of Scots law and law courts was guaranteed by the Treaty of Union and it may seem strange that appeals in civil cases are allowed to the House of Lords from a Scottish court. Any such case, however, is there decided by the law of Scotland before law lords only, and of these two at least are usually Scottish judges.

Poor Relief.—The Scottish poor law differed from that of England in various respects. There the workhouse test had been applied to poor people seeking assistance, from the reign of Elizabeth until the end of the eighteenth century, when, by what was called the "Speenhamland System", outdoor relief to the amount of over £6,000,000 a year was being given to supplement the low wages of farm-workers. In Scotland, outdoor relief had been the rule for centuries, and the workhouse test was applied only in a few large towns such as Glasgow, Edinburgh and Paisley. Other towns which had tried to maintain workhouses or "houses of correction" found it cheaper to give the poor a few shillings in their own homes. In England, the expense of poor relief was met by the "poor rate" in each parish, the first kind of local tax. Although Scottish parishes were also authorized to levy an "assessment" or tax for poor relief, generally the funds came from church collections, from fines imposed by the kirk-session for non-attendance, swearing and other offences, and from charitable bequests or "mortifications", as they were called. By 1800, however, charity was proving insufficient in most places, particularly in the towns. In 92 out of 878 parishes assessments for poor relief were imposed, the number of such parishes rising to 230 by 1845. Another feature of the Scottish system was the issuing of licences in each parish to beggars who alone were permitted to "thig" or beg on one or two days in the week or month. At the end of the eighteenth century, for example, there were 24 such licensed beggars in Irvine and 40 in Montrose. The "gaber-lunzie man" or "blue-gown", with his large brass badge or token, was by no means "the lowest of the low", and in Scott's *Antiquary* there is a pleasant study of one, Edie Ochiltree, a respectable and dignified personage. Finally, in the large towns there were "hospitals" for the aged and infirm, some of which were also used as workhouses for the poor, and which were maintained by a tax levied on the inhabitants, like the Town's Hospital in Glasgow, or by private endowments, like Cowane's Hospital in Stirling. By the middle of the nineteenth century there had been a great

Photo: National Museum of Antiquities of Scotland

Beggars' Badges

increase in the number of the paupers due to the recurrent depressions in industry and the influx of Highlanders and Irish, and the whole system of poor relief was breaking down in Scotland as it was in England.

Social Reforms.—The years following the passage of the Reform Act of 1832 saw many important social reforms. Those relating to industry were due mainly to the exertions of the "Tory philanthropist", Lord Ashley (later Earl of Shaftesbury). Other reforms, connected with poor relief and public health, were the results of the untiring efforts and zeal of a government official, EDWIN CHADWICK. Chadwick had taken a leading part in the inquiries carried out by Royal Commissions into the poor law and sanitary conditions. New arrangements for the relief of the poor were made in the POOR LAW AMENDMENT ACT, 1845. In every parish, Inspectors of Poor were appointed and parochial boards set up with powers to levy rates for poor relief. Poor-houses for the aged and infirm were set up for groups of parishes, and although, in general, outdoor relief still continued to be the rule (unlike the new English Poor Law system set up in 1834) the workhouse test was applied in some places, for example, Gallo-way, where the influx of destitute Irish had brought about the collapse of the outdoor system. Chadwick's PUBLIC HEALTH ACT OF 1848 aimed at controlling public nuisances and made the nation conscious of the dangers to public health from lack of proper sanitation. The cholera epidemics forced the large towns to tackle the problem of contaminated water-supply. About Dundee's main source of supply, the Lady Well, the Royal Commission on Water Supply had reported: "The water is bright, sparkling and piquant to the palate, but an analysis shows that this is nothing but a very thorough purified sewage, to the properties of decomposition of which it owes its pleasant flavour." But it was long before Dundee had an adequate water-supply. Glasgow Corporation in 1855 decided to bring the water by pipes all the way from Loch Katrine, and from 1859 a plentiful supply of pure water was available. Some older people still preferred to draw water from a well, for the Loch Katrine water, they complained, had "neither taste nor smell". Edinburgh, which had been more fortunate than Glasgow in its wells, was also at last compelled to use a gravitation water-supply, reservoirs being made in the Pentland Hills nearby. Aberdeen by 1866 was also using a gravitation supply drawn from the Dee more than 20 miles away. The first MEDICAL OFFICER OF HEALTH in Britain was Dr William Duncan, one of the many Scottish doctors who went south for a living; in 1847 he was appointed to the office by Liverpool Town Council. The first Scottish M.O.H. was appointed in 1862 for Edinburgh, the year after the accident in the

High Street which led to such shocking revelations about housing conditions.[1] Glasgow followed in 1863 and by the PUBLIC HEALTH ACT OF 1875 the appointment of a M.O.H. was made compulsory for all districts, eight years after the appointment of SANITARY INSPECTORS had become compulsory. By another act of 1875

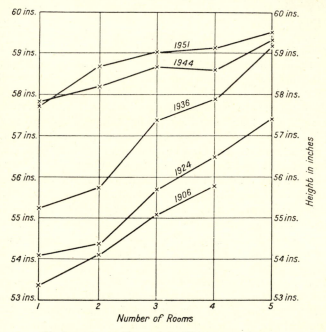

Environment and growth in Glasgow, 1906-1951

This diagram, showing the average height of boys of 13, is reproduced by permission from the Report of the Glasgow Schools Medical Service for 1951

powers were given to local authorities to condemn, demolish and reconstruct whole areas. But slum clearance proceeded very slowly in Scotland. In 1911 47.9 per cent of the population lived in houses of one or two rooms, in comparison with only 7.5 per cent in England and Wales. Even today the problem in the large cities is far from being solved.[2]

Famous Doctors.—Scottish doctors won great fame outside

[1] See p. 197   [2] See p. 317

Photo: Picture Post

Glasgow Tenements

their own country as early as the eighteenth century. The two brothers WILLIAM HUNTER (1718-83) and JOHN HUNTER (1728-93), who were born near Glasgow, both made their careers in London and rose to high positions. The elder brother first studied theology at Glasgow University and then medicine under Professor William Cullen before leaving for London where he became physician to Queen Charlotte as Dr Arbuthnot had been to Queen Anne. His brother, who followed him to London, became more famous still, was appointed surgeon to the King and is considered the father of scientific surgery. "Gregory's Mixture", which has been used as a medicine for almost two hundred years, is called after Dr JAMES GREGORY (1753-1821), professor at Edinburgh University, one of a celebrated Aberdeen family which provided no less than seven professors of mathematics, chemistry and medicine. The introduction of anaesthetics for surgical purposes in this country was the work of Sir JAMES YOUNG SIMPSON (1811-71), a native of Bathgate and a professor at Edinburgh University. His experiments, first with ether, which had been used as an anaesthetic in America, then with chloroform which he first tried out on himself and his assistants, helped to convince the British people, many of whom, strangely enough, thought that pain was intended by God as a "trial" for men and that it was wrong to do away with it. Anaesthetics made difficult operations possible; but, mainly because of that, deaths following operations actually became more common than before, many of them due to gangrene and sepsis or blood-poisoning. An Englishman, JOSEPH LISTER (1827-1912), professor of surgery at Glasgow University, suspected that the blood-poisoning in operation wounds was due to bacteria or germs getting into the wound. He started using an "antiseptic" lotion of carbolic acid on the wound, on surgical instruments, on the surgeon's hand and in the dressings in order to destroy the bacteria; he even had an assistant with a carbolic spray in the operating theatre. He first tried this new antiseptic surgery in Glasgow Royal Infirmary in one of the wards where the death-rate was high. In five years the proportion of deaths from blood-poisoning in amputation cases fell from 45 per cent to 15 per cent. Lister later became professor at Edinburgh University and was made a peer. His methods were improved by one of his successors at Glasgow, Sir WILLIAM MACEWEN (1848-1924), who was the first to operate successfully on the brain. Sir PATRICK MANSON (1844-1922), "Mosquito Manson", a native of Aberdeenshire, has been called the founder of tropical medicine; along with another doctor of Scottish origin, Sir RONALD ROSS (1857-1932), he helped to make the tropics more tolerable by the discovery that malaria was caused by a certain type of mosquito. But there were many other notable Scottish doctors, among the more recent being Sir ALEXANDER FLEMING, a native of Ayrshire, who discovered penicillin in 1929. Both Edinburgh and Glasgow Universities still

Photo: Harris's Picture Agency
Sir Alexander Fleming

attract each year from all over the world students who are keen to receive in the university classes and in the hospital clinics, the medical training that will fit them for the honourable profession of doctor. With the improvement in medical knowledge and public hygiene and the increase in the number of qualified doctors and pharmacists, the death-rate from many diseases gradually fell as can be seen from the table on page 199.

Social Insurance.—During the Boer War (1899-1902) many of the men called upon to serve in the Army were rejected because of their poor physique; in some areas like Clydeside the proportion of "rejects" was over 50 per cent. A typical Glaswegian of the poorer districts in the early part of the twentieth century was known as a "wee bachle", undersized, bow-legged or knock-kneed, ricketty because of a deficient diet in childhood and an upbringing in a city slum. A committee set up after the war to consider the causes of the high rate of rejection of recruits made various recommendations, as a result of which an act was passed in 1906, making provision for SCHOOL MEALS, but in Scotland little advantage was taken of the act. By another act, passed in 1908, MEDICAL INSPECTION of children in elementary schools was made compulsory. Neither of these acts had much immediate effect. Slums still existed and, although there was a great variety of cheap food from overseas, the diet of the poorer classes, particularly during unemployment, was miserably inadequate—tea, white bread, margarine, jam, skimmed milk having displaced the simpler but more nutritious fare of a century before. In 1908, another act, the OLD AGE PENSION ACT, which gave a pension of 5s. a week (7s. 6d. for a married couple) to those over seventy, helped to make it possible for old folk to keep out of the poor-house, a prospect which used to cast a gloom over thoughts of retiring from work. The sum was very small but it was hoped that a man would still save for his retirement and that his children would also contribute to his upkeep, thereby keeping alive the much-praised nineteenth-century virtues of thrift and self-help. By the NATIONAL INSURANCE ACT (1911) a new idea—that of compulsory social insurance—was introduced. Hitherto there had been voluntary schemes among workers for insurance against sickness, accident or death. By a small payment every week it was possible to make provision for a rainy day. Some of these schemes had been started by trade unions; others were independent FRIENDLY SOCIETIES established in the early part of the nineteenth century in Lancashire but with branches in England and Scotland, e.g., the Independent Order of Oddfellows, the Ancient Order of Foresters, the Loyal Order of Ancient Shepherds, the Independent Order of Rechabites (for total abstainers). Large public companies like the Prudential Assurance Company (founded in 1854) also carried on a similar kind of business among working people, some of their weekly payments being as low as a penny-a-week. The idea of compulsory insurance, already tried out in Germany and New Zealand, had been proposed by the Conservative Joseph Chamberlain, but it was under the Liberal Government of Asquith that the scheme was put into practice in 1911 by his Chancellor of the Exchequer, Lloyd George. For a payment of 4d. a week by employees whose wages were less than £160 a year, with similar contributions from their employers and from the State, the scheme provided medical service and sickness benefit. Another part of the scheme provided unemployment insurance for workers in certain industries, where work tended to be irregular, e.g., building trades. LABOUR EXCHANGES had been set up in 1909 and they undertook the payment of unemployment benefit until a man had found a new job. Both the health and unemployment insurance schemes were extended after the First World War to cover almost all employees, and after the Second World War a comprehensive National Insurance came into being. In 1914, however, although Britain had become a "welfare state", there were still very much distress among the poor and aged, still many preventable diseases taking their toll of human life, still plenty of social problems such as bad housing, lack of sanitation, drunkenness, waiting to be dealt with.

SOURCE EXTRACT
(See the table of statistics on p. 199)

EXERCISES

1. Which of the columns of statistics on page 199 shows the greatest improvement? Account for the disappearance or decline of plague, leprosy, malaria, smallpox, typhus and cholera.
2. In what respects was the food of the nineteenth-century townsman better or worse than that of the eighteenth-century townsman or countryman?
3. Explain: gaol-fever, kink-hoast, skeely woman, physick well, toddy, swats, partans, collops, Whisky Line, gauger, *bona fide* travellers, thigging, gaberlunzie man.
4. Write a sentence about each of the following: Forbes MacKenzie Act, Poor Law Amendment Act of 1845, Public Health Act of 1848, Old Age Pension Act, National Insurance Act.

5. Write notes on the following: William Hunter, John Hunter, James Gregory, Sir James Young Simpson, Lord Lister, Sir William MacEwen, Sir Patrick Manson, Sir Ronald Ross, Sir Alexander Fleming.

6. Find out when your town or village first received a gravitation water supply and when the oldest hospital and the local poorhouse were founded. (Are there any beggars' badges in your local museum?)

CHAPTER XIV

INDUSTRIAL PROBLEMS

Merchant and Craft Guilds.—The medieval merchant and craft or trade guilds continued to exist in Scotland until the time of the Industrial Revolution and are to be found even today in the large cities. They were associations of masters, not of their employees, but in certain other respects they resembled the earlier trade unions: e.g., they used their funds to provide charity for the dependants of any of the guild. The trade guilds or incorporations had nothing to do with trade in the English sense, that is, buying and selling. A tradesman in Scotland is a man who works at a trade or craft, e.g. a joiner or bonnet-maker or hammerman; those who engage in trade are dignified by the name of merchant. The MERCHANT GUILD in each town comprised the leading burgesses and for a long time there was little difference between the composition of the merchant guild and the town council.[1] In the fifteenth and sixteenth centuries, craft guilds were incorporated in the chief towns and soon they were claiming the right to be represented in the town councils. The practice of each burgh council varied according to its "sett" or constitution, but by the end of the seventeenth century most town councils included members of the crafts or trades incorporations, usually the "deacons" or heads of the crafts. The craft guilds in Glasgow, Aberdeen and other large burghs had common meetings and discussed common problems, their president being called

[1] See p. 168

the DEACON CONVENER; they also built for themselves a Trades House to rival the Merchants' House of the old-established merchant guild, which remained for long an important body. The head of the merchant guild, the DEAN OF GUILD, in time became more or less an official of the burgh, and the Dean of Guild Court supervised all kinds of matters relating to the merchants, e.g., weights and measures, and also disputes over property, e.g., boundaries or the erection of buildings. The craft guilds were jealous of their rights and tried to exclude any one not a member from practising his craft in the burgh. But as trade and industry developed, their monopoly was gradually broken down. The story is sometimes told that it was because of the objections of the Incorporation of Hammermen in Glasgow that James Watt set up his workshop in Glasgow University; but in fact, although there was probably some jealousy, he moved after two years into premises in one of the main streets of Glasgow without any trouble. The craft guilds or trades incorporations have survived in the large cities, their main function today being that of dispensing charity; in Edinburgh and Glasgow Corporations, in addition to the elected members there are also the Dean of Guild and the Deacon Convener of the Crafts. In other burghs, the Dean of Guild is simply a town councillor elected in the ordinary way and later chosen by his fellow-councillors as head of the Dean of Guild Court, where applications for erecting new buildings are considered. At the end of the eighteenth century, the journeymen and apprentices of the crafts, who of course did not share in the privileges of the "guild brethren", their masters, began to join together for common deliberation and action. As the Industrial Revolution brought more and more workers together, the tendency to form combinations naturally increased.

Working Conditions.—The Industrial Revolution, which helped to give Britain the leadership of the world in the nineteenth century, also intensified the age-long struggle between employer and employee. On the one side, that of the manufacturers, the merchants, the business-men—the capitalist class, as it came to be called, there were greater wealth and greater comfort; on the other side, that of the working-class, there were, not always but certainly during "bad times" or "depressions" in industry and trade, greater poverty and greater misery. The factory system had made possible the large-scale employment not only of men but also of women and children for long hours in an unhealthy and sometimes dangerous environment. These were the "wage-slaves" of the nineteenth century. In David Dale's mill at New Lanark, which was considered one of the best of its kind, in 1796 the daily hours of labour for children under 10 years of age were from 6 a.m. to 7 p.m. for 6 days a week, with 1½ hours off for meals and, in addition, through the kindness of Dale, school from 7.30 to 9 p.m.[1] In many other mills, children under 5 years worked beside their mothers, picking up cotton-wool from the floor under the machines, and were often asleep before the end of the long working-day. But the factory "operatives" were fortunate in comparison with the mine-workers. Although they were legally free since 1799, their conditions were still little better than slavery. Women and girls equipped with harness had to crawl on all fours, pulling hutches along low galleries, filthy and wet. Flooding, explosions, gas-poisoning, the collapse of roofs—these were daily dangers for everyone underground, and lung diseases were common among the men over 30 years of age. About one in three of the married women in Tranent in 1840 had lost their husbands through mine accidents or disease. In the factories, in the mines, and also in the homes of the handloom weavers, whose wages were so miserably low after 1815, conditions of employment were such as would be called intolerable today.

Robert Owen.—One of the first to stir the public conscience about working conditions was a Welshman, ROBERT OWEN (1771-1858), who in 1799 married a daughter of David Dale. In the following year he became manager and part-owner of his father-in-law's mills and settled down nearby with his wife at Braxfield, formerly the home of the famous "hanging judge" of that name. Starting work at the age of ten as a draper's assistant, Owen had risen to be manager of a cotton-mill in Manchester by the time he was nineteen. He was an odd mixture—a very efficient business man with novel ideas about improving the conditions of the working

[1] See p. 75

classes. Owen soon set out on a programme of reform at New Lanark. Although their hours were long, the 500 orphan children employed by Dale had been comparatively well-treated; but his other workers, of whom there were over 1500, lived in miserable slums, and were lazy, dirty and given to drinking. Owen was of the opinion that the character of a person depended on his environment and that good conditions in the factories and houses would make good workers and good citizens. He had new houses built, controlled the sale of alcoholic liquor, and opened a store where food could be bought cheaply. Not only did the workers benefit but also Owen and his partners, as the output of the factory was greatly increased. When the American War of 1812 stopped the cotton supplies he even continued to pay his men when they were out of work. He was against the employment of children under ten years of age and provided free education for his employees' children in schools where no corporal punishment was allowed. He later opened a nursery school for children as young as eighteen months, the first of its kind in Britain. In 1813 he published *A New View of Society* in which he propounded his views on the importance of environment. New Lanark soon became a centre for visitors from all over

Photo: Weaver Smith

Robert Owen

Europe, who came to admire the model factory, schools and village. The FACTORY ACT of 1802, which had been passed through the efforts of the first Sir Robert Peel, had proved a dead letter as there was no real attempt to enforce it. In 1815 Owen drafted a

Bill, strictly limiting the employment of children and providing for inspectors to see that it was carried out. He failed to get any encouragement from other factory-owners in Scotland; and the Bill, when at last it was passed with English support in 1819, was so altered that Owen disowned it.

Owen as Socialist.—By this time he was beginning to put forward the theory that poverty could best be treated by forming socialist communities of about 2,000 people, working together and sharing the product of their work. At first, his ideas were well received by many, including the Duke of Kent (the father of Queen Victoria) but he lost the support of the upper classes when he attacked the churches for their doctrine of original sin, as he maintained that man's errors were due to his ignorance and to his bad environment. His theories were tried out at Orbiston in Lanarkshire, under the leadership of Abram Combe, an Edinburgh "Owenite", and Hamilton of Dalziel, a local landowner's son, at the same time as Owen himself was in Indiana, busy establishing a community, called New Harmony. The Orbiston community collapsed after a few years on the death of Abram Combe, and New Harmony also, after £60,000 had been spent on them. From the Owenite communities came the idea of co-operative trading; although there had been a few before his time, the Rochdale Pioneer Co-operative Society, which made the idea of the dividend popular, was started in 1844 by men with Owenite sympathies. After Owen's connections with New Lanark mills ceased in 1828 he spent most of his time advocating reforms of various kinds. He was also responsible for forming the Grand National Consolidated Trades Union in 1833-34, when the working classes were feeling disillusioned after the Great Reform Act. It was hoped that all workers of all trades would join it but its growth was too rapid; the strikes attempted were too numerous so that the union collapsed. Although Owen's socialist schemes were failures and he has been criticized as a "starry-eyed idealist", he is regarded as the father of socialism, co-operative societies and trade unionism.

Government Control.—The Factory Acts of 1802 and 1819 had not attempted much and had achieved less because their enforcement had been left to local magistrates, who were unwilling to quarrel with a factory-owner, perhaps a neighbour or even a fellow-magistrate. There was a widespread feeling in the nineteenth century that the less the Government interfered with private enterprise, the better. This doctrine of *laissez-faire* was put forward by philosophers and economists but was, naturally enough, popular with the factory-owners and mine-owners, some of whom, as Disraeli, later Conservative Prime Minister, said, were enthusiastic members of the Society for the Abolition of Negro Slavery, but were unaware of the sufferings of their own child employees, many of them black enough. Although other factory acts were passed in 1825 and 1831, the first real attempt to regulate factory conditions came after the Reform Act of 1832. During Earl Grey's Whig ministry (1830-34), ROYAL COMMISSIONS were appointed to inquire into various problems, among them the conditions of factory workers. These commissioners obtained such clear evidence from employees and employers of the horrible and inhuman treatment of workers in factories that it convinced the public that reform was long overdue. The FACTORY ACT of 1833, which restricted the employment of children in factories, introduced a new and important principle, that of enforcing the act through inspectors appointed by the Government. Factory-owners complained that they would be ruined and many of them contrived to evade the regulations laid down. The "Tory philanthropist", Lord Ashley (later Earl of Shaftesbury) tried hard to persuade the Whig Governments to further reforms, but they were unwilling to offend the mill-owners, many of whom were their supporters. More commissions were appointed and more acts were passed. After the shocking revelations of the Mines Commission, Ashley's MINES ACT OF 1842 was passed, prohibiting the employment underground of women and children under thirteen years of age. Ashley's TEN-HOURS ACT (1847) was considered a great advance, but progress was slow outside factories. Even in the textile industry, the finishing processes of bleaching, dyeing and printing were not included till late in the century. In 1874, when a Factory Act fixed a working week of 56½ hours for women and children, a Scottish M.P., who was owner of dye-works in the Vale of Leven, denounced it as likely to "lead to idle habits". Gradually, almost all industries were brought under government control by the great FACTORY ACT OF 1878 and later acts, a Saturday half-holiday being made compulsory for most occupations in 1901. But it was not until the twentieth century that the shop-assistants, farm-workers and others had their conditions of labour regulated.

Co-operative Societies.—A long-standing grievance of the working classes in the nineteenth century had been the TRUCK SYSTEM, whereby the workers were paid either in goods of a poor quality or were forced to buy food, clothes, etc., at high prices in "truck-shops" or "tommy-shops" belonging to their employers. In the far-distant Shetlands, the fish-curers had introduced this system in the eighteenth century and the fishermen scarcely handled any cash. Even the shawl-knitters there, instead of receiving the few shillings of wages owing to them, were forced to take from the merchants fancy goods which they did not want. In the mining areas, almost everything was "trucked" to the miner except his coffin. The first Truck Act was passed in 1831 but others were necessary as employers were quick to discover loopholes. In districts where the "tommy-shops" did not exist, workers began to combine to buy provisions for themselves. As far back as 1769, the weavers of Fenwick combined for the purchase of oatmeal. Other early examples of co-operation among consumers were "victualling societies" in Glasgow, that of Govan (dating from at least 1777) and Bridgeton (1800), while the LENNOXTOWN VICTUALLING SOCIETY, the oldest in Britain, if not in the world, was actually paying dividends in proportion to purchases in 1812. ALEXANDER CAMPBELL, at one time Owen's secretary, was the chief propagandist for co-operative trading in the first half of the nineteenth century, although Owen's experiments seemed to some people to show the futility of the idea. Campbell was consulted by the Rochdale "Pioneers" before they started their Equitable Society with a capital of £28 in 1844. In ten years they had 1,400 members and an annual turnover of £45,000. Their success popularized the idea of the dividend, and co-operative societies sprang up in almost all industrial communities, which found them a welcome change from the "tommy-shops". To eliminate the middleman's profits, the SCOTTISH CO-OPERATIVE WHOLESALE SOCIETY was started in 1868, five years after a similar society in England, supplying the various retail distributive societies with goods at wholesale prices and paying dividends to the individual societies. The next step in the progress of the Scottish co-operative movement was taken in 1881, when the S.C.W.S. started a factory for making shirts. Before 1900 factories for almost all kinds of goods had been established, and, in addition, farms, coal-mines, ships, tea and cocoa plantations were owned by the S.C.W.S. In 1952 the total membership of Scottish co-operative societies was 1,271,634, the amount of sales £122,101,497, and the average rate of dividend paid out, 1s. 7d.

Trade Unions.—Although the Combination Acts of 1799 and 1800 were not repealed until 1824, trade unions of weavers and spinners continued to function in Scotland, especially in the Glasgow district. The Glasgow cotton spinners staged a strike in 1812, the leaders suffering terms of imprisonment, and later resorted to desperate measures in the period of post-war discontent after 1815. "Black-legs" or "scabs", who continued to work during strikes, were mutilated by having their ears cut off, marked for life by having vitriol thrown at their faces, and even murdered. When the Combination Acts were repealed in 1824, many new unions were formed and strikes were staged. The employers tried to break the unions by employing non-union men—starving handloom weavers in the factories and Irish immigrants in the coal-mines and ironworks. Strikes in those early days did not last long, and the victory was nearly always to the employer; the union funds were too small to support the strikers and their families, and, where the truck system prevailed, there was no credit for food, clothing or house-rent. Owen's Grand National Consolidated Trades Union collapsed soon after it was founded in 1833-34, and thereafter each trade formed its own union—the miners, the textile workers, the shipwrights, the engineers, the joiners, the ironworkers, etc. All through the century strikes were staged for increased wages, reduced working-hours, a Saturday

H

half-holiday, with varying success. The greatest trade unionist in Scotland in the mid-nineteenth century was ALEXANDER MACDONALD (1823-81), the miners' leader, who campaigned for the abolition of the truck system, the 8-hour working-day, and many other reforms. He was one of the first two working-men to enter Parliament, being returned in 1874 as M.P. for an English constituency. In 1873 there had begun what is called the "GREAT DEPRESSION" of the nineteenth century, industry and trade being at a low ebb for nearly twenty years. Disraeli's Government in 1875 passed an act giving trade unions legal rights of "peaceful picketing" and safe-guarding them from prosecution for any action other than what would be a criminal offence if committed by an individual. Industrial unrest however continued to be common during the long depression and again in the period before the First World War.

Photo: Picture Post

Keir Hardie

Socialism.—A natural development out of the co-operative and trade union movements was a political party, organized to agitate inside and outside Parliament for legislation in the interests of the working class. The earlier Chartist movement had not been a specifically working-class movement, although it was supported by the workers. In the second half of the nineteenth century there were founded various organizations which might be considered forerunners of the modern Socialist movement—the Christian

Socialists led by two clergymen, J. F. D. Maurice and Charles Kingsley, the novelist; the International Working-men's Association, founded by Karl Marx in 1864 in London, although it had little support in Britain; the Social Democratic Federation, which, started a few years earlier by Henry Hyndman, in 1884 adopted a programme, partly based on Marx's teachings; the Fabian Society, which was founded by a group of intellectuals including Bernard Shaw and Sydney Webb, who aimed at gradual reform. At the election of 1886, following the Third Reform Act, which doubled the number of voters in the country, two successful Scottish Liberal candidates put forward what might be called Socialist manifestos. They were ANGUS SUTHERLAND, a crofter's son who was returned as M.P. for Sutherland and R. B. CUNNINGHAME-GRAHAM, a laird who could actually claim a descent from the kings of Scotland and who became M.P. for the mining constituency of North-west Lanarkshire.[1]

Keir Hardie.—Among those impressed by the American, Henry George, whose *Progress and Poverty* (1879) had a great influence and who toured Scotland at this time, was the young JAMES KEIR HARDIE (1856-1915), a leader of the miners. He became convinced that the only hope of the working classes was to have a party of their own in Parliament, and in 1888 he helped to form the SCOTTISH LABOUR PARTY, with himself as secretary and Cunninghame-Graham as chairman. It was the first Labour Party in Britain but its programme was partly Liberal, partly Socialist—adult suffrage, payment of M.P.s, abolition of the House of Lords, Scottish Home Rule, state insurance against sickness, accident, old age and death, nationalization of banks, mining royalties and all kinds of transport, local prohibition of alcoholic liquors, free education, taxation of land values and incomes. Keir Hardie was returned as M.P. for West Ham in 1892, one of three Labour members in Parliament. He created a sensation on his first day at the House of Commons, where he arrived, wearing a cloth cap and red tie and accompanied by a brass band. The following year (1893), the Social Democratic Federation, the Fabian Society, the trade unions and the Scottish Labour Party combined under the chairmanship of Keir Hardie

[1] See p. 177

Photo : Picture Post

J. Ramsay MacDonald

to form the INDEPENDENT LABOUR PARTY, whose main objects were frankly Socialist—"collective ownership and control of the means of production, distribution and exchange". When the parliamentary LABOUR PARTY was founded in 1900 with the definite aim of promoting labour representation in the House of Commons, it was another Scotsman, J. RAMSAY MACDONALD who was its first secretary. Thus the Scots played prominent parts in the early growth of the Labour movement in Great Britain. It was a fitting climax to their years of effort that, when the first Labour government took office in 1923, it was under Ramsay MacDonald as Prime Minister.

SOURCE EXTRACT

Evidence of Isabella Read, 12 years old, coal-bearer,
Edmonstone Colliery, East Lothian.

"Works on mother's account, as father has been dead two years. I am wrought with sister and brother, it is very sore work; cannot say how many rakes or journeys I make from pit's bottom to wall's face, thinks about 30 or 25 on the average; the distance varies from 100 to 250 fathoms. I carry about 1 cwt. and a quarter on my back; have to stoop much and creep through water which is frequently up to the calves of my legs. When first down fell frequently asleep while waiting for coal, from heat and fatigue. I do not like the work nor do the lassies but they are made to like it. When the weather is warm there is difficulty in breathing and frequently the lights go out."

Report of Commission on the Employment of Children (1843)

EXERCISES

1. Write a sentence about each of the following factory acts: 1802, 1819, 1833, 1842, 1847, 1874, 1878, 1901.
2. Write short notes about the following: Alexander Campbell, Alexander MacDonald, Angus Sutherland, Cunninghame-Graham, Keir Hardie, Ramsay MacDonald.
3. Give an account of the career of Robert Owen.
4. Write a short paragraph on merchant guilds, craft incorporations, trade unions.
5. How much of the programme of the Scottish Labour Party in 1888 has been carried out?
6. Explain: tommy-shop, victualling society, blackleg, depression, peaceful picketing, Dean of Guild.
7. Find out when your local co-operative society was founded, how many members it has today, and the amount of the sales in the past year.

CHAPTER XV

SCOTTISH CHURCHES

The Church of Scotland.—In the eighteenth century the Presbyterian Church of Scotland was the national church, established and supported by the state, its existence being secured "for ever" by the Union of 1707. Apart from the parishes, mainly in the north-east, where Episcopalianism still held out, and the regions in the west and north where Catholicism lingered on, it was the church for almost all Scotsmen and Scotswomen. In the first half of the century, the Church of Scotland exercised a control and influence almost as great as at any other period of its history. The ministers and the elders of the kirk-session kept strict watch on the actions of their parishioners, and for absence without good cause from the church services, for swearing, drunkenness and immorality the culprit might be fined or made to stand in sackcloth on the "cutty stool" (short stool) or stool of repentance on a Sunday before the congregation. In the schools there was regular religious instruction, based on the Bible and Shorter Catechism, and when the minister paid his visit to a family, he would hear the children answer the questions from the Catechism.[1] In most homes, family worship was regular, morning and evening, as it still is in many parts of the Highlands; the father would conduct the service, which included a reading from the Bible, a psalm and a prayer. On Sunday (or the Sabbath, as it was called for preference) all ordinary pleasures were banned as profane, and only work of necessity or mercy was permitted, while attendance at church service was almost compulsory. In some of the towns, elders, known as "seizers", would patrol the streets on the look-out for anyone absenting himself from the church. The service, held in plain and austere surroundings, was simple, without much ritual. There was no instrumental music and the precentor or "lettergae" (often the schoolmaster) led the congregation in the singing of the metrical psalms, "giving out the line" which was thereafter sung by all. Prayers were not read (that savoured too much of the Anglican and Catholic churches) and even the Lord's Prayer was considered as inferior to an impromptu prayer. Nor was any minister highly regarded who read his sermon or who tried to be brief, for the Scotsman of the eighteenth century was a sermon-taster. Communion (or the Sacrament of the Lord's Supper) was dispensed twice a year or in country districts only once, partly because of the great expense of entertaining visitors from other parishes. The "Occasions", as they were called, lasted from Thursday to Tuesday, what with preliminary Fast Days and subsequent Thanksgivings, attracting crowds from far and near to listen to the various ministers, whose preachings from the "tent" (a wooden pulpit with a projecting roof) often lasted for hours. No work was done during these days and for some it was more of a holiday than a religious occa-

[1] See p. 244

sion, as can be seen from Burns's *Holy Fair*. It was in and around the cities that the severity of church discipline was first relaxed. As we have seen, many of the "Moderates" of Edinburgh and district, Principal Robertson, "Jupiter" Carlyle and others, were themselves literary men and permitted themselves recreations such as card-playing and the theatre which would have been abhorred by their fathers.[1] The austerity of the eighteenth century still lingered on in the Highlands, however, and is to be found there to a great extent today.

Secessions.—The Patronage Act of 1712, passed by Parliament in defiance of the Treaty of Union, was to have most unfortunate consequences for the Church of Scotland. Many congregations were unwilling to allow to the local landlord the right as patron to appoint a minister over their heads. The first break-away from the Church, the ORIGINAL SECESSION, was made in 1733 by four ministers, whose leader, Ebenezer Erskine, championed the right of the people to elect their ministers. The Seceders were earnest and devout but narrow-minded; they protested not only against patronage but also against the failure to re-impose the Covenants in 1689-90, the toleration of Episcopalian clergymen, and the repeal of the acts against witchcraft. They soon split up into smaller sects, which were sometimes joined by those who were annoyed at the "intrusion" of a minister by the local landlord. A more tolerant and liberal-minded body of Seceders was the RELIEF CHURCH, founded in 1761 by the Rev. Thomas Gillespie of Carnock in Fife. It was not very different from the established church and, as its name suggests, offered to members of the Church of Scotland relief from patronage. As disputes arose between patrons and congregations, and as the "Moderates" became supreme in the Church, the Seceders, of one kind or another, became more numerous, and in 1773 there were 180 congregations outside the Church of Scotland. Some other sects which differed more radically from the Presbyterian Churches were the OLD SCOTCH INDEPENDENTS (founded in 1768), David Dale being one of their most active lay preachers, and the CONGREGATIONAL CHURCH, the first congregation of which was founded in 1799 by James Haldane. Some of the Original

[1] See pp. 130-2

Seceders reunited in 1820 to form the United Secession Church, which in 1847 united with the Relief Church to become the UNITED PRESBYTERIAN CHURCH (the U.P. Church, as it was familiarly called) of about 500 congregations. Small remnants at each union remained outside; one of them, the "Auld Lichts" or

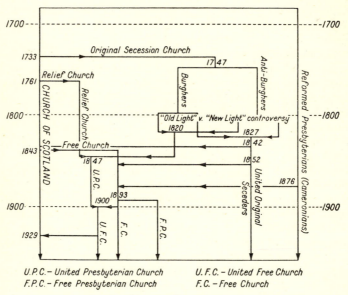

U.P.C. – United Presbyterian Church   U.F.C. – United Free Church
F.P.C. – Free Presbyterian Church   F.C. – Free Church

Presbyterian Sects after 1690

United Original Seceders, is frequently referred to by J. M. Barrie in his novels about "Thrums", or Kirriemuir. Between the sects there might be only some small difference in a matter of principle; almost all had the same kind of service and the same rooted objection to patronage. Before the U.P. Church was formed, the Church of Scotland suffered the greatest secession of all, so great that it has been called the "Disruption", which will be referred to later.

Episcopal Church.—The Episcopal Church in Scotland was

by no means dead after 1689. At the time of the Union, Episcopalian clergymen, mainly in the north-east and in the Highlands, were still carrying on their ministry in 165 out of about 900 parishes, and most of them remained loyal to the exiled Stewarts. In Queen Anne's reign, the Tory Parliament made things easier for them, but the failure of the Jacobite rebellions, in which Episcopalian lairds and clergy played a large part, brought disaster to them. Some of their chapels were destroyed by Cumberland and many of the clergy and laymen were imprisoned or transported to the plantations for offences under the Penal Acts of 1746 and 1748. But even before the death of the Young Pretender (1788) Jacobitism ceased to be dangerous; the Scottish Episcopalians began to grow in strength, especially after 1792, when the Penal Laws were repealed. Their numbers and resources increased in the nineteenth century through the arrival of immigrants from England and Ireland and the conversion of Presbyterian Scots, such as Sir Walter Scott and some who had been educated at English public schools. By the twentieth century there were more than 400 congregations in the Scottish Episcopal Church. Although it is in communion with the Church of England and is often called the "English Church", it differs from the Anglican church in various respects. In England bishops are appointed by the Crown (on the advice of the Prime Minister), but in Scotland nominations come from the clergy and laymen of a diocese. There is no archbishop in the Scottish Episcopal Church, but one of the bishops is elected by the others as a PRIMUS for life. The Church has a Prayer Book of its own, although it has a great similarity to the English Prayer Book, the use of which is also permitted. The Scottish Liturgy or Book of Common Prayer is partly founded on the Prayer Book of 1637, the introduction of which led to the riot in St. Giles' and the wars of the Covenants. The Scottish Episcopal Church has an interesting link with the Episcopal Church of the United States. In 1783, after the War of Independence, Samuel Seabury of Connecticut, who had been refused ordination by the English bishops, appealed to the Scots and was consecrated as bishop by their Scottish bishops in Aberdeen.

Presbyterianism in the Highlands.—Apart from one or two scattered areas such as Argyll, Sutherland and Easter Ross, Presbyterianism did not make much headway in the Highlands and Islands until the eighteenth century, but by 1800 it was firmly established except in a few Catholic and Episcopalian districts. One of the first duties of the Church of Scotland after it was established in 1690 was to send ministers as missionaries to the remoter parishes, and every incentive was offered to Gaelic-speaking students to settle in the Highlands. Where the people had an Episcopalian clergyman or were Catholic the new ministers had little success. In Glenorchy, when the former Presbyterian minister returned to his charge in 1690, he was escorted back to the parish boundary by the people, still loyal to Episcopalianism, with a piper playing "The March of Death". Although Episcopalian clergy were known to be in sympathy with the Jacobites, many of them were allowed to remain in their livings until their death. Some of the young Presbyterian ministers had a hard struggle. Aeneas Sage, the first Presbyterian minister in Lochcarron, used his prowess at putting the stone to impress the young men, who up to the time of his coming in 1726 had spent Sunday playing shinty, putting the stone and tossing the caber. As there were few Scottish-Gaelic books and only Irish translations of the Bible till well on in the century and as many of the people were illiterate, the ministers spent much of their time teaching the families they visited in their large parishes by "catechizing", taking the various questions from the Shorter Catechism. Later, this work was done by catechists, who travelled about, receiving hospitality for a few days in one home after another. The elders took a leading part in the work of the Church. At the annual communions which were attended by hundreds from neighbouring parishes, Friday was usually set apart for the "Men", leading elders who would discourse on a "Question", some point from the Bible which had perhaps given difficulty to an intending communicant. As the century advanced, the Highlanders became strongly religious,[1] and the soldiers of Highland regiments had a reputation far different from the rest of the army, which Wellington once described as "the scum of the earth, enlisted for money

[1] See pp. 49-50

or drink". General Stewart of Garth, writing in 1822, was able to say that after 79 years "no individual" (of the Black Watch) "has been brought to a General Court Martial for theft or any crime showing moral turpitude or depravity". Of the Sutherland Highlanders who served in South Africa in the Napoleonic Wars it was said that "they were a pattern for morality and good behaviour to every other corps", subscribing £1,400 for "books, societies and the support of the Gospel".

Revivals.—Highland Communions, often held in the open because of the large crowds, were solemn occasions, reminiscent of the conventicles of Covenanting times; sometimes the effect of a preacher's sermon was so great that it started off a revival of religion in the district. Such a revival began at Nigg, in Easter Ross, in 1739, a few years before the great revival at Kilsyth and Cambuslang, where, it was estimated, 30,000 attended communion in August 1743, and 3,000 communicated. In such revivals, when many became alarmed about their souls, praying-societies and fellowship-meetings were started, in which laymen could take the lead, but the minister's sermons on the Sabbath were still all-important. About 1859, a revival in north-east Scotland, led by James Turner, a Peterhead cooper, is said to have "converted" over 8,000 persons. In 1873 and 1883, two American evangelists, Dwight L. Moody and Ira D. Sankey, the first preaching and the second singing popular hymns, had also great success with their gospel-meetings in the north-east as well as in the Lowlands of Scotland. Since that time, small evangelical sects such as the Plymouth Brethren have had many adherents among the fisher-folk of the north-east coast, Orkney and Shetland. But the High-lands and Islands have remained a stronghold of Presbyterianism down to the present day.

The Disruption.—The right of patrons to present or "intrude" ministers to livings was still resented by the Church of Scotland even by those who had not seceded. In the first half of the nine-teenth century, the leadership of the Church passed into the hands of a strong "Evangelical" party, which was not prepared to tolerate patronage as the easy-going "Moderates" had done. In 1834 the General Assembly passed two acts which started off

what is called the TEN YEARS' CONFLICT, ending in the Disruption
of 1843. One of these acts, the VETO ACT, permitted the majority
in a congregation to veto or forbid the intrusion of a minister by
a patron against their will. The other, the CHAPEL ACT, allowed
ministers of the many
"chapels of ease" and
quoad sacra parish churches, which had been
built in populous areas, to
rank with the ministers of
the older or *quoad omnia*
parish churches. The
Moderator of the General
Assembly in 1834 and
the outstanding leader of
the Evangelicals at this
time was Dr THOMAS
CHALMERS (1780-1847).
Born at Anstruther, he
had a brilliant career at
St. Andrews University.
While a young minister
at Kilmany in Fife, he

Photo: *National Galleries of Scotland*
Dr Thomas Chalmers

continued to study mathematics, astronomy and economics,
published in 1808 an *Inquiry into the National Resources*. After
1810 he became more earnest in matters of religion and when
he was "translated" to the Tron parish of Glasgow, he proved
to be a most enthusiastic pastor, organizing charitable work
among the poor of the city slums and starting two weekday and
over forty Sunday schools. His eloquent preaching gained him
an enthusiastic following, and when he visited London in 1817,
after some of his sermons had been published, his reception
was such that Wilberforce said, "All the world is wild about Dr
Chalmers." He continued his hard work in Glasgow in another
parish from 1819 to 1823, when he went back as a professor to
his *alma mater*, St. Andrews University, leaving it after four
years for a chair at Edinburgh University. He still maintained his

interest in church affairs and helped to collect £300,000 for building over 200 new churches. He was one of those who insisted that poor relief should be a matter of Christian charity and not of local taxes, as was advocated by many at the time. In the conflict with the state which began in his year as Moderator, he was the natural leader of the "Evangelicals". The patrons were not long in challenging the two Acts passed. In Auchterarder parish, a minister was presented to the church with the support of only two out of the population of 3,000, and when the presbytery upheld the veto of the congregation, the case was taken to the Court of Session, which found in favour of the patron. The Assembly's Chapel Act was also declared illegal in the law courts. At last, in 1842 after bitter disputes, the Evangelical party issued a Claim of Right, drawn up mainly by Chalmers, claiming that although it was the duty of the state to maintain the Church it should not interfere in the government of the Church. They asserted this as a fundamental principle but the fact that only a small minority of M.P.s were Presbyterian gave added strength to their claim. Neither Peel's Government nor the Whig opposition would make a move to break the deadlock. At the General Assembly of 1843, led by Dr Welsh the Moderator, almost 200 ministers and elders walked out to form the FREE CHURCH OF SCOTLAND. Altogether, 451 out of 1,203 ministers surrendered their churches and their manses, some of them sacrificing stipends of £1,000 a year for the sake of their principles. In some cases, where the minister did not secede, the bulk of the congregation left so that the older parish churches were half empty. The new church grew quickly, due mainly to the organizing ability of Chalmers. Within four years over a million pounds had been raised and 654 new churches built; soon they began to build schools as well. Chalmers, who became first Moderator of the General Assembly of the new church and Principal of the Divinity College, died in 1847, worn out by his labours. The Disruption was an event which, happening in the middle of the Chartist period, overshadowed political happenings of the time; although it had some unfortunate consequences and caused bitter rancour in places, the men responsible earned the respect of the people of Scotland and England by their action.

Church Unions.—In the second half of the nineteenth century, a movement was afoot to unite the two great churches which stood outside the Church of Scotland. The U.P. (United Presbyterian) Church, which had been formed out of the earlier secession churches in the year of Chalmers's death, differed from the Free Church in certain respects. The Free Church stood for a state-established church, although they denied the right of the state to interfere in the internal affairs of the Church, while the U.P. Church was "Voluntary", i.e., opposed to state establishment. In the church services, the U.P. Church went much further than the Free Church in the singing of hymns (particularly after the revival meetings of Moody and Sankey) and in 1872 the use of instrumental music in the church was sanctioned. Many in the Free Church still maintained that only the psalms should be sung, while organs were considered as Anglican innovations and contemptuously referred to as "kists o' whistles". (In 1807, when the minister and congregation of St. Andrew's Parish Church, Glasgow, introduced an organ, said to have been built by James Watt, the Presbytery banned its use after the first service.) Some U.P. ministers also were prepared to accept the Westminster Confession of Faith only with certain qualifications, while it remained a fundamental standard of the Free Church. By the end of the century, however, a large majority of the Free Church were prepared to unite with the U.P. Church. By this time the foreign missions of the Scottish churches were to be found in many parts of Africa and India, and the claims of missionaries that separate missions caused confusion were among the arguments presented in favour of a union between two similar churches. In 1900 the Union was carried through and a UNITED FREE (U.F.) CHURCH was formed, leaving outside a small but determined minority in the Free Church, whose members became known as the "WEE FREES". In 1874 the Patronage Act had been repealed and it was inevitable that there should be another union, this time with the established Church of Scotland. Some of the U.F. Church did not like the idea of the church being controlled by the state in any degree whatsoever or of being supported by public taxes (the teinds). When acts were passed in Parliament in 1921 and 1925, declaring the Church's independence of the state and putting an end to the system of teinds, the way was clear and in 1929 1,457 parish churches and 1,441 U.F. churches combined to form the new Church of Scotland. The state connection is still maintained, however, by the Queen sending to the General Assembly each May the LORD HIGH COMMISSIONER, who takes up his residence as her representative in the Palace of Holyrood-house. The first oath taken by the Queen on her accession was one to maintain "the government, worship, discipline, rights and privileges of the Church of Scotland"; and it is the royal custom, when in Scotland, to attend Presbyterian services even although the sovereign is head of the Church of England. The Church is no longer so important in Scottish life as it was a hundred years ago or even in the 1880's when, out of a list of 72 leading men in Glasgow, 42 were ministers. The strict Puritanism of a century ago, which looked with disfavour on music, poetry, the theatre, innocent recreations and on any kind of breach of the sanctity of the Sabbath, has almost disappeared except for parts of the north and west of Scotland. But with it also has gone perhaps some of the moral training which helped to make the Scots highly respected all over the world.

Highland Catholics.—When Dr Webster took his census in 1755, the parish ministers reported just over 16,000 Roman Catholics in Scotland, of whom less than 1,000 lived south of the Highland line. Their numbers had been increasing in the first half of the eighteenth century, although the collapse of the "Forty-five" must have meant prison or death for many Catholics. During the seventeenth century Irish priests (including two sent by St. Vincent de Paul) had journeyed as missionaries to those of the "Old Faith" in the Hebrides and other Catholic districts. But there were long periods when the people were without any regular clergy at all. When Bishop Nicolson, appointed in 1694 as Vicar-Apostolic for Scotland, visited the Hebrides in 1700 he confirmed almost 1,000 in Benbecula and South Uist and over 3,000 in Moidart, where Catholicism had been strong since the reconciliation of Clanranald to the Catholic Church in 1624.

Nicolson's successor, Bishop James Gordon, was responsible for founding a humble seminary for training priests on an island in Loch Morar but after the "Fifteen" Rebellion it was moved to Scalan in Banffshire in 1717; in a few years native-born and home-trained priests, able to speak Gaelic, were at work among their people. Emigration meant a decline in the number of Highland Catholics. Often the priest was the organizer and leader of emigrants. One of them, Alexander MacDonell, who had been the first resident priest in Glasgow since the Reformation, took several hundred emigrants in three ships in 1802 across the Atlantic to settle with others of the MacDonald clan in Glengarry, Ontario, and became first Bishop of Kingston, Ontario. Many others poured into Prince Edward Island and Nova Scotia and their descendants have managed to retain both their old language and their old religion. It was estimated in 1908 that in Nova Scotia alone there were 45,000 Gaelic-speaking Catholics.

Scottish and Irish Catholics.—In Scotland itself the loss of Highland Catholics was, as we have seen, made up by Irish immigrants, mainly to the industrial south. Like the Free Church of Scotland after 1843, the Irish had to build new churches but, unlike the Free Church, their members were nearly all very poor and the sacrifices were proportionately much greater. The first Irish Roman Catholic church in Scotland was built in Paisley in 1808. The work of organizing a parish and collecting the money to build a church and a school fell upon the shoulders of the Irish priests, who knew best how to handle their flock. The mingling of the Scottish and Irish Catholics was not without some discord. Most of the bishops in the early and middle years of the nineteenth century were Scotsmen and they were accused by the Irish newspaper, the *Glasgow Free Press*, of favouring their fellow-countrymen by appointing them to parishes in which churches were already built, whereas Irish priests were given the task of starting such work. The Scottish bishops (like the Irish bishops) also condemned the violent political agitation for Home Rule among their flock. After an inquiry conducted by the English Archbishop Manning in 1868, the *Free Press* was denounced from the altars of all the Roman Catholic churches in Scotland

and ceased to exist. At a later date, the Ancient Order of Hibernians was banned for a period of ten years (1899-1909) when its activities were becoming too political. The emancipation of the Roman Catholics in 1829 allowed them to sit in Parliament and hold certain posts but it did not immediately place them on an equal footing. Up till 1897 Roman Catholics had to pay rates for Protestant schools without obtaining any support for their own schools; and it was only in 1918 that Roman Catholic schools were put on the same financial basis as Protestant schools. Although there had been Roman Catholic bishops in Scotland since the seventeenth century, it was not until 1878 that a full Scottish hierarchy was restored—two Archbishops, one of St. Andrews and Edinburgh and the other of Glasgow, and four bishops—twenty-eight years after the restoration of the Roman Catholic hierarchy in England. At the census of 1901 the Roman Catholic population of Scotland was given as 431,900 and in 1954 it had risen to 764,831.

Orange and Green.—As we have seen in the chapter—"Victorian and Edwardian Scotland"—this tremendous growth was accompanied by much strife in the nineteenth century and a revival of anti-Catholic feeling.[1] Part of this religious animosity came from the many "Orangemen" among the Irish immigrants, who brought with them their custom of celebrating with processions and demonstrations on each 12th of July, the anniversary of King William's victory at Boyne Water (actually fought on 1st July 1690). A fanatical anti-Catholic orator, John S. Orr, who summoned his audience with a trumpet and who called himself "Angel Gabriel," started off several riots in Greenock and Dumbarton in the 1850's. The death of a Protestant in a Kelso fight led to serious rioting there in 1856, a Catholic chapel being burned down. The Protestant v. Catholic feud continued to boil up every "TWELFTH OF JULY", when Orange "walks" or processions, headed by flute bands and with enormous banners portraying their hero, "King Billy", were wont to cause provocation by marching through Catholic districts. The worst affair occurred on the occasion of the centenary of the Irish patriot, Daniel O'Connell, in August 1875, when Irish Catholic

[1] See p. 179

demonstrations (in which green, not orange, was the predominant colour) started street fighting which went on for days in Partick, Glasgow. The rivalry even transferred itself to the field of sport: in Edinburgh hooligans, who called themselves Protestant or Catholic, fought one another at the games between the Heart of Midlothian and Hibernian football clubs, and similarly in Glasgow at the Rangers *v.* Celtic games, although the first match between these clubs in 1888 was friendly enough and was followed by both teams sitting down to supper together in the local Catholic hall.

SOURCE EXTRACT

Dr Chalmers in Cromarty, 1839

"Shortly after my return, Dr Chalmers visited the place on the last of his Church Extension journeys; and I heard, for the first time, that most impressive of modern orators address a public meeting, and had a curious illustration of the power which his "deep mouth" could communicate to passages little suited, one might suppose, to call forth the vehemency of his eloquence. In illustrating one of his points, he quoted from my *Memoir of William Forsyth* a brief anecdote, set in description of a kind which most men would have read quietly enough, but which, coming from him, seemed instinct with the Homeric vigour and force. The extraordinary impressiveness which he communicated to the passage served to show me, better than aught else, how imperfectly great orators may be represented by their written speeches. Admirable as the published sermons and addresses of Dr Chalmers are, they impart no adequate idea of that wonderful power and impressiveness in which he excelled all other British preachers."

Hugh Miller: *My Schools and Schoolmasters*

EXERCISES

1. Write a sentence about each of the following, explaining the origin of the name: Original Secession, Relief Church, U.P. Church, Free Church, U.F. Church.

2. Write notes on the following: Revivals, Scottish Episcopal Church, Scottish Catholicism, Orange-and-Green riots.
3. Explain: cutty stool, seizers, lettergae, "Occasions", "Intrusion", catechist, Primus, kist o' whistles, Wee Frees, "King Billy".
4. Explain the following stanzas:

    (a) The cheerfu' supper done, wi' serious face,
        They round the ingle form a circle wide;
    The sire turns o'er with patriarchal grace,
        The big ha-'bible, ance his father's pride.

                                    (Burns)

    (b) The auld kirk, the cauld kirk,
        The kirk that has the steeple;
    The wee kirk, the Free Kirk,
        The kirk wi' a' the people.

                                    (Anon)

5. Give an account of the life of Dr Thomas Chalmers.
6. Give an account of the history of your own church or of the local "parish church". (Find out the difference between a *quoad sacra* parish and a *quoad omnia* parish.)

CHAPTER XVI

SCHOOLS AND UNIVERSITIES

Scottish Education.—One feature of Scottish life which has long been singled out for praise is the educational system. How much of this praise has been deserved in the past or is deserved today? To answer both these questions would take up the whole of this book. But the story of Scottish schools and universities in the last two hundred and fifty years may help us towards finding an answer. The EDUCATION ACT OF 1696, making it compulsory for the heritors or landowners of each parish without a school to establish and maintain one, had been passed when Scottish education was at a low ebb. Most of the burghs possessed schools, some of them dating back to long before the Reformation. But there were many country parishes without a school and more

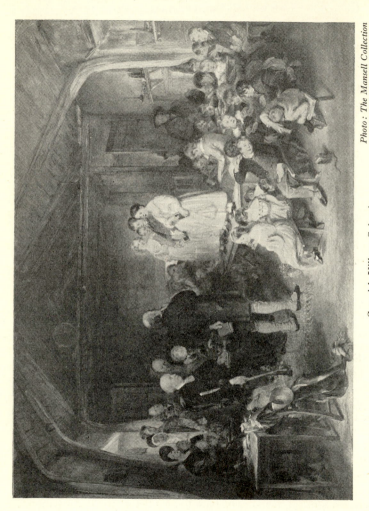

Photo : The Mansell Collection

Scottish Village School
The minister is catechizing four young scholars

than a century was to elapse after 1696 before it was possible to realize John Knox's ideal (expressed in the *First Book of Discipline*) of a school in every parish. At the end of the eighteenth century, according to the reports of over 900 parish ministers in the *Old Statistical Account*, there were still 10 parishes without a school. The chief difficulty came from the unwillingness of the heritors to pay the "stent" (a tax based on the annual value of their land), either for a parish school or a schoolmaster, even although the act of 1696 allowed them to make their tenants pay half the "stent". (This division of the "stent" between landlord and tenant has been carried on to the present day in the Scottish system of dividing rates between owners and occupiers.) Ministers and kirk-sessions tried to move heritors and tenants but there was no way in which they could be forced to pay their "stents" other than by peaceful persuasion. Like much other well-intentioned legislation, the Education Act of 1696 for "settling of the schools" was for long ineffective as it could not be enforced.

Rural Schools.—During the eighteenth century, in the remote districts where the population was widely scattered and the parish of great extent (like that of Glenelg, which was twenty miles long), there might be no PARISH SCHOOL or schoolmaster; or if there were, only a few of the children could attend. Too often, even in the more populous Lowlands, although there might be a schoolmaster, he found, instead of "the commodious house for a school" laid down in the act, that he had to take his scholars in the church itself, perhaps in the lower part of the tower, or in a family vault, or it might be in some dry-stone bothy with a turf roof and very little window light, or even in his own humble dwelling. For lack of desks or stools the children might sit on the floor, covered with straw or rushes which they themselves provided (as they also provided the peats for the fire in winter). In many parishes, both in the country and in the towns, there were DAME SCHOOLS for young children, taught to read and write by the "Dame", perhaps some genteel widow, who had been left without enough to support herself and her family. Sometimes a few parents who realized the benefits of education would combine to pay a teacher to look after their children, providing board and lodgings for him in turn. In this way, William Burnes, the poet's father, with some of his neighbours engaged a young student, John Murdoch, to teach their children, living with each family for a spell. In the Highlands and other remote regions there were by the end of the eighteenth century over 200 schools run by the SOCIETY FOR PROPAGATING CHRISTIAN KNOWLEDGE (S.P.C.K.), which also had about a hundred SPINNING-SCHOOLS for girls only. Other spinning-schools were set up in the Lowlands and Highlands by the Board of Trustees for Manufactures[1] and in the Jacobite districts by the Commissioners for the Forfeited Estates.[2] As the factory system developed in the textile industry, these spinning-schools tended to become sewing-schools providing instruction in reading as well as sewing.

Expansion.—By the beginning of the nineteenth century, although many of the children in the Lowlands were employed for long hours in coal-mines, cotton-mills and bleachfields, and in the far North even as late as 1820 there were only 500 in South Uist able to read out of a population of over 5,000, schools and schooling were being taken more seriously. An Act of 1803 provided for SIDE-SCHOOLS in large parishes. The Scottish educational system, backward as it may seem to us today, was greatly admired by visitors, and three times between 1807 and 1833 bills were introduced in the House of Commons to establish a similar system in England. The new interest in education led to the Government making grants of money in both England and Scotland from 1833 onwards, and in 1840 Inspectors of Schools were appointed for Scotland to see that the money was being properly spent. The Disruption of 1843 led to a great increase in the number of schools. Over 350 schoolmasters who had belonged to the Church of Scotland lost their posts, and partly for their sakes the Free Church set up new schools, more than 500 being founded within five years. In addition to the parish schools and Free Church schools, there were also Episcopalian schools, Roman Catholic schools and ADVENTURE SCHOOLS (or Venture Schools), run in their own home by cobblers or tailors who, being confined indoors by reason of their occupations,

[1] See p. 67   [2] See p. 37

would take a few pupils for 1d. or 2d. a week. Scotland was so well provided with schools of one kind or another that in 1872, when the SCOTTISH EDUCATION ACT was passed, education was made compulsory for children between five and thirteen years of age, whereas in England it was not until 1880, ten years after their first Education Act, that elementary schooling was made compulsory.

Village Dominies and Scholars.—The eighteenth-century schoolmaster or "dominie", as he was called, was sometimes a young student who had hopes of taking his degree one day; or he might be a "stickit minister", a man who had failed to qualify for the Church after his studies in divinity. His salary was only £5 a year, when the heritors and tenants all paid their "stents", but he eked out a living by performing various other duties— clerk to the kirk-session, registrar of baptisms and marriages, precentor or beadle in the church on the Sabbath. He was ap- pointed by the parish minister and the heritors, some of them elders of the Kirk, so that the school was closely linked up with the Church of Scotland. Among the dominie's other emoluments were the children's fees—1s. a quarter for the "3 R's" (reading, writing and 'rithmetic) and double fees if the pupil desired instruction in Latin or higher studies. On "Fastern's E'en" (Shrove Tuesday), which was celebrated as a holiday in most districts throughout the eighteenth century, cock-fighting was a great attraction, the dominie being the master of ceremonies, the schoolroom the cockpit and the local gentry and scholars the spectators. Each scholar brought a cock to the fighting, paying a penny entry fee to the dominie, who also claimed at the end of the day the "fugies", the cocks which would not fight. Even including these extras, few country dominies had more than £15 a year in 1803, when the act authorizing the building of side- schools also laid down a minimum salary, stated in the old Scot- tish currency (probably to make it sound better) as 300 merks, equivalent to £16 13s. 4d. Dominies of parish-schools, but not of side-schools, were to be provided with houses of not more than two rooms, which some critics of the act described as "palaces for dominies". Despite his humble salary the village schoolmaster was held in high regard. Although most of his pupils received instruction only in the 3 R's, the clever "lad o' pairts" was coached in Latin, Greek and Mathematics in order to proceed to University. Under the supervision of the one master there might be as many as a hundred scholars, ranging

Photo: Picture Post

Hornbook

from the serious student with his Livy or Tacitus to the young scholar learning his ABC and his figures from the "hornbook" (a paper pasted on a small piece of wood and covered with a sheet of transparent horn instead of glass). For all of them there was regular religious instruction, especially repetition of the psalms and the "CARRITCHES" (the Shorter Catechism). Writing was so often given to the pupils who would otherwise be idle while the master attended to one class or another that the penmanship was usually of a very high standard. After 1846, PUPIL TEACHERS, from the age of thirteen to eighteen, helped with the teaching of younger classes, while continuing to be taught themselves for 1½ hours per day by the schoolmasters. The MONITOR SYSTEM, although started by a Scotsman, ANDREW BELL (1753-1832) in Madras, was more popular in England than in Scotland. By it, a clever pupil or "monitor" was put in charge of a group of ten; he was taught the lesson which he in turn passed on to the others. Gradually, more and more women teachers also appeared as assistants; they were addressed as "Mem" (for Madam) even if they were only just out of their 'teens. The time was to come when they were to be in the majority in the rural schools.

Burgh Schools.—In many of the burghs, there were, as in the country parishes, Adventure Schools, Dame Schools and Sub-scription Schools, and in all burghs of a fair size there was a BURGH SCHOOL. In medieval times these had generally been connected with the Church but even before the Reformation the town councils had begun to control them, appointing and paying the master or rector, whose salary was about double that of the parish schoolmaster and was supplemented by fees and gifts, the most important being the CANDLEMAS OFFERINGS. On Candlemas (2nd February) there was a holiday in almost all burgh schools up to the first half of the nineteenth century, and money gifts were presented by the scholars to the master, who sat at his desk and acknowledged the gifts according to the amount—from no response at all if the sum were as low as six-pence, through "Vivat!" and "Floreat!" to "Gloriat!" for a guinea. The highest donor was declared King or Queen of the Day, which finished with a bonfire, the "Candlemas Bleeze". The burgh schools were also called GRAMMAR SCHOOLS, although only a few of the older burgh schools still bear that title, e.g., Aberdeen Grammar School. In the grammar schools, Latin was for a long time the main subject of instruction, the standard text-book of the eighteenth century being known as Ruddiman's *Rudiments*, or, in full, *The Rudiments of the Latin Tongue* by

THOMAS RUDDIMAN (1674-1757), at one time schoolmaster at Laurencekirk and latterly printer to Edinburgh University and keeper of the Advocate's Library. During the eighteenth century the hours of teaching were gradually reduced in most grammar schools. The seventeenth-century starting-times of 6 a.m. in summer and 7 a.m. in winter were extended to 9 a.m., but many schools still went on to 5 p.m. in summer and 12 noon on Saturdays. With the growth of trade and industry, some WRITING SCHOOLS and COMMERCIAL SCHOOLS were set up for the teaching of book-keeping, arithmetic, etc., the first at Dumfries in 1723; and in 1746, Ayr Town Council added book-keeping, navigation, surveying, mathematics and science to the curriculum of Ayr Grammar School. In the second half of the century there were established new schools in which there was instruction in modern subjects instead of in the classics, but for which, nevertheless, the classical name of ACADEMY was chosen. The first was Perth Academy (1761), and before 1800 there were also academies at Dundee (1786), Inverness (founded in 1788 but granted a royal charter in 1793), Elgin and Fortrose (1791) and Ayr (1794), most of them founded by public subscription. Other academies with royal charters were those of Tain (1810) and Irvine (1818), while Edinburgh's oldest school has been called the Royal High School since the reign of James VI. As the nineteenth century advanced, some of the grammar schools, adding the new subjects to their curricula, began to call themselves academies. In other burghs, grammar school and academy were amalgamated, usually under the name "academy", although in a few cases "High School" was the name chosen.

Schools for Rich and Poor.—In addition to the burgh schools there were in some of the larger towns other schools, originally founded as charitable institutions for poor children, such as George Heriot's and George Watson's Hospitals in Edinburgh, Hutchesons' Hospital in Glasgow, Morgan's Hospital in Dundee and Robert Gordon's Hospital in Aberdeen. About 1870, most of these hospitals and other similar institutions were transformed into fee-paying day-schools, the Edinburgh Merchant Company schools being the first to be changed. In England, similar endowed schools for poor scholars had become boarding-schools for the children of well-to-do parents. It was to these boarding-schools, which came to be known as "public schools", that the Scottish aristocracy began to send their sons even before the end of the eighteenth century. Three BOARDING-SCHOOLS were started near Edinburgh in imitation of the English "public schools"—Loretto (1829), Merchiston Castle (1833), Fettes College (1870) and a fourth boarding-school under the control of the Scottish Episcopal Church, Trinity College at Glenalmond (1847). Later, similar boarding-schools were started for girls and for boys but many Scottish parents who can afford to pay the high fees required still prefer to send their children to English boarding-schools. During the nineteenth century, wealthy bene-factors endowed schools which were soon able to compete with the older burgh schools. Such were the Dollar Institution (later called Academy) started in 1818, the Madras College in St. Andrews and Madras Academy in Cupar (later re-named the Bell-Baxter School), Milne's Institution in Fochabers, Morrison's Academy in Crieff and many others. At the other end of the scale, something was done for the poor children who could not afford to pay the small fees for the burgh schools and the parish schools. In some parishes there were charities whereby a few children were educated without payment of fees. There were certain very notable endowments, e.g., the Milne Bequest, the income from which (about £2,000 a year) was used to educate children in Aberdeenshire free of charge. In the large cities, with their slums and overcrowding, there was no schooling at all for many of the poor until late in the nineteenth century. RAGGED SCHOOLS were started by Sheriff Watson for poor children in Aberdeen in 1841 and by Dr Thomas Guthrie in Edinburgh in 1847. SUNDAY SCHOOLS, in districts of Glasgow where there was neither church nor day-school, were begun by DAVID STOW (1793-1864), a Glasgow merchant and philanthropist. He was helped in his work by Dr Chalmers and in time founded the Glasgow Infant School Society, with a model school, and the NORMAL SCHOOL or Training College for teachers (1836). Despite all these efforts, public and private, it was estimated in 1867 that about 1 in 6 of the children of school age in Scotland did not attend school, the proportion being as high as 1 in 2 in Glasgow.

Compulsory Education.—In 1872 the SCOTTISH EDUCATION ACT was passed, two years after a similar act for England, but differing from it in various respects. It set up a SCOTCH EDUCATION DEPARTMENT (the first word in the title being altered to "Scottish" in 1918) and placed all burgh schools and parish schools under the control of PARISH SCHOOL BOARDS, composed of men and women elected by ratepayers every three years. Education was made compulsory for children from five to thirteen years of age, those too poor to pay fees (which were later fixed at not more than 9d. a week per child) being given assistance from the parish rates. Most of the "voluntary" schools also became "public" schools at this time, obtaining grants from the rates levied on householders and also from Parliament. The only private schools remaining were the Roman Catholic, the Episcopalian and a few endowed schools, although all householders, whether Roman Catholic or Episcopalian, whether they sent their children to the public schools or even whether they had no children at all, had to pay the "school-rates". Parliamentary grants meant regular government inspection by officials, H.M. Inspectors of Schools, on whose reports the grants to schools depended—"payment by results". Gradually, a uniform system began to develop, although differences existed between one area and another, according to the amount of money which a parish school board would obtain from the rates for school buildings and teachers' salaries. Many of the schools at present used in Scotland were erected during the period of the school boards, which lasted from 1872 to 1918, and the name of the parish school board can still be seen on some parts of these schools. The system of compulsory education was extended by other acts. In 1883 the leaving age was raised to fourteen years (with certain exemptions if the pupil was proficient) and in 1891 fees for children from five to fourteen were abolished, although school boards could and did retain a small number of fee-paying schools. Common examinations for schools were instituted by the Education Department. The LEAVING CERTIFICATE examination, begun in 1888, soon became accepted as the gateway to the universities and the professions. At first there were only six subjects—English (including History and Geography), Mathematics, Latin, Greek, French and German (Science being added in 1899), and passes were awarded at three levels—lower, higher and honours. Later, in 1902, it became compulsory to gain a prescribed number of passes in a group of subjects and from 1906 to 1924 it was also necessary to pass first of all an Intermediate Certificate examination. (The name "Highers", given to the Leaving Certificate examination, goes back to the days of the two examinations.) Today, the Scottish Leaving Certificate is awarded for a pass even in one subject.

Recent Acts.—The present system of education is not radically different from that of the beginning of the century but certain changes have been introduced, notably those effected by three Acts of Parliament in 1908, 1918 and 1946, the last two having been passed at the end of the First and Second World Wars. Poorer children benefited in various ways by the 1908 Act: compulsory medical inspection of pupils was introduced, resulting in great improvements in personal cleanliness in slum areas, and school boards were allowed to provide cheap school meals and free books and stationery. Some school boards took advantage of these powers almost from the start. Free books, however, were not provided in certain areas until after the First World War (1914-18). Few school boards troubled about school meals but milk was supplied at a reduced price from 1934 and free after 1946. It was only in the Second World War (1939-45) that school meals became a feature of school life. By the EDUCATION ACT OF 1918, parish school boards were replaced by EDUCATION AUTHORITIES specially elected for the control of education in each county and large city. (As a result of the increased powers given to county councils in the Local Government Act of 1929, the *ad hoc* or specially elected education authorities were abolished and, instead of them, EDUCATION COMMITTEES of county councils and city corporations control education.) Voluntary schools, such as Roman Catholic schools, which had received grants from the state since 1897, were transferred in 1918 to education authorities, which were henceforth responsible not only for their control but also their expenditure. The 1918 Act, by abolishing school boards, helped to put an end to the distinction between schools of a wealthy city and those of a poor country parish. There were still differences between one county and another, but the EDUCATION ACT OF 1946 carried the levelling process still further by making all counties pay the same scales of salaries to their teachers. Instead of the old system whereby city school teachers received the higher salaries, teachers in remote areas are given an extra payment as an inducement to remain there. The 1918 Act had made provision for raising the school leaving age from fourteen to fifteen years of age and also for day continuation classes for those who had left school, but nothing was done to implement the Act for many years. The 1946 Act fixed 1947 as the year for raising the school-leaving age and also gave education committees wide powers to promote not merely day continuation classes as part of apprentice training but also all kinds of "Further Education" and "Youth Service".

The Changing Classroom.—Many other changes have taken place without an act of Parliament. Visual aids—magic lanterns, episcopes, projectors for films and film-strips, radio and television sets—are now considered almost as necessary in the classroom as the blackboard. More and more subjects have been added to the curriculum—Spanish, Italian, Russian and Hebrew in addition to the languages taught in the nineteenth century, technical subjects (woodwork, metalwork, engineering), commercial subjects and others. Examinations have also changed: they are not all written tests but may include practical and oral tests and even, at the end of the primary school stage, an intelligence test. Schools are much less grim in appearance than they used to be; today there are plenty of window spaces to give light and air. Nowadays, playing-fields and gymnasia are considered as vital to a school, whereas formerly there was no playing-field except a public park, and physical training (or "drill" as it was called) was performed in the school hall or playground. In the classroom, the atmosphere is not so austere as formerly. When a teacher of the nineteenth century in a city school had 70 to 80 children in his class, discipline had to be strict indeed. In the Code laid down by the Education Department in 1950, it was stipulated that classes in a primary school should not exceed 45 and in a secondary school 40, practical classes and those above the third year in secondary schools being smaller still. Large as these limits are, they are unfortunately still exceeded because of the shortage of teachers. Despite that, discipline does not today depend on the strap or "tawse" as it did fifty years ago. Whether the standards of education have declined in the same period it is difficult to say. Today the emphasis is less on the "lad o' pairts" and more on the average pupil. Grants of varying amounts according to the income of the parents have been paid since 1947 to children who remain at school after the age of fifteen years, the maximum being fixed at £50 in 1953. It is hoped that the bright boy or girl will be thereby encouraged to make full use of the education which the school has to offer.

Eighteenth-Century Universities.—It was the proud boast of Aberdonians in the eighteenth century that their city possessed as many universities as the whole of England. At that time and until 1860 when they were united, KING'S COLLEGE (founded in 1494) and MARISCHAL COLLEGE (founded in 1593) ranked as separate universities; but, as they were more to be compared with an Oxford or Cambridge college than with either of these universities, the Aberdonian boast need not be taken seriously. The other three Scottish universities in 1700 were the two pre-Reformation foundations of ST. ANDREWS (1412) and GLASGOW (1451) and the "Toun's College" of EDINBURGH (1583). In the early eighteenth century, each of the two southern universities might have two or three hundred students, many of them preparing for the Church. At that time, the young student, when he matriculated at fourteen, came under the care of one professor, his "Regent", for the whole course of four years. All the subjects, Greek, Logic, Ethics and Natural Philosophy, were taught by one person, the language of instruction being Latin. Professor Francis Hutcheson of Glasgow University was the first to break with this practice and start lecturing in English about 1730. Students had also formerly boarded with their "Regents", or

Photo: E.N.A

King's College, Aberdeen

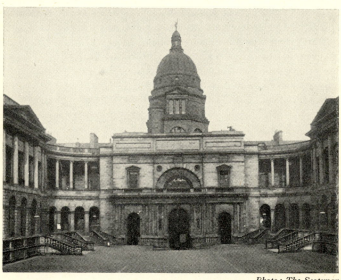

Photo: The Scotsman

Edinburgh University

lived in the college rooms under his supervision, being compelled
to converse only in Latin, to wear the scarlet gown and to eat at
common tables. But the system whereby "Regents" taught all
subjects was abandoned during the eighteenth century in favour
of separate professors for each subject, Edinburgh being the first
to do so in 1708 and King's College, Aberdeen, not until 1798.
At the same time, because of the great increase in numbers,
students began to live in lodgings in the town instead of in the
college. Although the system of common tables was retained at
St. Andrews as late as 1820, elsewhere the student depended on
cheap provisions and homely fare. Many a poor "lad o' pairts",
whose parents stinted themselves to provide for his education,
was compelled to "scorn delights and live laborious days" on a
diet of salt herring, oatmeal porridge or brose, and small beer.
Not all of the youths who went up to the university at fourteen
stayed for the full length of the course. The university degrees
had no great reputation, particularly as they were often conferred
on any candidate willing to pay the fees. Nevertheless, it is
doubtful whether there was ever such a galaxy of talent among
the professors of Scottish universities as in this period. You have
already read of Francis Hutcheson, the philosopher, and Adam
Smith, the economist, of Glasgow and Principal Robertson, the
historian, of Edinburgh.[1] Thomas Reid (1710-96), professor at
Aberdeen, along with Hutcheson, founded what is known as the
"Scottish School of Philosophy". But it was in science and medicine that Scotland excelled. William Cullen, Joseph Black,[2] the
Gregory family,[3] who have been mentioned in previous chapters,
were brilliant teachers who attracted students from many other
countries. As Nonconformists were barred from the universities of
Oxford and Cambridge and Trinity College, Dublin, many English
and Irish students attended Edinburgh and Glasgow universities.
Study at a Scottish university was also much cheaper than in
other countries; Dr Johnson, who thought very little of Scottish
universities, although he had a high respect for the learning of
the Scots he met, said that a student could live and learn at
one on £10 a year. In the fifty years before 1827, of 2,792 Edinburgh graduates in medicine, only 819 were Scotsmen, 706 were

[1] See p. 132   [2] See p. 58, p. 91   [3] See p. 214

I

English, 850 Irish, 225 were from British colonies and 192 were foreigners.

John Anderson's Legacy.—Professor JOHN ANDERSON (1726-96), from whom James Watt received the model of Newcomen's engine for repair, has other claims to be remembered by his fellow-countrymen. He was a brilliant, if erratic type of man, nicknamed "Jolly Jack Phosphorus". Born in the manse of Rosneath, he had studied at Glasgow University and had been professor of Oriental Languages before changing to Natural Philosophy (or Physics). He had strong Radical sympathies and at the time of the French Revolution he even presented a gun of his own invention to the French Assembly. When a professor in Glasgow, he ran twice-weekly "practical lectures" for working-men. At his death he left all his property for the establishment of a new university in Glasgow. This university, the "ANDERSONIAN", as it was called, at first had classes only in physics and chemistry, held in the Grammar School, and these proved very popular. The second professor in charge of the university, Dr BIRKBECK, started free classes for working-men in mechanics and chemistry, which became the MECHANICS' INSTITUTION, the first of many similar Mechanics' Institutes founded throughout the country. (Birkbeck College in London is called after him.) The "Andersonian" was for long the most famous school of chemistry in Britain and in 1886 combined with the Mechanics' Institution and other bodies to become the ROYAL TECHNICAL COLLEGE, the first and greatest in Europe. The beginnings of technical education and adult education can therefore be traced to John Anderson and his legacy. Today there are Technical Colleges in other cities and also Agricultural Colleges, Schools of Art, Commercial Colleges and Colleges of Music. Since 1946, moreover, many young people, who have started work, attend DAY-RELEASE SCHOOLS, where they learn not only commercial and technical subjects but also general subjects. Classes for adults in subjects like philosophy, political economy, art, music, literature, astronomy, geology, etc., are run in large cities and country villages, either in schools or community centres, by the WORKERS' EDUCATIONAL ASSOCIATION (founded in 1903) or the EXTRA-MURAL

DEPARTMENTS of universities. Education, in other words, need not stop at fifteen, but can go on to seventy and older.

Modern Developments.—The universities were reorganized and improved in many ways during the nineteenth century. Some relics of ancient customs have survived to the present day, such as the right of the students to elect their Lord Rector. Their choice usually fell on a politician of one or other of the two great political parties, and the election and rectorial address were often uproarious affairs. THOMAS CAMPBELL (1777-1844) was one of the most popular of Glasgow's Lord Rectors; his patriotic song, "Ye Mariners of England" has been a favourite with Glasgow students ever since. The courses for degrees were better regulated in the nineteenth century, and faculties of arts, divinity, medicine, law and, last of all, (in 1893) science were set up. Aberdeen's two universities were at last amalgamated in 1860, and in Dundee a university college was founded in 1881, later to be linked up with St. Andrews University. Women began to press for entry into the universities. The first step was taken by St. Andrews, which founded the diploma of Lady Literate in Arts (L.L.A.) in 1876; before the diploma was discontinued in 1920 it had been awarded to over 4,000 women. In Glasgow, Queen Margaret College was established in 1883 and incorporated in the University in 1892, when women were admitted to university courses. University education had always been cheap in Scotland and in 1901 it was made easier still for anyone who could pass the entrance examinations by the munificence of

Photo: Picture Post

Andrew Carnegie

ANDREW CARNEGIE, who gave over £10,000,000 for the founding of public libraries. By the CARNEGIE TRUST, set up in 1901, £2,000,000 was set aside for the encouragement of university education in Scotland by paying part of the students' fees. Bursaries to Scottish universities, although seldom large, were very numerous. With a bursary and the help of Carnegie, many a crofter's son or a miner's son went through university. In 1939, it was estimated that the proportion of university graduates in Scotland was four times higher than in England, but since the end of the Second World War the English proportion has risen. Large grants are now also made by education committees to assist university and other students not only with their fees but also with their maintenance, the allowance being sometimes as high as £160 in 1955, according to the income of the parents. It is thus possible to say that today there is full provision for education from the infant stage to graduation at the university and that no one need be debarred by financial reasons from obtaining as good an education as the country can offer him.

SOURCE EXTRACT

"*School*.—The schoolmaster's salary is 100 merks. The average number of scholars is 10. The smallness of the number is owing to the age and infirmity of the teacher, who is above seventy years of age; to his ignorance of the languages and particularly to his want of a schoolhouse. He has only a small cottage and an area of about 8 feet by 16, taken off the end of it as his school. . . . The fees for teaching to read English are 1s., writing and arithmetic, 1s. 6d. the quarter. He is also precentor, session-clerk, beadle, grave-digger, and yet his whole income does not exceed £8 stg. per annum. This, with the paltry accommodation, holds out little encouragement to a teacher of merit. Indeed, no man who possesses strength to lift a mattock, or to wield a flail, would accept of such a disgraceful pittance. In these times when there is such a general rise in all the necessaries of life, what progress in learning or in science is to be expected in any part of the kingdom, when that useful and necessary set of men are depressed by poverty?"

Account of Parish of Heriot, Midlothian, by Rev. Alex. Hunter, minister, in Sir John Sinclair's *Statistical Account* (1795)

EXERCISES

1. Write a sentence about each of the following: parish school, grammar school, academy, spinning-school, side-school, "Adventure" school, Ragged School, Normal School.
2. Write notes about each of the following: S.P.C.K., Monitor System, pupil teacher, Workers' Educational Association, Extra-Mural Department, L.L.A., Carnegie Trust, Professor Francis Hutcheson, Professor John Anderson, Thomas Campbell.
3. Write a sentence about each of the following acts: 1696, 1803, 1872, 1908, 1918, 1946.
4. Explain: stent, dominie, lad o' pairts, stickit minister, carritches, Fastern's E'en, Candlemas Offerings, regents (university).
5. Write an account of (a) the schools in your parish before 1872, if you live in the country, or (b) the oldest school in your town, if you live in one.
6. Find out about your own school as many facts as possible—date of foundation (if known), buildings occupied, numbers of pupils and teachers at different times, names of distinguished former pupils.

CHAPTER XVII

THE SCOTS OVERSEAS

Europe.—Up to and during the seventeenth century many a
young man had left Scotland for Europe to seek fame as a soldier
or fortune as a merchant. The same kind of emigration continued
on a much smaller scale in the eighteenth century, the Scots who
settled down in Europe being generally Catholic or Jacobite
exiles. After the rebellion of 1719, the two brothers Keith, the
Earl Marischal, George, and his brother, James, both entered
the service of foreign powers. James Keith, after an adventurous
career in the Spanish and Russian armies, became Field-Marshal
of Prussia under Frederick the Great, who also used his brother,
the EARL MARISCHAL KEITH, as a diplomat. FIELD-MARSHAL
KEITH (the names are confusingly similar) was shot dead at
Hochkirch in 1758 while leading a charge against the enemy for
the third time. In Russia, where General Patrick Gordon was
still remembered as the founder of the Russian Army in the reign
of Peter the Great, another Scotsman, Sir SAMUEL GREIG (1735-
88), born at Inverkeithing, was to help with the creation of the
Russian navy under Catherine the Great. In the Russian campaign of Napoleon, two of the generals on opposite sides were of
Scottish origin—the French Marshal ALEXANDRE MACDONALD,
born of a Jacobite family and said to be related to Flora MacDonald, and Marshal BARCLAY DE TOLLY, of the old Aberdeenshire
family, the Barclays of Tolly. Barclay's withdrawal in face of a
French army, three times the size of the Russian, laid him open
to the charge of cowardice; but his strategy, which has been compared with that of Wallace and Bruce, was at last vindicated. He
was commander-in-chief of the Russian armies at the battle of
Leipzig in 1813 and again in France in 1815. Some of Scottish
birth or origin achieved distinction in other spheres than those
of war or politics. There were many Scottish doctors in the
Russian service down to the middle of the nineteenth century;
two of them were from Dumfries-shire, JAMES MOUNSEY and

JOHN ROGERSON, physicians to the Empresses Elizabeth and Catherine respectively. MICHAEL LERMONTOV (1814-41), the Russian poet whose brilliant career was cut short by his death in a duel, was of the Scottish family of Learmonth; and the distinguished, Norwegian composer, EDVARD GRIEG (1843-1907), was grandson of Alexander Greig, who left his home near Fraserburgh to become a fish-merchant in Norway. There were still so many Scottish merchants in Sweden in the eighteenth century that eight of the thirty-three original members of the distinguished Royal Bachelors' Club, founded at Gothenburg in 1769, had Scottish names and one of the pioneers of the Swedish East India Company was a Colin Campbell.

Atlantic Migration.—But, as you know from earlier chapters, by far the majority of Scots overseas were those who had crossed the Atlantic. Many of those Scots in the north of Ireland, where the Plantation of Ulster had established a Scottish Presbyterian population, were among the earliest large migrations to Pennsylvania in the seventeenth century. The SCOTCH-IRISH, as they are called in America, emigrated partly because of their exasperation with the British government, which restricted their woollen industry in favour of the English and their linen industry in favour of the Scots. They also felt resentment against landlords who raised their rents and against an Episcopal Church to which they had to pay tithes. Over 200,000 of them, it is estimated, were settled before the American War of Independence in almost every colony, and they are said to have made ideal pioneers. Many of their descendants rose to high positions in the United States, the most notable being the two Presidents, ANDREW JACKSON, "Old Hickory", and WILLIAM MCKINLEY, who was assassinated by an anarchist in 1901. The trade between Glasgow and the American colonies led to some of the Lowland Scots settling there, like Colonel MacDowall in the West Indies and the Dinwiddie brothers in Virginia.[1] You have already read of John Paul or PAUL JONES, born at Arbigland in Galloway; he was the first commander of the United States Navy and his exploits would fill a book.[2] ALEXANDER HAMILTON, the lawyer who took a leading part in drafting the American constitution and put in

[1] See pp. 56-7   [2] See p. 106

order the finances of the young U.S.A., was born in the West Indies but was of Scottish parentage; he is said to have been at one time a member of the Trades House of Glasgow. You have read in the chapter, "A Century in the Highlands and Islands", how some Highland emigrants settled in North Carolina even before the "Forty-five" and how the stream of Atlantic migration after the War of Independence went mainly to Canada.[1] But, despite the attractions of Canada, many Scotsmen settled in the United States. ANDREW CARNEGIE (1835-1918) left his native Dunfermline for Pittsburg, Pennsylvania, with the rest of his family in 1848, when his father found it impossible to carry on his craft as a handloom weaver. Carnegie founded the largest steelworks in the world at Pittsburg and made a fortune, of which he gave away over £80,000,000 in benefactions. It was a descendant of Scottish (and Scotch-Irish) immigrants, WOODROW WILSON, who, as President, brought the United States into the First World War, and it was General MACARTHUR, the grandson of a Glasgow immigrant, who commanded the American forces in the Far East in the Second World War.

Canadian Explorers.—Many of the Highland Loyalists in the United States emigrated to Canada after the War of Independence; their settlements in Nova Scotia, Prince Edward Island and Ontario received more and more Highland emigrants driven out by the clearances and by overpopulation, especially after the collapse of the kelp industry. They brought with them to Canada their way of life, their Gaelic language and, in some cases, their own Gaelic-speaking priest.[2] The last time the fiery cross was sent round to raise a clan for battle was in Glengarry, Ontario, in the War of 1812, when the MacDonalds there raised a regiment, the Glengarry Fencibles, to fight the Americans. Along with the other United Empire Loyalists, they not only held up the American invasion forces but they crossed the frontier, capturing Detroit, Oswego and other towns before British help arrived. The opening up of Western Canada was in great measure the work of Scottish pioneers. Hudson's Bay Company, although originally an English concern, had so many servants and officials from Scotland (particularly Orkney, at which the company's ships

[1] See pp. 47-8   [2] See p. 240

made their last call on the voyage out) that it was referred to by
Henry Dundas as "a collection of douce Scottish gentlemen".
Little did he know of the toughness required to withstand Canadian weather, the bloodthirsty attacks of Red Indians, the perils
of voyaging by canoes down uncharted rivers and of blazing a
trail through primeval forest, not to mention the bitter enmity of
rival companies, also run by Scotsmen. Some of the Scottish fur-
traders explored the virgin territories to the north and west, as is
revealed by the names of these areas today. The MacKenzie

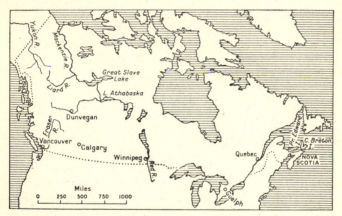

The Scots in Canada

River recalls the greatest explorer of Canada, Sir ALEXANDER
MacKENZIE (1763-1820), who was born in Stornoway and who
was appointed in 1787 as fur-trader at the most remote trading-
post of his company on Lake Athabaska. In 1789, with a party of
twelve French Canadians and Indians and three canoes, he
travelled by the Great Slave Lake down the river which bears
his name to the Arctic Ocean, returning to his trading-post after
breathless adventures and severe hardships. Not satisfied merely
with this achievement, in 1793 he crossed the Rockies and reached
the Pacific Ocean, the first man to do so from Eastern Canada.

He had previously set himself to study astronomy to assist him in exploration. For sheer physical endurance in the face of extremes of heat and cold, leadership in adverse circumstances and the successful execution of his plans, MacKenzie must be counted among the greatest explorers of history. After some years in fur-trading, MacKenzie became a member of parliament and ultimately returned to Scotland. Another fur-trader, SIMON FRASER, son of Scottish Catholic parents who had emigrated to the United States, explored the course of the river which now bears his name, passing successfully the terrible rapids on it. Other Scotsmen who opened up new territory in North-west Canada for the fur-trading companies were John MacLeod, the explorer of the river Liard, and Robert Campbell, the explorer of the Yukon.

Scottish Settlers.—Thomas Douglas, EARL OF SELKIRK (1771-1820), of St. Mary's Isle, Kirkcudbrightshire, was a man of different calibre from these fur-traders. He was genuinely interested in helping emigrants to settle in the prairie lands of Canada and had a bitter struggle with his fellow-countrymen in the fur-trading companies. Although his RED RIVER SETTLEMENT seemed to be a failure and he died broken-hearted, he laid the foundations of ordinary settlements in Winnipeg and Manitoba as distinct from fur-trading. Another, but successful, attempt at colonization was made soon after the death of the Earl of Selkirk by JOHN GALT (1779-1839), who became secretary of the Canada Company in 1826. Born at Irvine and educated in Greenock, he had already won great praise for his admirable sketches of Scottish life, like the *Annals of the Parish* and *The Provost*. In 1827 he founded the town of Guelph in the centre of a rich farming area, and he also opened up the surrounding country with roads, one of which led for a hundred miles through thick forest from Lake Ontario to Lake Huron. But Galt, like the Earl of Selkirk, aroused the jealousy of his countrymen in Canada, a clique of Scottish gentry known as the "Family Compact", and he was recalled after a year.

Canadian Politics.—While the settlers in the prairies and backwoods were busy with the heavy work that falls to the lot of the pioneer, the politicians of Canada were engaged in incessant wrangling and intrigue. Pitt's act of 1791 had divided the colony into two parts—Upper Canada (Ontario) being British and Lower Canada (Quebec) being French. The attempts of the British Assembly in Upper Canada and of the French Assembly in Lower Canada to gain some control of the government were frustrated by the British governors and the Scottish clique, the "Family Compact". In 1837, the discontent flared up into half-hearted rebellions. The leader in Upper Canada was WILLIAM LYON MacKENZIE (1795-1861), who had emigrated from his native Dundee in 1826 and achieved notoriety with his newspaper, the *Colonial Advocate*. He conducted a fanatical campaign against the governor and his clique, and was four times expelled from the Assembly, only to be re-elected. MacKenzie's rising faded out after an exchange of shots and he fled across the border to the United States. In Lower Canada, Joseph Papineau, the leader of the French nationalist movement, also started a rising which proved a fiasco. News of the dissatisfaction in Canada, however, roused the British government to action, and the EARL OF DURHAM ("Radical Jack") was sent out in 1838 to conduct an inquiry. As a result of the famous Durham Report (1839), Lord Melbourne's ministry decided to unite Upper and Lower Canada and grant the inhabitants responsible government.

Dominion of Canada.—The success of the Canadian Act of Union (1840), which paved the way for other British colonies, was in large measure due to two Scotsmen, the EARL OF ELGIN (1811-63), Lord Durham's son-in-law, whose tact and sympathy as Governor of Canada from 1846 to 1854 won the support of both French and British, and Sir JOHN A. MacDONALD (1815-91), who had been born in Glasgow, where his parents had settled temporarily after being evicted from their home at Lairg in the Sutherland clearances.[1] MacDonald, who was an adroit politician, was the chief architect of the Dominion of Canada brought into being by the British North America Act of 1867. Sir John, as he latterly became, was its first Prime Minister and by his promise of a Canadian Pacific Railway, he persuaded British Columbia to join the Dominion in 1869. It was no easy task for MacDonald to implement his promise, as many obstacles were put in his way;

[1] See pp. 48-9

but, at last, in 1885 the last spike in the railway was driven in at Craigellachie by Donald Smith, later LORD STRATHCONA, a native of Archiestown in Moray, who had been chiefly responsible for

By courtesy of the Canadian Army Liaison Establishment
This picture of Pipe Major William MacInnis of Kentville, Nova Scotia, shows the strong Scottish tradition in the Canadian army.

its construction. The C.P.R., which links the Atlantic with the Pacific Oceans, opened the prairies to settlers. It was mainly the creation of Scotsmen and its western terminus is, appropriately enough, Vancouver, where Alexander MacKenzie, who blazed the trail westward, reached the Pacific in 1793. Sir John Mac-

Donald died in 1891, after almost twenty years as Conservative Prime Minister, and was mourned by all Canada. He has been called "one of the greatest of Empire-builders and imperial statesmen". He helped to achieve the independence of Canada from Britain while still maintaining the loyalty to the mother-country and to him must be given the main credit for trans-forming Canada from a backward country, divided against itself, into a prosperous dominion. Canada, with all its past links with Scotland, is still the most Scottish of all the dominions. In the two world wars the Canadian Scottish regiments have acquitted themselves bravely. Scotsmen or the descendants of Scotsmen are still to the fore in Canada. The outstanding Prime Minister of this century has been WILLIAM LYON MACKENZIE KING, the grandson of the rebel, Lyon MacKenzie, and Liberal Prime Minister for over twenty years.

New South Wales.—Captain James Cook, on the first of his three great voyages, had claimed the south-east coast of Australia for Britain and named it New South Wales. (Two other examples of his "christening" of places, New Caledonia and New Hebrides, may have been connected with the fact that, although he was born in Yorkshire, his parents were Scottish.) In 1788, nine years after Cook's death, a settlement of 717 convicts, 183 of them women, was established at Port Jackson, some miles from Botany Bay, originally intended as the site but found to be unsuitable. (The name, nevertheless, was invariably applied to the penal settlement at Port Jackson, which was in time to become Sydney.) Not all the early convicts were of the criminal type. Some might have committed minor offences such as poaching, then punished in England by transportation, while others were political offen-ders; for example, Thomas Muir was transported there in 1793, only to be rescued by an American warship three years later.[1] Some of the earlier colonists in New South Wales were drawn from the soldiers sent out to guard the convicts. Australia's most important industry, sheep-farming, was started by one of these retired officers, JOHN MACARTHUR (1767-1834), born in England of Scottish parents. In 1794 he started his experiments in sheep-breeding, crossing Irish and Indian sheep and even introducing

[1] See p. 116

Spanish merino sheep from England, until at length he was able to produce fine wool. MacArthur had a quarrel with one of the Governors of the colony, William Bligh, whose overbearing conduct as captain of the *Bounty* led to the famous mutiny. There was much that was wrong with the young colony (rum-drinking was far too common and for many years rum was the medium of barter there) but Bligh's temper and tyrannical treatment of his opponents did not improve matters. His successor, Lachlan MacQuarie, Governor from 1809 to 1821, one of the ancient family that owned the small island of Ulva off Mull, was of a different type from Bligh, firm when necessary but humane and enlightened. He also had trouble with some of the free colonists, however, because of his policy of treating the "emancipists" or ex-convicts as ordinary citizens, even promoting them to official posts and inviting them to social functions at Government House. It was MacQuarie who gave the colony of New South Wales a respectable name so that settlers were no longer deterred from emigrating there. During his period of office, three Englishmen, Blaxland, Lawson and Wentworth, managed to break through the rocky western barrier of the Blue Mountains; beyond them they discovered marvellous pastures and the rivers to which they gave the names of the Governor—Lachlan and MacQuarie, and a native name, Murrumbidgee. The Governor who succeeded MacQuarie was another Scot, a native of Ayrshire, Sir Thomas Brisbane, after whom the capital of Queensland is named. During his rule, there was almost a sheep-farming mania in the colony. MacArthur, by that time a wealthy man, had started another important Australian industry, that of wine-making, planting his first vineyard in 1817. In the creation of what was to be one of Britain's most prosperous colonies, MacArthur and MacQuarie undoubtedly played the most outstanding parts.

Australian Exploration.—In the opening up of the continent after this time English and Scottish explorers shared most of the honours. New pasture lands in the north, the Darling Downs and Liverpool Plains, were discovered in 1828 by Allan Cunningham, a Scottish botanist who had come out from Kew to make a collection of plants. Young HAMILTON HUME, born in the colony of Scottish parents, was responsible for discovering the greatest river in Australia, later named the Murray River after a Scottish Governor, and for opening up the new land in the south where Melbourne was later founded. Sir THOMAS MITCHELL, a native of Craigend, Stirlingshire, was Surveyor-General of New South Wales for almost twenty years and by his well-organized expeditions brought to the knowledge of settlers the rich lands beside the Murray, Darling and Glenelg rivers, where the soil, he said, "was, as far as I can see, the finest imaginable, either for sheep and cattle or for cultivation". One of his last expeditions, in 1845, was for the purpose of reaching the Gulf of Carpentaria from Sydney but he failed. The first crossing of the continent from south to north was made from Melbourne by two Irishmen, R. O. Burke and W. J. Wills in 1860, but they died on the return journey across a barren wilderness. The second crossing was made in 1862 from Adelaide to Port Darwin, after two unsuccessful attempts, by JOHN MacDOWALL STUART, born in Dysart in 1815. He had accompanied Charles Sturt, the explorer of the Darling and the Murray rivers, on his expedition into Central Australia during which they were compelled to remain for six months beside the only well for miles around, under a glaring sun, until rain at last came to their rescue. Stuart never recovered from his severe privations, dying in England in 1869. Through his efforts, the Northern Territory was annexed, and along the route he pioneered, the telegraph cable was laid from the south to the north of Australia, to link up with that to Britain. When John Forrest, an Australian-born Scot, crossed the continent from west to east in 1874, the main physical features of Australian geography may be said to have at last been discovered. Although never very numerous in Australia, Scotsmen had taken a large part in the process of opening up the continent.

Commonwealth of Australia.—Not long after transportation to New South Wales was stopped in 1840, the colony was given a form of representative government and soon it was benefiting from the success of Lord Elgin's experiments in Canada. In

1855 responsible government was established with a two-chamber parliament and a ministry responsible to the lower house, the first Prime Minister being Sir STUART ALEXANDER DONALDSON, who, as his name testifies, was of Scottish origin. Later on in the century, the great champion of Australian federation was the Prime Minister of New South Wales, a Scottish lawyer, GEORGE HOUSTON REID, born at Johnstone, Renfrewshire, in 1845; and in 1901, the Commonwealth of Australia was inaugurated by a Scottish Governor-General, the Earl of Hopetoun, later MARQUIS OF LINLITHGOW. In Queensland, two Scottish premiers gained distinction in very different ways. It was Sir THOMAS MACIL-WRAITH, born at Ayr in 1835, who daringly annexed the eastern portion of New Guinea against the wishes of the British Government. The first Labour Government in Australia (and in the British Empire) was formed in Queensland in 1899 by a Scotsman, ANDERSON DAWSON. In still another respect, a Scotsman made a valuable contribution to Australian life. JAMES HARRISON, a journalist, made the earliest experiments in refrigeration of meat in Australia and the first cargo of frozen mutton was taken successfully to England in 1880 by the *Strathleven*, built on the Clyde and with refrigerating plant made by Clyde engineers on the principles of Harrison. Unfortunately, sheep-farming in Scotland was thereby struck a blow from which it took a long time to recover.

New Zealand.—In the early colonization of New Zealand Scotsmen took little part except for the activities of Presbyterian missionaries among the natives. In 1848, however, there arrived at Otago in South Island two ships with settlers to found a Scottish colony there. The leaders were Captain WILLIAM CARGILL, a veteran of the Peninsular War, and the Rev. THOMAS BURNS, a nephew of the poet, both strong Free Churchmen who had left the Established Church of Scotland at the Disruption of 1843. In Otago they founded a Scottish town, giving it the Gaelic name for Edinburgh—Dunedin. The colony grew slowly at first, the town of Invercargill being founded in 1857; but in 1861 gold was discovered in it and, as a result of the "gold rush" that ensued, the markedly Scottish character of the colony became less obvious. It was Scottish inspiration and enthusiasm, however, which led to the founding in 1869 of the University of Otago in Dunedin, the first in New Zealand. The Scots, as in Australia, carried out exploration, particularly of the difficult west-coast portion of South Island, and there are many names,

By courtesy of the High Commissioner for New Zealand
Pipe Bands Championships, Dunedin, New Zealand

in addition to Dunedin and Invercargill, as evidence of the strong Scottish element in New Zealand, e.g., Little Paisley, Oban, Clutha, Ben Nevis, Ben Lomond and Port Chalmers, from where in 1882 two Scotsmen, Davidson and Brydon, started the frozen meat trade which was to make Canterbury lamb so familiar to British housewives.

The Dark Continent.—The vastness of Africa, its torrid climate, its deserts and scarcely penetrable jungles, its warlike tribes and, not least, the opposition of those engaged in the slave trade combined to delay the opening up of the continent until comparatively modern times. As far back as 1768, the first journey of exploration was undertaken by a Scotsman, one of the many who have contributed to our knowledge of "Darkest Africa". JAMES BRUCE (1730-94), "the tallest man you ever saw gratis", was born at Kinnaird House in Stirlingshire, and, after studying at Edinburgh University, he became first a wine-merchant in London, then consul in Algiers. His journeys to Abyssinia between 1768 and 1773, during which he not only achieved his great ambition of discovering the source of the Blue Nile but also acted for a time as local governor, he described in his book, *Travels to Discover the Source of the Nile*. Unfortunately it met with a very critical reception, but since then many of the strange facts which Bruce "the Abyssinian" recorded have been found to be true. The year after Bruce's death, another Scotsman, MUNGO PARK, set off to explore the great river on the other side of Africa, the Niger. Park, who was born at Foulshiels near Selkirk in 1771, was tall and handsome, a man of splendid physique, and had qualified as a surgeon at Edinburgh University. He reached the Niger, the first white man to do so, but suffered great hardships, being more than once attacked by robbers; he would have died from fever were it not for the kindness of a negro merchant in whose house he lay ill for nearly seven months. On his return to Scotland in 1797, he published an account of his adventures, married and settled down as a surgeon in Peebles. But the urge to explore was irresistible and in 1805 he undertook another journey, this time with the backing of the Government. All the members of his expedition except one slave died or were killed. Park's journals and letters were to be an inspiration to later travellers who made attempts to discover the source of the Niger. One of the first was that commanded by Captain HUGH CLAPPERTON (1788-1827), a native of Annan in Dumfries-shire, who with his party discovered Lake Chad in 1823. Three years later, ALEXANDER GORDON LAING (1793-1826), an army officer who had been born in Edinburgh, led another expedition to find the source of the Niger and managed to reach Timbuktu, only to be murdered on the return journey. The conquest of the Niger was made finally by steamer. MACGREGOR LAIRD (1808-

61), a native of Greenock and a son of the founder of the well-known shipbuilding firm at Birkenhead, made an unsuccessful attempt with the Englishman, Lander, and later, after he had founded the African Steamship Company, equipped an expedition which finally reached the source in 1854. Its commander, an Orcadian, WILLIAM BAIKIE (1825-64), was at first the surgeon and naturalist of the expedition; after the wreck of the ship, he settled down among the natives, constructed roads, acted as doctor, translated parts of the Bible into the native language and opened up the region for commerce. It was the work of these men that led to the formation of the United Africa Company and the later colony of Nigeria.

Scottish Missionaries.—In West Africa, trade and the Bible went together: in South Africa, more often than not, they clashed. Even before the annexation of Cape Colony by the British during the Napoleonic Wars, there were already missionaries from the London Missionary Society at work in South Africa, a number of them being Scotsmen despite the name of the society. The desire of the missionaries to treat the Hottentots and other negroes on an equal footing with white men caused trouble with the Boers or Dutch farmers in the colony. The missionaries, too, did not view favourably further white expansion northwards and hoped to create independent self-governing Christian states among the native African races. The leader of the missionaries, the Rev. JOHN PHILIP (1775-1831), a native of Kirkcaldy and a Congregational minister, campaigned vigorously for the emancipation of the Hottentots and Bushmen, and in 1828 they were granted equality before the law. His efforts were warmly supported by the Churches at home, where foreign missions began to have a strong appeal. In those days, before the "Scramble for Africa" had developed, both the popular and the official attitudes were that the white men should be the guardian of the backward negroes and that the possession of colonies was a kind of sacred trust, "the white man's burden", as it was called. There is little doubt that the missionaries, among whom the Scots were most prominent, influenced public opinion very strongly in this respect, and John Philip may be considered as one of the creators of our modern colonial policy. The passing of the act abolishing slavery in 1833 combined with land-hunger among the Boers to make them decide to quit the colony and in 1836 they set off on their "Great Trek"; but British-Dutch rivalry lasted for the rest of the

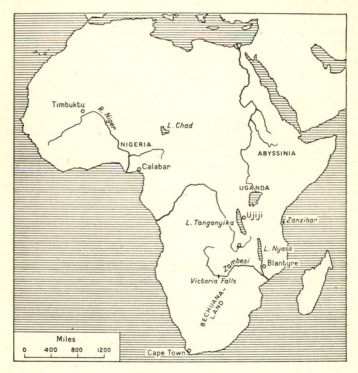

The Scots in Africa

century. Working quietly among the natives of Bechuanaland during these troubled times in Cape Colony was another Scotsman in the London Missionary Society, ROBERT MOFFAT (1795-83), born at Ormiston in East Lothian. He had been a gardener until he was twenty years of age, when he volunteered for mission work. During his long stay in Bechuanaland (1826-70) he acted not only as missionary but as farmer, engineer and translator of the Bible and *Pilgrim's Progress*. His mission-stations with their beautiful gardens became the centres of a Christian population; it was Khama, chief of the Bamangwato tribe in Bechuanaland, who visited Britain in 1895 to petition for the prohibition of alcoholic liquors in his land. Moffat's daughter, Mary, married David Livingstone, whose record as an explorer made him outstanding among Scotsmen in Africa. But there were many others who can only be briefly mentioned here but who are very highly honoured in the countries where they laboured—Robert Laws of Livingstonia, who did much to suppress the slave trade in Nyasaland; James Stewart, whose mission at Lovedale in Cape Colony trained teachers for native schools; Alexander MacKay of Uganda; Hope Waddell of Calabar; and the Dundee mill-girl, Mary Slessor of Calabar, a quiet, fearless woman who was actually appointed as a magistrate by the first Governor of Nigeria.

David Livingstone.—David Livingstone (1813-73) was born in Blantyre, Lanarkshire, in a tenement called Shuttle Row, in which twenty-four families each occupied one apartment. David's father, Neil, who had left his native island of Ulva as a boy, was a tea-merchant in a small way, travelling from door to door, and in so doing often took the opportunity to distribute religious tracts; for he was keenly religious, a Sunday School teacher and a total abstainer. Young David left school at the age of ten and until he was twenty-four worked in the cotton-mill at Blantyre, his hours lasting from 6 a.m. to 8 p.m. with brief intervals for meals. After the day's work, David and the other children had to attend school for two hours and there he learned to read Latin. So keen was he to study that it is said he would prop up his Latin grammar (Ruddiman's *Rudiments*) on the machine while at work. When he was about twenty years of age he decided to become a medical missionary. He studied first of all at the "Andersonian" University in Glasgow[1] and then at London, qualifying as a doctor and being ordained as a missionary by the London Missionary Society. He arrived in Cape Colony in 1841 and served for some years in Bechuanaland missions,

[1] See p. 258

marrying Robert Moffat's daughter, Mary, in 1844. On one occasion he was mauled so badly by a wounded lion that he never afterwards had the proper use of his left arm. Desiring to establish missions under native Christians, he set off in 1849 on a series of journeys to the north, crossing the Kalahari desert and discovering Lake Ngami. On one of his journeys, accompanied by his family, he penetrated still further north beyond the regions known to white men. It was in 1857 he first saw the Zambesi River and at once realized its importance. He felt that the evil slave trade could only be broken by starting other kinds of trade, and that meant opening up new routes from the centre of Africa to the sea. His first great journey of exploration with this end in view occupied from June 1852 to May 1856; during these many months of hardships, sickness and danger he crossed Africa from west to east, one of his many discoveries being that of the falls on the Zambesi which he named Victoria Falls. He was given a most enthusiastic reception on his visit to Britain after this expedition and his book, *Missionary Travels*, was widely read. Returning to Africa, he set out in 1858 on a second expedition, financed by the Government, and in the next five years carried out further explorations in the Zambesi regions and in the Shire, discovering Lakes Shirwa and Nyasa. Wherever he went, he quickly gained the confidence of the natives. He was appalled by the extent of the slave traffic; he later found that 19,000 negroes were sold annually by the Arab slave-traders at Zanzibar, while the Portuguese had almost as extensive a trade. His wife died in 1862 and, to add to his grief, his expedition was recalled in the following year. After another visit to Britain he returned to Africa for his third and last great expedition, again with Government support, this time to discover the source of the Nile. From 1866 to 1871 he was lost to the world, wandering about from Lake Nyasa to Lake Tanganyika, making valuable discoveries and observations, but all the time becoming weaker through recurrent illness. He was found worn out at Ujiji by H. M. Stanley, who had been sent out on a relief expedition by the *New York Herald* and who, after months of searching, finally greeted the lost explorer with "Dr Livingstone, I presume?"

Feeling that his duty was to remain, Livingstone declined Stanley's invitation to accompany him home; and on the morning of 1st May 1873 his servants found him dead, kneeling as if in prayer. Their devotion to him was so great that they carried his embalmed body to the coast, taking nine months over the 1,500 miles. At the simple service in Westminster Abbey, where his remains were buried, there were few left unmoved as the vast congregation sang his favourite second paraphrase, "O God of Bethel". Livingstone's fortitude, his perseverance, his strong sense of duty to God and his fellow-men, black and white, have made him a hero, not only of the Scots but of many other nations.

East India Company.—The whole of this book would be needed to give an adequate account of the achievements of the Scots in India, first in the East India Company (which although originally an English concern received many Scottish recruits from the time when Dundas was the leading member of the India Board of Control)[1] and later in the Indian Civil Service and the Indian Army. The number of Scottish names in Buckland's *Dictionary of Indian Biography* is some indication of their work in India; there are seventeen Grants, thirteen Stewarts, ten MacPhersons and many other Scottish names, Lowland and Highland. Not all of them played honourable parts; there were too many opportunities for intrigue and corruption in the East India Company. One of the MacPhersons mentioned was Sir John MacPherson, Governor-General in 1785-86 after the return of Warren Hastings to England; his vacillating methods earned him the sobriquet of "Johnny MacShuffle". During the French wars (1793-1815) British rule was extended over a great part of India, mainly due to the vigorous policy of the Marquis of Wellesley. In addition, valuable possessions elsewhere were picked up, as was the usual British custom, for use as bargaining counters at the peace negotiations. The almost bloodless annexation in 1796 of Ceylon from the Dutch was the result of the clever scheming of a St. Andrews professor, HUGH CLEGHORN; and it was the EARL OF MINTO, Governor-General in 1806-14, who was responsible for the acquisition of the islands of Mauritius and Java, although the latter was handed back to the Dutch

[1] See p. 109

in 1815. The chief credit for the remarkably peaceful development of the newly annexed lands and the consolidation of the older conquests was shared by four men—Sir Thomas Munro, Sir John Malcolm, Mountstuart Elphinstone and Charles Metcalfe, of whom the first three were Scotsmen. They believed that in making laws the British should respect Indian customs and traditions and that they should encourage the Indians by giving them positions of responsibility. The corrupt province of Madras was reorganized by Sir THOMAS MUNRO (1761-1827), a native of Glasgow who has been called "perhaps the wisest of Anglo-Indian statesmen" and who served the East India Company as soldier and administrator for nearly fifty years. It should be remembered that it was at the time when reaction was rampant at home that Munro and the other three were stressing the interests of the native population and laying the foundations of responsible government.

Westernization of India.—Scotsmen also took a leading part in introducing to India western education and culture. Although there are many today who regard this policy as unfortunate, there is little doubt of its importance: Indians who studied the political history of Britain could hardly fail to draw therefrom lessons that were most inconvenient to the British in India. Most of the schools set up at first were connected with missionary work. The first Scottish missionary of note in India was ALEXANDER DUFF, who was born near Pitlochry in 1806 and who arrived in Calcutta in 1829 after being shipwrecked twice on the way. One of his first steps was to open a school for Indians who would be taught through the medium of English. Calcutta through the jute trade with Dundee developed a strong Scottish connection. The rivalry between the Christian missions there led to the Scottish church being built with a steeple to overtop not only the Anglican cathedral but also all the other buildings in the city. Lord Macaulay (whose grandfather and great-grandfather had been Presbyterian ministers in the Outer Hebrides) did much to further the use of the English language in India by recommending in 1835 its adoption in state-aided schools. The idea that India was bound to benefit from the introduction of western civilization was at the core of the policy of the Scottish Governor-General, the EARL OF DALHOUSIE (1812-60), who in a brief rule of seven years annexed more territories, constructed railways, telegraphs, roads and canals, and encouraged forestry, agriculture, irrigation and mining. He took vigorous action in suppressing the social evils of India—suttee, thuggee, female infanticide and the slave trade, helped education with state subsidies and always strove to place the Indian on an equal footing with the European. His energetic methods, however, have been blamed for causing resentment which smouldered on after he left India and burst forth into flame in the Indian Mutiny of 1857.

Fighting Men.—You have read in the chapter, "The French Revolution and Napoleon", of Sir David Baird, the victor of Seringapatam (1799), at which Tipoo Sahib was defeated and killed.[1] Scottish regiments, it is estimated, formed at least half of the European forces during the wars against Hyder Ali and his son, Tipoo Sahib, although, as they lost at first a high proportion of their men from disease on the voyage out to India and on service there, one general asked the War Office not to send any more. At Sir Arthur Wellesley's first great Indian victory at Assaye (1803), where a French-trained army eight times larger than his own was defeated, two of the three regiments engaged were Scottish—the 74th and 78th Highlanders. (The elephant in the badge of the H.L.I. and the inscription "Assaye" commemorate its distinguished Indian service.) Scotsmen were also involved in what has been called the most complete and humiliating disaster that ever befell the British in the East. In the first Afghan War (1839-42), which originated in an attempt to bring Afghanistan under British control, the British envoy and his chief agent, who were both assassinated, were Scots; a Scottish general was also in charge of the army that was almost annihilated, one of the survivors being a Scottish doctor, William Brydon, who escaped by the Khyber Pass into India. The barefaced annexation of Sind in 1843 was accomplished by Sir CHARLES NAPIER (one of the celebrated Scottish family of that name) who himself described it as "a very advantageous, useful, humane piece of rascality"; *Punch* suggested for him a concise Latin

[1] See p. 119

summing-up of the expedition—*Peccavi*. In the suppression of the Indian Mutiny in 1857-58, the 78th or Ross-shire Buffs earned the title of "Saviours of India", eight V.C.s being awarded. The commander-in-chief of the British forces in the Indian Mutiny campaign was Sir Colin Campbell, later Lord Clyde (1792-1863). The son of a Glasgow carpenter, MacLiver, he assumed his mother's name, Campbell, for the sake of her brother, who gave him his education. Although he won great praise for his actions in India and particularly for the relief of Lucknow, he is best remembered for the part he played in the Crimean War (1854-55) in which he commanded the Highland Brigade, being almost the only British general who came out of the war with any credit. It was his battalions which stormed the heights of the Alma; at the critical moment when it seemed as if the British attack would have to be called off, he announced, "Highlanders never retire." Later, at Balaclava, under his leadership, the 93rd (Sutherland) Highlanders, "the thin red line of Balaclava", withstood the fierce assault of the Russian cavalry.

Scottish Regiments.—Apart from the Crimean War, the fighting of the British Army between 1815 and 1914 was all in colonial wars—in India, in Africa and in the Far East; and in victory and defeat, in the excitement of campaigns and in the monotony of occupation, both Scottish generals and Scottish soldiers have participated, as is testified by the battle honours of their regiments. Thus, of the Scots overseas in the nineteenth century, a considerable number have been those in the Army. In 1871 the reorganization of the Army was begun by Cardwell and ten years later infantry regiments ceased to be known by their numerical titles, which indicated their seniority according to the date of their formation. Instead, two single-battalion regiments were linked to form a two-battalion regiment with its own recruiting district. According to the Cardwell system, which prevailed till after the Second World War, one of the battalions in each regiment was on service overseas while the other battalion remained at home. Among the exceptions to the linking rule were those regiments which had numbers from 1st to 25th—the 1st Foot or Royal Scots, which had two battalions and was at this time given pipers again; the 21st Foot or ROYAL SCOTS FUSILIERS, in which Sir Winston Churchill served in the First World War; the 25th Foot or Edinburgh Regiment, which almost became the York Regiment, King's Own Borderers, but which after protests was named the KING'S OWN SCOTTISH BORDERERS. The 42nd Foot, having two battalions, retained its old name of the BLACK WATCH, and the 79th Foot or Cameron Highlanders also escaped linking with another regiment because of Queen Victoria's special interest, hence the name QUEEN'S OWN CAMERON HIGHLANDERS. Of those regiments that were linked, the 26th Foot or Cameronians amalgamated with the 90th Foot or Perthshire Light Infantry and are now the CAMERONIANS (SCOTTISH RIFLES); the 71st and 74th Highlanders became the HIGHLAND LIGHT INFANTRY; the 75th Stirlingshire Regiment was united with the 92nd Highlanders to form the GORDON HIGHLANDERS; and the 91st Argyll and the 93rd Sutherland Highlanders became the 1st and 2nd battalions of the ARGYLL AND SUTHERLAND HIGH-LANDERS. Some Lowland regiments lost their identity at this time. The 99th Lanarkshire became the 2nd battalion of the Wiltshire Regiment, and the 94th (formed out of the old Scots Brigade in Holland) the 2nd Connaught Rangers. By 1881, Scottish regiments had long since ceased to have mainly Scottish personnel. These were the days, however, when the tartan and the bagpipes were considered worth preserving as attractions for recruits. By the end of the century khaki was the colour for active service and the kilt is now retained for ceremonial parades or for walking out only. In addition to the above infantry regiments, there were the SCOTS GUARDS and a regiment of heavy cavalry, the ROYAL SCOTS GREYS (called the Royal North British Dragoons up to 1857). Yeomanry regiments of mounted volunteers also existed, e.g., the Lanarkshire Yeomanry, the Lovat Scouts, the Scottish Horse, the Ayrshire Yeomanry; after 1907 Territorial Army battalions were also created for most of the infantry regiments.

Empire-Builders.—Soldiers, explorers, missionaries, adminis-trators, statesmen—the list of distinguished Scots whose careers took them overseas has been a lengthy one and could be extended considerably. There were many other Scots whose lives were spent much more quietly—in backwoods settlements, on the prairies, in business firms in New York or Calcutta, and in a thousand and one other occupations. History too often selects the interesting and exciting episode and ignores the dull routine which is the common lot. The parts played by the ordinary Scotsmen overseas it is almost impossible to estimate. In this chapter you have been reading about the emigrants of the eighteenth and nineteenth centuries; but the flow of emigration has not yet dried up. Between 1901 and 1931 the population of Scotland increased from 4,479,104 to 4,842,980, that is, by 363,876. During the same period, however, over 884,000 emigrated from Scotland.[1] There has been almost constant emigration from Scotland for the last two centuries and by inter-marriage with men and women of other races the number of people overseas with Scottish blood in their veins must run into several millions. Not always is the present name an indication; Juan Domingo Peron, ex-President of Argentina, claimed to have a grandmother named MacKenzie. But naturally it is the British dominions and colonies that contain most of the Scottish race or their descendants, whose pride in their homeland is shown in the numerous Caledonian Societies, St. Andrew's Societies and Burns Clubs overseas. Some may regret that so many of Scotland's most able sons and daughters have left her shores, but what has been Scotland's loss has been other countries' gain.

SOURCE EXTRACT

Blantyre Works,
April 26th, 1838

"Revd. Sir,
    It occurred to me some months ago that I ought to state some particulars to you relative to my son David Livingstone, whose application is under your consideration in the hope that however unimportant the statements may be in themselves, they may assist you in coming to a decision regarding him.
    When he was about 13 years of age he asked me if I would allow

[1] See p. 309

him to learn Latin, our village schoolmaster being at that time commencing a class. Although we were in very humble circumstances I consented, not knowing what might be the design of the Most High respecting him; he had to work in the factory 12 hours a day, yet managed to keep at the top of his class while it existed. . . .

When he first mentioned to me his design of attending the University in order to study medicine I was much opposed to it, until he informed me that it was not to gain a livelihood he thought of doing so, his anxious wish was to be enabled to spend his life in the service of our Redeemer among the heathen; I no longer felt inclined to oppose his design, but felt thankful that such a thought was in his heart. . . ."

From the letter of Neil Livingstone to the Secretary of the London Missionary Society

EXERCISES

1. Write a sentence about each of the following Scotsmen: Sir Samuel Greig, Edvard Grieg, Andrew Carnegie, Sir Alexander MacKenzie, Earl of Selkirk, John Galt, William Lyon MacKenzie, Sir John A. MacDonald, John MacArthur, Lachlan MacQuarie, John MacDowall Stuart, James Bruce, Mungo Park, Robert Moffat, William Baikie, Rev. John Philip, Sir Thomas Munro.

2. In what way are Scots connected with the following places? Glengarry (Ontario), Great Slave Lake, Brisbane, Dunedin, Ceylon, Khyber Pass.

3. Explain the following: (a) "A collection of douce Scottish gentlemen"; (b) "Family Compact"; (c) "The tallest man you ever saw gratis"; (d) "The white man's burden"; (e) "Dr Livingstone, I presume?"; (f) "Peccavi".

4. Write a biography of David Livingstone.

5. Find out more about the careers of the Marquis of Dalhousie, Sir John A. MacDonald and Andrew Carnegie and write a short biography of each of them.

6. Find out from the *Dictionary of National Biography* or an encyclopaedia details of any Scot of your name whose career was mainly overseas.

7. Find out from a gazetteer how many other towns in the world have the same name as your own town or village.

8. Give an account of the infantry regiment whose headquarters are situated nearest to your school, mentioning the date of the formation of its battalions, their former names or numbers, their battle honours, etc.

CHAPTER XVIII

LEISURE TIME

Holidays.—Two hundred years ago the poorer classes had little time for leisure, and fifty years later, as the factory system developed, they had less. Saturday half-holidays came only late in the nineteenth century and Sunday was even then definitely a day of rest, when amusements or games were strictly forbidden. Fastern's E'en, Beltane, Hallowe'en, Hogmanay and New Year's Day remained for a long time rural festivals,[1] and the last three are still enjoyed as occasions for merry-making all over Scotland. The great cattle fairs like Falkirk Tryst were for many country people the big events of the year. In addition to the drovers and dealers, crowds thronged the fair ground, where at the stalls cheapjacks traded shoddy goods and at the whisky-tents drams were purveyed.[2] About 1800, Aikey Fair in Buchan attracted about 10,000 persons from the surrounding countryside, all decked out in their Sunday "braws", and sampling the wares of the stalls. In the towns the fairs had generally ceased to be markets. The Glasgow Fair over a hundred years ago was for some of the men a week's drinking orgy. On Glasgow Green were congregated circuses, collections of wild beasts, penny "geggies" (theatricals), waxworks, barefist boxers, fat ladies, tall men and midgets; and the din resulting from trumpets, bagpipes, drums, bells, and the shouting of showmen was such that, according to a *Glasgow Herald* writer of the time, "a thunderstorm would have passed unnoticed". In a few towns, horse-racing continued as an annual attraction, usually on May Day.

[1] See p. 20   [2] See p. 41

The traditional silver bell or small silver cup was awarded and a sum of money in addition; sometimes the horse races were run on the sands and, where suitable, a regatta for pair-oared and four-oared boats was held on the same day. The RIDING OF THE MARCHES, which at first had been regular in most burghs as a precaution against the encroachment of neighbouring landowners, continued in the nineteenth century in many of the smaller burghs as a local festival. Today, Lanimer Day at Lanark, the Common Riding at Hawick and Selkirk, and the Riding of the Marches at Linlithgow, Peebles, Lauder, Dumfries and elsewhere are still festive occasions. In the twentieth century, most workers have holidays (with pay) of a fortnight in summer and a few days at New Year. In offices and shops Christmas has also come to be regarded as a holiday, partly through the influence of English custom and the radio and partly through the encouragement of the Scottish churches, which no longer regard the observance as wrong. In addition, there are spring and autumn holidays, held "in lieu of the old fast days" at communion time, when all work ceased.

Beside the Seaside.—It was in the second half of the eighteenth century that the wealthier classes began to appreciate the health-giving properties of the seaside air. At the time when George III was helping to popularize sea-bathing in England by his annual visits to Weymouth, the Edinburgh gentry were able to indulge in the new pastime conveniently in the Forth. At Leith, a bathing-box with horse and servants could be hired in 1761 for one shilling. Helensburgh was laid out as a residential seaside resort in 1777,[1] and Dunoon, Rothesay and Largs also began to cater for summer visitors at about the same time. When the steamboat era arrived, seaside holidays became easier and cheaper. For long the Highlands were the chief counter-attraction for those who could afford a holiday with stage-coach travel. As early as 1817 there was a steamboat (belonging to David Napier)[2] on Loch Lomond and before 1850 there was at least one on almost every Scottish loch of any size—Loch Awe, Loch Ness, Loch Katrine and others. By 1850, the middle-class father might have a house at the coast, where his family would spend the summer

[1] See p. 150   [2] See pp. 152-3

months, while he himself would travel by steamboat or train daily to the city. Gradually, the working classes also began to spend the summer holiday "doon the watter" (as the Glaswegians called it) at one of the many resorts on the Firth of Clyde. An added attraction of the outings down the Clyde was the keen racing from pier to pier by rival steamers. In 1860, three vessels belonging to different companies were actually scheduled to leave the Broomielaw, Glasgow, at the same time, and similarly with the return run from Rothesay. Naturally, captains' tempers sometimes became frayed and collisions resulted. About the same time, there was fierce war between Sunday trippers and the local inhabitants of the coast towns who resented the desecration of the Sabbath by the "Sunday-breakers". At Garelochhead pier, the steamer was met on a Sunday by the proprietor, accompanied by his gamekeepers and foresters, carrying cudgels, and regular battles resulted. Towards the end of the century, similar affrays occurred at Dunoon, where the Glasgow "keelies" easily routed the ministers and their supporters. On the east coast (and in some resorts on the west coast) the seaside holiday was also a golfing holiday. On each side of the Forth there grew up holiday resorts where only sandy links or decayed harbours had been before.

Scottish Sports.—The two games which are considered most distinctively Scottish in origin (although probably both were derived from the Dutch) are golf and curling. Both were played for centuries before clubs were formed and rules drawn up for the games. The Edinburgh Burgess Club was founded in 1735; and at St. Andrews there was founded in 1754 a golfing society which became the ROYAL AND ANCIENT CLUB, whose rules were adopted by other golf clubs. In 1860 the first OPEN CHAMPION-SHIP was staged at Prestwick, the prize being a Champion Belt. One of the first champions was Tom Morris, senior, and when his son, "Young Tom", won it outright with three successive wins (1868-69-70), another trophy, a cup, was substituted for the belt. Although the "Open" is now sometimes held on English as well as Scottish courses and although the game is played almost all over the world, St. Andrews still remains the "Mecca" of golfers.

In curling, too, the rules of the game are those laid down in Scotland by the ROYAL CALEDONIAN CURLING CLUB, founded in 1838. Nowadays, since the invention of the artificial ice-rink in 1877 and the adoption of the game in countries with suitable winter climates like Canada and Switzerland, "bonspiels" (curling matches) are also played much more outside Scotland; but almost all curling-stones are made in the little village of Mauchline in Ayrshire. The game of bowls, although played from at least the Middle Ages in England and Scotland, had deteriorated by the nineteenth century as the greens were generally adjoining taverns. It was again in Scotland that the rules of the game were first formulated by the Scottish Bowling Association in 1892, and later adopted to a great extent by other national associations. Another native Scottish sport, SHINTY, was of Highland origin, although obviously similar to hockey in England and hurling in Ireland. In the eighteenth century, Highland ministers had to suppress Sunday shinty-playing but it continued to be popular; on New Year's Day it was general to have a game between neighbouring villages. Today, the Camanachd Association controls the game, which is especially popular in Inverness-shire.

English Sports.—It is from England that many of our other modern games have been introduced. CRICKET was played as early as 1790 on the College Green at Glasgow, and although Scottish weather does not favour the game, there are many clubs in all parts of Scotland except the Highlands. TENNIS is another game which depends on good weather. In its present form, lawn tennis is comparatively modern, dating only from 1874; a year after the first championships at Wimbledon, the Scottish championships were held at Edinburgh. ROWING similarly derived from England, where first at Eton, then at Oxford and Cambridge, it was established as the "manly sport" *par excellence*. As the amateur rule in rowing debarred anyone engaged in manual labour, professional rowing continued in Scotland until the formation in the twentieth century of a trades amateur association. In Scotland, races are rowed today not only in up-to-date "shells" but also in the old-fashioned "jollyboats", with fixed seats and no outriggers. By 1880, when the Saturday half holiday was

K

becoming general, many of our modern sports were thus organized with rules and with clubs in all the larger towns.

Football.—Most Scotsmen, if asked what was Scotland's national game, would reply, "Football", meaning Association Football. As far back as 1424 an act of parliament forbade the playing of football in Scotland, but it continued there, as in England, a popular game on holidays like Fastern's E'en and New Year's Day, when most of the male inhabitants of some towns engaged in a game with two or three hundred a side. It was in the English public schools and the universities that the two forms of the game were organized. The "carrying code" had its origin at Rugby school in 1823 and became popular in certain other public schools in England. "Old boys" of those schools which preferred the "dribbling game" drew up rules for the game in London in 1862 and formed the Football Association in the following year, thus giving the name ASSOCIATION FOOTBALL or "soccer", as distinct from RUGBY FOOTBALL or "rugger". The Rugby Union, which drew up new laws for the rugby game, was formed in 1871; two years later a similar SCOTTISH RUGBY UNION was founded in Scotland where the game had been introduced by "old boys" of English public schools and Scottish boarding schools. In the same year, 1873, the SCOTTISH FOOTBALL ASSOCIATION was founded to control the "dribbling game", and a competition inaugurated for the Scottish Cup, the winners being the Glasgow club, Queen's Park, which had developed out of the Young Men's Christian Association. Already, however, in the previous year, an international match had been played between Scotland and England at Kennington Oval, the entire Scottish team being members of Queen's Park and the result a goalless draw. The team formation of Queen's Park was then and for long after different from that of today: a goalkeeper, two backs, two half-backs and six forwards. Queen's Park, like all the other clubs in those early days, was a club of amateurs; today they are the only amateur club in senior football in Britain. In 1875 they were responsible for the introduction of new rules—the use of a goal bar instead of a tape, and the adoption of a fixed half-time, irrespective of the goals scored. Some of the early clubs have since then disappeared from the game, at least from senior foot-ball—St. Bernard's (Edinburgh), Vale of Leven and Renton. The last-named team (most of them from the village after which the club was named) gained the title of "Champions of the World" in 1888 when they won the Scottish Cup and thereafter defeated the English Cup winners, West Bromwich Albion. The growth of professionalism at the end of the nineteenth century adversely affected smaller Scottish clubs, which lost outstanding

Photo : T. and R. Annan

Queen's Park Football Club, 1875

players to wealthier city clubs both in Scotland and England. Some of the original Scottish clubs are still going strong. It was on Glasgow Green that Glasgow Rangers (founded in 1872) first played; now they have as their headquarters at Ibrox one of the finest stadiums in the world. Celtic, founded in 1888 for the pur-pose of raising funds for meals for poor Catholic children, has for long been the keenest rival of Rangers; unfortunately matches of the "Old Firm" have often been spoiled by "orange-and-green" hooliganism on the terracing. Scottish footballers acted as coaches in foreign countries like Czechoslovakia and Austria; but nowadays the pupils are fit to trounce their masters. It has been said that modern Scotland's heroes are the stars of the football field, and older men still recall admiringly games played by Bobby Walker (Heart of Midlothian), Jimmy Quinn (Celtic), Alan Morton (Rangers), Patsy Gallacher (Celtic) and the "Wembley Wizards" of 1928. The game, although not so universal as formerly, is played all over the country on Saturdays by seniors, juniors, juveniles, schoolboys, F.P. clubs, Boy Scouts and Boys' Brigade teams. Rugby football is generally considered the game of fee-paying schools and their former pupils' clubs; but it has a wide support in the Border counties. The rugby game also has its heroes, e.g., J. M. Bannerman, G. P. S. MacPherson and D. S. Drysdale.

Highland Gatherings.—Many other sports and games have acclimatized themselves in Scotland—hockey, ice-hockey, lacrosse, badminton, basketball, cycling. In the Highland games or gatherings Scotland has produced a sporting event with its own peculiar national appeal. As they are organized today at Aboyne, Braemar, Dunoon and elsewhere, they comprise athletic events, both field and track, and also piping and dancing competitions. Many of the competitors are in Highland dress and the Highland gatherings can be very picturesque, staged, as they are in many cases, in a setting of pine trees and heather-clad hills. They are not confined to the Highland area and the oldest meeting is said to be that of Ceres in Fife where it has been held ever since Bannockburn, while the people of Carnwath in Lanarkshire claim that their Red Hose Race (the winner of which receives a pair of hand-knitted red stockings) is the oldest foot race in Europe. At the beginning of the nineteenth century, some of these old-established meetings were organized with money prizes for a whole series of events—throwing the hammer, putting the stone, tossing the caber, wrestling, jumping and running. The BRAEMAR HIGHLAND GATHERING, which has been held regularly since 1832, was naturally patronized by Queen Victoria and became one of the social events of the Highland season. There was little specialization in sport in the nineteenth century; men

like Donald Dinnie of Aboyne or A. A. Cameron of Lochaber
at a later date were able to win prizes for half a dozen different
events. Professional athletics still survives in Scotland, mainly
because of the Highland gatherings. In 1883 the SCOTTISH

Photo: Picture Post

Tossing the Caber
(Sergt.-Major Starkey, Crieff, August, 1924)

AMATEUR ATHLETIC ASSOCIATION was founded and athletic clubs
were established for cross-country running in winter and track-
running in summer. Among Scotland's greatest athletes must be
reckoned two men who won the 400 metres at the Olympic
Games, which were revived in modern form in Athens in 1896.
These were Lieut. Wyndham Halswell of the H.L.I., who was

the victor at London in 1908 despite the obstructive tactics of
three American runners in the final, and Eric Liddell, later a
medical missionary in China, who won the title at Paris in 1924
after he had declined to turn out in the 100 metres final because
it was to be run on a Sunday.

The Open Air.—One result of the urbanization which followed the Industrial Revolution was a reaction among town-
dwellers, a movement "back to the land", not for the purpose of
farming but for recreation. As grouse-shooting and deer-stalking
developed, there was a growing danger of many areas being closed
to the public, and an association was founded in Edinburgh in
1844, becoming in time the Scottish Rights of Way Society.
It acted in defence of public rights of travelling by drove roads,
hill paths or other ways which were at one time open to public
use. The society contained a considerable number of lawyers
who were fond of walking or climbing, and, generally, the members were drawn from the middle classes. Some of the earliest
Scottish mountaineers were scientists, e.g., Professor James D.
Forbes (1809-68), the physicist and geologist who was one of the
first to scale the rocky heights of the Cuillin of Skye. Forbes
usually ascended by the easiest route, but in time there came
others who were interested not merely in reaching the summit of
a mountain but in climbing by the difficult way, by rocks, or
under difficult conditions of snow or mist. Such a man was
Sheriff Alexander Nicolson (1827-93), after whom Skye's
highest mountain, Sgurr Alasdair, is named. Snow-climbing was
practised by many who wished to gain experience for the Alps,
but the Scottish mountains also became respected for themselves.
In 1883, the Ben Nevis observatory was founded for the purpose
of taking meteorological observations over a sun-spot period, and
after the observatory closed in 1904 the tea-room at the summit
continued to give a welcome to the climbers of Britain's highest
mountain. The safety bicycle, which became popular after
1885, made cheap travel possible and more and more townsmen
began to spend their holidays not at seaside resorts but touring
at home or abroad. It was not, however, until the twentieth
century, between the two world wars, that walking for pleasure,

on the roads or over the hills, was taken up by great numbers of the people. The three youth organizations, the Boys' Brigade, founded in Glasgow by Sir William Smith in 1883, and the Boy Scouts and Girl Guides, founded by Lord Baden-Powell in 1908 and 1910 respectively, helped to give boys and girls an experience of outdoor life by their summer camps. Rambling clubs were formed by churches and various societies, and, under the guidance of a leader, followed rights-of-way over the moors. The American name "hiker", which originally was used for those who "hitch-hiked", or travelled by begging lifts from motorists or lorry-drivers, was applied to these ramblers or walkers. The Scottish Youth Hostel Association was founded to provide simple accommodation for walkers and cyclists at 1s. a night, the first hostel being opened in 1931 at Broadmeadows near Yarrow Water. As a result of these developments, many town-dwellers nowadays seek the countryside at holiday times and at week-ends, in summer and winter. Children from Glasgow and other schools are also given the opportunity of a month's course during the school session at Glenmore Lodge in the Cairngorms, where they not only study botany and geography but engage in climbing, sailing and even ski-ing.

The Fine Arts.—Leisure time is used for mental as well as for physical recreation. Literature, drama, the fine arts (music, drama, sculpture, painting, engraving)—all these have their appeal. It cannot be claimed that Scottish achievements in the sphere of the fine arts in the nineteenth and twentieth centuries have been outstanding. One reason advanced for the comparative neglect of the arts in Scotland is the long-standing puritanical tradition of the Presbyterian churches. Another reason, so far as the eighteenth century was concerned, is the lack of sufficient patrons possessed of wealth and taste. When these were present, as in the "Golden Age" of Edinburgh, Scotland produced Raeburn, who could be matched with the best in any other country at his time.[1] In the nineteenth century a Scottish school of landscape-painting was founded by Alexander Nasmyth (1758-1840), better known, however, for his portraits of Robert Burns. Among his successors was Horatio McCulloch (1805-

[1] See p. 139

67), whose romantic Highland scenes, e.g., *Glencoe* and *Misty Corries*, appealed to the current romantic tastes. Sir DAVID WILKIE (1785-1841) produced sentimental pictures of humble life, e.g. *The Penny Wedding*. The dramatic and historical type of picture was also very popular in Victorian times. Leading representatives of this school of painting were Sir WILLIAM Q. ORCHARDSON (1831-1910), whose *On Board H.M.S. Bellerophon*, *Ophelia* and many other pictures display elegant craftsmanship. His friend, JOHN PETTIE (1839-93) produced a similar type of painting, such as *Two Strings to her Bow* and *The Chieftain's Candlesticks*. A Scottish painter who anticipated the French Impressionists in his use of colour and light was WILLIAM MacTAGGART (1835-1910), born at Machrihanish in Kintyre, which he recalled in his pictures of sea and sky. At the end of the century, a number of young painters, under the leadership of W. Y. MacGREGOR (1855-1923) developed a new style, distinctive enough to merit the name of the GLASGOW SCHOOL. They delighted in a bold use of colour, and their free, vigorous painting was much admired. Of this group, E. A. Hornel, George Henry, Sir David Y. Cameron and Sir John Lavery all produced work of great merit, and they were succeeded by others equally brilliant —F. C. Cadell, Leslie Hunter, and S. J. Peploe, whose delight in colour he transmitted to his pictures of flowers, still life and scenes of Iona. In sculpture, few Scots have risen above a competent mediocrity in modern times except one of the Glasgow School, Pittendrigh MacGillivray, whose work shows a return to classical ideas. The Victorian delight in Gothic architecture led to a revival in England and Scotland which ended up with schools, railway stations and even public-houses being disguised as baronial castles. In reaction to this and as a development of the simpler, austere eighteenth-century Scottish architecture, CHARLES RENNIE MACKINTOSH (1868-1928) evolved a new functional style, and his building, the GLASGOW SCHOOL OF ART, is reckoned one of the first examples of the new functionalism in Europe. Although Glasgow was a city of commerce and industry, of dirt and slums, it could thus also claim to have contributed to the fine arts; and in its Municipal Art Galleries it gathered one of the

finest art collections in the country, to match those of the National
Gallery and the National Portrait Gallery in Edinburgh.

Poetry and Music.—To many Scots, there seems to be little
Scottish poetry after Burns and Scott; indeed, it has been said
that Burns is called "the national bard" because he is the only
one known to most Scotsmen. Yet, during the nineteenth century
there was a constant stream, almost a flood, of good and bad
songs which are still sung from concert platforms, some of them
sentimental like *Bonny Strathyre* and some of them ardently
nationalist like *Scotland Yet*. Although Gaelic is said to be a
dying language, bards in the Highlands, and more particularly
in the Hebrides, seem as numerous as ever; new songs, comic
and serious, appear each year at the *ceilidh*. The songs of the
Gael have undergone a revival, mainly due to collectors like
Marjorie Kennedy Fraser, although the settings which she has
made familiar in her *Songs of the Hebrides* have been criticized as
too sophisticated. No Scottish composer of note has appeared
unless we include in that category Hamish MacCunn (1868-1915),
a native of Greenock, the title of one of whose works, *Land of the
Mountain and the Flood*, indicates his style of music, and Francis
George Scott (b. 1880), a native of Langholm, Dumfries-shire,
whose settings of songs combine both older Scottish and modern
European idioms. The poets of the nineteenth century were not
numerous. Many of them produced their best work in dialect,
e.g., Mrs Violet Jacob in poems like her *Howe o' the Mearns* and
Dr Charles Murray in his poems of an exile in South Africa,
Hamewith. In the twentieth century, a poet of real power and
feeling with a masterly command of language arose in the person
of C. M. GRIEVE, who used the pen-name of HUGH MACDIARMID.
His beautiful early lyrics, published just after the First World
War, gave way to scathing satire in which he exposed the weak-
nesses of his countrymen and others. A fiery nationalist, he
has made a novel contribution to Scottish culture by the creation
of a synthetic Scots language, in which, gathering words from
different periods and regions, he knit them together into a
new tongue. This "LALLANS" has been adopted by many of
the younger "makars" of today, such as Douglas Young and

Sydney Goodsir Smith. Hugh MacDiarmid and his school are passionately devoted to Scotland and her cultural heritage, which they regard as being threatened by submergence in an English-dominated Britain.

Prose.—Since the death of Sir Walter Scott in 1832 there has been no Scottish novelist with a European reputation. Some of his imitators produced historical novels that were highly esteemed in their day but have not stood the test of time, the best of them being James Grant's *The Romance of War* (1846), which deals with the exploits of the Scots in the Peninsular War. ROBERT LOUIS STEVENSON comes nearest of Scott's successors to equalling his achievements. He was born in Edinburgh in 1850 and died in the Pacific island of Samoa in 1894 after some years of feeble health. In Alan Breck (*Kidnapped*) and Long John Silver (*Treasure Island*) he created two of the best-known characters of fiction; and his macabre *Dr Jekyll and Mr Hyde* has never ceased to thrill readers. Sir JAMES M. BARRIE (1860-1937) was a native of Kirriemuir, the "Thrums" of his *Auld Licht Idylls* and *A Window in Thrums*. These books, in which he depicted Scottish rural life, proved very popular but his combination of humour and pathos has not lasted well. His later work was almost all for the stage, on which he had several successes—*Quality Street, What Every Woman Knows, Mary Rose*, which are still performed regularly, while his *Peter Pan* has an ever-fresh appeal for children. Barrie's books on Thrums also produced imitators. The sentimental novels of Scottish village life, like *The Stickit Minister* of S. R. Crockett (1860-1914) and *Beside the Bonny Brier Bush* of Ian MacLaren (1850-1907) were best-sellers and earned for their authors, both ministers, and some others such as Annie S. Swan, the name of the KAILYARD SCHOOL. As an antidote to them, George Douglas Brown (1869-1902) wrote *The House with the Green Shutters*, a grim, realistic tragedy of the Scottish countryside. Two writers in the Stevensonian tradition were writing their first books at the same time as the "Kailyarders". NEIL MUNRO (1864-1930), the editor of a Glasgow evening newspaper, was the first Scottish novelist to portray the Highland character successfully, e.g., in his *John Splendid*, a historical romance of the

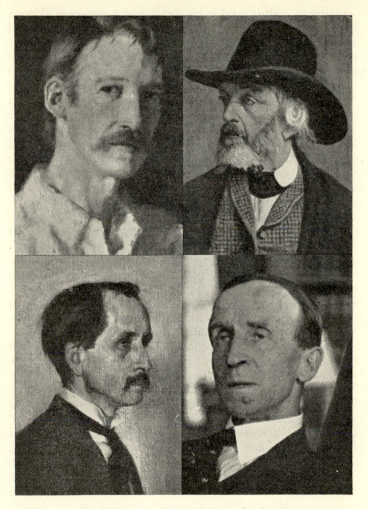

FOUR SCOTTISH PROSE WRITERS

R. L. Stevenson   Thomas Carlyle
J. M. Barrie   John Buchan

*Acknowledgements: Top Left, Top Right, Bottom Left, National Galleries of Scotland
Bottom Right, Picture Post*

seventeenth century, and in his sketches of a west-coast skipper, Para Handy. JOHN BUCHAN (1875-1940) wrote popular historical novels and modern thrillers as well as serious works of biography and history; as Lord Tweedsmuir, he was Governor-General of Canada for the last five years of his life. The quality of Scottish novel-writing in the twentieth century has been very high. Neil Gunn and Lewis Grassic Gibbon have found their inspiration in Scottish life on the Caithness coast or in the farmland of the Howe o' the Mearns. Eric Linklater and Sir Compton MacKenzie have been more cosmopolitan in their range and are alike skilful satirists of their times. Two novelists, A. J. Cronin in *Hatter's Castle* and George Blake in *Shipbuilders*, have portrayed town life in industrial Clydeside. There have been distinguished Scottish prose-writers other than novelists. THOMAS CARLYLE (1795-1881), born at Ecclefechan in Dumfries-shire, was translator, essayist, philosopher, historian and political propagandist. His *History of the French Revolution* is perhaps his best-known work, although today it is read more for its picture of Carlyle than for its account of the French Revolution. He had a great influence on his contemporaries, not least in Germany, which he greatly admired. Sir JAMES G. FRAZER (1854-1941), in his monumental *Golden Bough*, first published in 1890, helped to lay the foundations of the new studies of anthropology and sociology.

Drama.—Scotland was a backwater in the eighteenth and nineteenth centuries so far as the drama was concerned, despite the furore caused by John Home's *Douglas* as far back as 1756.[1] The opposition of the Kirk lingered into the nineteenth century long after the meetings of the General Assembly had been altered to permit the "Moderate" ministers to see Mrs Siddons.[2] In the cities, the theatres which were built generally staged English plays with English casts. The native Scottish dramatic talent flourished in the "penny geggies" (penny theatricals of the music-hall type), in stage versions of musical melodramas like *Rob Roy*, and in the pantomimes at Christmas. This was the background of the "Scotch comic", typified by Sir HARRY LAUDER (1870-1950), who with his songs and jokes presented a caricature of the drunken, close-fisted, kilted Scotsman that is to

[1] See p. 130   [2] See p. 132

be found in the humorous pages of the world's newspapers and
that, oddly enough, never fails to amuse the Scots themselves.
There was no outstanding Scottish playwright in the nineteenth
century, if we except J. M. Barrie, who wrote in England for the
English stage. It was not until the twentieth century that Scotland
produced a dramatist of distinction. JAMES BRIDIE (1885-1951),
in private life Dr O. H. Mavor, wrote *The Anatomist, Mr Bolfry*
and other plays which fail to reach the first rank only by a narrow
margin. He helped to found in Glasgow the Citizens' Theatre,
which produces not only ancient and modern masterpieces of
other nations but also new plays by Scottish authors. In the
period between the two world wars, 1918-39, Scotland became
very conscious of the theatre. Amateur groups in "Little
Theatres" and Women's Rural Institutes presented a great
variety of plays ranging from the one-act Scottish kitchen comedy
to the full-length drama of Chekhov or Strindberg. The Scottish
Community Drama Association started in 1927 an annual play
festival which had the effect of raising the standards of amateur
drama. This intense interest in the drama has been increased
rather than diminished by the cinema and broadcasting, which
provide ample opportunities for hearing and seeing new plays.
The EDINBURGH INTERNATIONAL FESTIVAL, started in 1947, has
emphasized the international and the musical aspects but it has
also revived some older Scottish plays, e.g., *The Satyre of the
Thrie Estaitis* and *The Gentle Shepherd*. The changed attitude of
the Church of Scotland is evidenced by the fact that it has its
own theatre in Edinburgh and that many churches now run their
own dramatic clubs.

Books and Newspapers.—In comparison with over a hundred
years ago, there has been a vast increase in the circulation of
newspapers and in the number of libraries and readers. Despite
the counter-attractions of radio and cinema, LIBRARIES are more
frequently used today than ever before. This is partly due to the
very much improved service offered by libraries, and partly to
the increased leisure time of the worker with his five-day week
and his wife with her labour-saving appliances in the home.
Scotland is able to boast of the first "itinerating library" in Britain;

it was started in East Lothian by Samuel Brown, Provost of Haddington, in 1817. There are now libraries in most village schools: and in some counties mobile libraries are even brought round by vans. Following the passing of the Libraries Act of 1853 free public libraries were set up in the large burghs, some of them receiving fine new buildings from the benefactions of Andrew Carnegie. For many people, however, libraries have no appeal and their only reading is in the newspapers. Scotland does not depend much on the British national dailies, except for two of them, the *Daily Express* and the *Daily Mail*, which have editions printed in Scotland. There are also six morning papers, nine evening papers and two Sunday papers produced in Scotland. The two leading newspapers, the *Glasgow Herald* (the present name of the *Glasgow Advertiser* which first appeared in 1783) and the *Scotsman* (founded in 1817 as a twice-weekly, costing 10d. a copy) have high reputations outside Scotland. The oldest Scottish newspaper is the *Aberdeen Press and Journal*, which, as the *Aberdeen Journal*, first appeared two days after the battle of Culloden in 1746. It was not until after the middle of the nineteenth century that these newspapers were published daily; the first Scottish daily paper was the Glasgow *North British Daily Mail*, which was started in 1847 but was absorbed in 1901 by the *Daily Record and Mail*. Scotland is also fortunate in its monthly and weekly press, some of the local newspapers being long-established, e.g., *Kelso Border Mail* (1779), *Ayr Advertiser* (1803) and the *Inverness Courier* (1817).

Leisure Today.—This survey of Scottish leisure time of the past two hundred years is necessarily incomplete. There are so many different ways of using leisure time; for one man it may mean the hectic pursuit of some sport, for another an hour or two with a book or an outing to the theatre, and for a third merely quietly puffing a pipe and blowing smoke-rings. Pipe-smoking has almost entirely displaced the snuff-taking of a century and a half ago; Scotland then seemed almost a nation of snuff-takers. Glasgow imported the tobacco from which the snuff was made, Mauchline in Ayrshire made the snuff-boxes or "sneeshin'-mulls" ("sneeshin'", for "sneezing", was another name for snuff)

and in tobacconists' shops in various parts of Britain you will still
see the figure of a Highlander advertising the sale of snuff. As
the pipe displaced snuff, so did the cigarette the pipe in the
second half of the nineteenth century. Today cigarette-smokers
form the vast majority of smokers, who, through the duty on
tobacco, contribute a large sum to the revenue, the figure in 1954
being over £600,000,000. Gambling, which was frowned upon
in Victorian Scotland, received a new lease of life by the introduction of greyhound-racing in the 1930's and of football pools,
which became a national craze after the Second World War.
CINEMAS became popular in the period just before the First
World War, and are still the resort of many people two or three
times a week. The film industry is largely based in the United
States, and an obvious effect of regular cinema-going, for good
or ill, has been the Americanization of outlook, manners and even
speech. Since 1922, when the British Broadcasting Company
started regular BROADCASTING from the first Scottish station,
5SC, at Glasgow, to the days when the British Broadcasting
Corporation runs three different sound programmes daily and
(since 1953) a television programme from Kirk o' Shotts, wireless
has been the greatest, and in some cases, the only cultural influence in people's lives. Listening has taken the place of reading a
book or going to the theatre or concert-hall or even to church.
But it has also had the effect of deepening the appreciation of
literature, music and the drama.

SOURCE EXTRACT

For Alasdair

Standan here on a fogg-yirdit stane,
drappan the bricht flees on the broun spate,
I'm thinkan o ye, liggan thonder your lane,
i the het Libyan sand, cauld and quate.
    The spate rins drumlie and broun,
    whummlan aathing doun.
The fowk about Inverness and Auld Aberdeen
aye likeit ye weel, for a wyce and a bonny man.

Ye were gleg at the Greekan o't and unco keen
at gowf and the lave. Nou deid i the Libyan sand.
    The spate rins drumlie and broun,
    whummlan aathing doun.
Hauldan the Germans awa frae the Suez Canal
ye dee'd. Suld this be Scotland's pride, or shame?
Siccar it is, your gallant kindly saul
maun lea thon land and tak the laigh road hame.
    The spate rins drumlie and broun,
    whummlan aathing doun.

Douglas Young

(Fogg, *moss*; yirdit, *buried*; liggan, *lying*; drumlie, *muddy*;
gleg, *keen*.)

[*Reprinted by kind permission of the author*

EXERCISES

1. Do you think the poet achieves a better effect by writing the above poem in "Lallans" than in modern English?
2. With what sports are the following associated: Tom Morris, Wembley Wizards, Donald Dinnie, Eric Liddell, Sheriff Nicolson. (Write a sentence about each of them.)
3. Write a brief account of one of the following: Royal and Ancient Club, Queen's Park F.C., Scottish Youth Hostel Association.
4. Explain the following: penny-geggie, Sunday-breakers, keelie, bonspiel, jollyboat, carrying code.
5. Write a sentence about each of the following works: *Treasure Island, Window in Thrums, Beside the Bonny Brier Bush, House with the Green Shutters, John Splendid.*
6. Write short notes on the following: Glasgow School, Charles Rennie Mackintosh, Edinburgh International Festival, James Bridie, Hugh MacDiarmid.
7. Give an account of any annual celebration in your district, such as riding of the marches.
8. Write a short history of your local senior football club, mentioning outstanding players and distinctions gained. (For this purpose, you should consult not only any books which have been written on the subject but also the back files of your local newspaper.)

CHAPTER XIX

TWO WORLD WARS

The Summer of 1914.—When Franz Ferdinand, Archduke of Austria, was assassinated at Sarajevo on 28th June 1914, few in Scotland dreamed that before the summer was out half of Europe would be at war. In the four years since the death of Edward VII and the accession of George V in 1910, Britain's own problems had occupied people's minds—the House of Lords crisis, the Irish Home Rule problem which seemed to threaten civil war in the spring of 1914, national strikes by railway-men and miners, the introduction of state insurance schemes for sickness and unemployment, and the suffragette movement with its "wild women" who smashed shop-windows, slashed famous pictures and put letter-boxes on fire. By the end of August 1914, however, there had landed in France the first hundred thousand of the British Expeditionary Force, which had been prepared for such an emergency by R. B. Haldane, the eminent Scottish lawyer and Secretary for War. In this B.E.F., there were, besides the few but well-trained Regulars and Reservists, many of the new Territorial Army which Haldane had formed, the first of the "Terriers" battalions to go into action being that of the London Scottish. Volunteers also began to pour into "Kitchener's Army", in response to the appeal of Lord Kitchener, the new Secretary for War, who shocked the public by his forecast that the war would last at least three years. (Later, in 1916, it was found necessary to introduce conscription, with certain exceptions for the "key-men" in industry.) The Navy, on which depended so much, used the new bases in Scotland, Rosyth, Invergordon and Scapa Flow, more than the old bases in England, so uncom-fortably near the enemy in a war in which it was difficult to pre-dict what would happen with many new factors—submarines, torpedoes, aeroplanes, zeppelins.

The Great War.—Little can be told here of the actual fighting during the war—the initial campaign to stop the German advance on Paris, the long-drawn out trench warfare punctuated by bloody battles like that of the Somme and the fruitless Dardanelles venture, the introduction of poison-gas and tanks, and the final break-through. Among the Scottish generals who earned distinction, Sir Ian Hamilton held the difficult command of the Dardanelles expedition, and Field-Marshal Sir DOUGLAS HAIG (later Earl Haig) was Commander-in-chief of the British forces at the end of the war. Casualties were terribly heavy; out of 812,000 killed or missing from the armed forces of Great Britain and Ireland, over 100,000 were Scotsmen. The war memorials erected in towns and villages after 1918 still show the long lists of those who gave their lives, and many who returned were disabled in one way or another. German air raids were carried out by zeppelins but generally did not reach as far as Scotland. Edinburgh was raided on several occasions but only a few casualties resulted. The sinking by U-boats of British ships led in 1916 and 1917 to great scarcity of certain foods, long queues forming at grocers' shops. The Government decided to introduce rationing on the basis of 8 oz. of sugar, 2 oz. of tea, 2 oz. of cheese, 5 or 6 oz. of butter and margarine, 1s. worth of meat, etc., per person. It was then that saccharines first made their appearance as a substitute for sugar and many people realized that tea could be drunk unsweetened. It was a long war, one which even in the last year Germany had seemed capable of winning, and the armistice or end of hostilities was welcomed with rapturous enthusiasm when it came on 11th November 1918.

Post-War Troubles.—"The war to end wars", as it had been called, brought much trouble in its train. The demobilized soldiers and sailors soon began to realize that winning a war did not necessarily mean more prosperity in their country. Prices were still very high, wages, although high, had not kept pace with prices and soon they were being cut by employers, who felt that only thus could they win back their markets overseas. As a result, over 2,000 strikes, great and small, occurred in Great Britain in 1919-20. During the war there had been more labour unrest on Clydeside than elsewhere in Britain; in 1916 some of the workers' leaders were imprisoned and in the following year some were deported to Ireland. In January 1919, when strikes were staged in various industries, a mass demonstration in George Square, Glasgow, came into conflict with the police, who cleared the square with a baton charge, over fifty being injured. Some of the strikes (e.g., those of the railwaymen and miners) were on a scale large enough to paralyse the work of the rest of the community. When employers offered reduced wages that the workers would not accept, they enforced a lock-out, one of which, in the textile industry, lasted for more than six months. In the coal-mines, the miners were resentful not only over the question of wages but also because the Government had not accepted the recommendation of the Royal Commission on the Mines in 1919 that the mines should be nationalized. Although the Government maintained that it would be wrong to implement a recommendation carried only by the casting vote of the chairman, Mr Justice Sankey, the miners felt that the decision was due rather to the influence of the mine-owners. In 1921, "sympathetic strikes" by other unions were promised but failed to materialize and the miners came out on their own, returning only when the Government had promised £10,000,000 in reduction of their wage cuts. After a brief boom period, Clydeside ship-builders found that pre-war clients from abroad were having their ships built in their own countries. Some of the yards on the Clyde closed down never to reopen.

Scots in Parliament.—It is little wonder that at the 1922 election, when Lloyd George's Coalition Government was defeated, and a Conservative Government came into power, the Labour Party won the largest number of seats in Scotland, with 30 members against 28 Liberals (more or less equally divided between supporters of Lloyd George and Asquith), 15 Unionists (or Conservatives) and actually one Communist. The Scottish Labour members comprised one-fifth of the party in the House of Commons and their representation was so strong in the West that Glasgow and district earned the name "RED CLYDESIDE". The Conservative Prime Minister in the new Parliament was ANDREW BONAR LAW (1858-1922), who was the son of a Scottish Presbyterian minister in Canada but who was educated in Glasgow at the High School there. At one time chairman of the Glasgow Iron Trade Association, he entered Parliament in 1900 and soon made a great impression because of his ability to speak without notes; later as Chancellor of the Exchequer in Lloyd

Photo : Picture Post
Andrew Bonar Law

George's Coalition Government, he delivered long, difficult budget speeches with only some figures on a single sheet of paper to help him. His tenure of office as Prime Minister did not last long, as he died after seven months, to be followed by Stanley Baldwin. When, after the election of 1923, the first Labour Government in Britain took office, it was also under a Scotsman, JAMES RAMSAY MACDONALD (1866-1937). He was born and brought up at Lossiemouth, and by hard work and study fitted himself for journalism and politics, joining the Independent Labour Party soon after it was formed.[1] He was appointed as the first secretary of the Labour Party in 1900 and sat in Parliament from 1906, although in 1918 he lost his seat because he had been a pacifist during the war. In MacDonald's ministry, in which he acted also as Foreign Secretary, there were a number of Scotsmen: the former Liberal, Lord Haldane, was Lord Chancellor, Arthur Henderson was Home Secretary, William Adamson was Secretary for Scotland and John Wheatley, one of the Glasgow group, was Minister of Health. As the Conservatives and Liberals outnumbered the Labour Party (also known as the Socialist Party) MacDonald's Government remained in office for less than a year

[1] See p. 228

and in 1924 the Conservatives came back to power under Baldwin.

Strikes and Unemployment.—In May 1926, following a lock-out by the mine-owners, who were insisting on a wage reduction, there occurred the GENERAL STRIKE: almost all other workers (the exceptions being those in essential services, such as food, lighting, etc.) came out in sympathy with the miners. In Scotland, as elsewhere in Britain, the public were without railway trains or newspapers for most of the ten days of the strike. Motor buses, which had only recently begun to operate on the roads, were in some cases able to offer an alternative service to the trains, if they were driven by their owners, as was possible in those days of one-bus firms. Tramcars were driven by volunteer drivers like university students and a few clashes with strikers occurred. Although strikes were fewer after 1926, the troubles of industry did not decrease. When another Socialist Government, with Ramsay MacDonald as Prime Minister, took office in 1929, they soon found themselves faced with the greatest slump in business of the twentieth century. The number of unemployed in Britain had seldom been less than 1,500,000 even although there was a steady flow of emigration. (Between 1921 and 1931, 329,000 went overseas from Scotland and at the census of 1931 Scotland's population actually showed a decline.)[1] When the figures of men "on the dole" (those in receipt of unemployment benefit) began to soar in 1931, the Socialist Government resigned and was replaced by a National Government, consisting mainly of Conservatives, with a few Socialists and Liberals, under Ramsay MacDonald as Prime Minister.

The Great Depression.—This was the period of continuous unemployment in many countries, known as the GREAT DE-PRESSION. In 1933, 407,000 workers in Scotland, in comparison with over 2,500,000 in England and Wales, were registered as unemployed (with many others unregistered). The unemployed were over thirty per cent of all the workers in Scotland, but in some industries the percentage was much worse, being twice as high in shipbuilding and little better in textiles. In John Brown's ship-yard at Clydebank, the giant Cunarder, then known only as No. 534 but later to be launched as the *Queen Mary*, was lying

[1] See p. 284

Photo: *Daily Herald*

Unemployed of the 1930's

on the stocks for almost three years, while thousands of riveters, platers, joiners, shipwrights and others were idle. The National Government, in a desire to reduce state expenditure, cut unemployment benefit and imposed a "means test" where a man or woman had been out of work for some time. When unemployment continued for a year or more, as was often the case, the condition of the unemployed and their families was one of great distress. According to Sir John Boyd Orr (later Lord Boyd Orr), a Scottish expert on nutrition, more than half of the population in 1936 existed on a diet insufficient to maintain proper health. The depression, which affected almost all the countries in the world, slowly lifted, but when the Second World War started in 1939, the unemployed total for the whole of Britain was still over a million, with Scotland's share almost 200,000. Why were Scotland's unemployment figures comparatively worse, and sometimes much worse, than those of England? Various reasons have been suggested. Scotland had remained much more dependent on a few main industries like shipbuilding, coal-mining and textiles, which had gained prosperity for her in the nineteenth century, whereas in England many new industries, e.g., motor-manufacturing and electrical engineering had developed. Scotland had made the mistake of keeping all its eggs in a few baskets. There was also a tendency for the sites of new factories that were started by British or American companies to be located not far from London and its huge potential market among a population of over eight millions. Thus the American firm of Henry Ford built their giant works at Dagenham in Essex. With the growth of large combines, the control of which often passed into English hands, there was also a "drift south" of industry from Scotland. In 1937 the Government made an attempt to reverse the process by setting up at Hillington, near Glasgow, an industrial estate with all the necessary facilities—buildings, roads, electricity, water supply—available, and in 1939 three other similar estates were established.

Second World War (1939-45).—In late September 1938, when there was a war scare over Czechoslovakia, people queued for gas masks (which fortunately were never to be required) and trenches were dug in the public parks as protection against air raids. The crisis passed but less than a year later, on 1st September 1939, when German planes were bombing Warsaw and other towns in Poland, there was carried out a mass EVACUATION of city children and their mothers to the country and to towns not likely

Evacuation, 1939

Photo: The Scotsman

to be targets for enemy bombers. During the broadcast of Neville Chamberlain, the Prime Minister, on Sunday 3rd September, announcing that war had been declared, the howl of the first siren or air-raid warning was heard; but for the next eight months there seemed to be little sign of the threatened *Blitzkrieg* (lightning war) in the west of Europe. For a short period after the fall of France in June 1940, Britain stood alone and invasion seemed imminent. On the south coast of England, the "Battle of Britain" went on in the air; on the coasts of Scotland as well as England concrete defences were built, barbed wire entanglements set up and poles erected on beaches or links that might be used for an invasion from the air. An AIR RAID PRECAUTIONS service was in readiness, and A.R.P. wardens patrolled the streets at night to ensure that no light showed through the bl nds or "black-out" curtains. The HOME GUARD of volunteers for local defence was formed, at first so poorly armed that pikes were recommended for drilling purposes. All fit young men were called up for service in the armed forces except those in "reserved occupations". For the next five years Britain was to be an armed camp; in Scotland, at one time or another, there were large numbers of Britain's allies, Poles, French, Norwegians and Americans. As London and the English ports were too near the German bombers, Glasgow and the Clyde became vitally important for Britain's food and supplies from overseas. Many convoys left from or came into the "Tail of the Bank" at Greenock and the giant Cunarders, the *Queen Mary* and *Queen Elizabeth* arrived regularly, not as ordinary passenger liners but as troopships crammed with thousands of soldiers.

Home Front.—Despite the distance from Germany, it was in Scotland that the Germans made their first air raid in October 1939, when bombs were dropped near the Forth Bridge, beside some ships of the British Navy. The conquest of Norway in 1940 enabled the Germans to carry out frequent "hit-and-run" raids on Shetland, Orkney and the north-east coast. The heaviest raid which the *Luftwaffe* delivered in Scotland was the "blitz" on Clydeside on March 13-15, 1941, 1,083 persons being killed. Over 4,000 houses (or about one-third of the total number of houses) were destroyed, and only 8 remained undamaged in the burgh of Clydebank. Civilians were thus made to feel the impact of the war, and for some time the number of casualties from air raids exceeded those on active service. In still another respect, civilians were worse off than servicemen: their rations were more meagre and, as there was also a shortage of non-rationed goods, shopping usually meant standing in queues. By cheap or free issues of milk, codliver oil and orange juice for infants and by the provision of school meals, the health of children was wonderfully maintained and the average measurements of the height and weight of school pupils actually increased during the war. With industry geared up to maximum production, there was no longer any chronic unemployment except among a few thousand "unemployable"; men worked overtime evenings and Sundays, and the number of women employed rapidly increased. Women indeed played a very important part in the home front also in the W.V.S. (Women's Voluntary Services), while many of them served in the A.T.S. (Auxiliary Territorial Service), the W.A.A.F. (Women's Auxiliary Air Force), the W.R.N.S. (Women's Royal Naval Service) and in nursing units overseas as well as in Britain. Because of the sinking of food ships by U-boats, farming became of vital importance and the WOMEN'S LAND ARMY was formed to help with farmwork. No longer able to import timber from Scandinavia, Britain was compelled to cut down its own forests and the country benefited from the afforestation carried out in the Highlands and Southern Uplands by the FORESTRY COM-MISSION, set up in 1919. In the middle of the war, also, the first steps were taken in carrying out a long-term plan of development of Scotland's water-power resources by the formation of the NORTH OF SCOTLAND HYDRO-ELECTRIC BOARD in 1943.

Victory and After.—The opening of the "Second Front" in Normandy in June 1944, coupled with the great westward drive of the Russians, proved too much for Germany. The war ended in Europe in May 1945, and in the Far East in August of the same year, not long after the dropping of the first atom bombs on Japan. In the six years of war the casualties were mercifully only about one-third of those in the First World War, partly because generals were less ready to squander men's lives need-lessly and partly because of the use of new drugs and new methods of treating wounded, e.g., by blood-transfusions. At the beginning of the war, there had been four Scottish infantry divisions, the 9th, the 15th, the 51st and the 52nd, none of them so Scottish in character as formerly. But, in the reorganization of the army that succeeded the fall of France, when the 51st Division was almost wiped out except for a remnant evacuated from St. Valéry on the Somme, the 9th Division disappeared and the 51st was reconstructed. Perhaps the most distinguished Scotsman of the war was Admiral Sir ANDREW CUNNINGHAM, afterwards Lord Cunningham of Hyndhope, whose exploits in command of the fleet in the Mediterranean included the victories of Taranto and Cape Matapan, and the covering of the invasions of North Africa, Sicily, Italy and South France. Although his achievements were less spectacular, Sir ROBERT WATSON-WATT, the scientist who developed "radar", also contributed a great deal to winning the war. When V.E. Day and V.J. Day (8th May and 15th August, the official days of celebration of the victories in Europe and Japan) had come and gone, Britain settled down to peaceful ways, realizing that wars, even if they have been won, have still to be paid for. Memories of post-war troubles twenty-five years before were still fresh in the minds of the older generation; but fortunately they were not paralleled by events after 1945.

Post-War Reconstruction.—The break-up of the wartime Coalition Government led by Winston Churchill and the defeat of the Conservatives at the election of July 1945 brought into power a Labour Government under Clement Attlee. It held power until October 1951, although with a much reduced majority after the election of February 1950. The Socialists carried out a programme of NATIONALIZATION of the key industries and services—coal-mining, iron and steel, railways, road transport, electricity and gas supplies—and also introduced a new health service and national insurance scheme. Full employment continued and there was a labour shortage in the country, especially acute in the coal-mining industry. To a certain extent this shortage was caused by the very large increase in the size of the Army, in which young men were compelled to serve for two years, the steady emigration of young Scots overseas (over 88,000 between the end of the war and the census of 1951), and the raising of the school leaving age in 1947, from 14 to 15 years; but, on the other hand, many more women continued in industry after the war, the proportion being almost one to every two men in 1950. There was an almost complete absence of labour unrest and strikes; no attempts were made to reduce wages, which gradually rose, along with prices, until they were about three times as high as before the war. The necessity for earning enough dollars to enable Britain to buy from the United States and Canada made the export trade to these countries of first priority.

Photo: Picture Post

Thomas Johnston

Scotch whisky, Harris tweed, woollen knitwear from Shetland and the border towns like Hawick were mainly reserved for export. Although there were plenty of problems still to be solved, it seemed that Scotland had taken on a new lease of life. Much of the credit for this revival was due to the energy and enthusiasm of men outside the Government. THOMAS JOHNSTON (b. 1882), who was first returned to Parliament as Labour M.P. in 1922, held the office of Secretary of State for Scotland in the National Government from 1941 to 1945 and took an active part in setting up the North of Scotland Hydro-Electric Board in 1943, becoming the chairman after he resigned his office as Secretary of State. After the war, as Chairman of the Hydro-Electric Board, the Scottish National Forestry Commission and the Scottish Tourist Board, he helped to revitalize the Highlands and he added to his multifarious activities in 1954 by becoming Chairman of the Scottish Broadcasting Council. The SCOTTISH COUNCIL (DEVELOPMENT AND INDUSTRY), under the chairmanship of Lord Bilsland, undertook the task of attracting firms, Scottish, English, American, Canadian and foreign, to the new INDUSTRIAL ESTATES. These were placed in or near former "depressed areas" and a great variety of light manufactures was thus introduced to Scot-

land—type-writers, cash registers, adding machines, clocks, etc.
By industrial exhibitions, also, new customers for Scottish firms
were gained. Instead of the haphazard growth of towns in the
nineteenth century, regional surveys were made and plans for
long-term development drawn up. New towns were founded at
East Kilbride near Glasgow and at Glenrothes in Fife and planned
for other places.

Housing and Health.—The greatest problem left over from
the Second World War was undoubtedly housing. Scottish slums,
the worst of any industrial country in Europe in the twentieth
century, were the legacy of the Industrial Revolution, combined
with the traditional Scottish style of building high stone tenements that lasted far too long. Although attempts at slum clearance had been made from the middle of the nineteenth century,[1]
there was no large-scale clearance by town councils until after
the First World War when, with the help of government subsidies, many new housing schemes were started. The improvement was not very noticeable in the statistics. In 1911, 47.9 per
cent of Scottish houses were of one or two rooms, as against 7.5
per cent in England and Wales; and in 1931 the corresponding
figures were 46 per cent and 5 per cent. The effect of overcrowding and insanitary conditions on the health has already been
mentioned. The infant mortality rate (that of the deaths of
children under one year) has been called one of the clearest
indications of the living conditions of the people. Scotland's
figures reflect only too clearly bad housing, poverty and malnutrition.

Infant Mortality Rate per 1,000 Live Births

	Scotland	England and Wales	Holland	Sweden	New Zealand
1886-90	121	145	175	105	84
1906-10	112	117	114	—	70
1936-40	76	55	37	42	32
1950	39	30	25	20	23

In the five years before the Second World War when unemployment was still serious, Scotland's infant mortality rate was

[1] See pp. 197, 212

actually the highest in western Europe except for Spain and Portugal. It was, as might be expected, worst in the large cities; in Glasgow itself, the rate in 1938 ranged from 47 per 1,000 in a middle-class residential district to 131 per 1,000 in a slum district. During and after the war, the figures steadily improved, mainly due to better food and better medical attention; in 1950 the rate for Scotland had fallen to 39 and in 1951 to 35. The general health standards of children improved at the same time, as has already been mentioned. The problem of re-housing had been made more difficult by the destruction of many houses in bombed areas and the deterioration or disrepair of others, while the population had increased. Immediately after the war the Government encouraged local authorities to make up for the lost six years by building "pre-fabs" (pre-fabricated houses, some of aluminium) and over 32,000 temporary houses were erected in Scotland in the first two years. At the time of the census in 1951, out of a total of 1,375,083 houses occupied by the population of 4,869,868 (an average of 3.54 persons per house) over 130,000 were new houses provided since the war, and by the end of 1954, the number of new houses was 261,729, nearly all owned by local authorities. Lest it may seem that slums have disappeared, it should be noted that the census of 1951 disclosed that Glasgow's percentage of houses of one or two rooms was 48 (compared with 8.4 per cent for London, 3.4 per cent for Liverpool, 2 per cent for Birmingham and Manchester) and that there were 15,402 "grossly overcrowded" houses, i.e., houses containing more than 3 persons per room.

Highlands and Islands.—To what extent have the Highlands and Islands shared in the revival of Scottish economic life since the Second World War? There have been many obvious improvements. The schemes of the NORTH OF SCOTLAND HYDRO-ELECTRIC BOARD—Grampian, Loch Affric, Loch Sloy, Tummel-Garry and others—have brought power to the glens. What a difference electricity has made to the life and work of the farmer and his wife! The coming of the country bus and the grocer's motor-van in the 1920's had already caused a social revolution, changing the habits, the ideas and the diet of the

country people by making regular contact with the towns possible. In the 1930's regular aeroplane services enabled the island
dwellers in Orkney, Shetland and the Hebrides to reach the south
in a matter of hours instead of days. The tourist industry also
benefited by these new forms of transport. With greatly improved housing in the crofting districts, and new village halls,
W.R.I.s (Women's Rural Institutes) and community centres,

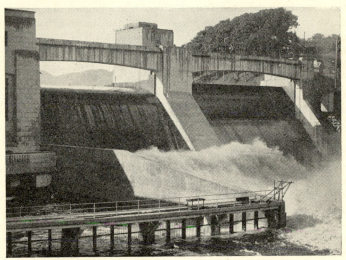

Photo: The Scotsman

Hydro-Electric Scheme, Pitlochry

many scattered villages of the north and west of Scotland now
enjoy a more sociable life than that of the large cities. In agriculture, several experiments are being tried—the eradication of
the bracken pest, the reclamation and utilization of peat-bog,
which with the afforestation schemes of the FORESTRY COM-
MISSION could transform the Scottish hills into productive land.
A few pioneering landowners and farmers have brought back
large-scale cattle-raising to the Highlands, which for two cen-

turies have been inhabited mainly by sheep or deer. By draining, liming and sowing of grasses, the permanent pastures are beginning to recover from neglect and from the ill effects of sheep farming. Quick-freeze plants, kippering stations, fish-oil and, fish-meal factories have been erected to help the herring industry, which between the wars seemed to be on the verge of collapse; lobster-fishing, which has given rise to a lucrative trade, has become more widespread. Factories have also been set up round the coast for producing from seaweed the alginates that have so many different uses, from the prevention of haemorrhage after operations to the preparation of hair-cream. The hand-woven heavy Harris tweeds of Lewis and Harris and the soft warm knitwear of Shetland are high-quality goods that are excellent "dollar-earners", as also is the malt whisky, which after being blended with the grain whisky of the south of Scotland, is sold all over the world. But despite all these welcome improvements there are still plenty of problems to be solved.

Crofting Problems.—In many areas depopulation still continues, and in this connection it must be remembered that hydro-electric and forestry schemes do not mean a large number of employees. In villages in Skye and on the mainland in Ross and Sutherland some of the crofters are too old to work their crofts and others are absentees living in the south except for an annual visit on their summer holidays. Crofting has generally shown a decline, despite the efforts of the Department of Agriculture; the crofts whose owners were given security by the Crofters Act of 1886[1] were in many cases too small to be economic (3 or 4 acres of arable with rights of common pasture). In Orkney, with larger holdings and good soil, the people have enjoyed a long spell of prosperity, different from the conditions of the other islands, like Shetland and the Outer Hebrides, where the crofter depends for his money income on some other occupation like fishing and weaving. By a new CROFTERS ACT OF 1955, it is hoped to encourage consolidation of crofts, although it is recognized that for many it is bound to be only a part-time occupation. Fishermen have many complaints—the loss of the large Russian market after the First World War, the depredation of British and foreign

[1] See pp. 184-5

trawlers which drag their trawls inshore, within the three-mile territorial limit, and ruin the spawning-grounds, and the reluctance of the Government to protect the native fishermen's rights, as, for example, the Norwegian Government does, and to provide large enough subsidies or loans for fishing-boats, gear, wharfs and factories necessary to revive the industry. The difficulty of transport to the southern markets is a handicap to other forms of food-production advocated, such as growing vegetables, for which the mild climate of the Hebrides is very suitable. The development of the Highlands and Islands has attracted the interest of many Scotsmen in the south, especially Scottish Nationalists who believe that, by a large investment programme such as is carried out in the British colonies, the many natural resources could be properly exploited and the region would be not only re-vitalized but would make a valuable contribution to the wealth of the whole country.

Scottish Home Rule Movement.—During the inter-war period there were many proposals for setting up a separate parliament and a separate government in Scotland. Some of them advocated almost complete separation from England and Wales and others only a limited form of "devolution" of administration.[1] On nine occasions after 1918, motions or bills proposing Home Rule in one form or another were brought before the House of Commons, with very large majorities of Scottish M.P.s of all parties in favour, only to be crowded out by pressure of other business. Many supporters of Home Rule felt that it would never come through the existing political parties despite the election promises of Scottish M.P.s. In 1928 they formed two groups, both seeking fairly similar measures of self-government, the National Party of Scotland and the Scottish Party, which united in 1934 as the SCOTTISH NATIONAL PARTY. An early success was gained in 1931, when Compton MacKenzie, the author, was returned as Scottish Nationalist Lord Rector for Glasgow University. But although several candidates stood for Parliament, they won only one seat in twenty years at a bye-election in 1945, when Dr Robert Macintyre was returned for Motherwell. There were many reasons for expecting the party to gain strong support;

[1]See p. 178

in particular, there was a strong feeling that the very much worse state of employment, housing and health, in comparison with England, as revealed by statistics every year during the "Great Depression", pointed to a neglect of Scottish affairs. The House of Commons, it was pointed out, was predominantly English in character and, as it suffered from chronic congestion of business, seldom found time to discuss Scotland. Further, even where there were separate Scottish departments, as for agriculture and education, too often their powers were limited by the Treasury in Whitehall. After the Second World War the nationalization of industry added another cause for grievance, as more and more it seemed that control was being centralized in London. In 1949 a SCOTTISH COVENANT was drawn up and signed by over two million people who thereby pledged themselves to press for a Scottish Parliament. A sensation was caused at Christmas 1950, when as a gesture of protest the Coronation Stone (the so-called "Stone of Destiny") was removed from Westminster Abbey to be left a few months later at Arbroath Abbey, where the famous Declaration of Scottish Independence had been signed in 1320. But the signatories to the Scottish Covenant have almost invariably voted for Labour or Conservative instead of Scottish National candidates at elections; and in 1955 the prospect of Scottish self-government being achieved by the victory of a Scottish Home Rule party seems no nearer than before.

Scottish Nationalism.—Although there is no immediate prospect of a Scottish Parliament in Edinburgh, Scottish nationalism is by no means dead, nor is it confined only to politics. The SALTIRE SOCIETY, founded in 1936, exists to preserve the Scottish heritage of literature, art, architecture and music and to foster a greater public interest in Scottish culture and history. But the political aspect still remains important despite the failure of candidates at elections. Both Socialist and Conservative Governments have been strongly criticized for the delay in the construction of a Forth Road Bridge and a Clyde Tunnel, for the failure to utilize Prestwick Airport and Rosyth Dockyard effectively and for the lack of any constructive policy for the Highlands. Not all hese critics are desirous of a separate government but they are very sensitive about Scotland's well-being. The attitudes of both major political parties to Scottish Home Rule have been similar. Scottish M.P.s maintain that separation would deprive Scotsmen of the opportunity of contributing to the solution of world problems, as defence, foreign and imperial affairs would not be considered by a Scottish Parliament. Conservative M.P.s regard the close links between English and Scottish industry and trade as obstacles to Home Rule, while Socialist M.P.s emphasize the benefits of planning on a large scale. It has been argued also that Scotland is too poor a country to stand alone, although the Scottish National Party not only vehemently deny this but point also to examples of other countries that have prospered after being separated from larger neighbours. Each of the major political parties has also been able to account for the ills of Scotland as due to the mistakes of the rival party; and various slight concessions to Scottish nationalism have been made at intervals, mainly in the devolution of Scottish administration. Thus in 1926 the Secretary for Scotland became the Secretary of State for Scotland; in 1939 the Scottish Office was transferred from Whitehall to St. Andrew's House in Edinburgh; new appointments were made in 1951 and 1952—a Minister of State, normally resident in Scotland, and a third Under-secretary of State. As we have seen in a previous paragraph, Scots themselves have undertaken direction of Scottish affairs through various Boards and Councils.[1] The effect of government concessions, Scottish self-help and a long period of full employment has been to damp down political agitation. But Scotsmen are still keenly conscious of their separate identity as a nation. They are proud of their own national institutions, their Church, their legal and educational systems and the achievements of former generations. If sometimes the criticism is made that the Scot is too aggressive in preserving his national heritage, it should also be remembered that there is much in it worth preserving.

Central Government.—The Secretary of State for Scotland is sometimes regarded as an unofficial Prime Minister of Scotland but his powers are very much more limited. He has four of his colleagues to assist him, the Minister of State and three Under-

[1] See p. 316

Secretaries who share the work of the four main departments at
ST. ANDREW'S HOUSE, Edinburgh—the Home Department (law,
police and fisheries), the Health Department (housing, public
health, registration of births, etc.), the Education Department and
the Department of Agriculture. A great part of the administration
of Scotland is carried on in government departments in London,
with subordinate Scottish officials in charge of matters pertaining
to Scotland—the Admiralty, the War Office, the Air Ministry,
the Ministries of Labour, Health, Housing, Transport, Supply,
National Insurance (in Newcastle), Fuel and Power, Board of
Trade and the Post Office, with the Treasury exercising a financial
control over all. For parliamentary elections, Scotland is divided
into 71 constituencies, the three university seats having been
abolished in 1950 as a result of the Representation of the People
Act of 1948. The number of Scottish seats in the House of Commons (71 out of 625) is high in proportion to the population. The
16 Scottish peers elected in Edinburgh by their fellow peers are
not the only Scotsmen who sit in the House of Lords; since 1782
those who hold peerages of the United Kingdom have the same
right as English peers, e.g., the Duke of Hamilton, who is also
Duke of Brandon. The SCOTTISH GRAND COMMITTEE[1] has considered Scottish bills at the committee stage since 1907 and may
also debate the second reading, a procedure which was first
adopted in 1948, while it discusses the Scottish estimates for six
days each session, its only opportunity for reviewing Scottish
affairs. The Scottish Grand Committee is not entirely Scottish,
as it also comprises enough English M.P.s to maintain the balance
of the parties in the House of Commons. Although the final vote
on the bill is decided by the whole house, this device of a separate
committee makes it possible for more time to be given to Scottish business. Questions to the Secretary of State for Scotland
are not allowed every day, but, because of the limited time available, only at intervals in rotation with those of other departments.

Local Government.—This is the concern of the county
councils and the corporations and town councils of the burghs.
Since the passing of the Local Government Act of 1929, committees of the COUNTY COUNCILS[2] and the CORPORATIONS of the

[1] See p. 178   [2] See p. 178

four large cities control various departments of local government, e.g. the Housing Committee, the Education Committee, the Police Committee, the Public Health Committee, the Roads and Bridges Committee, etc. The four cities, Edinburgh, Glasgow, Aberdeen and Dundee, have the odd name, "County of the City", attached to them. The committees of the county councils and corporations meet usually once a month, while the full council or corporation may also meet monthly or only three or four times a year. The COUNTY CONVENER, elected from among the councillors themselves, presides over general meetings of the council, and chairmen, similarly chosen, over the various committees. The LARGE BURGHS, with populations of 20,000 or over, e.g., Greenock, Paisley, Hamilton, Ayr, similarly control through committees all the functions of local government except education and, in some cases, police. SMALL BURGHS, of which there are 170, some with less than 1,000 inhabitants, e.g., Abernethy in Perthshire or New Galloway in Kirkcudbrightshire, have only limited powers, relating to housing, cleansing, lighting, parks, etc., while DISTRICT COUNCILS have even fewer functions, housing being reserved for the County Councils. The head of a town council, large or small, is called a PROVOST, and of a City corporation, LORD PROVOST. The last title is also borne by the chief magistrates of Perth, the senior burgh in the Convention of Royal Burghs, and of Elgin, although the right of the latter to the title is disputed and is not recognized at state functions. The senior magistrates are the BAILIES, who preside in rotation at the Burgh Police Court. There is usually also a DEAN OF GUILD,[1] whose office is a relic of former times when the Merchant Guild was itself represented on the council; the main function of his court today is to control the erection of buildings in the burgh. The other important official in the Town Council is the TREASURER, whose duty it is once a year to prepare estimates of expenditure and fix on a rate to be levied on all owners and occupiers of property, according to the assessed annual value or rent. The local elections are held at regular intervals, not like parliamentary elections, which, although they must be held at least once every five years, may happen more frequently if a government is defeated. On the

[1] See p. 219

second Tuesday of May every three years County Council elections are held, the first election after the Local Government Act of 1947 being in 1949. The municipal elections in cities and burghs, large and small, are held on the first Tuesday of May each year, only one-third of the corporation or council being elected each May for a period of three years, after which they are eligible for re-election. Although most local elections are run on the normal party lines, with the left-wing candidates calling themselves "Labour" or "Socialist" and the right-wing candidates "Moderate" or "Progressive", there are also successful "Independent" candidates, and votes are often cast for the man rather than the party. The most striking feature of local government today is the apathy of the citizens regarding it. While the poll in parliamentary elections may be higher than eighty per cent of the electorate in some constituencies, too often at municipal and county council elections the poll is only thirty per cent or less. The franchise which previous generations struggled so hard to obtain is little esteemed. The right to vote should, however, also be regarded as a duty; the more citizens take an enlightened interest in political affairs, national and local, the better chance there is of good government.

SOURCES

For contemporary history, newspapers and magazines are obvious sources of information, although they must be treated with caution, as they are subject to various kinds of bias. It is sometimes very difficult to find out about very recent events; but the back files of newspapers are available in large libraries and some of them have an index for each annual volume. Useful books of reference are the *Annual Register, The Statesman's Year Book, Whitaker's Almanack*, while the Stationery Office publishes regularly volumes of statistics on trade, industry, agriculture, health, education, etc. The volumes of the *Third Statistical Account*, compiled for each county and city, will provide when completed a full and detailed picture of Scotland in the middle of the twentieth century to compare with those of the two earlier statistical accounts.

EXERCISES

1. Write short notes about each of the following: Earl Haig, Sir Ian Hamilton, Andrew Bonar Law, James Ramsay MacDonald, Sir Andrew Cunningham, Sir Robert Watson-Watt, Thomas Johnston.

2. Explain the abbreviations: A.R.P., W.V.S., W.A.A.F., W.R.N.S., W.L.A., V.E. Day, V.J. Day, W.R.I.

3. Explain: Red Clydeside, Great Depression, depressed area, means test, *Luftwaffe*, *Blitzkrieg*, reserved occupation, dollar-earner.

4. Give an account of any incidents, such as air-raids, in your district in the First or Second World Wars.

5. Write short notes on the following: General Strike, Evacuation, Home Guard, North of Scotland Hydro-Electric Board, Scottish National Party, Scottish Covenant, Saltire Society, Scottish Grand Committee, Counties of Cities, Large Burghs, Lord Provosts.

6. To what extent may Scotland be considered to have experienced a renaissance since the Second World War?

7. What solutions have been proposed for the problems of the Highlands and Islands?

8. Give arguments *for* and *against* Home Rule for Scotland.

INDEX

	SOCIAL REFORMS	RELIGION AND EDUCATION
1700		1709. *S.P.C.K.*
		1712. *Patronage Act*
		1717. *Catholic seminary at Scalan*
	1729. *Edinburgh Royal Infirmary*	
		1733. *Original Secession*
		1739. *Cambuslang Revival*
1750		
	1769. *Fenwick victualling society*	1761. *Relief Church*
	1774. *1st. Miners' Emancipation Act*	1761. *Perth Academy*
		1792. *Penal Laws against Episcopalians abolished*
	1794. *Glasgow Royal Infirmary*	
	1799. *2nd. Miners' Emancipation Act*	1799. *Congregational Church*
1800	1800. *Robert Owen at New Lanark*	
	1819. *Factory Act (ineffective)*	1820. *United Secession Church*
	1831. *1st. Truck Act*	1829. *R.C. Emancipation*
	1833. *Owen's Trades Union*	1829. *Loretto School*
	1833. *Factory Act (inspectors)*	
	1842. *Mines Act*	1841. *"Ragged Schools" at Aberdeen*
	1845. *New Poor Law*	1843. *Disruption – Free Church*
	1847. *10 Hours Act*	1847. *U.P. Church*
	1848. *Public Health Act*	
1850	1853. *Forbes–Mackenzie Act*	
	1859. *Glasgow supplied with water from Loch Katrine*	
	1862. *M.O.H. in Edinburgh*	
	1868. *S.C.W.S. formed*	1872. *School Board's Education Act*
	1878. *Factory Act*	1873–83. *Moody and Sankey Revivals*
	c.1880. *Saturday half-holiday*	1886. *Royal Technical College, Glasgow*
1900	1908. *Medical inspection of children*	1900. *United Free Church*
	1911. *National Insurance Acts*	
	1913. *Temperance Act*	1918. *Education Authorities*
		1929. *Union of U.F. Church and Church of Scotland*
	c.1946. *Five-day-week*	1929. *Education Committees*
	1948. *National Insurance and Health Service*	1947. *School-leaving Age – 15*
1950		

WHAT THE PAPARAZZI DIDN'T SEE

BY

NICOLA MARSH

First published in Great Britain 2013
by Mills & Boon, an imprint of Harlequin (UK) Limited.
Large Print edition 2013
Harlequin (UK) Limited, Eton House,
18-24 Paradise Road, Richmond, Surrey TW9 1SR

© Nicola Marsh 2013

ISBN: 978 0 263 23692 7

Harlequin (UK) policy is to use papers that are natural,
renewable and recyclable products and made from
wood grown in sustainable forests. The logging and
manufacturing process conform to the legal environmental
regulations of the country of origin.

Printed and bound in Great Britain
by CPI Antony Rowe, Chippenham, Wiltshire

For Ange, Shanika and Kylie.

Thanks for the laughs and for providing me with plenty of interesting book fodder!

Looking forward to some interesting research trips!

CHAPTER ONE

LIZA LITHGOW'S STYLE TIPS FOR MAXIMUM WAG WOW IMPACT

The Lashes

The eyes have it. Whether attending a grand final at a stadium packed with one hundred thousand people, a glamorous nightclub opening or a BBQ with the team and their partners, bold eyes make a statement.

1. Prep with a hydrating cream.
2. Apply foundation over your lids.
3. Draw the perfect line with pencil then trace with liquid eyeliner.
4. Apply shadow of choice. Go for sparkle at night.
5. Finish with lashings of mascara.

If you need a little help in the lash department, extensions are the way to go. Individual fake lashes are pasted to your own, giving you a lush look that turns heads.

A full set of extensions takes about an hour. They last 3-6 weeks and will require refills at this time. Refills take 30 minutes.

The great thing about lash extensions is you choose whether you want natural or glamour. Though be warned: the longer-length 'glamour' lashes may result in questions like, 'Have you been to a fancy dress party?' or, 'Is there a *Priscilla: Queen of the Desert* revival at the local theatre?'

If you prefer *au naturel*, the key to luscious lashes is prepping with a good serum. Many cosmetic companies have them.

To open up the eye in preparation for mascara, eyelash curlers are essential. Best to heat them up slightly before applying pressure to the lashes for thirty seconds.

For more dramatic impact with mascara, wiggle the wand from side to side as you apply, ensuring good coverage at the base of the lashes. It's the density and darkness of mascara at the roots that gives the illusion of length.

And always, always, opt for waterproof. (You never know when your sport star 'other half' may shoot the winning hoop to win the national championship or kick the goal to break a nil-all draw in the World Cup.)

For a real wow factor with mascara, the darker the better. Black is best unless you have a very fair complexion, in which case brown is better.

Similarly with eyeliner. Stick to black at night and softer, smudged brown during the day.

For eyeshadow shades, stick to neutrals or soft pinks. Let your lashes do the talking!

IF LIZA LITHGOW had to attend one more freaking party, she'd go insane.

Her curves resisted the control-top underwear constriction, her feet pinched from the requisite stilettos and her face ached from the perpetual smile.

The *joys* of being a WAG.

Technically, an ex-WAG. And loving the *ex* bit.

The reportedly glamorous lives of sportsmen's

Wives And Girlfriends were grossly exaggerated. She should know. She'd lived the lie for longer than she cared to admit.

'One more pic, Liza?'

Yeah, that was what they all said. Not that she had anything against the paparazzi per se, but their idea of one last photo op usually conflicted with hers.

Assuming her game face, the one she'd used to great effect over the years, she glanced over her shoulder and smiled.

A plethora of flashes blinded her but her smile didn't slip. She turned slowly, giving them time to snap her side profile before she cocked a hip, placing a hand on it and revealing an expanse of leg guaranteed to land her in the gossip columns tomorrow.

Hopefully for the last time.

Being a WAG had suited her purposes but she was done.

Let some other poor sap take her place, primping for the cameras, grinning inanely, starving herself so she wouldn't be labelled pregnant by the media.

With a final wave at the photographers she

strutted into the function room, pausing to grab a champagne from a passing waiter before heading to her usual spot at any function: front and centre.

If this was her last hurrah, she was determined to go out in style.

She waited for the party peeps and hangers-on to flock, steeled her nerve to face the inevitable inquisition: who was she dating, where was she holidaying, when would she grant the tell-all the publishers had been hounding her for?

Her answer to the last question hadn't changed in twelve months: 'When hell freezes over.'

It had been a year since international soccer sensation Henri Jaillet had dumped her in spectacular orchestrated fashion, three years since basketball superstar Jimmy Ro had broken her heart.

Reportedly.

The truth? She'd known Jimmy since high school and they were the quintessential golden couple: king and queen of the graduation dance who morphed into media darlings once he hit the big time.

He'd launched her as a WAG and she'd lapped

it up, happy to accept endorsements of clothes, shoes and jewellery.

For Cindy. Always for Cindy.

Everything she did was for her baby sister, which was why a tell-all was not on the cards.

She'd grown apart from Jimmy and when reports of his philandering continued to dog her, she'd quit the relationship when he wanted out.

The media had a field day, making her out to be a saint, a very patient saint, and the jobs had flooded in. From modelling gigs to hosting charity events, she became Melbourne's latest 'it' girl.

And when her star had waned, she'd agreed to be Henri's date for a specified time in exchange for a cash sum that had paid Cindy's carer bills for a year.

Being tagged a *serial WAG* had stung, as people who didn't know her labelled her money-hungry and a camera whore.

She tried not to care, though.

The only people that mattered—her and Cindy—knew the truth.

And it would stay that way, despite the ludicrous sums of money being dangled in front of her for a juicy tell-all.

Yeah, real juicy. Readers would be distinctly disappointed to learn of her penchant for flannel PJs, hot chocolate and a tatty patchwork quilt.

As opposed to the rumoured lack of sleepwear, martinis before bed and thousand-thread sheets she slept on.

She had no idea why the paparazzi made up stuff like that, but people lapped it up, and judged her because of it.

What would they think if they knew the truth?

That she loved spending a Saturday night curled up on the couch with Cindy under the old patchwork quilt their mum had made—and one of the few things Louisa had left behind when she'd abandoned them—watching the teen flicks her sister adored?

That she'd prefer to spend time with her disabled sister than any of the able-bodied men she'd dated?

That every word and every smile at events like this were part of a carefully constructed, elaborate mask to ensure her popularity and continued work that would set up Cindy's care for life?

Being a WAG meant she could spend most of her time caring for Cindy; a part-time gig as opposed to a full-time job that would've taken her away from her sister.

It had suited their lifestyle, putting in infrequent appearances at galas or launches or openings in exchange for days spent attending Cindy's physiotherapy and occupational therapy sessions, ensuring the spasticity in Cindy's contracted muscles didn't debilitate her limited mobility completely.

She'd sat through Cindy's Botox injections into specific muscles to ease the pain and stiffness and deformity around joints, followed by extensive splinting to maintain movement.

She'd supported Cindy through intrathecal baclofen therapy, where a pump had been inserted into her sister's abdomen to deliver doses of baclofen—a muscle relaxer—into her spinal fluid to ease the spasticity and relieve muscle spasms in her legs.

She'd been there for every session of speech therapy, muscle lengthening and strengthening, splinting, orthotics, mobility training and activities of daily living management.

Putting on a façade for the cameras might have been a pain in the butt but it had been a small price to pay for the time she'd been able to spend supporting Cindy every step of the way. The financial security? An added bonus.

Cindy's care hadn't come cheap and if a magazine wanted to pay her to put in an appearance at some B-list function, who was she to knock it back?

She almost had enough money saved… After tonight she could hang up her sparkly stilettos and leave her WAG reputation behind. Start working at something worthwhile. Something in promotions maybe? Put her marketing degree to use.

Cindy had progressed amazingly well over the years and Liza could now pursue full-time work in the knowledge she'd put in the hard yards with her sister's therapy when it counted.

Cerebral palsy might be an incurable lifelong condition but, with Cindy's determination, her amazing sis had reached a stage in her management plan where the spasticity affecting the left side of her body was under control and she maintained a certain amount of independence.

Liza couldn't be prouder and could now spend more hours away from Cindy pursuing some of her own goals.

Though she wondered how many interviews 'serial WAG' would garner from her sketchy CV.

A local TV host laid a hand on her arm and she faked a smile, gushing over his recent award win, inwardly counting down the minutes until she could escape.

Think of the appearance money, she mentally recited, while nodding and agreeing in all the right places.

Another thirty minutes and she could leave her old life behind.

She could hardly wait.

Wade Urquart couldn't take his eyes off the dazzling blonde.

She stood in the middle of the room, her shimmery bronze dress reflecting light onto the rapt faces of the guys crowding her.

With every fake smile she bestowed upon her subjects, he gritted his teeth.

She was exactly the type of woman he despised.

Too harsh? Try the type of woman he didn't trust.

The same type of woman as Babs, his stepmother. Who at this very minute was doing the rounds of the room, doing what she did best: schmoozing.

Quentin had been dead less than six months and Babs had ditched the black for dazzling emerald. Guess he should respect her for not pretending. As she had for every moment of her ten-year marriage to his father.

A marriage that had driven the family business into the ground. And an irreversible wedge between him and his dad. A wedge that had resulted in the truth being kept from him on all fronts, both personally and professionally.

He'd never forgive her for it.

Though deep down he knew who should shoulder the blame for the estrangement with his dad. And he looked at that guy every morning in the mirror.

He needed to make amends, needed to ease the guilt that wouldn't quit. Ensuring his dad's business didn't go bankrupt would be a step in the right direction.

Qu Publishing currently stood on the brink of disaster and it was up to him to save it. One book at a time.

If he could ever get a meeting with that WAG

every publishing house in Melbourne was clamouring to sign up to a tell-all biography, he might have a chance. Her name escaped him and, having been overseas for the best part of a decade, he had no idea what this woman even looked like, but he could imagine that every one of her assets would be fake. However, it seemed Australia couldn't get enough of their home-grown darling. He'd been assured by his team that a book by this woman would be a guaranteed best-seller—just what the business needed.

But the woman wouldn't return his assistant's international calls and emails. Not that it mattered. He knew her type. Now he'd landed in Melbourne he'd take over the pursuit, demand a face-to-face meeting, up the ante and she'd be begging to sign on the dotted line.

At times like this he wished his father had moved with the times and published children's fiction. Would've made Wade's life a lot easier, signing the next J.K. Rowling.

But biographies were Qu Publishing's signature, a powerhouse in the industry.

Until Babs had entered the picture, when Quentin's business sense had fled alongside his common sense, and he had hidden the disastrous truth.

Wade hated that his dad hadn't trusted him.

He hated the knowledge that he'd caused the rift more.

It was why he was here, doing anything and everything to save his father's legacy.

He owed it to him.

Wade should've been there for his dad when he was alive. He hadn't been and it was time to make amends.

The bronzed blonde laughed, a surprisingly soft, happy sound at odds with the tension emanating from her like a warning beacon.

Even at this distance he could see her rigid back, the defensive way she half turned away from the guys vying for her attention.

Interesting. Maybe she was nothing like Babs after all. Babs, who was currently engaged in deep conversation with a seventy-year-old mining magnate who had as many billions as chins.

Yeah, some people never changed.

He needed a change. Needed to escape the expectations of a hundred workers who couldn't afford to lose their jobs. Needed to forget how his father had landed his business in this predicament and focus on the future. Needed to sign that WAG to solve his problems.

And there were many. So many problems that the more he thought about it, the more his head pounded.

What he needed right now? A bar, a bourbon and a blonde.

Startled by his latter wish, he gazed at her again and his groin tightened in appreciation.

She might not be his type but for a wild, wistful second he wished she could be.

Eight years of setting up his own publishing business in London had sapped him, sucking every last ounce of energy as he'd worked his butt off. When he'd initially started he'd wanted a company to rival his father's but had chosen to focus on the e-market rather than paper, trade and hardbacks. Considering how dire things were with Qu Publishing, his company now surpassed the one-time powerhouse of the book industry.

He rarely dated, socialised less. Building a booming digital publishing business had been his number-one priority. Ironic, he was now here to save the business he could've been in competition with if his dad had ever moved into the twenty-first century. And if he'd been entrusted with the truth.

Not that saving Qu mattered if Babs had her way.

The muscles in his neck spasmed with tension and he spun away, needing air before he did something he'd regret, like marching over to stepmommy dearest and strangling her.

He grabbed a whisky from a passing waiter and downed half of it, hoping to eradicate the bitterness clogging his throat. Needing a breather, he made his way to the terrace that wrapped across the front of the function room in wrought-iron splendour.

Melbourne might not have the historical architecture of London but the city's beautiful hotels, like the Westin, could hold their own around the world.

He paced the marble pavers in a vain attempt to quell the urge to march back into that packed function room and blast Babs in front of everyone, media be damned.

Wouldn't that go down a treat in tomorrow's

papers? PUBLISHING CEO BAILS UP SOCIALITE STEP-MOTHER, a real page-turner.

He wouldn't do it, of course. Commit corporate suicide. Qu Publishing meant too much to him. Correction, his dad had meant everything to him, and Wade would do whatever it took, including spending however long in Melbourne to stop Babs selling his legacy.

Qu Publishing needed a saviour. He intended to walk on water to do it.

He cursed and downed the rest of his whisky, knowing he should head back inside and make nice with the publishing crowd.

'Whatever's biting your butt, that won't help.'

Startled, he glanced to his right, where the bronze-clad blonde rested her forearms on the balcony, staring at him with amusement in her eyes.

Blue. With tiny flecks of green and gold highlighted by the shimmery dress. A slinky, provocative dress that accentuated her assets.

The whisky he'd sculled burned his gut. His excuse for the twisty tension tying it into knots.

Her voice surprised him as much as her guileless expression. Women who dressed like that usually wore calculating expressions to match their deliberately sexy garb and spoke with fake deference.

She sounded…amused. Concerned. *Normal.*

It threw him.

He prided himself on being a good judge of character. Hadn't he picked Babs for a gold-digging tart the moment his dad had introduced her ten years ago?

His people radar had served him well in business too, but something about this woman made him feel off-kilter. A feeling he wouldn't tolerate.

He needed to stay focused, remain in charge, to ensure he didn't lose the one thing that meant anything to him these days.

And as long as she was staring at him with that beguiling mix of fascination and curiosity, he couldn't concentrate on anything.

'Can't a guy have a drink in peace without being accused of drowning his sorrows?'

He sounded abrupt and uptight and rude. Good. She would raise her perfect pert nose in the air and stride inside on those impossibly high heels that glittered with enough sparkle to match her dress.

To his surprise she laughed; a soft, sexy sound that made his fingers curl around the glass as she held up her hands in a back-off gesture.

'Hey, no accusations here. Merely an observation.'

A host of smartass retorts sprang to his lips and he planned on using them too. Until he glimpsed something that made him pause.

She was nervous.

He saw it in the way her fingertips drummed delicately on the stem of the champagne flute she clutched. Saw it in her quick look-away when he held her gaze a fraction too long.

And that contradiction—her siren vamp appearance contrasting with her uncertainty—was incredibly fascinating and he found himself nodding instead.

'You're right. I was trying to take my mind off stuff.'

The corners of her mouth curved upward, the groove in her right cheek hinting at an adorable dimple. 'Stuff?'

'Trust me, you don't want to know.'

'I used to worry about stuff once.'

Intrigued by the weariness in her voice, he said, 'Not anymore?'

'Not after today,' she said, hiding the rest of what she was about to say behind her raised glass as she took a sip.

'What happened today?'

Her wistful sigh hit him where he least expected it. Somewhere in the vicinity of his heart.

'Today I secured a future for someone very important to me.'

He didn't understand her grimness or defensive posture, but he could relate to her relief. When he secured the future of Qu Publishing in memory of all his dad's hard work, he'd be pretty damn relieved too.

'Good for you.'

'Thanks.' She smiled again, sweet and genuine, and he couldn't fathom the bizarre urge to linger, chat and get to know her.

She wasn't in his plans for this evening. Then again, what did he have to look forward to? Putting on a front for a bunch of back-slapping phoneys and gritting his teeth to stop from calling his stepmother a few unsavoury names?

He knew what he'd rather be doing.

And he was looking straight at her.

'Do you want to get out of here?'

Her eyes widened in surprise before a disapproving frown slashed between them. 'You've got to be kidding me? I make polite small talk for two seconds and you're propositioning me?'

She shook her head, her disgust palpable.

'Let me rephrase that.' He tried his best smile, the one he used to win friends and influence colleagues. Her frown deepened. 'What I meant was that I've had a long day. Landed in Melbourne this morning, had to attend this shindig for work tonight and I'm tired of the schmoozing.'

He waved towards the balcony. 'Considering you're out here to get away from the crowd, I assume you've probably had a gutful too?'

Her wary nod encouraged him to continue when he should cut his losses and run.

'The way I see it, we have two choices. Head back in there and bore ourselves silly for the next hour or we can head down to The Martini Bar in the lobby and unwind before we head home—I mean, before we go our separate ways.'

The corners of her mouth twitched at his correction.

'What do you say? Take pity on a guy and put him out of his misery by saving him from another interminable stint in there?'

Damn, he'd made a fool of himself, blathering like an idiot. What was it about this cool, classy blonde that had him rattled?

He'd had her pegged wrong and he, better than anyone, should know never to judge the proverbial book by its cover.

'So you weren't propositioning me?'

Was that a hint of disappointment? Mentally chastising himself for wishful thinking, he mimicked her frown. 'Sadly, no. I'm too jet-lagged to—'

He bit off the rest of what he was about to say when her eyebrow arched.

Yep, he was stuffing this up royally.

'To what?'

At last, she smiled and it made him feel oddly excited, as if he wanted to see her do it again.

'To muster up enough charm to ensure you couldn't say no.'

She chuckled and he joined in.

'I like a guy with confidence.' She laid her

champagne glass on the ledge. 'Let's go get that martini.'

He didn't have to be asked twice. 'You really made me work for that acceptance.'

As he gestured for her to take the stairs ahead of him she cast him a coy glance from beneath her lashes. 'Didn't you know? You need to work your butt off for anything worth having.'

'Is that right?'

'Absolutely.' She nodded, strands of artfully curled golden silk falling around her face in gorgeous disarray. 'Nothing better than nailing a challenge.'

He bit the inside of his cheek to prevent laughing out loud, finding her utterly beguiling. In contrast to her sex-kitten persona, she was forthright and rather innocent if she hadn't picked up on that nailing remark.

Then he made the mistake of glancing at her and saw the moment her faux pas registered.

She winced and a faint pink stained her cheeks, making him want to ravish her on the spot.

'That didn't sound too good,' she said, wrinkling her nose.

'Now we're even,' he said, wondering what

they'd come out with after a few drinks under their belts. 'My mistaken proposition, your nailing suggestion.'

'Guess we are.' She eyed him speculatively, as if not sure what he'd say next.

That made two of them.

'Maybe we should stick to coffee tonight?'

'Why's that?'

That dimple flashed adoringly again. 'Because with our strike rate, who knows what'll happen if we have a martini or two?'

He laughed. 'I was thinking the same thing.'

'Coffees it is.' She nodded, expecting him to agree.

But there was a part of him that delighted in flustering this woman and he couldn't help but wonder how she'd loosen up with a few drinks inside her.

He leaned in close, expecting her to retreat a little, his admiration increasing, along with his libido, when she didn't.

'Actually, I prefer to live on the edge tonight. Why don't we have a martini or two and see what other verbal gaffes we can make?'

'As long as we stop at the verbal stuff,' she said so softly he barely heard her.

'Any other mistakes we make? Not our fault.'

'Oh?' He loved how she did the imperious eyebrow quirk.

'Haven't you heard?' He lowered his voice. 'What happens in The Martini Bar stays in The Martini Bar?'

With a surprisingly wicked twinkle in her eye, she nodded. 'That's if we stay in the bar.'

With that, she took to the steps, leaving him trailing after her, more than a little captivated by this woman of contrasts.

A woman whose name he didn't know.

Ah well, he'd have all night to discover it if he was lucky.

CHAPTER TWO

LIZA LITHGOW'S STYLE TIPS
FOR MAXIMUM WAG WOW IMPACT

The Lips

For the height of sophistication and glam wow, the perfect pout is where it's at.

Having a palette of colours for various looks is essential.

Co-ordinate colour with outfits.

Go bold with fire engine red for an awards ceremony or pastel pink for the season opener.

Keep lips soft; that means no lip liner!

For a fabulous femme fatale pout, preparation is key.

1. Gently exfoliate lips with a soft-bristled toothbrush.
2. Moisturize with a specialized lip balm.

3. Use a lip-fix cream which prevents colour bleeding.
4. Apply lipstick once. Blot with tissue. Re-apply.

For a subtle look, pat lipstick on with a fingertip.

For bold lips, apply with a lip brush.

Blot.

Reapply.

If you want a plump pout without the injections, try lipsticks with inbuilt 'plumpers'. These innovative ingredients are proven to increase lip volume by forty percent. Amazing! They also hydrate and restore collagen over time.

A dab of gloss in the middle of the lower lip is a subtle touch that adds real wow!

LIZA COULDN'T REMEMBER the last time she'd been out on a date.

One that hadn't been orchestrated as some huge PR stunt, that was. She'd attended the Logies, Arias and Brownlow Medal galas on the arms of a TV personality, a rock star and an up-and-coming footballer respectively. And on each occasion had been bored witless within the first ten minutes.

So what was it about this guy that had her laughing and fluffing her words and interested in spending some one-on-one time with him?

She'd made her required appearance at the book launch; she should head home, get out of this designer dress she'd been begged to wear and curl up with her e-reader and the latest juicy romance.

Instead, she watched *him* place their martini orders, shocked she didn't know his name, thrilled she didn't particularly care.

She never had fun or did anything on a whim. Ever.

Her life for the last ten years since her mum had absconded when she was eighteen and left Cindy in her care had been about weighing decisions carefully to see how they would affect her younger sister.

Everything revolved around Cindy and while Liza never begrudged her sis anything, knowing tonight would be the last time she'd have to put on her *fake face* had lifted a weight from her shoulders.

She could be herself from now on and Mr Martini had been in the right place at the right time. More than that, he'd intrigued her, and she couldn't say that about many men.

She'd watched him morph from uptight and judgemental to cool and a little goofy, with a hint of underlying sexiness that made her long-neglected hormones sit up and howl.

When was the last time she'd had sex? Probably not since she was with Jimmy, because while Henri had paid for her arm-candy status for a year, she wouldn't go *that* far as part of their deal.

And if she couldn't remember exactly, it meant it had probably been during the good period with Jimmy, which hadn't been the last year of their relationship. The year he'd progressively withdrawn, establishing emotional distance before the final break.

Her mum had done the same over the years. In both cases, their abandonment hadn't come as any great surprise but had hurt all the same. Hurt deeply.

But tonight wasn't the time to dwell on her

issues. Tonight was perfect for something else entirely.

She did a quick mental calculation.... Could it really have been four years since she'd been with a guy?

Maybe that explained her irrational urge to push the limits with Mr Martini. He'd be ideal for a celebratory fling, a little fun on a night where she felt like dancing down Swanston Street with her arms in the air.

Not that she'd had a one-night stand before but the way she was feeling right now? Edgy. Dangerous. A little outrageous. It could very well be a first tonight.

He stalked towards her, his ebony suit highlighting lean legs, broad shoulders, impressive chest, and she squirmed a little.

What would it be like to explore beneath that suit? To feel the warmth of a man's skin next to hers? The heat of passion? The yearning to lose herself in pleasure?

Cindy was her world and Liza never regretted assuming responsibility for full-time care, but it was at times like this she wished deep down for something she'd never have: a guy to come home to, a guy to warm her bed, a guy who wouldn't abandon her when the going got tough.

'You must really have a hankering for a martini,' he said, taking a seat next to her, far too close as a few synapses zinged with the need to touch him.

'Why?'

'Because you have an odd look on your face, like you want it real bad.'

Uh-oh. He could see her desperation? Not good.

'I'm thirsty,' she blurted, wishing the waitress would hurry up and deliver their damn drinks so she wouldn't have to stare into his knowing dark eyes.

'And I'm curious.'

That made two of them. She was curious as to why she'd agreed to this and why the hell she wanted him to be part of her freedom celebration tonight.

'How could two intelligent people like us, about to having a scintillating conversation, still be strangers?'

'Not anymore.' She stuck out her hand. 'Liza Lithgow.'

'Wade Urquart. Pleased to meet you.'

As his palm touched hers and his fingers curled around her hand, Liza could've sworn every sane reason why she shouldn't indulge in a night of incredible sex with this guy melted clean away.

'Your name sounds familiar.' He frowned, releasing her hand after lingering too long. She wasn't complaining.

'I'm hoping the next words out of your mouth aren't, "Haven't we met some place before?"'

He laughed. 'No need for glib lines. You're here, aren't you?'

'True.'

And with the dim lighting, the smooth jazz spilling softly from discreet speakers behind them and a gorgeous guy eyeing her speculatively, she was right where she wanted to be.

For tonight. Tonight, she was in the mood for celebrating. Shedding her old life felt amazing.

'Why did you agree to have a drink with me?' The waitress deposited their drinks and he raised a martini glass in her direction. 'You seemed to be in your element at that party.'

'Haven't you ever faked it?' She clinked her glass to his. 'What you see isn't always what you get.'

He stared at her over the rim of his glass, a slight groove between his brows. 'Have to say, you're an intriguing woman, and I can't figure you out.'

She shrugged. 'What's to figure out? We're two people who wanted to escape that party; we're having a drink, end of story.'

'Is it?'

His gaze locked on hers, potent and smouldering, and her breath hitched.

She took a sip of her martini, needing the alcohol to loosen her tightened vocal cords. 'You're expecting an epilogue?'

'A guy can always live in hope,' he said, downing his martini and placing the glass on the table in front of them. 'Honestly? I've had a crappy six months, my dad's business is under threat and I haven't met anyone as captivating as you in a long time. So excuse me if I don't BS you.'

Liza valued honesty. Most people didn't know the meaning of the word. How many times had friends, who'd hung around under the misguidance she'd take them places because of her lifestyle, vanished when they'd learned she had a disabled sister?

Stupid morons acted as if cerebral palsy were catchy. And they didn't stay to be educated either.

Even Jimmy had been awkward and stilted around Cindy, despite Liza explaining cerebral palsy was a physical disability caused by injury to the brain before birth.

Cindy had a milder form, with only the left side of her body affected by the debilitating spasticity that left her hand, elbow, hip and knee clawed, and some speech problems. She had been lucky in escaping ataxic—uncontrolled—movements and athetosis, the writhing movements.

Sure, the spasticity in Cindy's elbow, wrist and fingers made daily tasks like eating, dressing, writing and manipulating objects difficult, but they'd learned to cope best they could. Countless occupational therapy sessions had seen to that. And the ongoing physiotherapy to prevent deforming contractures made Liza eternally grateful for the job she'd had for the last few years.

After tonight, not anymore.

Having Wade clearly articulate what he wanted impressed her. Scared the bejeebies out of her, but definitely impressed her.

'Want to talk about the crappy six months or the business?'

'Hell no,' he said, loosening the knot on his tie and unbuttoning the top button of his shirt to reveal a hint of deliciously tempting tanned skin. 'The only reason I'm in Melbourne is to sort all that stuff out, but considering I arrived this morning it can wait 'til tomorrow.'

'Then why show up at the party at all?'

'Because sometimes we have to do things we don't want to.'

His frown reappeared and she had a feeling he did a lot of that. He'd been frowning when she'd first seen him on the balcony, deep in thought, incredibly serious. It was what had made her approach him. Because she used to look like that all the time when she didn't have her game face on, the one she donned along with her make-up before a public appearance.

She'd frowned a lot over the years, worrying about Cindy. About her care long term should anything happen to her, about her sister's health, about her financial security.

The latter had driven her to go to great lengths. Heck, she'd tolerated posing as Henri Jaillet's girlfriend for twelve months when most people couldn't stand longer than a few minutes in the egotistical soccer star's presence.

But those days were over. She'd invested wisely over the years and tomorrow, when her investment matured, financial security would give her the peace of mind she needed to get more carer help, leaving her more time to sort out her own future.

Why wait until tomorrow?

The thought wasn't exactly out of left field. She wouldn't be sitting here if she hadn't already contemplated celebrating her newfound freedom tonight.

But how did this work? She couldn't take Wade home; she'd never expose Cindy to that unless the guy meant something to her. Even Jimmy had hardly visited and she'd known him since high school.

Though that had been more due to Jimmy's unease around Cindy than not wanting to see her. She hadn't pushed the issue with him, content to protect Cindy from any vibes she might pick up from Jimmy. But it had hurt, deep down, that her boyfriend wasn't more open-minded and didn't care enough about her to accept Cindy as part of the package while they dated.

'Another drink?'

She shook her head. 'No thanks. After the champers I had upstairs, any more of this and who knows what I'll do?'

'In that case, maybe I should insist you try every martini mixer on the menu?'

She smiled, glad his frown had disappeared, but a little intimidated by his stare, the probing stare that insisted there was intention behind his teasing quips.

'You could try, but you'd have to carry me out of here.'

'Not a problem. I have a suite upstairs.' He winked. 'You could recover up there.'

Guess that answered Liza's question about how she'd go about *celebrating* with Wade.

The old Liza would've laughed off his flirtation and changed the subject.

The new Liza who wanted to kick up her heels for the first time in for ever? Surely she couldn't pass up an opportunity like this?

'Is that an invitation or a proposition?'

'Both,' he said, capturing her hand between

his, the unexpected contact sending a buzz shooting up her arm. 'Am I in the habit of picking up women I barely know at parties? No. Do I invite them back to my place? Rarely.'

He raised her hand to his lips and brushed a soft kiss across her knuckles, making her yearn for more. 'Am I hoping you'll say yes to spending the night with me? Absolutely.'

Liza had a decision to make.

Do the sensible thing, the responsible thing, as she'd done her whole life.

Or celebrate her new life, starting now.

'Do I accept offers to spend the night from guys? No.' She squeezed his hand. 'Have I had a one-night stand before? Never.' She slid her hand out of his. 'Do I want to spend tonight with you?'

She took a steadying breath and laid her hand on his thigh. 'Absolutely.'

CHAPTER THREE

LIZA LITHGOW'S STYLE TIPS
FOR MAXIMUM WAG WOW IMPACT

The Shape

The key to WAG wow is making the most of what you have.

Learn how to show off your best assets and how to visually change the body parts you'd rather hide.

Always, always, dress to suit your shape.

PEAR

a) Wear dark colours on the lower half of your body.

b) A-line skirts that skim the hips and bottom are flattering.

c) Accessorise with scarves, necklaces and earrings to draw attention to the upper half of your body.

d) Avoid light coloured trousers or any-thing too tight on your bottom half.

BUSTY

a) Go for flattering necklines with tops and dresses: turtlenecks, shirt collars, boat necks, V necks.

b) Go for high-sitting necklaces as they draw the gaze up.

c) Avoid baggy tops with no shape as they can make you look heavier and avoid anything too tight across the chest.

SHORT

a) Dresses ending above the knee are best.

b) Wear fitted tops and trousers (straight or bootleg).

c) Avoid cropped length pants as they make legs look shorter.

TALL

a) Wear different colours top and bottom to break up the illusion of length.

b) Wear horizontal stripes.

c) Wear well-fitted layers that skim the body.

d) Adding a wide belt can help create a nice shape.

e) Avoid wearing pants that are the incorrect length.

Remember, the key to appearing confident in the clothes you wear is to be comfortable.

How many times have we seen women tugging up their strapless bodices or tugging down their micro-minis? It's not a good look.

When you strut into a room, being confident in your body and the look you've created is half the battle!

As LIZA STARED out over the lights of Melbourne glittering below, she had second thoughts about her decision.

Was she really in Wade's suite, about to indulge in her first one-night stand at the ripe old age of twenty-eight?

She still had time to bolt. She'd thought it rather cute when he'd mentioned making a quick trip to the convenience store across the road, and it re-inforced his assertion that he wasn't in the habit of picking up women or expecting to have sex his first night in Melbourne.

But while he was buying condoms, she was mulling over reasons why this might not be such a good idea after all.

She maintained strict independence for a rea-son. Depending on anyone for anything inevita-bly led to heartache.

Not that she'd be depending on Wade for any-thing, but letting her guard down came with a price. It left her vulnerable to *feeling*, and hav-ing her defences weakened, even for a short time, made her skittish.

She'd loved her dad. He'd abandoned her with-out a backward glance.

She'd depended on her mum. She'd eventually left too.

She'd thought sweet, easygoing Jimmy would always be there for her. He'd done a runner too.

No, it was easier maintaining aloofness, not let-ting anyone get too close. And that was exactly what Wade would be doing shortly…getting ex-ceptionally close.

Ironic, it wasn't the prospect of some stranger seeing her naked that had her half as anxious as the thought of being intimate with him and enjoying it too much.

She'd never been a needy female and had tried to instil the same independence into Cindy despite her physical limitations, yet there was something about how much she wanted to be close to Wade tonight that terrified her.

She could blame it on her impulsive need to celebrate and do something completely out of character.

Or she could admit the truth, albeit to herself. That she craved a connection, even if only physical, for just one night.

The soft swoosh of the key card in the lock had her fingers clenching on the windowsill.

So much for escaping.

He entered and her tummy fell away in that uncharacteristic swoop that signalled she really wanted this guy.

She tingled all over from it, her nerve endings prickling and putting her body on notice, a heightened awareness that made her want to rub against him, skin to skin.

Then it hit her.

She'd never been so attracted to any guy before. Not even Jimmy, whose body she'd known
in intimate detail from the time they'd lost their
virginity together in the back seat of his car at
seventeen.

Because of the clothes she wore and the persona she presented to the world, guys assumed
she was an easy mark. Even while she'd been
dating Jimmy and Henri—albeit platonically in
his case—guys had hit on her.

Fellow soccer and basketball stars who assumed WAGs were up for anything. Commenta-
tors and managers and agents who thought WAGs
would do anything for stardom and recognition,
including accept outlandish proposals.

The whole scene had sickened her and, while
she'd seen enough hook-ups at parties in her time,
she'd never been remotely interested.

What made Wade Urquart so special that she
wanted to rip her clothes off the moment his
sizzling-hot gaze connected with hers?

'Glad you're still here.'

He closed the door and slid off his jacket, where
she caught sight of a tell-tale box bulging from

the inside pocket. What looked like a surprisingly large box for what she'd envisioned as a brief interlude.

Her skin tingled again.

'I contemplated making a run for it.'

'What stopped you?'

He stalked towards her, stopped less than two feet away.

'This.'

She laid a hand on his chest, felt the heat from his skin brand her through the expensive cotton of his shirt.

He didn't move as her palm slid upward. Slowly. Leisurely, as she savoured the contours of hard muscle, desperate to feel his skin.

He watched her, his gaze smouldering as her fingertips traced around his nipples, his breathing quickening as her fingers skated across his pecs, along his collarbone and higher.

When her hand reached his neck, she stepped closer, bringing their bodies less than an inch apart.

She could feel his heat. She could smell his expensive citrus aftershave. She could hear his ragged breathing.

She'd never wanted anything as badly as she wanted Wade at that moment.

With a boldness she'd had no idea she possessed, she tugged his head down towards her and kissed him.

The moment their lips touched Liza forgot her doubts, forgot her past, forgot her own damn name.

She couldn't think beyond their frantic hands and loud moans. Couldn't get enough of his long, deep, skilled kisses.

Her body ignited in a fireball of passion and she clung to him, eagerly taking the initiative, pushing him down on the bed so he lay sprawled beneath her like a fallen angel.

His lips curved into a wicked grin as she shimmied out of her dress.

Another first. Letting a guy see her naked with the lights on.

She didn't like being seen during intimate moments. She spent enough of her life in the spotlight, being scrutinised and evaluated, she didn't need it in the bedroom too.

But this was a new Liza, a new life.

Time to shed her old habits and take what she wanted.

Starting with the sexy guy beckoning her with a crook of his finger.

'Bronze is your colour,' he said, propping on his elbows when she straddled him.

'I like to colour coordinate my outfit and underwear.'

'While I appreciate the effort—' he snagged a bra strap and tugged it down, trailing a fingertip across her collarbones and doing the same on the other side '—I'd prefer to see you naked.'

He surged upward so fast she almost toppled off, but he wrapped his strong arms around her waist, anchoring her, holding her deliciously close. 'Now.'

She cupped his face between her hands and stared into his beautiful brown eyes. Eyes that held shadows lurking behind desire. Eyes that intrigued.

She briefly wondered if they were doing the right thing. Before ignoring that thought.

She wanted to celebrate her new life tonight. Having an exciting, impulsive fling with a hot guy who made her pulse race with the barest touch?

What a way to do it.

She inched towards him and murmured against his mouth, 'What are you waiting for?'

Wade knew Liza had vanished when he woke.

It didn't surprise him. He'd half expected her to disappear when he'd gone condom shopping.

Even now, after six hours of sensational sex and a much-needed two hours' sleep, he couldn't quite believe she'd stayed.

He'd known the moment they'd started flirting she wasn't the type to deliberately reel a guy in with the intention of a one-night stand.

She hadn't toyed with her hair or used fake coy smiles or accidentally on purpose touched him as so many women who came on to him did.

She hadn't pumped up his ego or been impressed by his trappings. How many times had women made a comment on his expensive watch, thinking he'd be flattered? Hell, even Babs couldn't go past a thirty-thousand-dollar watch without making some remark.

How wrong he'd been about Liza.

He'd likened her to his stepmother when he'd first seen her surrounded by lackeys at that party. The two women couldn't be more different.

Thoughts of Babs had him glancing at his watch and leaping out of bed.

He had a board meeting scheduled for ten this morning. A meeting he couldn't miss. The future of Qu Publishing depended on it.

While one-night stands weren't his usual style, Wade knew better than to search for a note or a business card or a scrawled phone number on the hotel notepad.

But that was exactly what he found himself doing as he glanced around the room, hoping for some snippet that indicated Liza wouldn't mind seeing him again.

He might not be in the market for a relationship but his time in Melbourne would be tension-filled enough without adding frustration to his woes.

He'd been lucky enough to meet an intriguing woman who made his body harden despite the marathon session they'd had. Why not stay in touch, date, whatever, while he was in town?

He might not know how long that would be, or how long it would take to ensure the publishing business that had been in his family for centuries was saved, but having someone like Liza to distract him from the corporate stress would be a bonus.

A quick reconnaissance yielded nothing. No contact details.

Disappointment pierced his hope. By her eagerness and wanton responses he'd assumed she'd had a good time too. And if she wasn't the one-night-stand type, why didn't she leave *something*? A note? A number?

Ironic, for a guy who didn't trust easily, he'd pinned his hopes on a virtual stranger trusting him enough to leave her contact details?

Then again, she'd trusted him with her body. A stupid thought, considering he wasn't naïve enough to assume sensational sex equated with anything beyond the heat of the moment.

A glance at the alarm clock beside the bed had him frowning and making a beeline for the bathroom.

He had a boardroom to convince.

Time enough later to use his considerable resources to discover the luscious Liza's contact details.

* * *

In all the years Shar, Cindy's caregiver, had stayed over, Liza had never needed to sneak past her 'the morning after'.

By Shar's raised eyebrows and smug smile as Liza eased off her sandals and tiptoed across the kitchen, only to be caught out when Shar stepped out of the pantry, the time for sneaking was long past.

Liza had been sprung.

'Good morning.' Shar held up a coffee plunger in one hand, a tin of Earl Grey in the other. 'Which would you prefer?'

'Actually, I think I'll hit the shower—'

'Your usual, then.' Shar grabbed Liza's favourite mug and measured leaves into a teapot. 'Nothing like a cuppa to lubricate the vocal cords first thing in the morning.'

'My vocal cords are fine.'

Liza cleared her throat anyway, knowing the huskiness came from too much moaning over the hours that Wade had pleasured her. Repeatedly.

Shar grinned. 'Good. Then you can tell me who put that blush in your cheeks.'

Liza darted a quick glance at Cindy's door.

'She's fine. Still asleep.'

One of the many things Liza loved about Shar was Cindy was the carer's priority. Liza had seen it instantly when she'd interviewed Shar for the job after her mum had left.

Liza had been a hapless eighteen-year-old, used to looking out for her younger sister but shocked to find herself a full-time carer overnight.

She'd needed help and the cerebral palsy association had come through for her in a big way. Organised respite care, assisted with ongoing physio and occupational therapy and sent part-time carers to help.

Liza had known Shar was the best when Cindy took an instant liking to her and the older woman didn't patronise either of them.

At that time Liza hadn't needed a mother— she'd had one and look how that had turned out— she'd needed a friend, and Shar had been all that and more over the years.

Liza couldn't have attended functions and cultivated her WAG image without Shar's help and they'd eased into a workable schedule over the years. Liza spent all day with Cindy and Shar came in several evenings a week, more if Liza's WAG duties had demanded it.

Liza had been lucky, being able to devote so much time to Cindy and support them financially. And when her investment matured today she'd be sure to give Shar a massive wage increase for her dedication, loyalty and friendship. And increase her hours to include days so Liza could find a job in marketing. One that didn't involve marketing herself in front of the cameras.

'Sit.' Shar pointed at the kitchen table, covered in Cindy's scrapbooking. 'Start talking.'

'Damn, you're bossy,' Liza said, not surprised to find a few muscles twanging as she slid onto the wooden chair.

She hadn't had a workout like that in…for ever.

Though labelling what she'd done with Wade a workout seemed rather crass and casual.

The passion they'd shared—the caresses, the strokes, the exploration of each other's bodies. She'd never been so uninhibited, so curious.

She knew the transient nature of their encounter had a lot to do with her wanton playfulness—easy to be bold with a guy she'd never see again.

So why did that thought leave her cold?

On waking, she'd spent an inordinate amount of time studying his features. The proud, straight nose with a tiny bump near the bridge, the dark stubble peppering his cheeks, the tiny scar near his right temple, the sensuous lips.

Those lips and what they'd done to her...oh boy.

'On second thought, I need more than a caffeine shot to hear this story.' Shar stood on tiptoe and grabbed the tin box storing their emergency brownie stash.

While Shar prepared the tea and chocolate fix, Liza wondered if she'd done the right thing in bolting. She had no clue about morning-after etiquette. Should she have left a thank-you note?

When she'd slid out of bed and done her best not to wake him, she'd dressed in record time yet spent another ten minutes dithering over a note. She'd even picked up a pen, only to let it fall from her fingers when she'd stared at the blank hotel paper with fear gripping her heart.

As she'd looked at that paper, she'd been tempted to leave her number. Before reality had set in. Wade hadn't questioned her or made polite small talk. He hadn't been interested in anything beyond the obvious. And that was enough of a wake-up call for her to grab her bag and get the hell out of that hotel room.

One-night stands were called that for a reason. That was all they were. One night.

The uncharacteristic yearning to see him again? To have a repeat performance of how incredible he made her feel? Not. Happening.

'Right, here we go.' Shar placed a steaming cup of Earl Grey in front of her along with two double-choc-fudge brownies on a side plate. 'Get that into you, then start talking.'

Liza cupped her hands around the hot cup and lifted it to her lips, inhaling the fragrant bergamot steam. Earl Grey was her comfort drink, guaranteed to make her relax.

She'd drunk two pots of the stuff the morning she'd woken to find her mum gone.

It hadn't been a shock. Louisa had been an emotionally absent mother for years before she'd left. Guess Liza should be grateful her mum had waited until Liza had turned eighteen before she'd done a runner, leaving her the legal guardian of Cindy.

Crazy thing was Liza had long forgiven her father for running out on them after Cindy's birth.

Men were fickle and couldn't stand a little hardship. She'd come home from her first day of school to find her dad shoving belongings into his car in front of a stoic mum.

Louisa had cried silent tears, holding a twelve-month-old Cindy in her arms, while her dad had picked Liza up, hugged her tight, and told her to take good care of her sister.

And she'd been doing it ever since.

While Liza might have forgiven—and forgotten—her dad, she couldn't forgive her mum as easily. Louisa had watched Cindy grow. Had been a good mum in her own way. But Liza had seen the signs. The subtle withdrawing of affection, longer respite visits away from the girls, the scrimping and saving of every cent.

Her mum hadn't left a note either. She'd just walked out of the door one morning with her suitcases and never looked back.

If Louisa expected Liza to be grateful for the birthday cards stacked with hundred-dollar bills that arrived every year on Cindy's birthday, she could think again.

Cindy needed love and caring, not guilt money.

Thankfully, with what Liza had done over the

last decade, Cindy's financial future was secure and they no longer needed her mum's money.

Now she needed to start doing stuff for *her* and first item on the agenda involved finding her dream job. One that didn't involve schmoozing or showing her best angle to the cameras.

She sipped at the tea, savouring the warmth.

'Could you drink that any slower?' Shar wiped brownie crumbs off her fingers and mimicked talking with her hand.

Liza placed a cup on the saucer and reached for a brownie, when Shar slapped her wrist. 'You can eat later. I want details, girlie.'

Liza chuckled. 'Better tell you something before you break a bone.'

Shar's hand continued to open and shut, miming chatter. 'Still not enough of this.'

'Okay, okay.' Liza leaned back and sighed. 'Henri's book launch was every bit as boring and pompous as him. I was doing the rounds, talking to the regular people. I got bored as usual.'

Then she'd stepped out onto that balcony and her life had changed in an instant.

Melodramatic? Hell yeah, but no matter where

her future led she'd never forget that one incredible night with Wade at the Westin.

'And?' Shar leaned forward and rubbed her hands together.

'I needed some fresh air, headed outside, met someone.'

'Now you're talking.'

Liza sighed. How to articulate the rest without sounding like a floozy?

'Shar, you know Cindy is my world, right?'

Shar's eyes lost their playful sparkle and she nodded, sombre. 'Never seen anyone as dedicated as you.'

'Everything I've done is for my little sis and I'd do it again in a heartbeat, but last night signalled a new beginning for me and when the opportunity to celebrate presented itself? Well, let's just say I grabbed it with both hands.'

Shar let out a soft whoop and glanced at Cindy's door. 'Good for you.' She leaned forward and wiggled her eyebrows. 'So how was he?'

Liza made a zipping motion across her lips. 'No kissing and telling here.'

Shar reached across and patted her forearm. 'All I can say is about time, love. You're a good girl, dating those dweebs to secure your financial future, making the most of your assets. About time you had a little fun.'

'There was nothing little about it,' Liza deadpanned, joining in Shar's laughter a second later.

'Hey, Liza, is it Coco Pops time?'

Liza's heart squished as it always did at the sound of Cindy's voice from behind her bedroom door. There was nothing she wouldn't do for her baby sister.

'You know the drill. Weet-Bix as usual,' Liza called out, draining the rest of her tea before heading to the bedroom to help Cindy dress.

'Are you going to see him again?' Shar asked as Liza paused with her hand on the doorknob.

Liza shook her head, the disappointment in Shar's expression matching hers.

Silly, as Liza didn't have time for disappointments. She had a secure investment about to mature, a new career in marketing to embark on and an easier life ahead.

No time at all to reminisce about the hottest night of her life and what might have been if she'd had the courage to leave her details.

'Trade you a pancake stack for the Weet-Bix,' Cindy said as Liza eased open the bedroom door.

The moment she saw Cindy's beaming, lop-sided smile, Liza wiped memories of Wade and focused on the number-one person in her life and her sole motivation.

Life was good.

She didn't have room in it for commanding, sexy guys, no matter how unforgettable.

CHAPTER FOUR

LIZA LITHGOW'S STYLE TIPS FOR MAXIMUM WAG WOW IMPACT

The Classics

You don't need money to create a WAG wow look. Designer bargains, vintage chic and good accessories can create an outfit that will have the paparazzi snap-happy.

To create a timeless, elegant look consistently, it's worthwhile investing in a few classic pieces, the items in any WAG's wardrobe that will always be in style.

- Little black dress. (A staple. Buy several: different lengths, necklines, fitting. The classic LBD is a lifesaver and can be combined with various jacket/shoe combinations to give the illusion of many different looks.)

- Jacket. (Make sure it's expensive and tailored. It will last for ever.)
- Heels. (Black patent leather stilettos will never go out of style.)
- Sunglasses. (Brand names are classy. Enlist the help of an honest shop assistant to ensure the shape/size suits your face.)
- Boots. (Black and brown leather boots can be worn with anything and everything. High heels and flats in both recommended.)
- Striped top. (Black and white stripes are a staple. Dress up or down.)
- Ballet flats. (Perfect to pop into your bag to use at the end of a long day at the Spring Racing Carnival or a long night of dancing.)
- Trousers. (Tailored black and beige will go with almost anything. Wide leg is elegant. Bootleg flattering.)
- Belt. (Thin, black leather. Classic.)
- Cardigan. (Cream cashmere, can't go wrong.)

- Clutch. (Smaller than a handbag yet makes a bigger statement.)

- Handbag. (Must carry everything including the kitchen sink but bigger isn't always better. Co-ordinate handbag to your outfit and shoes. Choose neutral colours: black, tan, brown. Mid-size with handles and shoulder strap best.)

- Jeans. (Discover which style suits you best and stick with it. But for maximum WAG wow, have denim in various cuts: skinny, bootleg, boyfriend, etc.)

- Trenchcoat. (Double-breasted, belted, beige. Classic.)

- Watch. (For timeless elegance, invest in an expensive watch. People notice.)

- Bling. (Take the 'less is best' approach. Diamond stud earrings. Thin white gold necklace. Unless your sports star partner wins the World Cup or Olympics for his team, then get him to buy you a diamond mine and then some.)

WITH CINDY ENGROSSED in her electronic tablet, Liza ducked into the shower, something she should've done the moment she'd arrived home to scrub off the lingering smell of Wade's aftershave.

Maybe that was why she hadn't? For the moment she towelled off, slipped on her skinny jeans and a turquoise long-sleeved T-shirt, and padded into the kitchen to say bye to Shar, she missed it—his evocative crisp citrus scent.

Irrational? Absolutely, but it wasn't every day an amazingly hot guy left his designer aftershave imprinted on her skin.

The perky hum died in her throat as she caught sight of Shar waving a stack of messages at her.

'These are for you.'

Liza raised an eyebrow. 'All of them?'

Shar nodded. 'I didn't want to bombard you when you first came in.'

'More like you wanted the goss and knew those would distract me.'

'That too.' Shar grinned and handed them over. 'Looks like some editor from Qu Publishing is mighty persistent.'

Liza groaned. 'Can't those morons get a clue and stop badgering me?'

'Doesn't look like it.' Shar pointed to the message slips in her hand. 'All those are from her.'

'No way.'

Liza flicked through the lot, twelve in all. Nine yesterday when she'd been out in the afternoon and later at the party, three while she'd been in the shower this morning.

'She said she'd call back in ten minutes.'

'Like hell.' Liza stomped over to the bin and dumped the lot. 'I'm sick to death of being pestered by this mob and I'm going to put a stop to it.'

Shar punched the air. 'You go, girl.'

Liza grinned. 'While I'm kicking some publisher butt, maybe you should stop watching daytime TV?'

'Careful, cheeky.' Shar shooed her away. 'You've got an hour before I need to leave, so hop to it.'

Liza didn't need to be told twice.

No way, no how, would she ever sell her story. Cindy needed to be protected at all costs and the last thing she wanted was a bunch of strangers reading about their lives and intruding.

For they would, she had no doubt. There'd be

book tours and blog tours and a social media explosion if she told all. It was why these Qu Publishing vultures were hounding her. They knew a best-seller when they saw it.

Laughable, really. What would they say if they knew the truth? That she'd invented a fake life to protect her real one?

That every event, every lash extension, every designer gown, had fitted a deliberate persona she'd cultivated to get what she wanted.

Lifelong security for her little sis.

And when her financial adviser rang today and gave her the good news about her investments maturing, she could put away her lash curler and hair straightener for ever.

Yeah, the sooner she set this publisher straight, the better.

She yanked on black knee-high boots and shrugged into a sable leather vest with fake fur collar. While being a WAG had been a pain, some of the perks, like the gorgeous designer clothes she'd got to keep on occasion, had been great.

She'd miss the clothes. She wouldn't miss the rest.

Time to hang up her stilettos and set the record straight.

* * *

Wade strode into the boardroom with five minutes to spare then spent the next thirty listening to a bunch of boring agenda items that could've been wrapped up in half that time.

He wished they'd cut to the chase.

The future of Qu Publishing depended on a bunch of old fuddy-duds that wouldn't know a profit margin if it jumped up and bit them on the ass.

The members of the board were old school, had been best buddies with his dad and, in turn, were *rather fond of his delightful wife Babs.*

When the chairman had articulated that little gem at the party last night, he'd wanted to hurl.

Was Wade the only guy who could see through her fake wiles?

By the board's decision to back Babs in her quest to sell Qu Publishing? Hell yeah.

He knew it would take a monumental effort to save this company. From the accounts down to the staff, Qu needed a major overhaul. And to do that they needed a cash injection, in the form of a mega best-seller.

Which reminded him. He needed to sign that

WAG to a contract today. He'd up the ante with a massive cash injection from his own pocket, a hefty six-figure sum she couldn't refuse. From what he'd heard in snippets from memos, her sordid tale would be a blockbuster. Serial WAG, dated an international soccer star and a basketball player, a media darling from magazines to TV, a practised socialite who'd appeared everywhere in Australia from all reports.

He couldn't care less if she'd dated the entire Socceroos team and what she'd worn to do it but that kind of gossip drivel made the average reader drool. And sold books.

Thankfully his company had branched out into the lucrative young adult market and were making a killing but Qu readers expected factual biographies, so no use getting too radical when he'd probably only have a few months tops to save the joint.

Yeah, he needed to get that WAG to sign ASAP. He'd get straight onto it, once this meeting wound up.

'And now, gentlemen, we come to the last item on the agenda.' The chairman cleared his throat and glared at Wade as if he'd proposed they collectively run down Bourke Street naked. 'As you've seen from the proposal Mr Urquart *Junior* emailed us yesterday, he wants to give the company three months to see if it can turn a healthy profit.'

Wade bristled at the emphasis on junior. He'd paid his dues in this company in his younger days, had done a hell of a lot more in London where his business was booming compared to this languishing one.

Thoughts of the disparity saddened him and pricked his guilt as nothing else could. If he hadn't been so pig-headed, so stubborn, so distrustful, he could've helped his dad while he had the chance. Could've done a lot more, such as mend the gap between them *he'd* created. A regret he'd have to live with for the rest of his life. A regret that would be eased once he saved Qu.

'To do this, he proposes Qu Publishing will have a *New York Times* best-seller on its hands within the year, along with accompanying publicity blitz in the form of social media, television and print ads.'

A titter of unease echoed around the conference

table and Wade squared his shoulders, ready for the battle of his life.

No way would he let Babs win. She'd made a laughing stock out of his dad; damned if he sat back and let her do the same to his dad's legacy.

'We usually put agenda items like this to a vote.' The chairman steepled his fingers and rested his elbows on the table like a presiding judge. 'But I don't think it's necessary in this case.'

Wade clenched his hands under the table. Pompous old fools. 'Gentlemen, if you'd let me reiterate my proposal—'

'That won't be necessary, Wade.'

The chairman's use of his first name surprised him, but not as much as his dour expression easing into a smile. 'Every member here knew your father and respected what he achieved with this company. But times are tough in the publishing industry. The digital boom has hit our print runs hard and readers aren't buying paperbacks or hardbacks like they used to. Economically, it makes sense to sell.'

Wade opened his mouth to respond and the chairman held up his hand. 'But we admire what you've achieved with your company in London.

And we like your ambition. Reminds us of your father. So we're willing to give you three months to turn this company around.'

Jubilant and relieved, Wade nodded. 'Thanks for the opportunity.'

'We understand the profits won't soar until we have that promised best-seller on our hands, but if you can prove to us we'll have that guaranteed hit with buyers' pre-orders in three months, we won't vote with Babs to sell Qu. Got it?'

'Loud and clear.' Wade stood, ready to hit the ground running. His first task? Get that WAG to sign on the dotted line. 'Thanks, gentlemen, you won't be sorry.'

He'd make sure of it.

The idiots were stonewalling her and Liza wasn't happy.

'You won't take no for an answer. Your editors won't take no for an answer so I'm taking this to the top.' She leaned over the receptionist, who, to her credit, didn't flinch. 'Who's your boss?'

The receptionist darted a frantic glance to her right. 'He can't see you now.'

'Like hell.' Liza strode towards the sole double doors where the receptionist had looked.

'You can't do that,' the perky blonde yelled and Liza held up her hand.

'Watch me.'

Liza didn't stop to knock, twisting the door-knob and flinging open the door before she could second-guess the wisdom of barging into a CEO's inner sanctum unannounced.

They were relentlessly harassing her; let them see how they liked getting a taste of their own medicine.

The editors wouldn't listen so the only way she'd get this mob to leave her alone was to have the order given from the top.

However, as she strode into the office her plan to clear up this mess hit a major snag.

For the guy sitting behind a huge glass-topped desk, the guy barking orders into a phone, the guy clearly in charge of Qu Publishing, was the guy who'd set her body alight last night.

Wade stopped mid-sentence as Liza barged into his office like a glamazon bikie chick.

She wore tight denim, a clingy long-sleeved

T-shirt, a black leather vest and the sexiest knee-high boots he'd ever seen.

By her grim expression and wild hair, make that an avenging bikie chick.

He'd expected to never see her again. Had secretly hoped he would.

After the crappy year he'd endured—learning his dad hadn't trusted him with the truth about his heart condition, accepting how far their relationship had deteriorated, his dad's death, Babs's sell-out plans—maybe the big guy upstairs had finally granted him a break.

'Set up a meeting with the buyers and we'll discuss covers and digital launch later,' he said, hanging up on his deputy without waiting for an answer.

He stood, surprised by Liza's stunned expression. Wasn't as if they were strangers. She'd obviously sought him out, though the dramatic entrance was a surprise.

Most people couldn't get past Jodi, the receptionist, he'd been told. His dad had raved about her and from what he'd seen of her work ethic in half a day, the woman was a dynamo.

Maybe Liza had been so desperate to see him she couldn't wait?

Yeah, and maybe that WAG would saunter into his office any second and give him her completed biography bound in hardcover.

'Hey, Liza, good to see you again—'

'*You're* the CEO of Qu Publishing?'

She made it sound as if he ran an illegal gambling den, her eyes narrowing as she crossed his office to stand on the opposite side of his desk. 'Oh, it all makes sense now. That's why you slept with me.'

She muttered an expletive and shook her head, leaving him increasingly clueless as he waved away Jodi, who'd stuck her head around the door, and motioned for her to close it. Jodi mouthed an apology before doing as he said, leaving him alone with an irate, irrational woman who stared at him as if she wanted to drive a letter opener through his heart.

He wished he'd stashed it in his top drawer once he'd done the mail.

'Time out.' He made a T sign with his hands and gestured towards the grey leather sofas. 'Why don't we sit and discuss this?'

Whatever *this* was, because he had no idea why she'd gone crazy on him for being CEO of Qu and what that had to do with having great sex.

Her lips compressed in a mutinous line as she marched towards the sofas and slumped into one, ensuring she sprawled across it so he had no chance of sitting nearby.

Ironic, when last night she couldn't get close enough. And the feeling had been entirely mutual.

Even now, with confusion clogging his head, he couldn't switch off the erotic images.

Liza straddling him. Underneath him. On her hands and knees in front of him.

The sweet taste of her. The sexy sounds she made. The softness of her skin. The intoxicating rose and vanilla scent that had lingered on his sheets.

Their night together had been sensational, the most memorable sex he'd had in a long time.

Hell, he was hard just thinking about it.

Then he looked into her dark blue eyes and saw something that shocked him.

Betrayal.

What had he done to make her look at him as if he'd ripped her world apart?

'You used me,' she said, jabbing a finger in his direction before curling it into a fist as if she wanted to slug him. 'Proud of yourself?'

'I don't know what you're talking about.' He poured a glass of water and edged it across the table. 'Can we backtrack a little so I have a hope in Hades of following this bizarre conversation?'

'Drop the innocent act. The moment I walked in here and saw you, everything made sense.'

Her fingers dug into the leather, as if she needed an anchor. 'Why you asked me to have a drink with you last night, inviting me back to your suite, the sex…' She trailed off and glanced away, her blush rather cute. 'Totally freaking low.'

She thought he'd used her. Why? None of this made sense.

'From what I remember, you approached me on that balcony. And from your participation in the phenomenal sex, you were just as into it as me.'

Her blush deepened as she dragged her defiant gaze to meet his. 'What I don't get is why you'd think I'd sell my story after I discovered your identity?'

She shook her head. 'Or are you so full of your-self you thought I'd remember the sex and sign on the dotted line?'

Pieces of the puzzle shifted, jiggled and finally aligned in a picture that blew his mind.

'*You're* the WAG we're trying to sign?'

'Like you didn't know.' She snorted in disgust. 'Nice touch last night, by the way. "Your name sounds familiar"? Sheesh.'

Hot damn.

Liza Lithgow was the WAG he needed to save Qu Publishing.

And he'd slept with her.

Way to go with messing up big time.

'Liza, listen to me—'

'Why the hell should I?' Her chest heaved with indignation and he struggled to avert his eyes. No use fuelling her anger. 'You *lied* to me. You *used* me—'

'Stop right there.' He held up his hand and, amazingly, her tirade ceased. 'Yeah, I knew Qu Publishing was pursuing a WAG for a biography but I had no idea that was you.'

'But I told you my name—'

'Which I had vaguely heard but, come on, I'd

only landed in Melbourne for the first time in six months a few hours earlier. I'd come into the office briefly before heading to that party. So yeah, I'd probably seen your name on a document or memo or something, that's how it registered.'

He leaned closer, hating how she leaned back. 'But everything that happened between us last night? Nothing to do with us publishing your biography and everything to do with...'

Damn, wouldn't do any good blurting out what last night had been about. He didn't need her feeling sorry for him. He needed her onside, ready to tell her story so the board gave Qu more than a temporary reprieve.

'With what?'

At least her tone had lost some of its vitriol.

'With you and me and the connection we shared.'

'Connections can be manufactured,' she said, her steely stare speaking volumes.

She didn't believe him.

When he'd first glimpsed her last night he'd associated feminine and bimbo in the same sentence. Then when she'd spoken to him, he'd re-evaluated the bimbo part pretty damn quick. He never would've thought her attractive outer shell hid balls of steel.

'Maybe, but the way we burned up the sheets last night?' He winked, trying to charm his way out of this godforsaken mess. 'I wasn't faking it. Were you?'

At last, a glimmer of softening as her shoulders relaxed and her glare lost some of its warrior fierceness. 'Forget last night—'

'Big ask,' he said, continuing with his plan to use a little honey rather than vinegar to coerce her into giving him a fair hearing. 'Don't know about you, but the way we were together last night? Pretty damn rare.'

She glanced away, but not before he glimpsed a spark of heat in those expressive blue eyes.

'And have to say, I was pretty disappointed this morning to find you gone, because I would've really liked to...'

What? See her again? Pick up where they'd left off? Prove their attraction extended beyond a first-time fluke?

Best he stop there.

He needed this woman onside to save his father's business. A business he should've seen was floundering before it was too late. Before his prejudices had irrevocably damaged his relationship with his dad and ended up with him not knowing his dad was dying before he could make amends.

Saving Qu, saving his dad's legacy, was the one thing he could do to make this semi-right. He could live with the guilt. He couldn't live with knowing he hadn't given this mission his best shot.

Her gaze swung back, locking on his with unerring precision. 'Look, I'll admit we shared something special last night. But I don't have room in my life for complications.'

He should drop this topic and move on to more important stuff, like getting her to sign. But he couldn't help teasing her a little. Maybe if she loosened up he'd have more chance of convincing her Qu Publishing were the only mob in town worth considering for her tell-all tale?

'And that's what I'd be if I called you for a date? Dinner? A movie?'

She nodded. 'You're a nice guy but—'

'Nice?' He winced. 'Ouch.'

She rolled her eyes. 'Your ego's not that fragile, considering you picked me up at a party after knowing me less than ten minutes.'

'And you're not as immune to me as you're pretending considering you agreed to a drink after knowing me less than ten minutes.'

'Touché.' The corners of her mouth curved upward. 'Let's forget last night and move on to more important matters, like why your office is bugging me constantly and won't take no for an answer.'

'Glad to hear the editors are doing their jobs.'

Her mouth hardened. Maybe he'd taken the levity a tad far?

'You think this is a joke?' She shook her head, her ponytail swishing temptingly over one shoulder, reminding him of how her blonde hair had looked spread out on the pillows and draped across his chest. And lower. 'I can't count the number of phone calls to my mobile. And now someone in your office has used underhanded tactics to discover my *unlisted* number and I'm being pestered at home? Poor form.'

She sighed and a sliver of remorse pierced his resolve to get this deal done today.

'I hate having my private life invaded and it's time you and your cohorts backed off.'

He should feel guilty but he didn't. While Liza didn't fit the typical WAG profile, she couldn't live the life of a famous sportsman's girlfriend without loving some of the attention. And having her private life open to scrutiny came with the territory.

All he wanted was to delve a little deeper, give his readers something more and they in turn would give him what he needed most: money to save Qu.

'What if we don't back off?'

He threw it out there, expecting her to curse and threaten.

He wasn't prepared for the shimmer of tears that disappeared so fast after a few blinks he wondered if he'd imagined them.

'Two words for you.' She held up two fingers. 'Harassment charges.'

Idle threats didn't scare him.

But the guilty twist his heart gave at the sight of those tears? Absolutely terrified.

He didn't handle waterworks well. Even Babs's

crocodile tears at his dad's funeral had made him supremely uncomfortable.

That had to be the reason he'd gone soft for a moment and actually considered backing down after seeing Liza's tears.

'Maybe if you gave us a chance to explain our offer, you may feel differently?'

Her expression turned mutinous. 'There's nothing you can say or do that will convince me to sell my story.'

Okay, he was done being cool. He'd tried the truth; she hadn't believed him. He'd tried charming her; she'd lightened up for a scant minute. Time to go for the jugular. And do his damnedest to forget that his lips had coaxed and nipped her in that very vicinity last night.

'A ghost writer, a mid-six-figure advance, a more than generous royalty percentage, all for a story that most people have probably heard before?'

Her glacial glare dropped the temperature in the room by five degrees. 'It's called *private* life for a reason. I don't give a flying Frisbee what people surmise or print or think about me. As of last night I'm done with all the hoopla so you and your cronies can invent a fictional story for all I care.'

The first flicker of unease soon gave way to fear. Wade never took no for an answer, not in the business world. But Liza's adamant stance put a serious dent in his confidence he could woo her to Qu.

He needed her biography.

Failure wasn't an option.

'Look, Liza, I'm sure we can come to some type of mutually beneficial agreement—'

'What part of *you can take your offer and stick it* don't you understand?'

With that, he watched his final chance at saving his father's legacy stride out of the door.

CHAPTER FIVE

LIZA LITHGOW'S STYLE TIPS FOR MAXIMUM WAG WOW IMPACT

The City

Depending how famous the sportsman, WAGs get to travel, but home is where the heart is. Here are my tips for getting to know beautiful Melbourne.

1. Acland Street, St. Kilda. (An iconic street lined with cake and pastry shops. Dare you to stop at trying one! And on Sundays, check out the market on the nearby Esplanade.)

2. Lygon Street, Carlton. (The Little Italy of Melbourne, a street lined with fabulous restaurants and cafés. Try the thin-crusted pizzas and the espressos. You

won't be able to walk past the gelato outlets without succumbing!)

3. Victoria Street, Richmond. (If you love Vietnamese food this street is for you. Choose from the many restaurants filled with fragrant steam from soups and sizzling dishes. And if you love to shop, check out nearby Bridge Road with its many brand outlets. Bargains galore!)

4. Southbank. (Stroll along the Yarra River and try to decide which fabulous café you'll dine in. Or check out the funky shops.)

5. Docklands. (If you like to eat by the water's edge, this area is for you. Many restaurants, many nationalities.)

6. Dandenongs. (The mountain range just over an hour from the city, where you'll find many quaint B&Bs, craft shops and cafés to explore. Also home to the iconic Puffing Billy steam train, which takes you on a leisurely ride through the lush forest.)

7. Phillip Island. (If you like cute animals

and the beach, you'll love this place. Stroll the surf beach and, at night, check out the fairy penguins.)

8. Federation Square. (In the heart of the city, Fed Square is home to restaurants, cafés and cultural displays.)

9. MCG. (WAGs in all sports codes have usually visited the Melbourne Cricket Ground at some stage. Home of the AFL Grand Final, watched by millions around the world. A visit to the sports museum here is worth it.)

10. Little Bourke Street. (In the heart of the city, Chinatown in Melbourne, lined with fabulous Chinese restaurants. Hard to choose!)

11. Chapel Street, South Yarra. (About ten minutes from the city, you'll find an eclectic mix of boutiques, restaurants and cafés here. Worth strolling to people-watch alone.)

12. Queen Victoria Market. (Food and fashion bargains, with everything in between. A fun way to pass a few hours.)

13. Daylesford. (This quaint town is in the heart of 'Spa Country'. The amazing baths at neighbouring town Hepburn Springs are a must visit. The area is home to gourmet food and artists. Visit the Convent Gallery for a combination of both.)

14. Brunswick Street, Fitzroy. (An eclectic mix of cafés, boutiques and clubs.)

LIZA HAD MADE it to the elevator when her mobile rang. Considering her hands shook with fury, she wouldn't have answered it if she hadn't been expecting her financial adviser's call imparting good news.

Her investments had matured and Cindy was set for life. The figures she'd crunched for long-term ongoing medical and allied health care had terrified her but now, after years of careful saving and investing, she could rest easy in the knowledge that should anything happen to her, Cindy would be financially secure.

It made every blister from impossibly high stilettos, every sacrificed chocolate mousse so not

to gain weight, every artful fend-off from a groping sleaze worth it.

Ignoring the death glare from the receptionist,
she fished out her phone, checked the number on
display and hit the answer button.

'Hey, Walden, good to hear from you. I've been
expecting your call.'

A long silence greeted her.

'Walden?'

A throat cleared. 'Uh, sorry, Miss Lithgow, this
is Ullric.'

Okay, so Walden's assistant had called instead.
A first, but not surprising considering Walden
had a full schedule whenever she'd tried to slot
in a meeting lately.

'Hey, Ullric. I'm assuming you have good news
for me about my investments?'

Again, a long pause and this time a finger of
foreboding strummed Liza's spine.

'About that…' His hesitancy made her clench
the phone. 'Afraid I have some bad news.'

Liza's heart stalled before kick starting with
a painful wallop. 'I don't like the sound of that.
What's happened?'

Ullric blew out a long breath that transferred

into annoying static. 'Mr Wren has disappeared and his clients' funds are gone.'

Liza's legs collapsed and she sagged against the nearest wall.

This couldn't be happening.

A delusion, brought on by the shock of discovering Wade had potentially used her.

Though she wasn't prone to delusions and Ullric's pronouncement underlined with regret seemed all too real.

'What—how—?'

'The fraud squad are investigating. His assets have been seized, but from what I've been told the client funds have been siphoned into offshore accounts.'

Liza swore. Several times. The only words she could form, let alone articulate.

'I'm sorry, Miss Lithgow. The police will be in touch and I'll let you know if I hear anything—'

Liza disconnected, the mobile falling from her fingers and hitting the carpet with a muted thud.

Her life savings.

Gone.

In that moment every stupid awards ceremony and dress fitting and magazine article she'd endured flashed before her eyes in a teasing kaleidoscope of humiliation.

Everything she'd worn, everything she'd said, for the last umpteen years had been to build a sizable nest egg for Cindy in case something happened to her.

And now she had nothing.

Tears burned the backs of her eyes and a lump welled in her throat.

What the hell was she going to do?

A pair of expensive loafers came into view and her head fell forward until her chin almost touched her chest. Great, that was all she needed to make her failure complete. Wade Urquart to witness it.

'I think this belongs to you.'

He picked up her mobile phone and held it out.

Liza was bone-deep tired. Exhausted to the core, where she'd regularly drawn on a well of courage to face the media, the crowds, the critics.

But she had to leave here with some snippet of dignity intact and right now, sitting in a crumpled heap on Wade's expensive carpet, she'd lost most of it.

'Here.' He dropped the mobile into her open bag and held out his hand. 'Let me help you up.'

'I think you've helped enough,' she muttered, but accepted his hand all the same, grateful for the hoist up, for her legs still wobbled embarrassingly.

'Are you okay?'

She couldn't look at his face, didn't want to see the pity there, so she focused on the second button of his crisp pale blue business shirt.

He'd lost the tie, a snazzy navy striped one that had set off his suit earlier. The fact she'd noticed? A residual tell from her WAG days when it paid to be observant about the latest fashion. And nothing at all to do with the fact she could recite every item of clothing he'd worn last night and what he'd looked like without it.

When she didn't answer, he placed his hand under her elbow and guided her towards his office. 'Come with me.'

Liza wanted to protest. She wanted to yell at the injustice of busting her butt all these years, and for what?

But all the fight had drained out of her when she'd hung up and it wouldn't hurt to have a glass of water, muster the last of her meagre reserves of courage and face the trip home.

Home. Where Cindy was.

Damn.

She'd had their future all figured out.

Now she had nothing. She now needed to find a job, and pronto. The idea of trying to juggle a new job and how it would affect Cindy's care, without the security of money... Pain gripped her chest and squeezed, hard.

The tears she'd been battling welled again and this time spilled over and trickled down her cheeks.

Wade darted a glance her way but she resolutely stared ahead and dashed away the tears with her other hand.

Thankfully, he didn't question her further until he'd led her to the sofa she'd so haughtily vacated five minutes earlier and closed the door.

He didn't speak, setting a glass of water in front of her and taking a seat opposite, giving her time to compose herself.

His thoughtfulness made her like him. And she didn't want to like him, not after what she'd discovered today.

In fact, when she'd huffed out of here she'd assumed she'd never see him again—and had steadfastly ignored that small part of her that had been disappointed at the thought.

She gulped the water, hoping it would dislodge the giant lump of sadness in her throat. It did little as she battled the hopelessness of her situation.

Her new life? In ruins.

Cindy's safety net? Gone.

She'd been screwed over by some smarmy financial adviser whose balls she'd crush in a vice if she ever laid eyes on him again. Yeah, as if that were likely.

Her financial ruin meant she was back to square one, but no way could she don designer outfits and start prancing around on some egotistical sportsman's arm again.

Mentally, she couldn't take it any more. Physically, late twenties was getting old for a WAG and she was done with the paparazzi scrutiny.

Which left her plum out of options.

'Want to tell me what happened out there?'

'Not really.' She topped up the glass from a water pitcher, grateful her hand didn't shake.

'I don't think my offer was that repugnant so it had to be something else.'

'It was your offer.'

The lie tripped off her tongue. Better for him to think that than know the truth.

That she'd lost her life savings and had no way out of this disastrous situation.

'You're not a very good liar.'

'How would you know?'

He raised an eyebrow at her acerbic tone. 'Because contrary to what you believe, I actually spent time paying attention to you last night and I reckon you've got one of the most guileless faces I've seen when you let your guard down.'

Damn, how did he do that? Undermine her with insight when he shouldn't know her at all?

'I can't talk about it.' She shook her head, tugging on the end of her ponytail and twisting it around her finger. 'Besides, it's my problem. There's nothing you can do about it.'

'Sure?' He braced his elbows on his knees. 'Don't forget, if you're ever in a bind all you have to do is accept my offer and you'd be set for life.'

As his words sank in, Liza's hand stilled and she flicked her ponytail back over her shoulder.

No. She couldn't.

But what other option did she have?

Agreeing to a tell-all biography would replenish her lost savings and ensure Cindy's security.

Relating a few stories to a ghost writer had to be less painful than going down the fake tan/lash extensions/hair foils route again.

She wanted to pursue a career in marketing and accepting this book deal would allow that.

The only catch was Cindy.

Liza didn't want the world knowing her private business and she wanted to protect Cindy at all costs. She'd done a good job of it so far, keeping her public persona completely separate from the reality of her home life.

Any publicity shots and interviews with Jimmy had been done at his palatial apartment, same with Henri. It had been important to her, deliberately misleading the press to think she lived with the sports stars so they wouldn't hound her or, worse, follow her.

Not that she was ashamed of the modest Californian bungalow she shared with Cindy, but her goal to ultimately protect Cindy at all costs meant she wanted their real home and the life they shared to be off-limits to the public.

The guys had never mentioned Cindy in interviews either, though she knew that had more to do with them not wanting to be tainted—even by association—with a disability they couldn't handle or had no knowledge of rather than her request.

Jimmy and Henri were too egotistical to want to field questions about their girlfriend's disabled sister so they'd pretended Cindy hadn't existed. While their apparent disregard had hurt, it had been exactly as she wanted it.

Her protecting Cindy over the years had worked, but how could she sustain that in a biography?

She had physically invented a façade all these years, playing up to the image of the perfect WAG.

What if she invented a story to go with it?

It wasn't as if she hadn't done it before when she'd been interviewed. She'd give a few scant details, an embellishment here, a truth stretched there. No one would be wiser if she did the same in her biography.

She could lay out the basics of her upbringing and focus on the interesting stuff, like her
relationships with Jimmy and Henri. That was
what people were really interested in anyway,
the whole 'what's it like dating a famous sports
star?' angle.

Yeah, she could do this.

Continue her WAG role a little longer, but behind the scenes this time. Had to be easier than
strutting in front of A-listers and faking it.

But she'd told Wade to shove his offer so appearing too eager would be a dead giveaway
something was wrong, and she didn't want him
prying.

If she had to do this, it had to be a strictly business deal. From now on, her personal life was off-
limits. Unless it involved inventing a little drama
for the ghost writer.

'What if I was crazy enough to reconsider your
offer? What would it entail?'

He masked his surprise quickly. 'We'd have
a contract to you by this afternoon. Standard
publishing contract with clearly stated royalty
rates, world rights, advance, no option to your
next book.'

Next book? Heck, she could barely scrimmage enough suitably juicy info for this one. Though she'd love to publish a book raising the awareness of cerebral palsy and give an insight for carers. It was something she'd considered over the years: using her high profile to educate people regarding the lifelong condition.

But then she imagined the intrusiveness on Cindy's life—the interview requests, the demands, the interference on her schedule and the potentially damaging physical effects linked to emotional fragility in CP sufferers—and Liza balked.

Cindy thrived on routine and the last thing Liza wanted for her sister was a potential setback. Or, worse, increased spasticity in her muscles because she got too excited or too stressed. Most days were hard enough to get through without added complications and that was what spotlighting her sister's cerebral palsy could do.

Embellishing her so-called glamorous life and leaving Cindy out of it would be a lot easier.

'How much is the advance?'

He named a six-figure sum that made her head spin.

Were people that desperate to read a bunch of stuff about her life?

Considering how she'd been occasionally stalked by paparazzi eager for a scoop while dating Jimmy and Henri, she had her answer.

'The advance is released in increments. A third on signing, a third on acceptance of the manu-script and a third on publishing.'

'And when would that be?'

'Six months.'

She laughed. 'You're kidding? How can you publish a book in six months?'

'Buyers are lined up. Ghost writer ready to start tomorrow if you can. Week-long interview process, two weeks writing the book, straight to copy and line editors, then printers.'

Liza knew little about publishing but market-ing was her game and she'd interned at a small publishing house while at uni. No way could a book get turned around in six months.

'Do you have a marketing plan?'

A slight frown creased his brow. 'Have to admit, Qu is lagging in that department at the moment. I want to bring the company into the twenty-first century with online digital instalments of books, massive social media campaigns, exclusive digital releases on our website.'

'So what's the problem? Hire someone.'

He tugged at his cuffs, the first sign she'd seen him anything but confident since she'd arrived. 'Turnaround time on this book is tight.'

'I'll say.' She shook her head. 'Six-month release date? Impossible.'

'And you can say that with your extensive publishing experience?'

She didn't like his sarcasm, didn't like the fact it hurt more.

'Matter of fact, I interned for a publisher during my marketing degree.'

'Next you'll be telling me you're applying for the job.'

And just like that, Liza had a bamboozling idea. For the first time since that soul-destroying phone call earlier, hope shimmered to life and gave her the confidence to make her idea happen.

'That's a great idea. Why don't you give me the marketing job on this book and I'll make sure it's the best damn book this company has ever published?'

He fixed her with an incredulous stare. 'Let me

get this straight. You want a publishing contract *and* a marketing job here? After basically telling me to stick my offer—'

'Call it a WAG's prerogative to change her mind.' She smiled, hoping it would soften him up. 'What do you say? Do we have a deal?'

'What we have here is you not telling me everything and then having the cheek to try and coerce me into giving you a job too.'

'Take it or leave it.'

Yeah, as if she could afford to call his bluff.

If he left it, she'd be back to strapping on her stilettos and smiling for the cameras again. She shuddered.

Those sensual lips that had explored every part of her body eased into a smile.

'You drive a hard bargain, Liza, but you've got yourself a deal.'

Liza could've hugged him.

She settled for a sedate shake of hands, though there was nothing remotely sedate about the way her body buzzed as his fingers curled around hers.

That part of her plan where she kept dealings with Wade strictly business?

Would be sorely tested.

CHAPTER SIX

LIZA LITHGOW'S STYLE TIPS FOR MAXIMUM WAG WOW IMPACT

The Big Chill

Melbourne is renowned for its chilly winters but that doesn't mean WAGs need to lose their wow. Here's how to beat the big chill:

1. Even though your body isn't on show as much, maintain moisturised, smooth skin. Indulge in home-made natural masks made from egg whites, avocado and honey. Exfoliate dry heels, lavish with moisturiser and wear warm socks to bed. Continue to drink two litres of water a day. Evening events will continue throughout winter and you need to be at your glamorous best.

2. Surround yourself with warm textiles at

home. Fluffy throws and cuddly cushions, perfect for snuggling inside.

3. Choose to stay home occasionally rather
than doing the constant social whirl of
nightclub openings, theatre and movie
premieres. Curl up with a hot chocolate
and watch DVDs.

4. Stay warm. Invest in a pair of snug Uggs
and a cosy blanket to cover yourself
with while curled on the couch.

5. Scented candles are perfect for creating
a winter ambiance. From vanilla to cin-
namon, infuse your room with warmth.

6. Whip up a feast. Check out new cook-
books. Invest in a slow cooker. Surround yourself with fresh ingredients
and herbs. And enjoy the results of your
labour while whizzing around a warm
kitchen.

7. Relax. Take a long, hot bath, slip into
comfy clothes, pour a glass of red and
curl up on the couch with the latest best-
seller.

8. Warm up. On rainy days, get active.

Whether yoga at home or a local Zumba class, having a workout is good for the mind, body and soul.

9. Rug up and take a walk. Head to a local park or the beautiful Botanical Gardens near the city.

10. A rainy day is perfect for all those little jobs you've put off: sort through your old photos, spring clean your closet, organise your filing cabinet. You'll feel satisfied and warm by the end of it.

11. Pep up your wardrobe. Investing in a few key pieces will glam up your look. A good quality woollen coat and black high-heeled and flat-heeled knee-high boots can be used for many seasons.

12. Check out other sports. While WAGs get to attend all her partner's games, why not learn about a new sport? Melbourne is the home of Australian Rules Football in winter. Pick a team. Don the colours and show your patriotism.

13. If all else fails and the cold is getting you down, book a weekend away to escape

and make sure it's somewhere tropical. Winters in Queensland are notoriously mild and after a two-hour plane trip you could be soaking up the sun.

WADE HAD GIVEN up figuring women out a long time ago.

He dated them, he wooed them, he liked them, but that was where it ended. Any guy who lost his head over a woman was asking for trouble.

He'd seen it firsthand with his dad.

Not that he'd begrudged the old man happiness. Far from it. Quentin had raised him alone after his mum died when he was a toddler, devoting his time to his business and Wade with little room for anything else.

Then when Wade had started uni Babs had come along and his dad had been smitten. Wade had been appalled.

He'd seen right through the gold-digging younger woman; probably why Babs had hated him on sight. The feeling had been entirely mutual.

But Wade had seen the way his dad lit up around Babs and while he'd tried to broach the delicate subject of age differences and financial situations, one ferocious glare from his dad had seen him backing down.

They'd been married within a year and, as much as Wade hated to admit it, Babs had been good for Quentin. They'd had a good ten years together but Wade had left for London after two.

He couldn't pretend to like Babs and he saw what the barely hidden animosity did to his dad. It caused an irrevocable tension between them and while neither of them mentioned it, it was there all the same.

Wade had stayed away deliberately, only catching up with Quentin on his infrequent trips to London, invariably alone. They talked publishing and the digital revolution and cricket but Wade never asked how Babs was and his dad never volunteered the information.

The fact he hadn't seen his dad in the fifteen months before his death? And that Quentin hadn't trusted him enough to tell him the truth about the heart condition that had ultimately killed him? The biggest regret of Wade's life and the sole reason he was here, trying to save the company that had meant the world to his dad.

He should've known about his dad's dodgy heart. He should've had the opportunity to make amends for deliberately fostering emotional distance between them.

Instead, guilt had mingled with his sorrow, solidifying into an uncomfortable mass of self-recrimination and disgust.

He didn't trust easily and his scepticism of Babs had ultimately driven his dad away.

He'd regretted it every day since his dad's funeral.

Hopefully, saving Qu would help ease the relentless remorse that he'd stuffed up royally when it came to Quentin.

While Wade had left Qu a long time ago, he kept abreast of developments and when rumours of employee dissatisfaction, low sales and financial strife reached him in London following Quentin's death, he knew what he had to do.

Throw in the fact his dad had barely been buried before Babs had started flinging around terms like 'white elephant' and 'financial drain' in relation to Qu, and Wade had had no choice.

He'd appointed his deputy as acting CEO in

London and hightailed it back to Melbourne as fast as he could.

Just in time too, judging by the board's lukewarm response to his plans to save the business.

As for his confrontation with Babs before the party yesterday…he'd been right about her all along.

Thank goodness his dad had been smart enough to leave a very precise will. Babs got the multimillion-dollar Toorak mansion and a stack of cash. He got the business.

But sadly, the bulk of his dad's shares had passed on to Babs too and that meant they now had equal voting rights with the board.

If she whispered in the right ears—and she had from all accounts—if it came to a vote they'd sell Qu Publishing out from under him.

He couldn't let that happen. He wouldn't, now he had Liza on board.

Thinking of Liza brought him full circle back to his original supposition.

He'd given up trying to figure women out.

Which was why he had no clue why she'd had a mini meltdown half an hour earlier. And why he didn't trust her complete about-face in regard to his offer.

One minute she'd been fiery and defiant, the next he'd found her in a defeated heap near the elevator.

Whoever had rung her had delivered bad news. And the thought it could've been some guy who'd devastated her rankled.

He'd assumed she was entanglement-free last night, but what if there was some guy in the picture, an ex she was hung up on? And why the hell did it matter?

Whatever had happened via that phone call, it had provided a major shake-up for her to switch from a vehement refusal to accepting his offer. It made him wonder, had it been a ruse? A plan on her part to get him to up the advance?

He didn't think so, for her devastation had been real when he'd found her crumpled beside the elevator. But his ingrained lack of trust couldn't be shaken and her vacillating behaviour piqued his curiosity meter.

Was Liza genuine or was she a damned good actress? And if so, what was her motivation?

Ultimately, it shouldn't matter. He couldn't af-

ford to be distracted. It would take all his concentration to ensure her biography hit the shelves
within a record six months. He had editors, buyers, online marketing managers and a host of
other people to clue in to the urgency of this release.

Not that he'd tell them why. Having a publisher
on the brink of implosion didn't exactly inspire
confidence in the buyers who'd stock this book
in every brick-and-mortar and digital store in the
country.

He needed their backing for this book to go
gangbusters following a speedy release. It would
take every moment of his time making it happen.

So why the persistent niggle that having Liza
stride into his office the first time, and later agree
to his offer, was the best thing to happen to him
on a personal level in a long time?

He'd been thinking about contacting her anyway, getting one of the company's investigative
hounds onto finding her. Thankfully, that wasn't
necessary. But the fact she was the WAG every
publisher in town had been hounding for a tell-
all? Threw him. And made him doubt his own
judgement, which he hated.

Had his first impressions been correct? Was she a woman not to be trusted?

He couldn't afford to have this book deal fall through and with Liza's abrupt about-face—shirking his offer then accepting it—what was to say it wouldn't happen again?

She'd verbally agreed to the deal but until he had her signature on a contract he wouldn't be instigating any processes.

Damn, he wished he knew her better so he could get a handle on her erratic behaviour.

She'd seemed introverted last night, reluctant to flirt, at complete odds with the image of WAGs he had.

In London, a day didn't go by without the tabloids reporting exploits of sports stars' wives and girlfriends, from what they wore to a nightclub opening to rumours of catfights.

The woman he'd coaxed into having a drink with him last night, the woman who'd later blown his mind with sensational sex, didn't fit his image of a WAG.

Which begged the question, what had Liza done to make her notorious?

What was her real story?

Considering he'd just emailed her a publishing contract, guess he'd soon find out.

Liza had less than twenty-four hours to come up with a plausible life story. One far removed from the truth.

She'd been in a daze on the tram ride home, stunned how quickly her life had morphed from orderly to disastrous.

Though it could've been a lot worse if she didn't have Wade's offer to agree to.

For as much as it pained her to contemplate he might have used her to get what he wanted, she'd be in real trouble if his publishing contract hadn't been on the table.

It had pinged into her inbox the moment she'd arrived home and she'd scoured the contract, expecting hidden clauses and a bunch of legalese. Surprisingly, the contract was straightforward and the sizable advance eased the constriction in her chest that had made breathing difficult since she'd taken that call from Ullric.

Once she'd forwarded it to Jimmy's manager—who also happened to be one of the best entertainment lawyers in the country—she sat down with a pen and paper, determined to have bullet points ready for her first meeting with the ghost writer tomorrow.

Wade wanted a specific kind of book: a complete tell-all highlighting the juicy, glamorous, scandalous aspects of her life as a WAG. Yet another reason why she'd have to leave Cindy out of it.

He'd also assured her the story of her life would be well written and focused on the facts, but Liza read widely and was wise enough to know ghost writers liked to embellish, taking a little fictional creativity along the way.

Let them. Considering she was doing the same thing, giving an embroidered account of her life while withholding important facts—namely Cindy's existence—she couldn't begrudge the writer that.

Why should she care? Wasn't as if the media had never invented stuff about her to sell papers or magazines.

While she'd been with Jimmy there'd been a never-ending list of supposed indiscretions. Smile at a world champion tennis pro and she was accused of having an affair. Lean too close to hear a rock star's boring diatribe at a nightclub, ditto.

She'd grown immune after a while, knowing it went with the territory. But not a day went by when she didn't feel like telling the truth and ramming her side of the story down their lying throats.

Then she'd arrive home after yet another movie premiere or restaurant opening or fashion-label launch, curl up next to Cindy on the couch, and know it was all worthwhile.

There was nothing she wouldn't do for her little sis. Including manufacture a life story to give the masses something they'd probably invent anyway, and secure Cindy's future in the process.

Liza arrived at Qu Publishing at nine on the dot the next morning, dressed to impress and armed with her extensive list.

She wanted to wow the ghost writer and to do that she'd donned her WAG persona, from sleek blow-dried hair to lashings of make-up, seamed stockings and sky-high black patent leather stilettos to a tight crimson sheath dress with long sleeves and a low neckline.

Power dressing at its best and if the reaction of the guys who passed her on Collins Street was any indication, she'd achieved her first goal: make a dazzling first impression.

She found it infinitely amusing that guys would barely give her a second glance when she did the grocery shopping with her hair snagged in a low ponytail and no make-up, wearing yoga pants and a hoodie, yet dressed in a slinky outfit with enough make-up to hide a million flaws and they drooled. Fickle fools.

As she paced the reception area she wondered if that was what had captured Wade's attention at the party. Her fake outer shell. Or was her name enough, when he'd wanted her to sign on the dotted line all along?

Then again, what he'd said had been true. *She'd* approached *him*. Engaged him in conversation. Even flirted a little, and he hadn't known her name. Not until later at The Martini Bar.

His admission had soothed her wounded ego for all of two seconds before she realised a smart guy like him would've researched her to get as much info on the WAG he wanted so badly, so would've known what she looked like from the countless pictures online.

Stupid thing was, she wanted to believe him, wanted to give him the benefit of the doubt that the way they'd hooked up at the Westin had been about a strong sexual attraction and a mutual need to escape.

But Liza had been let down by people her entire life, especially those closest to her, and had learned healthy distrust wasn't such a bad thing.

She'd idolised her dad. He'd left when he couldn't handle having a disabled daughter.

She'd idolised her mum. Yet her mother hadn't been able to handle things either. When Louisa had finally left it had almost been a relief because the tension in the house had dissipated and Liza had been more than happy to step up with Cindy.

She'd been doing it for years anyway.

While she wanted to hate Wade for using sex as a way to get her onside, part of her couldn't help but be grateful his offer had still been on the table after the way she'd stormed out of his office.

Without that contract and advance, she'd be screwed. And he'd given her a job to boot.

Not many executives would've given in to her

crazy demand for a job alongside a significant contract offer, but he'd done it.

Probably out of desperation to have her agree to his proposal but, whatever his rationale, she was grateful.

He'd agreed to let her focus on marketing her biography for a start, which was a good way to ease into her new career. She might have been handed a dream job on a platter but the fact she hadn't actually worked in marketing since she gained her degree six years earlier went some way in denting her fake confidence.

If she screwed this up, not only would she have an irate publisher on her hands, she'd be fired before her job had begun.

Along with spinning a bunch of embellished half-truths for the ghost writer, she had to spend her days coming up with whiz-bang marketing plans and meeting with Wade.

She didn't know which of the three options terrified her most.

As if she'd conjured him up, Wade opened his door and strode towards her, tall and powerful and incredibly gorgeous.

She'd rubbed shoulders with some of the most

handsome guys in the world, from movie stars to sporting elite, but there was something about Wade Urquart that made her hormones jump-start in a big way.

He wore his dark hair a tad long for convention and sported light stubble that accentuated his strong jaw. Throw in the deep brown eyes, the hot bod and the designer suit that highlighted his long legs and broad shoulders, and Liza wasn't surprised to find herself holding her breath.

For it wasn't the clothes that impressed her as much as the body beneath, and the fact she'd seen every inch, touched every inch, made her skin prickle with awareness the closer he got.

'Punctual. I like that.' His slow, easy grin added to her flustered state as she shook his hand and managed to look like an idiot when she snatched hers away too fast.

'I'm eager to get started.' She gestured at her bag. 'I've brought a ton of notes and pictures and stuff so we can hit the ground running.'

'That's what I like to hear.'

She fell into step beside him, having to lengthen her stride to keep up.

'I can't emphasise enough the speedy turnaround needed on this.' He stopped outside a conference room and gestured her in. 'There's a lot riding on this book being a runaway success.'

A wave of panic threatened to swamp Liza, mixed with a healthy dose of guilt.

Inventing a bunch of lies to protect Cindy hadn't seemed so bad when she'd been jotting notes last night, but hearing the hint of desperation in Wade's voice made her wonder about the wisdom of this.

What if one of her lies unravelled? What if she was declared a fraud? Or, worst-case scenario, what if Cindy was exposed in the process?

'Something wrong?'

Everything was wrong, but Liza had to do this. It was the only way forward that enabled her to provide a safe future for Cindy while following her own dream at the same time.

She was used to depending on no one but herself and to provide Cindy with that same independence, she had to make this work.

She faked a smile that had fooled the masses before. 'Let's get started.'

With a doubtful sideways glance, he gestured her ahead of him into the room, where he introduced her to Danni, the ghost writer, a forty-something woman who reeked of efficiency.

'I'll leave you ladies to it,' he said, glancing at his watch. 'And I'll see you in my office this afternoon at one-thirty, Liza.'

'Sure,' she said, not looking forward to the marketing meeting one bit.

She might be able to fake it for Danni, but Wade had seen her naked, for goodness' sake. Not much more she could hide from him.

Over the next four hours Liza laid bare her life. The life she'd pared back, embellished and concocted, that was.

Danni taped their interview, jotted notes in a mega scrapbook already filled with scrawl and typed furiously into a laptop.

Danni asked pertinent questions, nothing too personal but insightful all the same and Liza couldn't help but be impressed.

And relieved. This biography business was going better than expected and, according to Danni, she'd have enough information by the end of the week to collate into a workable chapter book.

When they finally broke at one-fifteen, Liza

had a rumbling tummy and a headache, but she couldn't afford to be late for her meeting with Wade so she grabbed a coffee from the lunch room, checked in with Shar to see how Cindy was, and made it to Wade's office with a minute to spare.

He barely acknowledged her entrance when she knocked and he waved her in, his eyes riveted to the massive monitor screen in front of him while on a speaker conference call.

Whoever was on the other end of the line was spouting a whole lot of figures that made her head spin; hundreds of thousands of dollars bandied around as if they were discussing pocket change.

She could hardly comprehend the advance Qu Publishing had offered her. It topped the other offers she'd had by two hundred grand.

Ironic, it hadn't been enough to tempt her when she'd had her investment maturing but, with her nest egg gone, beggars certainly couldn't be choosers.

'Sorry about that,' he said, clasping his hands together and resting them on the desk. 'Working on the pre-orders, which are all important.'

'How many people are interested in reading about my boring life?'

'Boring?' He spun the screen around, pointing at the spreadsheet covered in figures and high-lighted colours. 'According to the orders flooding in already, you're ranking up there with Oprah and Madonna for notoriety.'

He leaned back, pinning her with a speculative stare. 'Which makes me wonder, what have you done that is so newsworthy?'

Liza shrugged, knowing he would've asked this question eventually but feeling increasingly un-comfortable having to discuss any part of her life with him.

Rehashing details for Danni was one thing; bar-ing herself—metaphorically—to Wade another.

'Not much, really. My high-school sweetheart turned out to be a soccer superstar so we were thrust into the limelight early on.'

She smoothed a fray in her stockings, remem-bering how out of her depth she'd felt at the time. Photographers snapping their pic wherever they went, groupies slipping phone numbers into Jimmy's pocket constantly, autograph hunters thrusting pen and paper into his face regardless of appropriate timing.

It had been a circus but she'd quickly learned to play the game when a national magazine had offered her twenty thousand dollars for an interview.

At twenty-two and fresh out of uni it had been an exorbitant sum, and she'd grabbed it to buy a new motorised wheelchair for Cindy.

That interview had been the start. More had followed, along with interviews on talk shows, hosting charity events and appearing at openings for a fee.

Jimmy had encouraged her and with every deposit in her investment account she'd been vindicated she was doing the right thing.

Cindy would be secure for life. Liza never wanted her sis to struggle the way she had when their parents had left them.

Being abandoned was bad enough, but left without long-term security? Liza could never forgive her folks for that.

Not that she heard from them. Her dad had vanished for good when he'd left and her mum occasionally rang on birthdays and Christmas.

Liza never took her calls, letting Cindy chatter enthusiastically, while she wondered the entire time how a parent could walk out on their child. Especially a high-needs child.

'You travelled?'

She shook her head. 'No, I didn't want to become one of those women who clung to their man.'

And she couldn't leave Cindy for long stints, not that Wade needed to know that.

It was one of the things that had eventually come between her and Jimmy. He needed full-time glam eye candy on his arm wherever he went; she needed to devote time to her sister.

They'd parted on amicable terms despite what the press had said.

But her heart had been a teensy-weensy bit broken because he was the first guy she'd ever loved, the only guy she'd ever loved.

And he'd walked away, just like her folks.

Thankfully she'd developed a pragmatic outlook to life over the years and, while Jimmy continued to be plastered over the media, she was glad she'd stepped off his bandwagon.

'I thought that's what WAGs do. Pander to the

whims of their superstar partners. Hand-feed them grapes. Fan them with palm fronds.'

He was winding her up and her lips curved in an answering grin.

'You forgot being on call twenty-four-seven.'

He snapped his fingers. 'Thanks for clarifying.'

'Actually, you're not far off the mark.'

He arched a brow and she continued. 'You're on show every time you step out. Scrutinised all the time. It felt like a full-time job in the end.'

'Is that why you broke up?'

'Something like that.'

She didn't know if he was asking these questions in a professional capacity or assuaging his curiosity but for now she was happy to answer.

Sticking to the facts was easy. It was the potential landmine questions she'd need to carefully navigate.

'And then you dated a basketball star.'

She wrinkled her nose and he laughed. 'That good, huh?'

'Off the record? Henri and I had a convenient arrangement. Nothing more.'

Confusion creased his brow. 'How did that work?'

'He needed a girlfriend. I needed the lifestyle he provided.'

She threw it out there, gauging his reaction.

His eyes widened and his lips tightened, his frown deepening.

'I don't understand.'

She shrugged, as if his opinion didn't matter, when in fact it irked he thought badly of her. Not that it should surprise her. They hardly knew each other, despite one night of amazing sex. But for someone who'd spent the last umpteen years being judged by everyone, it really peed her off to add Wade to that list.

'Our arrangement was mutually beneficial. That's all anyone needs to understand.'

He recoiled as if she'd slapped him. 'I hope you'll be giving us more than that in the book.'

'My biography will be comprehensive.'

He continued to stare at her as if she'd morphed from an angel to the devil incarnate and she struggled not to squirm beneath the scrutiny.

When the silence grew painfully uncomfortable, she gestured to the stack of paperwork on his desk. 'Shall we discuss the marketing plan?'

'Yeah,' he said, his frown not waning as he

spread documents across his desk and picked up his pen. 'I have a few ideas but I want to hear what you've come up with.'

As Liza ran through an impressive list of ideas, from a massive social-media blitz via popular sites to weekly bonus e-serials to Qu Publishing subscribers, Wade wondered how he could have misjudged her so badly.

Maybe he could blame it on jet lag, because he could've sworn the livewire he'd wooed into bed a couple of nights ago was far removed from the calculated, cool woman who was happy to date as part of an *arrangement*.

He'd seen a lot of interesting couples in his travels, younger women with older men in it for the money and security. Hell, he'd seen it first-hand with Babs and his dad. So why did he find the thought of Liza hooked up with some slick sports star for the sake of *lifestyle* so unpalatable?

'What do you think?'

Damn, she'd caught him out.

'Sorry, I was still pondering your Twitter tribe idea. What did you ask?'

Nice save but, by her narrowed eyes, she didn't buy it.

'With the new e-releases of any sporting personnel three months before the bio launches, why not insert a snippet from the bio into the back of those books? Build a little anticipation?'

'Sounds great.'

She'd come up with some solid ideas and he was impressed with her work ethic. Pity he couldn't say the same about the rest.

'How do you feel about the serial WAG tag?'

She stiffened in surprise. 'That's out of left field.'

He shrugged, pretending her answer wasn't important when in fact he needed to know what made her tick.

Sitting across from her, the faintest rose fragrance scenting the air and reminding him of the way it had clung to his skin after their night in his suite, he had to know who the real Liza Lithgow was.

Was she the soft, hesitant woman he'd met at the party and spent a wild, passionate night with?

Or was she a gold-digging, plastic floozy who'd do anything to further her lifestyle?

'Call it publisher curiosity,' he said, hating how

her answers meant way more to him than on a publishing level.

'I've been called many things by the press over the years, serial WAG being on the tamer side.'

Her flat monotone suggested rote answers, when he wanted to know the *real* her. It annoyed the hell out of him.

'How did you put up with all that?'

'Came with the territory,' she said, darting a nervous glance at the documentation on his desk, as if she'd much rather be discussing business than her personal life.

Too bad. He wanted to know more about the investment his dad's company was riding on and right now he had the distinct feeling she was hiding something. Something that went beyond a need for some degree of privacy.

He couldn't pinpoint what it was but her general evasiveness, the look-away glances, the rote answers, seemed too trite, too polished, almost as if she'd rehearsed.

Crazy? Maybe, but he'd put his father's company and three hundred grand of his own money on the line for this book. It had to be a blockbuster and so far Liza hadn't inspired him with her careful answers and measured responses.

'You haven't told me why every publisher in Melbourne was clamouring for your exclusive story,' he said, prepared to keep interrogating her until she told him the truth.

'Don't you know?'

'Know what?'

'I slept with the entire Aussie soccer team,' she deadpanned. 'The English one too.'

He barked out a laugh. 'Don't believe you about the English. I would've read about that in London.'

'Pity my antics didn't make it all the way over there,' she said, her tone holding a hint of accusation. 'What is it you want me to say? That I danced naked at the Grand Final? That I had half the team and cheerleaders in my room one night?'

Her voice had risen and she lowered it, making him feel guilty for pushing her. 'Honestly? I have no idea why my story is so important, other than the fact I haven't given them a story before now.'

She held out her hands, as if no tricks up her sleeves. 'I've been reticent in interviews over the years. I pick and choose the ones I do and the questions I answer. Maybe that's built the mystery? Plus the fact I've dated two mega-famous Aussie sporting stars, people want to know, "Why her? What's so special about her?"'

He'd touched a nerve.

He could see it in the frantically beating pulse in her neck, in the corded muscles, in her rigid shoulders.

He could move in for the kill now he had her more animated and far removed from her trite answers, but something in her eyes stopped him.

She looked almost haunted. As if she'd seen too much, done too much, and was still reeling from it.

It made him even more curious. What or who had put that look in her expressive eyes?

'Want to take a break and meet back here at four-thirty?'

Liza nodded and stood before he'd barely finished the sentence. She was desperate to escape? Yeah, looked as if he'd definitely hit a nerve.

He watched her walk to the door, a goddess in sheer stockings, a tight red dress and heels that could give a guy serious ideas.

'Liza?'

She glanced over her shoulder and arched a brow.

'Good work on the marketing campaign.'

'Thanks.' Her smile lit her expression and made her eyes sparkle, the first genuine show of emotion all afternoon.

Interesting. Either this book or this marketing job meant more to her than she was letting on.

'See you later,' he said as she slipped out of the door with a wave, leaving him more bamboozled than ever.

Would the real Liza Lithgow please stand up?

CHAPTER SEVEN

LIZA LITHGOW'S STYLE TIPS FOR MAXIMUM WAG WOW IMPACT

The Day Spa

For a WAG to have true wow potential at any event, a visit to a day spa beforehand is a must.

Below is a list of treatments, from the basic to the sublime.

Worth the time and money investment for body and soul.

- Waxing
- Eyelash tint
- Spray tan
- Mani and pedi (skip the basic and go deluxe)
- Footbath/reflexology

- Body scrub
- Clay body mask
- Yoghurt body cocoon
- Massage (including scalp)
- Facial

If you're too busy to attend a day spa, set aside a few hours at home and DIY.

- Cooled tea bags or cucumber slices work wonders to de-puff eyes.

- Make your own moisturising face mask: Blend yoghurt, honey, avocado and aloe vera gel, paint on face with a foundation brush, let it dry for twenty minutes and rinse. Refreshed skin!

- Condition your hair with coconut oil. You can leave it in overnight for deeper moisturizing.

- Make your own exfoliating body scrub: 1 cup raw oats, 1 cup brown sugar, 1 cup olive oil. Mix together and apply on dry skin moving your hand in slow circles. Rinse off. Smooth skin!

- Make your own hand cream: add a few drops of tea tree oil, lavender oil and olive oil to a few spoonfuls of cold cream. (For a fruity smell, add a banana.) Blend. Slather over hands, wear rubber gloves while watching TV. For better penetration, place gloved hands on a hot-water bottle.

LIZA SURREPTITIOUSLY SLID the sleeve of her dress up to check her watch.

On the plus side, Wade had stopped interrogating her during their second meeting of the day and had concentrated on marketing plans.

On the downside, it was six o'clock and she was on the verge of fainting from lack of food.

Her tummy rumbled on cue and she wrapped an arm over it. Too late. His gaze zeroed in on it. The rumbles were quickly replaced by a horde of tap-dancing butterflies as she remembered the way he'd stared at her naked body on that unforgettable night.

Damn, she'd vowed not to think about that night again, especially when working. She'd done a good job of it so far, then all it took was one casual glance from *him* and the entire evening flashed across her mind in vivid detail.

His hungry stare as he'd propped over her, their bodies joined and writhing slowly.

His sensual lips as he'd kissed and nipped her elbows, her thighs, her stomach, every zone more erogenous than the last.

His skilful hands as he'd brought her to orgasm. Repeatedly.

Great. The butterflies had stilled, only to be replaced by a fiery heat that had her gritting her teeth to stop from squirming.

'Hungry?'

'A little,' she said as her stomach gave another growl akin to a muted roar.

He laughed. 'Sorry, I'm used to working through when I'm on tight deadlines.'

His eyebrows arched when he glanced at the time on his PC screen. 'Didn't know it was so late. Want to grab a bite to eat so we can keep working?'

'Sure.'

Thank goodness she'd had the foresight to ring Shar before this meeting started. With a four-thirty start she'd had a feeling it would run late.

'Been to Chin Chin?' He shrugged into his jacket. 'I've heard it's a favourite in Melbourne.'

'Good choice,' she said, surprised they were going out for dinner. 'Food's sublime.'

When he'd suggested grabbing a bite to eat she'd expected ordered-in sandwiches while he kept her chained to the desk.

Chained... Like how he'd pinned her wrists overhead as he entered her the first time....

Uh-oh. She needed to stay work-focused. And hope to hell he didn't pick up on her sudden shift in thoughts.

'Let's go.'

He opened the door for her and as she stepped through, with him close behind, a ripple of awareness raised the hair on the back of her neck.

It disarmed her, this unexpected physical reaction when she least expected it. Several times during their meeting she'd experienced a buzz from perfectly innocuous actions like their fingers brushing when handing over documentation or a lingering glance a tad longer than necessary.

She'd been deliberately brusque, determined not to botch this opportunity, which was exactly what would happen if she acknowledged the attraction between them now he was her boss.

And not forgetting that little technicality of him

potentially using her despite his protestations of innocence.

No, she'd be better off forgetting their night of scintillating sex and concentrating on getting her story straight for the book and making her marketing ideas fly.

She had enough complications in her life without adding fraternising with the boss to them.

They made small talk as they strolled down Flinders Lane and Liza tried to ignore the way people turned to stare.

Considering they were both tall and well dressed, she could attribute it to natural curiosity. Or she could acknowledge it for what it was: once a recognised WAG, always a recognised WAG.

When would people forget whom she'd dated and move on to the next 'it' girl? Sure, she'd milked her image for all it was worth, most recently hosting a reality show that had been a ratings disaster yet was the most talked-about event on social media sites for months.

But she was done with that part of her life. Wasn't that the main reason she'd slept with

Wade in the first place, celebrating putting her past behind her and moving on to a new life?

Ironic, her past had caught up with her and collided with her future.

When they arrived at the Melbourne institution, the nightly queue of eager patrons dying to try the fabulous Asian food was thankfully small but Liza knew they'd still be ushered to the bar downstairs to wait for a table to become available.

Not good. When she'd agreed to have a meal with Wade, she hadn't envisaged the two of them sitting too close in a bar.

A bar was reminiscent of their first night together and the last thing she needed right now was any reminder. Her body hummed with his proximity. Sharing a drink in a cosy setting? Not good.

Their wait for a table wouldn't be too long according to the hostess so Liza headed downstairs with Wade, trying to ignore his hand on the small of her back and the accompanying reaction that made her knees wobble a tad.

It worsened when they took a seat at the bar

and their thighs brushed. Hell, what had Liza let herself in for?

'Drink?'

'Soda with a twist of lemon,' she said, desperate to reassemble her wits and not needing alcohol to add to her bedazzlement.

'Technically we're off the clock, so you can have a drink, you know.'

'Isn't this a working dinner?'

He nodded but she didn't trust the glimmer of mischief in his eyes. 'Maybe I should order you a martini again and see what happens?'

'*That* won't be happening again,' she said, squeezing her knees together for good measure.

He laughed and nudged her with his elbow, the slightest contact making her body prickle with awareness. 'Never say never, I reckon.'

'We are *so* not going there.' She glared as if she meant business.

By his answering wink, he was thinking monkey business.

'I'll let you in on a secret,' he said, leaning so close his breath fanned her ear, pebbling her skin in the process. 'It's okay to flirt outside the office. Especially after we've already—'

'No flirting,' she said, unable to suppress a smile when he blew on her ear for good measure.

'That's better.' He touched a fingertip to the corner of her mouth. 'First time I've seen you lighten up all day.'

He traced her lower lip, lingering in the middle, and she couldn't have formulated an answer if she'd tried. 'Don't get me wrong, I like how focused you are on helping us meet this all-important deadline, but today?' He pulled a funny face, complete with crossed eyes. 'You were seriously scary.'

'Was not,' she said, enjoying his antics despite her vow to keep things purely platonic from now on.

She liked the fact he could switch from mega-powerful corporate CEO to teasing. It was one of the things that had attracted her that first night, the way he lightened up when they started talking.

'Yeah, you were.' He bumped her gently with his shoulder. 'But not to worry. I've got all night to get you to loosen up.'

'All night?' She wished.

'Figure of speech.' His wicked grin said otherwise. 'Though I have to tell you, I was pretty blown away when you barged into my office yesterday. It was like all my prayers had been answered.'

Liza didn't want to go there. She should change the subject, fake an emergency trip to the loo, anything to quell the irrational surge of jubilation that he'd been happy to see her.

'We really shouldn't talk about that night. It's unprofessional—'

'Why did you bolt without leaving contact details?'

A host of callous retorts designed to maintain distance between them sprang to her lips but Liza settled for the simple truth.

'Because I didn't think you wanted more than one night.'

There. She'd put the onus back on him. No way could he admit to wanting more without appearing a little needy.

'Considering we'd only just met, I don't think either of us knew what we wanted beyond the amazing connection we shared. But later…' he shrugged and turned towards the bar, but not before she'd seen a flicker of something akin to regret darken his eyes '…let's just say I was disappointed to find you gone.'

Liza admired his honesty. He sounded so genuine she could almost believe he hadn't known her identity when they slept together.

It made her curious. What would have happened if they'd had more than one night?

'For argument's sake, let's say I left my number.'

The waiter deposited their drinks and he took a sip of whisky before turning back to face her. 'I would've called you. Asked you for a date.'

'Before or after offering me a publishing contract?'

He grimaced. 'Got to admit, that does complicate matters now I know.'

There he went again, reiterating he'd had no idea of her real identity that night at the party. Maybe she should give him the benefit of the doubt?

For when it came to liars, she had a pretty good radar. She could tell when someone was uncomfortable with Cindy from ten paces and hated when people acted as if cerebral palsy were contagious.

It had driven a wedge between her and Jimmy, between most of her friends too. Which suited her fine, because most of them had drifted away as Jimmy became more famous and their lives changed.

It had started with her school friends pulling away, girls she'd grown up with and who she'd assumed she could always count on. But the more fancy events she attended with Jimmy, the faster the snide remarks started and she found herself not invited to their parties or dinners or girls' nights out.

Being abandoned by her friends had sucked and she'd learned to cultivate light-hearted friendships with acquaintances, fellow WAGs who stuck together out of necessity. But they'd pretty much abandoned her too once she broke up with Jimmy and Henri, and she missed her old friendships more than ever.

True friends stuck around through life changes. Guess she didn't have any true friends.

'Hey, you drifted off for a second.' He touched her hand and a lick of heat travelled up her arm.

'It's more than a complication now I'm working for you and you know it,' she said, re-evaluating the wisdom of working for him when his simple touch made her skin sizzle.

'Co-workers have relationships all the time these days,' he said, stroking the back of her hand with his thumb. 'And don't forget, the only reason you're working for me is because you blackmailed me into giving you a job.'

'Good point.' She chuckled, proud for pulling that masterstroke. 'So you're trying to get into my pants again on a technicality?'

His thumb paused and his eyes widened in surprise. 'Are you always this blunt?'

Not always. Most of her life she'd watched what she said and what she ate and what she wore, presenting a perfectly poised persona to the world, desperate no one saw behind the façade.

If she didn't let people get too close they couldn't hurt her. A motto she'd learned to live by the hard way.

So what was it about this guy that had her more relaxed than she'd ever been?

She took a sip of soda and shrugged. 'We've seen each other naked. I don't see the point in playing coy.'

He mouthed 'wow' and squeezed her hand before releasing it. 'Okay, least I can do is return the favour. I like you. You intrigue me. So while I'm in Melbourne, I'd like for us to see each other.'

Lord, Liza hadn't seen that coming. She'd thought Wade might put the hard word on her for another night in the sack. No way did she expect a quasi-relationship for the time he was in town.

She was tempted. Seriously tempted.

How long since she'd had great sex or indulged in genuine fun? Probably in the early Jimmy days, before the fame and the expectations associated with living up to the WAG label. She knew time spent with Wade would involve both sex and fun.

But what about Cindy and the lies she'd constructed to protect her?

If she started dating Wade, how long could she keep him from her place? How long before her lies unravelled and her carefully constructed story came crashing down?

She couldn't afford to have Qu Publishing renege on the contract, nor did she want to lose her first real marketing job.

Getting involved with Wade could compromise both.

'Wade, I like you—'

'I can sense a *but* coming.' He winced and pretended to clutch his heart. 'Give it to me straight. I'm a big boy, I can take it.'

She managed a wan smile. 'But I don't want to complicate our business arrangement.'

Disappointment downturned his mouth for a moment, before those lips she'd experienced over every inch of her body curved into a seductive smile.

'I understand. You don't know me that well. But the way Qu Publishing secured your book deal was by sheer persistence.'

He raised his glass in her direction. 'I don't give up easily. Challenge is my middle name.'

He clinked it to hers. 'Don't say I didn't warn you.'

Liza had been in a quandary when Wade offered to drive her home.

She'd wanted to refuse because it had been bad enough having him charm her over a delicious dinner of green Thai chicken curry and sampler plates of murtubak, slow-cooked beef and exquisite calamari.

But she'd wanted to get home fast so she could spend time with her sis before Cindy went to bed so she'd agreed.

And was now ruing the fact as he walked her to the front door.

Politeness demanded she invite him in for a coffee.

Self-preservation demanded she get rid of him ASAP.

'Thanks for dinner and driving me home,' she said, juggling her handbag from one arm to the other, hoping he'd get the hint.

'My pleasure.' He stilled her arm with a light touch on the forearm. 'Not going to invite me in?'

Damn. She admired his bluntness. But she hated being put on the spot.

'Don't think that's a good idea.'

His hand travelled up her arm in a slow caress before resting on her shoulder. 'Why? Scared I'll take advantage of you?'

'No. I just have a lot of work to do before my meeting with Danni tomorrow so—'

He kissed her, a stealth kiss that caught her completely off guard.

Her hands braced against his chest, ready to push him away as he backed her up against the front door.

But then his tongue touched her bottom lip, stroked it with exquisite precision, and she clung to him instead. Responded to his commanding mouth deepening the kiss to be sublimely erotic. Wanting more than *this*.

When his arms slid around her waist and pulled her flush against him, her body zinged with re-membrance. How it felt to be pressed against his arousal, how he'd masterfully seduced her with a skill that left her breathless.

She felt weightless, floating, as he kissed like a guy who couldn't get enough. And the feeling was entirely mutual.

When Wade kissed her, when he touched her, she forgot about responsibilities. She forgot about the stress of losing her money and Cindy's security. She forgot about the long list of doctor's appointments and physiotherapy sessions and hydrotherapy at a new pool next week. She forgot about finding a replacement carer for when Shar went on holiday next.

And she existed purely in the moment, revelling in this incredibly sexy guy's desire for her.

As the blood fizzed in her veins and her muscles melted, she wanted more than this kiss.

She wanted him. Naked. Again.

The thrill of skin to skin. The excitement of exploring each other's bodies. The release that left her boneless and mindless.

Until a massive reality check in the form of her buzzing mobile switched to silent vibrated against her hip.

Shar probably wanted to head home and here Liza was, indulging in a pointless kiss that could lead nowhere.

Regret tempered her passion. She eased away. Last thing she needed was for him to think something was wrong and want to talk or demand answers she wasn't prepared to give.

'Told you I wouldn't give up,' he said, cupping her cheek in a tender moment before stepping away.

'You should,' she said, but her words fell on deaf ears as he shot her one last wicked grin be fore strolling down her path like a guy who had all the time in the world to woo the woman he wanted.

An hour later, Liza had bathed Cindy, assisted with her stretches and helped her painstakingly make a batch of choc-chip muffins.

Every task took double the time with Cindy's clawed elbow and hand but that never stopped her sis having a go. Liza's admiration knew no bounds and whenever she felt her patience fraying she tried to put herself in Cindy's shoes.

Being a carer over the years had been tough, but imagine being on the receiving end? Of being dependent on others for activities of daily living that everyone took for granted? Needing help with bathing and dressing, cooking and cleaning?

Not to mention the never-ending rounds of therapy and medical interventions.

Liza had it easy compared to her sis and Cindy's amazing resilience and zest for life was what drove her every day.

'Were you talking to someone outside?'

The spatula in Liza's hand froze in mid-air,

dropping a big globule of muffin mix into the baking tin involuntarily.

'No one important,' she said, concentrating on filling the tin while Cindy popped choc chips into her mouth and chewed slowly.

'Sounded like a guy.' Cindy finished chewing and started making smooching noises.

Uh-oh. Shar had said they'd been busy in the kitchen when she'd arrived home but what if Cindy had seen that kiss?

'You should have a boyfriend,' Cindy said, her wobbly grin endearing. 'A proper one this time, not like those loser sports guys.'

Liza loved that about Cindy, her insightfulness. Most people saw the wheelchair and her physical disfigurement and assumed she was brain-damaged too.

While many people with cerebral palsy did suffer a degree of brain injury, Cindy had been lucky that way and she often made pronouncements that would've shocked most scholars.

'I'm too busy with my new job to date, sweetie.'

A half-truth. For the guy who wanted to date her happened to work right alongside her.

It could be convenient…if she were to lose her mind.

No, having Wade practically invite himself in sixty minutes ago reinforced she was doing the right thing in keeping things between them platonic.

She didn't want to let him into her life, into Cindy's life, when there was no future. While Cindy never talked about their folks abandoning them, it would have to hurt. The last thing she needed was Cindy bonding with Wade only to have him head back to London.

She wouldn't do that to herself—uh, to Cindy.

'I have a boyfriend.'

Liza smiled, having been alerted to Cindy's latest crush via Shar. 'You do?'

Cindy nodded. 'Liam Hemsworth. He's hot.'

'Personally, I prefer Chris.'

'No way.' Cindy popped another choc chip in her mouth. 'Though I guess that would work out well. They're brothers, we're sisters. Perfect.'

Liza laughed as she opened the oven door and popped the muffins inside. 'Tell you what. You do another ten hamstring stretches and I'll watch *The Hunger Games* with you again.'

'Deal.'

As Cindy manoeuvred her wheelchair into the next room Liza pondered her sister's observation.

You should have a boyfriend.

While she didn't need the complication, for a second she allowed herself to fantasise what it would be like having Wade fill the role.

CHAPTER EIGHT

LIZA LITHGOW'S STYLE TIPS FOR MAXIMUM WAG WOW IMPACT

The Home

While WAGs lead a busy social life, they do occasionally entertain at home. And even if they don't, what better way to unwind after a hectic game or a rowdy after-match function than kicking back in their cosy abode?

Here are a few tips to make your home entirely livable:

- *Make your entry-way inviting.* When your guests enter your home it's the first area they see. The entry-way should make a statement, give a hint of what's to come and draw the guest into the rest of the house. Pictures on the wall are the easiest way to dress up your entry-way. Same with floor coverings. Hall tables are a nice addition as you can dress them with signature or eclectic pieces.

• *Experiment with glass.* Glass instantly adds sparkle to a room. Experimenting with shapes and heights (vases, bowls, objects) is fun, and keeping them in the same colour palette is advisable. Varying shapes in like-coloured glass can be eye-catching.

• *Mix it up.* Every object in your home doesn't have to be an heirloom. If you like quality pieces, mix them up with a little kitsch. It's okay to have your favourite collection alongside that priceless vase. The whole point of collecting is to have a passion for it, finding items you really love, so why not show them off? They're a great conversation starter too.

• *Keep window dressings simple.* Whether you go for curtains or blinds, keep them simple. Don't let them overpower your furniture. Subdued tones work best but that doesn't mean you need to skimp on quality. The simpler the curtain, the better quality the fabric should be, like linen, silk, cotton or satin. Understated elegance is the key to setting off your room.

•*Layer your bed.* Your bed is usually the focal point of your bedroom and should be treated as such. Layering different fabrics on and around the bed (from a fabric headboard to lush linens) creates an inviting room. When layering, avoid clash of texture and colour by keeping it simple. Muted tones in green, blue and white work wonders.

WADE'S WEEK HAD been progressing exceptionally well.

Danni had completed the first draft of Liza's biography, the pre-orders were phenomenal and he'd managed to sneak another dinner with Liza, albeit for business.

This time she'd driven herself so had avoided his plans for more than a goodnight kiss on her doorstep. He didn't know whether to be peeved or glad she was so focused on her new job.

Considering he'd had his doubts about her when she'd secured this job, and her motivation behind it, he had to admit she'd impressed. Her dedication, her punctuality and her fresh ideas had given him new perspective on an industry he'd thought he knew inside out.

She was the complete professional and almost made him feel guilty for constantly picturing her naked. Almost.

They'd been too busy to catch up beyond snatched marketing meetings in the office, and for a guy who normally had his mind on the job twenty-four-seven he'd found himself being seriously distracted.

Those tight pencil skirts she wore? Disruptive, despite their sedate colours and modest below-knee length.

Those fitted jackets? The epitome of conservative fashionable chic.

Those blouses? Muted colours with barely a hint of cleavage.

But whenever she entered his office he had an immediate flashback to the night he'd seen beneath the clothes and he'd be hard in an instant.

He'd dated occasionally in London but no woman had affected his concentration like Liza. Ever.

When Danni had emailed him the first draft of

her biography he'd sat up all night devouring it on his e-reader. His obsession with her should've been satisfied. Instead, the more he discovered about her, the more she piqued his curiosity.

She'd delivered exactly what he wanted in terms of a tell-all, a juicy tale highlighting behind-the-scenes gossip in the soccer and basketball worlds.

She'd changed names to protect the innocent but he knew readers would devour the catfights and hook-ups and pick-ups, trying to figure out which real-life star and WAG inspired her stories.

This book would sell but her lack of personal details disappointed. She'd glossed over her childhood and teenage years, focusing on the glamorous drama that kicked in when her high-school boyfriend hit the big time.

He should've been glad, for she'd provided the page-turning hot gossip that sold books. But he'd be lying if he didn't admit to wanting to know more—a whole lot more—about the woman behind the fake tan and designer handbags.

If he had insight into what made her tick, he might understand her continued aloofness.

Her lack of enthusiasm at pursuing anything

beyond a one-night stand surprised him. Not from ego, but for the simple fact they still shared a spark. More than a spark, if the way she'd responded to his kiss seven days ago was any indication.

So why was she holding back?

It wasn't as if he was after anything hot and heavy. He'd been upfront with her about exploring a relationship while he was in Melbourne so anything too deep and meaningful wouldn't scare her off.

She'd refused. But her kiss said otherwise.

She wanted this as much as he did, which begged the question, why weren't they out at a movie or dinner or at his place right now?

Instead, he had to face his worst nightmare.

With impeccable timing as always, Babs knocked on his door and he braced for the inevitable awkwardness that preceded any confrontation with his stepmum.

Ridiculous, considering she couldn't be more than ten years older than him, if that.

'Wade, darling.' She breezed into his office and made a beeline for him.

'Babs.' His terse response didn't deter her from

planting an air kiss somewhere in the vicinity of his cheek.

Thank goodness. He preferred it that way. The less those Botoxed lips got near him, the better.

'Thanks for seeing me.' She took a seat without being asked. 'From what I hear we have a lot to catch up on.'

'Really?'

She hated his monosyllabic answers, which was why he did it.

'You're stalling the inevitable.' She waggled a crimson-taloned finger in his direction. 'It'd be best for all of us if Qu Publishing sold sooner rather than later.'

His fingers dug into the underside of his desk. 'I beg to differ.'

She wrinkled her nose. 'You always did.'

With a calculated pause, she leaned forward and he quickly averted his gaze from her overt cleavage spilling from an inappropriately tight satin blouse. 'It's what your father would've wanted.'

Low blow. Incredibly low. What did he expect? The woman was a gold-digging piranha and probably had already spent the money she'd anticipated from Qu's sale.

'My dad would've wanted to see his family legacy live on.' He forced a smile, knowing it would never reach his eyes. 'I'm surprised you wouldn't know that.'

The corners of her mouth pinched, radiating unattractive wrinkles towards her nose. 'We'd both be better off without a struggling business dragging us down. Digital publishing is the way of the future. Paperbacks are redundant.'

Showed how much she knew. Sure, the digital revolution was a boom for readers but, from the extensive research conducted by online companies over the last five years, there was room in the expanding market for *tree* books, as he liked to call them.

'I have figures to prove you wrong there.' He tapped a stack of documentation on his desk. 'Including record pre-orders for Liza Lithgow's biography.'

'That tart?'

Wade would never hit a woman, would never consider it, but he sure wouldn't mind clamping a hand over this vile woman's mouth and dragging her out of his office.

'Who'd want to read about her fabricated life?'

He wouldn't give her the satisfaction of asking what she meant.

'All those WAGs are the same. Fake, the lot of them. Happy to be arm candy for what they can get.'

Pot. Meet kettle.

Wade had heard enough.

'I'm not selling, Babs. The board isn't selling. They've agreed to give me three months to take this company into the black and they're men of honour.'

More than he could say for her. She wouldn't know honour if it jumped up and bit her on her nipped and tucked behind.

Her eyes narrowed, took on a feral gleam. 'You're pinning the success of this entire company on one book? Not a smart business decision. All sorts of disasters could happen before it hits the bookstores, like—'

'I really have to get back to work,' he said, standing and heading for the door, which he opened in a blatant invitation for her to get the hell out of his office.

She stood and strolled towards him, deliberately taking her time. 'I'll be at the next board meeting.'

'I'm sure you will,' he said, resisting the urge to slam the door as she stepped through it.

'What you're doing is wrong and your father would be appalled at the risk you're taking—'

This time he gave in to instinct and slammed the door.

'There's a book launch I want to suss out tonight,' Wade said, barely glancing up from his paper-work. 'We're going.'

Liza bristled. She didn't take kindly to orders, least of all from the man she could happily throt-tle given half a chance.

He'd been bugging her all week, using subtle charm and sexy smiles to undermine her. She'd weathered it all, had focused on work in the hope he'd forget this ridiculous challenge of trying to woo her.

He hadn't, until today. Today, he'd been brusque and abrupt to the point of rudeness and no one seemed to know why.

She should've been happy. Instead, a small part of her missed his roguish charisma.

'*We* may have other plans,' she said, in a man-ufactured sickly sweet voice.

He glanced up, the frown between his brows not detracting from his perfection. 'A rival com-pany is releasing a soap-opera starlet's bio. Pays to scope out the competition, get a few ideas for what works at these shindigs and what doesn't.'

Liza hated the hint of deflation she felt that his command had been pure business and not a burning desire to spend some time in her pres-ence outside work.

Crazy and contradictory, considering that was the last thing she wanted and she had gone to great pains to avoid any out-of-work contact since that kiss on her doorstep.

But a small part of her, the part of her that re-luctantly dredged up memories of their scintil-lating night together, yearned for a repeat.

Needless to say that part of her didn't get a look-in these days.

'Surely you've been to heaps of book launches? What's so special about this one?'

With an exasperated sigh, he flung his pen on top of the towering stack of paperwork threaten-ing to topple.

'I've heard they're trying an innovative give-away. Buy the book, get a download of another free.' He pushed aside the paperwork with one hand and pinched the bridge of his nose with the other. 'I want to see how well it's received by readers who prefer to hold a tree book.'

'Tree book?'

His mouth relaxed into a semi-smile. 'Paper comes from trees. Paperbacks? Tree books.'

'Cute,' she said, a broad term that could be applied to his terminology or the man himself when he lost the 'shouldering the weight of the company on my shoulders' look.

He'd been grumpy all day but she'd weathered it, assuming he had profit margins to juggle or worry about. The fact he'd cracked a half-smile? Big improvement.

'My dad used to call them that,' he said, interlinking his fingers and stretching overhead. It did little to ease the obvious tension in his rigid shoulders.

'He built an incredible company,' she said, surprised by his rare information sharing.

While Wade seemed content to interrogate her, his personal life was definitely off-limits.

The snippets she'd learned about the enigmatic CEO had come from colleagues, co-workers who'd given her the lowdown on Qu Publishing.

A company founded sixty years ago by Wade's grandfather, a company that had produced many best-sellers under Wade's dad, but a company that had floundered when Wade's stepmum had entered the picture and Wade had left to start his own company in London.

While no one would directly disparage Babs Urquart, Liza saw enough glowering expressions and heard enough half-finished sentences to know Babs wasn't well liked.

Apparently they blamed her for Qu's downfall. And so did their boss.

'You started out here too?'

His lips compressed, as if he didn't want to talk about it. 'Yeah. I left after a few years, started my own company in London.'

'Bet your dad was proud.'

'Yeah, though we lost touch over the last few years.' Pain flickered in his eyes and she wished she hadn't probed. 'Caught up infrequently. Snatched phone calls.'

He shook his head, the deep frown slashing his brow indicative of a deeper problem. Looked as if she wasn't the only one with parental issues. 'I resent that distance between us now. He had a heart condition. Didn't tell me 'til it was too late.'

Appalled, Liza resisted the urge to hug him. 'Why?'

Wade shrugged. It did little to alleviate the obvious tension in his rigid shoulders. 'Guess he didn't trust me to be there for him, considering I'd deliberately distanced myself from him.'

Liza didn't know what to say. She despised trite platitudes, the kind that Cindy copped from ignorant, condescending people.

And it was pretty obvious Wade had major guilt over his relationship with his dad, so nothing she could say would make it any better.

But she knew what it was like to be let down by a parent, knew the confusing jumbled feelings of pain and regret and anger.

'Kids and parents grow apart. Maybe it wasn't so much a lack of trust in you that he didn't mention his heart condition and more a case of not wanting to worry you because he cared?'

Wade's startled expression spoke volumes. He'd

never considered that might have been his dad's rationale.

'So you're a glass-half-full kinda girl?'

'Actually, I'm a realist rather than an optimist.' She had to be, because it was easier to accept the reality of her life than wish for things that would never eventuate. 'And whatever or whoever caused the rift between you, it's not worth a lifetime of guilt.'

His steady gaze, filled with hope, didn't leave hers. 'I should've been there for him and I wasn't.'

A mantra taken from her mum's handbook to life.

'He loved you, right?'

Wade nodded.

'Then I think you have your answer right there.' She tapped her chest. 'If it was my heart and I had people I cared about, I'd rather make the most of whatever time we had together, even if it was only phone calls, than field a bunch of useless questions like "How are you feeling?" or "Is there anything I can do?"'

She lowered her hand and continued. 'I wouldn't care about how often I saw the person or waste time worrying over trivial stuff like the length of time since we spoke. I'd remember the good times and want to live every minute as if it were my last.'

'Dad did travel a lot the last two years…' He straightened, his frown clearing. 'Thanks.'

Uncomfortable with his praise and wishing she hadn't blabbed so much, she shrugged. 'For what? Being a philosophising pragmatist?'

'For helping me consider another point of view.' Wade gestured at the office. 'Dad did a great job building this company and we were close. Until he got distracted.'

His frown returned momentarily and she knew it would take more than a few encouraging words from her to get him to change his mindset and let go of the guilt.

Deliberately brusque and businesslike, he shuffled papers on his desk. 'I'm here to ensure the company regains a foothold in the publishing market.'

'I thought that's why I'm here.'

She'd hoped to make him laugh. Instead, he fixed her with a speculative stare.

'How do you do it?'

'Do what?'

'Live your life under a spotlight. Fake it for all those people.'

Increasingly uncomfortable, she shrugged. 'Who said I was faking?'

He ran a hand over his face. 'Something my annoying stepmother said, about WAGs leading fabricated lives.'

A shiver of foreboding sent a chill through Liza.

What the hell was that supposed to mean? Did Babs Urquart know something? Or was she making a sweeping generalisation?

Lord, if her fabricated life ever became known they were all sunk and Wade would look at her with derision and scorn, not the continued interest that made her squirm with longing.

'Guess we all put on a front when we need to,' she said, thankful her voice didn't quiver. 'Nothing wrong with it if no one gets hurt.'

He didn't reply and his stare intensified.

'Is that what you're doing with me?' He placed his palms on the desk and leaned forward, shrinking the space between them. 'Putting on a front?'

Smart guy.

'Why would I do that?'

Yeah, as if he'd buy her feigned innocence.

'Because you're running scared. I want to date you, and I'm pretty damn sure you want to date me, but we continue to do the avoidance dance.' He beckoned her closer with a crooked finger. 'What I want to know is why.'

The longer he stared at her, his dark eyes intent and mesmerising, the harder it was to remember the question let alone formulate an articulate answer.

'Already told you. We work together. Too complicated.'

Her breath came in short, choppy punches, as if her lungs squeezed tight and wouldn't let the air out fast enough.

Her excuse for the breathlessness constricting her chest and she was sticking to it.

'Technically we don't work together. I'm here as an interim. You blackmailed me into giving you a job.' He waved a hand between them. 'You and me? We don't exactly fit the mould of corporate colleagues who shouldn't fraternise.'

He wore the smile of a smug victor. 'Got any other excuses?'

Yeah, Liza had plenty, but she'd never divulge

the real reason she couldn't date Wade. Not in a million years.

'For now, don't we have a book launch to attend?' She stood, put some much-needed distance between them. 'How's that for an excuse?'

'Damn flimsy, if you ask me,' he said, his gaze sweeping over her in admiration.

'I didn't.' She swept up her portfolio and tucked it under her arm. 'Email me the book-launch details and I'll meet you there.'

His frown returned. 'It's two blocks away. Makes sense for us to go together.'

When she took too long to respond, he added, 'I'll walk you back to your car afterwards. You know, in case you think I'll bundle you into my car and try to take advantage of you.'

She couldn't help but laugh. 'Okay.'

Wade shook his head. 'You're an exasperating woman, but if your marketing skills are half as good as your bio, Qu Publishing is going to love you.'

Her heart gave a funny little quirk at the L word tripping so easily from his lips.

As long as his publishing company was the only thing that loved her.

For as much as Liza secretly yearned for Wade, she didn't have room in her life for love.

Not now.

Not ever.

CHAPTER NINE

LIZA LITHGOW'S STYLE TIPS FOR MAXIMUM WAG WOW IMPACT

The Hair

For the ultra-glam events like the MVP Awards (and especially if your guy is favoured to win the Most Valuable Player award) it pays to indulge in a trip to a hair salon. Even if you don't go for a fancy up-do, blow-dried sleek hair is always in vogue.

For maximum do-it-at-home WAG wow, try the loose knot. It's sophisticated and relaxed and sexy all at the same time. The perfect 'do if you're aiming for understated elegance.

Here's how you do it:

• Wash your hair.

• Add a volumising mousse to damp hair.

- Blow-dry hair from the ends to the roots to create more volume.
- Use a comb to tease the crown.
- Using fingers, gather hair in a low pony-tail.
- Secure with a band.
- Fix into a loose bun with bobby pins and let strands fall.
- Finish with a light spritz of hairspray to secure.

If you're dying to try a different look but don't have the length required, hair extensions are an option.

But make sure they blend with your colour and get an expert to do them.

You don't want a clump of hair dislodging at an inopportune moment (like when the TV cameras are panning to you when your guy wins that MVP award!).

'DID YOU LEARN anything new at the book launch?'

'Yeah.' Wade screwed up his nose and rubbed

his chest. 'Cab sav and spinach-feta quiche don't mix.'

Liza laughed. 'That'll teach you for scoffing an entire tray of hors d'oeuvres.'

'I didn't have dinner. I was hungry.' The corners of his mouth curved. 'Your fault.'

'How do you figure that?'

'You wouldn't have dinner with me.'

She rolled her eyes. 'That's because you said we had a book launch to attend. For *work*. Remember?'

He heaved a sigh. 'Believe me, it's all I think about.' He took her hand as they entered the underground car park. 'Next to you, that is.'

An illicit thrill shot through Liza. She shouldn't be so happy Wade ranked her next to his precious business, not when she was determined to keep him at bay, but she couldn't help it.

The guy was seriously hot and she'd bet he invaded her thoughts a heck of a lot more often than she did his.

'We're not supposed to do this, for a million reasons—'

'Can't think of one right now.'

He'd pinned her against the wall before she could blink and plastered his mouth to hers.

The feel of his commanding lips wiped all rational thought from her mind as her body responded on an innate level that scared the hell out of her.

With this one, scorching kiss she remembered in excruciatingly vivid detail how he'd kissed his way all over her body.

How he'd caressed and stroked until she'd been out of her mind.

How he'd licked and savoured every inch of her skin until she'd melted.

His hands slid over her butt and pulled her flush against him.

Damn, how could something so wrong feel so right?

Liza wriggled, needing to push him off, get in her car and head home to Cindy.

Instead, as he changed the pressure of the kiss and touched his tongue to hers, she combusted.

She arched against him, revelling in the feel of his hardness. She wound her fingers through his hair, angled his head and kissed him right back, pouring every ounce of her repressed yearning into it.

He groaned. She moaned.

His hands were everywhere. Her skin blistered with the heat generated between their bodies.

He didn't stop. She didn't care.

Until the sound of a car engine starting on the level below penetrated the erotic fog clouding her head. And she realised what the hell she was doing.

She broke the kiss and dragged in great lung-fuls of air, her ragged breathing matching his.

'Don't expect me to apologise for that,' he said, resting his forehead against hers, his hands clasp-ing her waist, leaving her no room to move.

'I would, if I hadn't enjoyed it so much.' She rested her palms on his chest, wishing she had the willpower to shove him away. 'You won't take no for an answer, will you?'

He straightened and smiled down at her. 'You're only just figuring that out?'

'Maybe I'm a slow learner.'

'Or maybe you're running from something when it'd be better to confront it and grab it with both hands?' He squeezed her waist. 'By *it* I mean you should be grabbing *me*, of course.'

Laughter bubbled up in her chest and spilled out. She loved an intelligent guy. She loved a funny guy more. Love being figurative. Totally.

'I really need to get home and work on the marketing campaign.'

He humphed. 'And I really need to get home and work on it too.'

He released her and snapped his fingers. 'Here's a thought. Why don't we head home together and do some *work*?'

She chuckled. 'Don't hold your breath expecting me to ask your place or mine.'

'Not happening, huh?'

She shook her head. 'Nope.'

He ducked his head, nuzzled her neck, and the buzz was back. 'And there's nothing I can do to change your mind?'

Her libido whimpered and rolled over.

Her mind yelled, 'Easy!'

'Uh…no,' she said, too soft, too breathy, too needy.

'Sure?'

His lips brushed the tender skin beneath her

ear and trailed slowly downward where his teeth nipped her collarbone with gentle bites that made her body zing and heat pool low in her belly.

Sure? She wasn't sure of anything, least of all how she would get to her car, get in and drive home without him in the passenger seat.

'Wade, you're so—'

'Addictive?' He licked the dip between her collarbones.

'Wicked?' He deliberately brushed his stubbled jaw along the top of her breast.

'Sexy?' He edged towards her mouth, his lips teasing at the corner.

'Persistent,' she said, holding her breath as his lips brushed hers once, twice, soft, taunting.

As a car's headlights panned over them, Liza nudged him away. 'That'd be a great boost for the book's marketing. CEO AND WAG CAUGHT IN COMPROMISING POSITION UNDERGROUND.'

'All publicity's good publicity,' he said, completely unruffled while she felt dishevelled and flustered and turned on.

'Beg to differ.' She tugged down her jacket, straightened her blouse and smoothed her hair. 'Are you walking me to my car or not?'

'Lead the way.' His arm swept forward in a flourish, and as she passed him she could've sworn his hand deliberately brushed her butt.

Wade didn't play fair.

Then again, the way her skin tingled with awareness and her body seemed lit up from within, did she want him to?

Despite the urge to run from Wade as fast as her legs could carry her, Liza was glad he'd walked her to her car.

She wouldn't have made it otherwise. Her knees shook so badly after their impromptu make-out session in a dark corner of the underground car park, if it hadn't been for his steadying arm around her waist she would've definitely stumbled.

And her head was shrouded in a passionate haze, her only excuse for slipping up and not waving him away before they reached her wheels.

'You drive *this*?'

She slipped out of his grasp and fumbled for her keys. 'Yeah, why?'

'I pictured you in something swift and sporty.' Bemused, he walked around her ten-year-old people carrier. 'You could fit an entire football team in the back of this thing.'

Or a wheelchair, but that was on a strictly need-to-know basis.

'I like big cars.' She tried not to sound defensive. And failed, if his raised eyebrows were any indication.

'So it seems.'

She flicked the remote button to unlock the doors but he laid a hand on her forearm and stopped her from opening the driver's door.

'Wait.'

She couldn't. Because if she spent one more second around him in this befuddled mess she'd fall into his arms and beg for a repeat of that one memorable night they'd spent together.

'I really have to go.'

In response, he moved in closer, placing a hand on either side of her waist and pinning her between cold, hard metal behind and hot, hard body in front.

'Come home with me.'

Her heart lurched with longing but before she could protest he rushed on. 'You doubted my sincerity the first night we were together? Then let's start afresh. Make tonight our night. No work. No excuses. Just two people who are crazy about each other indulging their mutual passion.'

His heated gaze bore into her, unrelenting, demanding an honest answer. 'No complications at the office tomorrow. No second-guessing. Just you and me and an incredible night to be ourselves.'

Ah hell.

Liza was tempted. Beyond tempted.

Her body strained towards him of its own volition, miles ahead of her head in saying yes.

But what was the point? One more night would only solidify what she already knew.

She could easily fall for Wade Urquart given half a chance.

And she couldn't. Not with her responsibilities. Not with her life plan.

It wouldn't be fair to encumber a guy with Cindy's full-time care and she would never leave Cindy to fend for herself.

It was why she never considered a long-term relationship, why she would never marry.

Normally it didn't bother her. But she'd never met a guy like Wade before, the kind of guy who elicited wild fantasies, the kind that consisted of homes and picket fences and a brood of dark-haired, dark-eyed cherubs just like their dad.

'Stop thinking so hard.' He placed a hand over her heart and it bucked wildly beneath it. 'What does in here tell you?'

To run like the wind.

But she swallowed that instinctive response and reluctantly met his gaze.

She had to refuse.

But an incredible thing happened as her eyes met his.

She saw a confusing jumble of hope and vulnerability and desire, every emotion she was feeling reflected back at her like a mirror.

No guy she'd ever been with had been so revealing and in that moment she knew she couldn't walk away from him. At least for tonight.

'Okay,' she said, mimicking his action and feeling his heart pound beneath her palm. 'But this is a one-off, okay? We don't discuss it again or bring it up at the office.'

'Okay,' he said, swooping in for a kiss that snatched her breath and quite possibly her heart.

* * *

Liza didn't remember much of the short drive to Wade's Southbank apartment. She could barely concentrate on the road with his hand on her thigh the entire time.

He didn't speak, sensing her need for silence. She couldn't speak, not without the risk of blurting how he made her feel. Uncertain and flustered and on a high.

Hell, how bad would it be come morning after another amazing night in his arms?

She shouldn't have agreed, but the part of her that had had the life she'd planned ripped away following the phone call from her financial adviser's office still craved a little indulgence.

She was doing her best: with the biography, with the marketing job, with caring for Cindy.

She deserved a little break, deserved to feel good, and Wade was guaranteed to make her feel incredible, albeit for a few hours, tonight.

His penthouse apartment was everything she'd imagined: glossy wooden floors, electrically controlled slimline blinds, glass and chrome and leather. Minimalist chic. Reeking of money.

Not that he gave her much of a chance to study

it, for the moment they stepped down into the split-level lounge room he had his arms around her and backed her against a sleek marble-topped table.

'Do you have any idea how much I want you?' he said, framing her face with his hands, staring deep into her eyes.

The depth of his need shocked her, as if he'd given her a glimpse right to his very soul.

He shouldn't want her this much. It wouldn't end well.

But she'd come too far to back out now and she couldn't even if she wanted to. For she needed him just as badly. If only for tonight.

'I have a fair idea,' she said, undulating her hips against the evidence of how badly he wanted her.

He growled. 'Tease.'

'No, a tease would do this.' Her hands splayed against his chest, caressed upwards before stroking downwards. Lower. And lower. Stopping short of his belt buckle. 'A tease would also do this.'

She slowly slid the leather belt out, toying with the buckle.

'And this.' She flicked the top button of his trousers open.

'A tease would stop here.' She inched his zipper down, the sound of grating metal teeth the only sound apart from his ragged breathing.

'But I'm no tease.' She pushed his trousers down. Slid a hand inside his black boxers. Cupped his erection.

His groan filled the air and, empowered, she went for broke.

He let her undress him until he was standing before her, gloriously naked, incredibly beautiful.

Bronze skin, rippling muscles, hard for her.

'One of us is way overdressed,' he said, taking a step towards her.

'Wait.' She braced a hand on his chest. 'I'm admiring the view.'

'Later,' he said, bundling her into his arms. 'Much later.'

CHAPTER TEN

LIZA LITHGOW'S STYLE TIPS FOR MAXIMUM WAG WOW IMPACT

The Dream

WAGs of the New York Yankees may not harbour this same dream, but for WAGs all around the world New York City is *the* place to be.

From its iconic Manhattan skyline to its most recognised Statue of Liberty. From the Chrysler Building to the famed Empire State Building.

From its two most famous streets, Madison and Park Avenues.

There is so much to tempt a WAG.

Throw in:

The Metropolitan Museum of Art (The Met)

Central Park
The Flatiron Building
The Guggenheim
The Brooklyn Bridge
Times Square
Rockefeller Centre
Broadway
Carnegie Hall
Lincoln Centre
Madison Square Garden

And it's little wonder that most WAGs dream of being a part of New York.

So what are you waiting for? Book that airline ticket now!

LUCKY FOR WADE, he'd never had much of an ego. For if he had it'd be smarting.

Liza had done it again. Indulged in a wild, passionate, no-holds-barred night of mind-blowing sex. And then nothing.

The next day at the office she'd reverted to the cool, dedicated woman who'd wowed him with her business ethic that first day she'd presented her marketing ideas like a veteran.

That had been four weeks ago and nothing had changed.

Admittedly, they'd been incredibly busy, with her biography having the fastest turnaround he'd ever seen in all his years in publishing.

To have a book written, copy-edited, line-edited and in ARC format within a month? Unheard of, but he'd made it happen. He owed his dad that much.

Preserving a family legacy might be the reason everyone assumed was behind his drive to save the company.

Only he knew the truth. Guilt was a pretty powerful motivator.

And despite Liza's encouraging insights that his dad had loved him and that was why Quentin hadn't shared the truth about his heart condition, Wade knew better.

His dad had known how much he despised Babs, but he'd been too much of a gentleman to bring it up or let it affect their relationship initially. But with Wade's continued withdrawal, both physically and emotionally, he'd irrevocably damaged the one relationship he'd ever relied on.

For his dad not to trust him enough to divulge

the truth about his heart condition before it was too late? It hurt, deeper and harder than he'd ever imagined.

Wade regretted every moment he'd lost with his dad. Regretted all the time they could have spent together if he'd known the truth. Regretted how he'd let his superiority and judgement and distaste ruin their mateship. For that was what they'd had, a real friendship that surpassed a simple father-son bond.

Most of all, he regretted not having the opportunity to say a proper goodbye to his dad.

He'd regret his actions and the rift he'd caused until his dying day but for now he'd do everything in his power to ensure Qu thrived, as a token of respect for the man who had given him everything.

And he had the woman who'd sold her story to him to thank too.

He'd done as she said over the last few weeks. Remembered the good times with his dad.

Authors they'd signed together, books they'd published that had gone on to hit best-seller lists.

A patient Quentin teaching him golf as a teenager and the many hack games that had followed over the years.

The beers they'd share while watching the AFL Grand Final or the Grand Prix.

So many more precious memories he'd deliberately locked away because of the hurt. But Liza had been right. Holding on to guilt only made it fester and remembering the good times had gone some way to easing his pain.

She'd given him a wake-up call he'd needed and he hoped his surprise would help thank her.

He knocked on Liza's door, holding the Advanced Reading Copy behind his back. He wanted to surprise her and hoped she'd be as thrilled with how the story had turned out as he was.

He'd stayed up all night, devouring Liza's biography from cover to cover. When he'd speed read the first draft in e-format he'd done so with an editor's eye and hadn't really had time to absorb the facts beyond she'd delivered the juicy tell-all he'd demanded.

After reading the ARC last night, holding her life in *tree* format, he'd felt closer to her somehow, as if learning snippets from her childhood revealed her to him in a way she'd never do herself.

Of course, he'd hated her dating tales, insanely jealous of the soccer and basketball stars that had wooed her and whisked her to parties and elite functions, living the high life.

He had no reason to be jealous, for those guys were her past.

And what? He was her future?

Damned if he knew. It wasn't as if they were looking for anything long term. He'd spelled it out at the start and Liza did her best to maintain her distance when they weren't burning up the sheets those two times.

So why the intense disappointment she'd been willing to share part of her life with him, but only for the money?

The door opened and a forty-something woman with spiked blonde hair, no make-up and sporting a frown eyed him up and down. 'Yes?'

'Hi, Wade Urquart, here to see Liza.'

The woman's eyes widened as a sly smile lit her face. 'Nice to meet you, Wade. I'm Shar. Come on in.'

Shar ushered him through the door and it took a moment to register two things.

A pretty young woman bearing a strong resemblance to Liza was engrossed in a jigsaw puzzle alongside Liza.

The young woman was in a wheelchair.

Their heads turned as one as he stepped into the room, the young woman's lopsided welcoming smile indicative of some kind of disability, Liza's stunned expression a mix of horror and fear.

It confused the hell out of him.

Why was she horrified to see him? Was she scared he'd run a mile because she had a disabled relative, probably a sister?

The possibility that she thought so little of him irked.

He strode forward, determined to show her he was ten times the man she gave him credit for.

'Hi, I'm Wade.' He stuck out his hand, waited for the young woman to place her clawed hand in his, and shook it gently.

'Cindy,' she said, her blue eyes so like Liza's bright with curiosity and mischief. 'Are you Liza's boyfriend?'

'Yes,' he said, simultaneously with Liza's, 'No.'

Shar smothered a laugh from behind. 'Come on, Cinders, let's leave these two to sort out their confusion.'

Cindy giggled and Wade said, 'Nice meeting you both,' as they left the room.

Liza stood, her movements stiff and jerky as she rounded the table, arms folded. 'What are you doing here?'

'I came to give you this.'

He handed her the ARC, his excitement at sharing it with her evaporating in a cloud of confusion.

Why hadn't she told him about her sister Cindy? Did he mean that little to her?

They might not have a solid commitment or long-term plans but he'd thought they'd really connected on a deeper level beyond the physical.

At the very least they were friends, and friends shared stuff like this.

As her fingers closed around the creased spine from his rapid page-turning the night before, the truth detonated.

His hand jerked back and the ARC fell to the floor with a loud thud.

'There's no mention of Cindy in your bio.'

She glared at him, defiant. ''Course not. I don't want the whole world knowing about my sister—'

'What the—?' He ran a hand over his face, hoping it would erase his disgust, knowing it wouldn't. 'You're embarrassed by her.'

She stepped back as if he'd struck her, her mouth a shocked O.

Anger filled him, ugly and potent. He didn't know what made him madder: the fact she'd lied in her bio, the fact she was ashamed of her sister or the fact she hadn't trusted him enough to tell him anything.

He kicked at the ARC. 'Is any of this true?'

She flinched. 'My life is between those pages—'

'Bull.' He lowered his voice with effort. 'Leaving your sister out of your bio is a major twisting of the truth. Which makes me wonder, what else have you lied about?'

He waited for her to deny, wanted her to. But she stood there, staring at him with sorrow and regret, and he had his answer.

'I could lose everything,' he said, anger making his hands shake. His fingers curled into fists and he shoved them into his pockets. 'Your advance? Bulk of it came out of my pocket. Three hundred grand's worth.'

He should feel more panicky about the precarious position he'd placed his own company in to save his dad's—the advance was only the start, for he'd poured another half a million into the marketing budget for the bio too—but all he could think about was how Liza had lied to him. How she'd withheld the truth from him.

Just like his dad.

He'd told her about Quentin not trusting him enough, about how it affected him. Hell, she'd even given him that pep talk.

Yet she'd gone and done the same regardless.

'I earned that advance.' Her flat monotone made him want to shake her to get some kind of reaction. 'I gave you the story you wanted.'

'So what? I should be grateful?' His bitterness made her flinch. 'Should've known better than to trust someone like you.'

She paled but didn't say anything, her lack of defence riling him further.

'Guess you played me like those other poor suckers in your *biography*,' he said, not proud of the low blow but lashing out, needing to hurt her as much as she'd hurt him.

That was when the real truth detonated.

He wouldn't care this much, wouldn't be hurting this much, if he hadn't fallen for her.

A woman who didn't trust him, a woman who thought nothing of their developing relationship, a woman who'd done all of this clearly for the money only.

Reeling from the realisation, he did the only thing possible.

Turned on his heel, strode out of the door and slammed it behind him.

Liza sank onto the nearest chair and clutched her belly, willing the rolling nausea to subside.

She didn't know what was worse: feeling as if she was about to hurl or the breath-snatching ache in her chest.

This was why she never let any guy get too close.

This was why she never should've let Wade into her life.

And into her heart.

She had; despite every effort to push him away

and keep their relationship strictly business, he'd bustled his way in with charm and panache and flair.

And she'd let him. She knew why too. Because for the first time in for ever she'd felt cherished. Spoiled. As if someone was looking out for her rather than the other way around.

She didn't mind being Cindy's carer but for a brief interlude in her life Wade had swept her off her feet and taught her what it felt like being on the other side.

'Double mocha or double-choc-fudge brownies?' Shar bustled into the room, pretending not to look at her while casting concerned glances out of the corner of her eye as she tidied up a stack of magazines.

'Both,' Liza said, knowing she'd be unable to stomach either but needing a few more minutes alone to reassemble her wits.

'Okay. Back in a sec.'

Breathing a sigh of relief, Liza eased the grip on her belly and stretched. Rolled out her shoulders. Tipped her neck from side to side.

Did little for the tension gripping her but at

least she wouldn't get a muscle spasm on top of everything else.

Wade had ousted her lies. Worse, he thought she was ashamed of Cindy, when nothing could be further from the truth.

And the fact he hadn't let her explain, had stood there and hurled accusations at her, hurt.

Maybe she should've told him, should've trusted him with the truth. But her motives had been pure. She'd done it all for Cindy. Would do it again if it meant protecting her sister.

Now he knew the truth, where did that leave them?

'Here you go.' Shar dumped a plate of brownies and a steaming mocha in front of her. 'Looks like you could do with a good dose of chocolate.'

'You heard?' Liza picked at the corner of a brownie, shoved a few crumbs around the plate with her fingertip.

'Enough.' Shar winced. 'Didn't sound good.'

'Is Cindy okay?'

Shar nodded. 'Yeah, she was hooked up to the computer playing a game, had her ears plugged.'

'Guess I should be grateful for small mercies,' Liza said, the severity of her confrontation with

Wade hitting home at the thought of Cindy over-hearing what he'd accused her of.

'You didn't tell him about Cindy.'

It was a statement, not a question, and Liza didn't know where to begin to rationalise her behaviour.

'He seems like a nice bloke.' Shar sipped at her mocha. 'Good looker too.'

'Wade's…' What? Incredibly sexy? Persistent? Thoughtful? She settled for the truth. 'Special.'

'Then why all the secrecy?'

'Because I wanted to protect Cindy.'

'From?'

'Prying. Interference.'

'Ridicule?' Shar prompted and Liza nodded, biting her bottom lip.

'You'll probably hate me for saying this, but are you sure it's Cindy you were protecting and not you?'

Liza's head snapped up; she was shocked by Shar's accusation. 'What do you mean?'

Shar screwed up her nose before continuing. 'You've lived your life in the spotlight. TV-hosting gigs. Mingled with A-listers. Best parties. Best of everything.'

Shar paused, glanced away. 'Maybe you didn't want people knowing you had a disabled sister because you thought it would taint how you appeared to others in some way?'

'That's bull.' Liza stood so quickly her knee knocked the underside of the table and she swore.

'Then why so defensive?'

She glared at Shar. 'Because what you've just suggested is hateful and makes me look like a narcissistic bitch.'

Shar shook her head. 'No. It makes you human.'

Shar's accusation echoed through her head. Had that partially been her motivation? Was Wade right? Was she ashamed to reveal to the world she had a disabled sister?

Never in a million years would she have thought that, but if the two people in the world she was closest to—discounting Cindy—had jumped to the same conclusion, had she done it on some subconscious level?

She collapsed back onto the chair and tried to articulate her jumbled feelings. 'Because of what I've faced in the spotlight, I didn't want Cindy exposed to any of that.'

Shar pointed at the ARC lying on the floor.

'So what if you'd mentioned her in the book? Doesn't mean the media would've been beating down your door to interview her.'

'They might've.' Liza rested her feet on the chair and wrapped her arms around her shins. 'You've fielded enough calls to know how persistent they can be. It could've turned into a circus.'

'Or they could've respected your privacy and hers.'

Liza blew a raspberry. 'I hate it when you're logical.'

Shar winked. 'All part of the service.'

Now that Liza had come this far, she should tell Shar all of it.

'I did it for the money.'

'The biography?'

Liza nodded. 'That day I went to Qu Publishing's offices to tell them to stop harassing us? I had a phone call from my financial adviser's office.'

She took a deep breath, blew it out. 'My investment has gone. He scammed the lot.'

Shar blanched. 'Oh hell.'

'I said worse than that.' Liza hugged her knees tighter. 'I was still in the office. Wade found me in a crumpled heap. I had to accept his offer. The advance and royalties from the bio were the only way out.'

'Drastic times call for drastic measures.' Shar picked up the ARC off the floor and laid it on the table. 'If you didn't mention Cindy in the bio, did you stretch the truth in general?'

'A little.' She waved a hand side to side. 'Mostly stuck to the truth with the WAG side of things. Played up all that glamorous nonsense people lap up. It's what he asked for.'

'What about your folks?'

'I told the truth. Within reason.'

Even now, ten years after her mum had walked out on them, and over two decades since her dad had bolted too, Liza cushioned the hurt by justifying their appalling behaviour.

They didn't deserve it but the last thing she needed was for Cindy to realise the truth one day. That their parents had left because of her.

Cindy had been too young to know their father, had swallowed the story their mum had told: they'd grown apart and divorced. When in fact he'd been a coward, unable to cope with a disabled daughter and had taken the easy way out by abandoning them all.

As for their mum? Cindy wasn't a fool and had been stoic when she'd left. Louisa had emotionally withdrawn for years and Cindy had been philosophical, almost happy, when it had just been the two of them left.

Finding Shar at the time had been a godsend too and Liza knew she wouldn't have made it without the full-time carer and confidante.

'As long as you didn't tell blatant lies, I don't see what the problem is.' Shar picked up the ARC and flipped through it. 'What did he mean about losing everything?'

'Apparently the advance came out of his pocket.'

But from what she'd learned, Wade was loaded. Had his own publishing company in London.

Then again, she knew better than anyone that appearances could be deceptive. If his company was anything like Qu Publishing and the rest of the industry, maybe he'd taken a hit with the digital boom and was losing millions with falling print runs?

But her bio was already at the printers, ready to ship to the many bookstores that had pre-ordered by the thousands. And those pre-orders were like gold.

So what if she'd omitted Cindy? What the readers didn't know wouldn't hurt them.

He'd overreacted, probably smarting more from her omission than any real financial pressure.

Shar laid the ARC on the table and nudged it towards her. 'Maybe you should talk to him?'

'Are you kidding?' Liza shook her head. 'You didn't see how mad he was.'

'Give him time to cool off, then talk to him.' Shar took a huge bite of brownie, chewed it, before continuing. 'Besides, isn't he your boss? You'll have to talk some time.'

That was when reality hit.

She'd have to face up to work and see that devastation and disgust in Wade's eyes all over again.

The pain in her chest intensified.

Shar dusted off her hands. 'Go easy on him. I think he likes you.'

That's where the problem lay.

Liza liked him too.

Too much to be good for her.

* * *

After helping bathe and dress Cindy, Liza settled into the nightly routine of rubbing moisturiser into Cindy's dry skin.

It was their special bonding time, to relax and chat about their respective days. Liza had missed it on those evenings when she'd been on WAG duty. Guess it said a lot about her previous life-style that she would've rather been home with her sis than whooping it up with a bunch of fake socialites.

'That feels good.' Cindy closed her eyes and rested her head against the back of the chair as Liza spread the moisturiser evenly over her fore-arm with firm strokes.

'Your skin's looking great,' Liza said, always on the lookout for pressure sores or skin break-down, common side effects with CP.

'Thanks to you.' Cindy sighed as Liza increased the pressure slightly. 'Wade seems nice.'

'Hmm.' Liza deliberately kept her strokes rhythmic, not wanting to alert Cindy to her sud-den spike in blood pressure.

She didn't want to think about Wade now, didn't

want to remember the disappointment and cen-
sure in his eyes as he'd stalked out two hours ago.

His accusation cut deep. To think, he'd assumed
she was ashamed of Cindy…well, stuff him.

He wouldn't have a clue what it was like, trying to keep Cindy calm and avoiding stress that
could potentially increase her spasticity.

Liza had seen it happen, any time Cindy was
anxious, upset, agitated or excited. The medical
team had advised her to avoid such situations.
And that was the main reason Liza hadn't included Cindy in the book.

She couldn't run the risk of people invading
Cindy's privacy, pestering for interviews and potentially increasing the likelihood of those disastrous contractures.

The changes in Cindy's soft tissues terrified
Liza. The shortening of muscles, tendons and
ligaments could lead to muscle stiffness, atrophy
and fibrosis, where the muscles become smaller
and thinner.

And if those muscles permanently shortened
and pulled on the nearby bones the resultant deformities were a significant problem.

Her sis worked so hard at her exercises but Liza

constantly worried about contractures, where the spasticity in Cindy's arm and leg might reach a point where the muscles required surgical release.

Cindy co-operated most days but they'd had their battles over the years, where no amount of cajoling or bribery could get Cindy to follow her exercise regimen.

Liza hated playing taskmaster but she did it. Anything to avoid seeing Cindy in more pain than she already was.

Cindy coped with the chronic pain from minor muscle contractures and abnormal postures of her joints admirably but it broke Liza's heart every time her sis winced or cried out during her routine.

Liza stayed positive and tried to encourage as much as she could, for the possibility of a hip subluxation or scoliosis from the contractures was all too real and she wanted to avoid further medical intervention for Cindy at all costs.

So including her in the biography and having Cindy agitated or overexcited, leading to contractures?

Uh-uh, Liza couldn't do it. She'd never intentionally hurt her sister or put her in harm's way and that was how she'd viewed revealing Cindy's identity to the world.

As for Shar's insinuation that maybe Liza hadn't wanted to be tainted by Cindy's disability in some way, that was off base.

Liza would've loved to raise awareness for cerebral palsy, the association and the carers, and her tell-all would've been the perfect vehicle.

But Cindy came first always and she couldn't run the risk of her spasticity worsening.

'He said he was your boyfriend.' Cindy's eyes snapped open and pinned Liza with an astute glare she had no hope of evading.

'Guys get confused sometimes.' Liza reached for Cindy's other arm and started the massage process all over again. 'Smile and they think you're crushing on them.'

Cindy giggled, a sound Liza never tired of. 'Maybe that's the problem? You've been smiling too much at Wade?'

'Could be.'

Though Liza knew smiling would be the last thing happening when they met next.

Shar was right. She had to talk to him, had to calm this volatile situation before she lost her job. And maybe lost the guy.

CHAPTER ELEVEN

LIZA LITHGOW'S STYLE TIPS FOR MAXIMUM WAG WOW IMPACT

The Proposal

WAGs put up with a lot to stand by their man.

So it's only fitting a WAG deserves a special proposal.

Guys, here are some of the best places in which to propose to your devoted WAG (and actually put that W—Wife—into WAG!)

- Strolling along the Seine in Paris.
- Atop the Eiffel Tower.
- Cruising the Greek Islands on a private yacht.
- Top of the London Eye.
- Sunset on Kuta Beach in Bali.
- At the ball drop in Times Square, NYC, on New Year's Eve.

- Winery dinner in the Yarra Valley, Victoria.
- Hot-air balloon, anywhere.
- Camel ride, United Arab Emirates.
- Walking the Great Wall of China.
- Outside the Taj Mahal.
- Climbing the Sydney Harbour Bridge.
- Cruising the South Pacific.
- Midnight on New Year's Eve, anywhere.
- Central Park, any time.
- Spanish Steps, Rome.
- Diamond Head, Waikiki.
- In a buré over the water, Tahiti or Maldives.
- Scuba diving in the Great Barrier Reef.

AFTER THE BLOW-UP with Liza, Wade headed for the one place he felt safe.

The office.

It had been his refuge for as long as he could remember, whether in Melbourne or London, the one place he was on top and in total control.

Family? As changeable as the wind and, as his relationship with his dad had fractured because of Babs, he'd systematically withdrawn.

Girlfriends? Chosen with deliberation, the kind of corporate women who expected nothing and were content with a brief fling.

The publishing business had been the one constant in his life, the one thing he could depend on.

And now, courtesy of Liza's lies, he could lose that too.

It had taken a full hour of checking with his legal team and exploring all possible scenarios for him to calm down.

Even if Liza's bio weren't one-hundred-per-cent accurate, according to the contract wording the readers would have no recourse if the truth of Cindy's existence came out.

He'd assumed it wouldn't be a problem but needed to know for sure. After all, how many celebrities invented backgrounds and touted it as truth?

In the heat of the moment, when he'd realised she'd kept something as important as her sister from him, he'd snapped and said he could lose everything.

He'd thrown it out there to shame her; to intimidate her into maybe telling him the truth—why she'd done it—when in fact the eight hundred grand from his own pocket wouldn't make or break him.

Now that he'd calmed down enough to rationally evaluate the situation, he might not have lost his dad's company but he had lost something equally important.

The woman he loved.

How ironic that the first time he let a woman get closer than dinner and a date, the first time he'd learned what it meant to truly desire someone beyond the physical, had turned into the last time he'd ever be so foolish again.

And a scarier thought: was he like his dad after all? Had Liza played him as Babs had played his dad?

He wouldn't have thought so, the times they'd been intimate so revealing, so soul-reaching, he could've sworn she'd been on the same wavelength.

But she'd sought him out at the very beginning. She'd blackmailed her way into a job. Had that been her end game from the start?

Was their relationship a way of keeping him onside while she milked the situation for all it was worth?

Wasn't as if she hadn't done it before. According to her bio—if any of it was true—she'd been thrust into WAG limelight by default when her high-school sweetheart became pro, but with the basketball star she'd implied they'd had an understanding based on a solid friendship and mutual regard.

Yet when he'd studied the pictures of her and Henri Jaillet her body language spoke volumes. If the cameras were trained on her Liza stood tall and smiled, while subtly leaning away from Henri's arm draped across her shoulders or waist.

In the candid shots, she stood behind Henri, arms folded, shoulders slumped, lips compressed.

By those shots, she hadn't enjoyed a moment of their relationship yet she'd done it regardless, enduring it for a year.

What had she told him at the start? *What you see isn't always what you get.*

If so, why? Had it been to support her sister? Had she deliberately thrust herself into the limelight? Had it been for the adulation or was there more behind it?

That was what killed him the most, the fact he'd felt closer to her reading the bio, as if she'd let him into her life a little, when in fact she hadn't let him in at all.

He swirled the Scotch he nursed before downing the amber spirit in two gulps. The burn in his gullet didn't ease the burn in his heart and the warmth as it hit his stomach didn't spread to the rest of him.

He'd been icy cold since he'd left Liza's, unable to equate the woman he'd fallen in love with to the woman who'd hide her disabled sister out of shame.

His door creaked open and he frowned, ready to blast anyone who dared enter. Damn publishing business, one of the few work environments where it wasn't unusual to find employees chained to their desk to meet deadlines at all hours.

'Go away,' he barked out, slamming the glass on the side table when the door swung open all the way. 'I said—'

'I heard what you said.' Liza stood in the doorway, framed by the backlight, looking like a person who'd been through the ringer. He knew the feeling. 'But I'm not going anywhere.'

He swiped a hand over his face. 'I'm not in the mood.'

She ignored his semi-growl, entered the office and closed the door.

He watched her walk across the office, soft grey yoga pants clinging to her legs, outlining their shape, and desire mingled with his anger.

She sat next to him on the leather sofa, too close for comfort, not close enough considering he preferred her on his lap.

Her fingers plucked at the string of her red hoodie, twisting it around and around until he couldn't stand it any more. He reached out and stilled her hand, watching her eyes widen at the contact before she clasped her hands in her lap.

Great. Looked as if his touch had become as repugnant as him.

'We need to get a few things straight,' she said, shoulders squared in defiance. 'Firstly, Cindy is the most important person in my life and I'd never be ashamed of her.'

He waited and she glared at him, daring him to disagree.

'Secondly, I've spent most of my life protecting her and that's what my omission was about.

Ensuring she wouldn't cop the same crap I have all these years, which may have a detrimental effect on her condition physically.'

'How?'

'Extreme emotions or mood swings can increase the spasticity in her muscles, which in turn can lead to long-term complications. Serious complications that could lead to permanent deformities.'

A tiny sliver of understanding lodged in his hardened heart, cracking it open a fraction, letting admiration creep in. And regret, that he'd unfairly accused her of something so heinous as being ashamed of her sister when in fact she was protecting her.

'And thirdly, the rest of my life laid out in the bio? True. Not fabricated. Elaborated? Yeah.' Her fingers twitched, before she unlinked her hands and waved one between them. 'But you and I? All real. Every moment, and I'd hate for you to think otherwise.'

Admiration gave way to hope and went a long way to soothing the intense hurt that had rendered him useless until she'd strutted through his door.

But he wouldn't give in that easily. It might have taken a lot of guts to confront him now, so soon after their blow-up, but he couldn't forget the fact she'd shut him out when he'd let her in.

'Prove it.'

A tiny frown crinkled her brow. 'How?'

'Let me into your life.'

The frown intensified. 'I don't know what you mean.'

'I think you do.' He shuffled closer to her on the couch, buoyed when she didn't move away. 'I want to see the real you. Not the persona you've donned for years to fool the masses. Not the woman you've pretended to be from the beginning of our relationship. The real you.'

Liza stared at Wade as if he'd proposed she scale the Eureka Tower naked.

The real her? No one saw the real her, not even Cindy, who she pretended to be upbeat for constantly. The way she saw it, her sister had a tough enough life, why make it harder by revealing when her own life wasn't a bed of roses?

Liza had always done it, assumed a happy face even if she'd felt like curling up in bed with a romance novel and a pack of Tim Tams.

So what Wade was asking? Too much.

She shook her head. 'I can't—'

'Yeah, you can.'

Before she could move he grasped her hand and placed it over his heart. 'I'm willing to take a chance on us. Without the pretence. Without the baggage of the past. Just you and me. What do you say?'

Liza wanted to run and hide, wanted to fake a smile and respond with a practised retort designed to hide her real feelings.

But looking into Wade's guileless dark eyes, feeling his heart thump steadily, she knew she'd reached a turning point in her life.

She had two options.

Revert to type and continue living a sham.

Or take a giant leap of faith and risk her heart.

'An answer some time this century would be nice,' he said, pressing her hand harder to his heart.

'I'm taking Cindy to Luna Park tomorrow,' she blurted. 'Come with us.'

She waited, holding her breath until her chest ached.

She'd never invited anyone along to her days out with Cindy. It was their special time. To consider letting Wade accompany them, to see what the reality of being a full-time carer involved? Huge step. He'd wanted to see the real her and she'd thrown down the gauntlet.

His mouth eased into a smile and the air whooshed out of her lungs. 'Sounds good. What time?'

'Nine. We'll pick you up.'

He released her hand to rub his together. 'Great. I get to ride in the people carrier.'

'You're making jokes about my car still, even when you know it's used for a wheelchair?'

He tapped her on the nose. 'Hey, we're genuine from now on, okay? No holding back, no watching what we say. Full disclosure.'

Liza nodded slowly, wondering how he'd feel if he knew all of it.

She didn't have time to find out when he closed the distance between them and kissed her, effectively eradicating all thought and going a long way to soothing the emptiness when he'd walked out earlier.

She hated being abandoned. Dredged up too many painful memories.

She never wanted to feel that way again.

* * *

Liza didn't know what she'd expected when she'd invited Wade to accompany them to Luna Park on the spur of the moment.

She'd wanted to test him. To see how he acted around Cindy.

For when he'd walked out on her, she'd come to a few realisations. Wade was the only guy she'd ever genuinely cared about and for that reason, after seeing his disgust when she'd withheld the truth, she'd had enough of the lies and the fake life.

She wanted to be herself around him and that included Cindy. They were a package and if he couldn't handle her sister's disability Liza didn't want to get in any deeper.

Cindy was the deal-breaker.

By the way he'd teased and laughed and chatted with her sister, he'd passed with flying colours.

Liza had seen many people interact with her sister over the years. Some glanced away or pretended not to see Cindy. Some stared at her clawed elbow and wrist, at her scissored thighs, her equinovarus foot. Some patronised by speaking extra slowly or very loud. Some looked plain uncomfortable.

But from the moment they'd picked up Wade this morning he'd been at ease and, in turn, Liza had progressively relaxed as the morning wore on.

She liked not having to pretend around Wade. It was a nice change. Something she could get used to given half a chance.

While Cindy watched the roller-coaster ride with rapt attention, Wade sat next to Liza and bumped her with his shoulder.

'Having a good time?'

She smiled and nodded. 'Absolutely. I always have a ball when I'm with Cindy.'

'She's amazing,' he said, sliding his hand across her lap to grasp hers. 'And so are you.'

He waved at Cindy with his free hand as she glanced their way. 'Honestly? I don't know a lot about cerebral palsy. I'd planned on researching it last night but got caught up with conference calls.'

Liza admired his interest. Hopefully it meant his interaction with Cindy today wasn't just a token effort and he genuinely wanted to be involved in her life—which included Cindy's life too.

'It's basically a physical disability affecting movement, caused by an injury to the developing brain, usually before birth.'

The corners of his beautiful mouth curved upward. 'You sound like a medical dictionary.'

'With the hours I've spent with the medical profession over the years I reckon I could recite an entire library's worth of encyclopaedias.'

He squeezed her hand. 'What's her prognosis?'

'Normal life expectancy. The brain damage doesn't worsen as she gets older. But the physical symptoms can.'

Cindy laughed out loud as people on the roller coaster screamed when it plummeted and Liza smiled in response, never tiring of seeing her sister happy.

'Cindy's CP is pretty mild. She's diplegic, which means it only affects her arm and leg on one side. And she has spastic CP.'

Wade frowned. 'I hate that word.'

Liza shook her head. 'It's not derogatory. Spasticity means tightness or stiffness of the muscles. The muscles are stiff because the message to move is sent incorrectly to the muscles through the damaged part of the brain.'

'That makes sense.' He frowned, deep in thought. 'Can she walk?'

'A little. At home mainly, in her room, with the aid of a frame. But for Cindy, the harder she works her muscles, the greater the spasticity, so it's easier for her to get around in the wheelchair.'

Liza blew Cindy a kiss as she glanced towards them again and grinned. 'We're definitely lucky. Many CP sufferers have intellectual disabilities, speech difficulties, seizures and severe limitations with eating and drinking. Cindy's main problem is mobility.'

Wade shook his head, as if he couldn't quite believe her optimism. 'You're fantastic.' He nodded towards Cindy. 'The way you are with her? It's beautiful.'

Uncomfortable with his praise but inwardly preening, she shrugged. 'She's my sister. We've been doing stuff together for a long time.'

'What about your folks?'

She stiffened and he squeezed her hand. 'You glossed over them in your bio and you never mention them…'

Liza didn't want to talk about her flaky folks, not today, not ever. But after Wade's full-disclosure pep talk last night she'd have to give him something.

'I didn't want to make them look bad in the book. That's why I didn't say much beyond the basics.'

He frowned. 'How bad was it?'

'Dad took off when Cindy was a year old. Couldn't handle having a disabled kid. Mum progressively withdrew emotionally over the years, waited 'til I was eighteen, then she did a runner too.'

Wade swore. 'So you've been looking after Cindy ever since?'

'Uh-huh. The CP association hooked me up with Shar shortly after Mum left and she's been a godsend. More family than carer.'

More family than her parents combined. The old saying blood was thicker than water? Give her a long, tall glass of clear aqua any day.

'Do you ever hear from them?'

She heard the disapproval in his voice and didn't want to dampen this day. 'Mum rings on birthdays and Christmas, sends money as a gift, that's about it.'

Shock widened his eyes before she saw a spark of understanding. 'That's why you took the book deal, isn't it? You support Cindy financially.'

Liza struggled not to squirm. She didn't want to discuss this with Wade, didn't want him to know her private business.

There was disclosure and there was disclosure. And for a couple that were only just embarking on a possible future, she didn't want to muddy it with her sordid past.

'We do okay,' she said, springing up from the bench and dusting off her butt. 'Come on, I think Cindy's ready for that ice cream you promised.'

Disappointment twisted his mouth before he forced a smile. 'Sure.'

But as the sun passed behind a cloud and Liza shivered in a gust off Port Phillip Bay, she wondered if her sudden chill had more to do with Wade's obvious disapproval at her reticence than the fickle spring weather.

An hour after Liza dropped him off at the office, Wade strode into the boardroom.

He couldn't get the sound of theme-park rides and Liza's laughter and Cindy's giggles out of his head, or the taste of hot dogs and mint ice cream off his tongue.

It had been an incredible morning, seeing the real Liza for the first time, and he'd been blown away. By her dedication to her sister, by her level of caring, by her sheer joy in spending time with Cindy.

None of it was faked and it made him wonder why she'd gone to great lengths to hide Cindy's identity from him.

Sure, he bought her excuse about not wanting Cindy exposed to the kind of intrusion she'd faced with her lifestyle over the years and how emotional swings could increase the risk physically, but there had to be more to it.

He'd thought she might open up to him today of all days, for he'd seen how she'd looked at him. As if she'd really seen him for the first time.

It had made him feel ten feet tall, as if he could scale that giant mouth entrance at Luna Park and jog backwards on the roller coaster.

Then he'd made the fatal mistake of delving

deeper and she'd clammed up. Shut him out, as if the last four hours had never happened.

It killed him, because he had to make some fast decisions regarding his future and he hoped to have her in it.

He knew what the board were going to say, had been sent a memo by the chairman late last night after Liza had left the office.

Everything he'd worked so hard for, everything his father had achieved, would continue.

He'd saved Qu Publishing.

Liza's biography had saved Qu Publishing.

And rather than taking her out for a night on the town to celebrate, he knew when he broke the news neither of them would feel like champagne.

It meant the end of his time in Melbourne.

The end of his relationship with Liza before it had really begun.

For now he'd seen her with Cindy he knew she'd never leave her sister. She was too dedicated. And he wouldn't ask that of her.

What if they both came with him?

The thought exploded out of left field and he rubbed his temple, dazed and excited at the same time.

'Wade?' The chairman slapped him on the back and he dragged in a deep breath, needing to get back in the game.

His personal life could wait.

For now, he had a company to solidify.

Wade took his position at the head of the table. 'Thanks for coming, gentlemen.' He mustered a smile for his stepmother. 'Babs.'

Her lips thinned in an unimpressed line.

'As you know, thanks to the pre-orders of Liza Lithgow's biography, Qu Publishing has cleared all debts and is firmly in the black. And with projected profit margins from book sales, hardcover, trade paperback and digital, we're looking at enough capital to ensure viability for many years to come.'

He waited until the noise died down.

'So I propose a vote. All those in favour of selling Qu Publishing, raise your hands.'

There wasn't a flicker of movement at the table as a dozen pairs of eyes stared at him with admiration. All except one and he glanced at Babs, expecting to see her hand in the air.

Puzzled, he saw her hand rise above the table

to hover at shoulder height before she let it fall to her lap.

'Well, looks like the vote is unanimous—'

'I want to say something.' Babs stood and Wade's heart sank. What would she come up with now to derail him?

'Quentin loved this company and I know many of you blame me for distracting him from the office these last few years.'

Gobsmacked, Wade stared at the woman who had far more insight than he'd given her credit for.

'The truth is Quentin knew he had a heart condition, one that could prove fatal at any time. He wanted to make the most of our time together and I supported that.' She paused to dab under her eyes, the first time Wade had ever seen her show genuine emotion. 'This company reminds me of what I've lost and that's why I wanted to sell. To move on with my life while holding cherished memories.'

Babs' gaze swung towards him. 'Wade, you've done a great job saving this company from the brink, but I really want out. You can buy my shares and we'll call it even.'

Wade nodded, startled into silence by this turn of events.

He hated hearing Babs articulate his biggest regret: that his dad hadn't shared the seriousness of his prognosis. If he'd known about Quentin's fatal heart condition he never would've wasted so many years staying away because of the woman now looking at him with pity.

He didn't want her pity. He wanted those wasted years back. He wanted to repair the relationship with his dad, the one he'd fractured because of his intolerance. He wanted his dad to trust him enough to tell him the truth.

But he couldn't change the past. He'd have to take control of his future instead and never repeat the same mistakes.

He didn't know if Babs genuinely loved his dad, but he could understand her need to move on with her life.

Selling her shares to him would allow them both to get what they wanted: closure for her, preserving his dad's legacy for him.

Finally finding his voice, he cleared his throat. 'Thanks, Babs, I'll have the transfer papers drawn up immediately.'

She nodded, picked up her bag and sailed out of the door, leaving the board members watching him carefully.

What did they expect? For him to cartwheel across the highly polished conference table?

He might've been tempted if not for the fact he had serious business to conduct after this meeting.

Business far more important than Qu Publishing.

Business of the heart.

CHAPTER TWELVE

LIZA LITHGOW'S STYLE TIPS FOR MAXIMUM WAG WOW IMPACT

The Bachelorette Party

Once your sportsman has popped the question, it's time to move on to important things…like the bachelorette party!

Keep it classy.

Ditch the comedy genitalia paraphernalia.

Ditto strippers.

No club tours via bus.

Have fun with your girls without the tackiness.

- Book a swank apartment in the heart of the city, order room service, expensive champagne and watch chick flicks.

- A day spa package.
- A weekend away in a posh B&B.
- Eighties party.
- Hire out a renowned restaurant or use their private party room and indulge in fabulous food.
- River cruise.
- Cocktail party.

Recommended cocktails:

  - Frozen daiquiris
  - Millionaire cocktail
  - Boomerang cocktail
  - Bossa Nova
  - Mimosa
  - Pina colada
  - Brown Cow
  - Angel's Kiss
  - Avalanche
  - Chi-chi
  - Romantico
  - Pussy Cat
  - Margarita
  - Mojito

- ▫ Golden Dream
- ▫ Cosmopolitan
- ▫ Jumping Jack
- ▫ Flying Irishman

LIZA HADN'T EXPECTED Wade to show up again so soon after their morning outing.

When she'd dropped him at the office he'd been strangely withdrawn and while he'd mustered a genuine goodbye for Cindy he'd seemed almost disappointed.

She knew what the problem was. The way she hadn't been comfortable discussing her parents and supporting Cindy.

If he only knew how far she'd come in letting him get this close. She'd taken big steps forward today. Allowing him near Cindy, lowering her guard in front of him.

What did he expect? For her to blab all her deep, dark secrets at once? Not going to happen.

The fact he was waiting for her in the lounge while Shar and Cindy had a late supper on the back porch? Made her incredibly happy that he couldn't bear to be away from her for more than half a day. Or made her incredibly nervous that his impromptu visit heralded bad news.

'Drink?'

He shook his head. 'No thanks, I'd rather talk.'

'Okay.'

She perched next to him on the sofa, wondering if he noticed the threadbare patches on the shabby chintz. Seeing those patches made her angry. How hard she'd scrimped and saved, hoarding every cent away for Cindy's future, going without stuff like new furniture because she didn't deem it as important as having a failsafe should anything happen to her.

Instead, something had happened to her money and, while the advance and royalties would help, the thought of her sizable savings gone made her stomach gripe.

'Are you all right?'

'Yeah, why?' She met his gaze, knowing he was far too astute not to notice her jumpiness.

'You seem distracted.'

She tapped her temple. 'Making a to-do list for tomorrow up here. Always makes me seem scatty.'

He nodded, his grave expression saying he didn't buy her excuse for a second.

'I've got news.'

Trepidation taunted her, eliciting a hundred different scenarios, each of them worse than the last.

Pre-orders had fallen through. Bookstores had reneged. Online advertisers had pulled their backing.

'What is it?'

'With Qu Publishing in the black, I'm going back to London.'

The blood drained from her head and Liza's eyes blurred before she blinked, inhaled, steadied.

'My business is there and I've been away long enough.'

'Of course,' she said, grateful her tone remained neutral and well modulated, not shrieking and hysterical.

'I want you to come with me.' He took her hand, rubbed its iciness between his. 'You and Cindy.'

Shock tore through every preconception Liza had ever had about this guy.

He was returning to his life and he wanted her and Cindy to be a part of it?

If she didn't love him before, she sure as hell did now.

Love?

Uh-oh. Fine time to realise she loved Wade when she was on the verge of hyperventilating, collapsing or both.

What could she say? A thousand responses sprang to her lips, none of them appropriate.

She couldn't uproot Cindy. Couldn't lose Shar. Couldn't do any of this without the stability she'd worked so damn hard to maintain.

It had been her priority when her folks, particularly her mum, left. Try to maintain normality. Pretend everything was okay. That the two of them would be fine.

To tear all that away from Cindy on a whim to follow her heart?

Uh-uh, she couldn't do it.

Wade might have issued his invitation but had he really thought this through? Had he really considered what it would be like living with her and her sister? His place would need to be remodelled and that was only one of the many changes he'd have to cope with.

What if he grew tired of it? What if he couldn't handle having Cindy full time? What if Cindy grew to love him as much as she did and then he ended it? The emotional fallout from something so major would definitely have a detrimental effect on Cindy physically.

No, one Lithgow sister having her heart broken was enough.

She'd vowed to protect Cindy and, sadly, that meant giving up her one shot at happiness.

'Your silence is scaring me,' he said, continuing to chafe her hand in his, but no amount of rubbing could stem the iciness trickling through her veins and chilling every extremity.

'I—I think you're incredible for asking us to come with you, Wade, but we can't.'

His hands stilled. 'Can't or won't?'

'Both,' she said, wondering if that was the first impulsively honest thing she'd ever told him.

She'd spent a decade carefully weighing her words, saying the right thing, doing the right thing, yet now, when it would pay to be circumspect, a plethora of words bubbled up from deep within and threatened to spill out.

'The fact you care enough to include Cindy in your offer means more to me than you'll ever know, but I can't uproot her.'

She waved to the backyard where the sound of voices and laughter drifted inside. 'She's comfortable here, safe. It's the only home she's ever known and I can't move her halfway across the world.'

He willed her to look at him, his gaze boring into her, but she determinedly stared at their joined hands.

'She'll have the best of carers. I can afford it—'

'No.' The vehement refusal sounded like a gunshot. Short. Sharp. Ominous. 'I've always taken care of her and I'll continue to do so.'

He released her hand and eased away as if she'd slapped him. 'Is it so hard to accept help? Or are you too used to playing the martyr you'd do anything to continue the role?'

His harsh accusation hung in the growing silence while a lump of hurt and anger and regret welled in her chest until she could hardly breathe.

He rubbed a hand across his face. 'Sorry, that

was way out of line. But you need to realise you have a life too—'

'My life is here, right where I want to be,' she said, finally raising her eyes to meet his, seeing the precise second he registered her bleakness. 'Cindy is all I have and I'm not going to abandon her.'

'But you won't be.' He tried to reach for her and she wriggled back. 'You're not your folks, Liza, you're so much better than them. But the strain of bearing a constant load will eventually tell. It's not healthy shouldering the lot.'

He tapped his chest. 'Let me in. I'll be here for you. Always.'

That sounded awfully like for ever to Liza and it only added to her grief.

She'd be walking away from the best thing that ever happened to her.

But she didn't hesitate, not for a second. Wade was right about one thing. She wasn't her folks and there was nothing he could do or say that would make her put her needs ahead of her sister's.

She shook her head, the tears spurting from

her eyes like a waterfall, spraying them. 'I can't. Sorry.'

And then she ran. Ran from the house, ran from the man she loved, ran from a bright future.

Ran until her lungs seized and her legs buckled. Even then, she kept pushing, jogging four blocks before she registered the car cruising beside her.

When she finally couldn't take another step from sheer exhaustion, she stopped. Braced her hands on her thighs, bending over and inhaling lungfuls of air.

It didn't ease the pain.

She ignored the car idling on the kerb, ignored the electronic glide of a window sliding down.

'Get in. I'll take you home.'

Liza shook her head, willing the strength to return to her legs so she could make another dash for it.

She needed to escape Wade and his all-round goodness, not be confined in his car.

'I'm not leaving 'til you do.'

She lifted her head, mustered a glare that fell short considering sweat dripped in her eyes and her hair was plastered in lank strands across her forehead.

Then she glimpsed the devastation clouding his eyes and something inside her broke.

How could she treat this amazingly beautiful man so badly?

He didn't deserve this. He deserved a friendly parting, a thank you for giving her a job and a lifeline at a time she needed it most.

So she sucked in her bruised pride and hobbled towards the car, feeling as if a baseball bat had battered her as she sank onto the plush leather seat.

He didn't speak, intuitive to her needs until the very end, and it only served to increase her respect and love and gratitude.

When he pulled up outside her house, she mustered what was left of her minimal dignity.

'Thanks for everything.' Her breath hitched and she continued on a sob. 'I'll never forget you.'

She fumbled with the door lock, tumbled out of the car and bolted without looking back.

This time, he didn't come after her.

Wade packed on autopilot.

Suits in bags, shirts in the case, shoes stuffed in the sides, the rest flung over the top.

He liked the mindless, methodical job. Kept his hands busy. Good thing too, because otherwise he'd be likely to thump something.

Putting a hole in the wall of his penthouse wouldn't be a good idea at this point, as he didn't have time to organise plasterers to fix it.

He wanted to be out of here. ASAP. Sooner the better.

There was nothing left for him here any more. He'd done what he'd set out to do. Save Qu Publishing. Preserve his father's legacy.

Everything else that had happened? Blip on the radar. Soon forgotten when he returned to London.

Until he made the fatal mistake of glancing at the bed and it all came flooding back.

Liza on top, pinning his wrists overhead, her hair draping his chest.

Liza beneath, straining up to meet him, writhing in pleasure.

Liza snuggled in the circle of his arms, her hand over his chest, over his heart, keeping it safe.

Or so he'd thought.

With a groan he abandoned his packing and

sank onto the bed, dropped his head in his hands and acknowledged the pain.

He'd deliberately closed off after he'd left her house, had driven to his penthouse in a fog of numbness. It had worked for him before, when he'd made the decision to leave the family business and strike out on his own in London.

He remembered his dad's disappointment, his surprise, and the only way Wade had dealt with it back then was to erect emotional barriers and get on with the job.

It served him well, being able to compartmentalise his life and his emotions, forgoing one for the sake of the other.

But look how that had turned out, with his dad having a heart condition he knew nothing about and Wade distancing himself when he could've made the most of every moment.

Maybe his coping mechanism wasn't so crash hot after all?

Maybe he'd be better off confronting his demons than running from them?

Maybe he should lower the emotional barriers he'd raised to protect himself and take a chance on trusting someone again?

For that was what had hurt him the most with his dad: that their breakdown in trust had affected how he interacted with everyone, from his colleagues to his dates.

He didn't like letting anyone get close for fear of being let down, the way he'd felt when his dad had put Babs first at the expense of their relationship.

He'd never understood how Quentin could tolerate their strained relationship for that woman.

Until now.

Love did strange things to a guy and if his dad had been half as smitten with Babs as Wade had been with Liza, he could justify his behaviour.

It didn't make accepting their lost years any easier or the lack of trust he'd instilled in his dad because of his withdrawal, both physical and emotional, but it went some way to easing the guilt.

He wondered how different his life would be if he didn't run this time.

A thousand scenarios flashed through his head, the main one centred on Liza and him, together.

He'd thought he'd made her an offer too good to refuse, a magnanimous gesture including her sister. But the more he thought about it, the more he realised how selfish he'd been.

Had he really expected her to pack up, leave her support network and move halfway around the world to fit in with his life?

At no stage had he contemplated staying in Melbourne. It had been a given he'd return to London and expect her to make all the sacrifices. He should've known she'd never agree.

Maybe that was why he'd done it?

Issued an offer he knew she could never accept?

The thought rattled him.

He'd never been emotionally involved with a woman, had kept his dalliances emotion free. The way he saw it, inviting her to live with him had been a huge step forward.

But what if it wasn't forward enough?

He'd treated his dad the same way, not willing to see two sides of their story, intent on believing what he wanted to believe. It had ruined their relationship and driven an irrevocable wedge between them.

It irked, how he'd never have a second chance

with his dad. But it wasn't too late to make amends with Liza....

Wade leapt from the bed and headed to the lounge room, in search of his phone.

He needed to put some feelers out, set some plans in motion, before he took the chance of his lifetime.

This time, he wouldn't stuff up.

Liza cherished movie nights with Cindy. She loved curling up on the couch, a massive bowl of popcorn and a packet of Tim Tams between them, laughing uproariously at their favourite comedies they rewatched countless times.

But tonight, not even Peter Sellers and his Birdie Num Nums in the sixties hit *The Party* could dredge up a chuckle.

Sadly, Cindy had picked up on her mood too, barely making a dent in the popcorn and chocolate biscuits when she usually devoured the lot.

'Are you sad because Wade left?'

Reluctant to discuss this with Cindy, Liza dragged her gaze from where Hrundi V. Bakshi, Sellers's character, cavorted in a pool com-

plete with a painted elephant, and forced a smile
for her sis.

'Yeah, I'll miss him.'

A tiny frown marred Cindy's brow. 'Where is
he going?'

'London.'

'Wow.' Cindy's eyes widened to huge blue orbs.
'London looked amazing during the Olympics.
Wish we could go.'

Cindy crammed another fistful of popcorn into
her mouth, chewed, before continuing. 'Maybe
we could visit Wade there?'

Stunned, Liza stared at Cindy. She'd never
heard her sis articulate any great desire to travel.
The furthest they'd been was Sydney when
Jimmy had been up for a mega award, and Liza
had spent the entire time torn between caring
for Cindy and ensuring she presented the perfect
WAG front when on Jimmy's arm.

It had been exhausting and she preferred to
spend time with Cindy at home, while keeping
her travels for WAG duties separate.

Not that they'd been able to afford it. She'd
been so busy saving every cent for the future

she'd never contemplated wasting money on an overseas trip.

'Wade's a good guy. He likes you.' Cindy smirked and made puckering noises. 'I think you like him too.'

Liza sighed. If only it were as simple as that.

'London's a long way away, sweetie—'

'That's what planes are for, dummy.' Cindy elbowed her. 'You should buy tickets. We should go.'

Reeling from Cindy's suggestion, Liza nudged the popcorn bowl closer and gestured at the TV, grateful when Cindy became absorbed in the movie again.

She needed to think.

Not that she'd contemplate flying to London on a holiday, not after she'd worked so hard to replace part of her nest egg for Cindy, but hearing Cindy's request opened her eyes in a way she'd never thought possible.

Had she been so focused on providing financial security she'd lost sight of the bigger picture? That in an effort to protect her sister she'd actually been stifling her?

Guilt blossomed in her chest and she absentmindedly rubbed it, wishing it were as simple to ease the continual ache in her heart.

But since Wade had driven away last night, the pain had lingered, intensified, until she'd accepted it as a permanent fixture. Niggling, annoying, there until she got over him. Whenever that was.

Cindy laughed as Peter Sellers navigated his way around the party from hell while Liza contemplated the disservice she'd been doing her sister.

All these years she'd assumed Cindy had been content. But by her excitement about proposing a London trip, maybe Cindy was ready for adventures? Maybe she felt as if she was missing out somehow?

In building a secure life, had Liza transferred her fear of abandonment onto Cindy, ensuring her sister was cloistered rather than free to grow?

But she couldn't move to London with Wade. It just wasn't feasible or practical.

Then again, hadn't she lived a practical life the last decade? Faking smiles for the cameras, dressed in uncomfortable designer gear for events, pretending to like her date when she couldn't wait to get home at the end of a long awards night.

She'd built her entire reputation on a mirage, on a woman who didn't exist, to the point she hardly knew the real her anymore.

Yet Wade had taken a chance on her anyway.

He'd trusted her enough, loved her enough, to offer her a new life and had included her sister in it.

What kind of guy did that?

An honourable, understanding, caring guy. A guy who wasn't afraid of taking chances. Who wasn't afraid of letting people into his life.

Liza didn't like risks. Losing her folks and losing her savings had ensured that.

And if she couldn't take risks with her life, no way would she take risks with Cindy's.

Which brought her right back to the beginning of her dilemma.

She loved Wade. The only guy she'd ever truly loved.

But she'd let him go because she was too scared to take a risk, was too scared he'd eventually walk away from her.

'You're missing the best bit,' Cindy said, grabbing a Tim Tam and offering her the last one in the pack.

'It's all yours,' Liza said, draping a hand across her sister's shoulder and squeezing tight.

Everything she did was for this incredible girl by her side and she'd have to keep remembering that over the next few months while her shattered heart took an eternity to mend.

She'd like nothing better than to take a chance on Wade.

But as Cindy snuggled into her side, Liza knew some risks were too big to take.

CHAPTER THIRTEEN

LIZA LITHGOW'S STYLE TIPS FOR MAXIMUM WAG WOW IMPACT

The Wedding

With a WAG's busy lifestyle, planning a wedding is a monumental task.

For those with mega-famous sportsmen partners, it seems the eyes of the world will be on you throughout your big day.

Here are a few tips to get you to the altar, smile intact:

- Plan well ahead. Don't leave things to the last minute. And if it's too much, hire the best wedding planner in town and delegate.

- Choose a theme for the wedding and stick to it. Makes co-ordination easier.

- If intrusive crowds on your special day are going to be a problem, consider marrying overseas (a beach in Bali, Fiji, Tahiti).

- If paparazzi are a problem, sell exclusive rights to your wedding to one magazine and donate the proceeds to charity.

- When it comes to bridesmaids and groomsmen, less is best. Keep it simple, classy, elegant.

- Designer dress is essential.

- Trial hair and make-up months before the big day.

- Insist on tasting everything being served beforehand.

- Funky cakes may look fun on paper but stick to the classics.

- Madcap photos may appeal at the photographer's but when it's your big day captured you might not find the Groucho masks all that funny.

- Assign the rings on the day to the most responsible groomsman.

- Fresh flowers.

- Keep the guest list to close friends and relatives. Inviting the whole team may be your fiancé's priority but you don't want your wedding turning into an end-of-season trip rendition.

- Make sure your iPod is loaded with all your favourite songs and plug your ears on the way to the ceremony.

- Garter removal and bouquet throwing are yesterday.

- Prepare a classy speech. Why should your guy hog the limelight constantly?

- Most importantly, make sure you book your wedding completely out of your partner's sport season, taking into account drawn grand finals, replays and potential surgery due to injury.

- Look fabulous, strut down the aisle and WAG WOW!

WADE HAD NEVER been a gambler.

He preferred to weigh the pros and cons of any

decision carefully, consider all the options, before choosing the most logical, the most feasible.

All that sensible bull had gone out of the window when he'd taken the biggest gamble of his life and asked Liza to meet him here.

He didn't know if she'd show.

His message had gone through to the answering service on her mobile and her terse 'will think about it' texted response an hour later didn't bode well.

But he'd turned up at The Martini Bar anyway, hoping she'd take a chance.

For if there was one thing he was sure of in this godforsaken mess, it was her love.

She hadn't said it. Matter of fact, neither had he, considering she'd been too busy busting his balls and throwing his offer back in his face.

But he'd seen it in her eyes. The adoration, the tenderness, the agony at the thought of never being together.

He'd been through it all, a gamut of emotions ranging from devastation to optimism.

No more.

He might be going with his gut on this one but he'd applied logic to making it happen.

Every contingency plan had been put into place. Now all he needed was for Liza to say yes.

He nursed his Scotch, swirled it around, instantly transported back to the night they'd met, the night they'd shared a drink here, the night that had set him down this rocky road.

For a guy who never let emotions get in the way of anything, he'd sure botched this, big time.

He took a swig of his drink and glanced at his watch. Nine p.m. on the dot. Liza was a no-show.

He'd give her ten minutes and then he was out of here.

As pain lanced his heart he thought, *Who are you trying to kid?*

He'd probably end up sitting here all night if there was the remotest possibility she'd walk in the door.

As if his wish had been granted, he saw her enter, lock eyes with him and pause.

She looked stunning, from the top of her glossy blonde hair piled in a loose up-do to her shimmery turquoise dress to her sparkly silver-sequined sandals.

Guys in the bar gawked at the doorway and he wanted to flatten them all.

He stood as she made her way towards him, torn between wanting to vault tables to get to her and sit on his hands to stop from grabbing her the moment she got within reach.

The nearer she got, the harder his gut twisted until he could barely stand.

'Hey.' She hesitated when she reached him, kissed him on the cheek before taking a seat opposite.

'Thanks for coming.' He sounded like a dufus but he sat, relieved she'd made it. 'Didn't think you'd show.'

She held her thumb and forefinger an inch apart. 'I was this close not to.'

'Why the change of heart?'

She glanced away, gnawed on her bottom lip, before reluctantly meeting his gaze. 'Because you deserved better than the way I treated you the last time we parted.'

'Fair enough.'

He liked that about her, her bluntness. She might not have been completely honest with him the last few months, but her ability to call a spade a spade when it counted meant a lot.

He hoped she'd continue in that vein for the

rest of the evening; he'd settle for nothing less than the truth.

'Drink?'

'Anything but a martini,' she said, managing a wan smile.

'Sure? Because I kinda like what happens when you drink martinis.'

The sparkle in her eyes gave him hope. 'Soda and lemon for now.'

'Spoilsport,' he said, placing the order with a nearby waiter before swivelling back to face her.

'I was going to call you,' she said, her hands twisting in her lap before she slid them under her handbag. 'To apologise for the craziness after you asked me to move to London.'

'Not necessary—'

'Yeah, it is.'

The waiter deposited her soda on the table and she grabbed it, sculled half the glass before continuing. 'You caught me completely off guard. I mean, I knew you'd be heading back eventually but I didn't expect it to be so soon, and then you asked me to come along with Cindy in tow and I kinda flipped out.'

'I noticed.'

She matched his wry smile. 'I've never had anyone care about me that much to include Cindy in plans.' Her fingertips fluttered over her heart. 'It touched me right here and I didn't know how to articulate half of what I was feeling.'

That made two of them. He knew the feeling well. Bottling up true emotions, preferring not to rock the boat, seeking other outlets for his frustration rather than attacking the root of the problem.

If only he'd confronted his dad sooner, had a talk man to man, rather than skulking off to London with his bitterness. The last few years would've been completely different.

'So I want to say thanks, Wade. Your offer means more to me than you'll ever know.'

'But?'

Her gaze dropped to her fiddling hands. 'But ultimately my decision stands. I can't move to London to be with you.'

'Thought so,' he said, stifling a chuckle at her confused frown at his chipper tone. 'Which is why I'm changing the parameters of the offer.'

Her frown deepened. 'I don't understand.'

'I'm staying in Melbourne.'

Speechless, she gaped at him until he placed a fingertip beneath her chin and closed her mouth.

'I've installed my deputy as CEO in my London office. He'll run the place and answer to me.'

He sat back, rested an arm across the back of his chair, bringing his hand within tantalising touching distance of her bare shoulder. 'I'm taking over the reins of Qu Publishing. Finishing what my father started all those years ago. It's what he would've wanted.'

Another revelation he'd had while instigating steps to remain in Melbourne. It had been as if an invisible weight had lifted from his shoulders, the guilt he'd harboured in relation to the gap between him and his dad—by his doing—evaporating once he'd made the decision to run the company.

He knew it was what his dad wanted. How many times had they discussed it, before Wade had got jack of Babs and her influence over his father and had moved to London? Many times, and he'd seen his dad's shattered expression the day he'd told him of his plans to relocate and start a new business.

It had haunted him and, while they'd never

broached the subject again during their brief catch-ups over the years, he'd sensed his dad's disappointment.

Yeah, the decision to stay in Melbourne was the correct one.

Now he had to convince Liza of that.

'My offer still stands. Move in with me. Give our relationship a chance.' He touched her shoulder, slid his hand along the back of her neck and rested it there. 'I love you, Liza, and from a guy who's never said those three little words before, trust me, it's a big call.'

Tears shimmered in her eyes and he scooted closer, swiping away a few that trickled down her cheeks.

'A resounding yes would be great right about now,' he said, cuddling her into his side.

Her silence unnerved him but he waited. He'd waited this long to meet the love of his life, what were a few more minutes?

She sniffled, dabbed under her eyes, before easing away to look him in the eye.

'But Cindy—'

'The parameters of my offer have changed

somewhat.' He cupped her chin. 'I'm asking you to move in with me. Just you.'

Her eyes widened and she started to shake her head but his grip tightened.

'I'm blown away by your dedication to your sister, truly I am. I've never met such a self-sacrificing person. But I think you're using Cindy as a crutch. Hiding behind her. Afraid to go out into the world and take chances.' His thumb brushed her lower lip. 'Ultimately, sweetheart? That's not going to help either of you.'

Anger flashed in her eyes before she wrenched away. 'Who do you think you are, telling me what I feel and how I'm running my life?'

'I'm the guy who loves you, the guy who'll do anything to make you happy.' He laid a hand on her knee, surprised and grateful when she didn't shrug him off. 'If you'll let me.'

She glared at him a moment longer before she visibly deflated. Her shoulders sagged and her head drooped, and he moved in quickly to support her with an arm around her waist.

'Cindy wanted to go to London.'

She spoke so softly Wade had to lean closer to hear.

'It made me realise that maybe I've cosseted her too much.'

She shook her head and a few tendrils of hair tumbled around her face. 'I've spent most of my life trying to protect her but now I'm wondering...'

When she didn't speak, Wade said, 'What?'

She dragged in a breath and blew it out. 'I'm wondering if I did more harm than good, sheltering her the way I have.'

'You love her. It's natural you'd want to protect her after your folks ran out.'

'It's more than that.'

She glanced up at him, her forlorn expression slugging him in the guts. It took every ounce of his willpower not to bundle her into his arms.

'I think I used her. I liked having her dependent on me, because that way she couldn't abandon me.'

As her folks did.

Liza didn't have to say it, it was written all over her face: her fear of being alone.

'Is that why you're not doing cartwheels over my offer now? Because you think ultimately I'll abandon you too?'

She glanced away, but not before he'd seen her shock at his perceptiveness.

'I won't, you know.'

He grabbed her hand and placed it against his heart, beating madly for her, only her.

'I don't let people into my heart easily. I've never had a long-term relationship. It took me a while to trust you. I even pushed away my dad through sheer narrow-mindedness. But once I give it, it's all yours.'

He added, 'For ever.'

A tremulous smile shone through her tears. 'You're incredible, the most amazing guy I've ever met, but I've never depended on anyone before. I'd be no good at it. I'd muck up and you'd get sick of me and then—'

'Say it.'

'Then you'd leave me,' she said, so softly his heart turned over beneath her palm.

'There's no guarantees in life but how about this? I promise to love you and cherish you and look after you to the best of my ability. How's that?'

'Pretty damn wonderful.' She beamed and he

could've sworn the bar lit up like a bright summer's day.

'So no more secrets, okay?'

Her face fell. 'Then in the event of full disclosure, I need to tell you what happened in your office that first day.'

He had been curious but hadn't wanted to push for answers. With a little luck he'd have plenty of time for that: the rest of their lives.

'The WAG lifestyle? Why I put up with being arm candy for Henri when we weren't in a real relationship?' She winced. 'For the money. We had a signed agreement. I was building a sizable nest egg for Cindy's future in case anything ever happened to me.'

Yep, she was back to the abandonment issue. Considering what she'd been through with her folks he could understand that.

'That night we met? When I said I was embarking on a new life and wanted to celebrate? I was stoked to be putting my old life behind me. It had taken its toll and I was tired of faking it for everyone.'

Her fingers clenched, creasing the cotton of his shirt. 'My investment was maturing the next day and I had grand plans to tie up some of it in a guaranteed fund for Cindy in case of my death, and use the rest to modernise our place and buy her the best equipment. With that kind of monetary security, it was the beginning of a new life for me. I could finally pursue a career in marketing, my dream, and put the past behind me.'

A few pieces of the puzzle shifted and he had a fair idea what she was going to say. She would've never agreed to the publishing contract after vehemently refusing it unless she needed the money. Which meant…

'What happened to your investment?'

Her eyes darkened to indigo, filled with pain. 'My financial adviser absconded with the lot. Scammed millions in client funds.'

He swore. Several times.

'Yeah, I totally agree. The police are investigating leads but the likelihood of recovering my cash? Slim.'

'That's why you did an about-face with the publishing deal.'

She nodded. 'I needed that money as a safeguard for Cindy. It was the only way.'

He hesitated, glad they were talking things through but needing to know all of it, however unpleasant.

'I've seen how much you love Cindy, so you're not ashamed of her.' He grimaced. 'Sorry for saying that. So why did you really leave her out of your bio?'

'I always thought it was fear of her spasticity worsening and resulting in permanent deformities if her emotions careened out of control with the probable media circus.' She smoothed his shirt and let her hand fall, only to clasp his and squeeze. 'In reality? I think it's because I'm overprotective to the point of stifling. I've tried so hard to make up for our parents' shortfalls I've gone the other way and become smothering. I truly didn't want Cindy exposed to any media or ridicule, which can still happen for disabled people even in this enlightened day, so I cut her out of the story.'

'Did you ever stop to think how she'd feel if she knew that?'

Her brows arched in horror. 'I was doing it to protect her—'

'I know, sweetheart, I know.'

Maybe he needed to quit while he was ahead.

'You still haven't answered my original question.'

The corners of her mouth curved up and he had his answer before she spoke.

'I'll have to chat with Shar and see if she can become a permanent live-in carer. And I'll need a raise to cover it. Plus I still want to spend as much time as possible with Cindy.'

'Anything else?'

'Just this.'

She surged against him, grabbed his lapels, dragged him closer and kissed him.

The teasing wolf whistles of nearby patrons faded as her lips moved on his and he wished he'd had the foresight to book a suite.

When she finally broke the kiss, he grinned. 'That's a yes, then?'

'You bet.'

She cupped his face and stared unwaveringly into his eyes. 'And I love you too. How did I get so lucky?'

'*We* got lucky.'

He kissed her again to prove it.

EPILOGUE

LIZA LITHGOW'S STYLE TIPS
FOR MAXIMUM WAG WOW IMPACT

The Indulgence

Being a WAG can be demanding.

Always looking your best to avoid incurring the wrath of ruthless paparazzi.

Constantly being scrutinised by the public.

An expectation to attend all functions with your sports-star husband/boyfriend.

An expectation to support his team.

Turning a blind eye to the women slipping their phone numbers—and worse—into your partner's pocket.

But at the end of a long day—heck, at the end of a long season—it pays to indulge in whatever makes you feel good.

- Scented candles in the bathroom—lights off—and a long hot bath.
- Glass of quality champagne.
- A raunchy romance novel designed to distract.
- A classic chick flick.
- Expensive chocolate.
- Aromatherapy oils:
  - clary sage (good for relaxing)
  - chamomile (calming)
  - grapefruit (clears the mind)
  - geranium (balancing and harmonising)
  - rosewood (uplifting)
  - neroli (calms the mind)
  - marjoram (encourages sleep)
  - vetivert (reduces tension)

Liza hopes you've enjoyed her WAG wow tips.

While she may have left her WAG days behind, she regularly indulges in the above recommendations.

Though she's rarely alone in the bath, what with Wade to keep her company…

'WOW, CHECK THIS out.'

Cindy pressed her face against the glass pod of the London Eye, where they were perched on top with an incredible view of the city spread before them.

'Amazing, huh?' Liza slung an arm around Cindy's shoulders and squeezed.

'Sure is.' Cindy tore her awestruck gaze away from the view long enough to glance up at Wade. 'Thanks for bringing me, Wade. You're the best.'

'No worries, kiddo.' He dropped a kiss on the top of Cindy's head and Liza was sure her heart flip-flopped. Could she love this guy any more?

'Hey, what about me?'

Cindy rolled her eyes. 'You already know you're the best.'

'And don't you forget it.' Liza tweaked Cindy's nose before leaving her sis alone to enjoy the view.

When Wade crooked his finger, she happily moved into his embrace.

'You're incredible, you know that?'

He smiled and nodded at Cindy. 'So I've been told.'

'Well, I'm telling you again.' Liza snuggled

tighter, content in the knowledge there was no better place to be than Wade's arms. 'The way you put this trip together, checked out disabled facilities at all the hotels, did a reno on your apartment for Cindy to stay. Not to mention pulling together the digital companion novel to my bio highlighting cerebral palsy and the needs of carers to raise awareness...'

She stood on tiptoe and whispered in his ear. 'Remember how I was scared you'd leave me one day? Forget about it, babe, because I'm going to be glued to your side for life.'

He laughed and hugged her tight.

'Make that a promise and you've got yourself a deal.'

They kissed to seal it.

* * * * *

Mills & Boon® Large Print

November 2013

HIS MOST EXQUISITE CONQUEST
Emma Darcy

ONE NIGHT HEIR
Lucy Monroe

HIS BRAND OF PASSION
Kate Hewitt

THE RETURN OF HER PAST
Lindsay Armstrong

THE COUPLE WHO FOOLED THE WORLD
Maisey Yates

PROOF OF THEIR SIN
Dani Collins

IN PETRAKIS'S POWER
Maggie Cox

A COWBOY TO COME HOME TO
Donna Alward

HOW TO MELT A FROZEN HEART
Cara Colter

THE CATTLEMAN'S READY-MADE FAMILY
Michelle Douglas

WHAT THE PAPARAZZI DIDN'T SEE
Nicola Marsh

1013 Rom LP

Mills & Boon® Large Print
December 2013

THE BILLIONAIRE'S TROPHY
Lynne Graham

PRINCE OF SECRETS
Lucy Monroe

A ROYAL WITHOUT RULES
Caitlin Crews

A DEAL WITH DI CAPUA
Cathy Williams

IMPRISONED BY A VOW
Annie West

DUTY AT WHAT COST?
Michelle Conder

THE RINGS THAT BIND
Michelle Smart

A MARRIAGE MADE IN ITALY
Rebecca Winters

MIRACLE IN BELLAROO CREEK
Barbara Hannay

THE COURAGE TO SAY YES
Barbara Wallace

LAST-MINUTE BRIDESMAID
Nina Harrington

A SILVER LINING

A SILVER LINING

Anne Douglas

This first world edition published 2014
in Great Britain and the USA by
SEVERN HOUSE PUBLISHERS LTD of
19 Cedar Road, Sutton, Surrey, England, SM2 5DA.

British Library Cataloguing in Publication Data

Douglas, Anne, 1930- author.
  A Silver Lining.
  1. World War, 1939-1945–Social aspects–Scotland–
  Edinburgh–Fiction. 2. Love stories.
  I. Title
  823.9'2-dc23

ISBN-13: 978-0-7278-8403-9 (cased)

All Severn House titles are printed on acid-free paper.

Severn House Publishers support the Forest Stewardship Council™ [FSC™],
the leading international forest certification organisation. All our titles that
are printed on FSC certified paper carry the FSC logo.

MIX
Paper from
responsible sources
FSC
www.fsc.org   FSC® C013056

Typeset by Palimpsest Book Production Ltd.,
Falkirk, Stirlingshire, Scotland.
Printed and bound in Great Britain by
TJ International, Padstow, Cornwall.

Part One

One

There it went, dead on time, the One o'clock Gun from the castle sounding over Edinburgh, sending people's eyes to clocks and watches, making tourists jump and locals smile. Not that there were many tourists around on that November day in 1937, only city shoppers diving into Princes Street stores to escape from the 'haar' – the cold, wet mist that had been hanging about since morning.

Glad I'm not out in it, thought twenty-one-year-old Jinny Hendrie, sitting at her desk in the warmth of the accounts office of Comrie's Bakeries where she was working on staff wages. Maybe it would clear by going home time, which wouldn't be till half past five, ages away. Why, even tea break at three o'clock was far enough off.

Not that Jinny minded. She enjoyed her work, which was mainly with figures, assisting Mr MacBain who was the accountant in charge, though it had all been much more complicated than she'd ever imagined. Who'd have thought there'd be so much to worry about behind all the lovely bread and cakes sold by Comrie's, and the superior morning coffees and afternoon teas served in their cafés?

Not caring to make herself hungry thinking of delicious cakes, Jinny bent her dark eyes over the spread of wage packets she was preparing for delivery to the workforce the next day. All would receive cash, herself included, the only exceptions being Mr Whyte, the bakery manager, and Mr MacBain – Ross, as she was allowed to call him – who were paid by cheque. Her job was to make sure that everyone received the correct amount and that their wage slips tallied; the last thing she wanted was for one of the bakers to come round claiming she hadn't included his overtime.

Oh, my, better check everything again! But she was confident she'd made no mistakes and knew that the bakers and café staff trusted her – even if they did think she was too pretty to know how to count!

There was no doubt that she was pretty, with her dark eyes, her pointed chin and high cheekbones. She wore her dark hair rather longer than was fashionable – but what had looks to do with arithmetic?

She'd always been good at maths at school, and had gone on to more detailed study at a technical college, just like her attractive sister, Vi, two years her senior, who now ran the office of a clothing factory and grew touchy if anyone commented on her looks. But May, at twenty-four the eldest of the three Hendrie girls and a good-looking blonde, liked to say with a laugh that folk thought her just right to work in a West End hat shop. Maybe her sisters should change jobs? What an idea! They were happy where they were and in 1937, unemployment being what it was, if you had a job you hung on to it.

Accounts, where Jinny worked, was a large, airy room on the first floor of the double-fronted Comrie building at the east end of Princes Street. Next to it was the office of John Comrie, the owner of the business, while below on the ground floor was the largest of the cafés, with an attached kitchen and staffroom, and a bread and cake shop.

The bakery that provided Comrie's bread, cakes and scones was some way away in the Broughton area, but Arthur Whyte and Ross MacBain liaised regularly to discuss expenditure and the progress of various lines. Heavens, how they worked to keep tabs on everything! And Mrs Arrow, manageress of the Princes Street shop and café had to be careful, too, to keep an eye on sales.

Only Ross, however, was in charge of the complicated costing system that made sure customers got value for money and the bakery made a profit, though he said one day he would see that Jinny had knowledge of it too, which she was pleased about. In the meantime, of course, she had to work on the wages and be sure she got them right.

She rose and stretched, looked out of the window and saw that the haar was still masking the street, then turned her head as the door to Mr Comrie's office door clicked and Mabel Hyslop came through. In her late thirties, she was thin and narrow-faced, her brown hair rather sparse, and always keen to hear bakery gossip. She was efficient enough, though, working partly as Mr Comrie's secretary and partly as the office typist.

'Ross not back yet, Jinny?' she asked now. 'Mr Comrie's going to lunch with someone at two today but he says he'd like a word with you and Ross before that.'

'Me as well as Ross?' asked Jinny with interest.

'Yes. It's nothing to worry about, just to do with his nephew. Oh, here's Ross now! I'd better tell Mr Comrie.'

With a quick smile at Ross MacBain as he walked into Accounts,

Mabel hurried away while Ross shook drops of moisture from his hat and overcoat and looked across at Jinny.

'Haar's no better – I feel I've been wrapped in a great damp blanket. What was Mabel after?'

'Just came to tell us that Mr Comrie wants a word.'

'A word? Sounds ominous.' Ross ran his hands through his damp, copper-coloured hair and sat down at his desk. 'Wonder what that's about, then?'

'Just his nephew, Mabel says.'

'His nephew? He's not even here. Ah, well, all will be revealed.'

Such a cheerful face, thought Jinny, as she always did when looking at Ross – just the sort of face of a man who would never be taken aback by anything life had to throw at him. Or so you might think. In fact, it wasn't true. As she'd been told by others when she'd first arrived to work with him two years before, Ross had been taken aback – and deeply grieved – by the death of his fiancée from appendicitis shortly before their wedding. And though he never showed it, keeping his cheerful manner at all times, some people believed he was grieving still. Usually Jinny tried not to think about his sorrow, for that was his business entirely, but just occasionally found herself sensing something about him that made her think she was one of the few people who could see beyond his mask. Or maybe she just imagined it.

'I've done the wages,' she was beginning when Mr Comrie's door clicked again and the owner of the bakery – short, portly and in his fifties – came through and accepted the chair Ross leaped up to set for him.

'Ah, there you are, Ross, Jinny. I'm just off to lunch with my bank manager. Send up the usual prayers, eh?' Mr Comrie laughed, his narrow blue eyes crinkling in his heavy face. 'Just want to tell you that we'll be having a new man here from Monday next – my nephew, Viktor Linden, my sister's boy from Vienna.'

Vienna? Jinny's dark eyes widened. She vaguely remembered hearing that Mr Comrie's sister had married an Austrian and moved from Edinburgh years before, and that there was a nephew. But why should he be coming as a new man here? Did Mr Comrie mean he was coming to work?

It was Ross who put the question. 'Mr Comrie, that's very interesting news. Will Mr Linden actually be working here, then?'

'Of course, of course. He's only twenty-five but he's a very experienced confectioner. His father owns a splendid Viennese cake shop – what they call a *Konditorei* – and my sister tells me that Viktor's quite the star.'

'And he's coming here?'

'To visit Edinburgh again – he hasn't been here since he was a boy – and to see how we operate and get some experience of other systems. I also want him to make us some of his wonderful cakes. *Torten*, as they call them.' Again, Mr Comrie laughed. 'But of course he won't be staying long – a few months at most.'

'We'll make him very welcome,' Ross declared. 'I'm sure all the staff will be very interested to meet him. We've all heard about Austrian cakes.'

'Indeed. Well, I'll leave it to you to inform the staff, and I'll introduce him on Monday morning. No need to worry about his English – he's bilingual. My sister, Clara, has seen to that. Now, I must hurry. Can't keep the bank manager waiting!'

When their boss had rushed out, Ross and Jinny exchanged looks.

'Well, that's something new,' Ross commented, sitting down again at his desk. 'It will be good to see some of those amazing Austrian cakes being produced here.'

'Why are they so wonderful? We make lovely cakes ourselves – aren't we famous for them?'

'Of course, but these are different.' Ross was laughing. 'I must sound like a greedy schoolboy, but I went for a walking tour once in Austria and I've never forgotten trying their pastries and cakes when we finished up in Vienna. Chocolate, marzipan, nuts, layers of cream, raspberries—'

'Oh, stop, you're making me hungry!' cried Jinny, joining in his laughter. 'Think I'll put the kettle on.'

What an interesting bit of news, she thought as she set out cups and gave Mabel a call. Just fancy, a chap from Vienna working at Comrie's! All she knew about the Viennese was that they danced Strauss waltzes and made delicious things to eat, but now she would find out much more. Depending on what the new fellow was like, of course, and whether he was friendly or not. Anyway, he'd be something to tell her sisters at home about. They always liked to talk over their news at teatime.

Two

The Hendrie girls and their father, Joshua, lived over a watchmaker's shop in Fingal Street, off the Lothian Road. Josh, as he was usually called, worked as a scene-shifter at the nearby Duchess Theatre – a job he loved, having always had an interest in the theatre but 'not cut out', as he would say with a grin, to be an actor. Working with the sets, breathing in the atmosphere of the stage and mixing with the cast was the next best thing, and in the years following his dear Etty's death his work had helped him to get over the bad times.

Not as much as his girls had helped, of course. Sometimes he almost came out in a cold sweat when thinking what his life would be without them, for now that Etty'd gone they were everything to him. Such lovely girls, all of them, whose only thought was to make him happy, to make up as best they could for their mother's death. If they were ever to leave him, what would he do? But there was no sign of that at present, thank God.

There was only one thing he wished might be different about them: that they would feel as he did about the stage. They had the looks and the intelligence – they could have been stars, he was sure of it – but no, they wouldn't even give it a try. What a shame, eh?

'Honestly, Dad, can you see us dressing up and spouting all those lines!' Vi had cried, and May had shaken her lovely fair head while Jinny had laughed. When he'd said their mother would have liked it for them, their faces had changed and sadness appeared. Ma would have wanted them to be happy doing what they thought best for themselves, they told him, and with that he could say no more. Seemingly they were as happy as they could be, in the circumstances.

Coming home that evening through the last remnants of the haar, Jinny was herself thinking her family was a happy one. Even though Ma was no longer with them and they missed her still, the girls had all tried to keep their home as she had made it, and felt, especially when they came back after work, that they'd succeeded. All right, nobody claimed there weren't arguments, especially with Vi around, but they never lasted long. The girls soon made up and were content.

'Evening, Jinny,' called Allan Forth, the watchmaker, who was

also the Hendries' landlord, as Jinny approached the side door that
led up to the flat. 'Not been too bright today, has it?'

He was just locking up for the night, having closed the shutters
on his windows full of clocks, watches, tankards, toast racks, lockets
and necklaces, for in addition to his watch-making and mending
business, he sold a variety of merchandise suitable for presents. Though
Jinny often wondered how much of it he sold in these difficult times.

Still, he seemed to keep the shop going and to look after the
bungalow in the suburbs that had been his parents' after they'd left
the flat the Hendries now occupied. And Allan had never put up
the rent of that flat, which was very reasonable – maybe because
originally it was his father who'd been the landlord and he'd been
a pal of Josh's at the bowling club. Now he was dead, his wife too,
and it was tall, grey-eyed Allan who was their landlord. No changes
had been made, though, even if he was not a particular friend of
Josh's as his father had been. More likely he was a friend of May's,
thought Jinny with a smile – or wished he were.

'You're the last in,' he told Jinny, checking the lights on the bicycle
he used to ride home to Blackhall. 'Your dad and Vi have just gone
up and May was first. Said she had to do the cooking tonight.'

'It's her turn,' Jinny told him, noting that he must have left his shop
to talk to May. By the light of the streetlight she studied his good-
looking face with its sensitive mouth, always ready to smile. He'd be
right for May, she thought, and added: 'We girls take it in turn to cook.'

'Oh, yes, I know, May told me. Said she'd already made a hotpot
for you.'

'Did it last evening. Very efficient, May.'

'I'm sure,' he said fervently before finally beginning to wheel his
bike towards the Lothian Road, from where a hum of traffic could
be heard. ''Bye then, Jinny. Have a nice evening.'

'You must come and have tea with us sometime!' she called after
him. 'You haven't been for ages.'

With colour rising to his face, he did not stop but called back
that he'd like that very much, and Jinny, smiling again, watched him
pedal away.

The flat that had been Allan's home before it was her family's was of
good size, with a living room, a separate little kitchen, two bedrooms
– one double, one single – a boxroom and a bathroom. It was Josh
who nobly slept in the boxroom, having given up the double room
he'd shared with Etty to Jinny and Vi, while May had the single room.

How well placed they were in Fingal Street compared to the cramped tenement flat where they'd lived before, Jinny still thought whenever she came home. Ma had always hated that, having to share a WC on the landing with other families and fill up a tin tub to take a bath. She'd been so glad when Mr Forth had offered them his old flat at a rent they could afford, but used to shake her head and say that how things went for you in life was all down to luck. And so it was, thought Jinny, though there were some who said you made your own luck. Whatever the truth of that, one thing was for sure – good luck had run out for Ma, through no fault of her own, when she had been taken by the pneumonia that killed her.

Everyone was in the living room when she came in. May was setting the table while the hotpot she'd prepared for them all cooked in the oven, and Vi and Josh were sitting by the open fire, reading separate pages of the evening newspaper. Everything seemed warm and comfortable.

'Och, that's grand!' Jinny cried when she'd taken off her coat and moved towards the fire. 'Let me in, I'm frozen! Makes a difference, eh, having a fire like this instead of a kitchen range?'

'A range is more useful,' said Vi, looking up from her paper, her face so like Jinny's yet somehow subtly different, perhaps only because her thoughts were different and reflected her dissatisfaction with the world. While Jinny took things as they were Vi was all for reform, her dark eyes regularly flashing over some injustice, making Jinny feel guilty that her dark eyes weren't flashing too.

'You can cook on a range,' Vi added now, 'and get hot water and warmth. Can't say the same about a fire.'

'Why, there's a back boiler for the hot water!' Jinny fast retorted. 'Trust you to look on the dark side, Vi!'

'Only facing facts,' her sister replied with a sudden grin. 'I'll admit the fire's nice to sit beside.'

'Aye, come and thaw out, lassie,' said Josh, rubbing Jinny's cold hands. 'That haar's enough to chill your bones, eh?'

'It's just moving away now.'

'Thank the Lord for that, seeing as I've to get back to the theatre after tea.'

A handsome man in his late forties, with the dark eyes and hair his younger daughters had inherited, Josh looked across at May, who was bringing in her dish from the adjoining kitchen.

'That ready, May?'

'Quite ready, Dad. Come to the table and I'll dish up.'

Three

May's hotpot was excellent, with beef, potatoes and carrots, and as they all ate heartily Jinny said it was just the thing for a cold night and worth all her sister's trouble the evening before.

'Only thing is it's my turn tomorrow and I'm only doing sausages, so don't expect anything like this!'

'Can't expect beef every night,' Vi remarked. 'We're lucky to have it at all.'

'It was only brisket – pretty cheap,' said May.

'Aye, well, think of the folk in the tenements living on bread and dripping – if there's any dripping.'

'Come on, now, Vi,' Josh said easily. 'Don't spoil our pleasure in May's grand meal, eh?'

'I'm not, Dad, it's lovely – I'm only reminding you how it is for others.'

'And I don't need reminding, seeing as I was one o' the others, as you call 'em, when I was a lad.'

Vi lowered her eyes. 'Sorry,' she said after a moment. 'I know times were hard for you then.'

After another pause Jinny, to lighten matters, said cheerfully, 'Saw your admirer tonight, May!'

'What admirer?' asked Josh, instantly diverted and frowning, while May was already beginning to turn pink.

'Exactly – what admirer?' she responded quickly. 'Who on earth are you talking about, Jinny?'

'Why, Allan, of course! He'd just locked up when I got home, said he'd seen you, May, and you'd told him what you'd been cooking.'

'And how does a few polite words in passing make him my admirer?'

'He must have been watching out for you because you were so early back, and – you know – it's just the way he looks when he says your name. He's always been sweet on you, May – isn't that right, Vi?'

'Don't ask me, I've no time for all that romantic stuff,' replied Vi, shrugging, and Josh nodded in agreement.

'Nor me. Allan's a nice lad but he's never shown any romantic interest in you lassies that I've ever noticed.'

That you'd decided *not* to notice, thought Jinny, who knew her father couldn't yet bring himself to see that his girls might one day marry and 'leave the nest'. Aloud, to calm things down, she changed the subject again to her own exciting news from Comrie's.

'Guess what? We've a new chap starting next week and he's from Vienna! Mr Comrie's nephew, no less, and a qualified confectioner. He makes gorgeous Austrian cakes, so Ross says. I can't wait to meet him!'

'What makes him so exciting?' asked Vi. 'Because he's from Vienna, or because he makes gorgeous cakes?'

'I don't know if he's exciting or not – he'll be different, that's all.'

'There's nothing different at Madame Annabel's Hats,' sighed May. 'Except I did make a new hat today. A winter felt, dark red, with a curved brim – all set for Christmas.'

'And I had a new row with the foreman over starting hours,' put in Vi. 'I mean, it's ridiculous that women clock in at eight o'clock when they've everything to do at home before they come to work! Of course, Bob Stone said it wasn't up to him, I'd have to take it up with the union – as though I haven't done that already!'

'Uphill work there, Vi,' commented Josh, his eyes on what was left in May's dish. 'Any chance of me finishing that off, May? Don't want to waste it, eh?'

'Sure, we'll let you finish it, Dad, before you go back to work. What shall we do, girls? There's a Ronald Colman picture on at the Princes cinema – anybody keen?'

'I am!' cried Jinny, and even Vi said she wouldn't mind.

'All workers need escapism, eh?'

'Right, then,' said May. 'When we've done the washing up, we'll go – right?'

'Right!' they echoed, and while their father was on duty at the theatre they were far away in the country of Shangri-la, watching *Lost Horizon* in the cinema, caught up wonderfully in the escapism Vi said all workers should have, all their slight frictions forgotten.

Four

Monday morning came at last, a grey cold day but without the haar, and Jinny, early to work, hurried into Accounts even before Ross, who usually beat her to it. For some moments she stood irresolutely, wondering if the man from Vienna had arrived yet, before realizing that of course he'd be coming in with his uncle. He didn't usually arrive till getting on for nine.

'You're nice and early!' came Ross's voice and she swung round to find him smiling at her, knowing, of course, why she'd made her special effort.

'Not here yet?' he asked lightly.

'Who?'

'Oh, come on! *Herr* Linden, of course. Or, should I say *Der Leutnant*? That means lieutenant.'

'Whatever are you talking about, Ross?'

'I'm just guessing that he's done service in the army. Don't all Germans and Austrians do army service?'

'As though I'd know. Anyway, there's no need to make fun.'

Jinny moved to her desk and began to bang open drawers and look as though she was starting work, but Ross only laughed, and then of course she laughed too, for she could never be cross with him for long.

'Suppose I am being a bit nosy about wanting to meet him. It's just like I said to my sister – he's different, that's all. Maybe we won't see him at all today. Mr Comrie will want to take him to the bakery.'

But it wasn't long before they did see the man from Vienna, for Mr Comrie, arriving earlier than usual, brought with him a tall, straight-backed young man in a long dark overcoat and a trilby hat, which he swept off to reveal fair hair cut very short.

'Ross – Jinny – this is my nephew, Viktor Linden,' Mr Comrie announced. 'Viktor, may I introduce Mr MacBain, my accountant, and Miss Hendrie, his assistant.'

The young man, smiling gravely, gave a bow, then shook hands, first with Ross and then with Jinny, his hand cold and firm, his light blue eyes meeting theirs very keen, very direct. Was it Jinny's imagination or did his gaze linger a little longer on her than Ross? Her imagination, undoubtedly, she told herself at once, feeling foolish.

'I'm so glad to meet you,' he said now, his tone formal, his Austrian accent only slight. 'I'm so looking forward to working here at the bakery.'

'Everyone is looking forward to working with you,' Ross assured him cheerfully. 'We hope you'll be very happy here.'

'Very happy,' Jinny added quickly, not wanting to be seen studying the newcomer more than was polite but making no effort to look away from his face. It did not appear to her to be particularly foreign, just very good looking, the nose high bridged, the brow quite noble, the mouth finely shaped. That stubbly short haircut, though, did seem different and the way the young man held himself, so straight, so erect – wasn't that a bit like a soldier's style? Ross had joked about him, calling him '*Der Leutnant*', but perhaps he'd been right, after all?

Glancing at Ross, Jinny saw that he was looking slightly amused – as though he'd been thinking what she'd been thinking. But why be amused? If the young man had had to do military service, he couldn't be blamed for having the air of a soldier – and didn't the look suit him, anyway?

'I have two right-hand men in my business, Viktor,' Mr Comrie was saying. 'One is Mr Whyte, my bakery manager – you'll meet him soon – and the other is Mr MacBain here, who knows everything there is to know about costings, prices, wages, estimates, insurance and business in general. What I'd do without him I do not know, but I'm hoping I never have to find out! Right, Ross?'

'If you say so, Mr Comrie,' Ross answered, smiling. 'But don't forget, Miss Hendrie here is knowledgeable too. We'll both do our best to help you, Mr Linden, if there's anything you need to know.'

'Thank you, Mr MacBain, I appreciate that.' Viktor gave another little bow and turned to Jinny, who now lowered her eyes. 'Miss Hendrie.'

'Oh, I hope I'm not late!' cried a voice at the door and Mabel Hyslop came hurrying in, wrapped in a checked coat and woollen scarf, a beret over her thinning hair. 'My tram was full, I'd to wait for another, Mr Comrie, and I did want to be on time today—'

'Don't worry, you're not late,' he told her genially, 'we're early. Let me introduce my nephew, Viktor Linden. Viktor, meet Miss Hyslop, my secretary – another expert on all things to do with Comrie's.'

Mabel blushed, and there was the shaking of hands and more polite words again, until Mr Comrie ushered his nephew into his office, telling him to hang up his overcoat, exclaiming over his fine grey suit: 'My word, Viktor, you won't want to be wearing that in the bakery, will you? Is that what you wear in your Viennese place?'

'Not at all, Uncle, I wear a white overall and hat – see, I have them here in this bag.' Viktor smiled. 'I think I know the effect flour has on good suits!'

'Ha, ha, of course, you do!' Mr Comrie gave one of his ready laughs. 'But now, before we go to the bakery, let me take you down to meet the manageress, Mrs Arrow, and the staff of the shop and the teashop. Why, we might even have a coffee down there! They won't be open yet, but they'll open for us, eh? Miss Hyslop, I'll be with you later. Meantime, there are couple of letters on my desk to type.'

'Certainly, Mr Comrie.'

As soon as the uncle and nephew had departed, Mabel rushed into Ross's office, her eyes gleaming. 'Oh, my, what a handsome young man, eh? He'll have all the girls after him here, mark my words. Did you ever see such blue eyes? So keen – like sailor's eyes, I'd say!'

'As I think he seems like a soldier, we only need someone to say he looks like a pilot and we'll have him in all three services,' Ross said coolly. 'And I rather think the girls downstairs won't get very far.'

'Why not?' Jinny asked at once. 'There are some very pretty girls in the shop and the café.'

'Why, he's sure to have a *fraulein* of his own back home,' Ross said carelessly. 'Shall we get to work, then?'

'I'm sure I'm ready to do my work, Ross!' Mabel cried, her face puckering. 'No need to tell me, I promise you!'

'Nor me,' said Jinny, seating herself at her own desk as Mabel, sniffing, returned to Mr Comrie's office. 'Why so snappy, Ross?'

'I'm not being snappy. When am I ever snappy?'

'Not often,' she agreed, and gave him a long, level look. 'You don't like him, do you? You don't like Mr Viktor Linden?'

'I've only just met him.'

'Don't always need time to know what you think of someone.'

Ross shrugged. 'I expect he's all right. What did you think of him, then?'

'He's very good looking,' she replied obliquely, and began to study the wages book, while Ross, after giving her a return stare, suddenly laughed.

'I've just thought – if Mrs Arrow gives him a coffee downstairs he'll be in for a shock. Probably won't know what he's drinking.'

'Something wrong with our coffee?'

'No, no, it's just that in Vienna drinking coffee is almost a religion. There are so many kinds – maybe as many as fifteen – and all so delicious that you're absolutely spoiled for choice. Our one brand will seem strange to anyone used to Viennese ways.'

'Well, he's come here to learn about our ways, hasn't he?' Jinny asked quickly. 'And I'm sure he'll be very polite, whatever he thinks.'

'Of course,' Ross agreed. 'Of course he will.'

And no more was said.

Five

After the exciting morning, things seemed flat for Jinny. Viktor Linden had returned only once to his uncle's office – to collect his overcoat before going to the bakery, and though he had very definitely smiled at Jinny as he walked through Accounts, he didn't linger to speak. Ross was out at the time, which meant that if she and the Viennese had exchanged a few words she wouldn't have been inhibited by Ross's presence, but there it was – Viktor Linden hadn't stopped. He probably wasn't interested. Why should he be, when this was his first day and he had so much to see and learn and so many people to meet?

As she worked, totalling up figures and costs of ingredients used the previous week, she put the new man firmly out of her mind, deciding that Ross was probably right, he no doubt had a girlfriend back home, and anyway, why should she be so interested? She'd never been interested in the young men she had occasionally been out with – why should this chap from abroad be any different? Oh, because he was. Different.

When her lunchtime break came and Ross was back she went down to the shop, as she usually did, to buy at staff discount a couple of filled rolls to eat in the back room which adjoined the kitchen, and found the assistants agog with chat about Mr Comrie's nephew.

In between expertly wrapping up bread and cakes for customers, Kirsten, Polly and Rhoda were fizzing with excitement. Had Jinny met him, then? Was he no' a charmer? Such blue eyes and so tall! And such wonderful English! Why, they hadn't expected to understand a word he said, but he was so nice, so interested!

It was the same in the tea shop when Jinny went to pick up her cup of tea, with the waitresses – Audrey, Joan and Fiona – as full of admiration for Mr Linden as the shop girls, and even Mrs Arrow, the thin, sharp manageress, was keen to talk about him.

'Asked me if the customers liked to sit outside in the summer, and when I told him we never put out tables he said that folk in Vienna love to sit outside. And outside or in they stay for hours, just chatting away over a single coffee sometimes, and I said we'd never hold with that – why, we need the space!'

'Of course you do,' said Jinny at the door, cup in hand. 'But things are very different there.'

'So it seems. But I gave him a cup of our coffee and he seemed to like it. At least, he didn't say he didn't. And he said our cakes looked excellent.' Mrs Arrow suddenly frowned. 'Just hope he doesn't go making too many of his own, though. Mr Comrie muttered something about trying out his sort in the shop and in here too. I'm no' sure how they'll go.'

'Have to see what Mr Whyte thinks.'

'That's right. Arthur will sort it out. I mean, there's a slump on at the moment. Who's going to pay for elaborate cakes at a time like this?'

'I would!' cried Audrey, a redhead with a mind of her own. 'If Mr Linden was making 'em, eh?'

'Now, now, Audrey, let's no' hear too much of your opinions, eh?' snapped Mrs Arrow. 'I see a customer at table four looking round for service.'

'I'll go for my lunch,' said Jinny, escaping to the little room at the back and thinking ruefully that Mabel had been right – the girls at Comrie's would certainly be 'after' Viktor Linden. She'd not be joining in, then. No, indeed. And opening a copy of *The Scotsman* someone had left on the table, Jinny carefully studied the news, which wasn't too good, as it happened. There was no let-up in the depression yet. Japanese troops in their war against China had captured Shanghai. Someone in an article forecast war with Germany the following year.

Oh, dear. She put the paper aside. As soon as she'd finished her lunch she'd go round the shops and do a bit of Christmas shopping. That would cheer her up.

After a very routine afternoon she was glad to be going home. There was no doubt that, whatever she'd decided about putting the young Viennese man from her mind, she'd been disappointed not to have seen him again on his first day. It seemed like he'd been caught up at the bakery meeting the men who made the loaves and rolls and the two girls, Norah and Trixie, who decorated the 'fancies' and iced the Christmas and wedding cakes. Of course, the bakery would be where he'd be spending most of his time, especially if he was going to be making his own cakes; over here in Accounts she probably wouldn't see him at all. But then, there was a bit of a question mark over his making cakes, wasn't there?

'I suppose Mr Whyte will have to OK any baking from Mr Linden, won't he?' she asked Ross as she put on her coat. 'Mrs Arrow's worried that we can't afford his sort of elaborate cakes.'

'Old groaner, Mrs Arrow,' Ross answered with a grin. 'She's one for doing what we've always done. Madeira, Ginger, Sultana, Seed Cake, Swiss Roll – those are our staples. Anything a bit different doesn't get a look in.'

'Yes, but what will Mr Whyte say?'

'You mean, what will Mr Comrie say? He's all for letting his nephew show what he can do, and he has the last word. No need to worry about Viktor Linden's baking, Jinny.'

'I'm not worrying!' she cried, at which he smiled.

'Of course not. Why should you?'

'Goodnight,' she called. 'I'm away for my tram. Are you coming?'

'Got some things I want to clear up. Goodnight, Jinny. See you tomorrow.'

It's Vi's turn to cook tonight, thought Jinny, turning into Fingal Street, which meant they'd be having fish. They usually did when Vi cooked – easiest and quickest to do, she always said, and she was always short of time. There was her studying to fit in – she'd joined an evening class on politics – or she had to go to a Labour meeting, or do some canvassing if there was a local election coming. That trip out to the cinema the other evening with Jinny and May had been unusual for her, though she'd certainly enjoyed it.

Thinking of May, there she was, standing in the lamplight, talking to Allan Forth. At once, Jinny halted. They were standing so close together, so obviously enjoying their meeting that it seemed a shame to interrupt them.

'I was wondering, May,' Allan was saying, his eyes never leaving her face, 'if you'd care to come to the pictures with me one night this week? There's a good film on, *Lost Horizon* with Ronald Colman.'

'Oh, Allan, that would be lovely!' May hesitated. 'The thing is—'

'What?' he asked quickly.

'Well – no, it's all right, I'd like to go, Allan. What night were you thinking of?'

'Any night, May. Any that would suit you.'

'Wednesday?'

'Perfect. I'll come round for you at about half past six, shall I?'

'Half past six would be grand. Oh, here comes Jinny!' May's keen eyes had spotted her sister now approaching slowly up the street, and at once had stepped back from Allan at the same time as he moved away from her.

'Hello, Jinny!' Allan cried. 'Had a good day?'

'Oh, yes, you had the new man starting today, didn't you?' asked May, talking a little fast. 'What's he like, then?'

'All right. Speaks good English.' To Allan, Jinny added, 'He's Viennese.'

'Really? I've heard those Austrians make nice cakes.' Allan was pushing his bike away. 'Goodnight, then. May, I'll see you Wednesday, if not before.'

'Lovely. Goodnight, Allan.'

Not looking at Jinny, May hurried along to the side door to the flat, but Jinny was close behind.

'Wednesday?' she repeated.

'We're going to the pictures,' said May, and went up the inner steps so quickly Jinny couldn't catch her.

Six

'The pictures?' cried Jinny at the door of the living room. 'You and Allan?'

May swung round, shaking her head. 'Ssh! Dad'll be home and I don't want to tell him yet.'

'You'll have to tell him sometime, May. Best get it over with.'

'He'll be in a mood right through tea.'

'Yes, but then he'll accept it – what else can he do?' Jinny smiled. 'You're over twenty-one, eh?'

May sighed. 'All right, I'll tell him now.'

At the sisters' entrance Josh looked up from his evening paper, his face brightening.

'Hello, you two, you're back! Had a good day?'

'Same as usual,' May answered, moving towards the kitchen. 'Is that fish I smell?'

'Spot on,' cried Vi, appearing red-faced, a fish slice in her hands. 'Frying tonight – how did you guess?'

'Just genius,' said Jinny. 'And the fact that you usually do fish for us when it's your turn to cook.'

'Aye, but this time I've done chips as well. And they're all ready, so you'd better sit down. Dad, did you hear that?'

'We'll just wash our hands,' said May, sending a look of apprehension to Jinny, who mouthed, *Go on, tell him!*

But when they sat down to Vi's speciality, which was perfectly cooked, for if she only did one thing she at least did it well, it was clear that May was biding her time to speak to her father, and talk centred on the new man at Comrie's.

'So, Jinny, what's the German like, then?' Vi asked as she buttered some bread. 'Wasn't he starting today?'

'Yes, he started today, but he's Austrian, not German.'

'Same difference.'

'No, Austrians are not like Germans.'

'If we go to war with 'em, they'll be the same, all right.'

'Who says we're going to war?'

'Why the papers are full of this chap Hitler wanting to start a war with everybody. *And* he was born in Austria, too, so there you are.'

'I'll never believe that we'll go to war with Germany again!' Josh cried. 'We'd enough o' that last time. Was it all for nothing, then?'

'Don't worry, Dad,' May said quickly. 'The government won't let it happen. It's all just talk. Jinny, tell us about this new chap. Do you like him?'

'He's all right,' Jinny answered cagily. 'Very polite.'

'And nice looking?'

'Well, yes, fair, you know, and tall. But we didn't see much of him in Accounts – he was away to the bakery.'

'He's going to make some Austrian cakes?' asked Vi. 'A bit different to Comrie's Seed Cake and Madeira, eh?'

'I expect so.' Jinny, to hide her unwillingness to talk, leaped up to clear away their plates and, when they'd all had the remains of yesterday's apple tart, looked meaningfully across to May, who said she'd make the tea.

'Think she seems bit strange tonight?' asked Josh, moving to his fireside chair as May went into the kitchen 'As though she's got something on her mind?'

Jinny, looking down, said nothing.

'Seems just as usual to me,' Vi answered. 'May doesn't usually have things on her mind.'

'My imagination, then,' said Josh.

'Must be.'

No one said anything more until May, rather flushed, brought in the tea.

'Everything all right, pet?' asked Josh, taking his cup. 'I was saying you seemed a bit – what's the word? Preoccupied.'

'Me?' May's gaze on him was limpid. 'No, I wouldn't say so.

Though I have got a bit o' news. Allan Forth's asked me to go to the pictures with him. On Wednesday.'

A silence fell, enfolding Josh and his girls in a curtain so thick only Vi was brave enough to speak through it.

'What are you going to see?' she asked May lightly, though her dark gaze was on her father.

'*Lost Horizon*,' answered May.

'Why, you've seen that!'

'So? I suppose I can see it again. It's very good.'

'Very good,' agreed Jinny.

'Wait a minute, wait a minute!' cried Josh, setting down his cup with a crash. 'What's all this about you seeing Allan Forth, May? He's our landlord, for God's sake, and years older than you!'

'Five,' she said quietly.

'But what's he got to do with you? We don't know him like we knew his father.'

'He's had tea with us, Dad,' Jinny put in quickly. 'He's a friend, he isn't just our landlord, and we all know he's been sweet on May for ages – don't know why he's taken so long to ask her out.'

'Sweet on May?' Josh rose from his chair. 'I don't want him to be sweet on May! He's the wrong type for her, there's nothing to him, canna say boo to a goose – she deserves better than that!'

'What do you mean – I deserve better?' cried May with sudden passion. 'We're going to the pictures together that's all. And didn't you say the other evening that he was a nice lad? Has he stopped being nice because he's asked me out?'

'I want you to know I don't approve of you seeing him,' Josh said, pushing aside his chair and snatching his jacket from the back of the door. 'If you want to see him, I canna stop you – you're over twenty-one—'

'Certainly am!' said May.

'But I'm never going to say I'm happy about it – I never will be, and that's that. Now, I'm going back to work.'

Slamming the door behind him he went out, leaving the girls to sigh deeply and exchange hopeless looks.

'I suppose he doesn't want to think you might leave him, May,' Jinny said at last.

'It's only because he's lost Ma,' May declared. 'He's come to rely on us to fill her place.'

'He got very upset when I went out with Iain Baxter, that one I went to school with.'

'Gets upset about anyone,' said Vi. 'You're just going to have to take a firm hand with him, May. Now, I'd better get off to my politics class or I'll be late.'

'So we do the washing up?' asked Jinny. 'Och, nae bother, we don't mind, do we, May?'

'As long as Vi does it on Wednesday. Thing is, though, I'd just like to say that none of us is thinking of getting married, so Dad can stop going off like a rocket, eh?'

'Try telling him that,' Jinny laughed as they began to pile up the dishes, 'when you go out with Allan.'

'One trip to the cinema doesn't mean much.'

'It's a start.'

Seven

Wednesday, the day May and Allan were to go out, was when Jinny met the Viennese man again, though afterwards she rather wished she hadn't. Not because of anything he'd said or done – quite the reverse. It came about when Arthur Whyte, the bakery manager, brought Viktor across to Ross's office to sit in on one of the regular meetings on costings and sales. Seemed that Mr Comrie had expressed a wish for his nephew to get some idea of how expenditure and profit were monitored in a Scottish bakery, so that he could compare the system with the one at home, and Viktor, arriving with Mr Whyte, was interested. He still found time, before greeting Ross, to give Jinny a smile which she hastily, if a little shyly, returned.

'All going well, Mr Linden?' asked Ross, offering Viktor a chair. 'You getting to know the bakery?'

The Viennese inclined his head. 'Please, call me Viktor. Yes, thank you, I am enjoying my time there. Everyone is being so kind.'

'He is already planning to begin some baking of his own,' remarked Arthur Whyte, a chunky figure in his late forties, grey-haired and pleasant enough but best known for his keenness to save money. His smile now was cautious. 'Have to see how that goes, eh?'

'Indeed,' Viktor returned politely. 'But I believe my uncle would like me to make some of our *Torten*, as we call cakes, out of interest, perhaps?'

'Oh, yes, certainly, we'll be very interested,' Ross said agreeably.

'I know something of Austrian baking, Viktor, and I am a great fan. Jinny, will you pass me the stock book? Then we'll make a start.'

It was not usual for Jinny to sit in on the costings meetings, although Ross had instructed her on what was involved, and she now took her place at her own desk, her eyes on her work – until they just managed to light on Viktor sitting at a distance.

Yes, there was no doubt about it, she decided, observing him at her leisure. He was very attractive. She saw the way his blond hair seemed to fit his finely shaped head, and how he held himself so elegantly, his shoulders flat, his slim neck showing his youth. Maybe, after all, it was his looks and not just being Viennese that made him seem so different from the few young men she'd gone out with in the past? She was pleasantly dwelling on this question when, to her horror, he suddenly turned his head and their eyes met. He had caught her watching him.

A great rush of colour flooded her face from her pointed chin to the top of her brow, but she could not seem to detach her gaze from his and kept on looking as he returned her look and then gently smiled. Oh, God, what must he be thinking? She couldn't smile back, couldn't pretend she wasn't embarrassed, and even when she'd dragged her gaze away and was bending her head over her work, all she felt was the embarrassment and the painful flush staining her face that Viktor must have seen.

Even though she was staring down at a column of figures, she was aware that he had turned his attention back to the meeting where Mr Whyte was going on about . . . something to do with Swiss Rolls not selling well that week and should they cut down on numbers for a while? Better than losing money having to sell them off at reduced prices, eh?

How many Swiss Rolls did they need? Mr Comrie was asking, and Jinny sighed. Heavens, who cared? Usually she was interested in snippets of information she heard from the meetings, but just then she felt she'd rather be elsewhere. Anywhere, in fact.

Of course, she had to face Viktor when the meeting was over. Smile politely, as though she'd never been caught staring at him; wish him all the best with his cake making while he bowed and thanked her, giving no sign that there was anything between them. Well, there wasn't, except that she'd been caught gazing at him and could have kicked herself for being such a fool.

When Mr Whyte called from the door that they'd better be getting back to the bakery, Viktor buttoned on his overcoat, turned to thank

Ross for allowing him to sit in on the meeting and, with a last look at Jinny, left Accounts without another word. Was that all then? Her heart weighing her down, Jinny returned to her desk, feeling so crushed she didn't even remember it was her lunch hour until Ross reminded her.

'Hey, shouldn't you be gone?' he asked easily. 'Not so carried away by the sight of our *leutnant* that you've forgotten to eat, I hope?'

'Oh, what a piece of nonsense!' she flared, then lowered her eyes and muttered an apology.

'Sorry, Ross – shouldn't have spoken to you like that.'

'Not at all, I shouldn't have teased you, it never goes down well. All right now?'

'Of course. I'll get off to lunch, then.'

But still she lingered a moment. 'Meeting go well, Ross? Did Mr Linden enjoy it?'

'Seemed to. Asked some intelligent questions – maybe you heard?'

'No, I didn't hear.'

'Well, he certainly seems a bright lad. And, by the way, he's asked us to call him Viktor. Anxious to mix in, I suppose.'

'Yes, I suppose so.' Jinny glanced at the clock. 'I'd better run, then.'

'Take your time. I don't mind when I go to lunch.'

'I'll be back at one.'

Not caring to read Ross's expression, for it seemed to her that he knew she was upset, Jinny quickly left Accounts and made her way to the bakery shop downstairs, took her usual rolls and added a cup of tea from the tea shop. After the familiar chat with the girls she was glad to find herself alone in the back room, where she could desolately eat her rolls and think about how silly she'd been.

Gradually, though, she began to feel better. So he'd caught her studying him. What of it? She sipped her tea. A cat could look at a king, the saying went, and he needn't have found her gaze anything remarkable. He was new; he would expect to be a focus of interest. No need to worry, then.

But she had no sooner cheered herself up than she remembered Viktor's intense blue eyes.

'Did you ever see such blue eyes?' Mabel had asked. 'Like sailor's eyes, I'd say . . .'

Long-sighted sailor's eyes, then, that could have seen even from a distance that Jinny was looking at him because she was attracted to him. As, of course, she was. Attracted. She hadn't really admitted it to herself till then. More than attracted? Maybe. She'd heard about people falling in love at first sight. Was this what it meant? To have this line drawn between yourself and someone you'd just met? To want that person to feel the same?

Oh, it was all so crazy! Viktor Linden wasn't someone who was going to stay in her life, even if they did get to know each other. He came from another country and he'd be going back to it. There was no future to her feelings and the best thing she could do was to stamp them out – to let them die as a plant dies without light or water, not let them blossom.

Which meant that tomorrow, when she took the wages over to the bakery, she would just be very polite but cool if she saw Viktor, and let him see she wasn't especially interested in him. And she wouldn't be staying long at the bakery, in any case, as she had wages to take to the other shops. There, that was her little plan of campaign, and having worked it out Jinny felt better – so much so that she felt quite hungry and went back to the shop to buy a vanilla slice which she enjoyed with another cup of tea.

Wonder how May and Allan will get on this evening? she thought idly. And guessed very well, once they'd overcome their first feelings of strangeness at being together.

But first, of course, for May, there'd be the ordeal of tea with Dad to get through. Oh, heavens, and she, Jinny was cooking! Help! She'd better get home early and make sure everything was ready so that May could leave by half past six, hoping, of course, that Dad didn't make difficulties. Oh, why did folk want to do that?

As she ran back to Accounts at exactly one o'clock – there was the gun sounding off again – her only consolation in worrying about her father making difficulties was that, for a little while, she'd stopped thinking about Viktor Linden.

Eight

Ordeal by Tea. Yes, you could call it that, with Josh sitting at the table with a face of stone, Vi sighing with exasperation, and even cool May seeming to be on edge, fiddling with her knife and fork and looking at the clock.

At least her cooking had been all right, thought Jinny, serving

Josh and Vi second helpings of ham shank and split peas, but then May rose and said she must get ready and a dark red colour rushed to Josh's brow.

'Still going out, then?' he asked shortly.

'Yes, I am.'

'Even though I'm not happy about you seeing Allan Forth?'

'Dad, you know you're never happy when we go out with anyone.'

Josh frowned. 'When did I ever complain about you lassies going out?'

'Oh, Dad, how can you say that?' Jinny asked. 'You know the awful fuss you made when I went out with Iain Baxter.'

'That laddie you knew from school? He wasn't right for you, Jinny. Just like the fellows May was seeing weren't suitable for her. I wasn't complaining, just pointing out what was true.'

'And now you're saying the same thing about Allan?' May asked. 'Well, that certainly isn't true. There's nothing at all wrong with Allan, as you know very well. You've always been very friendly with him up till now.'

'Aye, well that was before I knew he was playing up to you behind my back.'

With a sigh of exasperation, May shook her head. 'Dad, I don't know what you expect! I'm a grown-up and can say what I want to do; there's no need for Allan to ask your permission.'

'Get going, May,' advised Vi. 'Don't argue any more. Dad's only holding you up.'

'Vi, I'll thank you to stay out of this!' Josh jumped angrily to his feet. 'It's between May and me and no one else!'

'Well, I'm going to get ready,' May told him calmly. 'So you should just sit down and finish your tea. Jinny's taken a lot of trouble with it, remember.'

'Och, I'm no' hungry.' Josh glanced at Jinny. 'Sorry, pet. I think I'll away back to work.'

But as he made no move, May caught at his hand and held it. 'Oh, please, don't be like this again,' she said softly. 'I'm only going to the pictures. I know you're upset but you needn't be. Even if we make other friends, we're still your girls, isn't that right – Vi? Jinny?'

'Sure,' said Vi.

'Oh, yes,' Jinny agreed. 'You have to remember that, Dad.'

Slowly he let go of May's hand and rested his sombre gaze on her face. 'Still my girl, May? I don't think so. These friends you talk about – you just mean Allan Forth. And who says he wants to be a friend?'

'He's a friend already!' she answered swiftly. 'A friend to this family. It's unfair for you to be so much against him.'

For some moments Josh was silent. Finally, he said heavily, 'Listen, May, since your ma died we've all made the best o' things, eh? Maybe we haven't been like we were before, but still as happy as we could manage. We never needed so-called friends wanting to come between us, spoiling what we had.'

'Are you saying we shouldn't have friends at all, then?' asked Vi, her tone blunt, her eyes hostile.

'Of course not! All I say is that you should have real friends, not fellows pretending to be what they're not.'

'You're hinting Allan is like that?' cried May. 'Dad, you couldn't be more wrong! He's sincere and honest in every way!'

'And causing trouble!' Josh, breathing fast, strode across the room and snatched his coat from a peg on the door. 'You go out with him if you want, May, but I'm telling you, he'll never be welcomed here by me! Now, I'm away.'

After he'd slammed the door behind him, just as before, and they'd heard his feet thundering down the stairs, the sisters sat in silence for some moments.

Finally, Vi spoke. 'He's like a five-year-old, eh? Throwing a tantrum if folk won't do what he wants. May, you'll just have to ignore him.'

'He's really upset,' she answered in a low voice. 'I hate to see him like that. Shows how deep his feelings are.'

'Never mind his feelings – he's no right to 'em.' Vi began to clear the table. 'Off you go, get yourself ready and go down to meet Allan.'

'Will you tell him – about Dad?' Jinny asked.

'Don't know yet. Look, I'm sorry to leave the clearing up—'

'Och, just go!' cried Vi. And May finally went.

But how pretty she looked, her sisters thought, when she was finally ready. Worries about her father or not, in her blue coat with matching hat of her own making and a blue scarf that brought out the colour of her eyes, she appeared only to be looking forward to her night out – her first with Allan Forth. Once again, Vi and Jinny marvelled at how she could set aside her feelings and present such a serene face to the world, and wished they could have shared her gift. No point in that, they were different and must make the best of it, but all they wanted now was for May and Allan – two lovely people – to enjoy their evening together.

'Thank the Lord she's not going to let Dad spoil things,' said Vi, crashing dishes into a bowl after May had run lightly down to meet Allan and walked away with him to the tram. 'There's a lot to be said for being calm as a cucumber, eh?'

'Think something might come of this going out?' asked Jinny, reaching for a towel.

'Don't ask me. You were the one who said Allan was sweet on May.'

'Depends if she's sweet on him, though.'

'I think she might be. Look at the way she defended him to Dad. That's what's got him worried.'

'Poor Dad. He makes himself so unhappy.'

'I've no patience with him. Face facts is what he should do. You and May will be sure to get married one day and leave the nest, and I'll depart to live my own life, eh? He'll have to get used to it.'

Jinny laughed a little. 'The way you talk, Vi! You're not really as hard as you make out, you know. And why shouldn't you get married one day anyway?'

'Because I'll have better things to do.'

'Maybe I will too, then. I'm in no hurry to get married – I like my job.'

'Especially when you can meet interesting guys from foreign parts, eh?'

Glancing away from Vi's amused gaze, Jinny made no reply.

Nine

Meanwhile, across the city, May and Allan, in the darkness of the cinema, their eyes on the screen, were conscious only of each other yet still not drawing close. Only as the film progressed did it seem natural that Allan should reach to take May's hand, that her eyes should turn to meet his, and that both should smile.

'That was a wonderful picture,' Allan whispered as the credits rolled at the end and they were blinking at each other in the returned lights. 'I suppose everyone would like to live in a place like Shangri-la where you'd never grow old and always be happy.' He looked down at May's hand in his. 'You wish there was somewhere like that in real life, May?'

'I don't know. I think, maybe, I'd rather have life as it is. I mean, where you'd know what you had was true.'

'Yes, I suppose I agree. And people can be happy in the real world, eh?' His gaze on her was steady. 'For instance, I'm happy now, just being with you.'

'It's the same for me, Allan.' But May was quietly withdrawing her hand from his. 'There's something I should tell you, though.'

'Oh?' He was trying to smile. 'Nothing bad, is it?'

'Well, it's just that – look, I don't want to make too much of it but my dad isn't keen for me to go out with you.'

Allan's effort at a smile disappeared. His eyes on May were wide, their look bewildered.

'What are you saying? I don't understand – your dad doesn't like me? But he does! We get on well. How can it be true that he's not keen for you to go out with me?'

'He does like you, really,' she said earnestly. 'It's hard to explain, but since Ma died, he's, well, he likes to think that we only need him.'

'You and your sisters? All three of you?'

'Yes. Well, Vi isn't interested in going out with anyone – it's Jinny and me that Dad gets worried about – I mean, if we . . . see people.'

'See young men, you mean,' Allan said quietly. He put his hand to his brow and shook his head. 'But this is just crazy, May. He can't keep you as little girls for ever, you have to grow up, have lives of your own—'

'I know, and I think he knows that too, deep down, but he can't accept it, that's all, so we have these . . . arguments.' May sighed heavily, then suddenly reached forward and took Allan's hand. 'The thing is I'm not going to take any notice of him. If I want to go out with someone I will, and as he says himself, there's nothing he can do about it.'

'Go out with someone,' Allan repeated, his eyes intent on hers. 'Would that be me? Do you mean you'd like to go out with me again?'

'Yes, I would,' she said softly.

'Even if it means upsetting your father? I don't like that, May. I don't want to cause trouble between you and your dad.'

'You'd rather we didn't see each other?'

'Oh, God, no!'

As the lights began to dim for the second feature, Allan pulled May to her feet.

'Come on, let's go,' he said urgently. 'We don't need to see the B-picture, do we? Let's just get out of here.'

They'd meant to walk home but the night air was so cold and the pavements so slippery with frost that they took the tram and sat together on the jolting bench seat, holding hands and closely studying each other's faces.

'This has been a blow,' Allan said quietly. 'And so unexpected.'

'I know,' May replied. 'It was for me, too, because you're different from other fellows. I mean, I knew Dad liked you, so I thought he might not mind so much if I went out with you.'

'If he sees all men as a threat there wasn't much hope of that.'

'No, but he's so obstinate – he won't listen to anything anybody says.'

Allan, his eyes brightening, squeezed May's hand in his. 'Did you defend me?' he asked softly. 'Against what, I don't know, but I suppose there must be something.'

'Only that you're older, which is a piece of nonsense as you're not that much older than me, and Dad was older than Ma, anyway. Don't worry about what he says, Allan. We've agreed, haven't we, to see each other?'

'Nothing will stop me from being with you, if it's what you want, May.'

'I've told you it is.'

'Just makes things a bit awkward, that's all. I mean, what do I say when I see your dad?'

'Be as you always are. If he wants to quarrel with you, say there's no point.'

'You make it sound so easy,' he was beginning, when she knocked his arm and began to rise from her seat.

'Our stop, Allan.'

'I wouldn't have minded travelling on,' he said with a laugh.

They made the walk up Fingal Street last as long as possible, keeping close together, their arms entwined, enduring the cold until they reached the Hendries' door, where they stopped and gazed at each other in the lamplight.

'I wish I didn't feel your dad was looking out,' Allan whispered. 'Think he might come down if he sees us?'

'No, he'll probably not be back from the theatre yet. He's one of the last to leave.'

'In that case . . .' Allan was drawing her into his arms when she stiffened and took a step back.

'He's here?' he asked, turning quickly to look down the street, but May shook her head.

'It's Vi. She must have been to one of her meetings – oh, Lord, why does she have to come back now?'

'Why indeed?' groaned Allan.

They stood still, facing Vi, who was jauntily approaching.

'Had a good time?' she cried brightly. 'Enjoy the picture?'

'Very much,' Allan answered politely. 'Certainly takes you into another world, eh?'

'Shangri-la? Yes, it's grand – as long as you remember it's not real.'

'Only have to come out into the cold here to know that,' May said, rubbing her arms. 'Suppose we'd better go in.'

'Och, don't let me interrupt things.' Vi hurried past them to the door of the flat. 'I'll go in and you two can say goodnight.'

'Goodnight to you, then,' called Allan, and when she'd gone and closed the door he turned eagerly again to May.

'Sorry about that,' she said, looking embarrassed. 'Vi came just at the wrong time.'

'She seemed pretty understanding, though.' Allan was slowly drawing May into his arms and bending his face to hers. 'Didn't linger.'

No further words were spoken as they stood very still, their eyes searching each other's faces, then let their mouths meet in their first kiss, a kiss that promised so much more, and finally drew apart, breathing hard.

'When can I see you again?' Allan asked urgently. 'I must see you, May. Will you come into my shop one evening?'

'Yes, I will, I promise. It's for the best, to meet like that.'

'You mean to keep out of your father's way?'

'He'll settle down, he'll be all right – don't worry.'

'I can't believe he doesn't like me, May. I mean, there's never been any hint—'

She put her finger to his lips. 'I told you, he'll be all right. We'll just have to give him time to get used to things. Now, I'd better go.'

'You won't forget? To come into my shop?'

'As though I would!'

He made to take a step towards her but she blew him a kiss and opened her door.

'Goodnight, Allan!'

'Goodnight, dear May.'

He watched as the door closed behind her, standing there for several minutes before walking away.

Ten

'Dad not back yet?' asked May, taking off her coat in the living room of the flat.

'Too early,' Jinny answered, studying her sister with interest. 'But have you had a good time?'

'Yes, did you enjoy seeing the picture all over again?' Vi put in with a laugh. 'Did you let on you'd seen it already?

'No, I didn't,' May told her coolly. 'Why should I? Anyway, I enjoyed it just as much the second time.'

'You certainly look happy,' Jinny observed. 'You'll be seeing Allan again, eh?'

'Ssh!' cried Vi. 'There's the door! Dad's back!'

The sisters looked at one another, Jinny with apprehension, Vi with a frown and May with her usual calmness. When their father came in, his face cold and set, it was she who stepped forward to greet him.

'Hello, Dad, want some tea?'

He stared. 'You're back then?'

'Of course I'm back!' She smiled. 'It wasn't such a long picture.'

Josh took off his coat and hung it on its peg. He moved towards the fire and held out his hands to the blaze.

'I don't want to hear about it,' he said over his shoulder. 'You know my views, May. If you don't tell me what you're doing, the better we'll get on.'

'Oh, Dad, don't be so ridiculous!' cried Vi as Jinny hurriedly set about making tea. 'You can't ask May not to talk about Allan! She's every right!'

'Do you mind not speaking to me like that?' Josh's face was mottled red. 'If May does as I say we can all get on as we were. I don't think I'm being unreasonable to want that.'

'Not unreasonable!' Vi gave a short laugh but May shook her head at her, and as Jinny poured the tea and handed round the cups an uneasy peace descended. Finally Josh stood up and said he was weary, he'd be away to his bed. Goodnights were said, with Josh looking at no one, and then he was gone and the girls sighed and relaxed.

'Oh, it's a shame Dad's being so difficult,' said Jinny. 'I mean, we usually get on so well.'

'Aye, it's especially hard for you, May,' Vi commented. 'Your first time out with Allan and he goes and spoils it all, eh?'

As her sisters' eyes rested on her, May's own gaze seemed far away and her mouth curved slowly into a small, secret smile.

'Not all,' she replied softly. 'I wouldn't say "all", Vi.' With that she rose and put the guard over the fire. 'Shall we call it a day?' she asked. 'Things will look better in the morning.'

'I shouldn't bank on it,' said Vi shortly. 'Dad shows no sign of coming round to things.'

'We'll just have to be patient. The good thing is that he does like Allan really and, remember, Allan is our landlord. Dad won't want to fall out with him.' May began to gather up the teacups. 'Look, I must get to bed – I'll just take these away. Goodnight, girls.'

'Poor May,' said Vi, standing up and yawning. 'She's putting a good face on it but she knows there'll be trouble if she and Allan get serious. Thank the Lord I've nothing like that to worry about.'

'Nor me,' said Jinny promptly, at which Vi gave her another of her amused looks.

'Aren't you forgetting *Herr* Whats-his-name? Don't look so embarrassed – I can tell you're interested.'

'I don't know what you're talking about!' Jinny flared, jumping up and making for the door. 'You just like to tease, eh? I don't know why.'

'Sorry,' said Vi. 'Honestly, I don't mean to upset you. I won't say another word.'

'Thank you!'

'Friends again?'

'Of course. As long as you forget about Mr Linden.'

'Wiped clean from my mind! cried Vi, as they put the light out and left the living room.

But not from mine, thought Jinny with a sigh as she made her way into the bathroom. Only Vi needn't know that.

Eleven

Friday. Wages day. For Jinny it was a day to enjoy, when she could make her rounds of the Comrie shops and the Princes Street café, as well as the bakery at Broughton Street, bringing the staff what they wanted and being welcomed on all sides.

'Here she is, then, good old Jinny! What have you got for us this week, then?' the bakers would cry. 'Our overtime gone up, has it? No' taken too much off, have you?'

'Everything's just as it should be,' she would always answer, smiling, and feel a wonderfully warm feeling inside at the sight of all the cheerful faces.

Actually, not all the bakers would be there. Those on the first shift who started work at four a.m., would have already gone off duty after sending their new loaves and rolls for early delivery in the van driven by cheerful, ginger-haired Terry Brown. But there would still be plenty of activity going on in the delicious-smelling bakery, as Jinny always liked to see. Men kneading, slapping and rolling out dough, or preparing cakes in the electric mixing machine; women icing and decorating fancies and large fruit cakes.

On that Friday morning in cold November, when Jinny arrived at the bakery, all her intentions of being cool with Viktor intact, she found Terry Brown back from his first deliveries, smoking a cigarette outside the door.

'Hallo, Jinny!' He gave her his usual grin. 'Want your lift over town?'

'Oh, yes, please! I'll just find Mr Whyte and give him the wages and then I'll be with you.'

'No' forgetting mine, eh?'

'Have it right here.'

Hurrying on into the bakery, Jinny returned the usual greetings with Alf, Ronnie and Bob loading up the big ovens set into the wall, and waved to Trixie and Norah, both attractive forty-year-olds who'd worked for Mr Comrie since leaving school, though Senga, the young trainee, didn't seem to be in sight. And nor was Viktor Linden.

'Mr Whyte around?' Jinny called, wondering where Viktor might be. Wasn't he supposed to be baking his own wonderful cakes?

'Right here, Jinny!' called Arthur Whyte, appearing from his small office. 'Good to see you. All present and correct?'

'Yes, except that I haven't got anything for Mr Linden. He's not been put on my list.'

'Oh, no, he wouldn't have been.' Mr Whyte spoke in a stage whisper. 'Mr Comrie's making special arrangements for him.'

'I see,' said Jinny, her eyes still checking round the bakery. 'I can't see him, anyway. Is he in today?'

'Why, of course. He's over at the small oven with Senga – don't you see him?'

Oh, yes, there he was, standing next to young Senga, a snub-nosed girl with a mass of thick brown hair stuffed into a cap, who was animatedly talking to him. Rather pushy, Jinny always thought her, and with a very good opinion of herself, but Viktor, dressed in a chef's white top and trousers with his hair also covered by a cap, appeared to be listening to her with great interest. Was she explaining how to work the oven? As though he wouldn't know!

Removing her gaze from Viktor – who hadn't seen her – Jinny followed Mr Whyte into his office, where they checked off her list and sorted the wage envelopes ready for distribution.

'Got time for some tea?' asked Mr Whyte when Jinny rose to leave, but she shook her head.

'Thanks, but Terry's giving me a lift to the Morningside shop – I don't want to keep him waiting.'

'All he'd do is light another cigarette.' Mr Whyte shrugged. 'And how he and other fellows can afford to smoke these days is a mystery to me. I mean, elevenpence ha'penny for twenty, eh? It's a lot. Take care not to get the habit, Jinny.'

'I'm far too sensible for that,' she said with a laugh.

But when she'd left him to open his office door, her laughter died. Seemed she'd be leaving the bakery with no chance to speak to Viktor Linden when she'd hoped she might somehow make it clear that she wasn't interested in him. If he hadn't been so busy chatting to Senga, or, at least, listening to her, she might have spoken to him then, but now it was too late. Better to forget her plan – maybe it wouldn't have worked, anyway – and just find Terry and head off for Morningside. So she was deciding when she saw Viktor making his way towards her, and then she stood very still.

'Miss Hendrie, how good we meet again!' he said as he snatched off his white cap and made one of his small bows. 'I was not expecting to see you at the bakery.'

'It's Friday, wages day. I always come here on Fridays.'

'You are responsible for the wages?'

'Among other things.'

Her little laugh was nervous. The one thing she'd wanted was to meet Viktor and convey to him that if he'd seen her watching him it was all a mistake, it didn't mean a thing. Yet here he was and she had the feeling that her eyes on him were showing just the sort of interest she was so anxious to deny. How had she ever thought she could do otherwise? Her plan had been ridiculous, would never have worked, and all she could do now was be polite and hope he wouldn't be able to read what her eyes were telling him.

'I didn't think you'd seen me,' she said quietly. 'You were busy at the small ovens.'

'Yes, with the young lady called Senga. Now that is a strange name – she told me it was another name backwards.'

'Agnes,' said Jinny shortly. 'It is used in Scotland.'

'Well, she has been very helpful.' Victor's smile was radiant. 'Today, I am to begin my baking and she was showing me the ovens which are a little different from those I know. But I still saw you, Miss Hendrie.'

Senga was Senga, but Jinny was Miss Hendrie?

'I wish you'd call me Jinny,' she told him.

'If you will call me Viktor.'

'I'd like to. It's a name we have too, but spelled differently.'

'And "Jinny" – that is a name short for another?'

'Virginia, maybe, but I don't know any Virginias. My real name is Jean – which is shorter, in fact, than "Jinny".'

They both laughed at that and Jinny would have relaxed, for she felt suddenly at ease with the young man looking at her with such interest, except that she was aware of another kind of interest coming their way. Not only from the bakers, but also from Trixie, Norah and, most obviously, Senga, who was gazing so intently at Viktor! Clearly she was another of the girls Mabel had said would be 'after' him. Only to be expected, wasn't it? But Jinny couldn't avoid an inward little stab at the thought.

'I must go,' she told Viktor. 'Terry's giving me a lift to one of the other shops – you've met Terry, our van driver?'

'Sure he has,' said Terry, suddenly joining them and speaking in a very loud voice, as though Viktor wouldn't otherwise understand him. 'Is that no' right, Mr Linden? Everything OK with you? Finding your way around?'

'Yes, indeed, thank you,' Viktor replied politely. 'Everyone is being very kind.'

'That's the ticket, folk are very friendly here. Jinny, you coming?'

As though I wouldn't be, she thought, but only smiled.

'Goodbye, Viktor, it was nice to meet again. Good luck with your cake making.'

'Thank you, Jinny.' He inclined his head. 'But I think you will soon be seeing what I have made. On Monday, I am bringing my cakes to the café.'

'The café? On Monday? Oh, I'll look forward to that – I really want to see your Austrian cakes!'

'Jinny!' Terry said warningly and as she hastily followed him out, looking back once, Viktor replaced his white cap and watched her go.

'Bit stiff, our Jerry friend, eh?' asked Terry, driving them easily and efficiently across town. 'All those wee bows and suchlike.'

'Viktor?' Jinny frowned. 'I don't think he's stiff – he's always smiling. And you needn't call him Jerry. He's not German, he's Austrian.'

'Reckon they're the same. Fought together in the war when my dad died.'

'My dad fought in the war as well, and it was horrible, but Viktor had nothing to do with it any more than we had.'

'All I'm saying is that Austrians and Germans have the same ideas. This chap Hitler even thinks the Austrians should be part of Germany, and I bet they do too.'

'I don't think you can say that. Anyway, Viktor's not to blame for what other people might do.'

'Viktor?' Terry gave Jinny a quick glance and grinned. 'Soon got to know him, eh?'

'Ross says he wants everyone to call him by his first name.'

'Never asked me,' Terry supplied.

'Look, let's talk about something else. He's not even really part of Comrie's.'

'Only the boss's nephew! And makes fancy cakes, they say. I can understand fellows making bread, but fancy cakes – best left to women, I'd say.'

Jinny, sighing, refused to be drawn into an argument, and no more was said until they arrived at Comrie's in Morningside, where they unloaded trays of small buns and doughnuts and Jinny thanked Terry for her lift.

'Always grateful, Terry.'

'Nae bother, you ken that.' He hesitated. 'Look, sorry if I spoke out of turn about Mr Linden, if he's a friend o' yours, I mean.'

'He's not specially a friend of mine, Terry. We've only just met.'

'Oh, well, I daresay he's a nice enough guy – just no' a Scot, eh?'

'Can't all be lucky!' She smiled. 'See you next week, then.'

'Sorry I can't take you on to Stockbridge, but I've to get Glasgow – need a part for the van.'

'That's all right. Plenty of trams.'

Taking the wages into the shop, Jinny found Terry's words echoing in her mind.

'If he's a friend o' yours, I mean . . .'

Were other people thinking that, too? Look how the bakery folk had stood, openly watching, as she and Viktor talked together! Her feelings must have been too obvious, then. To Viktor, as well? A little while ago she would not have wanted to think that, but since he had come to speak to her, since she had read something in his eyes, in his manner towards her, she no longer minded. Was it possible that they both felt the same?

As she greeted Phyl and Sal in the shop and met their usual teasing – had she brought them a rise that week, if not, why not, et cetera – she only laughed and accepted a cup of tea and one of the new doughnuts. It was amazing how much better she felt than when she'd set out that morning, especially thinking that on Monday she would be seeing Viktor again.

Twelve

Even if Jinny had not been looking forward to seeing Viktor again, she would have wanted Monday to come, for the weekend had been depressing in the extreme. Josh had shown no signs of 'coming round', as the girls had hoped, and as he was at home on Sunday and had seen May go out, obviously to meet Allan, his misery was like a great cloud hanging over Vi and Jinny, who had to go out themselves to be free of it. Not that they felt much better when they returned, for their father was the same as when they'd left him and refused to listen to any arguments they wanted to make on why he should let May see Allan and be happy about it.

'You're only making things worse for yourself,' Vi told him. 'I mean, you might have to accept Allan one day, mightn't you?'

Josh raised his shadowed eyes. 'What are you talking about?'

'Well . . .' Vi glanced at Jinny. 'May and Allan might want to get married, mightn't they?'

'Married?' cried Josh. 'She'd never want to marry Allan! I'm no' denying that she might want to marry – don't accuse me of standing in her way – but she'd never want to marry him!'

'Why ever not? asked Jinny. 'He's got his own business, he's got his own house, but the main thing is he's nice, he's kind – he'd be just right for May!'

'He's a milksop!' cried Josh, rising. 'He's got no personality! He's like a long drink o' water! I'd never want to see my May married to him.'

As his daughters stared, their hearts sinking at the way their father was inventing a character that didn't exist to suit his own ends, it seemed clear that there was no point in saying any more. When he threw on his coat and cap and said he was going out for some fresh air, all the girls could feel was relief, which lasted until he returned some time later. May also returned, and the dark cloud stayed with them until they thankfully went to bed.

Roll on Monday! was Jinny's last thought before drifting into sleep, which only came after she'd spent some time wondering how things would be when she saw Viktor and his cakes the next morning – and, of course, had decided what to wear.

Her new raspberry jumper she'd been saving to wear at Christmas was in the end her choice, though when Monday morning actually came and she arrived in Accounts wearing it, she felt a bit of a fool to be making such a fuss about how she should look to see Viktor Linden.

It was true, she did feel attracted to him, and had felt a definite interest in herself flowing from him, but where was the point in trying to take it further? Viktor didn't live in Scotland and would never live in Scotland. Within a few short months would be returning home to Vienna. To picture herself there – well, even her vivid imagination couldn't take her as far as that! Why on earth hadn't she just put on her old blue twinset?

'You're looking very smart,' Ross observed when he joined her in the office. 'Have I seen that jumper before?'

'No, I haven't had it long.' Jinny played with the papers on her desk. 'Thought I'd give it an airing.'

'The colour suits you.'

Exactly her own view. She flushed a little and gave her papers another shuffle.

'Have you seen Mr Comrie yet? He's coming in with Viktor this morning.'

'Bit early for him.'

'Yes, but Viktor's bringing in some of his cakes — they're going to try them out at the shop.'

Ross raised his eyebrows. 'You're very well informed. No one's told me about this.'

'Viktor told me when I took the wages to the bakery on Friday. I think it had only just been decided. He'll have been working over the weekend, I expect, to get the baking done.'

'And they're going to be sold at so much a slice, I suppose? What price has been set?'

'Oh, I don't know. I don't suppose Viktor had even thought about it.'

'Probably not,' Ross said coldly. He reached for the telephone. 'I'll give Arthur a ring.'

'You're not cross, are you?' Jinny asked quickly. 'It was always what Mr Comrie wanted, to try out the Viennese cakes here.'

'I just like to know what's going on, that's all.' Ross began speaking to someone on the line then put his phone down. 'Seems Arthur's on his way here. I'll discuss this when I see him.'

'I'm sure no one wanted to keep you in the dark, Ross. It's all happened so quickly.'

'I know. I'm sorry.' Ross gave a quick smile. 'Must be that Monday morning feeling, eh? Let's go downstairs and see if anything's happening.'

But Mabel was already coming in the door, her cheeks rather red, her look excited.

'Oh, Ross — Jinny — Mr Comrie's just arrived at the shop with Mr Whyte and Mr Linden. They've got the cakes — just the six — the poor boy's been working all weekend on them but they're beautiful! Oh, you must see them.'

'We're on our way,' Ross said shortly. 'Jinny here can't wait.'

'Nor can you!' she answered spiritedly, rather wondering at his manner. Usually so easy-going, he seemed to still be in a bad temper in spite of his apology. 'Aren't you the one who was praising up Viennese cakes to me?'

'Looks like I'll be praising up Viktor's, too. Come on, let's get to the shop and join the admirers.'

And admirers there were, standing around in the shop that was

not yet open, for not only was Mr Comrie looking down at the
large trays containing Viktor's cakes with the proud expression of a
new father, but Mr Whyte had something of the same look and
Mrs Arrow appeared astonished and her girls thrilled. As for Viktor
himself, and Jinny's eyes went to him at once, he was standing to
one side, wearing his jacket and flannels instead of his baker's whites,
and looking suitably self-deprecatory at all the excitement his cakes
were causing. At the sight of Jinny and Ross his smile changed,
broadened, and he took a step towards them.

'Miss Hendrie! Mr MacBain! Look, see my cakes – I have them
ready!'

'*Wunderlich!*' Ross commented with a grin, bending to see the
cakes, while Jinny, flushing, joined him, her eyes widening at the
works of art, as she judged the cakes on the trays to be.

There were six, as Mabel had reported. Two large chocolate cakes,
covered in the smoothest icing ever seen and carrying the magic
name of Sacher written in darker chocolate. Then two towering
layer cakes iced with a toffee-coloured glaze and decorated with
triangular sponge slices. And finally, two white iced cakes, on which
were beautifully made flowers of sugar paste and lines and shapes in
marzipan. Only six, yes, but with the general effect of so much
more, like a display for a grand buffet, perhaps, in some elegant
house or special hotel, something quite out of the ordinary. Certainly,
nothing like them had been seen before in Comrie's Bakery.

For a few moments no one spoke, then Mrs Arrow, clearing her
throat, looked across at Viktor.

'Tell me, Mr Linden, how did you make cakes like these in just
a weekend?'

'It is my job, Mrs Arrow.' He shrugged a little. 'On Friday and
Saturday, there was the baking. On Sunday, the icing. It was no
trouble to me.'

'Of course, I'd already organized the ingredients you wanted,' Mr
Comrie put in. 'But you did a grand job, Viktor – I think we'll all
agree on that?'

After an immediate chorus of approval Viktor spoke again,
saying that he would like to tell everyone a little about the cakes.
That the *Sachertorte* had been invented by a famous chef named
Sacher back in 1832 for Chancellor Metternich, and was the
favourite cake of Vienna. That the cake with the triangles was
the *Dobertorte* from the Hungarian border, and the white-iced cake
an almond sponge his own creation. He always liked to – what

was the word – improvise from time to time, but never with the most famous cakes, of course. He would never presume to do that.

After he'd finished speaking another silence fell until Mr Whyte, exchanging looks with Mr Comrie, said that now, of course, there were decisions to be made.

'True,' Mrs Arrow agreed. 'And I've a shop to open and the café to be made ready.' She clapped her hands. 'Girls, away you go, then!'

'Meantime, what's happening to these splendid cakes, then?' asked Ross. 'If they're to be sold here by the slice, what charge is to be made?'

'That's to be discussed,' Mr Comrie said firmly. 'Viktor, will you and Mr Whyte put the trays into the room at the back and we'll adjourn there. Mrs Arrow, we'll need you as well. Get the girls to open up this morning, eh?'

'Certainly, Mr Comrie.'

As the girls hurried to their tasks everyone else moved to the back room, Viktor and Arthur Whyte carefully bearing away the trays of precious cakes so they were out of sight of any arriving customers for the time being.

Thirteen

Their eyes moving from those cakes to Mr Comrie standing before them, everyone waited for him to speak. Viktor, close to his uncle, seemed unworried, but Jinny – who wasn't even sure she should be there – could tell that Mr Whyte and Mrs Arrow were on pins wondering what would be decided and probably already working out what they would say if they disagreed with Mr Comrie.

'Well, now,' he began, smiling round at the watchers, 'time to fix a price for Viktor's delectable cakes. I think we've decided, haven't we, to have slices from three in the café and three in the shop here?'

'That's what we decided,' Arthur Whyte agreed.

'Without me, actually,' Ross put in, smiling as though he wasn't annoyed, which he was. 'Of course I'm quite happy about it, provided the price is right.'

'That goes without saying, Ross,' said Mr Comrie smoothly, 'and I think we have discussed this in general terms already, haven't we?'

Ross shrugged. 'Perhaps so. What are the views on prices then?

We'll have to remember that the ingredients for these cakes are a good deal more expensive than for our usual cakes.'

'Exactly so.' Mr Comrie looked round again at his staff. 'That's why I'm suggesting a price of sixpence per slice in the shop and ninepence in the café.'

Silence fell. While Arthur Whyte and Mrs Arrow exchanged looks, Ross stared straight ahead, Jinny gazed at Viktor and Viktor gazed at his uncle.

'Sixpence and ninepence?' Arthur repeated at last.

'That's my suggestion.' Mr Comrie's smile was pleasant but his eyes were cold. 'You think they're too high?'

Arthur hesitated. 'They might be thought so,' he said at last.

'Compared with our usual prices,' added Mrs Arrow.

'As Ross has just said, the ingredients will be more expensive and we'll have to take account of that.' Mr Comrie's smile was fading. 'We haven't done any costings yet but I think the prices I've suggested will have to be charged anyway. Slices are not usually sold in the shop but are in the café. How much are we charging for a slice of cake there, Mrs Arrow?'

'Threepence!' she cried, as if to say, *You see my point?*

'Yes, well, that may be so, but I am certain that customers will see the difference between the Viennese cakes and our usual Madeira and so on. They will expect to pay more and, don't forget, there are still people with money about who come into Comrie's.'

Mr Comrie's face was rather red and his eyes were still cold.

'That being the case, perhaps you'd care to tell me, Arthur, what price you would like to see put on my nephew's cake slices?'

'Off the top of my head, Mr Comrie, no disrespect, you understand, but I'd say fourpence in the shop and fivepence in the café. If this doesn't take into account the difference in ingredients, I'd suggest that if the cakes become popular we'll sell enough to cover the difference.'

'Fourpence in the shop, fivepence in the café?' Mr Comrie's eyes were now flashing disapproval. 'Well, I don't know what you make of those prices, Ross, but I say they do not reflect my nephew's artistry and I'm not going to accept them. Mrs Arrow, please begin selling the cakes at the prices I've recommended and report back to me this afternoon. Ross and Arthur, I'll see you in my office, right?'

'Certainly, Mr Comrie,' they both chimed, while Mrs Arrow hurried away, saying, with an anxious face, that she'd send her girls to fetch the cakes, while Viktor and Jinny stood together uncertainly.

'Uncle, what about me?' asked Viktor. 'Shall I return to the bakery?'

'Take the rest of the day off,' his uncle ordered, wiping his brow. 'We owe you time, don't we? You worked the entire weekend.'

'That's kind of you, Uncle.'

As everyone else went, he and Jinny were left staring at each other, he looking so lost that her heart went out to him. Suddenly it seemed that everything had changed for him. One minute he was being praised to the skies, the next people in this strange country were squabbling over how much his beautiful cakes should cost. Probably that would never have happened in Vienna, and it had made him aware that he was far from home. Though he might have his uncle to turn to, being with him in Edinburgh was obviously not the same as being with his family and all that he knew.

Impulsively, she pressed his hand.

'Try not to worry about it, Viktor – the pricing, I mean. Everyone loves your cakes and they're sure to be very popular. This will all be forgotten in a day or two, you'll see.'

At her words, his face lit up and he pressed the hand she had put in his with so much warmth she could hardly pull it away. But of course, she had to go. Shouldn't be still downstairs, anyway.

'Jinny, thank you,' he murmured as she moved away from him 'You are so kind. I appreciate it very much.'

'I have to go back to Accounts, Viktor. And you must have a lovely day off.'

'No – wait – could not you be free too? Spend time with me?'

Oh, heavens, what was he saying? She felt as if she was almost physically spinning with joy, but there was no way she could take an afternoon off, just like that. No way at all.

'It's not possible. I'd love to but I can't. I'm so sorry!'

'Lunch, then?' His blue eyes were shining. 'We could have lunch? *Mittagessen?* I could meet you outside the shop?'

Lunch? She was still spinning. 'You could, yes, that would be grand. Thank you.'

'What time?'

'Twelve o'clock? That's when I go to lunch.'

'Till twelve o'clock,' he said solemnly, and their eyes met, holding them as though by physical bonds. 'I will meet you then.'

At last, as he formally bowed, she managed to leave him, hurrying from the back room through the café to the stairs, then upwards to Accounts where there was no Ross and no Mabel. Thank God for that. Long may they stay out of the office, or at least until twelve o'clock. For no one must see her looking as she did – so happy.

Fourteen

Of course, they did see her. First, Mabel, returning from the post office where she'd been buying stamps for the office. Next, Ross and Arthur Whyte, released from Mr Comrie's office, though Mr Whyte, his face grim, gave just the briefest nod as he passed by, and Mabel was only interested in getting back to her typewriter now that the meeting was over. Only Ross actually looked at Jinny before he sat down at his desk, but then he only laughed and held up his hands.

'Sixpence it is, for the shop, Jinny! And ninepence for the café. All that time waffling and we might just as well have said yes in the first place.'

'Did you say yes at all?'

He shrugged. 'For the try out, I did, but we're going to work out how much we'll lose on making the new cakes, and if they don't sell well . . .' He shook his head. 'It'll be sorry, Viktor. Thank you and goodbye.'

'Goodbye? He's going to be working here anyway.'

'Oh, yes, of course.' Ross gave Jinny a thoughtful look, but made no further comment, and both worked quietly until Jinny rose and said she'd be going for her lunch.

'Couldn't just find me our flour account before you go, could you? I'm planning to compare it with one from that new firm, Rowley's.'

'Do you need it now? I'm meeting . . . my sister. I have to go.'

'Your sister? The one in the hat shop?'

'Yes, May. Could I get the account for you later?'

'No, no, I'm just being lazy.' Ross smiled. 'Have a nice lunch, then. Take a bit longer if you like – you don't often meet May.'

For a long moment Jinny stared ahead, not looking at him. Then she met his eyes. 'All right, Ross, you win. I'm not meeting May, I'm meeting Viktor. I don't know why I had to lie about it.'

'Didn't want to be teased, perhaps?' Ross was looking rueful. 'And now I've teased you, anyway. I'm sorry, Jinny. Away to see Viktor, then, and cheer him up, but not too much.'

'What do you mean?'

'Well, he's not here for ever, that's all.'

'Think I don't know that?'

'All I'm saying is remember it.'

'I'll see you at one o'clock, as usual.'

'Fine.'

As she turned, to speed down to the street, Jinny's eyes were stormy and her colour high, but by the time she'd found Viktor waiting on the pavement a little way from the shop, Ross's words had already faded from her mind.

'Viktor!'

He had been looking down Princes Street over the gardens towards the castle, his shoulders back, his head erect, every inch '*Der Leutnant*', as Ross had called him. As soon as he heard Jinny's call, however, he spun round and went to her, taking her hands and looking down into her face, his own face brightening as he said her name.

'Jinny!'

'I hope I'm not late?'

'No, no.' He pushed back his hat from his fair hair and smiled a little. 'So good to see you, after my morning that was so . . . I must say *schrecklich*. No word in English will do.'

'*Schrecklich?* Does it mean awful? Terrible?' Jinny searched his face. 'Viktor, it wasn't so bad. I told you, everyone liked your cakes, it was only the price they couldn't agree on.'

'My cakes are not worth your six pennies a slice?' He grasped her hand. 'Come, let us forget it. Where may I take you for lunch?'

Careful of cost and not knowing how Viktor was placed for money, Jinny took him to a small café in the West End where they could have something light that would not be expensive. Of course, it was crowded, but they were lucky, able to spot a table as two city workers rose to leave, and settled themselves down at once, ready to talk.

Fifteen

'Such a beautiful colour,' Viktor remarked as Jinny removed her winter coat, revealing her raspberry-coloured jumper. 'May I say it suits you?'

'I'm glad you like it.'

She was surprised to find herself feeling quite at ease. Perhaps because Viktor had shown a vulnerable side she hadn't thought he had, or perhaps because she might indeed be the one to cheer him, as Ross had suggested. 'Not too much,' he had added, but she dismissed those words from her mind.

The waitress brought a menu and they chose mushroom soup, followed by sausages and mash for Viktor and a toasted sandwich for Jinny.

'What are sausages in German?' she asked. 'I'm sorry to say I never did German at school, but maybe the Austrian language is different anyway, is it?'

'It's a version of standard German, one that Germans understand, as we understand theirs. Just as you understand American and English English.'

'But did you know that Scots itself is a proper language?' Jinny smiled. 'I just speak with a Scottish accent. You do understand me, don't you?'

'Of course! Don't forget, I'm used to my mother's.'

'But now she'll speak fluent German. I don't speak one word.'

'And your first word will be the German for sausages?'

They laughed, all traces of stress vanishing from Viktor's face, making him look suddenly so young, Jinny felt she could visualize him now, not so much as a lieutenant, but a schoolboy. Handsome, of course, he must always have been handsome.

'*Wurst*,' he whispered, leaning across the table. 'That is your first word, but if you would like me to, I can teach you others.'

'I'd like it very much, Viktor. But first you must tell me about your Vienna. I know it's lovely.'

Viktor looked away. 'Not only lovely, it's splendid. Though maybe not quite as splendid as it was.'

'Why's that?'

He shrugged. 'Well, because of what we've lost. We had an empire, we were an imperial capital. Our emperor, Franz Josef, looked as if he would last for ever. But he died during the war and the empire died with him. Our country was defeated, and Vienna was defeated, too.'

'But it's still lovely? Still splendid?'

'Yes, well, it rebuilt itself and became beautiful again. Still had its palaces and boulevards, you know, and of course restaurants and coffee houses. But – I do not know how to put it – the people know things have changed.' Viktor sighed. 'Enough of that – here comes our soup!'

Over the soup, which Jinny was relieved to find was very good, he seemed to relax, grow lyrical almost, as he began to talk of the coffee houses back home, describing them simply as the best in the world.

'Jinny, I cannot tell you all that they mean to us in Vienna. For they are not just cafés, you understand, but places to gather and meet friends, to read the paper or talk all day, if you like – and never be asked to move on.'

'And they have wonderful cakes like yours?'

'Of course!' Viktor's eyes glowed. 'From the shops like my father's, where I learned my baking. How I wish I could show them to you!'

Their looks met and lingered, but the moment passed as the waitress removed their soup bowls and served their next course.

'*Wurst!* My favourite!' Viktor exclaimed when she had left them. 'You know, we have as many varieties of sausage at home as we have coffee.'

'Oh, dear! Do hope our sausages will be all right for you, then.'

'They are excellent, I assure you.'

'And what about our coffee?'

He gave a wary smile. 'Well, there I must confess, I am missing home.'

'I did wonder if you might be homesick.'

'Because of how I was today?' He shook his head. 'That was only because of what was said about the price of my cakes.'

'Viktor, I explained—'

'I know, I know, but let's not discuss it. Let us just enjoy being here, together.'

Lulled for a moment by the beauty of the idea, Jinny dreamily finished her cheese roll and was about to let Viktor order some of the local coffee he evidently didn't enjoy when some inner warning made her look at the café clock.

'Oh, no, look at the time! I have to be back by one and it's nearly that now!'

'Surely you can take a little longer?'

'Ross said I could, but I told him I'd be back as usual, I don't know why. Maybe I didn't want him to think I was using you to take extra time.'

'Would he have thought that?'

'Probably not. I suppose I was just cross with him and didn't want any favours.' Putting on her coat with Viktor's polite help, Jinny shook her head. 'Come on, let's go.'

The coffee cancelled, the bill paid, they left the café and hurried back towards Comrie's, but before they reached it Viktor slowed down and touched Jinny's arm.

'I am sure, you know, you need not worry,' he said gently. 'Ross will not be cross if you are late when he told you to take more time.'

'Oh, I know, it's just that – like I said – he upset me, so I wanted to make sure he'd no reason to complain.' Jinny laughed apologetically. 'I'm sure I'm not making sense to you – sorry.'

'Jinny, I'm sure you will always make sense.' Viktor's tone was light but his eyes were serious. 'And I'm sure, too, that you and Ross usually get on very well. Am I right?'

'Yes, it's true. In fact, I'm feeling sorry now that I've made such a fuss.' She put her hand on his. 'Viktor, I'm so sorry I have to go. It's been so lovely.'

'Lovely for me, too.' He held the hand she had given him. 'It has made me feel better – to be with you.'

'So, what are you going to do now, with your free afternoon?'

'I don't know. Sightseeing, maybe, though the weather is not good.'

'You must be so tired after all you did yesterday – why don't you just have a rest?

'Rest? I never rest.' He laughed. 'But I almost had help yesterday, you know.'

'Help? With your baking?'

'With the decoration. Senga asked if I'd like her to come in.'

'Senga!' Jinny's dark eyes flashed. 'What was she thinking of?'

'Well, she said she'd a lot to learn, and if she could work with me it would be a great help to her.'

'I'll bet! Viktor, you didn't let her come, did you?'

'No, no, I never want anyone around when I have work to do. Especially not someone who needs training.'

'So, you said no. Quite right, too.'

Watching her face with its obvious look of relief, Viktor made no comment, but as he released her hand he fixed her with an intense gaze.

'Jinny, we are wasting time. Tell me when I may see you again, before you vanish for the afternoon.'

'You mean, see me . . . not at work?'

'Of course. Not at work. When will it be?'

'Depends what would be best.' Her heart was beating fast. 'What about Sunday?'

'Sunday? That's too far away. Why not one evening? We could go to the theatre. I read in the paper that there is an Agatha Christie play on at the Duchess theatre.' Viktor's face was animated. 'It's called *Black Coffee*. They said it was very good.'

The Duchess Theatre, where her father worked? Oh, no, she'd have to tell him she wanted to go to the theatre with Viktor, and what in heaven's name would he say? What would Viktor say if she told him she couldn't risk it? But of course, she must risk it. If she wanted to see Viktor regularly she would have to tell her father soon anyway.

'I know the Duchess,' she said levelly. 'My dad works there – he manages the scenery and effects.'

'Why, that is wonderful!' Viktor cried. 'You will know all there is to know about the theatre! Shall we say we'll go, then?'

'Yes, why not? I'll book the tickets. No, don't say anything, it will be easier for me. Shall we try for Thursday? We can arrange when to meet later.'

'Fine. Excellent. I'll leave it to you, then, but I wish to pay.'

She put her finger over his lips and shook her head. For a long moment they gazed into each other's eyes, until finally she broke away and ran for Comrie's, looking back once to wave and to catch Viktor smile.

She couldn't have put it clearly into words how she felt when she reached Accounts and met Ross's interested gaze. Happy? Over the moon? Oh, yes, but also apprehensive, now that she'd realized what it would be like telling her father about Viktor. If he had thought Allan unsuitable what would he think of a foreigner, one whose nation had been his enemy?

'Had a good lunch?' she heard Ross ask, and from somewhere produced a radiant smile.

'Lovely. Sorry I'm late, though. And that I was – you know – a wee bit snappy.'

'No need to apologise. I was to blame.' Ross was putting on his coat and smiling. 'But there's good news for Viktor – did they tell you as you came through the shop?'

'No, I didn't stop. What good news?'

'All his slices have sold like hot cakes – pardon the pun – and several orders have been taken for the full-size versions. No need to worry about the price now – we're on to a winner.'

Sixteen

When their father had returned to his work at the theatre that evening, Jinny told her sisters of her fears. Of how she'd had lunch with Viktor and enjoyed being with him. Of how they wanted to see each other again and Viktor had suggested the theatre. Of how they'd agreed on the Duchess, though it was the last place Jinny would have chosen, and were planning to go on Thursday. But how was she going to tell Dad?

'Oh, for heaven's sake, you're not going to let Dad throw another tantrum, are you?' cried Vi. 'It's been bad enough with May here, still not allowed to mention Allan's name – such a piece of nonsense!'

'You tell me how to stop him throwing a tantrum then! If May couldn't do it, what chance have I?'

'You must be firm. We must all be firm. Tell him straight out that we're grown up now, not children any more, and we've a right to our own lives.'

'The thing is, we live here,' said May. 'It's Dad who pays the rent; he could just show us the door.'

'We pay our way!' Vi retorted. 'We don't live here for nothing, so it's our home as well as his. He wouldn't want us to go, anyway.'

'So, I tell him about Viktor and wait for the explosion?' asked Jinny. 'It's a shame, because Viktor seemed quite interested that Dad worked at the Duchess. I think he likes the theatre, he really wants to go with me, and if Dad had been OK about it he might have given us complimentary tickets.'

'I shouldn't ask him for any tickets if I were you,' said Vi with a mock shudder. 'That'd be adding insult to injury in his eyes. Giving free tickets to a man taking his daughter out – a foreigner at that!'

'Oh, don't!' Jinny wailed. 'I know exactly what'll happen. He'll say Viktor's from an enemy country, there's no future in it and that I'll be sure to get hurt. You wait, see if I'm right.'

'Suppose you might get hurt, but that's not the point, you should be free to do that. Just like May should be able to see Allan and talk about him if she likes.'

'True,' May agreed. 'But Allan has decided to have it out with Dad, anyway. He says we can't go on the way we are, and that's that.'

'That's good, but what will you do if Dad won't climb down?'

'We'll cross that bridge when we come to it. But Jinny, I think you should speak to Dad tonight as soon as he comes back. Tell him he needn't worry about you and Viktor, because you know the situation and you can cope with it.'

'Glad you've said all that,' said Vi. 'Because I think I hear Dad now, coming up the stair.'

'Oh, no, is it that time already?' cried Jinny, rising and looking as if ready to run. Even if she'd had any such thought, however, it would have been too late, for Josh, rosy with the cold, was already on his way in.

'Hello, girls!' he called, taking off his cap and coat and rubbing his hands. 'Got the fire made up? It's enough to freeze your hair off outside!'

In a good mood, wasn't he? That was because May hadn't been out for a day or two. The sisters all knew, without needing to put it into words, that their father's moods were a barometer registering May's evenings out, for when she was with Allan gloomy weather could be forecast, and when she stayed at home there was sunshine. As she was clearly at home that evening Josh, as he approached the fire, was the mellow, good-natured father his family loved, which didn't make it any easier for Jinny to know that she must soon bring this pleasant situation to an end.

'Like some tea, Dad?' asked Vi, leaping up from her chair.

'Aye, when have you known me to say no to tea? Won't have anything to eat, though, as I've had sandwiches with the lads. Might manage a biscuit.'

'The digestives are in the coronation tin,' May said, rising to join Vi, not only to help with the tea but to look meaningfully at Jinny, who was too concerned with gazing at her father to take their unspoken hint.

'How d'you like the play this week, Dad?' she asked with an attempt at casualness. '*Black Coffee* by Agatha Christie. I've heard it's good.'

'Aye, she can turn a fine plot.'

'As a matter of fact, I'm thinking of going to see it.'

'You are?' Josh sat up in his chair. 'Jinny, that's grand. You lassies haven't been to the theatre since I don't know when. It's all the pictures with you, eh?'

'I like a play sometimes, especially if it's a thriller.'

'What night are you going? I can get you some tickets.'

Instantly, Jinny's face flamed.

'Thursday's the night, but the thing is, Dad, I'm going with someone from work. He's – well, he's the new chap from Austria. I think I told you about him. He's Mr Comrie's nephew, just here for a short time, but he said he'd like to go to the theatre and we settled on *Black Coffee*. It's not new but it's had good reviews – should be worth seeing.'

All the time she'd been rattling on she'd seen her father's face change as he took in what she was saying, and the register of his barometer dropped from 'Set Fair' to 'Storm'. Now, as her sisters stood, watching, he held up his hand.

'Jinny, that'll do. I want to get it straight, what you're saying.'

'Don't be cross, Dad. There's nothing to be upset about.'

'When you're telling me you want to go out with a foreigner? Don't be cross, you say. It's what you girls always say, but I'm never cross, just worried, that's all. Worried you're storing up trouble for yourself. How can I stand by and let you go out with a fellow who's only a ship passing in the night? A German, or as good as, from a country that caused a war where millions died—'

'He isn't a German, Dad, and he'd nothing to do with the war, it's not fair to say that!' Jinny's eyes were shining with feeling, her colour still high, yet she was trying to appear reasonable, trying to make her case. 'He's just a cake maker, here for a few months, and he's nice, he's friendly – why shouldn't we go to the theatre together? You talk as if he's my young man!'

'That's how things start,' Josh said doggedly. 'You go out with a fellow, he wants to see you again, and before you know it you're in love and all set to get your heart broken. I don't want that for you, Jinny!'

'But you don't want May to see Allan either,' Vi pointed out, as she brought across a tray of tea things. 'She's not going to get her heart broken with him, but you still don't want her to see him.'

'We're talking about Jinny,' Josh snapped. 'What she wants to do is risky and she knows it. Girls don't go out with men when they know there's no future in it, and there's no future in this except heartache. Why should I say I'm happy about it when I'm not?'

'I'm just going to the theatre with Viktor,' Jinny said in a low voice. 'That may be the end of it.' But she knew her heart didn't believe her, and neither did Josh.

'The thing is you don't want it to be,' Josh said, fixing her with his dark eyes so like her own. 'Look me in the face and tell me that's no' true.'

A silence fell as her family waited, and Jinny, lowering her own gaze, knew what she should say, knew what she wanted to say, opened her mouth to say it – and then closed it again. She couldn't say it.

'There you are,' Josh said with grim satisfaction. 'Pour the tea, Vi. I think I've made my point.'

'I'm still going to the theatre with Viktor,' Jinny said, clearing her throat. 'He wants to pay for us, anyway, so you needn't worry about complimentary tickets.'

'I wasn't going to.' Josh reached forward and took a biscuit from the plate May had set down. 'Let's consider this subject closed. For the time being.'

Later, at bedtime, Jinny's sisters tried to console her, but she said she didn't need consoling. She'd just go her own way as May had done and let Dad say what he liked. She knew the situation, knew what it would mean if she and Viktor did become close and he had to leave her, and would be prepared. It was her heart that was involved, after all – no one else need worry.

'Oh, Jinny,' May sighed. 'Maybe Dad's right. It might be wiser not to see him, eh?'

'Who wants to be wise? Anyway Viktor might not want to see me again after this next time, anyway.'

Somehow, no one thought that likely.

Seventeen

The clash with her father had certainly spoiled Jenny's pleasure in looking forward to her theatre visit with Viktor. Perhaps she'd had her misgivings as soon as he'd suggested the Duchess, for it meant she'd had to mention it to her father, and the thought of Josh's likely views on her meeting with Viktor had been enough to cast a cloud over her excitement. The reality of hearing his actual views, however, had been even worse than she'd expected, and though she'd put on a good act when Viktor came over from the bakery to check their arrangements, she wasn't sure she could keep it going when they met for the play.

'All well?' Viktor had asked, grateful for finding her alone in the office. 'You have the tickets?'

'Oh, yes, I was lucky. I got a couple of stalls – all they had left.'

At least, as he stood close, she could take pleasure in remarking again on his fine features, his vivid blue eyes, his attention that was all on her, and feel that Dad couldn't spoil any of this, at least. Or, could he? He'd reminded her, as if she needed it, that these looks, this attention, would not always be close, for one day Viktor would have to go away.

'Now, you know the arrangement,' Viktor was saying softly. 'I'm going to pay for the tickets. Perhaps you could let me have them?'

'I'd like it to be my treat, Viktor. No arguments.'

'Jinny, it is not possible that you should treat me. I have an allowance from home and I have a salary here – it is best that I should pay. Come on, now!'

'This time, I'd like to pay.'

'There will be another time?' he asked quickly.

'If you'd like it.'

He smiled. 'I think you know the answer to that. Very well, then. I give in, for this time only. What time shall we meet on Thursday?'

'At seven o'clock? The play begins at half past.'

'Excellent.' He glanced at his watch. 'I'd better go before Ross finds me. I'm not supposed to be here.' His blue gaze held hers and he seemed to want to say more, but finally turned to the door.

'Till Thursday, then?'

'Till Thursday.'

For some time after he'd left, she sat at her desk staring into space. Only when Ross came in noisily, bringing with him a rush of cold air and wearing a heavy coat and hat brushed with rain, did she smile and put down her pen, as though she'd just been interrupted from hard work. She was acting a part again, of course; it seemed to be becoming a habit.

When she saw Viktor waiting for her outside the theatre, however, there was no need to act any part, for the great rush of feeling that consumed her then was genuine and natural, and though she hadn't experienced it before she knew it for what it was. As she stood looking at him before he looked at her, studying his straight shoulders, his height, his elegance in his dark coat and his hat set at an angle over his blond hair, all thoughts of her father's disapproval melted from her mind and she was filled with elation that this man was really waiting for her, that he really wanted to be with her. He might in fact return what she now recognized in herself for him, though she still didn't put that into words.

'Viktor?'

At the sound of his name, he turned, his face lighting up, and at once he was with her, making a pathway like an arrow through the crowd around him, smiling down at her as he touched his hat and took her arm.

'Jinny, you're here! Wonderful!'

'As though I wouldn't be! I've been looking forward to it all day.' She held up her bag. 'And I've got the tickets – let's go find our seats.'

Everything seemed so magical. Joining others searching for their stalls, looking up at the people in the boxes, the circle and the edge of the 'gods', sensing the atmosphere that went with the anticipation of a live performance that was not found going to a cinema.

Why don't we go to the theatre more often? Jinny found herself wondering. And be interested in it, like Dad? But at the thought of her father working somewhere behind the scenes her mind reared away and she glanced quickly at Viktor as they took off their coats and settled into their seats. Don't let me think of Dad, she pleaded wordlessly. Don't let him spoil this for me.

'Very good seats,' Viktor commented. 'I think we should enjoy this.'

'I'm sure we will. But do you know about Agatha Christie in Vienna?'

'Know about Agatha Christie? Of course we do! My mother has all her books in English and I've read them, in English and German. Such good plots! But this, of course, is a play. I don't know it at all.'

'No, I don't. But it has Hercule Poirot in it, so it should be like the books.'

'Here is the programme – we must study the characters.' Viktor hesitated a moment, then put a wrapped package into Jinny's hands. 'First, you must have a chocolate.'

'You've brought chocolates? Oh, Viktor, that's so kind!' As she read the name on the box, Jinny's eyes widened. 'And these are very special – the best – but so expensive! You shouldn't have spent so much!'

'They are to celebrate something special, Jinny.' Viktor's smile was radiant. 'Our first evening together. It means so much. And also—' He paused. 'I expect you can guess what else might matter to me.'

She thought, but only for an instant. 'That the customers liked your cakes? Viktor, of course they did! I knew they'd be a success.'

'I could only hope, but now I am so happy.' He lowered his voice. 'For those two things.'

'Shall we open them now, before the play begins?' asked Jinny, feeling almost dazed by his apparent pleasure in being with her. 'I can't wait to taste them.'

They spent a happy few moments deciding which ones to try first before the lights dimmed, the safety curtain rose and there they were, transported into the house of a famous physicist shortly to meet his end by foul play, as Hercule Poirot would discover. The spell Agatha Christie could cast so well was beginning its work.

Eighteen

Absorbed as they were in following the plot, time passed quickly until suddenly it was the interval, the lights were coming on and people were stampeding for coffee, while Jinny and Viktor were blinking at each other and smiling.

'Enjoying it?' asked Jinny.

'I am; it's just the thing to relax with. But would you care to go for coffee?'

'Oh, it's such a scrum – let's just stay here and have another chocolate.'

They made their choices – caramel for Jinny and marzipan for Viktor. 'Of course, I am Viennese – we love marzipan,' he said, laughing.

'You are half Scottish, too,' Jinny remarked. 'Because of your mother.'

'That's true. Poor Mother.'

'Why do you say that?'

'Well, she will be missing me. I am an only child. "All she has", she sometimes says, though of course she has my father and they are very happy.'

'You're all alone? I've got two older sisters, May and Violet – we call her Vi. But my mother is dead.'

'Ah, I'm so sorry. That must have been a terrible loss for your family and your father.' Viktor's eyes had moved to the curtains drawn across the stage. 'Is he working here tonight? Behind the scenes somewhere? That must be strange for you, to think of him so close, yet not seen.'

Jinny was silent, bending her head away from Viktor, who, quick to sense a change in her, waited for a moment, hoping she would look at him.

When she did not, he took her hand. 'Is everything all right, Jinny?'

She wanted to say 'Oh, yes, of course' but, raising her dark eyes, said nothing.

'I don't want to pry,' he murmured, 'but I feel you are suddenly not happy. Please tell me if there is something troubling you – but only if you want to, that is understood.'

'I suppose I should tell you,' she said slowly. 'If – if we want to see each other again.'

'We do,' he said at once, and she felt his hand around hers – dry, firm and reassuring.

'Well, it's just that after Ma died, my dad came to depend on us – my sisters and me. We made him happy again, he said. But as we got older and, you know, wanted to go out with people, he got upset. He thought we shouldn't think of it, that home, that the four of us, must be enough. You can guess that there has been . . . trouble.'

'I can,' Viktor said strongly. 'I understand completely.

'I don't see how,' she said hopelessly. 'Men are always so free.'

'Jinny, I understand what you are telling me, because – because my mother is the same.'

Jinny's eyes on him had widened. 'Your mother is . . . like my father? I never would have imagined it.'

'Of course you wouldn't have, if you think all men are free. I've never been free since I grew up and wanted a life of my own. It's just because she loves me so much, of course, but whenever I wanted to go out with a girl – and there haven't been so many – my mother could not stand it. My father used to take my side, but she could never accept that there might be others in my life.'

'Yet she let you leave her to come here? That must have been very difficult.'

'It was my father's idea that I should come, and yes, it was difficult, but in the end, Mother gave in.' Viktor smiled. 'So, here I am. With you.'

'Seemingly, we're in the same boat,' Jinny said, trying to speak lightly. 'I can't get over it – that you should have my sort of problem.'

'Not when I'm here, Jinny. Here, I am free to ask you to go out with me.'

'You won't mind if you don't meet my dad? He doesn't want me to see you but I'm not going to give in to him.'

Jinny looked around at people returning to their seats – it was time for the second act of the play.

'But quick, before the bell goes, tell me: these girls you used to see back home . . . were any of them . . . are any of them . . . special to you?'

He laughed, delighted at her little show of jealousy. 'Not one, *liebchen*, not one!'

And then the bell did go; people hurried to take their seats, the lights went down, the curtains opened, and Jinny and Viktor held each other's hands tightly and sat as close as they could while still in two seats. Interested in the stage, of course, but so much more fascinated by each other.

After the play they stood in the frosty night air outside the theatre, buffeted by going home crowds, staying close.

'May I take you home?' Viktor asked. 'Do we catch a tram?'

'No, we can walk down from here to Lothian Road, then turn off for our flat in Fingal Street. You don't mind walking? It's a fine night.'

'I like walking.' Viktor took her arm. 'This cold air will do us good – reminds me a little of home, though it's much colder there, of course.'

'I expect you'll go skiing?'

'For holidays, yes. Many people enjoy skiing and skating.'

'Sometimes, in a hard winter, folk here like to skate, but I don't know anyone who's been skiing. No one can afford to go abroad.'

'I wish you could come with me some time.'

Jinny laughed. Another impossible wish, that was, on a par with visiting Viktor's father's cake shop in Vienna. Best just to think of what was wonderful here and now, which was walking arm in arm with Viktor, feeling him close and knowing he wanted to be with her.

They continued to walk, step for step, down the busy city road lined with people going home from cinemas, the theatre, pubs and late-night cafés, some looking highly respectable, others scuffling and shouting in hoarse voices Viktor couldn't understand.

'Neither can I,' Jinny told him. 'When they get to drinking the laddies aren't too clear – maybe just as well! But here's our turning. It's quiet here.'

Walking slowly, for their time together was running out, they walked past the shuttered shops and lighted upstairs windows of the quiet street, pausing at last outside Allan's shop to look up at the Hendries' flat.

'That's us,' said Jinny. 'As you can see, we're over a watchmaker's. The man who owns it is Allan Forth, our landlord and my sister May's admirer. In fact, I think they are in love.'

'And there has been trouble?' asked Viktor, turning to look down at her.

'Yes, with my dad. Allan's father was a very good friend of Dad's – you'd have thought Allan would be ideal, but no. Dad can't find a good word to say about him. He won't even let May mention his name. It makes us so angry.'

'It is, in fact, very sad. Your father is making himself very unhappy – he's really the one to suffer.'

'Yes, but he brings it on himself. Nothing we say can change him.'

'Just like my mother,' Viktor said heavily. 'This is all so familiar.'

By the light of the street lamp, Jinny studied his face, which had taken on a seriousness that contrasted with his earlier look of happy contentment. And there was, too, something in his eyes which seemed to show that in his thoughts he was far away from Fingal Street. Probably he was thinking of his mother, who had made him so unhappy when he'd wanted to see girls. So what would she make of him now, out with Jinny? Well, thank God she didn't know. As he'd said earlier, in Edinburgh, he was free, even if Jinny wasn't.

With a sudden movement he seemed to bring himself back to his surroundings and, gently taking Jinny's arm, moved her a little way down the street.

'Away from the lamp,' he whispered and kissed her swiftly and sweetly, releasing her so she could look into his face as he smoothed back her hair and then kissed her again. This time the kiss was long and passionate, but afterwards he stepped away, shaking his head.

'Jinny, what will you think of me? Kissing you like that the first time we've been out together? I really do apologise – please forgive me!'

'Viktor, there's nothing to forgive. I wanted you to kiss me. It was lovely.'

'But does your father come this way? How terrible it would be if he were to see us!'

'He won't be along yet, and what's so terrible about one kiss? Don't worry about it.' She drew him back into the lamp light. 'Viktor, I've had a grand evening. Thank you.'

'I should be thanking you – it was your treat.'

'You brought the chocolates!'

'Which reminds me—' He put the box into her hands. 'You must finish them. And now, I must say goodnight.'

'I wish you could have come in to meet my sisters. Maybe another time . . . when my father isn't due back.'

'Another time . . . all I can think of is when we can meet again. Jinny, when will it be?'

'Sunday? Sunday afternoon?'

'When? Where?'

'The Scott Monument, two o'clock?'

'Jinny, you are an angel. I'll see you then, if not before. I may be bringing my cakes in on Saturday. But now, I'd better let you go.'

'You know the way to your uncle's? From Princes Street, go to the Queensferry Road, cross over the Dean Bridge and Belgrave Crescent is on your left.'

They hesitated, longing to kiss again, but only waved as they separated, Jinny to go inside the flat, Viktor to walk away fast.

Pray God he doesn't meet my dad, thought Jinny, for Josh would be sure to guess who a tall stranger would be, leaving Fingal Street at this hour. Oh, well, if he saw him, he saw him. They wouldn't speak, that was for sure.

'Had a good time?' asked her sisters.

'Oh, I can't tell you!' Jinny cried. But she told them, all the same. Or, at least, as much as she wanted them to hear.

Nineteen

While Jinny was getting ready to meet Viktor on Sunday afternoon, and Vi was pulling on heavy shoes to go walking with friends, May was hovering around looking strangely anxious. As she had already told her sisters, today was the day, the time of the decision, when Allan 'had it out' with their father, telling him outright that they couldn't go on the way they were. No, Allan must be accepted, or . . . what? Well, that was the question.

'Supposing Dad just says no?' asked Vi, her head emerging from a heavy sweater. 'What's your bargaining counter?'

May sat down on Jinny's bed, her lovely face so troubled that Jinny gave her a sudden hug, at which May sniffed and looked as if she might cry.

'Allan says I must leave.'

'Leave?' Vi and Jinny cried in unison.

'Leave and go where?' asked Vi.

'Find somewhere to stay — a bedsitter, maybe — and then . . . get married.'

'Married?'

Her sisters stared at May, then at each other, and Vi gave a short laugh.

'Why are we so surprised? I'm sure getting wed is what Allan wants anyway.'

'But I don't,' May answered quickly. 'I mean, not yet. I need time to save up for the wedding — I want that to be paid for by me, not Allan.'

'Well, just keep the idea of leaving home as a threat,' Vi advised. 'You might find it works. Now, I've got to go.'

'Me, too,' said Jinny, putting on her outdoor coat. 'Oh, May, I'll be thinking of you.'

'Even when you're with your Viktor?' May managed a smile. 'Maybe, if Dad listens to Allan, he might be easier on you, Jinny.'

'I'm not counting on it. He's not been speaking much to me lately.'

Vi, who had left them, came back to put her head round the door. 'If you want Dad to listen to anybody you'll have to wake him up first. He's fallen asleep by the fire. Just thought I'd warn you.'

As soon as Jinny had left, hurrying with breathless anticipation to meet Viktor, and Vi was on her way to walk up Calton Hill, Allan, very pale and stern, arrived at the flat's outer door.

'Is he in?' he asked May, who had flown down to let him in.

'He's asleep over the Sunday paper.'

'I'll have to wake him up, then.'

'No, let me.'

Like two conspirators, they were breathing hard as they faced each other, their eyes fearful.

'Come on,' May whispered. 'Let's get it over with.'

A great Sunday silence seemed to hover over the living room as they approached Josh, asleep in his chair, his paper on the floor beside him and no sound coming from him except a slight whistle as he breathed in and out.

'So damned peaceful,' Allan muttered. 'You wouldn't think he could cause so much trouble.'

'Ssh!' said May as she bent to shake her father gently by the arm. 'Dad, wake up! Wake up, there's someone to see you.'

A strangled noise came from his throat and he stirred in his chair. Then his eyes opened. Dark, unknowing eyes stared into May's face, then recognition came.

'May? What's – what's wrong?'

'Dad, it's Allan. He's come to see you.'

With a cry, Josh sat up straight, his colour deepening to an angry red, his gaze going to Allan standing before him as May moved away.

'Allan Forth? What the hell is he doing here? I thought I said he wasn't to enter this house, my home!'

'Don't speak about him like that!' May cried. 'This is my home, too, and I invited him. We want to talk to you and you must listen.'

'I'll be damned if I'll listen to him!'

Rising to his feet, Josh looked down on Allan, who did not have his height but who was standing his ground, not looking away. As Josh stared at him with flashing eyes, Allan reached across and took May's hand.

'Mr Hendrie, do you want to lose your daughter?' he asked quietly.

'What do you mean, lose her? May will never leave me.'

'She will, if you don't accept me. We want to marry – not now, in the future – but if you won't give us your blessing, and continue to stop May even mentioning my name and forbid me in this house, which I actually own, May will leave you and we'll be wed. Do you want that to happen?'

Josh's flush had died away, leaving him looking white and suddenly much older. For a long moment he held Allan's gaze, then turned to May.

'May, this isn't true, is it? You'd never leave me like that? Leave the family? I can't believe it. I won't believe it!'

'Dad, have you ever thought what would have happened if Ma's father had refused to let her marry you? Wouldn't you have wanted her to come to you?' May's usually calm face was showing a passionate feeling that Josh did not recognize, that was surprising even to Allan.

'Wouldn't you?' she cried, moving closer to her father. 'But you were lucky – Granddad liked you, they were happy for you to marry Ma. All we're asking is that you'll do the same for us.'

'Mr Hendrie, you liked my father,' Allan said urgently. 'And I know you liked me – until I fell in love with May. You thought I'd take her away from you, but that's not true. If you'll accept me she'll still be a part of the family, and I'll be a part, too. Isn't that the way the world works? For God's sake, Mr Hendrie, let us be happy. Let yourself be happy. Please, give us a chance!'

A silence fell and deepened. Josh was standing like stone, his eyes on the floor, his hand sweeping his brow as the two young people watched, their hands clasped and hearts beating fast, and waited.

Finally, Josh sank back into his chair. 'I don't know,' he began. 'I don't know . . . if I can.'

'Can be happy?' asked May.

'Can . . . do what you want. It's too much – to lose you, May. I lost your mother, but I thought I had my girls.'

'You have, you have!' May said, her voice trembling. 'It's like Allan says, it's the way of the world. People grow up and marry, but they don't have to go away. The family grows bigger, that's all.'

'I'd have another father,' Allan murmured. 'You'd have a son. I promise I'd be a good one.'

'Oh, God, I don't know . . .' Josh shook his head. 'It's true, I did like your dad, Allan, and I did like you, but to be happy about you and my May . . . I haven't been able to face it. I still don't know if I can.'

'We won't be getting married for at least a year, Dad,' May told him. 'Everything will just go on as usual, till you get used to it.'

'Aye, well, all I can say is we'll have to see how things go. I'm no' promising I'll be happy. Don't ask that.'

'But you'll let Allan come here? You'll let me mention his name?'

Josh, struggling, got the words out. 'If it's what you want.'

May and Allan exchanged looks. There was no doubt that Josh wasn't happy – his tone could only be called grudging – yet it was more than they'd hoped for; it was truly a breakthrough. As Josh sank into his chair and asked if they'd have a cup of tea, it was all they could do not to embrace in front of him, but they were sensible, and knew that what they had was fragile and must be carefully handled. There would be time, later, to celebrate.

It was only when May was handing tea and cutting the sponge cake she often made on Sundays that she ventured, very cautiously, to mention Jinny.

'Dad, do you mind if I say . . . about Jinny—'

'What about her?'

'Well, she says you haven't been talking to her lately. I know you're not happy about the Austrian chap she's seeing, but couldn't you, you know, discuss it with her and try to understand?'

Josh set down his cup and fixed May with a dark, brooding stare. 'Try to understand? I understand, all right. She's just storing up trouble for herself, getting involved with a foreigner who's already said he's no' staying here. Where's the future in that?'

'Maybe she's not thinking of the future,' Allan suggested. 'Maybe she's just enjoying being with someone different. It's not often a girl here meets a guy from Vienna.'

'And when he goes home, she's quite happy then? When he says goodbye, it's been nice knowing you?' Josh gave a hard laugh. 'You've only to look at her, sitting around, all starry-eyed, to know she'll never be able to do that. She's going to be very unhappy, I promise you.'

'Well, maybe we should just try to support her,' May said desperately. 'People can't help falling in love, can they?'

'And maybe this Viennese fellow will want to stay here, anyway,' said Allan. 'Isn't his mother Scottish? She obviously decided to follow her heart and moved to her husband's country.'

'Women often follow their men,' Josh declared. 'Doesn't happen often the other way round. No, he'll away home and Jinny will be left to pick up the pieces. There'll be nothing we can do.'

'Except talk to her,' said May. 'Say you will, Dad.'

'All right, all right, I'll talk to her.' Josh took another slice of cake. 'As though it'll do any good.'

Walking round the battlements of Edinburgh Castle with Viktor, Jinny would have agreed with Josh that talking would not change how she felt. In some ways, being with Viktor had widened her horizons. In other ways, her universe had definitely shrunk to contain just one man and that was Viktor. No amount of talking could ever change that.

Twenty

There were very few places to have tea on an Edinburgh Sunday, but Jinny and Viktor found a little café in Rose Street that was open and gratefully squeezed in to escape the dark and cold.

'None of your grand cakes here,' Jinny whispered to Viktor, 'but the scones look all right.'

'And Scottish scones are famous,' Viktor answered as a waitress brought a menu. 'Shall I order, then?'

'You could have toasted teacakes if you'd rather. Teacakes are another thing we're good at.'

But they settled for tea and scones and, until they came, took pleasure in studying each other's faces and talking about the castle, the first of the Edinburgh 'sights' on Jinny's list for Viktor to see.

'If only the days weren't so short at this time of year,' she sighed. 'And on Sundays there's nowhere to go in the evening.'

'At least the shop windows look wonderful, dressed for Christmas, even if the shops aren't actually open. Which reminds me . . .' Viktor paused. 'About Christmas – I meant to tell you earlier . . .'

Again, he halted, watching the waitress set down their tea things and a plate of fruit scones, after which they busied themselves spreading the scones with generous amounts of butter.

'Tell me what?' asked Jinny, pouring the tea.

'That I'll be going home for it. Christmas, that is.'

She set down the teapot, her dark eyes wide. 'Going home for Christmas? Why, you've only just come!'

'I know, and I had no plans to go back. It was arranged that my parents would come over and we'd have a Scottish Christmas and New Year – my mother's idea. My father was in a state about leaving his business with his assistants. But now it seems my mother's health has not been good and she doesn't want to make the trip, so I said I'd go home.' Viktor's eyes on Jinny were appealing. 'I'll only be away for the week – it's not long.'

'Oh, well, if your mother's not well of course you'll have to go.' Jinny ate a piece of her scone, keeping her gaze on her plate. 'I expect she'll be missing you anyway, won't she?'

'You're thinking of what I told you about her?'

'Well, you did make out she couldn't do without you, like my dad says about my sisters and me.'

'She agreed to my coming here, though. And it's natural to want family at Christmas. If she'd been fit we'd have all been together at my uncle's.'

'Yes, well, as you say, you'll only be gone a week.'

Viktor caught at Jinny's hand across the table. 'Why did I say it would not be long? It'll be a lifetime, to be away from you.'

She raised her head. 'You mean that?'

'You know I do!'

Happiness was restored and the café seemed filled with sunlight, even though outside the city remained gripped by winter, and as they drank more tea and took a second scone each, Viktor's Christmas departure seemed very far away.

Eventually, of course, they had to leave, and as they met the cold

rush of air in the street Jinny, clinging to Viktor's arm, said she
supposed she'd better go home.

'Oh, why?' cried Viktor. 'It's not late. You need not go yet.'

'I think maybe I'll go back and sweeten up Dad by not being
late.'

'From what you've told me he's not likely to be sweetened unless
you stop seeing me.'

'That's not going to happen. But come on, you can walk me
home.'

'A little more time together – that's good.'

As they faced the bitter wind and made for the Lothian Road,
Jinny looked up into Viktor's face. 'Mind if I ask you something?
It's about your uncle.'

'Uncle John? Why has he entered your head?' Viktor laughed.
'What is it?'

'Well, I was wondering – have you told him we've been out
together?'

Viktor hesitated for only a moment. 'No, I haven't.'

'But doesn't he wonder what you do? I mean, going to the theatre,
for instance. Does he think you went on your own?'

'Well, he's out so much – to Rotary and so on, that he's hardly
ever in when I go out, and so far he's never asked exactly what I
do.'

'I suppose that's easier.'

'Yes, much easier than someone checking on you all the time.'

'But would he – you know – mind if he thought you were with
me?'

'No, why should he?'

'I don't know.' Jinny walked in silence for a few moments. 'He
might not think it's a good idea.'

'I don't see why. He's not like your father.'

'But you're only here for a short time; he might not want you
to get involved.'

'Is that what you think, Jinny?'

'No! You know I couldn't think that. I don't let myself think of
how long you'll be here.'

'Nor do I!'

Viktor stopped and drew her into his arms, holding her close and
disregarding passersby. They began to kiss and continued kissing,
strongly and passionately, over and over again.

'Don't let us spoil this,' Viktor whispered as they finally drew apart, catching their breath. 'All that matters is that we have found each other and are together now. Who knows what will happen in the future?'

But Jinny was too out of breath to answer, and too enchanted to consider anything but the present.

After a lingering farewell outside the flat in Fingal Street, Jinny was dreamily mounting the stairs only to find Allan Forth appearing above her with a smiling May in the background.

'Allan? What are you doing here?' asked Jinny.

He, too, was smiling. 'There's been a development. I'm allowed to come to the flat now. I'm off, but May will tell you all about it.'

'When I've said goodbye to you, dearest. Wait there, Jinny.'

Standing in wonder at the flat door, Jinny waited for her sister, who eventually came back, looking, Jinny told her, as though she was a cat who'd been drinking the cream.

'You should know – you look the same yourself.'

'Do I?' Jinny blushed. 'Oh, well, never mind, tell me what's been happening.'

'You know I told you what Allan was planning to say to Dad? Well, he said it, and it did the trick. As soon as Dad heard I'd leave and marry Allan straight off if he didn't turn reasonable, he more or less caved in. I asked him how he'd have felt if Granddad had refused to let him court Ma, and that brought it home to him as well – that he had to change. In the end he agreed to let Allan visit here. We're to have a long engagement but get married in the end, and that was that.' May flung her arms round Jinny. 'Oh, I'm so happy, Jinny – so relieved!'

'And I'm happy, too. For you.' But then Jinny drew back a little. 'How about me, then? Is Dad going to speak to me again? Am I allowed to go out with Viktor without thunder in the air?'

May's smile faded. 'I don't think Dad's happy about Viktor yet. He says you'll end up with a broken heart.'

'That's my business, May. He's no need to interfere!'

'I did get him to agree to talk to you, Jinny, so let's see how things go, eh? Vi's back – she's frying up some cold potatoes and bacon. We haven't had any tea yet.'

'Smells good,' Jinny said cheerfully as she and May entered the living room, and Vi, bouncing in from the cooker, grinned, while Josh looked up from a mystery novel he was reading but said nothing.

'Hello, Dad!' Jinny called.

'Dad,' warned May, as he returned to his book again.

'Hello, Jinny,' he replied at last. 'Been out with that German, then?'

'Austrian, Dad. Yes, we went round the castle and had some tea in Rose Street.'

As May began to set the table, Jinny sat down by the fire and held out her hands to the blaze. 'He's going home for Christmas. His mother's not well.'

'Oh, yes?'

Josh turned a page of his book and Jinny, glancing across at her sisters, sighed heavily and asked herself: if this was what Dad called talking, it wasn't exactly a breakthrough, was it? One step forward, how many back? But what did it matter? As she turned her eyes to the fire and watched the leaping flames, all she could see was Viktor's handsome face as he drew her into his arms, and all she could think of were his kisses. No cold treatment from her father could blank those things from her mind.

Twenty-One

In the December weeks that followed, Jinny and Viktor met outside work as often as they could, though each had decided that they should play down their relationship at the bakery itself.

'Imagine the teasing!' Jinny had exclaimed to Viktor, without adding that she really didn't want folk such as Senga pointing the finger and delighting in thinking Jinny would be left high and dry when Viktor returned to Vienna. As though Senga wouldn't have changed places with her at any time! You only had to see the way her eyes followed Viktor, and to know how disappointed she'd been when Bob and Norah had been chosen to help him with the making and decorating of his cakes that had become so popular.

Jinny's idea, then, was to keep her affair with Viktor secret, hugging it to herself with special elation, while Viktor himself was relieved that his uncle need not know about his feelings for Jinny – at least for the time being. He might not object. On the other hand, he might inform his sister, and the last person Viktor wanted to be told was his mother. He would certainly not be telling her himself when he went home at Christmas, for what she didn't know couldn't hurt her. Whether or not she would have to know sometime was a question he kept at the back of his mind, just as Jinny kept the knowledge that he would one day return to Vienna at the back of hers.

Were they living in a fool's paradise? That was another question not to be asked, though when they were together they might well have considered they were in paradise anyhow. Other considerations could be put aside while they went to see films or plays, visited the sights on Jinny's list — museums, galleries, the Canongate, the Palace of Holyroodhouse — or walked in wintry landscapes outside Edinburgh, while Viktor put German names to the things they saw and Jinny practised her pronunciation.

What her father thought of the continuing relationship was plain enough, but he no longer spoke of it, saying very little at all, in fact, to Jinny. Although grieved by his attitude, she had trained herself to put up with it. Meanwhile, as time flew by, she and Viktor made the most of what they had, dreading farewell even for a short period.

'My uncle says with Christmas coming I must do some overtime.' Viktor sighed. 'Work with Bob and Norah so that they can be sure of supplying orders while I'm away. Seems everyone wants my *Sachertorten* for Christmas cakes here, though at home we usually have the *Stollen*. That's the marzipan fruit bread, you know.'

'Oh, don't let Mr Comrie make you do more hours!' Jinny cried. 'Time is slipping away so fast, soon you'll be away and I'll be on my own!'

'Why, I have been told there is staff party to look forward to. You'll be able to dance with Terry Brown and Ross and I'll be jealous thinking of it.'

'There'll only be an old gramophone for the dancing, and you are the only one I'd want to be dancing with, anyway.'

'Though Terry and Ross are very nice fellows, particularly Ross.'

'Yes, and Ross does know about us, you know, though he'd never tell anyone else.'

'As I say, he is a nice fellow.'

It was true that Ross knew about Jinny and Viktor, not just that they were seeing each other but that Jinny was very deeply into the relationship and unwilling to listen to any advice he would have liked to give her. In fact, he no longer gave her any, only smiled indulgently when he saw her looking particularly excited at the end of the day, when it was obvious she was looking forward to meeting Viktor.

Sometimes, catching that smile, Jinny felt bad that Ross seemed to have so little in his life compared to her. He had friends he played golf with, she knew, and he also did some charity work, raising funds for tenement children, but when he went home to the house he'd inherited from his late father there was no one there to greet him, no girlfriend for him to arrange to meet, have a meal with or take somewhere. At least, she'd never heard that anyone had taken the place in his life of the dead fiancée, and she was sure she would have been told.

Once, she'd asked him what his interests were, and he'd told her he liked working with his hands, as a change from getting the poor old brain to work in Accounts all day. Perhaps what he did would not be interesting to her, but he liked to make things in wood – small furniture, book cases, tables, and such.

'Why, I think that *is* interesting!' Jinny had cried.

But none of it made up for his being so much on his own in her eyes. None of it was to be compared with what she had, which was being with the person she loved and who loved her. For though she and Viktor had never actually declared their love for each other in words, their eyes said it for them. Certainly, only love could cause the pain she felt as she looked at the calendar every day and saw that the day was drawing nearer and nearer when he must leave for home, and she knew from Viktor's face that he was feeling the same.

Maybe they were foolish to feel so tragic about one week's separation, but then a week was a week, and time could stretch and seem like a year, if you were missing somebody.

Twenty-Two

On the day before he left, which was 22 December, they agreed to have a farewell meal together, for Mr Comrie was to see Viktor off at the station, which meant they could not meet there to say goodbye.

'I didn't want him to come,' Viktor said wretchedly over their dinner, 'but he thought he was doing me a favour, driving me to the station, so what could I say?'

'Never mind. Everybody says it's awful, saying goodbye at the station.'

Jinny took a wrapped parcel from her bag. 'It's better here where I can give you this and you can take it back to put in your luggage.'

'Oh, Jinny, it isn't a present, is it? cried Viktor, turning the parcel in his hands. 'You shouldn't have been spending your money.'

'As though I wouldn't want to give you a present at Christmas!'

He smiled fondly. 'Well, as a matter of fact, I have something for you.'

He fumbled in his pocket as the waitress removed their plates and asked what they'd like next.

'Just coffee, I think,' said Jinny, adding in a low voice to Viktor, 'if you can bear it.'

He gave the order and when the girl had gone, put a very small package into Jinny's hands.

'Oh, Viktor!' Her eyes were dancing. 'May I open it now?'

'Strictly speaking, we should wait for Christmas Eve – that's when we open presents at home. But as we're not going to be together then . . . yes, let's open ours now.'

Viktor was the first to reveal his present, which was a fine history of Edinburgh, complete with illustrations, something he said he truly wanted and had been thinking of getting for himself, but would Jinny write in it for him? Here was his fountain pen – she could write something now.

'What shall I put?' she asked, taking the pen.

'With love to Viktor, from Jinny, Christmas, 1937.'

'With love?'

'With love.'

He leaned forward, his eyes tender, his hand seeking hers, but she was blushing and writing what he'd told her. 'With love to Viktor . . .'

'That's the first time that word has actually been used,' she remarked quietly.

'Though it's always been there, Jinny. That's a fact. Would you like me to say it again?'

'I think I would.'

'*Ich liebe dich*, I'll say, then. And you know what that means?'

'I love you.'

'There, now you've used the word, too.'

He sat back as the waitress appeared with their coffee and began to replace the Christmas wrapping paper around his book. 'Aren't you going to open my present?'

Still flushed, she waited for the waitress to go, then looked down at the small, neat package he had given her. 'I'm too excited.'

'Ah, but I want to know what you think. Please . . . open it.'

Inside the wrapping was a small box and inside the box was a brooch on a velvet pad. A beautiful brooch, showing white, star-shaped flowers, so exquisitely fashioned that Jinny was mesmerized, already thinking it the most wonderful thing she'd ever be given.

'Viktor, what is it?' she whispered. 'What's the flower?'

'Why, the Edelweiss, of course! Our national flower, as well as Switzerland's and maybe Hungary's. It's a mountain flower, anyway.'

'But it's so beautiful, Viktor! Where did you find it – I mean, an Austrian brooch in Edinburgh?'

'You'll never guess where I got it, never. But it was somewhere very well known to you.'

'Well known to me? Where? I can't think! Tell me, Viktor, tell me!'

'What is next door to where you live, Jinny? What sort of shop?'

'You mean . . . Allan's shop?' She was shaking her head in wonder. 'I can't believe that Allan had a brooch like this – it'd be such a coincidence!'

'No, I went there secretly and asked him if he could find one for me, and he said he'd do some asking around, which he did and was successful. A jeweller in Glasgow specializes in continental jewel-lery and had just what I wanted. That's how I got it.'

As Jinny continued to look astonished, Viktor gently took the brooch from its box and pinned it to her dress. 'I'd better say it's not what you could call valuable,' he said quickly. 'Only costume jewellery, but well made and something to remind you of me.'

'Viktor, I'll treasure it all my life.'

'Just as I'll treasure my book. Now, we'd better drink this coffee before it gets cold.'

When they had left the restaurant and were making their way to Fingal Street, Viktor told Jinny more about the Edelweiss – how the Emperor Franz Josef had ordered it to be the insignia of the Austrian/Hungarian mountain troops, and how young men had once climbed mountains to find the flower for their sweethearts, the higher the mountain the better for their reputation.

'And I only bought it for you from a shop,' Viktor finished, laughing. 'I must climb a mountain or two to find the real thing when I get home.'

'Oh, don't!' Jinny sighed. 'You know how much your brooch will always mean to me, and I can't bear to think of you going home.'

'Think about the New Year – that's what I'm doing. Only a day or two later, I'll be back.'

They stopped to kiss and hold each other close before walking on, finally passing the closed door of Allan's shop next to the flat and pausing again to look in his window, in which he only showed clocks.

'So Allan has met you,' said Jinny. 'He must have liked you – and you must have liked him, mustn't you?'

'A very pleasant man, I thought he was, kind and helpful.'

'He never said a word about you to me.'

'I told him the brooch was to be a surprise and he promised not to tell you.'

'I think I'll keep it a secret until Christmas, then I'll wear it and thank Allan for helping you find it.'

'And I'll keep my book a secret until Christmas Eve, and when I read it I'll think of you.'

But will you say who gave it to you? Jinny wanted to ask, though she didn't put the question into words. There must be nothing to cause worry to either of them on this last evening before their separation, and as she went quietly into Viktor's arms for a long, passionate farewell, she put everything from her mind except their love.

Only her sisters were at home when she finally let herself into the flat, which was a relief – no Dad to face with Viktor's kisses fresh on her lips, only sympathetic looks from May and Vi.

'Poor Jinny,' murmured May. 'Does it seem a long time till New Year?'

'It had better be,' laughed Vi. 'I haven't done my Christmas shopping yet.'

'I suppose it's only a week – I shouldn't be making such a fuss.' Having removed her brooch from her dress and put it into her bag while on the stairs, Jinny now took comfort that it was safely there and asked whether Dad was rather late back.

'Yes, they're preparing for the pantomime. The theatre's closed at the minute – it reopens on Boxing Day.'

'What's the show this year? Are we going?'

'You bet,' Vi answered. 'It's *Aladdin* – my favourite. And Dad's getting us tickets.'

'One for Allan, too,' said May happily. 'Who'd have thought it?'

'I'm so pleased for you,' Jinny murmured, which was true, but already her thoughts had moved from her home to the man who was returning to his home the following day, and she was wondering, just to cheer herself up, if in the future he and she might have a home together. Well, why not? There was no harm in dreaming.

Twenty-Three

How the time dragged for Jinny after Viktor's departure! It didn't matter that she had plenty to do at work before the holiday, and of course, the staff party to think about, she still felt that the days were empty and her life was just marking time until she saw Viktor again.

The staff party, always held on Christmas Eve in the Princes Street café after its early closing, was not something she expected to enjoy; it was more just a duty to get through, though Ross did try to make it as pleasant as possible. But even he caused a surprise, appearing with an attractive young woman whose burnished copper hair was the same colour as his own, leading to guesses that she was his sister, though nobody had heard that he had one. In fact, she turned out to be his cousin from London, who was staying with her parents at Ross's home for Christmas.

'Meet my cousin, Lorna,' he told Jinny. 'My uncle and aunt are having a quiet evening but Lorna has bravely agreed to accompany me. Lorna, this is Jinny, my valued assistant.'

They shook hands and murmured politely, Jinny still taken aback to see Ross escorting a pretty girl, for this was a first for him, surely? She'd always thought of him on his own, not willing to replace his lost love, and maybe she should be glad to find him getting over his loss at last. If that was the case, for Lorna was his cousin, not a girlfriend. Cousins, though, were not quite the same as sisters.

'It's lovely to meet everyone,' Lorna was saying, her green eyes moving round the crowded café where Comrie's staff members were enjoying drinks, sandwiches and mince pies, or endeavouring to dance to a gramophone in very limited space, while Mr Comrie and Mr Whyte looked on, smiling and at the same time checking that none of the bakers drank too much.

'And to be in Scotland,' Lorna was continuing. 'Because I'm really a Scot myself – it's just my father's business took him to London.'

'Our loss,' said Ross. 'But it's nice you're here now.'

He does seem fond of her, thought Jinny, her feelings strangely mixed on the issue, but then Terry Brown arrived to ask Lorna if she'd like to risk a turn on the floor, and as she accepted and they moved away, Jinny was the focus of Ross's kind gaze again.

'Getting through it?' he asked softly. 'I know how you're feeling.'

'I'm being silly about it. He'll only be gone for a few days.'

'Days, or years?' He laughed a little and, looking at the couples on the makeshift dance floor, seemed about to ask Jinny if they shouldn't join them, when Norah, wonderfully smart in a blue taffeta dress and jacket, appeared at his side.

'Come on, Ross, this won't do. Let's see you on the floor for the quickstep. and no arguing!'

'Who's arguing?' asked Ross, holding up his hands in surrender, and as he was led away Jinny laughed, thinking she would go for another drink and maybe try a mince pie, when she felt a touch on her arm and turned to find Senga at her side.

'Think she's had too much blackcurrant cordial?' she asked, nodding towards Norah.

'She's just in the party spirit,' Jinny replied coolly, noting that Senga, though looking very young, could still seem confident, even arrogant, her dark brown eyes never warm as brown eyes could be, and her mouth a straight, expressionless line.

'No' like you, then, Jinny,' she said now. 'What's the matter? Missing your young man?'

'I don't know what you're talking about!'

'Oh, come on – everybody at Comrie's knows there's something going on with you and Viktor Linden.'

Stunned, Jinny had no answer. What Senga was saying couldn't be true, could it? They'd been so careful. She realized Senga was watching her and wanted to answer her but, before she could think of what to say, Senga had begun to laugh.

'You should see all the chaps knocking each other in the ribs when you come over on wages day and try no' to look at Viktor and he tries no' to look at you! And even Norah and Trixie have to stop themselves from smiling. Why all the secrecy, anyway? What've you got to hide?'

'Nothing,' Jinny answered huskily. 'It's just that . . . we don't want to go broadcasting our feelings to everybody.'

'To Mr Comrie, more like. He's about the only one who doesn't know already.'

'Why should we worry about him?' Jinny cried, trying not to let Senga see she'd hit a nerve.

'Well, there's sure to be trouble when the time comes for Viktor to go home, eh? And he won't want trouble with his nephew.' Senga was silent for a moment as the record playing for the dancing came to an end and couples began to return from the floor. Finally, she gave Jinny a long, hard look.

'You may think I envy you, Jinny, but it isn't true. I wouldn't want to be mixed up with a foreigner, especially one who's a German, or as good as. I mean, what'll you do if there's a war?'

'Why should there be a war, Senga? And Viktor isn't a German – why don't folk believe that?'

'I said as good as.' Senga, seeing Terry approach, was smiling. 'You watch which side he'll be on if we go to war, then you'll know what he is.'

Twenty-Four

'Hello there, you lovely ladies!' Terry had taken out a handkerchief and mopped his brow. 'Why aren't you dancing?'

'We weren't asked!' Senga replied smartly. 'You were too busy dancing with Mr MacBain's cousin.'

'What a looker, eh? None o' my cousins look like her. But come on, let's all go for another drink – my treat, eh?'

'That's rich, seeing as they're provided by Mr Comrie.' Senga laughed. 'You coming with us, Jinny?'

'No thanks, not yet. Just want to say goodbye to Ross.'

When she'd found Ross, now back with Lorna, Jinny said she had a lot to do back at home and she'd better be going.

'Oh, what a shame!' cried Lorna. 'But I suppose it is Christmas Eve – you'll be busy.'

'I've got the car; may I give you a lift home?' asked Ross. 'Lorna, you stay on and I'll come back for you.'

'No, no, thanks all the same, Ross.' Jinny was very earnest. 'I want to walk for a bit; I've got a headache coming on.'

Shaking hands with Lorna, she wished her and Ross a merry Christmas, said she'd just say thanks to Mr Comrie and make her other goodbyes.

'See you after Boxing Day, Ross!'

'After Boxing Day, Jinny. Have a lovely holiday with the family.'

Well, perhaps she would – she'd always enjoyed Christmas with her family before, and there'd be presents to exchange and the showing of her brooch next morning. Much depended on how Dad was, of course, and that remained to be seen. In the meantime, when she'd made all her goodbyes at the party, it was grand to be out in the fresh night air and to be on her own, seeing only strangers in the streets and not thinking of Senga's words, only of Viktor.

But how pleasant her home looked, she thought as she went into the living room. How Christmassy! Clearly her sisters had been busy while she was out, putting up balloons and paper chains, and with the fire crackling, her mother's old glass decorations and the Woolworth's tinsel glittering on their little tree, all was as cheerful as a Christmas card. May was setting out her mince pies on the table while Josh was lying back in his chair, looking relaxed, and Vi, sorting about in the Christmas box, was seeking the Christmas tree fairy.

'Got her!' she called, standing up with the rather battered little celluloid doll in her fingers. 'You're just in time to put her on the top, Jinny, though I reckon she's about ready to retire. Might get a new one next year.'

'Shame!' cried May. 'We've always had that fairy; she's a tradition.'

'That's right,' agreed Jinny. 'She's not ready for her pension yet.'

'Put her up, then!' Josh ordered, and Jinny obediently fastened the doll to the top of the tree then stepped back with her family to admire the result.

'Looks lovely,' she commented. 'You've done a good job, Vi. In fact, you both have. The whole place is transformed!'

Vi tossed back her dark hair and shrugged. 'Just makes me think how much we have. I mean, when you consider how many bairns across this city will be lucky if they get anything to eat at Christmas, never mind presents and a tree.'

There was a short silence, then Josh said, rising from his chair, 'You're no' the only one remembering them, Vi. A percentage of the Boxing Day takings from the panto is going to a children's charity.'

'We do care,' added May. 'We give what we can.'

I should give more, thought Jinny, and be like Ross, not just think of myself and Viktor.

'We need to change the system,' said Vi. 'It's fine giving to charity; the point is no one should need it.'

'Agreed,' said Josh. 'But for now it's Christmas Eve. Can we have our mince pies and a cup of tea?'

'It's all ready,' said May with some relief. 'Jinny, we never asked you – how was the party? Did you have a good time?'

'It was the same as usual. Yes, I suppose we had a good time but I missed having a mince pie – yours look nice.'

'Help yourself, and merry Christmas, eh? Merry Christmas, Dad, merry Christmas, Vi!'

'Merry Christmas!' they called back and, as May passed the cups, Jinny whispered in her ear, 'And tomorrow you'll have Allan here for Christmas dinner – think of that.'

'Thanks to Dad,' May whispered back happily, and Jinny's eyes moved to meet her father's. Dark eyes looked into dark eyes until, hardly daring to venture it, Jinny smiled – and after a long moment of suspense, Josh smiled back.

Better not spoil things by saying anything, thought Jinny, but it was a start, eh? A hope for reconciliation?

Twenty-Five

Christmas certainly made a difference to Jinny's spirits, though when alone all her longing for Viktor rushed back to consume her, and the time till his return seemed, as Ross had joked, to be years, not days.

Still, it had been sweet to see Allan arriving on Christmas Day with his bottle of wine and box of chocolates, his eyes only for May, yet making a valiant effort to greet Josh as though there was nothing to worry about. And the good news was that Josh responded pretty well – not exactly with warmth, but then not with coldness, either.

The girls flew about preparing the dinner with May, the expert, in charge of the crackling on the roast pork while Vi and Jinny prepared the vegetables and put on the pudding to steam away, leaving the two men to sit by the fire and chat. Which, of course, annoyed Vi, who declared such a division of labour, always weighted against women, to be ridiculous.

'Oh, don't say anything!' whispered May. 'There's no point.'

'If you keep on saying so there certainly isn't!' cried Vi.

But Jinny wasn't getting involved. She'd taken a break to show Allan she was wearing the brooch he'd found, and ask in a whisper what he'd thought of Viktor.

'Oh, I thought him a very nice young man! A bit foreign in style, you know, but so polite and so good looking!'

'He was really pleased you'd found this brooch for me, Allan. Everyone thinks it's beautiful. Even Dad.'

'You liked it, Mr Hendrie?'

'Liked what?'

'Jinny's Edelweiss brooch?'

'Oh – yes. Very nice.' Josh's tone was non-commital.

Vi called across, 'Come on, Dad, you were impressed! We all were!'

'I said it was nice – what more do you want? Now, how about joining in the carols on the wireless?'

Two steps forward, one step back, that's the progress with Dad, thought Jinny. But at least there had been those steps forward for May and Allan, and there had been that smile for her last night. How would it be if one day she saw Viktor with her family, like Allan today? So much was against their love it was hard to picture him in her home, but why shouldn't it happen? She determined fiercely that it should – especially as, on a day like this, any idea of war seemed very far away.

Boxing Day brought the panto, and how they all enjoyed that! More than enjoyed it, really. Rather, they were grateful for the way they could give themselves up to a world that didn't exist, find a true escape from all their worries while watching larger-than-life characters weaving through an impossible story, singing, dancing and finding bliss in the grand transformation scene that the sisters especially admired. Their father, after all, was working away behind the scenes on that, and if there'd been any justice, would have been brought on for the line-up for the applause at the end. Still, he enjoyed his work and always said that that was his reward.

'You have to admire him,' Allan had remarked when they were all together in the interval. 'He's a very clever and resourceful chap.'

'Nice of you to say that,' said May.

'Well, I mean it. I do admire him and still remember that train he put on for Arnold Ridley's *Ghost Train* play. You said he and the stage director had worked together on that, but it was your dad who had to create the effect.'

So lovely for May that such a nice fellow as Allan would be coming into the family, Jinny was thinking, but couldn't help feeling a stab of envy – until she decided again that one day, yes, she would see Viktor in her home, accepted by her father, and joining in all that her family did, being a part of their lives.

Even going to the panto? Her lips curved in a smile. She couldn't imagine what he'd make of something so peculiar to her own country. Whatever would he think of Widow Twankey in *Aladdin* being played by a man? And of Aladdin himself played by a woman – the principal boy, of course, dressed in the shortest costume ever, to display her splendid legs? And then there'd be the slapstick and the jokes, and the singing with the audience joining in, and then the wonderful ending, when everyone was set to live happily ever after. Why shouldn't he enjoy it all?

One day, she decided, she would take him along to see a panto-mime, and it would be just one more strand for him to learn about and enjoy, as she would learn German and all the things he would teach her about Vienna in their future life together.

A happy daze seemed to occupy her then, and she had to concentrate hard to return to her seat for the rest of the performance. Already, in her mind, she was seeing Viktor arriving at the station, stepping off the train and looking for her, and they were meeting at last, holding, touching, their eyes filled with delight – had it not really happened, then?

Not then, but only eight days later, when she'd taken an extra day's holiday, all that she'd dreamed came true. She really was on a Waverley Station platform, seeing Viktor's train come steaming in from London. She really did see his handsome face at one of the doors, his far-sighted blue eyes searching, finding, smiling – and then he opened the door and hurtled out with his cases, dropping them as she ran to him and they were in each other's arms.

'Oh, Jinny, *liebchen*!' he was murmuring against her face. 'It's been so long! So long without you! Wasn't it long for you?'

'Never ending, never ending! But you're back now and I'm so happy!'

At last, their mouths were able to meet in a first ecstatic home-coming kiss that seemed as though it would never end, when a voice sharp as a shot close by made them made them spring apart, their faces stricken.

The voice was Mr Comrie's.

Twenty-Six

The bakery owner's face was scarlet, his round eyes outraged as his gaze went from Viktor to Jinny and back to Viktor.

'What's the meaning of this?' he asked, oblivious of the flow of passengers from the London train hurrying around the tableau of their three standing figures.

'I come to the station, Viktor, to give you a lift home, and what do I find? My nephew kissing one of my own employees, a young woman whose welfare I'm responsible for, as I am for all who work for me!'

'Uncle, I didn't know you were coming to meet me,' Viktor interrupted. 'I didn't expect you to come.'

'That's obvious! But I knew which train you were likely to get, and I thought I'd do you a favour and take you home quickly as you'd be tired. And all I see is you and Miss Hendrie, behaving in a way that shows me there's been something going on between the two of you behind my back for who knows how long?'

Taking off his hat, Mr Comrie mopped his brow with his hand then, replacing the hat, pointed to Viktor's cases. 'Pick those up, Viktor, and come home with me – you as well, Jinny – I want the truth from both of you about what's been going on and what you've got to say for yourselves. What your mother's going to say, Viktor, is another matter.'

'My mother?' cried Viktor, stricken. 'Uncle, there's no need to bring her into this!'

'We'll discuss that when we're out of this public place, if you don't mind. Come away now, the pair of you – the car's parked nearby.'

Following Mr Comrie's plump figure, Jinny walked by Viktor's side without any conscious feeling of putting one foot in front of the other. To be plunged from delight to the fear of unknown consequences was almost too much to bear, and even Viktor, she felt, could not help her now, though when she looked at him he smiled in encouragement. As though he could make things better! There was too much at stake. At that very moment she might be facing the sack – 'not a suitable person for his workforce', Mr Comrie might say. And as for Viktor, he might be made to go home. She caught her breath, thinking of it, seeing the wonderful feeling they shared as a glistening bubble rising away from them, waiting for Mr Comrie's stick to burst it.

In the car, Viktor was made to sit next his uncle at the front while Jinny sat at the back, and for the drive to Mr Comrie's house, in an elegant terrace off the Dean Bridge, no one spoke, the atmosphere carrying so much tension that the trip for Jinny was an ordeal. At one time, she knew, she would have been fascinated to see where Mr Comrie lived because that was where Viktor lived, but now she felt so numb with apprehension that all she wanted was to learn what was going to happen so she could somehow face it.

Opening his front door, Mr Comrie ushered the young people into a handsome hallway and, as Viktor set down his cases and caught Jinny's hand in a strong squeeze, a middle-aged woman wearing a dark dress and her grey hair in a bun came forward.

'There you are, Mr Comrie!' she cried, though her eyes were on Jinny. 'And Mr Viktor! Did you have a good time in Vienna, then? How was your ma? And your father?'

'Not too bad, thank you, Mrs Orchard, and I had a very good time—' Viktor was beginning, when Mr Comrie interrupted to say she would hear all the news later.

'For now, Mrs Orchard, we'd like some tea in my study, please. I have some things to discuss with Miss Hendrie here from Accounts. Jinny, this is my housekeeper, Mrs Orchard.'

After exchanging polite greetings, Jinny, followed by Viktor, was shown into a large, high-ceilinged room furnished with shelves of books, a mahogany desk and comfortable chairs, at which Mr Comrie pointed. 'Take a seat, please. Tea won't be long. Then we can talk.'

Twenty-Seven

Silence fell. Jinny, glancing at Viktor for possible comfort, thought he seemed calm as he sat in his armchair, but when he met her gaze she saw in his eyes the same sort of anxiety that he must see in hers. He smiled, and his smile was as encouraging as before, but though she tried she couldn't manage to smile back. For this was no time for smiling.

She'd never before felt so ill at ease, so afraid for the future, which was now so much in the power of another person. Could she really lose her job for kissing a man on a station platform? A man she loved? Circumstances alter cases, it was said, and it seemed to her quite possible that in this case Mr Comrie would consider himself within his rights to give her the sack.

'Tea, Mr Comrie,' Mrs Orchard announced, entering with a loaded tray. 'And I've brought some of my shortbread, Mr Viktor, as I know you like it, eh?'

'I do, Mrs Orchard. Scotch shortbread is not served in Vienna, but when I've learned to make it perhaps it will be.'

'That'd be grand. Shall I leave it to you to pour, Miss Hendrie?'

It was the last thing Jinny wanted to do, but as Mrs Orchard withdrew she poured the tea with a shaking hand and passed the cups. Only Viktor ate some shortbread, which he said he should to please the housekeeper, and after the tea was drunk Mr Comrie put the tray on to a side table and sat down to face his nephew.

'Now, Viktor, you can tell me how long this affair has been going on and who knows about it?'

'It's not an affair, Uncle.'

'Whatever you care to call it, then. I say again, how long has it been going on, and who knows about it?'

Viktor sighed and moved uneasily in his chair. He looked across at Jinny, who was winding her fingers together, and whose dark eyes were fixed on him.

'How long has it been going on?' Viktor shook his head. 'I suppose since we first met.'

'First met?' echoed Mr Comrie. 'You mean, as soon as you saw Jinny you decided to make a play for her?'

'A play?'

'Oh, don't pretend to misunderstand me, Viktor. You know what I'm talking about, and I want to make it plain that I blame you for this whole thing. Jinny would never have thought of getting involved with you if you hadn't swept her off her feet.'

'That's not true, Mr Comrie!' Jinny cried, stung into finding her voice. 'We were both attracted from the beginning and before we knew what was happening, we were in love. Viktor never swept me off my feet. Our love just happened.'

Mr Comrie stared, then shook his head. 'If that's true, the situation is worse than I thought. The two of you must have been making eyes at each other at work, at my bakery, no doubt with everyone looking on and enjoying it.'

'No, never!' cried Viktor, his face a mask of anger. 'It was never like that, Uncle! How could you think that of us? No one knows, no one saw. We kept it secret, is that not so, Jinny?'

As he turned indignant blue eyes on Jinny, her own gaze fell. Of course, he hadn't been at the staff party so he didn't know what Senga had told her about the laughing and tittering that had gone on behind his back and hers, and she'd had no chance to tell him. But what could she say now? Mr Comrie's gaze was upon her, and with a sinking heart she realized he had correctly guessed the truth of the matter.

'Well, Jinny?' he asked impatiently. 'Do people know, or do they not?'

'They don't know,' she said after a pause, deciding it was better not to mention Ross's name. 'But I think some have guessed.'

'Guessed?' asked Viktor. 'Who says they have guessed?'

'Never mind,' his uncle snapped. 'It's plain to me that you've become the object of gossip – my own nephew who I had such hopes for! Well, it's got to stop – I won't have it. I'll phone your mother this evening, Viktor, and as you know what she'll say, I think you should arrange to go home as soon as possible. As for you, Jinny, your best plan is to forget this affair ever happened. It was never going to work out; you're both from different countries, you have no future together and that's all there is to it.'

'And did my mother's love for my father not work out?' Viktor asked quietly. 'They were from different countries and they've been happy together for years.'

Mr Comrie hesitated. He put his hand to his brow, and for a moment or two looked away from his nephew's level gaze.

'That was different,' he said at last. 'Your mother was willing to go to your father's country. What if Jinny doesn't want to? What if her father doesn't want it, either? I don't suppose he's happy about your seeing Viktor anyway, is he, Jinny?'

'He doesn't know Viktor.' Jinny suddenly turned a passionate dark gaze on her employer. 'But I do, Mr Comrie, and all I can say is that I want to be with him, wherever he is!'

'Oh, Jinny,' Viktor murmured. 'Jinny . . .'

But Mr Comrie was holding his head and almost groaning. 'God, what a mess, what a mess! I don't know what to say, I really don't. The thing is you've given yourselves no time. These things happen, they don't always last, and with you two – for heaven's sake, consider the difficulties! You don't even know which country you'd want to be in!'

'If you'll give us some time, Uncle, we can work something out,' Viktor said desperately. 'Let me stay until November, when I'm due to leave, and if we still feel the same—'

'What? What then?'

'Well . . .' Viktor's eyes went to Jinny, who was standing with her head down, her hands clasped together, looking suddenly so young, so vulnerable that he stretched out his hand to her as though his touch would give her strength. But she didn't take it, perhaps didn't see it, and he dropped it to his side.

'Then we make decisions,' he said in a low voice.

'Decisions,' Mr Comrie repeated. 'But have you forgotten your mother, Viktor? She will be very upset, very upset indeed about all this. She'll want you back home, and you should go.'

'I know what she wants, and I've no intention of doing it,' Viktor said with sudden firmness. 'I'm not going home to stay under her eye as though I were a child. If you won't keep me on here, Uncle, I can find a job elsewhere. I believe that there are other firms interested in what I can do.'

'Other firms? What other firms?'

With a slight shrug, Viktor mentioned two well-known names, at which his uncle became agitated. 'No, no, Viktor, that won't do! Your Viennese cakes belong with Comrie's! It was my idea to bring you over, and I've been the one to encourage and promote them. To make them elsewhere would be utterly disloyal!'

'You'd like me to stay on with you, then?'

'Yes. Yes, I would. It's only fair to me that you should!'

'So what about my mother, wanting me back home?'

Mr Comrie hesitated. 'I'll – I'll leave telling her for the moment. Maybe you're right – she needn't know the situation yet. It would only upset her.'

'You'll give us time, then, to make sure we know how we feel?'

'Until you are due to go home. And then, as you say, you make your decisions.' For some moments, Mr Comrie stared at his nephew. 'At least you are being sensible, Viktor. But you must promise me that you will keep your feelings to yourselves when you're at work. There must be no more scenes like the one at the station.'

'That was just a welcome home, Uncle. At work things have always been different, anyway.'

'Very well. There's just one more thing, and this is for you, Jinny. You say your father hasn't met Viktor. I think he should meet him as soon as possible. In my opinion, he has that right.'

'He has,' Jinny said bravely. 'It's whether he'll agree to it is the point.'

'Well, do what you can.' Mr Comrie heaved a great sigh. 'Now, I think we should get you home. What a day this has turned out to be!'

Viktor moved to stand next to Jinny. 'Thank you, Uncle. I'm glad we've made things clear. I'll take Jinny home – you needn't drive us.' His glance on her was tender. 'We'll take the tram.'

Twenty-Eight

When they had settled together on the wooden seating of the Sunday tram that finally appeared, Viktor made Jinny turn her face to his and took her hand.

'You were very quiet back there,' he whispered, 'letting me do the talking.'

Her dark eyes were steady. 'Except when I told your uncle . . . what I did tell him.'

'That you'd be glad to be with me wherever I went?' Viktor pressed her hand hard. 'That meant a lot to me.'

'You knew it, anyway.'

'You put it into words.'

'And words are important.'

'*Liebchen*, what are you meaning? I haven't been saying the right things? Did I not say "*Ich liebe dich*"?'

She looked down at his fingers clasping hers. 'You did, and I know the translation. But what did you mean when you told your uncle that if we still felt the same after a certain time, we'd make decisions?'

Viktor gazed around the tram, which was only half empty yet still showed enough pairs of eyes and ears for him to look back at Jinny with some concern. 'Let us wait for our stop. This is not the place to talk, I think.'

'It's not,' she agreed, but withdrew her hand from his so that he would not feel it trembling.

It was better in the darkness of the street, when they'd alighted and could walk together without fear of being overheard, when there was just the two of them ready to face momentous things.

'What did I mean?' Viktor asked. 'It was what I had to say. That if we still felt the same about each other, we'd decide to be together.'

'You think we might not feel the same?'

'No! No, Jinny, of course not. I said that to please my uncle; I knew it was what he wanted to hear. That we were prepared to be reasonable.' He looked anxiously into her face. 'You understand my reasons, Jinny?'

'Oh, yes, yes, I do! But, you see, we've never talked about the future, have we?'

'You mean I have never put anything into words? I suppose that is true.'

'But why not, Viktor? Why not put things into words?'

'Because—'

He drew her to a halt, and took her gently into his arms. 'Because I suppose I was thinking that you are still so young, Jinny. I thought again today how young you seemed, how vulnerable, and that's what's always been in my mind.'

'I'm not young, Viktor! I mean, not too young. You're only a few years older than me, anyway, so what are you talking about?'

'Those years matter, Jinny. They've made me feel responsible for what I'm asking of you and I used to wonder sometimes if it was too much. I mean, expecting you to move into my life, giving up what you have here. I wanted you to be sure.'

'Well, now you know I am. I've never been so sure of anything before. I agree, we had to let your uncle think we needed time, but it's just like I said; I want to be with you, wherever you are.'

'But maybe it's still right, *liebchen*, to take this time my uncle is giving us. We'll take it and be happy. We will feel the same at the end of it, but we'll have proved to my uncle that we're right to make a life together.'

'So it's right in every way to take the time,' she whispered. 'I feel better now that we've decided what to do.'

'And maybe my uncle has done us a favour.' Viktor smiled. 'But let's not talk any more. Just let me kiss you.'

'In the street?' she asked teasingly. 'What will your uncle say?'

'The street is dark and there is no one to see us. But if you do not wish it—'

He was laughing, and so was she. They both knew what they both wished, and kissed long and passionately, time scarcely seeming to exist, except that they did eventually have to part and continue on their way to Fingal Street.

Here at last was the Hendries' flat; here were its windows that
drew their gaze, as though they might see Jinny's father looking
down. Of course, he wouldn't be, he'd be at the theatre, where
another performance of the pantomime would be about to begin,
and yet they felt his presence.

'Somehow I have to persuade Dad to meet you,' Jinny whispered.
'And he is very difficult to persuade.'

'Maybe I should be a surprise? One evening you should just bring
me in and see what he says.'

'He's always at work in the evenings.'

'A Sunday, then. A Sunday afternoon?'

'We could try it, but there's no knowing how he'd take it.'

'I say we do try it. Next Sunday.'

'Next Sunday?' She gazed at him fearfully. 'All right, then, if you
think it might work.'

'We must make it work. Even if he does not want to meet me,
I want to meet him.'

After a long moment they stared at each other, then again went
into each other's arms, and again for some time did not part. If only
they could stay like this for ever, Jinny thought, but of course they
lived in a real world, not a dream world. Next day they would be
back at work, and how would things go for them then?

In fact, they went surprisingly well. Fortified by their secret
knowledge that they would one day have a future together, there
was a difference, a sort of confidence, in Jinny and Viktor that
was somehow recognized by others at the bakery. There were one
or two knowing smiles on the first day Viktor was back, but no
one went further, no one made remarks, and even Senga only
gazed warily at Jinny, perhaps wondering why she seemed so much
more at ease.

Apart from Mr Comrie, no one, of course, knew about the scene
at Waverley Station, but when Jinny returned to work the following
day she was quick to tell Ross. He was his usual sympathetic self,
commiserating with her on the shock of it and glad that nothing
terrible was about to happen because of it.

'I'm so glad Mr Comrie is allowing Viktor to stay, Jinny, and that
you'll have the time to make the right decisions. That's sensible.'

Decisions. That word again.

'Yes, well, you see, Viktor was serious all along, Ross. Everyone
said I was storing up trouble for myself, that I'd be left heartbroken,

but it's not going to be like that, not at all. All Viktor wanted was for me to be sure.'

'And, of course, be sure himself?'

'Both of us, yes, but this time thing is only a formality. We know how we feel. Why should we change?'

Ross hesitated. 'And at the end of this formality, what happens next?'

'We'll be together.'

'You mean marry? And live where? In Vienna?'

'In Vienna, yes. That's where Viktor will be working.'

'That's wonderful, then.' Ross smiled. 'For you, not for me. Where am I going to find another assistant?'

'There's some way to go before you need worry about that.' Jinny's expression had clouded. 'I haven't taken Viktor to meet my dad yet. There will be stormy weather ahead.'

'If he doesn't give his blessing, I suspect you will manage without it.'

'I want it, though, I do want it.' Jinny gave a heartfelt sigh. 'Wish us luck, Ross. Viktor's coming to meet Dad on Sunday.'

'Jinny, you know I wish the pair of you all the luck in the world.'

Twenty-Nine

For some time before the fateful Sunday, Jinny, of course, was in a state of nerves, and when the day itself finally arrived she was on pins, watching her father and wondering about his plans.

The weather was wintry – he wouldn't want to go out, would he? On the other hand, May and Vi, who were both in on the secret, had to go out so as to leave the field clear, May to meet Allan, Vi to visit a friend. Maybe that would encourage Josh to go out too?

'He won't,' May told Jinny in her bedroom before she left. 'This is his time to relax and he'll sit in his chair reading the paper, just as he did before Allan came that time.'

'Allan? Oh, yes, he came on a Sunday, didn't he?'

'And all went well then, so it will today. Just remember that, Jinny. Dad had to accept Allan, didn't he?'

'But Allan's a Scotsman, Viktor's not.'

'Never mind. He's the one you want and Dad will have to see that. Courage, Jinny!'

'You do make me feel better, May.'

'There you are, then!' cried May, and hurried out to meet her own beloved.

At least she was right about what Josh wanted to do, for he did indeed sit by the fire and read his Sunday paper, snorting over news items that amused or annoyed him, while Jinny, her eyes on the clock, set out buttered scones and the remains of the Christmas cake for tea. Half past three was the time Viktor had said he would come, and at twenty-five minutes past, with a last glance at her father, Jinny left the living room and ran down the stairs to open the door.

Viktor was already there, waiting, his hat and overcoat covered in sleet, his face reddened with cold, but as she drew him inside, his eyes shone.

'*Der tag, liebchen*, the day is here. All will go well, I feel it.'

'I'm just so nervous, Viktor. It means so much, what happens.'

'Our luck will hold, you'll see.'

He took off his hat and kissed her quickly, then let her take his damp coat and lead him up the stairs, by which time his colour had faded and he looked, in spite of his brave words, as nervous as she felt.

'Dad,' Jinny said hoarsely, 'I've brought someone to see you.'

He looked up, his eyes a little unfocused, as though sleep was ready to claim him, but when he saw the tall blond figure in the doorway, everything cleared. Sleep was banished, the newspaper cast down, and Josh was sitting ramrod straight in his chair, his eyes alight with raw feeling.

'Who's this?' he cried. 'Have you invited that German into my house, Jinny? If that's who he is, he can turn round and go. I'll no' entertain him here!'

'Viktor is Austrian, not German, as you very well know, Dad, and, yes, I have invited him here. He wants to meet you.'

'I want that very much, Mr Hendrie,' Viktor said, stepping forward.

'Well, I don't want it at all. Just go, eh? You're no' welcome here.'

'Dad, we have something to tell you.' Jinny moved closer to his chair. 'It's very important. Please give us a chance and listen to us.'

'Please listen, Mr Hendrie,' Viktor put in. 'Please let me tell you that my intentions are good.'

'Intentions? I know what your intentions are!'

Josh stood up, his gaze on a level with Viktor's, his gaze unrelenting.

'You want to court my daughter to please yourself, be all lovey-dovey, take her out, turn her head, and then, oh, my, it's time to go! Goodbye, Jinny, goodbye! And that's that – except that my lassie is crying her eyes out!'

'It's not like that, Mr Hendrie.' Viktor's face was white but he was keeping himself well in control, his head up, his shoulders straight. 'I care for your daughter; she cares for me. We are planning to make a life together.'

Josh grew pale, his dark eyes widening as he looked from Viktor to Jinny.

'Is this true, Jinny?'

'Dad, it is.'

'We're going to give ourselves time, Mr Hendrie, before we announce anything,' Viktor went on, 'so that you and my uncle can be sure we know what we're doing. But you can see why I wanted to meet you. It's very important to us both that you're happy about our plans.'

'Important?' Josh repeated. 'I'll say it's important! But I already know all I need to know. You're a foreigner, you'll be leaving Scotland one day and there's no way Jinny will be going with you. She will never give up her family and her country, so all this talk of decisions and me being happy is just a waste of time!'

'My mother is Scottish, Mr Hendrie. She married my father from Vienna and made her home with him there. They've been very happy.'

'Maybe, but Jinny isn't like your mother, she'll never leave us for you, never!'

'Oh, Dad, that isn't true,' Jinny instantly wailed. 'I love Viktor and – and if he goes back to Vienna, I'm going too.'

'To Vienna?' Josh asked hoarsely, and at the look of desolation that swept over his face as he took in her words, for the first time, with a great inward pang, Jinny recognized just what she would be inflicting on him and her family if she left them for Viktor.

Was she being selfish? Yes, lovers were selfish, but she'd never really thought until then what effect her going would have on those left behind, and as her face crumpled and the tears pricked, she went to Josh and threw her arms around him.

'Oh, Dad, I'm sorry, I'm sorry! It's not what I want to do – to leave you and May and Vi – it isn't! But when you love someone, you have to follow wherever they go, eh? Wouldn't Ma have followed you?'

He shook his head, unable to find his usual flow of words to answer her, but held her close as she leaned against him, still holding back the tears, until she finally released herself.

'Let's not discuss this any more just now,' she whispered, dabbing at her face with a handkerchief. 'We have time ahead. I'll put the kettle on and we'll have some tea.'

'That would be very nice,' said Viktor, who had been standing apart, his eyes cast down. Josh, however, seemingly still stunned by Jinny's bombshell, simply sank into his chair and said nothing. Even the presence of Viktor, still in his house, failed to cause him to rally.

Jinny, glancing at her father as she set out the tea things, knew that he had never believed that Viktor could be serious about her, which was why he was now so shocked. He'd been like Mr Comrie, believing Viktor to be just playing around, but now he knew that that wasn't true and that she might one day go to Vienna, he couldn't take the blow. But she understood how he felt, oh, she did, and could no longer blame him. In this situation there was no way out from hurting somebody, and facing the fact that she would be doing the hurting, Jinny felt so bad she could have cried again over the teacups.

'Come and have some tea, Dad,' she called, trying to sound just as usual, and when he did stir to sit at the table, he finally managed to speak.

'Have you thought what'll happen if there's a war?' he asked, taking a buttered scone and studying it. 'It'll be no place for our Jinny to be if she's in a foreign country then. She'll be an alien.'

'I haven't heard that Hitler wants a war with Great Brtain,' Viktor said slowly. He too was studying a scone, which he eventually tried. 'I can't see that it would be of any advantage to him.'

'The papers say he wants world domination.'

'Oh, that's an exaggeration. All he wants is to give Germany some pride again, after what happened when they lost the war.'

'Well, from what I've read, he's keen to make your country join with Germany.'

'Our chancellor doesn't want that.'

'How about you?'

Viktor drank his tea. 'I'd prefer to remain as we are.'

'Let's not talk any more about Hitler,' Jinny said uneasily. 'Viktor, what do you think of my scones?'

'Excellent! I must introduce them back home, along with Mrs Fortune's shortbread.'

'If you like our baking so much, you might consider staying here,' suggested Josh, watching Viktor closely. 'Why not? Why not you stay in Jinny's country, instead of her going to yours?'

As Viktor opened his mouth to speak, Jinny leaped up to add water to the teapot.

'No more discussion,' she declared. 'We can talk another time. Dad, more tea?'

As he took the cup she had refilled, she touched his hand. 'Listen, I want to thank you – for letting Viktor stay.'

'I say the same,' Viktor put in quickly.

'Och, there's no point in fighting any more.' Josh's tone was heavy. 'What you've told me changes everything. For the worse.'

'Don't say that!' cried Jinny.

'What else can I say? It was bad enough when May fell for Allan, but at least' – Josh's voice shook – 'she's staying in her own country. I thought you'd be staying, too, Jinny. I thought you'd no future with Mr Linden. I thought I'd no need to worry—'

Suddenly he stood up and, looking at neither Jinny nor Viktor, moved away from the table.

'If you don't mind, I'm away to my bed. I just want . . . to rest.'

'Certainly, Mr Hendrie.' Viktor was on his feet, his face contrite. 'I'm so sorry if I've upset you.'

'Dad, try not to worry,' Jinny murmured. 'Nothing's been decided—'

But Josh had already left them.

On the stairs, where they were to say goodnight, Viktor put his hand under Jinny's chin and gazed into her face. 'My poor girl, you look exhausted.'

'So do you.' She took away his hand and stretched up to kiss his mouth. 'I'm so sorry, Viktor, it's all so hard for you – for all of us. You'll be wishing I was a Viennese girl in a *dirndl* and my hair in plaits.'

'I do *not* wish you were anyone but yourself, Jinny!' He crushed her to him, and as he released her his expression was bleak.

'Today, it has been good, though, that you have seen . . . how things might be. The reality of what we might want to do.'

'Viktor, it's all right.' She searched his face, her eyes tender. 'If I leave my family I'll feel bad, I know I will, but I'll still want to go with you – that's not going to change.'

'We have time ahead to be sure of that. Let's leave it for now, and try to be happy with what we have.' Viktor took a deep breath and smiled. 'I want to tell you that although he doesn't care for me, I liked your father. I think I understand him – and he looks like you. Or, of course, you look like him.'

'Viktor, that's nice of you. Fancy you saying you liked Dad when he wanted to throw you out! You will come again, then? Meet my sisters? They're dying to meet you!'

'Of course I will!'

As they clung together for one last passionate embrace, suddenly the future seemed very slightly brighter, and when they had to part, they knew they'd meet tomorrow.

Thirty

In the end, rather than having Viktor come to the flat again, it was decided that he, with Jinny, should meet May and Vi one day for lunch.

'Just our usual place will be fine,' Jinny told him. 'May can easily walk there from the hat shop and if we make it in February, when Vi's taking a few days off, she can come too.'

'Vi is the one who works for a clothing firm?'

'Yes, in Accounts like me. She's very keen on social reform, very political. May's just calm and sweet.'

'Engaged to the nice watchmaker who found your brooch for me?'

'And, surprise, surprise, has been accepted by Dad. Sort of.'

'Me next, then,' Viktor said cheerfully, though both knew, of course, that his case was very different from Allan's.

A date was fixed for mid-February and on a dismal wet day, Viktor and the sisters gathered at the small West End café Jinny had suggested and, after they'd hung up their umbrellas and mackintoshes, introductions were made and they sat down to order.

Tomato soup, Welsh rarebit and macaroni cheese were the choices, plus Viktor's sausages, and as they ate they all made easy conversation, with May and Vi covertly sizing up Viktor, while he remained his usual courteous self.

He likes them, thought Jinny with relief, and they like him. Even Vi, always less outgoing than May, seemed to be resting her dark eyes on Viktor's handsome face with approval, though of course

she'd be reserving true judgement on him until she knew more of
his views on how the world should be run. So far, so good, though,
with May really seeming charmed, and Viktor the same.

'So sorry you had a bit of trouble with Dad,' May told him, as
she finished her Welsh rarebit – a dish that had intrigued Viktor
because of its name. 'He'll come round, though, I'm sure. He has
with Allan, anyway.'

'I understand his worries,' Viktor replied. 'The situation is not easy.'

'People can alter situations,' said Vi. 'Depends if they know what
they really want.'

'That's what's not easy,' put in Jinny. 'Sometimes you want
everything.'

'I'll get the pudding menu,' Viktor said smoothly. 'They do a very
nice jam tart here.'

'Tell you what I've been seeing lately in the papers,' Vi remarked
when the puddings had been ordered, 'and that's the name of your
chancellor, Viktor. Kurt Schuschnigg?'

'Vi always reads the foreign news,' May confided. 'More than I
do, I'm afraid.'

'Yes, he's been in the news lately,' Viktor agreed. 'For his meetings
with Hitler.'

'Looks like they haven't gone well,' said Vi. 'Seemingly, Hitler
wants this *Anschluss*, and your chancellor doesn't.'

'What's an *anschluss*?' asked May.

'It means "union",' Jinny told her, with some pride. 'So, here,
the union of Austria with Germany. I looked it up.'

'That's correct.' Viktor's smile was strained. 'I hope it will not happen.'

'Doesn't Hitler usually get what he wants?' asked Vi.

'Well, there's talk of our chancellor organizing something to find
out Austrians' views. If most people don't want it I don't see how
Hitler can force it through.'

Vi raised her eyebrows. 'You don't? From what I've heard he's
good at forcing.'

'Whatever happens, I wish I could have been there.' Viktor glanced
quickly at Jinny. 'Only to vote, I mean. This is so important.'

'Oh, yes,' she agreed, but a coldness was running down her spine
and it was with obvious effort that she asked if he would be going
home. 'Just for the vote,' she added hastily.

'No, no, I don't think I can do that. I'll just have to rely on
others to do the right thing.' Viktor's expression brightened. 'I see
our puddings are on the way. I'll order coffee to follow, shall I?'

'Brave man,' said Jinny, feeling better. 'Viktor has a problem with our coffee,' she told her sisters, who laughed.

'Suppose you know why we're a nation of tea drinkers, then?' asked Vi. 'Maybe you should start serving coffee along with your *Sachertorte*, eh?'

'A brilliant idea,' said Viktor.

Everything was so relaxed, so pleasant, that when they stood outside under their umbrellas they agreed they must all meet again, next time with Allan.

'And our treat,' said May. 'It's been so nice, Viktor. We're so glad we've met you and we want to thank you, don't we, Vi?'

'Certainly do. I say we should all go to the theatre as well. Get some tickets from Dad. He likes us to take an interest in his handiwork.'

'I'd like that very much,' Viktor told them, raising his hat as May set off for her hat shop and Vi went to catch a tram. 'Jinny, I mean that. Your sisters are delightful – I'd be very happy to meet them again.'

'So glad,' Jinny replied, taking his arm as they turned to make their way to Comrie's. 'I can tell they were very impressed with you.'

'Can't believe that. But May, she's so lovely – and Vi, she's like you! Very sharp, too, I should say. I can see her doing well in politics.'

'Anything that will let her make things better for ordinary folk.' Jinny glanced up at Viktor as they splashed along the streaming pavements. 'Viktor, I'm sorry you're so worried about things back home. I can tell you are, but it may all work out well, you know. You're right, I'm sure – Hitler can't force a union of Germany with Austria if the people don't want it.'

'Yes, that's what I think. Or, at least, I hope.'

But only a few weeks later they had to read in the paper that Hitler and his Nazis had marched in triumph into Vienna and been accepted by the Austrians. Hitler had cancelled the peoples' plebiscite, Chancellor Schuschnigg had resigned and might be facing imprisonment, and the *Anschluss* was now a fact. Austria and Germany were one.

Thirty-One

'I can't believe it,' said Viktor, sitting with Jinny in the lounge bar of a West End hotel, his face so pale, so distraught, he seemed quite strange. They had planned to go to the pictures, but when he met Jinny from work he seemed so low in spirits that as soon as he asked if they could go for a drink first, she'd agreed. After all, the hotel was not a pub, where women would not generally be welcome, and though she knew her father didn't like her drinking out, a glass of wine wouldn't hurt. He wasn't to know about it, anyway.

'I knew you'd be upset when you saw the papers today,' she said, studying Viktor worriedly, after the waiter had served their drinks – a sweet German wine for her and a Scottish beer for Viktor. 'You were hoping it wouldn't happen, weren't you? This *Anschluss?*'

'Of course I was. I never thought Austrians would welcome Hitler the way they did.'

'Though you've never said much against him yourself, Viktor.'

'Not while he didn't try to interfere with my country. But uniting us with Nazi Germany makes me see him very differently. There's always been talk against him, of what he's doing to Jewish people, for instance, but I never knew quite what to believe. Now I think I can believe anything.'

'I read it was the Austrian Nazis who welcomed him to your country. Did you know about them?'

Viktor sighed heavily. 'Oh, yes. My uncle let me telephone my father today. He feels as bad as I do, but he told me a lot of his customers are Nazis and are very keen for the union. So they're the ones who've let it happen.'

'And what does your mother think of it all?' Jinny asked after a pause.

'Oh, she's absolutely furious! She's never wanted to be part of Germany – she remembers the war too well.' Viktor gave slight smile. 'She wants me to go home, of course.'

Jinny set down her glass, her face showing her feelings. 'Viktor you won't, will you? You won't go back home yet?'

'It's just that everything's so uncertain, Jinny. Our fate is tied up with Germany's now. What they'll do, what we'll do, and if there's a war—'

'There won't be a war, Viktor! There's no need for you to go home early. We agreed, didn't we, that we'd give ourselves time before we made things official, and how can we do that if you leave me now?' While she kept her gaze fixed on his face, she was close to tears, fighting not to let them fall. 'Tell me you won't go!'

'*Liebchen*, don't worry, I'm not making plans to go back yet.' He reached across to press her hand. 'I've discussed it with my uncle and we've agreed I should stay on unless there is a real threat of war.'

'Thank God,' she said simply, withdrawing her hand from his so that she could wipe her eyes. 'I don't know what I'd have done if you'd left me now. I mean, I'm not ready – not prepared—'

'But Jinny . . .' He hesitated. 'You do realize that if Germany does start a war, I'll have no choice but to go back? Now that we are part of Germany, I'll be eligible for war service.'

'On their side? Oh, Viktor! How can you fight for Germany when you don't trust Hitler?'

'What else can I do? I'll be conscripted.'

As the words sank in, Jinny shivered. 'I never thought you'd be talking about fighting – I mean, at all. It's like a bad dream, a nightmare—'

'But may not happen in real life, Jinny.'

'It might.'

'I was painting the darkest picture, that's all.' Viktor sat up, straightening his shoulders, running his hand across his brow. 'Look, I'm sorry, *liebchen*, it seems I've been unloading all my fears on to you, and I shouldn't have done because we don't know what's going to happen. I may have been frightening you for nothing. There may be no war, no question of my going into the army. Please forgive me.'

At once she brightened, a smile lighting her whole face, her eyes softening with a look of love as she touched his hand. 'Viktor, there's nothing to forgive! If you aren't going home yet and we can just follow our plan – oh, that's all I want!'

'I want that too.' He looked down at their glasses. 'Would you like another drink, Jinny? Or should we still go to the cinema and see that picture you mentioned?'

'I don't want another drink, thanks, but I'd love to see the picture. Just to relax for a bit . . . move into another world.'

'What's it called, then?'

Jinny looked a little embarrassed. '*The Divorce of Lady X* – sounds silly, but it's supposed to be a comedy.'

'About divorce?'

'I think it all ends happily. Merle Oberon's the star – she's lovely – and Laurence Olivier.'

'And he's handsome, I suppose?'

When they'd put on their coats, hats, scarves and gloves against the winter wind outside and Viktor had paid the bill, he opened the double doors of the hotel and held them wide for Jinny.

'Come on, then, let's move into this other world and forget ours for a bit.'

'Not all of it,' said Jinny as she took his arm, and together they ran down Princes Street for their tram.

Thirty-Two

As the year 1938 progressed through spring to summer, it seemed strange to those worrying about possible war that everything seemed so normal. Though Hitler's name appeared in the papers often enough, it was usually in connection with Czechoslovakia or the Sudetenland, and didn't, to the general public, seem to involve Great Britain. What, after all, was the Sudetenland? Something to do with Germany? Nothing to worry about, anyway.

In Scotland, there was the British Empire Exhibition, opened by George VI in Glasgow in May, to provide excitement and pride, and even though the weather was dismal, crowds flocked to see the handsome 'palaces' and stands concerned with arts and trades, while all thought of the international situation was put aside.

Certainly, no one discussed it at Comrie's Bakery, where life continued as usual, except that Viktor's cakes became ever more popular and he and his assistants had to struggle to meet demand. Which seemed, in fact, to suit Viktor, who threw himself into his work with so much dedication he began to look far from well and excited the motherly attention of Mrs Arrow, who said he needed beef tea and glasses of stout to 'build himself up', while Mabel Hyslop even went so far to speak to Jinny about it.

'It's really worrying to see a young man look so run down,' she remarked one coffee break. 'I really think you should have a word with him, Jinny.'

'Why me?' Jinny asked, flushing and avoiding meeting Ross's eye.

'You're the one to do it, dear – everyone knows you two are close.'

Jinny drank her coffee. 'As a matter of fact, I have told him he's doing too much, but he – well, he has a lot on his mind at the minute.'

'Oh, yes, I can quite see that, poor boy, being in a foreign country and so on. I expect he'll be wanting to get home.'

'He's due home in November, Mabel.'

'Yes, but he might want to go earlier – just in case anything happens. Though it all seems to have gone quiet, eh?' Saying she'd better get back to work, Mabel collected the coffee cups for washing and removed herself, at which Jinny gave a sigh of relief.

'Poor Mabel,' said Ross. 'She's only trying to help.' He gave Jinny a meditative look. 'I take it Viktor is not going home yet?'

'No, he isn't. But it's true what I said – he does worry.'

'About the *Anschluss*? I can believe a chap away from his country would be worried if it suddenly became part of another one. But you're worried too, aren't you, Jinny? You're not looking a whole lot better than Viktor.'

'I've got Dad to think about,' she said after a pause. 'He was upset before, to think I might go to Vienna, but now it's a part of Germany he thinks the worst has happened.' She sighed and looked down at the column of figures she should have been adding up. 'He always did call Viktor a German – says now he was right all along.'

'I'm sorry, Jinny. Look, if you ever want a shoulder to cry on, you know mine's available.' Ross studied her, concerned.

'I do, Ross, and thanks.' She gave a weak smile. 'But listen, you might be able to tell me something – I don't want to ask Viktor as I'm trying not to talk to him about Hitler. But what is this Sudetenland Hitler's so interested in?'

'The Sudetenland? Well, I'm no expert – only know what I've picked up from the papers – but apparently it's a part of Czechoslovakia. About three million Germans live there from the time it was Bohemia, and Hitler wants them to have self government. The problem is that the Czechs say no.'

'And Hitler's annoyed?'

'You bet, but we and France are on his side and they've told Benes – he's the Czech President – to do what Hitler wants. Instead, Benes has started mobilizing troops.' Ross shrugged. 'Can't see Hitler accepting that.'

'He'll go to war?' Jinny asked fearfully.

'He might.'

Germany could go to war? Jinny's heart plummeted. That meant Austria would also go to war. And Viktor too? He'd said nothing, but maybe he was already thinking again of going home? Of becoming a soldier? No wonder he seemed so low recently.

'Hitler hasn't declared war yet,' she said, trying to appear calm. 'Maybe he won't?'

'Well, we'll do all we can to prevent it. But if you're worrying about Viktor, I think he'll be all right. He's over here, that's the good thing.'

'But he might want to go home.'

'He needn't, unless there's a definite declaration. There'll be a lot of diplomatic activity going on behind the scenes, and the whole thing could be sorted out without war. You could tell him that, Jinny.'

'I will, but whether he'll listen or not, I don't know.'

As they'd arranged to meet at lunchtime, at least she'd have a chance to speak to Viktor then, for which she was grateful. Returning at last to her work, she knew she could not have got through the day without knowing what she had to face.

But it was all right. As soon as Viktor saw her anxious face, he held her hands outside the bakery and managed a smile.

'*Liebchen*, what have you been thinking? That I'm planning to go home again? No need to worry – I'm not.'

'But Ross was saying that Hitler might be going to declare war on Czechoslovakia, and that would mean—'

'I know what it would mean, but I speak regularly now to my father and he says the talk at home is that Hitler will be holding his fire. Nobody knows, of course, what's in his mind, but there's every chance he doesn't want to start a war at present.'

'Viktor, that's wonderful! Wonderful! I've been so worried – and you've been looking so down lately. I thought you were sure to want to go back—'

'Not yet. Come on, let's have something to eat.'

Over a secluded table in their usual café, Jinny studied him, seeing beyond his smile the lustreless look of his fine eyes, the dispirited air that had replaced his confident manner, and she shook her head.

'You are feeling low, aren't you? People seem to be noticing . . . Are you ill—'

'I know, I get advice on all sides. Should have a holiday, should have beef tea, should have milk stout, whatever that is!' He shrugged. 'But there's nothing wrong with me. It's just that I feel weighed down by what's happened to my country. And that my people let it happen. You can understand that, Jinny?'

'Of course I can! It's no wonder you feel bad, when Austria has lost its independence.'

'Not just its independence.' Viktor's voice was low. 'It's lost its heart.'

They ordered their usual soup but were without appetite, and afterwards had only coffee and called early for the bill.

'I'd better get back to the bakery,' Viktor told Jinny outside the café. 'We are having so many orders now we have to work flat out to keep up.'

'It's too much, Viktor. You're doing too much.'

'No, it's good to be busy. Helps me to forget for a while.'

'You know what I think?' she asked, with an attempt at lightness. 'You should help yourself to a great slice of your own *Sachertorte* – that would be better than Mrs Arrow's beef tea or milk stout!'

'*Sachertorte?*' Viktor gave a genuine laugh. '*Liebchen*, have you never realized that I don't like cakes? Especially my own. I am like someone in one of your sweetshops who never eats a chocolate.'

'Oh, Viktor, it's so good to see you laugh! Promise me we'll be happy again one day, when all this is over!'

'When I think of you, Jinny, I'm happy now,' he said seriously, and touching his thin cheek, she wondered – could she believe him? But as they separated, he to return to the bakery, she to Accounts, she knew in her heart that at that time it would take more than thoughts of her to make him happy.

Thirty-Three

She found only her father and Vi at home when she let herself into the flat, May being out with Allan, but Vi was busy cooking and Josh was listening to the wireless.

'Let's just get the news,' he told Jinny, meaning she was not to talk, which was no hardship as she didn't feel like talking anyway. Vi, though, was ready to chat when Jinny joined her at the gas cooker, first asking how poor Viktor was, as he'd been so down in the dumps when they'd all gone to a play recently. And then, keeping her voice down, she reported that she was sure something was up with May.

'How d'you mean?' asked Jinny, beginning to strain the potatoes ready for mashing.

'Well, when she went out she just seemed, you know, all agog about something.'

'She's usually in a happy mood when she's meeting Allan.'

'Aye, but this was something special. I didn't ask her what was going on – she was in a hurry – but we'll see how she is when she comes back.' Vi was opening the oven and inspecting her fish pie. 'This looks done – thought I'd give you a change from my fried haddock. Let's serve up and get on – I've a meeting tonight.'

Oh, good, thought Jinny as they served the meal and called to Josh to the table. It looked like she'd have a nice quiet evening to herself, maybe do her mending, listen to the wireless and try not to think how much she'd rather have been with Viktor. Down in the dumps he might be, but he was still the one she wanted to be with, and always would be. Lucky May, out with her dear Allan!

Lucky May indeed, for when she came home – quite late – she brought Allan with her and a piece of good news too, as her family only needed to look at her to realize. Josh was back from the theatre, Vi from her meeting, and Jinny, feeling virtuous, had finished all her mending, but all eyes were on May, looking so flushed and lovely in her blue jacket and matching dress as she stood in the doorway next to a smiling Allan.

'What is it?' Josh asked shortly. 'What's happened?'

'Oh, Dad, Vi, Jinny – we have something to tell you!'

'Not that it's really news,' put in Allan.

'It's official news,' said May, and she held out her left hand, on which a ring was glittering. 'We're engaged!'

There was a short silence, then Vi and Jinny sprang to their sister and hugged her, while Josh rose slowly to his feet.

'Engaged,' he repeated.

'I know I should have spoken to you first, Mr Hendrie,' Allan said hurriedly, 'but I think you knew what was going to happen, didn't you? We did say, right from the beginning, didn't we? I'm afraid I told May I'd be collecting the ring today, and when we met I couldn't resist putting it on her finger.'

'Collecting the ring?' Josh repeated. 'It's no' from your shop, then?'

'Oh, no, I've nothing in stock I'd want to give May. I knew the very one she liked – we'd seen it in the window of a jeweller's in town and I had her finger measurements, so I went back and got it, and here it is!'

Everyone, even Josh, studied the diamond ring on May's finger, which was beautifully set in a little circlet of pearls and was, apart from Jinny's Edelweiss brooch, the prettiest thing they'd ever seen.

'It's truly lovely,' Jinny said softly, and kissed first May and then Allan. 'And we're all so happy for you, aren't we, Dad?'

'Come on,' ordered Vi. 'Congratulate them, or at least Allan. Isn't that what you're supposed to do?'

'You are happy, Dad?' May asked, her voice trembling. 'I want you to be pleased – so much.'

'Aye, all right, then,' he said gruffly. 'If you're happy, I'll . . . I'll say I am.'

'Oh, Dad!' She threw her arms round him and kissed him, while Allan stood waiting to shake his hand.

'Pity we've nothing to offer in the way of celebration,' said Vi. 'You should have given us warning.'

'Don't worry, we've got a celebration planned for Sunday at my place. May's going to do lunch for us and you're all to come. Right?'

'As though we'd say no!' cried Vi, and everyone laughed as Jinny said she'd make the usual tea, which would have to stand in for a celebration for the time being.

It was while she was making the tea that Allan told her quietly that if she wanted to bring Viktor on Sunday, he'd be very welcome.

'Oh, but what about Dad?' whispered Jinny. 'We wouldn't want to cause trouble.'

'Ask Viktor first and see what he says, then we'll speak to your father.'

It sounded such a wonderful idea, Jinny couldn't believe it the next day when Viktor said he was most grateful but he really didn't think he should come. Just as Jinny herself had feared, he didn't want to cause trouble on her sister's lovely day, but he sent his congratulations and wished her every happiness.

And so do I, thought Jinny sadly. My lucky sister, May.

All she could hope was that she and Viktor would be happy too. There was no alternative she could bear.

Thirty-Four

As the wet, dreary summer progressed, May's happiness was all that cheered Jinny. She and Viktor still met when off duty, going around together to cinemas, cafés and so on, just like any couple who might soon be ready to declare their love to the world. Except that Jinny never felt they were like other couples in that way at all.

She knew how things had been for her and Viktor before his country had been annexed by Germany, and could tell the difference between how he'd been then and how he was now. He'd been so happy in those early days, running to meet her, his blue eyes shining, desperate to spend time with her. Whilst now, though he still wanted to be with her – yes, she was sure of that, sure he still loved her – now a change had come over him, cancelling out that delicious anticipation and making him seem preoccupied with a world that was outside theirs, a world she couldn't know.

They had stuck to their plan of waiting until November before telling the world of their love, but how were they to know now how their love would be affected by what had happened to Viktor's country? Or by the anxiety caused by Hitler over possible war?

In spite of all this, she had to believe that when the time came they would still be able to marry and that she would go to Vienna, for even if the international situation worsened, she was determined that she and Viktor would be together. How it would all work out, she didn't know, but if they loved each other, which they did, it would work out somehow. Whatever change had come over Viktor, of that she was certain. The important thing was just to keep going as normally as possible and see what happened. Just what everyone else was doing, no doubt, in Great Britain and in France.

In August, though, things took a turn for the worse. Reports came out that thousands of German soldiers were massing on the Czech border, and though no action was taken, there was a feeling in the air that trouble was simmering and might soon come to the boil. In September, Hitler made a speech at the huge Nuremberg rally, guaranteed to stir the pot by calling Czechoslovakia a 'fraudulent state'. It was after this that the British Prime Minister, Neville Chamberlain, asked for a personal meeting with Hitler, which was granted, and on the fifteenth of September he arrived at Berchtesgaden, Hitler's home in the Bavarian Alps. The people of Europe held their breath.

'What do you think will happen now?' Jinny asked Viktor, whose face wore its usual look of strain.

'Nothing good, I'm afraid.'

'Why do you say that? We've got a great empire and Mr Chamberlain's our prime minister – why shouldn't Hitler listen to him?'

'He might listen, but he'll still do what he wants to do. And he won't care about your empire, except to conquer it.'

'You used to say he wouldn't be interested in attacking us!'

'That was before he took my country,' Viktor said bleakly.

There was nothing left to do but wait to see what the papers said after Chamberlain had returned home, and when they appeared, it seemed that there might be some hope of a settlement. But it was not to be. Though Czechoslovakia had eventually agreed that parts of the Sudetenland could be returned to Germany and Hitler had seemed to be satisfied, only a week or so later he demanded all of the Sudetenland. After another trip to see him, Chamberlain admitted that the stage looked set for war.

Gas masks were being issued, air-raid shelters were being built, and everyone was beginning to fear the worst, but there was one last hope. Mr Chamberlain, it was reported, had left for yet another meeting with Hitler, this time in Munich. If it were to fail, well, the abyss might be waiting, but no one cared to think about that.

The thirtieth of September was the day Mr Chamberlain was due back, and, like the whole country, staff and customers at Comrie's were agog for news. Being a Friday and wages day, Jinny, as part of her routine, went with Terry as usual to the bakery, where of course her eyes instantly sought out Viktor.

He was at his work table, surrounded by layers of sponge cake and bowls of an elaborate egg and butter cream, seemingly completely oblivious to his surroundings as he poured caramel syrup over one of the sponge layers which he then set aside and called, 'Bob!'

As Bob came hurrying over, Jinny moved forward, smiling. 'Viktor?'

He looked up and for a moment stared, as though he couldn't take it in that she was near him, then returned her smile. 'Jinny! What are you doing here?'

'Don't expect Viktor to know it's pay day!' cried Senga, coming over from her work icing small cakes to laugh with Terry, who had sauntered along to join her. 'He doesn't have to think about it like the rest of us!'

'Pay day, of course,' Viktor only replied mildly. 'Nice to see you, Jinny. Just wait till I get Bob to pour this caramel over another layer.'

'We're doing a *Dobertorte*,' sandy-haired Bob announced proudly as he picked up a pan of caramel syrup. 'That's the Hungarian cake with layers, you ken, and the Devil's own job to make – aye, and we're doing two!' He rolled his eyes.

'Oh, yes,' Jinny said hurriedly, nodding coolly to Senga before fixing her eyes on Viktor again. 'It's not just pay day today, though, is it? Mr Chamberlain's coming back from Munich and he might have good news, Aren't you excited?'

'You bet,' said Bob.

'Sure,' said Terry, 'I'm walking on pins till we hear.'

'Me, too,' said Senga.

But Viktor's blue eyes on Jinny showed no excitement, no shine, and after a moment he looked away. 'There is no point in getting excited, as there will be no good news.'

'You don't know that!' cried Jinny.

'Whatever Mr Chamberlain brings back from Hitler, it will not be peace.'

He sounded so definite, and yet so defeated, they all stared at him in surprise, Jinny with a hollow feeling inside, as though she'd been expecting something good and been refused.

'I don't understand—' she was beginning when she heard Mr Whyte's voice calling to her.

'Jinny, have you got the wage packets? How about coming to my office?'

'On . . . on my way!' she called, turning, then looking back at Viktor, at which he moved swiftly to her side. Disregarding interested eyes, he put his hand on her arm.

'Jinny, may I see you this evening?'

'We don't usually meet on a Friday.'

'I know, but I'd like to, tonight.'

At the urgency of his tone, the appeal in his eyes, she knew she could not refuse.

'All right. I'll ring May at the shop to say I won't be home.' She hesitated. 'You'll come to Accounts?'

'Outside. Let's meet outside.'

'Till tonight, then.'

Now the appeal in his eyes had faded as his face took on its defeated look again, but Jinny had to move on, into Mr Whyte's office, leaving Viktor to return to his table.

At first he did not speak, only stared down into a bowl of butter cream, then raised his eyes to Bob.

'Finished covering that top layer?'

'Aye, I hope it'll be OK. This is no' ma favourite cake to make, you ken. Too fiddly.'

'You're doing very well, Bob. I am confident you will be able to take over from me when I leave.'

'Oh, God, Viktor, that's no' yet, is it?'

'We'll just let the caramel on the top layers almost set,' Viktor replied smoothly, 'and then we can begin assembling the cakes. Six layers for each. Think you remember what we do?'

'We fill the cakes with the butter cream, and just before the syrup sets on the top layers, we cut it into sections.' Bob groaned. 'And hope it doesna crack, eh?'

'If you oil the knife it shouldn't crack.' Viktor smiled. 'Well done, Bob. Don't forget to ice the sides of the cakes with the butter cream and finish off the tops with a few twirls of icing.'

'Don't move away until I've done all that, eh? Cutting thae sections, it's nerve-racking!'

'Don't worry, you'll be fine,' Viktor told him, clapping him on the back. 'I promise you!'

'Bit of a pessimist, young Viktor,' Terry remarked when he and Jinny were on their way to Morningside. 'According to him, we can't win, whatever happens.'

'If there's no war, he'll be pleased,' Jinny declared. 'I know he will; he couldn't be anything else.'

'Well, if he isn't happy, the rest of us will be, that's for sure. I reckon folk'll go mad with relief if we get a promise of peace. I mean, who wants another do like the last one?'

Thirty-Five

Terry was proved right, for when the news came through that Mr Chamberlain had arrived at the airport declaring there was to be 'peace for our time', the BBC reported that the whole country appeared to be going wild. As he waved the piece of paper Hitler and other politicians had signed, promising that there would definitely be no war, the cheers for him echoed. He was called a hero; he was summoned to Buckingham Palace to meet the king and queen; he was cheered again in Downing Street, feted everywhere he went on the day that no one had dared to hope would ever come.

For Comrie's, the news came before closing time and, like everyone else, staff and customers were hugging and shaking hands, some even shedding a few tears – Jinny, for one. As she and Mabel hugged Ross and shook hands with a beaming Mr Comrie, she felt her eyes smart, but she'd never been happier, for in the euphoria of the moment she was sure that Viktor's depressing thoughts would not survive the really good news they'd all heard. 'Peace for our time' – what could be more wonderful?

Now the two of them could go ahead in the knowledge that the future held no fears, and Viktor would realize that her love for him was as strong as it had ever been.

Although Mr Comrie regretted that he couldn't provide drinks for everyone, he declared that Accounts people at least should have a wee dram of his good whisky, or maybe sherry, if Jinny and Mabel would prefer?

'I think I'd better have the sherry,' Mabel said, giggling. 'I'm sure to feel a bit tipsy, anyway.'

'What better day than today to feel tipsy?' asked Mr Comrie and, as Jinny also opted for sherry, Ross caught her eye and winked, indicating he thought Mr Comrie had already sampled his own whisky. Why not, though? For this was a very special day.

'It's so good to see you looking so happy,' Ross whispered to Jinny as they moved to the windows to look down on crowds of shoppers stopping to shake one another's hands. 'All seems to be going right at last.'

'Oh, yes, I couldn't feel better, and I know Viktor will be feeling the same.'

'No doubt of that.' Ross drank some whisky. 'This news will have special meaning for him.'

'And for me, Ross!'

'Yes, but I'm thinking of his country. Now it won't be drawn into a war alongside Germany. And his country does matter to him, doesn't it?'

'Very much,' she answered, looking into her glass. 'Ross, mind if I use the office phone to ring May? I'm meeting Viktor instead of going home.'

'Of course you can ring her. And I'm not surprised you and Viktor want to go out tonight. This is a time for celebrating.'

'Will you be, too?' Jinny asked with unashamed curiosity

'Oh, yes! I promised that if we got good news I'd take Lorna out for a meal.'

'Lorna?'

'My cousin, you remember? Came up at Christmas with my uncle and aunt, but she's on her own this time. A friend got married here last week and Lorna's stayed on for a few days.'

'Oh, nice,' remarked Jinny, remembering the pretty redhead at the Christmas party. And she was genuinely pleased that Ross would be out 'on the town' that evening. Was he really coming out of his shell at last?

'More sherry, Jinny? Mabel?' asked Mr Comrie. 'Another whisky, Ross?'

They thanked him but refused, as it was in fact already time to finish work. What a relief! Though even Mabel wasn't tipsy on one drink, they really felt quite intoxicated with the events of the day and their avoidance of the abyss. Though they would all have to be back at work on Saturday morning, the evening was theirs to enjoy, and as Jinny began to run down the stairs she felt on wings, she was so happy. Until, suddenly, her steps slowed.

A memory of Viktor's face as she had last seen it – so depressed, so defeated – flashed into her mind and drew her eventually to a halt. Supposing . . . Supposing, when she saw him, he appeared just the same? If, in spite of so much joy on every side, he hadn't changed? No, it wasn't possible. Now that there was a definite agreement for peace from all who'd signed Mr Chamberlain's document, including Hitler, Viktor must be happy about it. He must be feeling as she was feeling . . . mustn't he?

She moved slowly onwards, down the stairs as far as the door to the street. When she went through that, if Viktor was there, waiting, as soon as saw him she would know. Yes, just from his face, she would know. And sure enough, when she pushed open the door and saw him waiting in the street, she did.

Thirty-Six

As soon as she saw him waiting, wearing a light overcoat over his suit and a dark trilby hat over his fair hair, she knew he hadn't changed. He hadn't been won over by Mr Chamberlain's paper. There would, in his opinion, be no peace. All this she knew from his face, though its look was different now, being neither depressed nor defeated, but unhappy — which did not deter her from deciding to argue the case for Hitler's wanting peace as soon as she got the chance.

'Viktor, you're here already!' she cried as cheerfully as she could. 'Not getting wet, are you?'

'I believe the rain has stopped,' he replied, holding out a hand. 'But do you have your umbrella?'

What were they talking about? Rain? Umbrellas? When the world might be righting itself around them and they should be celebrating?

'Sorry, I never thought about it.' She slipped her arm into his. 'So, where are we going? Our usual place?'

'I've booked at Ritchie's in the Old Town. You said you liked it when we went before.'

'Oh, yes, but it's a bit smart. I'm not dressed for it.' She looked down at her everyday blue coat and put her hand to her blue beret. 'I see you've put on your suit.'

'You look lovely, you always do.'

'Ritchie's is more expensive, too.' Her face brightened. 'Viktor, are you celebrating, after all? I should tell you, I've already had a sherry from your uncle.'

'A sherry? What next?' He laughed as they made their way through good-humoured Princes Street crowds towards a tram stop, though it seemed to her that his laughter was not quite natural. Or was she seeing things that weren't there? Maybe, but she didn't believe he was celebrating — at least, not in the way he should be. If she could only get him to believe what everyone else was happy to believe, how much happier he'd be . . .

They were early at the restaurant but glad they'd booked for it was unusually busy, with many people deciding to dine out in recognition of Mr Chamberlain's heroic act in saving the country from war. Wine was flowing and the talk was loud, but Viktor, ordering a bottle of a German wine he liked, said it was all to the good if people were noisy.

'If we want to talk, no one will be listening,' he explained, studying the menu as Jinny studied him. Though the restaurant lights were far from bright, she could see now that he seemed not just unhappy but also on edge, his eyes staying on the menu, evidently unwilling to meet hers.

'Are we here to talk?' she asked lightly. 'Because I do want to say a few things myself.'

'Oh?' At last, he looked at her. 'What sort of things?'

'Well, I can tell that you're not going to accept we now have peace, and I'm going to persuade you to change your mind. Be like everyone else, Viktor! Be happy that Hitler is sincere and doesn't want war, and let's get on with our lives!'

Very carefully, he laid down the menu and again rested his eyes on her face. 'Jinny, please listen to me. It's not true what you say about Hitler and it will do no good to believe it. I only wish it were otherwise.'

As Jinny opened her mouth to reply, a waiter appeared to serve their wine, followed by another, who asked if they were ready to order.

'Are we?' asked Viktor. 'Any preferences, Jinny?'

They settled on a melon first course, followed by a poultry dish, and breathed a sigh of relief when both waiters had gone.

'Now I can answer you,' said Jinny eagerly, but Viktor held up his hand.

'Let's leave it for now. There's a lounge here, if you remember, where we can have coffee and won't be disturbed. That will be best.'

Suddenly she was afraid, with a coldness surrounding her heart that was not soothed by the wine she began to sip. 'You really do want to talk to me?' she asked hesitantly, keeping her eyes down when he said he did.

Better not try to read his face. And better not drink any more wine, in case a clear head were needed. *Thud, thud, thud* went her heart, and it was with relief that she saw their waiter arriving with their first course. Now there would be something to do, thank God, other than worrying about what Viktor wanted to say.

Thirty-Seven

All too soon they were together in the lounge, coffee on the table before them, no one else around except a couple in the corner who had no eyes for them. Only a nearby mirror seemed to show another couple, but it was just their reflections, Jinny's and Viktor's, both looking pale, their eyes dark smudges, even his – but that must have been a trick of the light.

'Mind if I smoke?' he asked, as Jinny turned her gaze from the mirror.

'You know I never mind. Is this coffee all right for you?'

'Not bad at all. Better than most.'

'That's good.'

Watching him light a cigarette, she saw that his hand was trembling. He was nervous, then. Nervous, and unhappy.

'What is it you wanted to say?' she asked, drinking her coffee, her own hand trembling as she held the cup.

'I – the truth is – I don't want to say it.' He drew on the cigarette. 'Perhaps you've guessed what it is, anyway?'

'Just tell me.'

'Jinny – *liebchen* – I have to go back to Vienna. Quite soon. It's not much earlier than I would have gone anyway, but I don't want to delay.'

Silence descended. The couple in the corner rose and went out. No one else came. Jinny did not speak.

'Please,' Viktor said at last. 'Please, say something, Jinny. I know how you must be feeling, I feel so bad myself—'

'I'm trying to take it in, Viktor, what you've told me. You've made a decision to go home? And that's yours alone? I thought we were going to make a decision together? Isn't that what we said?'

'Things have changed. We don't have the same choices now.'

'Why? All that's changed is that there's going to be no war. I'd have thought that'd make things easier for us.'

He shook his head. 'Jinny, please, listen. It's as I said, Mr Chamberlain has not achieved peace, whatever is written on his paper. Hitler has no intention of honouring his promise and, when he's ready, he will strike. I have to be in my own country when that happens. I can't afford to be trapped here, where I'd just be interned as a foreigner. You do see that?'

'No, because I don't know why you're so sure that Hitler wants war. How do you know? You can't know!'

'I do know,' he said wearily, and with a last draw on his cigarette, stubbed it out. 'I know because my father has told me what his Nazi customers have told him. Hitler has no respect for Chamberlain, he finds him irritating and foolish, and will have no hesitation in going to war with Great Britain when the time comes.' Viktor stretched out his hand to take Jinny's. 'So you see, my dearest, why I must go home.'

'Yes, I see,' she said quietly, staring down at their clasped hands. 'You have to go, so you must take me with you.'

It was Viktor's turn to fall silent. He withdrew his hand from Jinny's and ran it over his face as she sat watching, her eyes alight, her lips parted.

'Why not?' she cried. 'Why not, Viktor? If we love each other?'

'Oh, Jinny, we do, we do! But there is no way you can come with me to Vienna the way things are. You'd be a foreigner, from a country likely to be an enemy – it would never work out. I could never let you do it.'

'But if we were married? I'd be with you, part of your family—'

'It would make no difference – you'd still be under suspicion. And how would your family feel, if war comes, as it will, and you were living in an enemy country? You could never put them through that.'

She was silent, coming face-to-face as never before with the difficulties, the near impossibility, of sharing the life of the man she loved in the present situation. If he was right and war between their two countries came about, he would not even be with her in Vienna but in the army, fighting her countrymen and women. She would be alone, regarded as an alien, an enemy, maybe even interned, as Viktor said he would be if he stayed in Scotland. There was no hope, no hope at all, of their being together, whichever country they were in.

Great tears began to fill her dark, tragic eyes and then slide silently down her cheeks. With a long sigh wrenched up from her unhappy heart, she dabbed at the tears with her hankie and rose to her feet.

'I think I should go home now, Viktor.'

'Of course.' He leaped up to be near her. 'I'll just get the bill and call a taxi.'

'A taxi? What are you talking about? We never take taxis.'

'Tonight, we will.'

'No, I'm taking the tram. You needn't come, Viktor. I'd like to be on my own, to sort out things out in my head. Where's my coat, then?'

His face quite white, he ran after her as she moved to the main restaurant, where a waiter helped her put her coat on and she pulled on her dark blue beret.

'Wait, Jinny, wait!' Viktor cried, scrambling into his raincoat. 'I have to pay the bill—'

She halted, shrugging. 'Be quick, then.'

People were staring but it was all right, she was not embarrassing him, they were not having a tiff at the end of their evening as lovers sometimes do. What was going wrong for them went much deeper than that, and it would have been childish not to leave together.

'Thank you,' Viktor said as they walked fast to the tram stop. 'Thank you for waiting, Jinny.'

'Thank you for dinner.'

'Oh, God, Jinny, you're not going to stop me taking you home, are you? I know how you are feeling, and I feel terrible about it, but it's not the end for us. We'll write, we'll keep in touch, and when it's all over we'll be really together. Truly together.'

'What are you saying, Viktor? We're engaged?'

He hesitated. 'You know we are. Not formally, maybe—'

'Not formally at all.'

'There is a reason, for that.'

'What reason?'

'Jinny, this isn't the time or place to talk. Let me come with you now—'

She turned her head, saw a tram in the distance, and sighed. 'All right, then, all right. I give in.'

'Thank God,' he said simply and, when the tram arrived, climbed on with her and sat close on the wooden seating. Both were exhausted and did not speak until they were in Fingal Street, outside the Hendries' flat.

Jinny said quietly, 'Tell me the reason, Viktor. Tell me why we can't be formally engaged.'

'It's difficult, Jinny. I don't want to sound too . . . pessimistic . . . but you have to think of the . . . situation.'

'If you're talking about the war, that shouldn't matter.'

'I'm talking about going to war, and—' He stopped. 'Look, you must know what I'm trying to say.'

'Going to war and not coming back?' she asked huskily. 'Viktor, that's why we should be engaged. So that I'd always have that, always know that's what we both wanted.'

'No,' he said definitely. 'No, if anything happens to me, I want you to have your own life. A properly fulfilled life, not just a string of memories. That's why I'm not going to let you tie yourself to me until we can be properly together.' He drew her into his arms and kissed her gently. 'So, let's just think of that happening, *liebchen*. Being together, making love – and don't ask me how often I think about that – but secure. In a world without war. That's what we have to work for, because it's all that matters.'

She leaned against him, her tears returning, wondering how she could have thought of not letting him be with her to say goodnight. It was the pain, she supposed, of his deciding to go home without her – it had been so hard to bear, especially when she'd been so happy thinking there could be something so different for them, now that there was peace. But Viktor did not believe in Hitler's peace. He was looking ahead to war and going off to fight, even accepting that he might not come back, and working out how things might be for her if he didn't.

Thinking of that, she clutched him compulsively, kissing him with all her strength and love.

'I think about making love, too,' she whispered. 'And sometimes I've wished – I've wondered – if we could be together like that. I mean, why not, Viktor?'

'You know why not, Jinny. Afterwards you might think differently, have regrets—'

'No, no, I wouldn't. If we were engaged.' In the light of the street lamp, her drenched eyes were tender. 'It's not too late, you know.'

'It's too early,' he said softly. 'Our time will come, though, I promise you. One day it will come.'

After they'd held each other in a vain attempt at comfort, Jinny slipped from his arms and took out her key.

'Would you like to come in for a minute, Viktor? No one's home yet – there's no light on.'

'I . . . maybe I'd better not. If your father were to see me he'd be upset.'

She was about to say not to worry, but instead smiled a little ruefully and waved at three figures in the distance.

'I see my sisters and Allan,' she murmured. 'They must have been out celebrating. But you must still come in.'

He didn't, though, and instead, when the sisters and Allan arrived and there'd been laughter and hugs, said he must get back.

'Oh, what a shame!' cried May. 'We've been over to Allan's to celebrate – had some of the neighbours in and had a wonderful time. Didn't we, Allan? Didn't we have a grand time?'

'With mine the only dissenting voice,' remarked Vi. 'Well, I had a grand time too, but shouldn't have done, really, seeing as I think Mr C. should never have signed that document with Hitler. Giving him everything he wanted! It was disgraceful!'

At which May said she was calling time on any more of that talk and now they must all go inside and she'd put the kettle on. Did Viktor really have to go?'

'I'm afraid so, but it's been wonderful to meet you all like this. Jinny, I'll see you tomorrow?'

Their eyes met.

'Tomorrow,' she agreed, and watched as he went down the street until she could see him no more, when she turned to join the others and hoped they wouldn't notice she'd been crying.

Thirty-Eight

Within three weeks, Viktor had gone. The worst three weeks of Jinny's life, she'd thought them. Until she said goodbye to him at Waverley Station and walked unseeingly back to Comrie's. It was then she realized that every day ahead was to be like this, filled with the searing pain of loss, and felt her knees almost buckle and her head swim, as though she had some sort of flu.

That Viktor felt the same – and she knew he did from his anguished face at the train window – gave her no comfort. In a way, it only made her feel worse, for his unhappiness seemed to make it clear that there was no real hope for them. If he could have been cheerful, telling her that this parting was only temporary and they would meet again soon, she might have been able to rally to cheerfulness too.

But of course, he couldn't pretend things weren't as they were, or that his clear-sightedness was mistaken – otherwise they would not have been saying goodbye. Even though they promised to write, and Jinny even said she'd be taking German lessons at evening class, they both knew this parting could be one of sorrow only, for there were no guarantees they would ever meet again.

How kind folk were, though! Jinny had never imagined her situation would bring such sympathy. Even her father, who was so relieved she was not going to Vienna, had taken her in his arms and said, 'Lassie, lassie, don't cry, he'll be back, eh? If there's no war, you'll see him again,' and she'd sobbed but been so grateful that he should try to help her.

And her sisters, of course, did all they could, trying to think of things to cheer her, pointing out that Viktor might have got it all wrong and there'd be peace after all, though Vi did not believe it, and May couldn't stop wondering what she would have done if she'd been left as Jinny had been and her Allan had gone to foreign parts.

The staff at Comrie's, though, were the most surprising to Jinny, for she knew there'd always been those who'd prophesied disaster for her if she went out with a foreigner, as well as those who'd teased and laughed, or felt a certain envy, and they might have taken a gloomy satisfaction in seeing her as she was now – abandoned, as it were. Yet that hadn't been the case at all. They'd all made a point of showing sympathy – from the bakery workers to the shop and café staff – with even Senga strangely showing some heart. Especially when she and Terry, out of the blue, announced their engagement at Christmas, and Senga, showing her ring, had whispered to Jinny, 'I'm that sorry, Jinny, I am, honestly.'

At which, Jinny, astonished, almost burst into tears, but with true sincerity wished her and Terry every happiness.

As for Accounts, her own workplace, it was here that she gained the most comfort. Not from Mr Comrie, who never seemed to want to look at her, perhaps because of feelings of guilt that his nephew had departed. Nor from Mabel, who was always shaking her head as though she'd known all along that something like this would happen. No, it was from Ross that the most comfort came.

The difference between him and everyone else was that he knew the whole background to her love affair with Viktor, had in a sense been through it with her having always been there, always ready to listen. Sometimes, it was true, he'd felt it necessary to warn her of possible future unhappiness, but usually he'd accepted her love and understood what it meant to her. And now that Viktor had gone, though his love hadn't died for her, as she'd been able to explain to Ross, if not to others, he knew just how much she was suffering, being now alone.

'You're so kind,' she told him once. 'You understand how I feel, but you don't keep asking me how I am or telling me I'll soon feel better or anything. I appreciate that.'

'Well, I know from experience that it's pointless telling people they'll feel better one day. They probably will, but it takes time. In your case, though, there is hope, isn't there? That you and Viktor will be together again one day?'

'Hope? I don't know. I have a feeling that I'll never see him again.' Jinny caught her breath. 'But it's much worse for you, Ross. I shouldn't be complaining to you.'

'Actually, I'm at last feeling better,' he said, after a pause. 'I'm not forgetting – I'll never forget her, but I'm . . . beginning to live again, you might say.'

'Ross, that's wonderful! Oh, I'm really pleased for you.'

She would have liked to know if his pretty cousin, Lorna, had anything to do with Ross's return to the world, but could scarcely ask that. Perhaps it was just a coincidence, anyway, that he'd been seeing her when he was getting better.

'Teatime!' cried Mabel, appearing in the office with a tray of cups of tea and a plate of biscuits. 'I'll just clear a space on your desk, Ross. Jinny, are you all right, dear? Feeling better?'

'Yes, thanks, Mabel,' Jinny said with a sigh.

'Oh, dear, poor Mabel,' Ross said, when she'd gone. 'She means well, though.'

'You always say that.' Jinny managed a smile. 'Look, do you want to OK these bills? I've put them in order if you want to look through them.'

'Fine. Let me just ask you, though – how are your German classes going? You finding them useful?'

'Oh, yes, I'm not doing too badly. Don't think I'll be able to write my letters to Viktor in German any time soon, though.'

'You do write to each other?'

'Of course. Not every day or anything, but yes, we write. It's our lifeline.' She smiled a little. 'Even though Viktor's written English isn't as good as his speech. Sometimes his sentences sort of look like German, if you know what I mean.'

'The main thing is you're in contact.'

'Like I say, we have our lifeline.'

Thirty-Nine

At least Jinny had that. A lifeline, made up of Viktor's letters. And though she didn't know if she would ever see him again, as Ross had said, she had hope. Hope, and her job, and peoples' kindness – she could manage. As long as they still had peace.

And peace they seemed to have. Maybe it really was true that Hitler didn't want war. And if it were – Jinny hugged the thought – she might have more than hope . . .

Until, that is, the news came on 15 March 1939 that Hitler had attacked what was left of Czechoslovakia. Then her hope died – and not just hers. The whole world saw the move for what it was – a beginning and an ending. The ending of peace; the beginning of World War Two.

For it was plain enough that Hitler would not stop at taking Czechoslovakia. He had his sights set on Poland, who would not give in to his demands on territories, and though Chamberlain had finally agreed that Great Britain would stand up to him, along with France, they had little hope that he would listen to them.

It was on 1 September that he invaded and bombarded Poland, and it was on Sunday, 3 September that Great Britain, having promised to support Poland, sent Germany an ultimatum. If, by 11 a.m, there had been no end to hostilities, war would be declared. No reply was made; no hostilities were ended. Therefore, at 11.15 a.m, Mr Chamberlain broadcast to the nation that Great Britain and Germany were officially at war.

Still grouped around the wireless after that fateful message had ended, the Hendries and Allan Forth sat for some time without speaking, only their eyes revealing their shock. Finally, Josh cleared his throat and looked around at his family.

'So, where do we go from here?' he asked. 'Back to 1914? The trenches? I canna believe it.'

'There won't be trench war this time,' Allan responded. 'This time it'll be the turn of the bombers.'

'Oh, no!' cried May. 'What'll we do?'

'Find the nearest air-raid shelter,' said Vi. 'They've been building 'em all over the place.'

'You canna fight a war just from the air,' said Josh. 'There'll have to be battles and troops, just like always, before we're done.'

'Oh, agreed.' Allan glanced at May. 'But this time they won't wait for volunteers. There'll be conscription – for men of the right age.'

'And women, they say, sooner or later,' put in Vi. 'Which is only fair.'

'Never!' cried Josh. 'You mean you lassies'd have to go to war? That'd be a piece o' nonsense, eh?'

'I wouldn't mind going,' Jinny said quietly. 'Like Vi says, it's only fair.'

As her family looked at her, May stretched out a hand to touch hers.

'What about Viktor?' she asked softly. 'You haven't mentioned him lately.'

Because she hadn't heard from him since he'd said he would be joining the army. Although he hadn't spelled it out, clearly he would find it more difficult to write to her then, and now that war had been declared between their countries, neither of them would be able to write. Maybe that was easy to understand, but it didn't make it any easier to bear.

'I don't expect to hear from him now,' she said after a pause. 'Now that he's in the army and we are at war.'

'In the army?' Josh repeated. 'You mean the German army?'

'Of course she means the German army,' Vi snapped. 'What else?'

'And you say he's no' a Jerry?' Josh asked. 'I always said he was, and now you see I was right.'

'He's an Austrian!' cried Jinny. 'That's all he wants to be. It's not his fault that his country's part of Germany now!'

Everyone waited for Josh to make some sharp riposte but when he didn't, only sat and filled his pipe, his face grey and weary, May rose to her feet.

'Come on, girls, let's get on with the Sunday dinner. Might as well have something good to eat.'

'While we've got it,' said Vi, joining her on the way to the kitchen.

But Jinny's thoughts, as she slowly stood up, were far away from roast beef and Yorkshire pudding.

Part Two

Forty

It was 1940 and a day in late June – a time of summer, when the Princes Street gardens Jinny could see from Accounts were in full bloom, and people hurrying by were lightly dressed and looking just as usual. Except that they weren't, of course; they were people at war, people under threat, people more vulnerable than they'd ever been in their lives. For France had fallen.

Jinny, totalling up figures on her adding machine, still could not believe that France had surrendered and that a British expeditionary force, originally sent to help, had earlier had to be rescued by boats from the German army now in control of Europe. It just didn't seem possible that Hitler had been so triumphant, taking – as well as France – Norway, Belgium, Luxembourg and Holland, so that all that remained to be conquered was Great Britain. Just across the Channel.

'Aye, it'll only be a matter of time before Hitler's here,' her father had said when the news about France's defeat had come. 'What's to stop him, eh? That wee strip o' water where our laddies were rescued? Forget it. We'll just have to prepare ourselves for what's going to happen.'

'Dad, you shouldn't be so defeatist!' Vi had cried robustly. 'We've got our defences, we've got an army; we won't be just giving in and opening the door for Hitler.'

'That's right.' May had added, with a voice that shook, 'Allan hasn't been called up for nothing.'

Poor May, her family thought as she looked down at her wedding ring. Still only a newly-wed, really, for her quiet registry office wedding had taken place in April, and she was now on her own in Allan's house while he'd been called up and was in Aberdeen doing basic training. Everyone had been happy that wedding day, except for Josh, though he'd surprisingly done his best not to show his feelings. But after only a weekend's honeymoon in the Borders, Allan had had to report to his unit. After which there'd been one terrible piece of news after another, culminating with the fall of France. It was when that news had broken that May had come over, so that they could be together as a family and discuss what they might do. As though there was anything they could do!

First would come the bombers – that was Hitler's practice – then the troops. There would be resistance, as Vi had said, and Mr Churchill, who'd taken over as prime minister from Mr Chamberlain in May, would no doubt be planning with his service chiefs their contingency plans at that moment. But why should Great Britain succeed in blocking Hitler when everyone else had failed? All that was sure was that the British people stood alone against a so far unstoppable army. For how long?

What am I doing? Jinny suddenly asked herself, putting down her pen and looking round the pleasant accounts office, at that moment filled with sunshine. This was all crazy, eh? Carrying on as though everything was normal? Any minute now, Mabel would come in with their tea and they'd all take their break as usual, yet Jinny had only to look across to Ross's desk and see Mr Lennox, Ross's replacement, checking some invoices to know that she was right and that nothing was at all normal.

Oh, how she missed Ross! He'd been gone since September, having volunteered for a Scottish regiment soon after the outbreak of war, and his place had been taken by Hugh Lennox, an old friend of Mr Comrie's and a retired accountant. After Ross's training, Jinny had felt she could have managed the office herself, and might have said so once, but now just let it go. Of course, it was good to have Mr Lennox anyway and he had certainly lost none of his skills, but every time she looked at him – and he was quite handsome in his way, with smooth grey hair and strong features – she was reminded that he wasn't Ross and that the old, pleasant way of working had gone and might never return.

Other things had changed, too. Comrie's, for instance, which was struggling to provide a service to its customers under difficult wartime conditions. There was a shortage of supplies, of course – flour, sugar and eggs, and pretty much everything else. There were new rules and regulations that had to be followed, such as the replacement of all breads by a so-called 'national loaf', a solid, wholemeal affair few people liked, and had the extra disadvantage that it could only be sold when a day old. The official intention was so that folk wouldn't try to eat too much when it was new, which as Mr Comrie said was a piece of nonsense if ever there was one!

As for his staff, Mr Comrie was in despair. Of his bakers, only Alf, who was over forty-one and not eligible for call-up, was left, which meant that Norah Mackie had been required to help out.

Imagine Norah, a woman, being a professional baker! But she was happy enough, her own work of decorating cakes being no longer required, there being so few cakes made and those only of the plainest type.

It was just as well, perhaps, that Trixie had departed to work in munitions, for there might not have been enough work for her, and certainly not for Senga, the trainee, though she was now married to Terry and 'expecting', while Terry no longer drove the van, for which there was no petrol allowance anyway, and was now serving in a Border regiment.

Not only Trixie had left to work in the munitions factory at Portobello – Audrey from the Princes Street shop was another who'd gone for the better money, leaving Mrs Arrow with only Fiona and Joan to help, about which she bitterly complained even though the café, at least, was no longer anything to worry about, Mr Comrie having closed it in 1939.

'Aye, there was no way we could keep that going, what with all the rules and regulations and nothing much to offer,' Mrs Arrow had said at the time, but she still liked a little moan to Jinny about her difficulties.

'So little to sell in the shop!' she would sigh as Jinny stood waiting to eat her sandwiches at lunchtime. 'I mean, compared to what we used to have!'

Of course she never mentioned Viktor's Austrian cakes, as there was no Bob to make them, even if they'd had the ingredients, and they wouldn't have made them anyway, would they? Who'd want Jerry cakes now?

In fact, no one ever spoke Viktor's name – certainly not to Jinny, and certainly not to Mr Comrie, who must be feeling bad enough that his nephew was probably fighting with the Germans by now. How Jinny was feeling it was thought better not to ask.

How was she feeling, then, on that apprehensive day so soon after the fall of France? She wasn't even sure herself.

Forty-One

How did she feel? Glancing over to Mr Lennox again, Jinny saw that he was still absorbed in his work, and after a moment's wait she picked up her bag from under her desk and took from its inside pocket a small box and a photograph. Removing the lid from the box, she looked down at her brooch, her Edelweiss, and as she remembered her joy, her utter happiness a the time it had been given, tears pricked her eyes and blurred the white flowers, so beautifully made, resting on the fine gold stem.

Would she ever have believed, when Viktor had given her the brooch, that she would be afraid now to be seeing his countrymen marching with Germans down Princes Street, as they would have marched in Paris and all the places they'd overrun? Might she even see Viktor himself? Oh, no, that wasn't possible! He wouldn't let that happen. He wouldn't be like those Nazis, so triumphant . . .

Yet as she put the brooch away and turned to his photograph, a snap she'd taken herself on one of their city walks, she had to admit that she didn't really know what Viktor was like now. He had not wanted to fight for Hitler before he went home, but time had passed and he might have changed. People did change, didn't they? And she had not heard from him for more a year. Time enough maybe for him to no longer be the man she had loved.

For she was no longer sure she still loved him. There was her problem and her pain, which was not the same as that she'd suffered when she was first without him. Then she'd felt only loss. Now she felt guilt. How could she not love Viktor just as much as ever when they'd been so happy together? Shared a love that was true? A year was a long time to manage alone, maybe, but how was it possible that she could allow the memory of his face, once so beloved, to begin to fade?

As her eyes again studied his photograph to remind herself of his fine, handsome face, she felt a great stab of grief cut through her heart like a knife, and as she thrust the photograph back into her bag she gave an involuntary sob. Oh, God, had Mr Lennox heard? He had.

'All right, Miss Hendrie?' he called.

Miss Hendrie . . . He always called her that, saying he was far too old fashioned to use colleagues' first names, which only made Jinny miss Ross all the more.

'Fine, thanks, Mr Lennox,' she answered, pushing her bag under the desk again as Mabel brought in tea, followed by Mr Comrie, who said he was on his way out to a doctor's appointment.

'All this stress and strain — it's not good for me,' he announced as Mabel gave Jinny and Mr Lennox their tea. 'Arthur Whyte's just rung to say there's more trouble over our flour allocation — I mean, what does anyone expect? We feed the nation on fresh air or what?'

'You're sure you don't want tea before you go, Mr Comrie?' Mabel asked as he clamped his trilby hat down on his head and strode to the door.

'No, no, I'd better get on my way. Though why we're worrying about anything I couldn't really say, after the news about France. What hope is there for us, Hugh, eh?'

After a quick glance at Jinny, which seemed to warn her against mentioning his nephew — as though she would! — Mr Comrie finally departed, allowing Mabel to sink into a chair and fan herself with her handkerchief.

'Mr Comrie talks about stresses and strains,' she remarked, 'as though he's the only one suffering. But I'm sure we're all on edge, eh? I feel quite bad myself, thinking about an invasion.'

'He's in charge, he has the responsibility,' Mr Lennox replied rather coldly. 'And these worries take their toll.'

'That's just what I'm saying — on all of us.' Rather pink in the face, Mabel stood up. 'May I take your cup, Mr Lennox?'

'Thanks, but I'm not quite finished. I'll bring it through.'

After she'd left, her head held high, Mr Lennox gave Jinny a slight smile. 'I'm afraid I've upset her, haven't I?'

'I shouldn't worry about it, Mr Lennox. As Mabel says, everyone's on edge at the moment.'

Why indeed worry? she asked herself, draining her own cup and setting it down. Why be touchy about things that didn't matter, when for all they knew they might have no future. At least, not as an independent country?

How she wished she could get away! Away from Mr Comrie and Mr Lennox and Mabel, and the flour allowance and the sugar shortage, and who would do what to help Mrs Arrow or Mr Whyte at the bakery. Was there not something else she could do? Something more worthwhile? Something that would put all these worries at Comrie's into perspective?

And maybe put her guilt over Viktor's fading image into perspective, too?

But what could she do? Where could she go?

With a sigh, she collected Mr Lennox's cup and her own and took them through to wash them, but with this little duty done and returning to her work, no answers to her questions came to mind.

Forty-Two

As the evening was so warm and close, Vi – whose turn it was to do the tea – announced that they were going to have salad and Dad would just have to put up with it.

'We're lucky to have it, *and* the boiled ham I managed to find, so don't go complaining,' she told him as they sat down to eat, at which he shrugged.

'Who's complaining? If I think salad's rabbit food, it's still food, eh? I know we're lucky. As long as Herr Hitler's no' crossing the Channel yet.'

'Don't!' cried Jinny. 'Don't joke like that!'

'Only way to get by, pet. Joking, I mean.'

'Nothing on the wireless yet?' asked Vi.

He shook his head. There'd been no news of movements across the Channel so far. Not that they could take comfort in that. It was still early days and no doubt Hitler was perfecting his bombing plans so that Great Britain would be attacked from the air before the troops came over. London, of course, would be his first target, but Scotland would not be forgotten. The Scots would be sure to need their air-raid shelters, just like folk in the south.

'I don't feel very hungry,' Jinny said, putting down her knife and fork. 'Sorry, Vi.'

'Oh, come on!' Vi had drawn her dark brows together. 'That's just silly talk! We have to eat; we have to keep going. And I got some lovely raspberries at the market – no cream, of course, but there's a wee bit of sugar. Just have to be careful.'

'Anything Jinny doesn't want you can give to me,' Josh said cheerfully. 'I need my strength for this farce we're putting on at the minute. Talk about scene changes! I feel I've run twice up Arthur's Seat by the time we've finished!'

'Full house?' asked Vi.

'You bet! To think they closed the theatres at the beginning of the war! Soon found out that was a bad idea!'

'I think I'll have some of the raspberries, anyway,' said Jinny, who was feeling slightly better seeing her father in a good mood, which was probably his aim.

After he'd left for work, the sisters washed up and turned on the wireless, but there was no news to alarm them, only a woman's educated voice talking about a wonderful 'response'.

'Response to what?' asked Vi.

'Ssh, I think she's telling us,' said Jinny.

'The number of young women responding to the Princess Royal's call for volunteers – "Your King and Country Need You!" – has been most gratifying,' the broadcaster was continuing. 'And I can assure everyone that they will be doing a thoroughly worthwhile job in the ATS, working alongside our brave soldiers and meeting new people, knowing they are responding to the call to help their country in her time of need. Now, it only remains for me to thank—'

'Think we'll cut out the thanks,' said Vi, switching off the set. 'But that's interesting, eh? All those lassies running off to join the ATS?'

'ATS?' Jinny repeated. 'What exactly does that stand for?'

'Auxiliary Territorial Service – it's the women's army.'

'Doesn't sound like it's for women.'

'No, I think I read there'd been trouble finding the right name. The women's air force and the women's naval service have got W for women in their titles – WAAF and WRNS – but nobody worked out how to put it in for the army. Still, what's in a name, eh?' Vi smiled. 'Fancy volunteering?'

The two pairs of dark eyes met.

'You know, I just might,' Jinny said slowly.

'You what?' Vi's mouth had dropped open. 'You don't mean it? Why would you want to leave Comrie's until you have to? We'll probably all be called up when they get round to passing an act for it.'

'I just felt today that I couldn't stick it any longer. I know it's nobody's fault, but the young men are away fighting and the rest of us are just going on about rations and how much flour we can have and all the rest of it. I know it's important – folk have to eat – but I'd like to get away, do something that matters.' Jinny smiled nervously. 'Couldn't think what – and then just now, hearing the wireless—'

'And you decided to join up? Well, I'm struck dumb, I really am!'

'Struck dumb, you?' Jinny tried to laugh. 'Do you think I shouldn't go for it?'

'Oh, I don't say that. If you're really fed up with Comrie's, why not? But Mr Comrie won't want to lose you, will he? How's he going to manage?'

'He's got his old buddy, Mr Lennox, working there instead of Ross, so he doesn't need me. There isn't as much to do as there used to be. We've had to cut down so much.'

Vi's look was dubious. 'And Dad? Have you thought what he'd say if you joined the army? He doesn't think women should go to war.'

'I don't suppose they'll be letting women really go to war. We'll probably just be back-up.' Jinny leaned forward. 'But it'll still be worthwhile to join up, eh?'

'Yes, I think it will. Remember, we said it was only fair that women should be conscripted like the men.' Vi took out a packet of cigarettes and lit one. 'I wouldn't mind volunteering myself.'

'Why don't you?'

'Until I'm officially called up I think I'd better stay with the firm. Since the changeover to uniforms we've been snowed under with paperwork and most of the men have gone, leaving you know who to carry on.' Vi studied her cigarette. 'Besides, we can't both leave Dad, can we?'

'Why, I never thought I'd hear you say that!' cried Jinny. 'You always say that men should be able to look after themselves and not depend on women to do everything for 'em!'

'I know, but he's lost May, and if he loses you too he'll be in a state. It'll be better if I stay on till I get the call.'

'You're just a great softie, after all,' Jinny said, laughing. 'Now it can be told!'

'None of that!' Vi grinned and offered her cigarettes. 'Here, have a smoke to celebrate your new life, eh?'

'No, thanks, I don't fancy smoking. You know I never have.'

'Wait till you're in the forces – you'll be smoking like a chimney! I'm told everybody does.'

Their talk had been so absorbing it had quite taken their minds off the danger that might be coming their way, but when they tuned into the BBC at nine o'clock, there was still no news of German bombing or invasion, and once again they breathed sighs of relief.

They were not to know that, within a few short weeks, everyone in the country would also be heaving sighs of relief, for it had become clear that Hitler would never invade Britain. He had gambled on winning a battle of the air in the skies over England, beginning in July and ending in September with defeat for him and his air force. The young British pilots, in their Spitfires and Hurricanes, had brought respite from fear for their countrymen and women, and though their cities had to endure German bombing, they no longer needed to picture German troops marching through London, or, indeed, Edinburgh.

'Never in the field of human conflict has so much been owed by so many to so few,' said Winston Churchill of the Battle of Britain, and the words of gratitude echoed throughout the land.

But in late June, when Jinny sat with her sister, planning her new future – all that lay ahead. Her immediate problem was how to break the news, first to her father, then to Mr Comrie, that she would soon be going away. In theory, they should be prepared for it, as all young unmarried women would certainly be conscripted sooner or later. In practice – well, in spite of what she'd told Vi, she didn't know how her news would be taken. With some apprehension, she watched Vi calmly smoking, and decided she must just wait and see.

Forty-Three

Jinny told her father first. On the following Sunday, it being a fine afternoon, it was decided she and Josh should take a tram to the Botanic Gardens, stroll round the extensive grounds, maybe look in at the hot houses and have a cup of tea. Finding cafés open on Sundays in Edinburgh was not easy, but it was possible to have tea at the Botanics, even if there probably wouldn't be anything much to eat.

'Very nice,' remarked Josh when they were sitting in the crowded tea room, looking out at trees and lawns. 'I appreciate this – I don't see enough greenery in my line o' work.'

'More tea?' asked Jinny.

'Aye, please. It's thirsty work, all this walking, and that hot house nearly finished me. Shame Vi's not with us, though. She should see a tree or two, eh?'

'She's out with her friend – you know, Marion,' Jinny told him, knowing of course that Vi was under her orders to be elsewhere while she broke her news to her father. When she had passed him his tea, she cleared her throat and took courage to speak. 'Dad . . . there's something I want to tell you—'

'Oh?' His dark eyes, so like hers, were instantly alert. 'Something good?

'It's just I've been thinking – well, no, I've decided, really – to volunteer for the ATS.'

He set down his cup. 'You've what?'

'Decided to volunteer, Dad. Seemingly, they want ten thousand women for the service. The Princess Royal came on the wireless and asked girls to join. For king and country, she said, and I thought . . . I thought I'd like to do something to help.'

'For king and country?' Josh raised his eyebrows. 'That's why she wants you to go? All I can say is that half the fellas that went last time for king and country never came back, and the rest were never the same again. I should know; I was one.'

'I know, Dad, it was a terrible war, a terrible waste, but this one is different. We have to fight Hitler because he's a tyrant; he's trying to enslave the world. That's why I want to do my bit.'

As he said nothing, she went on eagerly: 'But I won't be fighting like the men, you know, Dad – no one's saying that. I'll just be helping, that's all, doing back-up sort of jobs.' She laughed a little. 'Nothing in the front line!'

'What'll they say at Comrie's if you go?' he asked after a few quiet moments. 'Why can't you just stay there till they bring in this bill to conscript women? You'll be needed, eh?'

'Mr Comrie's got a retired accountant to stand in for my boss. They'll be able to manage without me. And I'm tired of what I'm doing there; I want to do something useful.'

Suddenly seeming to tire of her efforts to persuade her father to see her point of view, Jinny sat back in her chair and sighed, at which Josh shrugged,

'OK, if it's what you want – go ahead. Volunteer. Might be for the best.'

She jolted herself upright, staring at him with large, astonished eyes. 'You won't mind, Dad?'

'I don't say that, all I'm thinking is . . . it might be a good thing for you to meet other people.'

'Other people? Well, of course I'd be meeting other people!'

'Other men, Jinny.'

She was mystified. He had never wanted his girls to meet 'other men', to have lives away from him – why should he so suddenly have changed? Then it came to her. Because of Viktor. The men she would meet would be soldiers. British soldiers, men Josh might relate to, but that wouldn't matter. All that mattered was that any man she met in her new life would not be a foreigner who might take her away to live in his country. She would not be lost to her own country, to her own family, to Josh. She could now understand his thinking, but of course he didn't know anything of her present feelings for Viktor. How could he, when she didn't even fully know them herself?

'To meet other men is not my reason for joining the ATS,' she said, a little unsteadily, her heart beginning to ache at the thought of Viktor and how she didn't know whether he was alive or dead. 'But if you don't mind me going, it'll make me feel a lot happier.'

'Aye, well. maybe I shouldn't have mentioned the men, Jinny. It was just a thought. Thing is if you do join the ATS it'll give you a new life and if that's what you want, so be it.' Josh rose to pay for their tea and gave an uncertain smile. 'We'd best get going, eh?'

As they returned home, she couldn't really believe her luck – that she'd so easily got through the hurdle of telling her father her plans. If he liked to think she might make new relationships that would break her attachment to Viktor, best let him think so. If she had no thoughts of making new relationships herself then that wasn't something he needed to know.

All she had to do now was brace herself for her interview with Mr Comrie, and hope he would not think she was deserting Accounts for no good reason.

In the event, he took the news of her intentions so well that she was a little taken aback. Was she not to be missed at all? But when he expressed surprise at her decision to volunteer for the services, yet no real regret, she knew it was not because her work was inferior, only that he was confident his friend, the male and professional accountant, would manage very well without her. Of course, she should have expected that sort of reaction, Mr Comrie being the sort to believe a man always had a head start on any woman where work was concerned, and she had to admit Mr Lennox was very well qualified and experienced.

Still, it would have been nice if Mr Comrie had seemed genuinely sorry to lose her. He had said, of course, that her job would be waiting for her when the war was over, and patted her kindly on the shoulder when she turned to leave his office – she must make do with that. At least she could take comfort from the fact that others at Comrie's seemed sorry she was going – Mabel, for instance, who said Accounts just wouldn't be the same, and Norah Mackie and Mr Whyte, who were quick to lament over the departure of another familiar face. As for Mrs Arrow and her bakery staff, they made her promise to let them see her in her uniform as soon as she got some leave.

'But no getting wed to some soldier laddie and disappearing altogether!' Mrs Arrow cried on Jinny's last day.

'No fear of that!' Jinny answered.

And, of course, no one mentioned Viktor.

Forty-Four

The worst goodbyes were to her family, events having seemed to move so quickly that no sooner had she been accepted for the ATS than she was ready to go, those last kisses and hugs with her dad and sisters bringing tears to her eyes but quickly over and her new life coming up fast.

To begin with, as had been explained to her, there would be four weeks' basic training at one of the many camps, with an issue of uniform, or as much as was available, as there were usually shortages of various items. There would also be injections and checks for hair lice and social diseases – 'Nothing personal!' the woman officer who had been informing Jinny of what lay in wait for her had said with a laugh. 'We just have to be careful, you know.'

'Oh, yes,' Jinny had agreed, blushing, and thinking she'd be glad when all that was over. Where would she be sent first was the question. It turned out to be a training camp near Berwick-upon-Tweed, so not too far away. She might have had to go anywhere, from Aberdeen to the south of England.

Even though easy to reach, it was daunting to arrive at the spartan camp and meet up with a crowd of strange young women, all eyeing each other up and down before being directed to an army hut where they collected bedding and made up their own beds.

Surely she would never get to know any of these girls, thought Jinny as she and the other 'rookies' struggled to put together the three thin mattresses that made up what were known as 'biscuits', the look of which boded ill for comfort.

Her eyes went over those girls nearest to her – the tall, thin one with glasses, for instance, and the little, snub-nosed, sandy-haired girl who looked quite petrified; the couple of blondes who had already gravitated to each other, and the plump, cheerful young woman who had declared that if she could sleep on that terrible 'biscuit' on her bed, nothing would surprise her more.

Oh, but there were so many others, all speaking with different accents, all wearing different clothes: some smart and expensive, others shabby and well worn – all, except maybe the little sandy one, trying to put on a good front and at least finding something to laugh about when they tried on their army underwear.

'Help, will you look at me in these khaki knickers?' one of the blonde girls cried. 'I bet even my old granny wouldn't be seen dead in 'em!'

'Well, let's hope we're not either,' the tall girl with glasses retorted. 'Actually, I think the shoes are the worst – talk about clodhoppers!'

'And they've run out of khaki stockings,' the plump girl reported. 'We're going to look a bit odd in uniform wearing the ones we came in, eh?'

'Can't be helped,' snapped the woman sergeant overseeing their uniform allocations. 'The main thing is to remember to look as smart as possible with whatever you've got. Buttons polished, shirts and skirts ironed, hair neatly tucked into your cap. And not too much make-up!'

'Oh, dear, I'm not looking forward to the drill,' Jinny heard someone whisper, and as she was rather apprehensive about that herself, she was relieved to know they would not begin square-bashing until tomorrow. For now, they could go along to the cookhouse for a break, try what tea tasted like in enamel mugs and chew on the thickest ham sandwiches they had ever seen.

All very wearying, that first day, but at last, when they gathered in their off-duty room, some names began to be attached to the girls around Jinny, making her feel a little more at ease.

The tall, thin girl was Brenda, who had been working in her father's pharmacy and would eventually train in pharmacy herself, while the blonde couple were Georgina and Verity, not known to each other but with the same idea that being in the ATS would be 'fun'. 'Hope you're not disappointed,' commented Molly, the plump one, adding that she wouldn't mind a bit of fun herself, although her reason for volunteering from her office job was because she wanted to contribute to the war effort.

'That's a bit like me,' said Jinny, giving her name and explaining her background, and as Molly grinned and shook hands, she felt she might have already have made a friend, if only for four weeks.

Although there was a wireless and a gramophone in the off-duty room, most of the girls were so tired they didn't mind being told to go to bed, where they would learn the worst about their mattresses when they tried to sleep. Next day, there'd be PT and various lectures, as well as the dreaded drill – better be prepared.

'Don't worry about oversleeping,' the corporal who was supervising them said with a laugh. 'I'll be in early to call you – "Wakey, wakey, rise and shine" – and that means your shoes!'

Forty-Five

Jinny's bed was at the end of the hut, next to that of the little sandy-haired girl, who had said scarcely a word since she arrived and seemed most desperately shy. Poor kid, thought Jinny, resolving, once they were in their issue pyjamas, to speak to her before 'lights out'.

'Hello, I'm Jinny Hendrie from Edinburgh,' she whispered across. 'Are you settling on all right?'

The girl gave a timid smile. 'Oh, hello. I'm Sukie Woodman, from Worcester. I thought you were Scottish – I could tell by your voice.' She hesitated. 'To tell you the truth, I'm a bit scared. I've never been away from home before.'

'Nor me. I bet most girls here haven't, unless they were away at school, or something.'

'Bet those blonde girls were.' Sukie murmured. 'They don't seem a bit worried by anything.'

'That's blondes for you.' Jinny smiled. 'But it's a bit of a shock for most of us, being here, I'd say. Still, we volunteered, eh? Can't complain.'

'I never thought what it would be like. I just wanted somewhere to go.' Sukie shivered a little and tried to draw her thin blanket more tightly over her, but it was clear that she'd already found that nothing stayed tightly around the 'biscuits'.

'I live with my auntie,' she said after a moment. 'Me mum and dad are dead, you see. And it looks like me job in a shoe shop'll not be lasting much longer – the manageress says there's not enough work for both of us now, and Auntie'll never want to me to stay if I can't pay me keep.'

'Oh, surely—' Jinny began, but Sukie shook her head.

'No, no, I had to find somewhere else and when I heard the ATS wanted volunteers I thought it'd be for me, but now I'm worried I won't be able to keep up and they'll throw me out.' In the gloomy light of the hut, Sukie's hazel eyes were large and woebegone. 'Then what I'll do, I don't know.'

'They won't throw you out,' Jinny declared. 'No need to worry about that. They need you. And you'll be fine – remember, none of us knows anything. We're here to be trained and once you're trained you'll be posted and do a good job, I promise you!'

'You really think so?'

'Certainly do!'

'Lights out!' called the corporal. 'Everybody try to get some sleep. Need to be fresh as daisies tomorrow, eh? Goodnight, all.'

Well, she'd done her good deed for the day, Jinny thought as she listened later to the sound of Sukie's regular breathing. Fingers crossed, all would go well for that poor girl who'd so far had so little good luck.

But what of herself? As she lay awake in the long dark hut, shifting uncomfortably on her 'biscuit', aware of strangers all around and that home was much farther away than just a trip from Berwick might seem, Jinny wondered. Had she done the right thing, giving up all she knew in order to do something that might or might not be useful? Tears pricked her eyelids as she thought of her usual nights spent sharing a room with dear, prickly Vi. Of her father, back from work, in his chair smoking his pipe and sounding off about items in the newspaper. Of May, away from her old home, yet still so often popping in, always ready with a sympathetic ear, even with such real fears of her own about Allan.

Why had Jinny left them? To have a change from Comrie's? Well, in spite of Mr Comrie being so indifferent to her leaving, she'd been doing a good job there and she should maybe have continued to do it, until her conscription came. If, in fact, it ever did. The government hadn't even got a bill together, had they?

Round and round her thoughts whirled, until suddenly – it seemed no time at all – she opened her eyes and it was daylight.

'Wakey, wakey!' the corporal was crying as girls were leaping out of bed, complaining that they hadn't slept a wink, hurrying to wash and dress in their new uniforms, trying to be ready for all that lay ahead.

Maybe things didn't seem so bad as in the night, Jinny decided. She too hurried around, pausing to smile at Sukie and wave to Molly. She too was asking what was for breakfast in the cookhouse along with everyone else. And how the devil did you get these 'biscuits' to stay together?

Of course, come the night, she guessed she'd be tearful again, thinking of home, but the cure for daytime seemed to be to keep as busy as possible, and there was no problem there.

Forty-Six

It was said – the girls had heard it – that senior officers were constantly surprised at the way a group of young women 'rookies' could, in only four weeks, be transformed into a smart, well-trained marching squad that could equal that of the men.

'Equal?' the girls would have cried if they'd had the chance. 'We're better than the men!'

Well, no one would go as far as that but there was no doubt that at the end of their basic training the girls were a credit to their instructors, had mastered all fear of the drill and were even prepared to admit that their introduction to army life hadn't been as bad as they'd thought it might be.

Of course, the discipline was always there, and could be irksome – 'far too much nit-picking and fussing over regulations' was a common complaint, and why did there have to be so many pamphlets dealing with everything under the sun? When they thought about it, however, it did seem to make sense that every category of army life was covered, which meant you at least knew where you were and could quote 'regulations' if need be.

The best thing for most of the rookies was that as the days went by they got to know one another, made friends and felt a shared comradeship that was particularly helpful, especially if anyone was feeling homesick or worried.

Sukie, for instance, was still very unsure of herself in the early days, in spite of encouragement from Jinny. But the more she discovered she could do what was required of her the better she performed her tasks and she visibly gained in confidence. It was true she was the despair of the PT instructor, being so small and slight, and seemingly unable to master the handling of the gym equipment, but she did her best and, as Jinny told her cheerfully, there was no question of her being 'thrown out' just because she couldn't leap over the vaulting horse! Plump, good-natured Molly had the same problem, but didn't let it worry her, and Sukie, who'd done so much better in her new life than she'd ever believed she could, showed her new spirit by not worrying either.

'Everyone's been so kind,' she told Jinny. 'I'm really surprised, you know.'

'Well, apart from a sergeant I won't name and one or two officers, I think I'd say the same,' Jinny answered.

Of course, there were always folk you didn't like – you just had to put up with them – but on the whole, Jinny found she got on with the people around her very well, learning everyone's names and backgrounds, and sometimes felt rather sad that at the end of their basic training they would all be saying farewell and moving on. Who knew where?

By this time, they had all have been assessed for the jobs that would suit them most, with their postings soon to be announced. Then would begin their real work for the army, and they would discover just how much they could offer towards the war effort. Before that happened, however, a dance was organized with the soldiers of one of the Border regiments, and great excitement reigned as the girls gave up worrying about where they might be posted to concentrate instead on looking attractive, finding some decent make-up and getting their hair right.

'But won't it feel odd to go to a dance wearing uniform?' asked Verity, frowning. 'That'll be a first.'

'Oh, what's it matter?' Brenda retorted. 'We are supposed to be soldiers.'

'When it comes to dancing I don't feel a soldier at all!' said Georgina.

'I'm not really looking forward to it,' Sukie confessed to Jinny,

her face taking on her old woebegone look. 'I've never been one
for dances.'

'But why not, Sukie?'

'Well, I always think no one will ask me to dance.'

'Oh, what a piece of nonsense, as they say where I come from.
The chaps will be sure to ask you.'

'I don't look like you, Jinny. I . . . don't get noticed.'

'All you need is a bit of lipstick and your hair swept off your face
and you'll be fine. Trust me.'

'You always cheer me up,' Sukie said, managing a smile.

The dance went well. The soldiers, smart in tartan trews, were eager
to see the new 'talent', as they called the latest intake of rookies,
and wasted no time in taking partners for the opening quickstep,
played by a local band. One of the first on the floor, Jinny was
gratified to note, was Sukie.

'The lipstick must have done the trick,' she remarked to Molly,
just before they were themselves being asked to dance, at which
Molly laughed and told her she'd done a good job there.

'Poor little Sukie – she's like a different person from the waif that
first arrived, thanks to you.'

'Not just me. I think we've all been changed by joining up. Shame
we'll lose touch, eh?'

'Let's see where we get sent – we may meet up again.'

At that point they parted to join the crowd on the floor, and
from then on there wasn't much time for talking. For one strange
moment Jinny thought of Viktor when a tall, fair-haired soldier
danced by with Georgina, and though his looks were not really like
Viktor's, they were similar enough to make Jinny catch her breath
and feel the familiar stab of pain for lost love she always felt when
she remembered Viktor.

'Hey, penny for 'em!' asked her partner, a ginger-haired corporal,
having noticed the far-away look in her eyes. 'Where've you gone,
then?'

'Oh, sorry, I was just remembering something—'

'Something you should've done?'

'No, no.' She gave a quick smile. 'Nothing to worry about.'

'That's a relief. You're supposed to be enjoying yourself, you
know.'

'And I am!'

When the music drew to a close and they stood clapping, Jinny felt it was true, she was enjoying herself – as long as she did not look back.

The interval brought a curtain of cigarette smoke and the usual thin coffee and thick sandwiches, but as the drill hall had no licence there was no alcohol, which meant everyone behaved themselves, laughing and flirting until the band struck up again.

'Oh, I'm having such a good time,' Sukie whispered to Jinny before she returned to the floor with the cheerful young soldier who had first asked her to dance. 'You were so right, you know. Right about everything.'

'Oh, that's me!' laughed Jinny. 'Always get things right – I don't think!'

Still, when she and the rest of the girls were dancing again and she was being careful not to think about anything but the present, it did seem to Jinny that so far her new life was working out well. 'So far', however, being the key words here. So much depended on where she and the others were sent next, and they wouldn't know that till Monday, they'd been told.

But when Monday came and Jinny knew where she was going, she rather wished she didn't.

Forty-Seven

'Royal Army Pay Corps,' she told her family when she arrived home for a week's leave and had put aside her uniform for a pretty dress. 'Can you believe it? I spend half my time in Civvy Street doing wages, and when I join up for a new life where do I get posted? The Pay Corps!'

Josh and Vi, who'd taken time off work to welcome Jinny home, exchanged glances with May, who'd come over from the hospital where she was now working as a nurses' aide, the hat shop having closed for the 'duration'.

'Seems to make sense to me,' Vi observed, shaking the teapot before topping up Jinny's cup. 'I mean, you won't need much training, will you?'

'That's right,' said Josh. 'And they probably thought you'd be good at the work.'

'Well, I don't know, I think I agree with Jinny,' put in May. 'When you sign up for a new life you don't expect to be doing the same old thing.'

'It might be quite different work,' Vi suggested. 'Maybe more interesting. Where did other girls get posted, anyway?'

'Oh, all over the place,' answered Jinny, thinking back to that day when everyone found out where they were heading. How Sukie had been told she'd be joining the Royal Army Ordnance Corps to be dealing with all kinds of stores and was delighted, while Verity and Georgina would both be doing anti-aircraft work with the Royal Artillery and declared themselves thrilled. As for Brenda and Molly, their postings appeared to be top secret, probably deciphering codes, others had guessed, but they were both brainy girls so it was expected that they'd be selected for something like that.

In fact, the whole intake seemed to be going to do something interesting, except for Jinny, who sighed as she thought about it.

'Daresay I was the only one who wasn't too excited, but I expect it'll work out all right,' she said lightly. 'Like Vi says, the work might be different from what I did before. I'd better not complain.'

'Shame you can't work in Scotland, though,' said Josh. 'Are there no pay offices here, then?'

'Oh, they never like to send you close to home,' Jinny told him. 'So I'm going to Chester in Western Command. There'll be ATSs there, but any men'll probably be unfit for combat – so I've been told. They've probably been wounded. Not badly enough to be invalided out, but not able to fight.'

A silence fell as they all considered Allan, who had yet to be tried in battle, but who must face it sooner or later and then must trust to luck. Better not think about it.

'I should get back to the ward,' May said, rising with a sigh. 'But it's been so lovely to see you again, Jinny. That four weeks you were away seemed like forever.'

'You can say that again,' muttered Josh, also getting up. 'I'll be away and all, but it'll be grand to think you'll be here, pet, when I come back for tea. Come here and give me a hug, eh?'

'It's grand to be back,' said Jinny, hugging and kissing May and her father. 'Can't tell you how I missed home to begin with. Your letters were a big help, but the tears were often flowing, I can tell you!'

'And to think you needn't have gone yet,' commented Josh, shaking his head. 'But that's water under the bridge, eh? You're in the service now, and it seems to suit you. Did they get you marching in your training?'

'You bet, and we thought we beat the fellows hollow!' Jinny laughed. 'Oh, it was all a lot better than I thought it would be. I made some good friends and we had some grand times.'

'So, I've nothing to fear?' asked Vi, shrugging. 'I won't do as well as you, Jinny. I'm not your easy type, that's for sure, but I am wishing I could get away like you and do something useful.'

'Oh, don't say it,' groaned Josh, making for the door. 'I don't want to lose you as well!'

'Away with you, Dad! I'm not going yet, anyway. May, will you come back for your tea? I'm cooking for Jinny tonight – and yes, it's fish!'

'Oh, yes, I'll be back!' cried May as she and Josh hurriedly left and Jinny stood up, stretching, and said she'd unpack her few things.

'Nice to be back in civvies again – do you know, we had to wear our uniforms for the dance – they were all we had.'

'So, you went to dances?' asked Vi. 'They wouldn't be for me, but – don't tell Dad – I've changed my mind and am seriously thinking of volunteering. It might be some time before they start conscripting women and I want to get on with it.'

'As I said, you'll enjoy it, Vi, as I have so far, but still, you know, it's grand to be home.' Jinny smiled. 'And I've a whole week here before I need worry about the Pay Corps. Tomorrow I think I'll look in on Comrie's – see if the place hasn't fallen down without me, eh?'

In the bedroom where her bag was waiting to be unpacked, she first opened the little drawer under the dressing-table mirror where she kept her few pieces that were precious. Her mother's locket, a last present, was there, with a necklace or two and a ring that had been her grandmother's, but what Jinny was taking out now was the Edelweiss brooch Viktor had given her. Every so often she liked to look at it, though she never wore it and certainly would not take it with her on her ATS posting.

Why remind herself of happiness that was gone? She couldn't answer that, except perhaps that she felt it was right not to block everything from her mind. She didn't actually know what had happened to Viktor. They could still meet after the war, even though that might be years away, and if it was true his image had faded, the memory of it could still surprise her. Take Saturday night, when she'd seen the fair-haired soldier dancing with Georgina and been reminded of Viktor. How that look had sparked off the old pain again, until she'd been brought back to the present! Just as the lovely Edelweiss was bringing it back now.

After a moment, Jinny replaced it in its box and turned to begin her unpacking. It was strange to be at home again, the training camp already a memory! As she put away her few things she purposefully began to sing a popular song, reassuring herself that she felt better, able to look forward to the future. There was no point at all in thinking about the past.

Forty-Eight

Comrie's. There it was, in busy Princes Street, looking not too different from when she'd last seen it. Jinny, smart in a dark green dress and navy jacket, stood for a moment looking at her old work-place, remembering how things had used to be. Of course, by the time she'd left, change had already come – the windows were almost empty instead of displaying the selections of mouth-watering scones and cakes as in pre-war days, the staff so reduced in size as almost to be described as 'skeleton'.

And now there was something she'd never seen before outside Comrie's and that was a queue. The shop had always been busy, of course, the girls kept on their feet serving so many customers, but queues? No, there'd never been queues, but Jinny knew she should have expected one. Queues in wartime were a fact of life, especially for food. At the baker's, at the butcher's, at the grocer's, for if you could reckon on receiving foods that were rationed, any extras in short supply had to be queued for, which made life difficult for those at work, such as Vi.

'Had to take time off to get that fish we had,' she told Jinny. 'There's something to be said for being in the forces, eh? All food found!'

'Such as it is!' Jinny had retorted.

Feeling a little self-conscious now, she was wondering how she could get into the shop to say hello to the staff without being accused of queue-jumping. People were said to be cheerful about the problems of their changed lives, but some of the women outside Comrie's were looking pretty glum – Jinny doubted that they'd take kindly to a girl pushing ahead and trying to take their place, as they would see it. Still, she'd have to get in somehow.

Plucking up courage, she spoke to those at the front of the queue. 'Mind if I go in? I don't want to buy anything, I'm on leave from the ATS and just here to see the people I worked with.'

Without smiling they stared at her, taking in her great dark eyes, her pretty dress and jacket, and then looked at one another.

'Aye, let the lassie in,' one said. 'She's doing her bit, eh?'

'Go on, then,' another said, 'but if we catch you putting any teacakes into that handbag of yours, you'll be for it!'

'There was laughter as Jinny said, 'No teacakes, I promise!' and with a relieved laugh made her way into the shop.

Inside, there still people queuing right up to the counter, where Joan and a young girl Jinny didn't know were darting about, putting items into paper bags, while Mrs Arrow was calling in a sergeant major's voice: 'Only *one* fruit pie per customer, please. We're going to run out as it is.'

'And what's the good of one wee fruit pie for a family?' someone in the queue demanded.

Mrs Arrow retorted, 'Take it or leave it! We can't sell what we haven't got.'

'The pastry's just like cardboard, anyway,' another voice muttered, and there were sighs and laughter, but by then Mrs Arrow had spotted Jinny and rushed round the counter to greet her.

'Jinny, is it really you – looking that well, eh? My, it's grand to see you!'

'I've only been away a month,' Jinny murmured, embarrassed, 'though it does feel like more!'

'Well, we're really pleased to see you, anyway. Still got Joan, you see?'

'Hello, Joan!' cried Jinny, waving, as Joan looked up from putting a large pallid loaf into a flimsy paper bag and smiled, as the unknown young girl, thin and fair, smiled too.

'That's Peggy,' Mrs Arrow whispered. 'A school-leaver I managed to get, not doing too badly, though terrified of the customers. But just imagine what it's like trying to satisfy 'em, Jinny. It's terrible, I'm telling you! I mean, take thae fruit pies – there's never enough and it's true what they say, 'the pastry's just like cardboard', but we canna get the ingredients to make it any better, and Mr Whyte feels that bad. Even the fruit's out o' tins and nobody'd eat it if there wasn't a war on, but there you are, we have to do the best we can, eh?'

'I'm sure you're doing a wonderful job, Mrs Arrow, and it's grand to see you, it really is.'

'I wish I could give you a cup o' tea, but as you can see, we're rushed off our feet—'

'That's quite all right—' Jinny was beginning when her eyes widened and her lips parted as a copper-haired man in a sports jacket and tweed trousers came into the shop from the stairs, and Mrs Arrow waved.

'Ross, look who's here!' she cried. 'Jinny's come visiting, too!'

'Jinny?' he cried.

'Ross?'

Like the old friends they were, they hugged and shook hands, then burst out laughing.

'Talk about snap!' said Ross. 'I never thought to see you here, Jinny, and looking so well. You're a sight for sore eyes!'

'And you're looking well, too, Ross. Are you on leave, then?'

'I am, thank the Lord.' Ross's brown eyes were shining. 'But it's just so nice to see you, Jinny, I can't believe my luck. I came in to see how everyone was and to have a word with Hugh Lennox, but I never imagined I'd see you!'

'And I never thought I'd see you.' Jinny's eyes were as bright as his. 'I've just finished my basic training and I'm on a week's leave, so thought I'd call in here.'

Noting the interested eyes of Mrs Arrow, and all around her, Ross took Jinny's arm. 'We're a bit in the way here, how about going for a coffee? If we're lucky we can get one at Logie's.'

'I'd love to, Ross, but I was going up to see Mr Lennox and maybe Mr Comrie—'

'Ah, you can see them later. Come on, we've some catching up to do, haven't we?'

'All right, then, let's go! 'Bye, everybody.'

''Bye, Jinny, pet, and Ross!' cried Mrs Arrow. 'Or, should I say, Lieutenant MacBain?'

'Lieutenant?' repeated Jinny, remembering how Ross had liked to call Viktor that so long ago, or so it seemed.

'It's only second lieutenant, as a matter of fact,' Ross was saying. 'And I'm just Ross to you, Mrs Arrow.'

'An officer, though?' said Jinny. 'Well done, you.'

'Come on,' he said hastily. 'Let's go to Logie's.'

Forty-Nine

Logie's being Logie's, the best department store in the city, there was still a certain pre-war feel about the restaurant with its white-clothed tables and attentive service – even if the waitresses were either very young or rather old, the coffee weak and there were only biscuits, no scones. None of that mattered to Jinny and Ross as they sat at a window table, ready to exchange news and enjoying being together.

'This reminds me of when we used to share the office,' Jinny remarked after the waitress had brought their coffee and shortbread. 'Sometimes we'd have a good old talk. Usually when you wanted to give me advice, I seem to remember.'

'That's all you remember? My giving you advice?'

'No, of course not. I'm joking. I know we talked about lots of things.'

Ross was silent for a few moments while sampling the shortbread. Perhaps he was remembering that she had rarely taken his advice, except on work matters, thought Jinny. Perhaps he wanted to ask about Viktor, for his advice had often concerned him, but if that were the case he didn't put his question into words.

'I did hear you'd volunteered for the ATS,' he said at last, 'and now you say you've finished basic training. How did you like that?'

'It wasn't too bad at all. Och, you should have seen us marching! We thought we were so wonderful – much better than the men, we said!'

'Bet you were, too.' Ross passed the shortbread. 'Like one of these? I don't suppose they've much butter in 'em but can't expect it these days. Did you hear all Mrs Arrow's groans? If you see Mr Whyte he'll bend your ear about shortages as well. But tell me, where've you been posted?'

'Would you believe, the Pay Corps! Just because I used to do the wages! I'm pretty disappointed, really.'

'Is it a command pay office, or a regimental one?'

'A command one, near Manchester.'

'Ah, well, that'll be different work for you. You won't be paying out soldiers' wages, more likely dealing with public monies for military services. Might be more interesting.'

'It certainly sounds it! Thanks for telling me that, Ross – it's quite cheered me up. But now you must tell me what's been happening with you. It's not hush-hush, is it?'

He stirred his coffee, his face suddenly bleak. 'No, I think everyone knows about the evacuation of Dunkirk.'

'Dunkirk? You were involved in that, Ross?' Jinny's voice was hushed. 'I'm so sorry.'

Like most people, she had heard about the chaotic scenes that had taken place after the Allies, who'd been trapped by German forces following the Battle of France, were rescued by all sorts of little ships. It hadn't been possible to take the men off from the shore, and some had had to spend hours wading though the sea while waiting for an enemy attack which fortunately had not come. But though the evacuation had been something of a miracle, it could never be called a triumph, especially when it was remembered how many Allied soldiers had been killed earlier and how much equipment had been lost. It was no wonder that, as he recalled it, Ross's face was dark.

'No need to be sorry for me and the rest of us who were saved – we were lucky. All I can think of is the men who died before.'

'But have you been all right, Ross? I mean, have you recovered?'

'I'm fine, and I haven't been anywhere dangerous since. At the moment, my battalion is stationed in the south but we steer clear of London. That is not the place to be in the Blitz – it's taking a pasting, all right. But let's talk of other things.'

With some effort, Ross smiled and caught the eye of their waitress. 'How about another coffee? Then you must tell me about your family.'

'They're very well. Except that May is always worrying about Allan, of course. I'm not sure where he is at the moment. Dad's working flat out at the theatre which is selling out every night, but Vi is pretty discontented. I think she might volunteer too.' After a pause, Jinny asked casually: 'And how about your cousin? Lorna, wasn't it? Have you seen her lately?'

'Lorna? No, no. She's another volunteer – she joined the Wrens some time ago. She's down in Portsmouth. I haven't seen her for a while, though she writes now and again. Which reminds me, why haven't you and I been writing? You must give me your new address.'

'Oh, I will.'

Fresh coffee arrived and Jinny sat back in her chair, feeling strangely relaxed. In spite of their distressing talk of Dunkirk and the London Blitz, being with Ross again was so very pleasant she could almost say that she felt . . . not happy, she couldn't go as far as that, but at least at ease. As though she could put her worries behind her.

'What are you smiling at?' Ross asked, smiling himself.

'Was I smiling? I didn't even know.'

'I was hoping it meant you were feeling happier.'

At that, she sat up, knowing that his remark was more of a question — one she should answer. When she did, her voice was low. 'I still think of him. Viktor, I mean.'

Ross's brown eyes were steady on her face. 'Of course. It's natural that you would.'

'I think of him because I want to know what's happened to him, and because he meant so much. But . . . I don't know how to put it . . . I don't want to sound cold . . . and fickle . . .'

'I know you're not, Jinny.'

She shook her head. 'But I have changed, Ross. I never thought it would happen, but I don't feel the same. Viktor was everything to me, and now he seems . . . so far away. A sort of shadow.'

She looked away, to the people in the street below, all hurrying somewhere so purposefully, unaware of one another's troubles — and everyone would have troubles. Oh, yes, today they would. 'Sorry, Ross,' she murmured, 'if I don't seem happier.'

'I understand. I've been through something of the same myself.' He raised his hand to the waitress. 'But let's not talk of that now. I'll get the bill, shall I?'

Out in the street, amid all those hurrying people, they stood together, their eyes meeting, their faces serious.

'Ross, it's been lovely,' Jinny told him. 'It's a wonderful treat to see you again.'

'And for me to see you.' Ross put her arm in his. 'I'll walk back with you to Comrie's, if that's where you're going?'

'Yes, I'll look in on Mr Lennox — maybe see the bakery folk another day.'

But Comrie's came into sight too quickly. Although there was no longer any queue to observe them, they had no wish to say goodbye within sight of the shop window, and drew to a halt before they reached it.

'Jinny, I was wondering . . .' Ross began with an unusual

awkwardness. 'If you're on leave and I'm on leave, could we perhaps meet again? It would be a shame not to.'

'I'd like that very much, Ross, but are you sure it'd be all right?'

'Why shouldn't it be?'

'We'll, you're an officer and I'm not. We're not supposed to mix, are we? Bad for discipline, they say.'

'Oh, come, we're old friends, we've a right to mix on leave. And we're not in the same unit – that's when the discipline problem crops up.' Ross grinned. 'Same old conscientious Jinny! Look, apart from anything else, we'll be in civvies – I don't see any military policeman reporting us.'

'All right, then, if you're sure. When shall we meet?'

'Tomorrow night? There's a play I wouldn't mind seeing at the Raeburn – not your dad's theatre, I'm afraid, but I think you might find it interesting.'

'What is it?'

'*Time and the Conways* by J.B. Priestley. He's pretty good, usually. What do you think?'

'I think I'd like to go. Thank you, Ross.'

'Great. I'll book tickets. Starts at half past seven – shall I call for you a bit for that?'

'Our flat's right out of your way. I'll meet you at the theatre.'

'I'll call for you, it's no trouble,' he declared so firmly she didn't argue.

'OK, I'll be waiting, then, Ross. But now I'll pop in to see Mr Lennox, and then go and queue at the butcher's – Vi told me he's got some sausages.'

'Good luck!' he called, laughing, and they parted, after a cloud or two, in sudden sunshine.

Fifty

Ross was early coming to collect Jinny, but she didn't mind. She was ready, anyhow, and had given the living room a tidy up too, which was a bonus.

'Come on up,' she told him when she'd run down to answer his knock, and with alacrity he followed her up the stairs, looking well-turned out in a dark suit and carrying a bunch of mixed flowers.

'Jinny, you're looking lovely!' he exclaimed when she'd shown him into the living room. 'Such a pretty dress! Is it new?'

'No, it's ancient – hard to get new clothes these days.' She glanced down at her rose-pink dress, one of her favourites, which suited her colouring so well, and laughed. 'I often wear it – you must have seen it loads of times.'

'Sorry, but that's me – a hopeless case. Please accept this little bouquet as a peace offering.'

'Ross, they're beautiful!' She took the flowers, putting her face close to smell their scent. 'Wherever did you find them?'

'There's a wee florist's still open on the south side, and as I couldn't get you any chocolates, I thought these anemones and such would do instead.'

'I'm thrilled,' she answered, feeling at his mention of chocolates another little reminder of Viktor, a memory she quickly put from her mind. 'Just let me put them in water and then I'll get my coat, but we've plenty of time – you're nice and early.'

'That's me again, always catch the train before the one I want,' he answered jauntily, his gaze moving round the living room, taking in the well-filled bookcase, the heavy sideboard and chairs, the long window with pretty curtains, and the open fireplace that was so attractive compared with the usual kitchen range.

'Nice room, Jinny,' he called as she set a vase containing his flowers on the table. 'But are you on your own? I thought I might meet Vi.'

'Och, she's out at a meeting – or is it her evening class? Vi's rarely in, and May, of course, doesn't live here now. She and Allan have a bungalow his parents left him.'

'And your dad's at the Duchess?'

'Yes.' Jinny had taken her coat from a peg, and smiled thanks as Ross helped her into it. 'I wish he could have met you, Ross. I know you'd get on well.'

'Maybe another time,' said Ross, and as she waved him through the front door which she then locked, she noted his words.

Another time, did he say? Was this theatre outing not to be a one-off? Perhaps he wanted company? He was, of course, on his own.

They took a tram to the theatre in Morningside, as Ross had no petrol for his car, and taxis were mainly for emergencies, as he said with some apology, which made Jinny laugh.

'Why, we never take taxis, anyway, Ross! What an idea!'

'Only the best for you,' he said, grinning.

'Which is a dear old tram. Look, we're at the theatre already!'

The Raeburn, where a crowd was already gathering, was a small, old-fashioned building, known in recent years for its adventurous programmes, although, as Ross remarked, the Priestley play might well have appeared at the Duchess, J.B.'s work being so popular.

'*Time and the Conways* is one of his time plays,' he explained when they were settled in their seats in the stalls. 'He's written several, all based on the theory that time is sort of simultaneous, the past, present and future being one. I'm not sure I go along with it.'

'I think I've read about it,' Jinny said, studying the programme. 'But J.B. Priestley didn't invent it, did he?'

'No, that was a chap called J.W. Dunne. Cynic that I am, I can't help wondering if Priestley just saw the theory as a new peg to hang his plays on. But let's see what we make of it, anyway.'

When the curtain went up on the first act, set in 1919, with the Conway family feeling happy and optimistic, Jinny found herself thinking how agreeable it was to be beside Ross, different though it might be from the first time she'd gone to the theatre with Viktor.

How excited and strung up she'd been then, when they were watching Agatha Christie's *Black Coffee*, whereas being with Ross, her one-time boss and her old friend, was, of course, very different. Everything was so easy and pleasant and in no way nerve-racking. Yet, in its way, it was exciting, too. For this evening out was so much a departure from everything they'd known when they'd worked together, it had rather made them seem different people. Just as nice, though, in the case of Ross, who no longer felt like her boss.

Better concentrate on what was happening in the play, she decided at last, so that she could talk intelligently about it when they had coffee in the interval. But, oh dear, by the time she got to it they'd reached the second act, set years after the first, and everything, it seemed, was going wrong for the characters. How was Time going to help there? Only, as someone explained, if people can see it as something that does not progress in a line but includes the past, present and future, and helps them to overcome their suffering.

'Gives them a second chance?' Jinny asked doubtfully when she and Ross were having their coffee in the interval. 'I must say, I don't really understand what Priestley's getting at.'

'Nor me,' Ross admitted. 'Though I'm all for second chances.'

'That's because you have a generous nature.'

'Have I?'

'Of course. You don't go in for judging people, do you?'

'I have my prejudices, all the same. Remember how I didn't like Viktor at first? And I'd really no reason for that.'

'I remember,' said Jinny, smiling a little. 'Well, maybe that shows you're human, after all.'

'Hey, was there any question of it?' Ross laughed and stood up. 'There goes the bell. Let's see how the third act works things out – if it does.'

Fifty-One

The third act, like the first, was set in 1919, with the Conways and others appearing to be in their original optimistic mood. It soon became clear, however, that already there were signs of future disaster, with the play seeming to suggest that it could be avoided if only the lessons of Time could be learned. Somehow, one or two of the characters found hope and it was on that brighter note that the curtain fell, leaving the audience to make of it what they could.

'Happy about that?' Ross asked cheerfully as they joined the crowd leaving the theatre. Seeing the look on Jinny's face, he added, 'No, can't say I am, either. Yet it was interesting, wasn't it? I mean, it gave us something to think about.'

'Oh, yes, I enjoyed it,' she said quickly, 'it was different.'

'But we still need convincing that Time's going to make things easy for us?' Ross put his hand on Jinny's arm. 'I see a tram on the horizon. We'd better get to the stop.'

'You're coming back to Fingal Street with me?'

'Of course! No arguments, please.'

'I'm not arguing. I'd like you to come.'

That was true. Even though Jinny knew the shadow of Viktor would be with her as they made their way to Fingal Street, she was happy to be with Ross.

Outside the flat, there was the usual halting by the streetlight, the gaze up at the windows, the hesitation before the goodbyes. With Viktor, of course, there had been much more – desperate kisses, fierce embraces – all the delight and sadness of a parting between lovers. With Ross, there would be . . . what? A handshake, a friendly peck on the cheek?

'Why don't you come in?' Jinny cried suddenly. 'Just for a minute? Vi should be back, and probably Dad, too. You could meet them.'

'I'd like to very much – if you think it's not too late?'

'No, no, come on – I'll open the door.'

Josh was indeed back, sitting in his chair by the fireplace, being brought tea by Vi and just about to switch on the wireless when Jinny and Ross walked in.

'Hello, Dad!' cried Jinny. 'I've brought someone to say hello to you and Vi.'

'Nice,' said Vi, setting down Josh's cup and advancing to shake Ross's hand. 'So you're Ross? We've heard so much about you.'

'Groan,' he said lightly, but his gaze was on Josh who had risen, pipe in hand, to fix him with a hard stare.

'We got your note, Jinny – knew you were going out with your boss. A Priestley play, eh? We've had a couple of his things at the Duchess. Mr MacBain, how d'you do?'

'Oh, please, Mr Hendrie, call me Ross.'

Josh nodded and sat down again, drawing his cup towards him. 'Well, you'd better have a cup of tea,' he said gruffly. 'Jinny, get your boss a cup.'

'He's not my boss now, Dad – we're both in the army. Ross is a second lieutenant.'

'That right? First over the top, in my day, the officers, but war's different now, eh?'

'You'll have a cup of tea?' Jinny whispered to Ross, but he said perhaps he should be going.

'I'm sorry to look in so late, Mr Hendrie, and Vi – may I call you that? But I'm very glad to have met you both. I've heard a lot about you, too, you know.'

'All glowing reports, I'm sure,' said Vi. 'But it's been good to meet you.'

'Aye, very good,' put in Josh. 'Take care now, Ross. Do your best against Hitler!'

'I will indeed, Mr Hendrie,' Ross answered, smiling, as he was steered to the door by Jinny. When they had reached the street she gave a huge sigh of relief.

'What a hit you were with Dad!' she cried. 'You know what he can be like. So, what's your secret?'

'I think we were just two soldiers together – both with going to war in common.'

'Well, it was grand to see.' Jinny took Ross's hand. 'Thanks for the evening, Ross. It was lovely, I really enjoyed it.'

'Me, too.' He hesitated. 'Maybe we could meet again? I don't want to monopolize you – I know you've your family to see – and friends—'

'Well, I'm going to Glasgow with Vi tomorrow. We're hoping to see if they've got anything in the shops that we haven't.'

'I see.'

'But I'm free the next day.'

He brightened. 'You are? May we meet, then?'

'I'd like to, Ross. Where shall we go?'

'Think it'll have to be local. Travel's so difficult these days. Trams, buses – they've either got reduced timetables or they're packed out.' Ross smiled ruefully. 'And the entire coastline seems to be a restricted area.'

'Still plenty to see in Edinburgh.'

'That's right. Look, I have to see my lawyer tomorrow – he's doing the paperwork for my tenant's new lease – but I could come later, about two? How about we decide then where to go?'

'That'd be fine. But I didn't know you had let your house, Ross.'

'Oh, it's been let since I joined up. Not much point in keeping it empty except for my leave.'

'I did see it once, when you asked us all round once at Christmas.'

'And I wish you could have seen it again. Unfortunately, I don't live there any more.

'Where've you been going to, then, when you've left me?'

'I'm a member of the Northerner Club – I can stay there.' Ross laughed. 'Don't worry, I'm not on the streets. Not yet, anyway. Look, I'll see you the day after tomorrow then, at two?'

'The day after tomorrow.'

'Goodnight, Jinny.' He gave her a quick kiss on the cheek. 'Have a good day in Glasgow.'

'I don't suppose we'll buy a thing. Goodnight, Ross.'

Oh, I do hope they don't say anything about him, she thought, returning to the flat. I just can't face a great interrogation.

But as soon as she went into the living room, Vi asked, 'Are you sure Ross is just your boss, Jinny?'

'Was. That's all over for the duration.'

'Well, he seems pretty friendly for a boss.'

'Ross is a friendly chap. We always got on fine at Comrie's.'

'Seems a grand Scottish fellow to me,' Josh put in. 'Ready to fight for his country – that's the thing.' He tapped out his pipe on the grate. 'A big improvement on the last man you brought here, Jinny.'

'He's not to be compared with Viktor, Dad.'

'You can say that again.'

As she lay in bed later, going over the evening, she thought how right she and her father had been. Ross was not Viktor, and if at one time that wouldn't have been in his favour, things were different now. Being with him, she had been able to relax, feel calm and know all was well, yet there was no consciousness of dullness or boredom. No, there had been that little spice of excitement brought about by the change from all they'd known before in their surroundings, an excitement that made the thought of the day after tomorrow – well, quite exciting too.

Fifty-Two

At two o'clock on the dot, Ross arrived to collect Jinny for their afternoon out, looking cheerful in casual clothes and without a hat. his copper hair glinting in the sun.

'How was Glasgow?' he asked, as Jinny, wearing her navy jacket with matching skirt, hurried down the stairs to meet him. 'Any luck finding anything?'

'Yes! I got soap and make-up and two tea towels.' She laughed as they stood outside the flat in the autumn sunshine. 'Imagine being thrilled at finding tea towels! But everything's so short these days, you're lucky if you find anything.'

'Too right. By the time this war's over we'll all be dressed like scarecrows. And you'll still look, as they say, like a million dollars.'

'Ross, what a lovely compliment!' She slipped her arm in his. 'So, where are we going?'

'How about a gentle walk up Calton Hill?'

'Gentle suits me. I like Calton Hill – wonderful views without climbing.'

'And easily followed by tea – if we can find any. We'll away, then.'

Sitting together in the tram, there came again that wonderfully pleasant feeling of ease in each other's company. And when they began to walk up Calton Hill from the east end of Princes Street, there was still that feeling of rightness between them, of affinity shared.

Of course, there was nothing new for them to see on Calton Hill – they were both Edinburgh people, they knew it well – but the object of their day out was not to see something new as though they were tourists, just to enjoy time together. As they had in the past in the office, but that, of course, was different.

Often, as they followed the road up to the highest point, from where there was the magnificent panoramic view over the city, their eyes kept meeting, as though to say, 'isn't this the life?'

'Beats being on the parade ground,' said Ross, looking across the city to the Forth. 'I really am grateful to you, Jinny, for taking pity on an old guy on leave.'

'Old guy!' She laughed. 'You're only thirty!'

'Must seem old to you.'

'Of course it doesn't!' She took his arm. 'Come on, let's go down and see the monuments – if you can manage without a stick!'

'Cheek! I'll race you down, if you like.'

'No takers.'

Laughing, they made their way down the hill to see the famous monuments again: one to the dead of the Napoleonic Wars, always called 'Scotland's Disgrace' because it was never finished, another a great tower devoted to Nelson.

'See the time-ball at the top of the tower? Ross asked Jinny. 'That comes down at one o'clock to give the time signal to shipping. The one o'clock gun is its supplement. Which, of course, I'm sure you know.'

'I don't mind being told again.'

He laughed. 'That's the only problem with going to places in Edinburgh – we've seen them all before.'

'Yes, but don't you think it's worth coming here just for the air?' Jinny had taken off her blue beret and was breathing deeply as she shook her dark hair free. 'I mean, you're not far from Princes Street, yet you might be miles away in the country.'

'Let's sit for a while, then,' said Ross. 'We could take that bench over there if you're not too cold.'

'No, I'm warm after our walk.'

They took their seats on the bench, sitting close and not talking at first, just appreciating where they were. People passed them on the way to the top and they smiled and waved, so full of wellbeing, and equally full of goodwill to strangers.

'I like this,' Ross said after a while. 'Being here with you.'

'We've been together often enough.'

'You mean, in the office? You must admit, Calton Hill is different.'

Or are we different? wondered Jinny.

'What did you mean?' she asked aloud, 'when you said you understood about my change of feeling towards Viktor?'

Ross looked away for a moment. 'I was thinking of Annette,' he said at last. 'When she died, I thought the place she'd left could never be filled, that I'd always be missing her. For years, I thought that. But then, as I told you once, I began to feel better, as though I was back in the world again. What I didn't tell you was that I found, as you did with Viktor, that her image was fading.'

Ross, still looking away, gave a long sigh.

'Then I felt guilty. I thought it shouldn't happen, but gradually, as I began to think of her without pain, I realized it was natural. She had gone, I was still here, and life had to move on. I knew I would never forget her, that what we'd had would always be precious to me, but I had to realize it was over.' Ross turned his eyes on Jinny. 'Finally, I did – realize it.'

'You really felt better? There was no more guilt?'

'The guilt went with the pain.'

'You should never have felt it, anyway.'

'Nor should you, over Viktor. For whatever reason, he's no longer in your life. You must move on, too.'

'But I don't know what's happened to him, Ross. That's what different for me. He might still come back.'

'And if he did? You think you might care for him again?'

'No, Ross, I don't.' Her dark eyes were suddenly full of pain. 'But he did seem wonderful, didn't he?'

'So you thought,' Ross said shortly.

'Yes, well he was different from anybody I knew. So romantic, you see, coming from Vienna, and everything. I truly did believe I loved him. Well, I did, I know I did, but maybe we were never meant for each other, things were too difficult for us.' She shook her head. 'Whatever it was, it's over now. There's no way of going back.'

When she had finished speaking, a silence fell between her and Ross, while the sky began to darken as the clouds rolled over the city from where no lights could be seen.

'Time to go,' announced Ross, rising and giving his hand to Jinny, who stood beside him, straightening her skirt and pulling on her beret. 'What shall we do about finding some place to eat?'

'We can always get a cup of tea somewhere.'

'It's a bit late for teashops, and I feel like something more than tea. There's a place in Thistle Street sometimes has a menu to offer. Want to see what they have?'

'It's worth a try,' said Jinny.

Fifty-Three

They were in luck, the Thistle Street restaurant could offer two choices for their early supper – a beef casserole and baked haddock. Both chose the haddock, having had too much tough beef in army cooking, and when the waiter had taken their order, sat back, relaxing, yet also covertly eyeing each other with special interest.

Do we look different? Jinny wondered. She'd asked herself the question in the restaurant cloakroom when she'd combed her hair and splashed her face before putting on a little powder, and decided that they must. After all, they seemed different now from those two people who worked in Accounts. Something must surely show in their faces? Not really, it seemed.

Somehow, Jinny couldn't resist talking of Lorna again, as though she thought her something of a threat. A threat? she asked herself. Why should she regard any woman Ross might be interested in as a threat? She didn't bother to work it out, but as soon as they were eating their fish and drinking the pre-war wine Ross had chosen, heard herself saying, 'You know, Ross, at one time I thought you were keen on Lorna.'

'Lorna?' He stared in surprise. 'You're not serious? She's my cousin.'

'Cousins are sometimes attracted to each other. And she's a lovely girl.'

'She is, but she's the nearest I have to a sister. I could never think of her in any other way.' Ross smiled. 'Imagine your thinking I might!'

'I'm sure a lot of other people at Comrie's thought the same when you brought her to that staff Christmas party.'

'They understood when they knew she was my cousin. I thought you would have done, too.'

'Well, yes, only I did get the impression you were interested in her, and I suppose I was a bit surprised. But I knew I wanted you to be happy, so I was happy too – for you.'

'You wanted me to be happy?' Ross gave a wide smile. 'Jinny, that was nice of you. You always were a caring sort of girl.'

'But I was wrong about you and Lorna?'

'Wrong to think there was any sort of romance between us. I'm sure Lorna would be amused at the very idea. If I think of her as a sister; she probably thinks of me as an uncle!'

'A very attractive uncle, then,' said Jinny firmly, which brought another smile from Ross.

Reaching Fingal Street again to say goodnight, their steps were slow as they approached the door to the Hendries' flat. When they finally stopped, Jinny looked up at Ross and asked him what he was thinking.

'You seem worried. Is anything wrong?'

'Not at all, Jinny. I'm just getting the courage to ask you what day you go back.'

'Tuesday. What about you?'

He sighed deeply. 'Monday.'

'Oh.'

'I've got one more day.'

'Sunday.'

'And I suppose you'll be seeing your family then?'

'Yes, May's asked us over. She's managed to get a joint. It's a big treat.'

'I see. Well, your family comes first, of course. Can't expect you to see me again – you've been very good as it is.'

'Ross, I've had a wonderful time.' Jinny stood in thought for a moment or two, then her face lit up. 'I know, Ross! You could to come to May's as well! You said you'd like to meet her.'

'No, no, thank you, I wouldn't intrude. It's a nice idea, but I couldn't ask it of your family.'

'Seems a shame not to say goodbye tomorrow. If you're worried about sharing the joint, how about if we met in the evening?'

'The evening?' Ross's brown eyes were bright. 'You think we could?'

'Yes, why not?' Jinny was searching her handbag. 'I'll just give you May's address. You can come to her house and have a cup of tea with us, then we can go out somewhere. Got a pencil?'

When the address, written on a scrap from Ross's notebook, had been safely put away, they stood for a while, not seeming sure how to say goodnight. Then Ross gave Jinny one of his quick kisses.

'Until tomorrow, then.'

'Until tomorrow.'

'We're good friends, aren't we?' Ross asked. 'Special friends?'

'Special friends.'

'Goodnight, Jinny.'

'Goodnight, Ross.'

Special friends? Her family would think so, Jinny thought, when she told them Ross was not only coming to tea but spending the evening with her – again. So, what did special mean? Hard to be sure what was in Ross's mind, or in fact in her own, and soon they would be far apart, anyway. But at least they needn't say goodbye until tomorrow.

Fifty-Four

'May, that was grand,' Josh said, sitting back in Allan's armchair in the comfortable sitting room of the bungalow. Sunday dinner was over and had been a great success, with the joint so like something pre-war that they couldn't believe their luck.

'Can't think how you got it,' Josh went on. 'Was it a miracle or what?'

'Sweet-hearting the butcher, maybe.' Vi laughed. 'Blue eyes are such a help, eh?'

'Vi, what a thing to say!' May cried, for once losing her calm. 'As though I'd go around sweet-hearting, as you put it!'

'Oh, I didn't say you'd do it deliberately – just give a smile or two.'

'Now, Vi, stop your teasing,' Josh said easily. 'You know May would never go making up to the butcher – let's have our tea in peace.'

'Listen, I'd just like to say something.' Jinny cleared her throat. 'Ross is coming round later to call for me and meet May. It's his last day of leave and we thought we'd go out.'

'To meet me?' May smiled. 'That's nice. I've heard so much about your boss, Jinny.'

'On a Sunday?' Josh asked, sitting up straight. 'Where will you go?'

'Oh, there's always something open – with so many folk about these days.'

'I've never heard there was anything open.' Josh was now staring hard at Jinny. 'You've been seeing a lot o' this Ross this last week, eh?'

Jinny hesitated, glancing at her sisters, who were quietly watching. 'Yes, I have. We've enjoyed meeting up again.'

'As friends, eh?' asked Vi.

'Yes, why not? He has no family and he's glad to have a companion.'

'And that's all there is to it?' asked Josh.

'Oh, yes.'

'I haven't met him yet but he's always sounded very nice, from what Jinny's told us,' said May.

'He is nice,' Vi told her. 'Dad likes him.'

'Aye, I do,' said Josh, sitting back in his chair. 'He's a Scottish laddie, keen to fight for his country. That's the sort I like.'

'Why didn't you invite him to share our roast?' asked Vi. 'Bet he'd have enjoyed that.'

'He said he didn't want to intrude,' Jinny replied. 'He'll just have a cup of tea.'

'And be very welcome for that,' said May.

He was early, of course, that being his way, but, as May had promised, he was made very welcome, first being introduced to her, then greeting Josh and Vi again with his easy, natural manner.

'You'll have a cup of tea?' May asked.

'Thank you, I'd like that.'

Ross was looking round the pleasant room that had been furnished by Allan's parents but already bore some of May's touches – new curtains and cushions and lamp shades she had covered herself. He turned back, complimenting her, but she only sighed a little.

'I had great plans once, though I was lucky to get as far as I did. Now, of course, Allan's away and that's all I can think about.'

'May, you're doing good work at the hospital,' Josh put in. 'Don't forget that.'

'Might I ask where Allan is?' Ross asked May gently.

'Well, I'm not sure. He did mention Crete when he came on leave, but in his letters he never says.'

'Must be difficult for you, May, on your own.'

'Oh, we're all in the same boat, aren't we? And I've got Dad and Vi. Miss Jinny, though.' May smiled and rose, saying she'd make the tea, and when her sisters went out to the kitchen with her, Josh looked at Ross.

'Your regiment is still in this country, eh?'

'That's right, Mr Hendrie.'

'Can't say where, I suppose?'

'Oh, I think I can tell you it's the Isle of Wight.'

'Way down a bit from here, that. Where d'you think you'll go next, then?'

'Ah, well, that I can't say. But it will be abroad.'

'Not to fight Jerry?'

'Not yet.'

'But there'll be fighting wherever you go. Take care of yourself, if you can.' Josh put out his hand, which Ross shook. 'I'll wish you all the best.'

'Thank you, Mr Hendrie. I appreciate that.'

'Now, here come the girls — let's see if they've rustled anything up for tea. May told me she'd only one egg. Now, what can you make with that?'

'Scones!' May called across, setting down a tray. 'No cake, though, I'm sorry to say.'

'Home-made scones? What could be better?' asked Ross, smiling at Jinny and her sisters, savouring the family atmosphere he had not himself known for many years.

Fifty-Five

When he and Jinny prepared to leave May's some time later, there were more good luck wishes for Ross, as well as hopes that they might find something open for their last night out.

'Aye, what there'll be on a Sunday night in Edinburgh, I canna think,' Josh told them. 'There's nothing open, eh? Dead as a door-nail — that's Auld Reekie on a Sunday.'

'As a matter of fact, we do have a place to go,' Ross told him. 'My dad belonged to the Northener club in Abercromby Place, and I took out membership too. You can get a meal there, even on a Sunday, and women are welcome, as guests or members.'

'You're taking Jinny to the Northener?' cried Vi. 'Help, she'll be about thirty years younger than everybody else, if what I've heard is true.'

'Hey, what about Ross?' asked Jinny. 'He's not old!'

'Probably the youngest member,' admitted Ross, 'but you must admit, it's handy, having a place to go on Sunday evening!'

'You know what?' asked Jinny a few minutes later on the tram. 'I haven't even begun to think about my new posting. I thought I'd be so nervous, but it's all just gone out of my mind.'

'You'll be fine with the pay office, Jinny. You certainly don't need to be nervous, anyway.'

'Think I'll get a stripe?'

'You're sure to. You'll be a lance corporal in no time. The sky's the limit for you.'

'I don't think so! But listen, I'm getting nervous now, going to your club. I mean, am I dressed right?'

'In your navy suit? You're perfect.'

'Is it true that everyone's ancient?'

'Well, they won't see twenty-one again. But they're OK. Middle-aged, mostly.'

'As you say, it is a place to go.'

'That just about sums up what clubs are for,' Ross said wryly.

The Northener, as it turned out, was a comfortable, well-kept establishment, without the subdued atmosphere usually associated with men's clubs because of its mixed membership. Certainly, the women Jinny saw when she entered the dining room with Ross were talking freely, and though well-dressed, not so smart that she felt she needed to worry.

'The food's not particularly exciting,' Ross whispered as they were seated at a corner table for two. 'But they've got their problems with rationing the same as everyone else.'

'I'm not worried about the food. After May's roast I'm not really hungry.'

'We can just have a ham salad, then, if you like. And some wine?'

'Oh, no thank you, no wine.'

'Just coffee to follow, then.'

The ham in the salad turned out to be corned beef, but it wasn't too bad, and the coffee served to them when they'd moved to the lounge was good and strong.

'Nice,' commented Jinny. 'It's not often you can get coffee like this. Even pre-war, Viktor was always complaining about our coffee—' She stopped and coloured, but Ross shook his head.

'You don't have to worry about remembering Viktor,' he said

gently. 'He was an important part of your life and memories don't just disappear. I should know. I lived on them for long enough.'

'It's just a bit disconcerting for me, that's all.' Jinny finished her coffee and set down her cup. 'Better make a move, I suppose.'

'I don't want to. When we go we'll be on our way to saying goodbye, and I'm not looking forward to that.'

'Nor am I.' Jinny rested her eyes on Ross's face. 'These few days have been so nice, Ross. I've really enjoyed being with you.'

'Tell me something.' He leaned forward a little. 'Do you see me – after these few days – in a different light?'

'From the office?'

'Yes, from the office.'

'It's odd, but you've just put into words what I've been thinking. I do see you in a different light. Is it the same for you with me?'

'Very much so. That gap away from each other, away from the office seems to have made us into two different people.'

'Two new people,' suggested Jinny.

'New people after years of already knowing each other and liking each other – does that seem crazy?'

'No, just special.'

'And we did say we were special friends.'

'We did.'

For some time, they stayed where they were, studying each other, then Ross reluctantly stood up.

'Think we'd better go or they'll be turning down the lights. I'll just sign the bill.'

Fifty-Six

Outside in the elegant New Town street, where they could hardly see each other's faces in the blackout, Jinny sighed and slipped her arm into his.

'I don't know that I want you to take me home, Ross. It's too sad.'

'Come on, we have to say goodbye.'

'Maybe I could come to the station?'

'That'd be worse. I hate station farewells. I know what they're like. No, Fingal Street it is. Back to the tram stop.'

'It isn't as though I even know where you're going,' Jinny said when they were together on the wooden slatted tram seat. 'I mean, I know you're in the south, but you won't be staying there, will you?'

'We don't stay anywhere for ever, but I'll be writing to you. You'll know where I am then.' He moved his hand to take hers. 'And I'll be sure to get more leave one of these days, and when I do, I wanted to ask you – would you be willing to try to wangle leave yourself? So we could meet again. Would you want to do that, Jinny?'

'I would, though whether I'd get it just when I wanted it I don't know.'

'As long as you want to see me again, that's all that matters.'

'I don't know why you have to ask, Ross. We are special friends, aren't we?'

He pressed her hand hard. 'That's right. We are. As well as old friends who seem new. So we said.'

'And it's true,' said Jinny.

Though they put it off as long as possible, the time came when they reached the Hendries' flat again and stopped in the darkness of Fingal Street, below the blacked-out windows.

'This is it, then,' said Ross. 'Goodbye time. Or, we could just make it *au revoir*?'

'That does sound better,' Jinny agreed, looking up into his face that was so hard to see.

'And we are going to try to meet again, aren't we?' Ross took her hands. 'I just want to thank you again, Jinny, for making this leave so special – there goes that word again.'

'It was special for me, too.'

'But you had your family to see, yet you spared time for me. That's what I appreciate.'

'I had a wonderful time, Ross. I want to say thank you, too.'

They were silent for a while, waiting to make the final farewell.

'Wish I could see you better.' Suddenly, Ross drew Jinny closer, and the thought came to her: now he would kiss her, with one of his friendly little pecks . . .

But a friendly little peck, it wasn't. As his mouth met hers, she was so taken by surprise at the passion of the kiss that she did not at first respond, but as it lengthened and deepened she found herself kissing him back with a pleasure she'd never expected to feel. Could this really be herself and Ross?

'Special,' he whispered, as they finally drew apart. 'That was special. You didn't mind?'

'No, I didn't.'

'Oh, God, I think I'd better go. The longer I stay the more difficult it is to leave. Look, I'll write to you and we'll meet again. Promise?'

'Promise.'

'*Au revoir*, then, Jinny.' He smiled in the darkness. 'I'll be seeing you, as the song says.'

'*Au revoir*, Ross.'

She watched him as best she could – saw him straighten his shoulders, wave and walk away, but soon he swallowed up into the darkness and all she had of him was the sound of his footsteps ringing out until there was silence. All she could do then was to open the front door and climb the stairs.

'Guess what?' cried Vi as soon as she saw her. 'I've done it!'

'Aye, she's done it,' Josh said from his chair. 'She's written her letter.'

'What letter?' asked Jinny.

'My letter of resignation,' Vi said grandly. 'I'm joining the ATS, like you. Oh, I can't stick around here any longer – I have to do something.'

'And what I'm going to do, I don't know,' said Josh glumly. 'I mean, who's going to do my tea? Who's going to take care o' the house?'

'I'd have to go anyway, Dad. They'll be calling the women up next year, that's for sure. And May says she'll come over and do some cooking for you. She won't have to go in the forces – she's married.'

Vi looked across at Jinny. 'How d'you get on at that posh club, then? Och, I bet it was like having a meal in a graveyard, eh?'

'It was very nice and very comfortable.' Jinny took off her jacket. 'I enjoyed it.'

'You look a bit down, all the same. Saying goodbye to Ross, eh?'

'It was a bit sad. But I've still got a day of my leave left. Maybe we can do something?'

'Aye, I'm taking the day off for that. After I've been to the recruiting place we'll fix up something. Cheer you up before you've to go to that Pay Corps place.'

'That'll be difficult. I'm terrified.'

'You'll be fine, a clever lassie like you,' Josh said, rising. 'Now, I'm away to my bed. Wish I could be with you tomorrow, Jinny, but I canna make it. You get leave again, soon, eh?'

They all, unusually, kissed goodnight, and then Jinny was lying awake thinking about Ross, about that surprising kiss, about where they were going, if anywhere. And then her nerves came back and it was some time before she could sleep, worried as she was about her posting.

Fifty-Seven

Within a week, the worries were over.

Hard to believe when Jinny remembered how nervous she'd been when arriving on her first day at the rather splendid Pay Corps premises, so anxious, so wearied by the crowded train trip. Cigarette smoke had hung like a pall in the carriage and was still in her hair when she reported to the ATS sergeant, along with two other newcomers she'd met at the entrance. Turned out they'd managed to find a taxi from the station, where Jinny had followed instructions and taken the bus.

'You going where we're going?' one of them, a lanky young woman with reddish hair had asked, before introducing herself as Josie Marriott and her companion, thin and fair, as Pauline Sanders. 'Reporting to Sergeant Abbott?'

'That's right. I'm Jinny Hendrie.'

'From Scotland?' asked Pauline.

'How did you guess?'

They laughed as a soldier who had to let them in took their names, ticked them off on a list and escorted them to plump, black-haired Sergeant Abbott, in a room where there were uniformed girls but only two men. All looked up from their work and smiled.

After that, it had become hazy. Just as it had on Jinny's first day at the training camp. So many different girls' faces, so many different heads of hair – fair, dark, ginger, mousy. So much to take in all at once.

I'll never get this lot sorted out, thought Jinny, but at least the two men stood out, and Captain Norton, the officer in charge, was easy to distinguish, he being a man too – tall, with a limp and metal-framed spectacles. He shook their hands, said he was sure they'd enjoy their posting, and handed them back to Sergeant Abbot, who in turn had brought forward a girl with two stripes on her sleeve who said she was Corporal Holt and would be taking them to their billet.

'It's a country house not far away,' she told them. 'Mind walking?'

They said they'd be glad of the fresh air and, as they only had small kitbags to carry, there was no problem.

'Be prepared, usually, to march to the office and back,' Corporal Holt added crisply. 'But you'll all be good at marching, eh? Being straight out of basic training?'

'Don't know about that,' said Josie.

'Oh, I hope so,' said Pauline.

'Right then, quick march!' said the corporal. 'No, I'm only joking.'

The billet was really rather grand, or had been before it was requisitioned. The rooms were large and high-ceilinged, the fireplaces made of marble, the floors parquet blocks, and the windows, covered in anti-blast strips, were long and elegant. Even the dormitory where the three new girls were given beds showed signs of its former splendour as the upstairs drawing room.

'Not bad, eh?' asked Josie, slinging her bag on to her bed. 'Gracious high living, except for the furniture.'

'We could certainly do a lot worse,' Corporal Holt remarked. 'The pay office was custom built and it's a nice place to work, but for us they've just got to find accommodation where they can. Sometimes in schools or colleges, old houses with leaking roofs and no bathrooms. I tell you, you're lucky here.'

When they'd washed and unpacked, they were returned to the headquarters to have a cup of tea at the canteen and were told to report back to Captain Norton.

'But don't worry,' the corporal said, before leaving them, 'real work'll start tomorrow. The captain'll just give you an introductory chat.'

'Phew, I could do with this,' sighed Pauline, drinking her tea. 'Been on the go since crack of dawn.'

'Where from?' asked Jinny.

'Essex.'

'And I'm from Dorset,' put in Josie, lighting a cigarette and avoiding, like the others, the appraising looks from a couple of soldiers eating doorstep sandwiches at the next table. 'But I'd just like to get started, find out what we have to do. I was in the accounts office of an insurance firm so I reckon I should be OK, but I'd just like to know.'

When Jinny had said that she too had accounting experience, Pauline cried 'Snap!', which made Josie declare that it was plain to see why they'd all been selected for the Pay Corps.

'Maybe, but I'm still feeling nervous,' Jinny admitted. 'I'll be happier when I know what's expected.'

That was discovered soon enough, when Captain Norton outlined what the work of the command pay office entailed.

'Not dealing with pay parades,' he had told the newcomers, 'but the paying of all bills, handling all the public monies involved in military services, the payments for requisitioned houses and land, renewal of equipment, or special reasons for replacing uniforms and so on. The office also gives advice on technical matters and on various costings of establishments. So, you see, we have a wide remit and plenty to do.'

He gave a mild smile and removed his glasses for a moment to rub his eyes.

'And of course there'll be all the routine bits to learn as well – how invoices are handled, who signs what and that sort of thing, but I know your backgrounds and I don't think you'll find anything you're asked to do too difficult.'

'How many ATS girls are here, sir?' Josie asked him as he replaced his glasses.

'Eighteen, counting you three. All very friendly – you'll soon get to know them.'

Maybe, Jinny had thought, but so it had turned out, and by the end of the week she had indeed got to know a number of her colleagues and agreed that they were friendly. She'd also found her way around the headquarters, taken a trip into town to look at the shops, received a letter from Vi all about her recruitment, and had found time to write one in reply. There was nothing, as yet, from Ross, but she knew a letter would come. No doubt of that.

As for the work, Ross had been right – it was more interesting than doing the bakery wages, or paying out soldiers' pay. In fact, she was fascinated by the variety of the jobs that came her way and had no trouble in learning the routine.

'Shouldn't be surprised if you get your stripe soon,' Sergeant Abbot commented, and Jinny thought, now, that would be something to tell them back home . . . and Ross, of course.

Fifty-Eight

Waiting to hear from Ross, she had been wondering what sort of letter he would write. Friendly, cheerful, or . . . romantic? After that farewell kiss of his, she wasn't sure what to expect. Just how far did 'special friends' take them? Not so far as love letters, she guessed, and so it turned out, for when his first letter arrived, it was as Ross himself had always seemed to her – kind and understanding, generous of spirit, with the added bonus here of humour and descriptions of life on the Isle of Wight without giving too much away. He did, however, sign the letter 'with love', which didn't necessarily mean anything. People would sign Christmas cards 'with love' when there was no actual love involved.

Still, it was a lovely letter, and she wasn't at all sure that she could equal it. She'd never had to write many letters and felt she didn't have the skill to write amusingly of her routine at the pay office, or her not very exciting daily life.

All the same, she was relieved in a way that Ross's first letter had not been romantic. There was certainly something special between them, something they had not shared when they worked together, and it had been hard to say goodbye. Maybe they were moving towards a true relationship, but it was easier, maybe, as things were in their unsure world, to let that develop gradually and take things as they came until they could be very sure themselves. After what had happened between herself and Viktor, and how her feelings had changed, the one thing she wanted was to be sure.

At least, the way Ross had written to her, she knew what style to aim for in her reply, and spent a whole evening trying to produce something that would equal his for lightness of touch and humour, several times tearing up efforts that did not satisfy until, finally, she achieved a short account of her new life that might interest him. She sealed it up before she could change her mind and put it ready to post on her bedside locker.

'Finished it?' asked Josie, getting up from her bed on which she'd been lying, reading a magazine.

As Jinny only stared, Josie came over and nodded at the letter to Ross. 'I mean your letter. My, you had problems, eh? Or, am I speaking out of turn? Sorry, just ignore me.'

'I'm not much of a letter writer,' Jinny said stiffly.

'Nor me. And letters to young men are always the worst, eh? My chap is much better at writing than I am – I'm for numbers, not words – but letters are important to fighting men and you have to do your best.'

'I know.' Jinny hesitated. 'This one was to my ex-boss. We're . . . good friends.'

Josie's narrow grey eyes appeared a little amused, but she only asked if Jinny would like to go for a cuppa in the canteen.

'Yes, all right, I could do with something.'

'After all that effort,' Josie said with a smile.

The canteen was, as usual, wreathed in smoke and full of ATS girls, all known by now to Jinny, who knew their names, their backgrounds and their interests, just as they knew hers. How quickly it could happen, she reflected, that you could become absorbed into a crowd you hadn't known existed before! And here they all were now – Barbara, Alice, Shirley and the rest, some talking to each other and some to soldiers, though these were in short supply. Jinny knew their names, too, but not so much about them. Girls were always more forthcoming – they liked to talk, Jinny supposed.

'None of the fellows here is able-bodied,' Josie whispered to Jinny over their pale coffee. 'I mean, if they were able-bodied they wouldn't be here, they'd be on active service.'

'I suppose they've all been injured already.'

'Well, Captain Norton was, in France before Dunkirk, I've heard, but often I think if they end up here they're just not that fit.' Josie lit a cigarette, offering the packet to Jinny, who shook her head. 'I suppose that's where we come in – we certainly seem to be in the majority at the pay office. How're you liking it, then?'

'Fine, I've settled in pretty well, I think. I was nervous to begin with, especially with so many strange faces around, but it's as it was in basic training – I soon got to know everybody.' Jinny sipped her coffee. 'I've even got one girl writing to me now.'

And that was Sukie, still grateful to Jinny for her help and doing well, it seemed, in her own posting.

'Is that right?' Josie laughed. 'Bet you find it easier to write to her than your ex-boss, eh? Oh, dear, there I go again – sorry, none of my business!'

'Here's Pauline,' said Jinny, glad to be changing the subject as Pauline came up to join them with tea on a tray, a cigarette dangling from her lip.

'Hey, you two, you're ahead of me!' she cried, setting down her tray and stubbing out her cigarette on a tin ashtray. 'I just nipped out to the chemist's to get myself some shampoo. "Light Touch" it's called – guaranteed to make me a blonde bombshell. What do you think?'

'I think your hair's fine as it is,' said Josie. 'Who's to notice here, anyway?'

'Why, there's an engineers' regiment putting on a dance at the weekend!' Pauline cried. 'They're outside Chester but Sarge says they're laying on a bus for us. We'll all be going, won't we?'

'When is it?' asked Josie.

'This Saturday. Jinny. You want to go?'

Jinny hesitated. 'I suppose so – if everyone else is – but I don't know if I'm all that keen.'

'Come on, it'll make a change,' said Josie. 'You don't have to go out with any guys if you don't want to, though they'll be sure to ask you. Just have a night away from here, I say.'

'I wouldn't mind going out with somebody,' Pauline murmured. 'I know you've got your young man, Josie, but at the moment I'm fancy free, and that's not as much fun as it sounds.'

'Wait till you appear as the blonde bombshell – the lads will be queuing up!'

'Oh, Josie, you're such a tease,' said Pauline, finishing her tea and laughing. 'You never know, I might surprise you all.'

Why didn't she want to go to the regimental dance? Jinny wondered as she went to bed that evening. Somehow she couldn't summon up any enthusiasm, though everyone in the dormitory was talking about it. Catching sight of the letter still on her locker, she thought of Ross with a sudden, warm feeling of remembrance. Was he the reason? Was she worried that he might not want to see her dancing with other men? No, she didn't really think so. Ross was Ross, not the type to get worked up. He knew how to kiss, though – and there was another memory. Smiling a little, as the lights went out, she prepared to sleep.

Better go to the dance, anyway, she decided – she didn't want to appear as an outsider – and as her eyelids grew heavy and she could hear Edith in the next bed beginning to snore, wondered if she should have her hair trimmed, or if it would do.

Fifty-Nine

Cigarette smoke, of course, was already hanging over the improvised dance floor in the sergeants' mess when the pay office staff arrived on the following Saturday evening to join the waiting soldiers and girls from other ATS units. An army band was tuning up in one corner, eyes were being cast around at possible partners, and for those sitting out there were wooden chairs placed round the walls. It was all very similar to the dance at the training centre, but larger, thought Jinny, who had in the end had her thick dark hair cut, but like everyone else had not had to worry about what to wear, as they were all in uniform.

'Doesn't seem like a proper dance, does it?' whispered Pauline, whose hair was now a strange straw colour that had had her running around earlier, asking everyone if they thought it looked OK. 'Be honest now, just say,' she'd implored, but as no one had wanted to be honest and they were all as polite as possible, she'd decided not to try to re-do it and was 'hoping for the best'. By which she meant success at the dance, which was not like a proper dance, in her view, as they had no dresses to wear.

'We'd never have got 'em in our kitbags,' Josie reminded her, her eyes busy looking round the room. 'This is wartime, don't forget. But here comes the CO to start things off.'

After a few words of welcome from the commanding officer, the band began to play a foxtrot, partners were selected and the dance began. There was no shortage of soldiers for the girls, some chaps indeed having to wait their turn, and were already cheekily turning the dance into an 'excuse me', which caused a few dark looks, though the girls were not complaining. Pauline, in fact, was truly enjoying herself. Jinny, pleased for her, smiled as she saw the blonde head in the distance, turning from side to side, quite like a professional, as the dance progressed.

She herself was much in demand, soldiers calling her 'dark eyes', and 'gorgeous', and didn't object too much until a tall, raw-boned sergeant with a high-bridged nose and piercing grey eyes claimed her for a quickstep and told her he wasn't having any of that 'excuse me' nonsense.

'I've been waiting for a chance to dance with you,' he told Jinny. 'Saw you come in and thought, "Wow, what a looker!" and then lost out till now – so watch out, other guys, they'll be on fatigues if they try to interfere.'

'Heavens, it's only a dance,' Jinny said uneasily. 'People are just enjoying themselves.'

He looked down at her coldly as he expertly guided her round the floor. 'I've told you – no one cuts in with me.'

And no one did, though Jinny caught plenty of glances from soldiers coming his way and moving on with haste. Obviously, he was a tough one; not many would care to trifle with him.

'You're from the pay office, that right?' he asked her. 'And Scottish, eh? How d'you like being in England?'

'This part is lovely.'

'I'm from Manchester myself. Name's Bart Randall. And you are . . . ?'

With some reluctance, she told him. How long was this dance going on? She was beginning to feel trapped.

'Jinny,' he repeated. 'Well, Jinny, how about a trip to the pictures with me sometime?'

As his sharp gaze rested on her, she couldn't think what to say. She was never going to go anywhere with him, but how was she to refuse gracefully? How avoid the full battery of those cold eyes meeting hers?

'Oh, that's – that's very kind of you,' she heard herself murmuring, 'but—'

'But what?' he asked starkly.

'Well, I don't really go to the pictures much.'

'Come off it, everybody goes to the pictures. What else is there to do? What you're saying is that you don't want to go with me, is that it?'

The dance at last had come to an end, with the bandsmen putting aside their instruments. It seemed it was the interval, thank God – now she could get away . . .

'Thank you very much, it was nice dancing with you,' she said quickly, 'but I see my friends over there—'

'Wait a bit, wait a bit.' He took hold of her wrist, not hard but with definite intent – it was clear he wasn't going to let her go without a struggle. 'Just why don't you want to go out with me? You don't like sergeants, or what?'

'I have someone,' Jinny snapped, her dark eyes suddenly flashing. 'I don't want to go out with anyone else. And now, would you please let go of my wrist?'

'I don't see any engagement ring, Jinny.'

'I didn't say we were engaged. And it's nothing to do with you, whether we are or not!'

'All right, all right.' Slowly he let go of her wrist and shook his head at her. 'Quite the firebrand, aren't you? Well, I don't want to take another guy's girl – if he exists. All I'll say to you is you don't know what you're missing.'

With which parting shot, he marched across the dance floor as though he were on the parade ground, leaving Jinny to hurry across to where Josie and Pauline were standing, Pauline looking flushed and excited, her hair seeming brighter than ever, and Josie looking at Jinny with interested eyes.

'What was all that about? Thought you were going to have a stand-up row with that sergeant!'

Jinny shivered, not looking round in case she saw Bart Randell again, and as Josie drew on a cigarette she almost wished, if it would calm her nerves, that she could have one herself.

'He was awful,' she whispered. 'Wanted me to go out with him and, when I said no, took it as a personal insult.'

'They do, they do – it's a question of manly pride, dear. "Who are you to turn me down?" Et cetera, et cetera. I hope you told him what to do.'

'I did my best, but he held my wrist and I thought he might not let me go, but of course he did in the end. I just hope I don't have to see him again.'

'What a shame!' cried Pauline. 'Now the fellow I was dancing with just now is so nice. Did you see him? Curly hair, lovely smile . . . He's getting us some coffee. You want one, Jinny?'

'I'll say,' said Jinny.

When Pauline's cheerful dancing partner had passed her one of the coffees he'd brought, she felt better, though still alarmed at the thought of meeting Bart Randall again. There was also a certain amount of wonder in her mind that she'd been so quick to mention she had 'someone', and that the someone she'd thought of had been Ross. Should she have described him like that? Well, they were, after all, special friends. More than friends, you might say, though it was true they had not really spelled out what their feelings might be, despite their passionate kiss. Ross had been keen, though, for them to meet again, and that kiss . . .

Oh, whether or not it had been right to describe him as her 'someone', she knew, as she sipped her coffee, how much she would have given to have been with him then, how much she did in fact miss him. If only she could have skipped the rest of this dance to go back to the billet to write to him!

No such luck – the band was beginning again, and already Pauline was waltzing with Curly-top, Josie with a lean, freckle-faced corporal, and a nervous-looking engineer had come to ask Jinny to take the floor with him. At least he wasn't Sergeant Randall – quite the reverse, in fact, seeming too worried about his dancing to make conversation.

'I'm not much of a dancer,' he muttered in a soft West Country accent. 'Expect you can tell that already?'

'Don't worry, you're doing very well.'

'Quickstep is bad enough,' he went on, finding his voice, 'but the waltz – I can't get the hang of the timing! Never thought when I volunteered for the artillery that I'd have to dance.'

'It's supposed to be fun!' Jinny said, laughing.

'Things are only fun if you're good at them,' he told her bleakly, and she had to agree that there was something in that.

The rest of the dance passed off without problems, except for one sticky moment when Jinny saw Bart Randall moving by with a blonde girl who was not from the pay office, and at his scornful blue stare Jinny flinched and began to talk animatedly to her partner, who seemed amazed that she had so much to say.

'Wasn't too bad, was it?' asked Josie later, when they were back in their dormitory. 'Apart from your little run-in with that sergeant, of course.'

'As I said before, I just hope I don't see him again.'

'I can set your mind at rest there. That dance was the battalion's farewell – I heard it on the QT from one of the chaps. They don't like broadcasting their movements until they actually go, so I don't know the date, but it'll be soon.'

'That's a relief. Can't think why he asked me out then.' Jinny looked suddenly anxious. 'You don't suppose he'll be left here, do you?'

'Not he! I bet he's the kingpin of the whole thing. You've only got to look at him to see he'll know everything.'

'Well, if you hear any more on the grapevine, let me know.'

'Such a shame you had to meet him,' commented Paulie, back from the bathroom and draped in a towel. 'But what did you think of my chap, then? Chris Fielding, he's called. Didn't you think he was sweet? Did I tell you he's asked me out?'

'I'm sure everybody around heard that!' Josie exclaimed. 'Wednesday night at the flicks, eh?'

'I'm so glad he's in the Pay Corps and not an engineer,' Pauline said with satisfaction. 'He's got bad asthma, you know, and I'm sorry about that, but it does mean he's staying here.' She put a hand to her lips. 'Oh, dear. Do I sound selfish? Sorry, girls. I know you have fellows who'll be fighting somewhere.'

'No need to apologise,' said Josie. 'There isn't one of us who wouldn't feel like you.'

Later, when the dormitory lights were out and Jinny was lying awake, she thought of Ross and of her renewed wish to be with him again, to feel safe, protected from the likes of Sergeant Randall. And then she felt ashamed about playing the 'little woman', as though she needed protection, when she was perfectly capable of looking after herself. Except that to think of being with Ross was just so comforting, she couldn't blame herself too much for wanting to have his shelter.

When would they, in fact, meet again? On Christmas leave, perhaps? That's if they could get Christmas leave, which was doubtful. Deciding to hope for the best, she fell asleep.

Sixty

In the event, neither Ross nor Jinny managed to get Christmas leave, and though Jinny succeeded in being given New Year leave instead, Ross wrote that he didn't expect to be home before Easter. His present to her was a pretty silk scarf he'd found locally, while hers to him was a pair of silver cufflinks from an antique shop in Chester. Lovely gifts, but they had had to be exchanged by post instead of in person, and there was the disappointment, but it couldn't be helped. So many folk were so much worse off, Jinny felt she couldn't complain, and in fact she knew she was lucky, being able to go home for Hogmanay. Not only would she see her father and May, there was the added bonus of seeing Vi, who had leave from the driving course she was taking following her basic training.

'Oh, I'm so excited about it!' she told the family when she arrived the day after Jinny. 'You know I had a few lessons before the war – didn't get round to taking the test – but when they asked me after basic training if I'd like to drive for the army and that I'd be trained for it, you bet I said yes!'

'And you're on the driving course now?' asked May. 'I'm sure you're looking very well on it!'

'Aye, you look grand,' Josh agreed, 'And so does Jinny – it's only your poor old dad who looks his age these days, eh? Going downhill fast without my girls around me.'

'Oh, Dad, what a thing to say!' Serene May was actually frowning. 'Especially when I'm always coming round!'

'Och, that's true, and I don't know what I'd do without you, pet.' Josh grasped her hand. 'But I used to have you all, eh? All my girls together. Didn't know how lucky I was.'

'It's only for the duration,' Vi said easily. 'Then we'll be home again.'

'And how long is the duration going to be?' Josh demanded. 'I think we're in for years of war before we finish off Hitler, if we ever do. He's won everything he's taken on – except the Battle of Britain. I don't see him giving in very easily.'

'You're not supposed to talk like that, Dad,' Jinny told him, shaking her head. 'Think victory, that's the word. And he didn't win the Battle of Britain, so that shows he can be defeated.'

'That's right,' Vi agreed. 'And in the meantime, we have to do what we can for the war effort, though I'm glad I'm not expected to do any fighting. In fact, I told the ATS selection folk that I wasn't interested in doing anti-aircraft stuff – "Ack-Ack" as they call it – as shooting down planes was not for me, but when they offered me driving, like I say, I was thrilled. So, that'll be me – army driver.'

'Driving what?' asked Josh. 'Thae great army lorries you see thundering through Edinburgh?'

'Oh, no, it'll be ambulances. I'll probably be attached to a military hospital, no idea where, but I'm delighted. It's just what I wanted.'

'That's wonderful, Vi,' Jinny told her, with May agreeing and Josh nodding his head.

'Sounds grand, Vi, think I needn't worry about you, then. But what do all the fellows think, having you women driving around the place, then?'

'What fellows? They're needed for active service. Nearly all the drivers I've met lately have been women, and damn good they are!'

'So, you're not meeting many men,' May said thoughtfully, catching Jinny's eye.

But Vi only snorted her disapproval of the idea. 'No men,' she declared. 'Or, at least, very few.'

And May and Jinny, still exchanging glances, didn't need to put their thoughts into words. Vi was the same dear old Vi. She hadn't changed a bit.

Of course, wartime Hogmanay was not the Hogmanay they all knew. In a city where you couldn't show a light in the blackout without being in trouble with the air-raid wardens, there didn't seem to be much point in trying to meet outside to see the New Year in, and the numbers of revellers were down, anyway, with so many men in the forces.

People did still go out – some to pubs, some to take in the night, some to do their first-footing, arriving at doors with bits of coal and Christmas cake if there happened to be any left. The Hendries, however, decided to spend New Year's Eve at home, where May joined them, with the plan of staying the night so that she needn't go home in the dark, and Josh opened a bottle of port he'd been keeping for some time for their toasts.

'Absent friends' was first, and Jinny thought of Ross, though at the same time wondered, as ever, where Viktor might be, and May, of course, raised her glass to Allan.

'Any news of leave for him?' Jinny whispered. 'I don't really like to ask.'

'Well, I daren't even talk about it,' May answered, her blue eyes very bright, 'but in his last letter he said there was a chance that he might get back in the spring some time. Nothing's sure, but it's just so grand, being able to hope.'

'Poor lad,' Josh muttered. 'Here, let's have a top up and toast the New Year.'

1941. They thought about it. After the long months they'd already endured, it was a temptation to hope that the year to come would bring an ending to the hostilities, but Josh had already made it plain how little faith he had in that, and the girls, in their hearts, had to agree with him.

Still, there were their glasses ready and the toast to be made, so they made it.

'To the New Year!' they cried. May added, 'May it bring peace, and everyone back home!'

'Aye, bring us peace,' Josh echoed, and they sipped their port, set down their glasses and hugged one another, smiling and kissing. But as the last stroke of Big Ben's midnight chimes on the wireless died away, somehow they couldn't bring themselves to say, as they'd always said in the past. 'Happy New Year!'

Sixty-One

Although she had not been able to see Ross, Jinny felt better from having her leave. She was so very glad to have seen her family again – Josh, May and Vi, who was so soon to be embarking on her new life as a qualified ATS driver. There'd been friends to meet up with too and, of course, the staff at Crombie's, where she'd visited everyone she knew – Mrs Arrow, still moaning about their present difficulties and her girls, so worked off their feet; Norah, still helping out as a baker; Mabel, still typing for Accounts and getting on rather better with Mr Lennox, but always nostalgic and sighing for the 'old days'.

'Oh, it's not the same,' she told Jinny, who had asked her out for a sandwich lunch in the West End. 'Not the same at all. Mr Lennox is all right, but Ross he is not, and Mr Crombie's so depressed these days, not knowing what's happened to his family.'

'You mean his sister and her husband in Vienna?' Jinny asked carefully.

'Yes, Viktor's parents.' Mabel's eyes slid away from Jinny's. 'He hasn't heard from them at all, but I told him it wasn't likely he would, seeing as they're in an enemy country. How would they be able to get letters out to him? I mean, there'll be no diplomatic help there now.'

'I was thinking of asking him about them.' Jinny looked down at her dry cheese roll. 'But I didn't want to upset him.'

'Best not to say anything,' Mabel agreed. 'And I suppose you've no news of Viktor, either?'

'No, no news at all. He couldn't write to me and he could be anywhere with the German army – they're in so many countries.'

'Such a shame for you, dear.' Mabel's tone was sympathetic, her eyes sharp with curiosity. 'At least you've got your work in the Pay Corps, though. I'm sure you're a natural for that!'

'Oh, yes, I might get a stripe one day,' Jinny told her with a laugh. 'Though Ross, of course, is an officer.'

'You keep in touch with him, dear?'

'Just a letter now and again,' Jinny said smoothly. 'How about another of those drinks they call coffee?'

It was on her last day of leave, when she'd been trying without success to buy some tobacco for her father in Princes Street, that, of all people, she met Senga Brown pushing a pram in which a large baby was sleeping.

'Senga, fancy meeting you!' she cried, at which Senga stopped and gave a pleasant enough smile.

'It's me should be saying that to you, Jinny. I thought you were in the ATS, and here you are in Princes Street. So, where's your uniform?'

'I am in the ATS, but I'm on leave, going back tomorrow, so I'll be wearing my uniform then, all right. I've just been looking for some tobacco for my dad, but there doesn't seem to be any.'

'Tell us something new – there's never anything you want in the shops these days.'

The two young women studied each other, privately deciding that the other looked well, and then Jinny looked in at the baby, a boy named Gordon, and the image, Jinny said, of his father, Terry Brown.

'Look, he's got the same ginger hair!' she exclaimed, but Senga put her finger to her lips.

'Ssh, he's teething and only just gone off – I don't want him to wake up before I see what Mrs Arrow's got for me at Crombie's today. Want to walk along?'

'Mrs Arrow?' repeated Jinny, walking beside the pram. 'I saw her the other day. What does she find for you, then?'

Again, Senga put her finger to her lips. 'Just one or two rolls, you ken, and a few buns. Saves me queuing.'

'That's grand. But are you managing all right, Senga, with Terry away? Do you know where he is?'

'No details, but he's in the Middle East somewhere. His letters are always being censored – great bits blocked out. But I'm doing OK. No worse than any other lassie with a husband in the forces. How about you?' Senga's voice was casual. 'D'you ever hear from Viktor?'

Sighing inwardly, Jinny shook her head. Did these people who asked after Viktor not realize it might be painful for her to admit she knew nothing of him? But perhaps she shouldn't judge them; it was only natural they should be interested in a man who had once been a colleague. And, of course, her attachment to him was widely known and had, in Senga's case, been upsetting. At least she was happily married now, even if her worries over Terry must be acute. It should come as no surprise that she might ask Jinny for news of Viktor.

'I don't know what's happened to him,' she admitted. 'We've rather lost touch.'

'Just as well, Jinny,' Senga said with some satisfaction. 'I mean, he is the enemy now, eh? It never would've worked out, would it? Once the war came?'

'Perhaps not.'

'And you've no' found someone else?'

Preferring not to answer, Jinny shook her head again. 'Here's Crombie's,' she said brightly. 'Hope you have some luck with the rolls and buns, Senga. It's been nice seeing you.'

Remembering the custom of giving babies money, she opened her bag and took out two half-crowns, which she laid on the baby's pram cover.

'For his money box, Senga. Sorry I didn't get it to him earlier.'

'Ah, that's nice of you,' Senga said, smiling. 'It was very nice to meet you, too, Jinny. Take care, then, and good luck!'

'Remember me to Terry!' Jinny cried and, after watching Senga push her pram into the shop, to the annoyance of the queue that had formed some time ago, she turned to make her way back home.

All the talk of Viktor had been unsettling. She didn't want to dwell on her past love for him and her lack of knowing whether he was alive or dead. Best think about her family and how she must soon say goodbye to them again, and then, maybe, to wonder if there might be a letter from Ross waiting for her when she returned from leave. Yes, that was something cheerful to think about – a ray of sunshine on this dark January day.

Sixty-Two

She was in luck – there was indeed a letter from Ross waiting when Jinny returned to the pay office, and it contained hope of news to come of his own leave. Couldn't go into details, he wrote, but it looked promising for April.

April? Jinny's rising spirits fell. As it was now only January, April seemed an age away, but after a little thought she decided it was just as well he wasn't coming any earlier, for there would be no way she could get any more leave herself before some time had elapsed. Even April would be difficult, but she'd try for it anyway. All she could do now was write back to Ross as soon as she could, giving him news of her time back in Edinburgh, and then get on with her daily routine. It was what most people were doing, anyway, though Pauline had seemed particularly starry-eyed since Christmas.

'Things going well with Chris?' Jinny asked during one coffee break, and Pauline's smile was wide.

'Oh, yes! We really do hit it off well. It's just so lovely being with him. I didn't really want to go home for Christmas, though of course I enjoyed it, and Mum and Dad are always so keen to see me, anyway.'

'And you were better off than me,' Josie said, lighting a cigarette. 'I never even got Christmas leave, did I? Roll on my week away in February.'

'No hope of seeing your chap?' the others asked.

'Not a snowball's.' Josie shrugged. 'All you can do is put up with it.'

As they left the canteen, she moved closer to Jinny, letting Pauline go ahead.

'Listen, have you heard that Enid and Shirley are being posted?'

'No, where?'

'Salisbury, but the point is they're lance corporals, right? And they're being made up to corporal and leaving, which means there'll be vacancies for us.'

'For a stripe?' Jinny's eyes shone. 'I wouldn't mind getting promotion, but Sarge hasn't said a word . . . Why should it be us?'

'Oh, she's always saying we work well and should be going up the ladder – things like that.' Josie tapped Jinny's shoulder. 'We can but wait and see, but I reckon things look hopeful. Might cheer you up a bit, eh?'

'Who says I need cheering up?'

'You've looked a bit down since you came back. I wondered if it might be something to do with your ex-boss. OK, I'm being nosey again, but it might help to talk about it. I mean, is he important, or isn't he?'

'Honestly, Josie!' Jinny hesitated. 'All right, he's important, but there's nothing settled. It's all a bit up in the air.'

'He's probably worrying about the war. Some guys think it's not fair to ask girls to make commitments when . . . well, you know what might happen.'

'He's only in the Isle of Wight,' Jinny said, paling a little. 'And I don't even know exactly how I feel myself.'

'Oh, I think you do,' said Josie, nodding her head. 'And remember, he won't be staying in the Isle of Wight.'

Which was what Ross had once said himself, Jinny reflected, returning to her desk to pay more bills for army requisitions and prepare the invoice copies. It was true that he would not be staying in the Isle of Wight, and where he went next was anybody's guess – except that it would not be anywhere safe. Oh, Josie – why did she have to stir things up?

But of course, she hadn't. Anything she'd made Jinny say was just what she thought, anyway. Yes, Ross was important, and no, Jinny wasn't exactly sure how she felt. Or was that not exactly true? She waited for his letters and wanted to see him . . . Perhaps it was she who was afraid of commitment, then? Was it because of her change of heart over Viktor? As she knew so well, though, Ross wasn't Viktor . . .

Looking up, her eyes a little glazed, she found Sergeant Abbott's gaze fixed on her thoughtfully as she stood in the office doorway, and smiled uncertainly – at which the sergeant moved away.

Oh, dear, had she been found daydreaming at her desk? No hope of her stripe, then. But what on earth did a stripe matter, the way things were? Nothing, really. It would just be nice to have, that was all, as a reassurance that she was doing well, doing her bit, as the saying went. But she decided to put it out of her mind and concentrate on the work in hand, which she wanted to get right, stripe or no stripe.

★　　★　　★

Only a few weeks later, when wintry January had melted into dreary February, both she and Josie were awarded their stripes and took satisfaction in telling their families and the men in their lives.

'Of course, my Rickie's already a sergeant,' Josie said with a laugh, 'so you might think he wouldn't be impressed with my one stripe, but he's been really sweet about it. Wrote straight back when he got my letter, and that's not like him.'

'Ross wrote straight back, too,' Jinny told her, 'and guess what – he's got his second pip! He's a lieutenant now, but he was really nice about my stripe.'

'A stripe's a stripe, and anything that makes the men realize we're not playing at soldiers has to be good. Any news of a posting for Ross, by the way?'

'Not any that he's given me, but I have the feeling there's something in the wind that he's not telling me about.'

'Probably knows the censor would black it out, anyway, if there's something you'd really like to know.'

'All I'm really waiting for is news of his leave. Seems so long, Josie, since I last saw him.'

'And you say you're not sure of how you feel,' said Josie with a smile.

February became March and there was still no news of when Jinny and Ross might meet, but at least there was good news from Vi, who had completed her driving course with flying colours and was now settling into a posting with a military hospital in Devonshire.

'I'm really enjoying this,' she wrote to Jinny. 'Driving around narrow little roads, collecting patients and doctors, filling in on any other errands that crop up. Sometimes I have to go quite far afield and it's always a worry about petrol, but up to now everything's been OK. I really feel I've got the job I wanted – not actually killing anybody, but contributing to the war effort. Hope that doesn't sound too weedy?'

'Not weedy at all,' Jinny had written back. 'You're doing a grand, necessary job and I'm proud of you!'

Of course, she knew that Vi would only say, 'Enough of that sort of talk!' But it was true what she'd written – she was proud of her sister, who'd volunteered for a difficult job, which could only get worse if situations arose when casualties were high. In a way, she half-wished she could do something the same herself, for there was no doubt that she was very safe and comfortable where she was.

But she knew she was good at her job and it was certainly one that had to be done; she tried not to do too much soul-searching over it. Just keep going, day after day, and hope the time would come when she and Ross would meet again.

But when she finally received his letter telling her he was coming and would be in Edinburgh by the end of April, she could scarcely believe it. Even when she was told she could only have a weekend pass instead of leave, her spirits remained high, and when the time came to travel up to Edinburgh she felt she was moving there on billowing clouds. They supported her until they were replaced by Ross's passionate hug upon greeting her on Friday evening at Waverley Station.

Sixty-Three

'I can't believe you're here,' Jinny said breathlessly. 'I can't believe it's really you!'

'I feel the same,' Ross told her, still holding her close. 'Seems an age since we last met.'

'An age,' she agreed, releasing herself to look at him as people from the train surged by. 'But you look just the same. A little thinner, maybe—'

'No, no, I'm no thinner!' He laughed. 'Not on a diet of army stodge! And you look wonderful, Jinny, really lovely. So smart in your uniform!'

'With my one stripe? If anyone looks smart, it's you, Ross. Here, let me see your second pip – oh, very grand!'

'Come on, let's not waste time; let's get out of here. We'll have to take a tram – can't see any taxis at the moment . . .'

'Always looking for taxis,' she said fondly. 'The tram will be fine. But where are we going?'

'I thought we'd have a meal at the club and then – I don't know – I expect you'll want to see your father?'

'He won't be back from the theatre. I'll see him later, and May sometime tomorrow.'

'That's fine. I wasn't expecting you to get a weekend pass just for me.'

Did he really think that? Well, it was true, she did want to see her father and May, but the object of this visit was in fact to see Ross. She hadn't been able to think of anything else since she'd had news of his leave. Which told her something, didn't it? Told her quite a lot.

'All right to come to the club, then?' Ross asked as they climbed the slope from the station. 'I think you enjoyed your visit before.'

'I did. But are you sure no one will make trouble if I'm not commissioned and you are?'

'No one will say a word,' Ross said firmly. 'The club's like a sanctuary, and no one's young enough to be in the services, anyway, so they won't notice anything.'

At the club that seemed so much the same, as though untouched by conflicts outside its walls, they were given a corner table as before, and it was true, as Ross had said: none of the elderly patrons looked as though they would want to take any notice of the rank of army people. In fact, one or two smiled at the attractive young couple dining near them, and Jinny smiled back, thinking what a pity it was that there had to be any different ranks at all, but maybe the army wouldn't function without them? With Ross sitting opposite her, his brown eyes riveted on her face, she soon forgot to worry about it, anyway.

What they had for dinner scarcely registered, and the fact that now there was no wine on offer at all was of no importance. All they wanted was what they had, to be together again, to talk about their different army lives, to study each other, to make the most of the short time they would have.

The only thing that rather distracted Jinny was that she couldn't truly be sure that Ross wasn't keeping something from her. His face seemed at first sight to be as open as ever, yet, every so often, she would have the feeling that there was some shadow crossing his features and that there were words trembling on his lips that were never said.

'Ross,' she said at last, when they were taking coffee in the lounge again, 'is there something wrong?'

'Wrong? No, of course not. Everything's wonderfully right – can't you tell?'

'Yes, but somehow I have the feeling that you want to tell me something yet you never do. So what is it? If there's something I should know, I'd like you to say.'

'I was going to tell you sooner or later,' he answered after a pause. 'But then I thought, why spoil the first time we meet again?'

He gave a wry smile. 'Seems I didn't reckon on your eagle eye, Jinny.'

'You're too honest to keep secrets, Ross.'

'I've always known I wouldn't make a spy.'

Jinny sipped her coffee, then set down the cup. 'Well, what is it, then?' she asked, with a little impatience. 'What is it that I need to know?'

'It's just that . . . this leave I have, well, it's not ordinary leave . . . it's embarkation leave.'

'Embarkation?' Her impatience had died. She knew now why he hadn't wanted to tell her what she needed to know. 'You're being posted from the Isle of Wight?'

'We all are. The battalion is on the move.'

'Where to, Ross? Can you tell me?'

Again, he hesitated. 'India.'

'India? Oh, no, Ross, no! Why should you go there? You won't be fighting Germans; it's not involved in the war . . . why should you go to India?'

'Certain tribesmen are attacking British stations on the north-west frontier. We've been given the job of sorting them out.' Ross moved his coffee cup to and fro. 'That's the situation, Jinny. I agree, we won't be fighting the Germans, perhaps for some time—'

'Some time . . .' Jinny's voice was very low. 'How long will you be going for, then?'

'We don't know.' He raised his eyes to hers. 'Depends on the situation, but it might be . . . hell, I don't know. You can see why I didn't want to tell you.'

'I suppose wherever you went' – her voice was trembling – 'it would have been as bad. I mean,' she tried to laugh, 'I don't want you fighting Germans, either.'

He caught at her hand and pressed it. 'One day, you have to believe it, the war will be at an end and we'll be free of anxiety, free to live our own lives again. That's what you have to hang on to, Jinny, and in the meantime . . .' His eyes on her were tender. 'We have our weekend.'

'Our weekend,' she repeated. 'Yes, at least we have that.'

Sixty-Four

In spite of all their efforts, however, they could not take real pleasure in their weekend. They had looked forward to it for so long, wondered if it would ever happen, but now that it had, the news from Ross of his embarkation had cast a shadow they could not lift.

Of course, they still carried out what they'd planned, meeting early the next day to climb Calton Hill again and look out at the views over the city that Ross said he'd carry with him to India, have lunch at the place they'd found in Thistle Street, then walk for a while below the castle in Princes Street gardens.

'I suppose I should look in at Comrie's,' Ross said as they found a bench and sat together. 'I won't be seeing them for a while.'

'You could,' Jinny answered. 'I'm sure they'd appreciate it, but I don't think I'll come with you.'

'I'll leave it till Monday, then.' Ross looked bleakly toward the castle, Jinny's hand firmly locked in his. 'I have a couple of days left after you've gone tomorrow.'

Tomorrow. The word sent an arrow piercing their hearts. Tomorrow they must say goodbye.

'Come on,' said Ross, leaping up, 'there's time to go to the Botanic Gardens. I'd like to see them before I leave, then have a cup of tea. If they're still doing teas.'

'Where shall we go this evening?' Jinny asked as they went for yet another tram. 'Were you thinking of the club again?'

'No. Someone told me of a place in George Street where they still have quite decent food. I thought we might try that.'

'I've got a better idea. Why not come back to Fingal Street? If you don't mind having something light? I got some salad stuff in this morning and there's ham and cheese. No coffee, I'm afraid, only tea.'

'Jinny, that's a marvellous idea! Just to be alone, the two of us . . .' Ross's eyes were shining. 'Who cares about coffee?'

The thought of being by themselves raised their spirits for the first time that day, and by the time they arrived at the flat in Fingal Street they were so keyed up for this first time alone, they'd managed to put tomorrow's goodbyes from their minds.

'It's not going to be much of a meal, Jinny said nervously as she laid out the things for their supper. 'I wish I'd been able to boil eggs, but of course, Dad's got no eggs.'

'Jinny, come here,' Ross said gently. 'Stop worrying about what we eat. I don't give a damn.'

As soon as she'd moved into his arms, she sensed his transformation from special friend to man in love, and knew she felt the same herself. Knew she'd crossed from not being sure of her feelings to being so sure she was glad to kiss him as passionately as he kissed her, and to lie close to him on the old sofa. If only – if only – they stared at each other wildly, longing to put what they wanted to say into words, until Ross stood up and gave a long shuddering sigh.

'It's no good, Jinny. We can't risk it.'

'Can't? Folk do this all the time, Ross.'

'And regret it.'

'Not always.'

'Maybe not, but I'm not talking about the usual worry, though it is a worry when we're parting tomorrow. I'm thinking that I might be away for years, you won't see me, and as the time goes on, you might . . .'

He halted, looking down at her with those brown eyes that had always been so kind, so concerned, and now were more troubled than she'd ever seen them.

'Might what?' she whispered.

'Not feel the same.'

'You think because my feelings changed for Viktor they'd be likely to change about you? This is different, Ross. I promise you I'm not going to change.'

'There's time involved, Jinny. It can do strange things. And I don't feel I can ask you to wait. When, apart from anything else, I might – well, you know what might happen—'

'Don't, Ross,' she said quietly. 'Don't talk about that.'

'But you see why I'm not going to ask you to be committed to me? It just wouldn't be fair.'

'Do you think you will stay committed to me?'

'Yes. Yes, I do. I'm sure.

'Then why shouldn't I be sure, too?'

'You're younger, you're beautiful, you could meet someone – anybody—'

'No,' she said steadfastly. 'I won't meet anybody, because I don't want to. Look, let's not talk about this any more. Let's not think about the future, just today.'

'Today,' Ross agreed, and their mouths met in long, long kisses, until Jinny drew away, sighing, and suggested they have something to eat.

'As though we were hungry,' she added, with a laugh.

'It looks very good,' Ross remarked, taking a plate. 'This was such a wonderful idea of yours, Jinny, having time alone.'

Especially for their last evening, both were thinking, but neither put that into words.

Sixty-Five

After they'd eaten what they could, they sat close together on the sofa, Jinny resting her head on Ross's shoulder, while he put his arm around her. They felt so completely as one there seemed no need to talk, but Jinny at last sat up and asked Ross what she knew was an impossible question: how long did he think the war might last?

'Oh, Jinny, what a thing to ask!' he answered with a groan. 'Years, I should say. We're nowhere near defeating Hitler, and we've now got Mussolini to worry about in North Africa. There's talk that Rommel and the German Afrika Korps will soon be arriving, and that's bad news too. Rommel's a very talented general – no one fancies being up against him.'

At the dismayed look on Jinny's face, Ross shook his head and held her close for a moment. 'Look, I don't want to upset you,' he murmured, smoothing back her hair. 'We shouldn't just be looking on the dark side. "Look for the silver lining" – isn't that what people say?'

'Trust you to be optimistic!' Jinny said, sighing. 'Not everyone can see it.'

'OK, there is a bit of good news I've just remembered.'

'I wish you'd tell me, then.'

'Well, there's another rumour going about that Hitler's planning to attack Russia. If he does – and they say he's already got German troops massing on the borders – he might well be shooting himself in the foot. Russia's so vast, has such a terrible climate, as well as the Red Army, that it's unlikely he'll succeed there, and if he loses a huge amount of men, he'll be weakened.' Ross, looking hopeful that he had cheered her, turned Jinny's face towards his. 'Does that sound encouraging?'

'I don't know.' The words 'German troops' seemed to be echoing through her mind, coupled with 'huge amount of men', and just for a moment the question arose: would Viktor be among them? If only she knew what had happened to him . . . It seemed right that she should, they'd been so close once . . . But now the man she loved was gazing at her, and she leaped to her feet, saying she would make some tea, her father would soon be home from the theatre and would be delighted to see Ross.

How quickly their weekend was running away from them, she thought with a pang as she put on the kettle and set out cups. Already, Saturday, their main day, was almost over. To come, there would be their passionate yet melancholy parting, followed by the night to lie alone, and tomorrow, after their last meeting, Ross would see her to the station, for he'd changed his mind about railway farewells, and that would be it. No more contact except for letters – for how long? Years, perhaps, Ross had said.

Years? At the thought, her heart was as heavy as stone, but she stoically made the tea, hearing her father's step on the stairs, and resolved to be as totally committed to Ross as he'd said he would be to her. And when the years were past and the war was over, then, maybe, they could think about their happiness. Maybe.

'Why, Ross, hello!' Josh was crying. 'My, isn't it grand to see you, then? Let me shake your hand.'

Everything worked out just as Jinny had thought it would. After the long goodnight in the street and she had watched Ross move reluctantly away, she lay awake most of the night, wishing she had not had to spend it alone, and in the morning, after a sweet visit from May, she and Ross went out together, just walking in the city, before having lunch, for which they had no appetite, at a George Street hotel. Then it was back to Fingal Street for Jinny to change into her uniform, pack her kitbag, kiss Josh goodbye and hurry with Ross to the station for the train to Chester.

'You really shouldn't be seeing me off,' she told him. 'You did say you hated station farewells.'

'I did, but this time I don't want to waste any time I could spend with you. Every minute is precious.'

'I know, I know. I'm glad you came.'

They were standing close on the platform, surrounded by other couples and families saying goodbye. Already some were crying, and Jinny was close to tears herself, yet trying to keep them back, at least until she was on the train.

'This is where we promise to write,' Ross said softly. 'But we will write, won't we?'

'We will. I don't need to promise.'

'Nor do I. But if there's a delay in our letters, you'll understand, Jinny? We're going to have to travel a hell of a long way, and I've no idea how things will be in India. There may be times when I just can't write, but it won't mean I haven't been wanting to—'

'Ross, don't worry about it. I'll be grateful for anything that comes.'

Jinny's words were brave, but her face was pale, for her train was arriving, and it was time for the last embrace, the last long kiss. In spite of herself, a sob escaped her as she wrenched herself from Ross's arms and saw the misery on his face. Reaching up, she kissed him one more time, then turned to board the train, but he was with her still, trying to make a path for her between the soldiers already waiting, who called out, 'Watch it, darling!' until they saw the look on Ross's face and said no more.

Finally she was aboard, staying close to the open window, and as the train began to move she waved and waved, as Ross waved too, until he was a speck on the platform and she was alone, even though surrounded by others. Then she let the tears fall.

'Oh, you poor thing!' Pauline exclaimed when she and Josie first saw her on her return. 'Must've been awful, saying goodbye.'

'He'll come back,' said Josie. 'Don't worry.'

'And I've got some news,' Pauline told her. 'Though I don't want to make a big thing of it—'

'Go on, Jinny'll be pleased for you,' Josie said shortly. 'We all are.'

'Fact is,' Pauline whispered, 'I'm engaged.'

'Why, that's wonderful!' cried Jinny. 'Yes, I am pleased for you, Pauline. Of course I am!'

'Show her the ring,' ordered Josie, and Pauline duly showed off the pretty ring on her left hand, which Jinny praised with quite genuine feeling.

'What are the plans, then?'

'Oh, no plans yet. Maybe a wedding next year.'

Pauline's face was so wreathed in smiles, Jinny gave her a quick hug, and tried not to compare her own lot with her friend's. It was good that someone was happy, eh? But as she turned away she caught the sympathy of a fellow sufferer in Josie's eyes, and had to go into the bathroom before she began to cry again.

Sixty-Six

Now began the long years without Ross that Jinny had braced herself to face. Sometimes she wondered what she would have done without his letters, that gave her not only the joy of knowing she was loved, but the courage to keep going, and supposed that she would have had to survive, just as people without such support had to survive. But, oh, she was so glad she had them, and when it happened that he was unable to write, even though he had warned her that there would be such breaks, she felt quite bereft until she saw the familiar handwriting on an envelope again.

Like everyone else, she followed the war news with avid interest, noting not long after Ross had left that he'd been right about Hitler's invasion of Russia, which happened in June. Not right, maybe, that Hitler had made a mistake, for when three million German troops poured into the attack, with three thousand tanks, it seemed at first that Russia was not retaliating well.

'Oh, dear, bad news,' said Pauline. 'Chris says the critics of Hitler have got it all wrong. He's winning again in Russia, just like everywhere else.'

'Except over here,' Jinny reminded her, but she too felt troubled in case Hitler was proving invincible, before she again found herself wondering if Viktor was one of those millions of German army troops involved. He had become so shadowy, however, that her thoughts didn't linger on him, especially when the news came later in the year that the Russians had suddenly begun to fight back, with all the strength people had always expected of them. Even when Leningrad was put under siege by the Germans, the people there did not give in, which showed, everyone said, how difficult they would be to beat as a nation.

Still, there seemed no real hope of victory over Hitler until, in December 1941, the Japanese without warning attacked the American Pearl Harbor, which brought America into the war. True, the Japanese had joined the German Axis, but now that America, with all its huge resources, was one of Britain's allies, at long last there was something to be cheerful about. That was on a national scale, but also, for Jinny and May, there was something personal, for though it still seemed unbelievable, Vi, it appeared, had acquired a young man. As Christmas approached, she wrote to Josh and her sisters, saying she would be coming home on leave and bringing 'a friend'. The friend's name was Barry Graham, a sergeant stationed near the hospital where she was based.

'All right if he has the little bedroom, now that you've got May's room?' she asked Josh. 'Barry's parents are dead and he has nowhere to spend his leave, so I invited him home. I'm sure you'll like him – I do, anyway.'

'Vi's bringing a fellow home?' Josh cried to May. 'I don't believe it – she's never taken the slightest interest—'

'She says she likes him,' May pointed out. 'And he is an army sergeant, Dad. He's doing his bit, so you'll probably like him too.'

'I did think I could rely on Vi not to start bringing fellows home,' Josh retorted. 'Och, seems I've lost the lot o' you!'

'Hang on, no one says Vi is going to marry this Barry,' May said reasonably. 'Let's wait and see what happens, eh?'

But May lost no time in writing to Jinny, asking her to do her best to get leave, so that they could both see what Vi's young man was like, and Jinny, marvelling over that phrase – 'Vi's young man' – wrote back to say she'd move heaven and earth to get home to meet this amazing fellow. Her luck was in – she was given her leave – and on Christmas Eve she arrived home to find May and her father, who'd finished early at the theatre, ready and waiting for Vi and the unknown sergeant.

'It all looks lovely,' she told May. 'The fire burning and the little tree with the dear old fairy on the top, just as always.'

'Remember how Vi once said she should be retiring? We weren't having that!'

'Ssh!' cried Josh. 'I hear the door. They're here.'

Silence fell as Vi, in uniform, appeared in the doorway, ushering in a tall man, also in uniform, who took off his cap and stood smiling, looking from one expectant face to another.

'Dad, May, Jinny – this is Barry,' Vi announced. 'Barry, may I introduce my father and my sisters? You've heard all about them. Here they are.'

He stepped forward to shake Josh's hand, a strong-faced man in his thirties, with short, clipped brown hair and light blue eyes – not handsome, yet pleasant to look at, and with the army way of holding himself: very erect, very straight-backed. Jinny could imagine him being good on the parade ground, yet his manner now was easy and relaxed, although his eyes on Josh were perhaps just a little anxious.

'Mr Hendrie, I'm very glad to meet you,' he said in a northern English accent. 'It's so kind of you to have me for Christmas – I do appreciate it.'

'That's all right,' Josh muttered, clearly impressed. 'Glad you could come. May, Jinny, shake hands with Mr Graham.'

'Barry, you mean!' cried Vi. 'We don't stand on ceremony. Any chance of a cup of tea? We're parched and had to stand all the way to Waverley.'

'Tea's coming up,' said May, when she and Jinny had greeted Barry. 'Vi, show Barry his room while I get the cups.'

'I'd just like to put a few things under that Christmas tree, if I may,' Barry said, taking up his bag. 'Only a few odds and ends, but I did get a bottle of whisky for you, Mr Hendrie – I hope it's OK.'

'A bottle of what?' Josh shouted. 'I've no' seen any whisky since the start of the war!'

'He'll be your friend for life now,' May told Barry with a laugh.

He replied seriously, 'I hope so.'

In this way began a truly pleasant Christmas, with all the difficulties and shortages disregarded, as May and Jinny did their utmost for Vi's sake to make Barry feel at home. Even though their own loved ones were far away, the sisters took genuine pleasure in Vi's radiant acceptance that she could fall in love, just like anyone else, and were happy to see how beautiful she looked, and how she and Barry seemed right for each other. Of course, they couldn't know him in the short time since he'd arrived, but Vi knew him, and the way things were going they were prepared to trust her judgement.

'Oh, he is right for me!' she exclaimed when Josh had taken Barry to a Boxing Day football match and the girls were alone in the flat. 'He's perfect for me, shares all my ideas about equality and human rights – that's how we came to go out together, after we'd met at a hospital dance. We danced a bit, and then he told me he'd worked in a factory before the war and been the trade union repre-sentative and, of course, that got me started. By the end of the evening we were already fixing up to meet again.'

Vi gave a wide smile and sighed. 'All I've got to worry about now is how soon he'll be posted away, but so far there's no sign of it, so, fingers crossed, eh?'

'Fingers permanently crossed,' said Jinny. 'I've heard that Ross's regiment is leaving India, but only for North Africa, so there's still no chance of seeing him.'

'And Allan's in Tobruk,' put in May. 'No chance of seeing him, either.'

'Now I really understand what you're going through,' Vi said quietly.

Christmas leave was over, but before she left, while Barry was doing a last check round in his room, Vi caught her father's arm.

'Dad, do you like him?' she asked fiercely.

'Barry?' He looked down at her, his dark eyes serious. 'Vi, I do. If my girls have to go, I want 'em to be with a fellow who'll be right, and Barry's right. A grand lad, och, yes. If he's the one for you—'

'He is!'

'Then I'm happy for you.' He gave her a quick hug. 'And I hope all goes well for you both. Goes without saying, eh?'

'Thanks, Dad,' Vi answered, sniffing a little, as Barry came out, ready to go, and then there were handshakes, brief kisses and more hugs with May and Jinny, and final waves as the couple left for their tram to the station.

'That's it, then,' murmured May. 'Christmas is over.'

'Still got Hogmanay,' Josh said.

'I'll be away before then,' said Jinny. 'Anyway, I don't feel like celebrating. Who knows what the New Year will bring?'

'But have you ever seen Vi looking better?' asked May.

'Never,' they agreed, and then were silent, thinking of what might happen, for Vi and Barry, for all of them, in the time to come.

Sixty-Seven

What happened to Jinny was that, after being awarded a second stripe, she got posted. To Salisbury! Oh, no! She didn't in the least want to go and leave everyone she knew to start afresh in Southern Command. Oh, why couldn't they leave her where she was?

'You must suffer for promotion,' Josie told her. 'What about me? I'm getting a second stripe, too, but I have to go to Aberdeen.'

'Well, I haven't got any stripes,' Pauline said cheerfully, 'but I'm on my way as well. Might as well tell you now.'

'On your way where?' asked Jinny.

'Home. To my mum and dad. Can you believe it? But I've got no choice.'

'Just because you'll be married?'

'No, because I'll be getting the green ration book. Now, do I have to spell out what that means?'

Green ration book. Jinny and Josie exchanged looks. They knew that green ration books were only for expectant mothers, to make sure they had the food they needed.

'Yes, it's true,' Pauline said, laughing. 'I'm in the club. Jumped the gun, I'm afraid, and Mum's furious. Has to be only a register office wedding now, you see, with just her and Dad, and Chris and me, of course. Sorry, girls, I can't invite you, but if Mum can get the stuff, I'll send you a bit of wedding cake.'

'Congratulations, anyway!' cried Jinny, embracing her. 'What's it matter if the baby wasn't planned? I think it's wonderful, anyway.'

'And for you the war is over,' Josie added, smiling. 'If I could knit I'd make some bootees; as it is, I'll be sending a christening mug. Oh, but we're going to miss you, Pauline!'

'We're all going to miss one another,' Jinny said bleakly. 'Just think of Josie and me having to start all over again.'

'As corporals, though,' Pauline reminded her. 'You'll do fine, both of you, and I'm going to wish you all the best. You and your fellows, too. We'll keep in touch, eh?'

Of course they would. For a time, anyway. But Jinny was worrying how she would get on in a new place, and of how she must let Ross know as quickly as possible, hoping that her letter would get through, for of late their letters to each other had been slow to arrive, with some, Jinny feared, not arriving at all. The only good news, really, was that she'd been awarded that second stripe. Corporal Hendrie. It sounded good.

Only two weeks later, she left for Salisbury, butterflies fluttering inside her, but once she arrived it wasn't so bad. It was all right, in fact. Her new billet was in another large house, not unlike the one she'd been used to, the pay office was just what she'd expected and the people she met were friendly and helpful. Another captain, another sergeant, more ATS faces to get used to, and new recruits she'd been told she'd be training, but all looked promising.

I think I could settle here, she thought, and was surprised at how easy her move had been.

'First, a short course,' announced Captain Horton, erect, very military in bearing but missing fingers from one hand, his reason for no longer being on active service. 'Just to familiarize you with a corporal's duties and the techniques of training others. Sergeant Teller will fill you in and I know from your records that you're a quick learner so you'll have no problems. Nice to have you with us, Corporal Hendrie!'

'Nice to be here, sir,' she replied.

Sixty-Eight

It was here in Southern Command that she was to stay for the rest of the war, observing – at the safe distance she felt rather guilty about – the long progression of events that was finally to bring about the end, though she wasn't to know, of course, when that would be until it happened.

So many battles, so many 'theatres of war', to use a phrase liked by the BBC. She found it depressing to read and hear of so many, and all involving people hoping to kill other people. But that was what war meant, and you just had to keep on remembering that this war, against fascism, was a just one.

All the same, it was terrible to think of the suffering involved. In Russia, for example, where the continuing fighting with the German attackers was causing thousands of deaths and casualties. In the Far East, where Japan had taken Singapore, Hong Kong and Burma in ruthless fashion and had so far held off British advances. In North Africa, where the British were fighting the Italians and Rommel, the most feared of German generals, and where there were immense numbers of casualties after cat-and-mouse warfare.

Naturally, Jinny's anxieties were very much centred on that particular 'theatre', for it was there that Ross and Allan were both involved. Every day she dreaded receiving a telegram, heaving sighs of relief when none came – until, following the great battle between Rommel and the British General Montgomery at El Alamein, the news came from May that Allan was to be invalided home. A shell had exploded close to him during the battle and his hearing had been badly affected.

He was alive, that was the main thing, but poor chap, how terrible that he should not be able to hear properly! Jinny resolved to see him as soon as possible, but along with her sorrow for his troubles was her anxiety over Ross. She'd heard nothing, which might be thought of as good news, but then again, might not. If only she could see him again . . .

When she did manage to visit Allan, by then at home, it was to hear that the doctors had found he had some residual hearing and had fitted him with two powerful hearing aids. Even with these he would not be able to serve again in the forces, and might be advised to study lip reading, or signing, in case his hearing deteriorated even further.

'Not such good news,' he told Jinny, his voice sounding odd – rather distorted, in fact – 'but it could have been worse. That's what I keep telling myself.'

'You're alive,' May said softly. 'You're here. And that's all that matters.'

'I should say so!' Jinny cried, noting with distress Allan's haggard looks and the lines of strain around his eyes. Also, he seemed constantly to be holding his head forward, as though it would help him to hear, and when it didn't, he would fiddle with his hearing aids to try to make them work better. Which did very little good.

'What are you planning to do?' Jinny asked, speaking as clearly as she could. 'Will you open your shop again?'

'He's thinking of it,' said May, as Allan did not reply. 'But he's worried how he'd manage with the customers. I've told him I'll help, but he could always get them to write down what they want done if he can't hear them.'

'The hearing aids must surely do some good?' Jinny asked.

'Oh, they do, they do. It's just a question of getting used to them.' May was doing her best to appear as calm as usual, but the lines of strain were appearing round her eyes too. 'I'm sure we'll work something out.'

'Of course you will!' cried Jinny.

Before she left, she asked if Allan had any news of Ross, but he managed to tell her that the two had not met. He was sure she would have heard if he'd been hurt, however, and no doubt he was now involved in further activity in North Africa. There was a lot to do, even though the battle of El Alamein had been won.

'But you won't be doing it, thank God,' said May, then glanced at Jinny and bit her lip. Quickly, she touched her sister's hand. 'Ross will be all right, Jinny, I'm sure of it. As Allan says, you'd have heard if he wasn't.'

In fact, only a day or two later, she received a letter from him that had miraculously filtered through. He was fine, had come through without trouble, with only a slight shoulder wound that was already healing, and she was not to worry. One of these days they would meet again, no question!

And in May 1944, though she could scarcely believe it, his words came true. Thin and worn, though bronzed and smiling, he arrived in Edinburgh for his first leave in years, which was, even then, only to be a couple of days, and Jinny was there at Waverley to meet him, on only a short leave herself. It wasn't long, but it was enough, it was everything – yet as he came towards her, seeming at first a stranger, she hesitated, so anxious to greet him but not sure how she should. Until, that is, she saw his brown eyes searching her face, those same brown eyes she had always found so comforting, and in a moment she was in his arms, the years rolling away, and they were strangers no longer.

'I never thought this day would come,' she whispered, tears unshed, ready to fall. 'And you look so well, you've not changed at all—'

'Come on, that's not what I see in my shaving mirror,' he laughed. 'But it is true of you, Jinny. You're as lovely as ever, just as you've always been in my dreams these years away. Now, are there any taxis, do you think?'

'You and your taxis! There might be, if we're lucky. But I want to ask you, Ross, will you stay with us instead of going to the club? There's a small room you could have.'

'That would be wonderful, just what I want. But still, let's hunt down a taxi!'

Sixty-Nine

The brief leave passed like a dream. Sometimes, when they were alone, with moments of rapture that stopped just short of 'going all the way', as some described it; sometimes with long catching-up talks of how the world had been for them in the years that had passed, when Ross said all there had ever been for him had been warfare and thoughts of Jinny.

'I used to worry about you,' he told her. 'Of how you were not meeting other people because of me, and then, of course, I'd worry in case you were!' He lowered his eyes for a moment as he spoke and held her close. 'Was I wrong to do that? You wouldn't blame me?'

'Of course I wouldn't! It'd be natural to worry. But you never had any need, Ross.' Jinny moved back his copper-coloured hair and smoothed his brow. 'I used to go to the pictures, or to dances, but always in a crowd. Soldiers did sometimes try to make dates but I always put them off, and, you see, I'm here now. Isn't that so?'

'It is!' he cried. 'And I'm a damned lucky fellow, is all I can say.'

'Let's just hope your luck holds, then,' she said quietly. 'And I don't mean with me.'

'It will, it will, I promise you.'

Their talk shifted to the future of the war, with Ross being so optimistic that Jinny's heart lifted a little.

'You really think we can beat Hitler now? That would be wonderful!'

'I do think that. He's not exactly a spent force, but ever since he was defeated in Russia – and you remember the Germans surrendered back in 1943 – there's been a question mark over his powers to survive. And now you know what's coming, don't you? Why my regiment's back home?'

'You mean, D-Day?'

Now her heart was plummeting again. D-Day – the date when the Allies were to enter Europe that everyone talked about and no one outside the top brass knew when it would be – would for her be the biggest nightmare yet if Ross were to be part of it. Vi had said, in confidence, that Barry, at present at some unknown place abroad, would almost certainly be included in the D-Day assault, and Jinny had shivered to think about it. Now it looked as if—

'Oh, Ross, you're not going to be involved, are you? Do you mean that's why you're back?'

'I'm afraid so,' he replied seriously. 'We're home for preparation and training. It's what we've been working towards for some time; it's something we have to do.'

'It will mean killing, terrible killing.'

'And victory, Jinny. If we want to overcome evil we have to have victory over Hitler. Lives will be lost – on both sides – but it's the only way.'

She knew he was right, that victory was essential and must be paid for, but the price – it was so high she couldn't bear to think about it, and leaped up to begin making preparations for their meal. May and Allan were to join them, and Josh, too, for he was taking time off from the theatre for Ross's last night.

'What did you think about Vi finding a lovely young man?' May asked Ross over the wonderful gigot lamb chops she'd given Jinny, having been thrilled to be offered them by her butcher. When he'd heard about Allan he had been even more helpful to May, though Vi would probably still have put his helpfulness down to May's beautiful blue eyes.

'I'm very pleased for her,' Ross said now. 'Barry sounds like a damn good soldier, and from what I've heard he and Vi are really suited.'

'Aye, she's happy,' Josh put in. 'And Barry's such a grand lad, you have to be happy for her, eh? Just hope he comes through what's ahead, along with all you young men.'

There was a short silence after that, with Allan heaving a deep sigh and Ross finding Jinny's face and saying, 'Don't worry, we'll be fine!'

If only he's right, she prayed. If only they all come through, Ross, Barry and all the young men who meant so much.

But when D-Day arrived on 6 June, and the first Allied assaults were made on Normandy, though Ross survived, many of the other young men with him did not. And one of these was Barry.

Seventy

All those who knew Vi expected her to be stoical over the death of Barry, and so she was. Though it must have been hard to endure the euphoria of other people seeing an end to the war at last, she showed no emotion, driving her ambulance when she returned from a short time at home with the same dedication she'd always displayed. Only her face, so lacking in light, in any expression, revealed her feelings.

'Oh, to see her not crying, not giving way, makes me want to weep,' May told Jinny, and Jinny, trying to imagine how she would have managed had it been Ross who'd been killed, could only agree. There was something so poignant about Barry's death, coming when there was real hope of victory after all the years of fear, that it made the grief of the Hendries very real, and because they could not share it with Vi herself, all the more difficult to accept.

Josh, in particular, was very affected. Such a fine young man, he would say, such a wonderful soldier. What good times they might have shared in the future, liking the same things such as football and going out for a pint! He might have been the son Josh had never had, mightn't he? And talk of a son was something his girls had never heard from their father before.

All they could do was let Vi come to terms with her grief in her own way while they did the same, always thinking of her. In the world outside, the fighting went on that would eventually see the death of Hitler in his bunker. Nothing was easy – everything had to be taken after a struggle, but gradually the Allies reached their objectives, taking Rome, Florence and Athens, liberating Paris and finally crossing into Germany and reaching Berlin in April 1945. With the writing on the wall for Hitler, he ordered the destruction of everything that might be of use to his enemies, but his people were unwilling to put up resistance, being more concerned with escaping the Russians who would not have forgotten Germany's attempt to overpower their country. It was the Russians, however, who, along with the Americans, encircled Berlin, and whose iron grip would cause trouble in the future. But when Germany had officially surrendered, all the Allies and their people at home could think of was celebrating victory, which they did on 8 May 1945, with immense joy and relief.

Of course, there was still the war against the Japanese in the Far East to be won, which the families of those involved bitterly pointed out, but after all they'd been through no one could deny the survivors of the war in Europe their chance to celebrate. Whatever happened tomorrow, today they would dance and sing, light bonfires, have street parties and, if they could find anything to drink, make toasts to everyone in sight.

As for the Hendries, they had their own private celebration of a different nature, which was the birth of May and Allan's daughter on the day after the German surrender.

'No street party for me!' May had declared, laughing, when Josh came in to see her and his new granddaughter, who was to be named Victoria, and he'd shed a tear or two before hurrying to a phone box with all the money he could find to ring first Vi, who said she was delighted, and did sound so, and then Jinny at her billet.

'And she's to be called Victoria?' asked Jinny, experiencing a little twist of feeling at the name, which was so close to Viktor's. 'Oh, but that's wonderful, Dad, thanks for telling me. Oh, I'm so happy for them – now all I want is to be demobbed and to be at home!'

And with Ross, she added to herself. But when would that be? Please God, let it be soon, she prayed. Like everyone she knew, she'd had enough of her temporary wartime life and longed to get back to her own. It was true, she'd made some good friends – Josie, for instance, and Pauline, now the mother of a fine son, and young Sukie, and hoped they'd keep in touch, but there was a real life waiting for her somewhere and a real love. How soon before she could find them?

Seventy-One

With the process of demobilisation not beginning until June 1945, it was not to be expected that she'd be home very soon, but she was pleasantly surprised when her turn came six months later and the following January she was once again returning to Accounts. Not yet with Ross, though he was due to take up his old post soon, then Mr Lennox would depart and everything would be as it had always been.

Not quite, for Comrie's Bakery was not the same. Shortages, difficulties of every sort, made the atmosphere after the first euphoria of victory strained and tense, as it was in so much of post-war Britain, and it didn't help to see the newsreels at the cinema that showed the horrors of the German concentration camps, or the photographs of the atomic bomb explosions that had certainly brought the war in the Far East to an end, but had also destroyed two Japanese cities in the most terrifying manner. And then there were the endless problems of refugees everywhere, the misery of devastated cities, and the realization that everywhere there was so much to be done.

It was no wonder that Mrs Arrow took comfort in her usual complaints about supplies, and her new ones about the girls back from munitions being so discontented they'd already had enough of the queues and critical customers. Who'd won the war was the question. Nothing seemed different now there was peace.

★   ★   ★

All of this, Jinny might have expected to hear on her first day back, but what she had not expected was the news Mabel rushed to tell her, even before Mr Lennox had arrived.

'Mr Comrie's not in this morning,' she told Jinny, drawing her urgently into his office. 'He only manages the afternoons these days, poor man. He's not at all well. But he wouldn't be, would he? After the news he got not long ago.'

'What news?' asked Jinny, beginning to worry.

'Well, it was terrible. Someone in Vienna – a friend of the family – wrote that they'd been trying to trace him, you see. They knew Mrs Linden had a brother and they wanted to tell him—'

'What? Tell him what, Mabel?'

'Why, that she'd been killed in the bombing of Vienna, dear, and her husband too. Their bakery was completely destroyed. A direct hit, it seems.' Mabel's eyes were bright and intense. 'Viktor's parents, eh? But no one knows, the friend of the family said, where Viktor is. And you don't, do you, dear?'

'No, I don't know.' Jinny, her face white, turned away. 'I think I'd better get back to my desk, Mabel. Thank you for giving me that news.'

'Well, I knew you'd want to know. But you're looking awful pale, Jinny. Are you all right?'

'Fine. It's just – been a bit of a shock.'

Mr Lennox had just arrived when she returned to the accounts office, and held out his hand to her. 'Welcome back, Miss Hendrie! It's good to see you here.'

'Thank you. It feels a bit strange.' She sat down, putting her hand to her brow. 'I've just been hearing about Mr Comrie's sister and her husband in Vienna.'

'Oh, my word, yes, that was terrible news. He's been very badly hit by it. Not himself at all.'

'I'm not surprised.' Jinny tried to rally. 'Suppose I should try to get on with some work—'

'Don't worry about that this morning, Miss Hendrie. You look as though you're feeling shocked yourself. Why not go and have a cup of tea?'

'You're very kind, Mr Lennox. And you've been wonderful, taking over, the way you did.'

He smiled. 'Had to do my bit. But we'll be having Mr MacBain back soon, I expect. Then I'll be on my way. But you go and have your tea. Work can wait.'

★   ★   ★

Later, when she was at her desk again, she stared unseeingly at a pile of bills she was meant to pay, her thoughts dwelling on Viktor's parents and Viktor himself – whether he were alive or dead, and whether he would ever know what had happened to his parents.

And poor Mr Comrie, losing his sister and her husband, and possibly his nephew, too, the talented young man he had so much admired. She must try to see him when he came in and give him her sympathy. And in her lunch hour, she would write to Ross, whose support she had never needed more.

As soon as Mr Comrie arrived after lunch, Jinny leaped up from her desk and asked very politely if she could have a word.

'Of course, Jinny, of course! I was going to welcome you back, anyway. Come into my office.'

He had lost weight, his jacket hanging loosely on his once plump frame and his face gaunt, marked by new lines of strain, but he tried to smile as Mabel withdrew and Jinny accepted the chair he pushed forward.

'How was the ATS, then? You glad to be back?'

'It wasn't too bad at all, being away, but yes, I'm glad to be back.' Jinny hesitated. 'Mr Comrie, I hope I'm not speaking out of turn, but I'd just like to say how sorry I am about your sister and her husband. It's terrible news.'

'Yes.' He looked down at his blotter and played with a pen. 'It's been hard to take – the two of them, Clara and Bruno. I couldn't believe it at first.'

'I didn't even know Vienna was bombed so much.'

'Oh, yes, there were oil refineries, depots, that sort of thing. The city's been ruined, I've been told – bomb craters everywhere, buildings just shells. It'll take years to rebuild.'

'I'm so sorry.'

'I wanted to go over there but it's not possible. Travel is very difficult, and I'm not fit, Jinny. I'm not able.' Mr Comrie ran his hand over his brow, his breathing suddenly rasping, filled with effort. 'And then there's Viktor to think about. You don't know anything?'

'I haven't heard anything from him, Mr Comrie. I have no news at all.'

For some moments he sat very still, his breath becoming even more laboured, one hand at his chest, but then he began to fiddle with a desk drawer as drops of sweat gathered on his brow.

'Oh, God!' he whispered. 'My chest – the pain – Jinny, call . . . call Mabel. My tablets . . . I need them—'

For a second she sat, frozen, then leaped to her feet. 'Yes, Mr Comrie!' she cried, and ran like the wind to find Mabel, who rushed in with Mr Lennox at her heels. 'The tablets!' Jinny cried. 'Where are they?'

'In his drawer! Quickly, Jinny, some water!'

But Mr Lennox was already on his way, and as Mabel found the tablets and shook out two, he returned with a glass of water which he managed to make Mr Comrie drink as Mabel gave him the tablets.

'He's bad,' Mr Lennox whispered. 'Look at his colour! I'm going to ring for an ambulance. Wait here with him, Miss Hyslop.'

'He's collapsing!' she cried. 'He's losing consciousness!'

'Just stay with him – the ambulance won't take long; we should be in time—'

But it appeared that time had run out for Mr Comrie. By the time he reached hospital he had gone too far down his last path, and the following morning the staff at Comrie's were informed that he had died the previous evening, in spite of all efforts to save him.

Seventy-Two

The unexpected death of its owner threw Comrie's into confusion. For who was now the owner? What would the will say? Now that Mr Comrie's sister and her husband were dead, there were no relatives to inherit the business, except for his nephew, Viktor, whose whereabouts were unknown, and who might even be dead, too. Was he even a beneficiary, anyway? If it turned out that he was and had to be found, would the business have to be closed for probate, and would everyone lose their jobs, even if only temporarily?

These were genuine worries that Ross, who had arrived back early, his demob having been unexpectedly brought forward, was able to put to the lawyers. They agreed to a meeting with the staff, at which they announced that Mr Viktor Linden was indeed the sole beneficiary of his uncle's will, and that the business would not go into probate but be allowed to function until the results of a search already underway for him were known. In the meantime

Ross, as the senior accountant, would be required to keep track of all finances, and wages would be paid.

'Thank God they let you home early,' Mr Whyte told Ross fervently. 'I don't know what we'd have done without you. I'm no good at talking to these legal fellows.'

And with everyone agreeing with Mr Whyte's words and thankful to know where they stood, Jinny, back with Ross in Accounts, sneaked a kiss and told him he was their saviour.

'What did I do? I only asked John Dixon to talk to the staff and he should have done that earlier, anyway.'

'Well, it's wonderful that it's sorted out, at least for the time being.'

'I suppose so, but I'm pretty upset to have lost Mr Comrie. And what's going to happen if Viktor turns up and begins changing everything, as he'd be entitled to do?'

'I don't think he's going to turn up, Ross.' Jinny's tone was quiet, yet definite. 'I believe he's dead. If he were alive he'd have found a way to get in touch with me when the war ended.'

'You think that?' Ross asked uneasily. 'Is that what you want?'

'No! Well, only to know what had happened to him. I would like to know that.'

And she was to know, rather sooner than she'd ever imagined.

Some days later, while Ross was dictating letters to Mabel in Mr Comrie's office, Jinny sat working alone at her desk. A wind was rattling round outside, there was the promise of sleet, or even snow, and the accounts office was by no means warm, but Jinny, absorbed in her calculations, scarcely noticed. Nor did she notice when the door behind her opened. Only when a voice said her name did she turn round, and then her heart gave a lurch and the blood left her face.

A spectre was standing in the doorway. Or so for a moment it seemed. But he was not a spectre, he was a man, one she hadn't seen for all the years of the war but instantly recognized.

'Viktor?' she whispered. 'Viktor?'

Wearing a long, black overcoat marked with sleet, he was still tall, still handsome even, his bristling short hair still fair, but the etched lines around his eyes and his mouth told their tale. He had known suffering.

Oh, God, what had happened to him? Jinny's heart was thudding as her gaze rested on him – so much the same yet so different, so marked by what he'd known and she could not imagine. Even his erect military carriage had left him, and if Ross had once called him *Der Leutnant*, he would not do so now.

'Yes, I'm Viktor.' He gave a faint smile. 'Clever of you to recognize me.'

'I – I thought you were dead,' she stammered. 'Where have you been?'

'To hell and back. Or, if you prefer, a Russian prisoner of war camp.'

'You . . . were in Russia?' Jinny, now trembling so hard she could scarcely speak, felt as though she were in some sort of dream, talking to someone she'd believed lost or dead, as one might in dreams. But this was no dream, this was real. This was Viktor . . . real . . .

'How – how come you're here?' she asked, holding her cold hands together. 'How did you leave Russia?'

'God knows. Suddenly, after the German surrender, they let us go, though how we weren't shot in the first place I have no idea. Not many prisoners were taken – on either side. Jinny, may I come in?'

'Oh, I'm sorry, please do! And let me take your coat – it's quite damp.'

She hurried to hang up his coat with her trembling hands, noting that the suit he was wearing was too big for him and of cheap material, and he smiled again as he caught her glance.

'A charity purchase after I'd burned my prison uniform, or what was left of it.'

She hesitated, still trying to accept that he was there, standing before her, amazed that she could speak at all. 'Viktor, I was so sorry to hear about your parents. It must have been terrible for you, to come back . . . to find . . .'

Instantly his face appeared to shut down and he looked away, and Jinny, now feeling almost faint, said he must see Ross, he was just next door.

'Ross? He's here? He was in the army?'

'Oh, yes, went right through the war. I was in the ATS myself – the women's army. But please sit down, Viktor, while I tell Ross you're here.'

As soon as he saw her face, Ross leaped towards her, his hands outstretched, while Mabel stared, her mouth slightly open and her eyes wide.

'Jinny, what is it?' cried Ross. 'What's happened?'

'He's back, Ross. He's in our office . . .'

'Who? Who's back?'

'Viktor.'

There was a brief, trembling silence. 'Oh, God,' said Ross.

After a moment they all went into Accounts, Jinny and Mabel following Ross, who had managed to recover his poise as he shook Viktor's hand.

'This is amazing, Viktor! To see you back here, when we thought – well, we didn't know what to think.'

'I've been in a Russian prisoner of war camp since 1942.' Viktor's voice faltered. 'I only just got back to Vienna a few weeks ago.'

'They let you out? That was lucky.'

'Luckier that they took me in the first place.'

'I'm sure that's right. We heard a lot about what happened in Russia. You . . . know about your uncle?'

'I do now. When I first came back, I didn't. Didn't even think of him, when I found—' Viktor stopped, couldn't speak.

Ross said gently, 'I can't even imagine how it was for you.'

'Yes, well, when I could, I thought of him and was planning to get in touch, of course. It was only when I saw the lawyers' notice that I discovered he was dead.'

'Notice?'

'They put a German notice in all the main papers, asking Viktor Linden to get in touch regarding his late uncle's estate and then gave their details.' Viktor put his hand to his head for a moment. 'I couldn't believe it at first, but then I knew I should come over. I borrowed the money for the air fare and managed to get a flight. I saw Mr Dixon this morning and he told me about my uncle.'

'And the will?'

Viktor's face was impassive. 'And the will.'

'Let us welcome you as the new owner, then.'

'Oh, yes,' said Jinny, as Mabel nodded with enthusiasm. 'We wish you all the best, Viktor.'

He turned his shadowed, reddened eyes upon her. 'There are some things I'd like to discuss with you, Jinny. Would it be convenient for you to come for lunch with me – at Logie's, say?'

She glanced immediately at Ross, whose anxious eyes had instantly found hers. 'I expect that'd be all right, wouldn't it, Ross?'

'Perfectly all right,' he said hoarsely.

'We'll get our coats, then.'

*   *   *

Trying not to show how strange she found it to be with Viktor again, how fiercely gripped she felt by memories of the past, Jinny walked beside him from the shop, not looking at Mrs Arrow or her assistants, just keeping on through the falling sleet to Logie's.

'A table for two, please,' Viktor said to a waitress, and when she had escorted them to window seats and taken their coats, they looked at each other but did not smile.

'Like old times?' asked Viktor. 'Or perhaps not?'

Jinny did not reply.

Seventy-Three

They ordered the vegetarian cottage pie, as the waitress said it was better than the beef version, with just coffee to follow.

'I shan't eat much of whatever we have,' Viktor remarked. 'I eat only very little.'

'Why is that? We eat anything we can get.'

He shrugged. 'After years of cabbage soup they say it will take time to get back to ordinary food.'

'Oh, Viktor, how awful! You're so very thin.'

'Never mind about me.' His eyes were steady on her face. 'I wanted to speak to you to tell you I am sorry that, once the war came, I was never able to write to you. I knew you would be hurt, wondering where I was, but there was no way of letting you know.'

'I did realize that.'

'That's good, then. But once the years began to stretch out, I never expected you to wait for me, you know. That would have been unreasonable.'

She flushed a little. 'I did wait – I mean, for a long time—'

'Quite. But then you forgot me.'

'Viktor—'

'It's all right, I understand. I became unreal. It happens.'

'Wasn't it the same for you with me?'

'Perhaps. Where I was, everything outside became unreal.'

The waitress came with their order, and while Jinny began to eat, Viktor took a mouthful, then played with his fork. 'That's the way it was, you see,' he went on. 'Only my life in the army seemed real to me. And it was the same in the camp. Life centred on what happened there – there was nothing beyond.'

'Try to eat something,' she urged, but he shook his head.

'Even my parents went from my mind,' he said in a low voice. 'They only returned to me when I got home. But by then, they were dead.' His fingers clenched around his fork. 'Both dead. Like Vienna. It's in ruins, Jinny. A dead city. All is gone.'

She put down her knife and fork, her eyes filling with tears for him. 'I'm so sorry, Viktor, so sorry. If only there was something I could do—'

'For me?' His mouth twisted. 'There's nothing anyone can do for me. I must accept what's happened to my parents and think of Vienna, the people of Vienna.'

He shook his head, suddenly touching Jinny's hand. 'But I didn't ask you to see me to talk of my troubles.'

'Viktor, it's all right, you can talk to me. I want to hear—'

'No, there are other things I want to say.' His gaze on her was deeply intense. 'The first is that I'm happy for you, now I've seen you with Ross.' He lifted his hand as she tried to speak. 'No, he's right for you, and it's plain from just seeing you together that you love each other.'

She was silent, wanting to say it was true, but not finding the words.

'The second thing,' he went on, 'is that I'm not going to keep the bakery or my uncle's house. I'm going to sell them both and return to Vienna.'

'Vienna.'

'Yes. I'm going to help in the rebuilding of the city, but first it will be necessary to help those who are struggling now as though they are refugees. No homes, no money, no jobs. All they had, taken. That charity I mentioned to you does excellent work for all who need it and I'm going to work for them. It has been arranged.'

'That's wonderful, Viktor, but what about your career? Your cake-making?'

'My cake-making.' His smile was bitter. 'I can't imagine anything less needed than *Sachertorte* at the moment. I have found other things to do, now that my life has been spared.'

She could say no more.

When they'd had coffee, she asked diffidently if she might pay for the lunch, Viktor having no money, but he was dismissive.

'That will not be necessary. I've been given something in advance from the estate by the kind Mr Dixon. And to give you lunch again, just this once, has given me great pleasure.'

'Thank you, then. I appreciate it.'

When they had put on their coats and left the restaurant for the ground floor, Viktor put his hand on Jinny's arm. 'Before we go back, Jinny, may I tell you something?'

His eyes were suddenly as blue as she remembered them and, for a moment, gazing up at him, she saw beyond the gaunt façade of the returned soldier to the man she had once loved. It was true, that love was over and she had a new love that would always be hers, but she would not forget Viktor, just as, it seemed, he would not forget her. For, in those last moments they had together, he put a promise into words.

'I want you to know, Jinny, that I will always remember you, my Scottish love. The war drove us apart and now you have a new future with someone else, but I'll remember what we had – and maybe you will, too, I hope, with some affection?'

'I will,' she said quietly. 'I still have my Edelweiss brooch, but I won't need it to remember you.'

He was silent, studying her face, then bent and kissed her cheek. 'Good luck, Jinny, and also to Ross.'

'And to you, Viktor. You'll let us know how things go for you?'

He smiled. 'Perhaps.'

When they returned to Accounts, it was to find Ross waiting with every appearance of anxiety, but as soon as Jinny went to him and pressed his hand, he relaxed and smiled.

'Had a good lunch? Logie's seem to do better than most places for food.'

'Never mind the lunch, Ross, Viktor has some news,' Jinny said quickly. 'He's going to sell Comrie's and his uncle's house and go back to Vienna.'

Ross for a moment said nothing, his gaze resting on Viktor. 'Sell Comrie's?' he repeated. 'Is that definite?'

'Quite decided, Ross. I have other plans than running a bakery. I have been telling Jinny I want to do something for the people of my city. They've been affected badly by the war and now that I'm all right – or will be, soon – my plan is to help them rebuild their lives.' Viktor sighed. 'Then perhaps we can rebuild Vienna.'

'I see. That sounds admirable.' Ross appeared thoughtful. 'I don't suppose you've any idea yet of an asking price? I mean, for the bakery, not your uncle's house.'

'Nothing is arranged yet. I have to see Mr Dixon again soon to discuss the matter.'

'You will, of course, be hoping for a good offer. Money is always useful.'

'I am not looking for too much,' Viktor answered cautiously. 'I shall need money for what I want to do; otherwise, I don't any longer consider it important.'

Ross folded his arms and fixed Viktor with a long, serious gaze. 'May I ask you, then, if you would consider me as a purchaser?'

'Ross!' cried Jinny, her dark eyes enormous, 'what are you saying? You can't afford to buy Comrie's!'

'Perhaps not by myself, but I know that Arthur Whyte would be interested in joining with me. He has money that came to him recently and we sort of discussed a purchase before we knew that you'd inherited, Viktor. As I have what my father left me, depending on the price, I think we might just manage it.'

'I can't believe it!' Jinny cried. 'It seems impossible.'

'Not at all,' Viktor declared. 'I think Ross's suggestion is just what my uncle would have wanted. He'd believe that Ross and Arthur would be the right people to run Comrie's, as I do also.'

'You mean that?' asked Ross.

'I do. In fact, it would relieve my mind if I thought someone like you would take on my uncle's business, Ross. It meant so much to him.'

'It would mean a lot to me, too, and to Arthur Whyte.'

'Shall we see Mr Dixon, then, and see what can be arranged?'

'If you're sure.'

'I am sure,' Viktor said steadily.

And the two shook hands.

'I'm in another dream,' Jinny whispered when Viktor had taken his leave, promising to meet Ross at Mr Dixon's the next day. 'I never knew you had any money, Ross!'

'You'd have found out one day, wouldn't you? When I stood up at the altar and said something about 'with all my worldly goods I thee endow'?

She stared at him, a light taking over her face as her lips parted and her eyes shone. 'This isn't a proposal, is it?'

'What else?' He drew her to him. 'We've never spelled it out, what we'd do, but we always knew, didn't we? Now I think I should buy the ring before all my money goes on Comrie's. Shall we go shopping on Saturday?'

When Mabel came in and found them kissing, she blushed deeply. 'Oh, dear, I'm sorry, I'm sure . . . just had your letters to sign, Ross. Has Viktor gone, then?'

'Yes, but I'll be seeing him tomorrow,' Ross told her. 'We have something to discuss.'

'Do you think it will really happen?' Jinny whispered.

'I've every hope that it will.'

And so it proved. Ross and Arthur Whyte's offer was accepted by Viktor to much celebration at Comrie's, while Viktor returned home to regain his health and to work, as he'd promised, for those in need in Vienna.

'Take care,' he'd told Jinny and Ross on his last morning. 'Be happy. Keep in touch.'

'We will,' said Ross, 'but mind you do the same.'

When the final embraces had been made and the taxi bearing Viktor had driven away, Ross turned to Jinny and stood with her in silence for a little while. Then they moved into each other's arms, content.

Seventy-Four

It was some weeks later that the Hendries gathered, together with Ross, Allan and three godparents, for the christening of baby Victoria at the local kirk, and afterwards for tea at a small café, which had even managed to provide an iced cake. The meal was over, the cake sliced and served, and now Josh was on his feet, ready to say a few words and call for a toast.

'First, I want to say a few words about myself,' he began as Victoria slept peacefully in her carrycot. 'There was a time when I was all for my girls staying at home with me. I couldn't imagine a time without them, but after what we've all been through, I managed to learn a valuable lesson. What's important is that whatever happens we come through the bad times, we still love each other, and if there are new people in the family it just expands, that's all, and there's still room for everybody.

'So, I want to give my blessing to Jinny and Ross, who are going to be married, as I've already given it to May and Allan, who's doing so well with his shop again, and to Vi and her Barry, who is no longer with us. She'll forgive me for saying that I've been worrying about her, but she says she has plans to make people's lives better and will be happy in her own way. Maybe she'll try for the council, and – who knows – parliament. Isn't that right, Vi?'

'That's right,' Vi agreed and managed a smile as people tapped their approval. 'But get on with the toasts, Dad, eh?'

'Aye, I've talked long enough. I'm proud of you, my family and friends, and the new little lassie as well – may she grow up in a better world. Shall we drink to that?'

They drank to that and then to Barry, to all those who had gone before, and finally to the future.

'May there be peace in the world,' said May, speaking distinctly as she turned to look at Allan, who smiled and bent to pick up Victoria, as Jinny and Ross led the kisses and hugs and joined with everyone's hope: that one day May's wish might be realized.

A SMALL STIR

Letters on the English

by James Bridie

and Moray McLaren

HOLLIS & CARTER

MADE AND PRINTED IN GREAT BRITAIN BY THE CHISWICK PRESS,
NEW SOUTHGATE, LONDON, N.II, FOR HOLLIS AND CARTER, LTD.,
25 ASHLEY PLACE, LONDON, S.W.I

First published 1949

"A small stir of the Scots—soon blown over."

Petition of the Cornishmen to Henry VII

LETTER I

From James Bridie to Moray McLaren

Drymen
29th July, 1948

My dear Moray,

The French, the Irish and, above all, the Scots are forever yapping and howling and complaining that the English don't understand them. They are pleased with themselves for being so inscrutable and angry at the English for being so stupid. On the face of it, this is unfair.

It seems even more unfair when we reflect that the English take ten times more trouble to understand their neighbours than their neighbours take to understand them. I myself, a Scot, have taken some trouble—short of living among them—to understand the English. My trade of libretto writer for stage performances has made this necessary. A dairyman must familiarise himself with the habits and customs of cows. Yet I am uneasily aware that I have got nowhere near the root of the matter.

Can you help me? You have hunted among them a good deal. I understand that the walls of your Highland fastness carry some splendid specimens of stuffed Englishmen. You talk, moreover, their language.

The language difficulty is a great barrier between races. It is a greater difficulty when two languages are of some similarity. I can talk more comfortably to Arabs than to Englishmen or Americans because I do not know a dozen words of Arabic. On the other hand,

1

I have an almost idiomatic knowledge of English, though I have to struggle hard with the accent.

This matter of accent is often a very painful thing. In conversation with the English I find myself unevenly balanced between what we call Kelvinside English, which I despise, and Music Hall Scotch, which I do not speak very well. I cannot talk Well Off for more than two or three sentences at a time. This dilemma makes it hard for me to concentrate on what the English are saying to me. I have to cover my wandering attention by talking too much.

It is the more embarrassing because I know what importance the English attach to accent. For example, no Englishman with a trace of the Borough Road in his speech can make any way in the world unless he has at least ten thousand a year behind him, or a large Trade Union to push his claims to recognition. In 1945, 'when Death was on thy drums, Democracy, and with one rush of slaves the world was free', the English made it a condition that the revolutionary leaders should speak the language of Eton, Winchester and Haileybury. Mr. Morrison and Mr. Bevin themselves had, with varying success, to learn to speak Well Off.

Now, you undoubtedly speak Well Off as to the manner born. I am not quite sure, but I rather think that you have County connections. All the world over, from Land's End to John of Groats, County connections are very valuable. The voice may be the voice of either Jacob or Esau, but it has a confident ring in it. It has, as they say, background. The social scramble, upwards or downwards, has injected no anxious overtones into it.

It is different with us of the bourgeoisie. Our careful

2

consonants, our open vowels betray us. We know it. It is a poor patch to our self-esteem to tell the English that they cannot speak their own language—that the best English is spoken in Inverness or Dublin or Belfast. We know that, purity or no purity, the most important kind of English is a kind that we cannot speak. We despise each other for our attempts at it.

Here am I asking for instruction and giving it! An absurd habit of the Scotch. Quite like dear old Socrates, whom we do not otherwise resemble. He did it with the better grace, but we do it more natural. Unintentionally.

My own intention was to remind you that the English are likely to trust you. You are hardly a foreigner at all. You affect some John Bullishness in your dress and your small mutton-chop whiskers, and you take snuff. Your manners are good and your demeanour is gentle, amiable, and rather diffident, though you have a turn for clean-cut and seemly invective now and again. Many a one of the auld Enemy must have opened his heart to you without thinking for a moment that you were other than himself.

Tell me, then, about England. Supply the facts. If the facts puzzle you, and whom do they not? I shall try to order them and explain them. I am, or have been in my time, a student of Botany, Zoology, Physics, Chemistry, Physiology, Pathology and Anatomy. If that is not a scientific training, what is? It is freely at your disposal.

It will be a very strange thing if the fusion of your field work and my laboratory work does not produce a study of great value to you and me and, perhaps, to the

3

whole world. The Americans, for example, next to their longing to be loved and understood by other races, have a passionate desire to understand the English. This passion drove such men as Henry James and T. S. Eliot to become Englishmen themselves, the better to study this fascinating people. I cannot think but that they were frustrated in their quest. Their Imago-Englishman, their Anima-Englishwoman are altogether too complicated to be the real thing. These great men lacked our Scottish objectivity. They are not authoritative. Let us, dear Moray, aim at being authoritative. It is a noble thing to be and there is money in it.

Perhaps I should not have mentioned money or the American Market. We must not dazzle ourselves at the outset. Let us be animated principally by the wish to do good. Or, better still, let us put making money and doing good out of our minds and be soul-hydroptic with the sacred thirst for knowledge. This will guard us from the temptation to show off. I must warn you against this temptation and take my wise advice to myself. We know ourselves to be very clever chaps and it is a terrible pitfall for clever chaps to be forever displaying the superior quality of their education and their almost embarrassing wealth of cute ideas.

The Irish are very prone to this fault when they take up writing, though it was an Irishman who once told me of an impertinent fellow who, in the first five minutes of their acquaintance, told him how much money his father had. 'I just yawned', he said, 'in his face.' The display of wit and erudition can be no less vulgar than the display of wealth. Even in masterpieces like *Ulysses* and *Finnegan's Wake* such vulgarity is continuously offensive and Dr. Oliver St. John Gogarty is so often and so far beyond speaking about that it is a wonder he is received in respectable society.

Let us be warned by these barbarians across the channel. I often think that we Scots are not far removed from barbarity ourselves. If we own a silk hat we too often parade it incongruously while we are otherwise dressed in a loin cloth and brown boots. On second thoughts, not very often. We have a tradition of sound education in Scotland that lingers long after the education itself has disappeared. It is our substitute for the English tradition of gentility. It is not, we feel, a thing to make a song and dance about. Perhaps I should not have mentioned it.

If there is, after all, little need to warn ourselves against this kind of unseemly behaviour, there is even less danger of our being guilty of race superiority. The Scots have always been famed for their dignified humility. They know themselves to be perfervidly ingenious and to be the admiration and envy of all other peoples. It would be most shocking if they were addicted to rubbing it in. They can be tolerant of and even amused at the Englishman's pretensions to having a Scottish great-grandmother. It is only natural that one should be proud of one's ancestry. It goes without saying that we shall approach our little piece of ethnology in a truly modest and open-minded fashion. To do so comes natural to us. We need take no credit for it. We cannot help it. We can only be thankful that we carry such a useful bit of equipment.

Let us then, as some damned fellow or other has repeatedly so finely put it, march forward confidently towards our great task. I think you had better begin with a general survey, or appreciation. At the present stage you undoubtedly know what you are talking about a good deal more than I do. Besides, you began it. It was your idea. God send it prove to be a good one.

Aye yours,

James Bridie.

LETTER II

From Moray McLaren to James Bridie

Journeying from Ireland to Scotland
4th August

My dear J.B.,

It is right of you, though a trifle embarrassing, to remind me that the idear of writing to each other about the English was mine—I include the 'intrusive r' even in this first written sentence to conform to your conception of my 'well off' speech. I include it also to remind you that the *lingua franca* of easy or standard English (I admit to no more than that) has many sounds that are ugly phonetically, and meaningless grammatically. It is well, for those who possess this speech naturally, as for those who aspire to it, to remember this. There are far more imperfections in standard English in sound and in sense than in standard French. In that tongue the elisions and intrusions are a matter of form and not of careless habit. Standard French has nothing, or very little to do with class. The possession of pride in the language is fairly equally distributed in all who desire to have it. This (as you rather more than imply) is not so in English, or at least in that form of communication which the English, the Americans, the Irish and the Scots use amongst each other. This, however, is too fascinating a subject to launch upon so early. Let me tell you how the project of publishing letters upon the English first came to me.

I was sitting in the smoking room of my club in London one evening during the last year of the war. It

7

was fairly full; and the atmosphere was murmurous with that amiable hum of not very meaningful talk at which the English are so adept. Our club rather goes in for the convention of conversation; and clichés, platitudes and unostentatious greetings droned about the room like the pleasant sound of bees upon a hot summer afternoon. In the middle of all this the first V2, or rocket bomb, on London arrived a little over a hundred yards from us. It nearly destroyed a public house which I had just left, buried itself in the clay of London and exploded.

The effect was really startling. Owing to the fact that the explosion happened subterraneously there was at first no rush and rumble, only a kind of groan from the earth. The whole club (I refer to the physical structure and not to the members) was moved from beneath. It rose perceptibly, gave a grunt, and then settled back again like an old lady who, sitting in a deep armchair, had found herself suddenly troubled with the wind. Then there was the partly comical, partly macabre business of hearing the explosion first and the shriek and whistle of the approaching bomb afterwards. This, to the imaginative, could not but underline the elementary fact of the suddenness of life. At one moment one was sitting there talking and drinking: at the next—well, one was *still* sitting there talking and drinking. It was all so different from the chugging approach of the V1 or the blitz warning to which we had grown so accustomed. I repeat: the effect was startling.

Only three men in the room, however, showed signs of being startled, an American, an Irishman, and myself. It was not that we were frightened. It was a little bit

8

late in the war for that. The American had been on many night flights over Berlin. The Irishman had returned from the post D-Day Western Front. My own war had not been without incident. No, it was just that the whole thing had been so unexpected and remarkable that one felt inclined to remark upon it in a rather more pointed manner than usual. But what was more remarkable was that no one else of the dozen or so men in the room saw fit to remark on it. They were all English.

Later the American, the Irishman and I found ourselves talking about this at the bar. The American was warily and platitudinously sentimental. He talked about English phlegm, Englishmen changing for dinner in the jungle, and so on. The Irishman was cynical and mildly witty. He put it all down, with a wealth of illustrations, to a mixture of pose and insensitivity, and to the national complaint of constipation which had been increased by wartime food. He told, not without grudging admiration, of how when he had been driving in a taxi at night, the whole cab had been moved from one side of the road to the other by the blast from a bomb. The cab had been uninjured, so the driver had driven on without remark, merely saying at the next traffic lights, 'If he ain't careful he'll go too far one of these days'.

I, who knew the English so much better than these fellow foreigners, I, who had read this sort of thing that they were saying in countless articles and books, sighed and said little. Then I produced a dozen different generalisations which I had intended to be subtle. They were, however, only statements that I at once qualified and brought to no satisfactory end. Eventually I stopped.

'It's hopeless', I said. 'They can't be pinned down.'

'Someone ought to write a book about them', said the young American eagerly.

'Hundreds have', I told him. 'But I'm tired of reading the sentimental or abusive outpourings of Americans, the flatulent pedantry of the Teutons, the finnicking, tittering subtlety of the French, the well-bred evasions of the Spaniards or Italians or, for that matter, the complacent remarks of the English on themselves.'

'You ought to write one yourself', said the American.

'Impossible, I know too much and too little.'

'Write one in collaboration with someone else then.'

'With me', suggested the Irishman.

'The book would be all about Ireland.'

'Then what about me?' put in the American. 'We could write letters to each other when I get back to the States, and we'd make it into a book of correspondence.'

I shook my head. 'I should spend all my time correcting your mistakes. It would be a perfect literary example of the negative and the positive combining to make nothing.'

'Then write one with another Scot', they both said together.

'Not a bad idea', I agreed.

Then something happened to put the matter out of my mind—possibly another bomb. The idea, however, was not dead. It must have lain dormant within me. For, one day this summer, dreaming at Drymen or girning in Glasgow, the conversation between you and me turned upon the English. When I got home the old idea revived itself. I telephoned and put it to you. With your characteristic lowland generosity and impetuousness you agreed at once—and proceeded to crown your agreement by sending me the first letter. So here we are launched upon a venture in the eighteenth-century convention of writing letters to each other in public.

Some of our friends may smile at our claim to be able to talk about the English in a really objective manner, you whose 'libretti' are as well known in the West End as in Scotland, you with your membership of The Garrick and your innumerable connections, social, literary, and political with London and England, I who speak like an Englishman and who have spent nearly as much of my life in England as in Scotland. They will use of us (but in a more friendly spirit I hope) those terms with which our critics sometimes belabour us—arch, puckish and elusive of you. They will say of me (with a smile) that I am being self-consciously and aggressively Scottish Nationalist, and that I am glorifying the accident of remote provincial birth to a ridiculous extent.

You and I know that that is nonsense. For all your London-running and transatlantic-showing 'libretti', your world travels, your friends in every country and so on, you remain for anyone who knows your work (and more important yourself) as obviously a Scot as Scott, as obviously Scottish as Yeats was Irish. It would be an impertinence for me to underline this fact. I, I am a smaller fish and, as you point out, superficially of more doubtful colouring. I do not have as large a body of written work as you have to attest to my nationality. However, it pleases me to inform you that I am never taken for anything but a Scot in England, even if, alas!

I am sometimes taken for an Englishman in my own country. To be done with this short but necessary fit of introspection let me say this. Despite the circumstances to which you allude in your first letter, despite the partly Scottish, partly English, partly Cosmopolitan education of my forebears and myself, I have never since childhood felt anything but a foreigner in England. This goes, as they say, for such older relatives of mine as I remember. The sensation is far from being disagreeable. How dull it must be to feel at home everywhere. I have often pitied those weary chameleon-like cosmopolites who claim that they 'never feel abroad'. I understand, though I do not sympathise with the remark of a recent Monarch of the United Kingdom. He was recovering from a severe illness, and was advised to go to the South of France to recuperate. 'Damn abroad', he is said to have said, 'abroad's bloody.' My, and I'm sure your version would be 'Bless abroad, abroad's lovely.'

In spite of all this foreignness about which I have been quoting, how rarely placed we are to write about the English. We really do know them better than all the Continentals put together. We share the same *form* of language with them, but lack the vulgar sentimentality or equally vulgar dislike that the Americans have for the English. We lack too that acute Anglophobia which understandably afflicts nearly all Irish writing about the English. The strongest emotion of dislike which I have ever felt for the English (and I think you will agree with me here) has been irritation. I keep my really active hatred for some of my fellow countrymen and some of my fellow Celts.

And how good it would be for the English for you and me to write about them objectively. In their amiable, galumphing, good-natured way they are always ready, in farce, comedy or in sentimental writing to treat us, the Irish and even the Welsh as foreigners. They are always ready to emit a guffaw over our national peculiarities or shed a saccharine tear over our romantic past. Oddly enough they are always brought up with a jerk, and resent it when we treat them as foreigners, when we submit their peculiarities to laughter or applaud their virtues as something rich and strange.

Finally how good for us to write about them. We would, in the process, clear our minds, and those of many of our compatriots, of a good deal of cant. Moreover, as you rightly point out, there may be money in it. The English, however different they may be from the rest of mankind, share one universal quality of the literate world. They love reading about themselves

How then, after all this not altogether useless circumlocution, shall we start? There are a number of subjects I should like to suggest to you. For instance, the volatility and high emotional pressure of John Bull. This, as you will remember, was broached in G.B.S.'s preface to *John Bull's Other Island*. We could push the argument further from our point of view. There is the much discussed but never solved problem of the contrast between the Englishman's high productivity in art and his official and personal view of art. There is that enigma the Englishwoman, the Englishman in love. There is the English, the most irreligious yet the most

Godloved race in Europe—well, if not loved by God, at least well treated by Him. And so on and so on.

These, and other subjects will emerge. In the meantime, since your trade and mine is 'words', I suggest that we begin with the English language and what they have done with it. What do you think? Any variations, modifications or alterations gratefully accepted.

Yours,

Moray McLaren.

LETTER III

From James Bridie to Moray McLaren

Drymen
17th August, 1948

Dear Moray,

Words? I don't know about that. You see, the Southerners haven't got the monopoly of written English. The American dramatist, Maxwell Anderson, once said that the first qualification of a writer of plays was that he should be an Irishman because the Irish write the best English. The second qualification was to be a Scotsman, because the Scots write better English than the Irish.

There may be something in it. Can you think of a Sassenach writer who wrote better classical prose than Swift's or better colloquial prose than Boswell's. A great many living Englishmen write very good prose, but has a single one of them attained to either Shaw's penny plain or O'Casey's tuppence coloured? Has the great Sir Max himself (who is, I believe, not entirely Anglo-Saxon) ever attained to the delicate mastery of Linklater and Neil Gunn at their best? Aren't *The Scotsman* and *The Irish Times* at least as well written as the London *Times*? I should have thought so.

Don't let us talk about literature yet. We are trying to get behind façades and all literature is ninety per cent façade.

We shall get badly muddled if we begin to bother ourselves about how they talk English. I remember once sitting in an orangery in Malvern. I was in exceedingly

15

good company. Gordon and Emily Bottomley were there. Harold and Laura Knight were there. Yvonne Arnaud and Phyllis Shand were there. Time was more valuable than most time, but we spent over an hour discussing how to pronounce the word 'whale'. It was alleged that the Scots pronounced it 'hwale' and the English pronounced it 'wale'. The English asserted that it was correct to say 'wale' and I affirmed and repeated that the letter 'h' was retained for some useful purpose. The matter was referred to Miss Arnaud, who was a very bad judge, because she does not give two hoots how the English and the Scots pronounce their own language and makes herself intelligible in a language all her own.

How much better would we have been employed if we had discussed the deadly immortal monster itself! How idle of us to waste even part of a rare occasion on foolish points of pronunciation!

At the same time, I must say that the English are too careless about their rich and beautiful language. It may be wrong to say 'hwale', but it is much worse to say 'wale'. Anyhow, the Scots don't say 'hwale'. The long, impressive 'w' can be discerned on the horizon long before the important aspirate explodes on the ear. It is an English joke to make a great fuss of aspirates. At the few times when an aspirate ought to be taken seriously, why do they ignore it? I have heard educated Englishmen exploring the why and the wherefore and the when, while discarding entirely the element that makes these words so touching and plaintive. Surely this is not right.

Would it be true to say that in this matter, as in

other matters, they are abominably at the mercy of fashion? Nowadays they are not obleeged to refer to a cup of tay; but not so long ago they were, and to-morrow they may be again.

. . . . .

Hic hiatus. It is now the second of September. Whatever chain of thought I had in this letter has been broken by the Edinburgh Festival. Also round here-abouts I have read in a *Times Litt. Sup.* tuppenny reprint the best essay on the English that I have ever read. I hear that it has been credited to Maurois, Cyril Connoly—or 'Conolly' is it?—and Bernard Shaw. In fact a Scotsman wrote it. The English attribute many fine qualities to the Scots, but not wit, and the article is a witty one.

You have probably read the essay. In case you haven't, let us postpone its discussion till we can agree that it is our new Authorised Version. For, indeed, it is very true and can be used as a text when we get to the length of sermonising at each other.

Where were we? Trembling on the brink of the assertion that the English are no good at English. Trembling? Nay, our little trotters were already ploughing furrows in the slippery sand dunes. What a good thing and from how many points of view the Edinburgh Festival is!

Let us go back. Let us go back to your esteemed favour of the fourth of August.

I see that you suggest discussion on the volatility and high emotional pressure of John Bull. This will do very well.

Let us ignore those who say that John Bull does not

17

exist, or that he is a composite of Kentishmen, Dales-
men, Manchestermen, Wessex aborigines and what not.
We remember quite well that we are talking about
costermongers, generals, bargees, sailormen, judges,
comedians, potters, cheapjacks, policemen, lavatory
attendants, novelists, actors, engineers, financiers,
crossing-sweepers, jockeys, bailiffs, lords, and 'dear
little sillies' in Chelsea 'who do not know what they
are.'* If we are looking for the Highest Common
Factor, volatility will help. It is common to nearly *all*
Englishmen, in whatever part of the country or sphere
of life they were born. It is, moreover, impossible to
convince any Englishman that his fellow-countrymen
are volatile. This impossibility shows that we are on
the right track.

If we say to an Englishman, any Englishman, 'The
English are volatile', he will reply, 'No. You are wrong.
The French are volatile.' We shall pause for a moment
on this answer.

The English have two Creeds, a Secret Creed and an
Open Creed. The belief in certain national characteristics in others is the link between the two creeds and
is powerfully and potently held. Thus, the Irish are
witty, but find it impossible to be serious. The Germans
are sentimental. The Americans are boastful. The
Scots are mean. The Africans are jolly, with a childlike jollity. The Dutch are picturesque. The French
are logical, but volatile. The Russians are subtle. The
Welsh are dishonest. And so on.

All this is what the Neo-psychologists call trans-

* Barrie, Sir J. M., Bart., Scottish author of the early twentieth
century, on fairies in some play or other he wrote.

ference.   Qualities persons dislike in themselves are firmly attached to other people in the hope that they will not sully the fair forms of their own Imagines.

So it is with volatility which, I understand, is the quality of being volatile.   It is a disposition to exhale or evaporate, to be more or less freely diffused in the atmosphere at ordinary temperatures.   It has come also to mean—or, perhaps originally meant—flightiness, levity, giddiness.   In human beings it may, as you suggest, be associated with high emotional pressure.

The sons of John Bull and his consort Sal (who was, of course, a Volatile) are volatile in every sense of the word.   It is hidden from them that they are so, but this need not surprise us.   Take the simple instance of a railway carriage.

It is one of their little jokes among themselves that they are silent in railway carriages.   It would take a surgical operation to make a Scot see any sense in this joke.   They are extremely talkative in railway carriages. They attack entire strangers with accounts of their business, their private life, their sentiments about things in general.   In another of their jokes they are shown as good-hearted simpletons.   If they were so they would be easy meat for the con man, who likes people to open their hearts to him.   Fortunately, they are not good-hearted simpletons; but it is undeniable that they are terrible blethers.

Unless his *vis-à-vis* is a very suspicious looking character indeed or too obviously a member of a lower social grade, the Englishman will at once diffuse himself into the atmosphere.   His travelling companions are made welcome to the inner places of his soul long before the train reaches Rugby. Indeed, your friend Mr. Belloc, who is partly French and has accordingly had the giftie given him, has laid down many splendid rules for defeating this habit of the English and for preserving the privacy which is mankind's delight and right. He says that he has gone so far as to feign insanity, and this may well be so. One wonders whether the general company regarded it as in any way noticeable.

All really celebrated Englishmen whose blood was not alloyed by a foreign gene have almost consistently behaved like madmen. If you say that Newman, Wesley, Neville Chamberlain, Matthew Arnold, Martin Tupper, Spurgeon, W. H. Smith, Herbert Spencer, Milton, Bacon or Sir Frederick Leighton were not flighty, you have insufficiently studied their lives. It is not necessary for me to reply with C. J. Fox, Wolfe, Lord Shaftesbury, Shelley, William Pitt or Dr. Johnson who were all obviously daft. Behind grave countenances the men I have mentioned first concealed a quite ineluctable levity. The great Englishman is always a lunatic with a strongly practical side. Otherwise the English would not permit him to be great.

But you began all this, Moray, and you are the expert. Tell me, please, in what respect you have found the English volatile.

And God bless you.

J.B.

LETTER IV

From Moray McLaren to James Bridie

Glasgow, 14th September

My dear J.B.,

After I had read you in your last letter trying to edge me into a definition of volatility (when I had said that the English were volatile), I went straight to the dictionary. I wanted to know whether I really meant what I said when I used the word. In a correspondence such as ours, partly deliberately casual, partly spontaneously formal, I find myself using words often for the sound and the look of them rather than for their sense. I don't know that, in the circumstances, this is altogether wrong. Still, it is as well now and again to pull oneself up. Words are not only our professional but our national preoccupation.

It is impossible to avoid the subject of words at the beginning of such a correspondence as we have undertaken. English words (though not always English meaning) form our greatest and most continuously present link with the English. The fact of this link obtruding upon our consciousness all the time during our dealings with the English only serves to illuminate and remind us of our constant differences from them.

I agree with you that we were on the verge of hinting that the English aren't very good at English. I would go further. I would assert that most of the English are bad at English. By most of the English I mean those who are not professionally accustomed to the use of written words. On the whole, considering the huge output

21

of written English in England in the last thirty years, I think the general level of writing is remarkably high, and is improving. This is true of casual and anonymous journalism as well as of the more careful and deliberate writing. You have only to compare the columns of a newspaper before 1914 or a popular and forgotten Edwardian novel with their counter-parts to-day to agree with me. Writers of all classes in English and in England are expressing themselves more clearly, more concisely and are avoiding, without apparent effort, the *clichés* which weighed down the expression of most people who took a pen in hand in the first decade of this century.

This is not so in spoken English, which is the usual use of English of the vast majority of those who inhabit England. I *know* that the spoken English of most Englishmen is an insult to a noble language. I have the impression that it is getting worse. Not only is it everywhere spoken in a slovenly and ugly manner, but it is deprived of all but the crudest common currency of meaning by a shrinking vocabulary and a reliance upon the current cant phrase. The *cliché*, having been routed in written English, is now the tyrannical enfeebling ruler of modern English speech.

This is true amongst all classes in England. The well educated and the highly born are just as bad as the lower middle and the shopkeeping classes. They chatter and babble incessantly, wearisomely and embarrassingly in a flow of catchphrases and with a paucity of words expressing nearly nothing. One gets the impression that they have become so accustomed to the sound of the wireless that they cannot endure silence or reflection or the necessary pause to produce the proper words to say what they mean. They therefore open their mouths to make a series of sounds which they call conversation. This protects them from the terror of silence, but leaves the larger part of their minds free (as Maugham puts it) to thinking about the more important subjects of business or fornication. This drooling kind of English talk is now spreading to the working classes themselves and is poisoning the wells of common English speech.

I am not old enough to have more than childish memories of popular or conventional English speech before 1914. I am convinced, however (and you, from a slightly longer memory, may be able to confirm this), that English speech forty years ago was not so badly infected by this disease. Surely it was more racy, more humorous, more pathetic, and if sometimes more pompous, more exact. I believe, on no more grounds than intuition, that the conversations recorded in the lower middle class home of Mr. Pooter (The *Diary of a Nobody*, 1895) were faithfully reproduced even though they may have been artistically arranged. I believe that if the Grossmiths were alive to-day and were to write another *Diary of a Nobody* about a modern London petty suburban household, they would not have anything like so rich a material to work upon. This would not be because the situations to-day would be less ludicrous or pathetic, but just because a 1948 Mr. Pooter would not have the words in which to express his thoughts or to describe his actions, misfortunes or longings.

I know, of course, that there is nothing very new

in this diatribe against modern English speech. I only let myself go on the subject because I think it is germane to our theme—The English. What is it that has laid the English people, Northern and Southern, so open to this disease? How can their forefathers have invented so great a language, their present writers write it, on the whole, so well, and they themselves debase it thus on their tongues? It is easy to talk about the effect of the talking machines in the cinema, the influence of America, the mental indolence of thought brought about by the spread of literate illiteracy nourished on *Daily Mirror* strip cartoons and so on. But these, and all the other reasons usually brought forward won't do. For these things are prevalent in other countries; yet in no other land in Europe is the national language so degraded as it is in the generality of English speech.

This brings me to the point that I have been so laboriously reaching. While the quality of speech in Scotland has declined—mainly through contact with the English—it has not deteriorated in anything like the same way. Our compatriots who have stayed at home, or who have exported their nationality with them, may speak with an effort, slowly, pawkily, pedantically, or they may occasionally pour out their words in an excess of feeling which it is embarrassing to listen to. But they do seem to speak as individuals and not as talking machines. They do give the impression that they are using words, not catchphrases, to express whatever they are meaning. That meaning may be something platitudinous, or dull, or philosophical, or grossly sentimental—or something much better than any of these things. But they do take the trouble to express it in their own way.

The Irish, for whom I imagine you to have an irritated affection—despite your violent abuse of them in private conversation—have not debased their own use of English at all. Forget all the stage Irish you have ever heard, all the 'witty' Irish stories, all the sentimental tales of Celtic-struck returning travellers. Forget all your (and my) admiration for Swift and Shaw and O'Casey. Forget the whole façade, or genuine architecture that they shew, or have shewn, on their behalf to the world, and just do one thing. Be a fly on the wall of a Dublin public house, a flea in the crevices of a first, second or third class railway seat in Ireland. Be a tired, disgruntled reporter in the Dail, an irritated Englishman or Scot waiting for a late bus in an Irish country town. In short, put yourself at any disadvantage you can think of and just be an audience to them talking, so long as they don't know you are an audience—and listen.

You will hear English spoken vividly, expressively, often crudely, sometimes beautifully, but always richly and with a full sense on the part of the speakers of the wealth of the language at their disposal. They always have a word, a phrase, a simile or, in extreme instances, a metaphor to suit the occasion or thing that they are talking about. Above all they seem never to repeat themselves in their use or their order of words. It is not that their vocabulary is so much larger than the Englishman's (the inventor, it must never be forgotten, of their language) but that they always have a fresh arrangement of familiar words to suit their

25

description of or comment on even the most ordinary events or objects. The *cliché* in Irish conversation is unknown. And this quality, mark you, is not the prerogative of romantic peasants, romantic *nostalgie de la boueic* pub haunters in Dublin, romantic politicians, poets and all the rest of the fraternity of Irish characters with which we are so familiar in books and plays about the Irish. It is enjoyed by Irish business men, clergymen, doctors, tramdrivers and cinema attendants. They remain in spoken language Elizabethans.

Yet they too have their gutter press, their American films, their wireless. So have the French and the Germans, whose spoken language has far from declined in the last thirty years. Why is this? Why have the English uniquely debauched so noble an inheritance as their language? Is it, in some remote way, connected with the fact that while the English have produced the greatest and richest poetry of the modern western world, they despise the poet more than they do any other artist?

If you think that this is extravagant, reflect honestly on what would be your reception in all but the intellectual parts of English society if you were known not as a well-known dramatist but as a well-known poet. There are excuses on hand for all other artists in England. The novelist or the dramatist is a clever fellow who with luck might put you in his books or plays. He is usually, and often wrongly, considered entertaining. The painter has behind him a long tradition of excusable bohemianism. This has been acquired either abroad in romantic circumstances or in the equally romantic life of the studio. He is often genuinely picturesque to look at and is frequently a gentleman. Moreover, his mere technical ability to put down on canvas or on paper what he sees or thinks he sees is an accomplishment which most people, English or not, envy. 'If only I could draw faces like that I'd do nothing else all day long', is a very common remark. There is also something of the same respect for the exclusive ability of the musician, particularly the interpretive musician. His manners and appearance are often more difficult to put up with than are those of the writer or painter. None the less, he is usually accepted and forgiven as the gifted inhabitant of a world of sound forbidden to most of us. This is not so with the poet. He, in England, is widely distrusted. To announce your profession as poet is to proclaim that your job is being that of a dreamer, an idler, a *poseur*—and this from a race that has produced Shakespeare, Milton and Browning! It is as if it were disgraceful to be a musician in Germany, a painter in France, a ballet dancer in Russia or a big business man in America. Can you explain it? And do you see any connection between this comparatively recent contempt of the art of poetry in England and the recent decay of spoken English? Probably not. But I merely throw the question out.

As I was saying, I went to the dictionary to learn what it said about 'volatile'. It has, of course, an exact scientific meaning which, equally of course, I was not concerned with. It has also two not very consistent figurative meanings—movable and gay. Surely a person can be movable, inconsistent or inconstant and unpredictable in his emotions and opinions without being gay. It is also possible to be gay and expressive without being movable and inconstant. Compared with the English, the French, the Italians and the Irish Celts are gay. It is, however, always possible to tell how they will react individually or collectively to most circumstances. Not so the English. I was certainly not accusing them of being gay—however much they may talk in railway carriages. I was merely thinking of their tantalising mobility of emotion and thought.

It is not that they do not have certain deep general, if ill defined principles, or that they do not sincerely wish to keep to their word. It is merely that the emotions that spring from these deep principles are kaleidoscopic in their variations, and that their own honest interpretation of their word is, to foreign observers, often variable and incomprehensible. Anyone who is not an Englishman but who has had constant dealings with them must be able to think of many many examples of this individually and collectively. Let me but give one which has often struck me in my profession, as a journalist, a writer of books, and, during the war, an odd kind of Foreign Office official.

I am only middle-middle aged, but I have seen them change their opinion of the Germans violently four times, of the French three times, the Poles twice and of the Russians, most violently of all, three times. Their view of the Americans is almost as mobile as the Americans' own view of the rest of the humanity—but then the Americans are the most volatile people in the world. The English do not make these somersaults of emotion and opinion out of opportunism, but because of deep unshakable convictions. They sincerely believe in abstract justice, that the bullying of the weak by the strong is evil, that unprincipled aggression is wrong. The only drawback is that it is lamentably easy for any cynic or crank (usually a crank) to convince them that the hero or heroine of yesterday is the brute of to-day, or vice versa. Fortunately these strong but unselfcontrolled instincts have been, up to the present time, guided by the most venerable system of law in Europe and the fairly constant policy of their much abused Foreign Office. Will these guiding traditions continue to keep in control? I don't know. There are many signs that they are weakening. If they do weaken and completely lose their grip of the honest, emotional sentimental, volatile English heart and mind, there will be loosed upon the world a tempest of temperament beside which the storms of Latin and Slavonic behaviour will seem like zephyrs.

There are, as I have said, many other instances of the English volatility of temperament. Perhaps you can, if you feel inclined, add some from your experiences. There have been also, many more detailed and better pieces of writing about it—particularly Shaw's essay on Nelson and Wellington. But the English remain stolidly and unshakably convinced of their stolidity and immobility. Nothing that you or I, or any Irishman or Frenchman can say will ever affect this, their most precious illusion about themselves. They have another illusion. They are so poetic that, as Chesterton put it, they sometimes even dream that they are prosaic. But that is another matter.

By the way, talking about other matters, what about

the English and God as the subject of your next remarks?
You, at any rate, must believe in the existence of the
English and we are fairly sure to disagree about God.

Yours,
Moray McLaren.

LETTER V

From James Bridie to Moray McLaren

7th October, 1948

Dear Moray,

I am answered and you are probably right. You might have added that these highly benevolent people are also capable of being extremely ruthless. The point was made in a recent article in *The Times Literary Supplement.** In this unexpected and very brilliant essay the Irish, the Welsh and the Lowland and Highland Scots were called as witnesses.

It is true that the Boer War shook the conscience of the English in a way hardly appreciated by foreign students. When they realised why and how they had fought in that campaign they honestly determined to be better boys in future. Since then they have had a remarkable record of almost chuckle-headed magnanimity in the field of foreign and imperial politics. The old tiger burns with a more subdued and fitful glow. He is still there, however. As soon as he has served his contemporary purpose, it is true, he withdraws his claws and sits on the mat like the fat cat and the English forget about him as quickly as they can, as they forgot about that once popular figure, Bomber Harris. The people of Hamburg and other places no doubt still remember this aspect of English volatility.

Let that flea stick to the wall. You have asked me what I think about the English and God. You have hinted that we are likely to disagree about God. Why

* 7th April, 1948.

in God's name shouldn't we? In most authoritative text-books on the subject it is laid down that nobody knows much about God or is likely to do so till the great Day of Judgment. This leaves plenty of room for speculation on the nature of the Deity. I think that the Englishman speculates in a characteristic way and it is his speculations I should like to consider without bothering you with my own.

I have been conscious for a long time that the Englishman has a secret religion. It is possible to attend all the places of worship of all the denominations from Berwick to the Lizard without gathering any very clear idea as to Who or What the Englishman thinks he is worshipping. In Scotland, Wales and Ireland it is far otherwise. There, undoubtedly, the lineaments of an anthropomorphic god (or of a variety of anthropomorphic gods) are clearly discerned. These gods, Welsh, Scottish or Irish, take an arbitrary and decisive interest in human affairs from the smallest to the greatest. They keep many of the inhabitants in a continuous state of awe-struck apprehension. Nobody knows what they will do next, but in other respects they are as real as Victorian fathers.

Except in some Non-Conformist circles this attitude is rare in England. Indeed, the word Non-Conformist is an indication that this is so. It means that the majority, even the Catholics, conform. That is to say, they follow the convenient fashion. Religion is a matter of behaviour and not of passionate belief. I am using the word religion in the sense in which the Englishman uses it in common conversation. He uses it to denote a certain seemly and unexacting routine of the order of the cold bath or of the whisky and soda at bedtime.

No, not precisely of that order. I have just recalled the fact that no English gentleman discusses religion in mixed company. Perhaps it is pigeon-holed with 'shop' or with ritual hygiene. Important enough in its place, but. . . .

Religion is not exactly tabu as a subject for discussion. I have heard it discussed in the anteroom of an Officers' Mess. A number of subalterns (temporary, I hasten to say) were grouped in a semi-circle round an Army Chaplain who had his back, figuratively and literally, to the wall. The young men had gin in their hands and were already slightly flown with it.

I heard the familiar opening gambit, 'I don't pretend to be a religious man, but . . .', and I joined the group. The youths were, it appeared, instructing the Padre in basic religion as it should be presented to the troops. To do them justice, they had been at considerable pains to understand the troops. They had not, apparently, taken the same pains to master the principles of theology. The Chaplain, an Englishman himself, was very patient. Too patient, I thought. In the face of continuous interruption he attempted to propound some axioms of the sort familiar to every Sunday School infant. He translated these into subalternese or public school jargon. It was baby talk. It was pitiful. Nobody listened. The subalterns were bursting with half-baked ideas and were determined to be heard.

In a little while, I could stand it no longer. I said, 'Good God, gentlemen, does it not occur to you that the Padre has been working at his job for twenty years and may be expected to know something about it? Tell *me*, if you please, how to look after the sick and I will show the Padre how a lot of ignorant cattle should be answered.'

At that time I was the most important Doctor in the city of Baku and they did not dare to accept my challenge. In any case, Medicine was a subject one had to learn. Religion was a simple, natural process. One could make it up as one went along—out of one's own head. I believe that many Englishmen take this view of religion when they think about it at all.

It is far otherwise with the Englishman's Secret Religion. There is Law, in that, with powerful sanctions behind it. The nature of this Law is very difficult to determine. Here, indeed, we have a tabu on discussion, and a tabu of the most formidable character.

I cannot pretend to know anything about it. I know of the tabu, of course, and I am convinced that the caste system plays a very big part in its constitution. It also appears to be rigidly held by a huge majority of Englishmen of all types. Beyond this, I am only guided by casual manifestations I have met in my travels.

I think that I have told the following story in some book or other, but, as nobody ever reads my books, I shall tell it again. It was, for me, a very illuminating incident.

I was sitting in a restaurant with a friend of mine called Tomkins. He was a grey-haired man, a solicitor in some County Town. He was a well-read person, with a keen and original wit and a philosophical mind. He had talked extremely well. The dinner had been good. The wine had been plentiful. The sweet of the night was on the horizon. A timeless evening. An enjoyable evening.

A man named Chickering-Puttle came in to the restaurant with a spectacular lady. Both of us knew him slightly and he gave us a jovial wave. I felt a little proud of being waved to by Chickering-Puttle because he had once played football for his university, which was Oxford or Cambridge. I forget which. This toadying feeling of delight rather irritated me. I suddenly disliked Chickering-Puttle heartily. Indeed, he wasn't a very likeable character. He was rather a noisy, aggressive fellow, with an unpleasant slyness about him and a taste for unfunny smut. I said to Tomkins, 'When I make my fortune and institute my Museum of Bounders I shall give Percy Chickering-Puttle a beautiful large glass case right in the middle of the main hall.'

Tomkins looked at me strangely. 'My good fellow', he said, 'are you aware that Chickering-Puttle is a Blue?' With a shaken facetiousness I asked, 'A blue what?' Tomkins said, 'They are most frightfully particular whom they make Blues.'

I asked him who were those who were most frightfully particular, and he said that he preferred not to discuss it and called for the bill. He never spoke to me again.

This is a true incident and it worried me a great deal for a long time. If Tomkins had professed your faith and I had said 'To Hell with the Pope' he would have laughed at my ill manners and changed the subject; but this insult to his inner life bit deeper.

A friend of mine was walking over a moor. He was a boy at the time and was daydreaming. He suddenly hit his shoulder against the corner of a house that wasn't there. Without seeing the house he became aware of its general shape. He was so strongly aware of this that he built the house in hideous Scots baronial forty years later on that very moor. I have stayed in it.

It was some such impression I got of the Englishman's religion in the restaurant with Tomkins. I should be hard put to it to make even the roughest sketch plan. To tell you the truth, my vision rather frightened me. My curiosity urged me to sit down and draw the building or reconstruct the dinosaurus but something told me that I had better beware.

The secret religion has some kind of relation to what you and I understand as religion, but I am not sure whether it is incidental. Perhaps there is a clue in the different treatment accorded to Wesley and Newman severally by their fellow countrymen. Those Englishmen who did not accept the evangel of either Wesley or Newman reacted very differently to each of them. Newman retained their respect. They burned down Wesley's parsonage. Why?

Whatever the Englishman's conception of the Universe may be it is certainly that of an ordered Universe with a place for everything and everything in its place. The place of England in this Universe is naturally a very important one. It is essential that this position should not be disturbed.

An Englishman will tolerate disorder up to a point and provided that it is the right kind of disorder. Indeed, he is very fond of disorder within reason. He likes, as was once said, the sound of breaking glass. Empty bottles and torn newspapers amuse him and he finds peeling wallpaper, cracked plaster and even dry rot amusing and touching. But any interference with the essential structure is something up with which he will not put.

Tell me, please, do you agree that there is an essential structure? Of what is it composed and have you any idea of its general outline? I shall tell you whether it agrees with my own shadowy conception.

As ever,

J.B.

From Moray McLaren to James Bridie

Gaiety Theatre, Ayr, 9th November
My dear J.B.,

Round about 1860 (the plummiest period of mid-Victorianism) a respected and well-loved squire died in his small manor house in one of the more obscure Dorset vales. On the Sunday immediately after his death the village worshippers, including some visitors, approached the church for "Morning Prayer" at eleven o'clock. They were met by a notice posted on the church door which said 'Out of respect for the late Squire's memory there will be no Service this Sunday.'

The person who told me this story was an elderly, extremely Scottish relative of mine whose passion, in certain moods, for the exact search for truth was only equalled by his vivid imagination in other moods about what 'ought to be true'. As I write of him, the memory of his infuriating, attractive, lovable, capricious, pedantic characteristics comes back to me so forcibly that I can see and hear him in imagination much more vividly than I can many others who, though they have survived him by many years, lack the kaleidoscopic though clear personality which he had. He combined in himself more of the jarring, complicating, sometimes triumphant elements of our nation than has any other Scot I have known. It occurs to me that he might be useful to me later on as an excellent contrasting mirror (if such a thing exists) to hold up to the English. I have only to think of him, only to hear, over a lapse of many years, his voice upon my inward ear, to have before me—well, the perfect specimen of what the Englishman is not.

But it is not with him, but rather with his story of the dead Squire that I am immediately concerned. I don't know whether the story was true or not. It doesn't matter. It obviously ought to have been true. And, in any case, it illustrates a point which I would like to make about the Englishman's religion. You speak of its secrecy—and I take your point—I wish to underline its innocence.

When I first heard the story of the dead Squire I laughed. But, the more I have reflected on it, the more am I inclined to smile, and smile affectionately at it. There is really something rather touching about it.

I happen to know the church which my relative was talking about. It is a fine comfortable seventeenth-century building, erected upon the now completely obliterated ruins of an earlier and Catholic foundation. It is set at the end of a good long village street with fairly prosperous shops in it. The parish is large and entirely agricultural—green hummocks of cultivated hills and soft valleys with slow streams in them. If it were not in Dorset it might easily have been in Barsetshire—but it really does exist, and, I'm not making it up. My elderly relative had, by marriage, some connections in that part of the world. Until some fifteen years ago some of them were still there. That is how I know it. The Squire's line became extinct with his death. I heard little of him, even in my boyhood, save that he seems to have been worthy of the respect and love which he inspired. His Manor

House, after the usual process of selling and reselling, became too uneconomic a proposition for any single family to support. Nor was it sufficiently picturesque for it to be a rich man's toy luxury. Some school or hostel or something took it over well before the war. During the war it was of course occupied by troops. What has happened to it now, I do not know.

The seventeenth-century church was architecturally and historically contemporaneous with the Manor House. By historically contemporaneous I mean that both Manor House and church arose in the form that they did as a result of the same political and religious processes in the reign of James I of England and the early years of Charles. Their early foundations must have been shaken a trifle by the Commonwealth. And a whiff of political rather than religious incense may have drifted under the nostrils of the vicar and the squire in 1687 and 88. But apart from these two events the two buildings must have gone on serving the needs of the parish and of each other uninterruptedly until the latter part of Victoria's reign.

The church still stands (or did until just before the war) and is still used for public worship. But like the Manor House it had long become, if not uneconomic, too large for its purpose. Only a sprinkling of villagers were scattered about its echoing nave during Sundays in the 1930's. In 1860 I should imagine that its box pews must have been comfortably filled from many valley farms and cottages as well as from the village nearby. There must have been a brave show on Summer Sunday mornings when all the countryside gathered together to mumble their responses, sing their hymns and afterwards meet and talk together with each other and the Squire and the Vicar in the churchyard. The death of the childless old man who had so long presided at these gatherings must have been a real loss to the parish. I can well understand the Vicar and his church-wardens not having the heart to hold public service the Sunday after his death.

This, perhaps somewhat sentimentalised, picture of that 1860 Sunday morning is not intended to mean that I believe that all the previous gatherings over which the old man had presided had been entirely secular. I should imagine that at that time the majority of that large but remote congregation accepted such religion as was taught to them with the simplicity of country people all over the Western World. If they mourned the loss of their Squire I do not think any of them considered anything so appalling as his extinction or obliteration, certainly nothing so dreadful as Hell, or so uncomfortable as Purgatory. They were more likely to conceive of him as already ensconced in one of those 'many mansions' promised to his kind in 'My Father's House'.

Religion for most of them surely meant no more than the pursuit of a kind of life here on Earth which would, in the end, procure an indefinite prolongation of or an achievement of a great state of comfort not very different from the earthly social comfort of an English rural existence. It certainly did not (according to my assumption) mean to them ecstasy, terror, awe, a sense of overwhelming Majesty, Power, Beauty, nor that equally overwhelming panic of the soul that dares to ask itself the question 'Why?' They were not appalled by the prospect of annihilation, nor did they greatly fear the possibility of eternal torment, nor yet did they fear uneasily that they might not be quite able to support eternal bliss. They could not think of the Beatific Vision. Therefore they were not fearful of it. Perfection did not greatly trouble them; for it was no concern of theirs. And as for infinity—well, their instincts had already made them feel what Einstein was later scientifically to propound. They had 'rumbled' infinity without bothering much about it. That is what I mean when I say their religion was innocent.

I conceive that this innocent, childlike attitude towards religion came from the fact that up to the beginning of this century the English had been for a long time easily the most comfortable nation in Europe, certainly in the United Kingdom. *On the whole* the English people were not so continuously forced, as were their neighbours, to face the problem of Eternity. The Here and Now was in general quite comfortably sufficient.

I can see you already beginning to grow impatient with these generalisations (except the last about the comfort of the English which you surely cannot deny) and with my imaginary view of English rustic religion over forty years before I was born. Of course there are a thousand qualifications and exceptions. Of course Wesley had swept through rural England over a hundred years before the date I'm talking about, swept through it inflaming precisely the kind of people I have been thinking of with ecstatic visions and with Holy Awe and Dread. Of course in every community, no matter how remote and traditional, there were always individuals who were the forerunners of the hero of Masefield's *The Everlasting Mercy*. Of course long even before 1860 much of England had been ravaged by the slavery of the Industrial Revolution. Of course, even in the most beautiful and apparently prosperous agricultural corners there were disease, dirt, poverty and cruelty and so on. None the less I think that the imaginary picture I have drawn of a community that in my mind once inhabited a place I was to know years later on is based on a broad fact. I may have made it highly coloured, but I am fairly confident that it is typical of what was once the more simple Englishman's attitude towards religion. And I know what I mean when I describe it as innocent—though whether I have succeeded in conveying that meaning to you, I don't know.

I believe that that, innocent, sometimes attractive, sometimes infuriating attitude of the decent typical Englishman towards God and Eternity *has* lingered on. It has lingered on through decades of depression, near disaster and intense discomfort. It has lingered on despite the fact that the majority of Englishmen have ceased to believe in the Christian Religion and merely regard God as a vaguely beneficent First Cause—or more probably don't think about Him at all.

That innocence of mind towards these huge problems has left as a heritage that peculiar lack of bitterness which may be very comfortable to live in, but it never ceases to puzzle and often to annoy the foreigner whether he come from North of the Border or across the Channel, whether he be atheist, Catholic, agnostic or Wee Free. It is surely the heritage of that innocence that has produced the type of mind you described in

D

your last letter when you recalled the group of young officers who simply could not see that the Padre's was a skilled and professional job. Their grandfathers, for the most part, innocently and unquestioningly accepted the Vicar's teaching of the Christian religion—so what was there to worry about? They, the young men, equally innocently and unquestioningly accepted the newer doctrines which had imperceptibly grown up around them, the doctrine that if you were a decent fellow, behaved according to a generally accepted moral code and didn't 'do harm to anyone else' you were all right—so what was there to worry about? It is certainly a comfortable and kindly as well as innocent attitude of mind. Though whether it will face the test of Eternity or not neither you nor I know. Certainly, should we differ on the point, neither of us would be able to convince the other.

And that brings me up with a jolt. The first jolt is that, when I come to think of it, many of these generalisations I have been making about the religion of the decent fellow, the moral code, the doing no harm to anyone else, etc., could apply to many young and middle aged people outside England. I am thinking of hundreds in our own country, many in Scandinavia, Germany and even in France. And yet, and yet I cannot help feeling that there is a difference between the native English product of this sort of thing and the foreign version. The English invented it first. They took to it naturally, easily, and without that slightly despairing indifference, that near cynicism, which so often accompanies the faith of the decent fellow when it flourishes on un-English soil. In short (and this really

44

is the last time I'm going to use this word) they are more innocent about it.

The second jolt is, of course, the fact that I have allowed myself to run on to such an extent that I am in danger of provoking a theological controversy between us on points on which we may or may not agree, but which have little to do with the English. I apologise for this. But I think I have stopped myself just in time. We set out at the beginning of this correspondence on what, I suppose, was to be a partly deliberate, partly casual but certainly objective causerie on the subject of the English. I think you will agree that it would be impossible for two Scotsmen with the kind of background that we have had to undertake such a thing without the subject of religion cropping up somewhere. As far as I am concerned it has cropped up again and cropped down again. I shan't let it appear further in anything that I write to you. But I've honestly tried to be objective in the matter, my dear J.B., and not to flourish my own fundamental views on the 'faith of the decent fellow'—which have, I repeat, nothing to do with the subject. I have tried merely to view with an outsider's eye the Englishman's innocent religion (there, I've used it again) and not to pass judgment on it.

I escape from the position in which I have nearly found myself by the same device by which I entered it— the mention of my elderly relative who originally told me the story of the dead squire. He was an extra-ordinary character, yet very typical. I imagine that there must be others like him about in Scotland to-day.

He was a profoundly religious man to whom it never

occurred to doubt the essential tenets of the Christian religion, nor of certain political views which he held, and in which he was brought up. Nevertheless this did not prevent him indulging in, even delighting in the most fantastic somersaults of speculation on the minutiae of his religious and political convictions. This used to infuriate his English and German friends. He spoke German well. They could never make up their minds whether these fireworks or mental gymnastics were the fruit of Celtic lightheartedness or Scottish Lowland pedantry. At any rate they were inoffensive to their solidly held convictions. I do not think that they ever doubted his sincerity. It was his method of expressing it that maddened them. It delighted me: for I love to see a mind playing with a trivial point, just as I love to see a kitten playing with a ping pong ball. Delighted though I was I shared the Saxon and Teutonic doubt as to the source of this nimble pedantry. My relative was half pure Highland and half Edinburgh stock. Whence came this flippant seriousness?

It should not be supposed that the irritation and anger was all on one side in these discussions with his Southern theological and political friends. He was as maddened by their matter of factness, their straight unparenthetical argument as they were by his agility. They crashed straightforwardly up the trunk of the tree of any argument, heedless of what they left behind on the way, or what they damaged. He, monkey like, could not forbear to explore each branch, each twig of every tree until he got to the top triumphantly. It infuriated him to hear their laughter at his often useless meticulousness which they dismissed as pedantry. For over half his life he was sightless. It may be that his curiosity about things of the mind was exaggerated by his blindness. I think it merely brought out and underlined a national trait which for lack of a better word I will call Scottish mental bisexuality.

It is a commonplace to label the various nations of Europe according to sex. Despite the most reckless generalisations and exceptions, there is a good deal in this habit. Whatever you may say, I affirm that the English are the most male nation in Europe, the French the most feminine. We are a curious blend of the two; and you will often find that blend in the one person. My elderly relative was the best example I have ever come across. The unswerving logicality of his mind was masculine. The capricious and instinctive way he used his logic was feminine—and particularly irritating to his English friends who could not but recognise the calibre of his brain, but were put off by the movements of that brain. Their method (and it used to irritate him to the point of fury) of showing their own dislike of his mental agility was to burst into guffaws of laughter.

The memory of those long silent guffaws brings me to the point which (having I hope disposed of religion) I should like to lay before you as the next theme for your pen—the insensitivity of the English. They are kind, they are amiable, they are warm-hearted, generous and have produced the best poetry in Europe since the Renaissance. But surely no nation can more clumsily, heavy footedly trample over other people's sensibilities than the English.

Doctor Samuel Johnson was one of the greatest and most typical Englishmen of all time. His tour in

Scotland has been made the subject of much pedantic prickliness on the part of our compatriots—some of it justified, some not. One thing, however, I find it very difficult to forgive. When Boswell took him to see the ruins of Dundonald Castle of Robert Bruce, the patriot king, Johnson stood amidst the ruins and roared with laughter so loudly that, as Boswell put it, 'the ancient walls rang again'. When asked why he was laughing Johnson said that it was the size of the building that had amused him. 'Why, King Bob's palace is no more than a hovel.'

Could anyone but an Englishman have behaved so? Not even a German, I think. Yet Johnson was one of the most warm-hearted and (when he chose) the kindest of men. But he was an Englishman.

Yours,

Moray McLaren.

LETTER VII

From James Bridie to Moray McLaren

21st November, 1948

No, no, Moray. No, no, no, no, no. The English are not insensitive. And if there is one thing they hate, it is hurting other people's feelings. From time to time they may treat what they call 'natives' like dogs (or used to); but how well they treat dogs! I have seen an Englishman put off his sleep for a week because he had hurt his dog's feelings.

I think that you are being misled by folk tales and, it may be, by the Englishman's well-known sense of humour. An uncle of mine used to instance, 'He jumped. And we hadn't got no blanket. And he broke his bleeding neck' as the typical English joke. It cannot be denied that there is truth in this.

When I was an undergraduate I once had lunch with Mr. Hilaire Belloc (be seated; be covered, I pray you). His favourite English joke, he said, was the one about the stranger in the railway carriage who recited a long list of personal misfortunes and then asked 'What would you do in my case?' 'I believe I should cut my throat', said his interlocutor. 'That is exactly what I have done', said the stranger, lifting his head to display a grisly gash from which he bled to death in a few seconds.

But this is not insensitivity. Any psychologist will tell you—at great length and with a lot of drivelling, sham-Greek words—precisely what it means. It is St. George pulling the dragon's tail. It is playing with death and violence, diminishing those hateful things by making them small and ridiculous.

Without getting Bergsonish or Freudian, we can easily conjecture why Dr. Johnson made his joke about King Bob. He knew poverty and the agony of putting a brave face on it. He also knew all about Boswell's 'feelings'. Why should he have had any compunction in dealing with those powerful and aggressive instruments? Mr. Boswell, dancing like a weasel, was taking an unholy delight in anatomising the old man's feelings. He was taking enormous trouble to display them in outlandish surroundings for his own private satisfaction.

Anyhow, a great deal of what is called Scottish sentiment *is* funny. To anybody who knows the people who indulge in it, Wallacethebruceism, Charlieoverthewaterism, Puirrabbieburnsism, Bonniebonniebanksism, Myainfolkism and Laymedoonandeeism, those not very various forms of Scottish Sentiment, are very comical indeed. The Scot himself, greeting heartily beneath his bonnie briar bush, has been known to smile through his tears.

It is a solemn thought that foreigners, when they differ substantially from what Mr. Churchill calls the English way of life, do tend to buffoonery. The Englishman respects and admires, say, the Frenchman's energy, intelligence and skill in the social arts; but he thinks it funny when two hairy little men solemnly kiss each other. And it *is* funny. It is no sign of insensitivity when an old friend, an Englishman, tells an old friend, a Frenchman, that he finds it amusing.

The Scotsman's adoration for ruins that he does nothing to preserve and for traditions he only keeps to vulgarise sometimes makes an intelligent Englishman laugh. It is not for the Scot to complain.

The fact is that the Englishman's tact is notorious. I once said that tact was skill in the management of fools; but the Englishman's tact is more than that. It has enabled him to impose his will upon vast, alien civilisations. When he wrote off India, for example, he hardly paused to consider the three hundred year old miracle he had performed there. It is true that the Raj rested partly on fear; but four hundred millions of extremely sensitive people cannot be ruled by fear alone. Can they? They must be understood. They must not be offended in material matters. Men robbed of their freedom are covered with broken blisters and angry furunculi. By and large, those tender brown skins were handled with ineffable skill and tenderness. If we say that the English had no right to be in India in the first instance, we make it all the more wonderful that so many generations of Indians found their intolerable circumstances so tolerable.

Then there are the porters at Euston and the porters at Waverley—to say nothing of the porters in Paris. There are the English representatives on UNO and the representatives of any other nations you care to name. Even the ill-named English continental tourist, with his Crippsian face and his covey of governesses— so far as I can make out, his outstanding characteristic is shyness, and shyness is exaggerated sensitivity, surely. I am told that English ladies sometimes scandalise the natives of Europe by wearing slacks or even shorts. It is much, much stupider to be scandalised than to wear shorts.

No, no. The English are polite and considerate. Other peoples are more polite. Others are more considerate. But none combines the two things so well, so generously and so naturally.

I am making a pilgrimage to London by to-night's train. I hope to meet several Englishmen. None of them will, I think, really understand me or my nation and he will have no idea at all of our innermost thoughts, of what we reverence or to what we aspire. But I shall be disagreeably surprised if anybody treads on my toes deliberately or punches my vaccination mark. If he does he will certainly have Scots blood in his veins.

As ever,

J.B.

LETTER VIII

From Moray McLaren to James Bridie

Glasgow, 22nd *November*

My dear J.B.,

I am glad of the tone of your last letter for it gives me the chance to disagree with you flatly, and to say, at the same time, one or two things about the English which I have long wanted to get off my chest. Up to the present, I think we have flirted with each other's views too amiably—seeing the other fellow's point of view too much, and all that sort of thing, a failing in myself which I have always had to struggle against. Also we have been, I think, a little too polite about our great, amiable, noble, infuriating Southern neighbours.

Now to begin with Sam Johnson (a man whom I admire and love so much that I won't allow anyone but myself to say a word against him), I am amazed that you don't see the point about my King Bob story. Believe me, it isn't that Robert Bruce was one of our compatriots that offended me. Indeed R.B. was, in many ways, a dubious character whose story stirs my blood considerably less than does that of many more obscure Scots in our country's past. It was Sam's manner that made my gorge rise when I first read the story in the new unexpurgated Hebridean Journal. It would have risen equally violently had the story been connected with a Corsican, French, Icelandic or even American national hero.

I have little doubt that poor Boswell's 'provincial' enthusiasms must have irritated Johnson just as his

53

Corsican period must have jarred and bored the great man too. Indeed Boswell's febrile, pawky yet how human and Christian love for undertaking causes sometimes by no means ignoble must have made him tiresome to many other men, and of other nationalities than Johnson's. The mystery of Boswell (apart from the industry of his masterpiece) was that he was able to hold the friendship and indeed affection of so many differing men despite the fact that he was so continually making such an ass of himself in such a Scotch way.

What would some of the other celebrities (not English) whom Boswell cultivated and sought out have said in similar circumstances? I think that they would have behaved thus: Voltaire, had he been conducted to the ruins of Dundonald Castle by the eccentric young Scotsman, would have at once displayed his immense historical erudition. He would first of all have talked about Bruce's doubtful patriotism, his un-Scottishness as compared with Wallace. He might then have questioned the usefulness of the Scottish Kingdom which split the island of Great Britain into two. He would have talked (as he subsequently wrote) about the unhappy fate of Stuart kings of Scotland, thus arousing Boswell's romanticism and capacity for identifying himself with romantic persons of the past. Finally, he would have pulled Boswell's leg about his own feudal Scottish background without Boswell knowing anything about it. Rousseau would have romanticised the scene and occasion intolerably, but in beautiful French prose: he would have ended in a torrent of discussion of himself. Paoli, the greatest gentleman of them all, would have done his best to sympathise with his guide's local patriotism, but would in the end have found the enthusiasm he had aroused tedious and impracticable. At last he would have tactfully steered them both away from the scene and the topic.

The point is that, however satirical, sardonic, absurd or wisely bored any of these foreigners might have been, none of them could have brought himself to behave as did Sam Johnson, one of the greatest and most typical of all Englishmen. None would have roared with laughter at the ruins *because they were so small*. If you can't see that such behaviour is tactless and insensitive and typically English, nothing that I can say will make you do so.

I wonder whether you have me on the illustration you draw from the *British* Raj in India? This is a subject on which, from my childhood, I have been fairly well grounded. Four generations of my mother's family (all Scots) held high executive positions in 'The Raj', first of all in the East India Company and finally in the Indian Civil Service. At the time of my early childhood, India was littered with uncles and relations who had been brought up to *serve* India. I think that the secret of the success of the British Raj in India was largely due to the fact that there were many families such as mine (English, Scots or Irish) who had sucked in the tradition of service and tolerance towards the Indians with their mother's milk. My grandfather, who was the greatest of our lot, and the last of the line in the big way, used bitterly to complain of the young Englishmen who came into 'the Service' without the idea of service. That they acquired the idea eventually, and for the most part, was to their credit. But it was an acquisition that was a part of immense tradition outside themselves. Still, your point remains; and I can't make up my mind whether you have me on it or not.

However, put against it the immense insensitivity, tactlessness, how you will, that the English have displayed in other ways. It is not that they were brutal or particularly oppressive towards the Irish, the American Colonists, the Scottish Highlander or any other strange people who came under their sway. It is just that (as long as they were powerful enough to do so) they thought them funny or savage or charmingly outlandish, or all three—*and* shewed it. Perhaps that is better in the long run than brutal exploitation (Teutonic) or cynical disregard, sometimes combined with exploitation (Latin), but it is more annoying because it is more tactless and more insensitive.

All this is changing now, almost pathetically so. The Englishman is no longer, as he was in the days of our childhood, conscious of being God's chosen race. He finds himself having to contend equally or often on unequal terms with people whom he would before have dismissed lightly as Dagoes, Dutchmen or Yankees. He may find them disagreeable, and their way of behaviour unscrupulous, but they are too powerful and too dangerous to be dismissed as funny. There has therefore come over the English mind in particular, and the British mind in general, a much keener awareness of the fact that the inhabitants of this island have to share the world with foreigners on equal terms. Indeed the journals of to-day, both popular as well as intellectual, tumble over each other in printing articles which purport to understand the foreigner's point of view. I have said that this change of view is almost pathetic. I mean it. Though I have spoken harshly about the Englishmen's nineteenth-century insensitive insularity, I see it go with something of a sigh. It is like an ancient building falling into disrepair. And, as you yourself have pointed out, we Scots are liable to be sentimental about ruins.

There is another quality of the English that I see departing with regret. And this time the regret is not romantic or sentimental but wholly reasonable. One of the greatest qualities of the English (and I believe it to have been particularly English) was the universally recognised sense of the honour of the Englishman's word. When I say universally I mean everywhere on the Continent of Europe. European languages and slang abound in sayings to prove this. When a French-man says he will meet you at five o'clock *à l'heure Anglaise* he means that he will turn up at five exactly and not at five thirty and expects you to do the same. There are similar sayings in Italian and Polish. And time is a thing which the Italians and Poles are adept in wasting. 'The English hour' is to them something particularly sacred just because they find it particularly difficult to keep. When a dock hand at Barcelona gives or extracts a promise *Palabra Inglesa* he is doing his best to make that promise a sure and certain one. Who taught these quite humble people to invent these phrases of common speech? It was generations of English travellers, merchantmen, sailors and even politicians. I do not think that the German language contains a similar saying. But the slavish way in which the German upper classes used to imitate English punctiliousness shewed that they were well aware that there was something behind that punctiliousness worth striving after.

This sense of verbal honour was something that ran right through all levels of English society. When charwomen as well as dukes said that they would do such and such a thing they usually did do it. At least they could be more depended upon to do it than could their continental counterparts. It is, I suppose, a platitude, but none the less one worth repeating, that this verbal honour sprang from an abstract sense of justice. The duke's refusal to support a shabby measure in the House of Lords was usually disinterested; just as the charwoman's complaint that 'it ain't right that Mrs. Jones next door should have to wait for her old age pension' was disinterested. This abstract, sometimes mistaken, but wholly disinterested sense of justice is (or was) a quality much more strongly developed in the English than in their neighbours (including the Scots) where pragmatical or selfish motives were more likely to be behind men's public actions—great or humble.

How tragically we have seen this tradition decay in domestic matters. It might be argued that this is only a part of the general decline in standards following general disaster. Maybe; but I wish we could have kept this sign of decline at home and not have let it be seen abroad. *Perfide Albion* was said by an irritated and frustrated Napoleon—it is the only continental saying running counter to the sayings I have mentioned.

Now it is spat out by every little guttersnipe politician in Europe.

I know that this letter has been, even for me, unusually egotistical, but I can best illustrate what I mean by this changed foreign attitude towards England by what I experienced myself.

During the war I worked in an odd department about which I am not supposed to write or talk much. But I am, I imagine (since the publication of a book by my late chief, Sir Robert Bruce Lockhart), allowed to say that during the last two years of the war I was in constant touch, both officially and friendlily, with Mr. Mikolajczyk. He was, of course, the exiled Polish Prime Minister who took on the job after Sikorski's death. He had not long come into power when the British Government were compelled (to put it charitably) to take an opportunist view of the Soviet's demands in Eastern Europe. The war was far from over, and we had to keep the Soviets still in it. To do so, according to the Poles and some others, we promised away a great deal of territory and prestige which it was not ours to promise.

I hasten to say that I'm not proposing to raise once again that weary, sad old subject of whether Great Britain did or did not betray or connive at the betrayal of Poland and Eastern Europe in 1944. Nor do I consider myself well enough informed to guess whether that betrayal, if it were a betrayal, was necessry for our survival. All this sort of thing has been hammered out and yammered about on the wireless and in the press at the time of writing—ten years after Munich. But what I have to say is that it was intensely interesting

E   59

and humiliating to observe the reactions of those who, rightly or wrongly, conceived themselves to be betrayed in '44.

Mikolajczyk was, is, a Poznanian, that is to say, one of the Western, more stolid and unflashy Poles. To look at or to talk to he is rather like an English yeoman farmer or Aberdeenshire small laird. Much of his entourage was of the same kind. Those that were from Warsaw or the Eastern provinces were more Europeans than Poles. They were, with a few military exceptions, not the sabre-rattling, landowning Polish romantic kind. Yet all of them said the same thing about the position they found themselves in.

They said, 'How is it that England, you English' (for the purposes of the argument I was English) 'can do this to us? We might have expected it of the French, we would not have been surprised at the Italians, had they been allied to us. Had we been so foolish as to link ourselves with the Germans, we would have been certain of it—but the English! They have never betrayed anyone yet. Why should we be the first to be sold for twenty-nine pieces of silver?'

It was useless to argue with them. It would have been futile to have pointed to the precedent of Czecho-slovakia. Facts, even if one had felt inclined to use them, would have been of no avail against the reason-over-riding feeling of hurt and amazement at having been let down by England. One might have said to them, 'What is the point of saving your country if our country and the whole of Europe goes down?' They would merely have said, 'England entered the war on our side. England guaranteed us. England surely always keeps her word at whatever the cost.'

And it was with such words echoing in one's ears that one said goodbye to young Polish parachutists departing perilously for home on moonless nights.

It was this almost unreasonable, yet so understandable exhibition of pain at the cheapening of England's word that brought home to me for the first time how highly prized that word had been on the continent of Europe.   Of course one had heard about *l'heure Anglaise* and *palabra Inglesa* before, but, to be frank with you, I had half thought of these sayings as partly mockery of the English punctiliousness.   I had not realised how deep a feeling they had expressed.

Do you agree with me that the European reputation of the English word was the most valuable invisible asset that the English had acquired until the 1930's? Or do you think that I am too obsessed with the Continental view of this island?   Do you think that the magnanimity with which the English government (at the time of writing) is 'writing off' the British Empire recompenses for the loss of face on the cheapening of the English word?   Do you, in short, think that the kind of enforced amiable generosity which the English government is going in for now makes up for the disappearance of that arrogant insensitive rectitude which I have been trying both to pillory and to defend in this letter?   What do you think Samuel Johnson would have said about it?   Or do you think that that is a question like 'Have you stopped beating your wife?'

Yours,

Moray McLaren.

LETTER IX

From James Bridie to Moray McLaren

Drymen
15th December, 1948

You are quite right, dear Moray. I do not understand you. If you correctly recreate Messrs. Voltaire, Rousseau and Paoli, and if I had been Boswell, I should have found their treatment of me intolerable. I could answer you by saying that these celebrities did not, in fact, behave to Boswell as you say they would have behaved in King Bob's palace. But that would be beside the point, and we mustn't get beside the point, must we?

At the same time, I suggest that Old Sam behaved to that dangerous and brilliant little man of genius exactly as he had been taught to behave. It was all done by kindness, I admit, but it was none the less firmly done, however spontaneously the performing elephant appeared to wave his trunk and roll the barrel. Good God, how little you appreciate the capabilities of the inordinate Jamie. You talk of Voltaire pulling his leg.

I do not know whether Boswell was born in the breech presentation. Probably not, or he would certainly have put it on record. If he was, that was the first and last time his leg was ever pulled.

On second thoughts, perhaps Voltaire would have spoken in your way. And Rousseau. And Paoli. That is to say, they might have attempted egotistically to display their own characters for Boswell's benefit. It is the way of celebrated men to attempt this. I have

62

noticed it. I have noticed it less in the English than in the members of any other nation. Among my rather small collection of English celebrities, I cannot think of one who took the pains to 'put on an act' with me. The Scots, the Irish, the Welsh, the French, the Russians and the Jews worked very hard indeed. So did the Americans, who worked even harder than the rest.

I reminded you in my last letter that tact is skill in the management of fools. If the saying is true (and I think it is), then it would be the height of insensitivity to direct tact at such a one as James Boswell. You are quite wrong to bracket tact and sensitivity together. Indeed I should be surprised to find them co-existing in the same person.

Do *you* appreciate tact? When Lord Rosebery's tenant-farmer took a big spoonful of his *surprise* and blurted out, 'Pudding's froze!' the ex-premier took a spoonful himself and remarked, 'By Jove, so it is.' Lord Rosebery was a Scotsman. Sam Johnson would have explained. Which of these would have put the farmer at his ease and guarded him against the abominable sniggerings of his fellow guests? Which would have thought of the mortification suffered by the farmer in the long watches of the night when he ultimately learned the truth? Which would have been tactful and which sensitive? Eh? Pull yourself together.

I did a tour of Southern Ireland during the early part of the recent war. An Irish ploughman-poet told me that the saddest thing about the War for the landward Irishman was the breaking off of the visits of the English horse-coupers. These men, he said, were magnificent company, intelligent, friendly, funny, fine holders of their drink and as honest as the day. They were sadly, even desperately, missed. The time of all the year was the time when their innocent, generous laughter was heard in the pubs and over the bog. I don't suppose they were particularly tactful. At least Paddy didn't mention it.

You know about this. You have met it in your travels. Now you fear that it has all gone.

I'm told that the musk flower suddenly lost its scent simultaneously all over the world. Strange, if true. If the Englishman has lost his characteristics it must be even stranger. I do not believe it. I am not, as you appear to be, a disciple of M. Lysenko.

You may be right in saying that *Palabra Inglesa* is not so highly regarded abroad as it used to be. But is there not a simple explanation for this?

Are you not confusing the Englishman with his rulers? What contribution has been made by any English Government whatever to the proud reputation that an Englishman honours his bond? English Governments compare favourably with many other Governments in reliability; but, in the past, they have only been indifferently honest. Few Englishmen would set their standards of personal honour by the behaviour of English Governments in history. Like good trustees, the Governments have put the conveniences and necessities of their trusteeship first. It may be disingenuous of the Englishman to be content with this. After all, he is responsible technically and actually for the acts of his Government; but how far is he morally responsible?

You know quite well how English Governments are

chosen. At election time you are asked to choose between two entire strangers who advocate two opposing views with neither of which you may be in agreement. These persons are selected by two small groups of busybodies. If you are neither a Socialist nor a Tory, you have no say in the matter at all. If you make the best of a poor job and vote, you have a stake of three places of decimals in the person who is elected.

The elected is one of six hundred persons chosen for their eloquence or their surplus leisure. If those of his way of thinking are in a majority, he helps to choose a Prime Minister. This gentleman rules the land with the assistance of a committee of his own choosing and is the keeper of the King's and the Englishman's conscience. The chain of responsibility is really very long and thin.

For ten years the foreigner has known the Englishman only in print or in khaki. Most of the print has expressed the views of the Government, whose knowledge of the English is derived from political meetings and conferences with 'contact men'.

If, for ten years, our only contact with the English had been through print or khaki, this little study of ours would not be the valuable document we take it to be. The truth surely is that the Englishman is only content under incompetent Government. The less he is governed, the better he likes it and the better he behaves. Indeed, the word 'government' is a rather new and unpopular word. We thrived better under ministries and even administrations. A servant when he ruleth is no more pleasing to him than it was to King Solomon. It is little wonder, then, that his servants are often to be found mis-representing him and causing him to go about with an habitual red face. Quite often he is driven to express an opinion that even the proudest Malvolios of them all cannot ignore. You recall Chinese indentured labour, no doubt, and the Hoare-Laval pact. In each case he forced his trustees to behave themselves, although it was contrary to his material interests.

When he was fighting for his life he was not, perhaps, so scrupulous. At least, the fact that his rulers had been guilty of sub-standard morality took longer to penetrate to his conscience. This is by no means to say that his conscience no longer existed. The Englishman is not characteristically a liar, a traitor or a thief and I do not see him becoming one in my lifetime.

You say that a decay in personal honour is tragically evident in domestic matters. I am not sure that I know what you mean. The English have their share of scoundrels. They also have much more than their share of rules and regulations. The breaking of rules and regulations springs as often as not from sheer impatience, and when one is impatient one is not always too particular to which rules one breaks. But it takes a lot of twisting and fiddling to turn an honest man into a rascal. As a good Calvinist, I draw a very sharp line between human goodness and human badness and I find no general badness in the English. It is wonderful how much of the law they contrive to keep.

Mrs. Patrick Campbell once said that Moses made only ten commandments because he felt that he was getting silly and had better stop. Don't let us begin discussing the loosing of moral ties, the decline of home influence, juvenile delinquency and the crime wave. The measure of the Englishman's moral sense is his genuine horror at these unsurprising phenomena.

When the Englishman is again let loose on foreign parts and when he has (probably rather brutally) cured the locals of their present hysterical habit of shooting at him, it will soon be discovered that he is still by far the most trustworthy being in the world. If he hurts your feelings, I am sorry; but you can't get back at him that way. He is over-rated, I think, as a sportsman, but not as a fair dealing man of his word. Unless, of course, he is corrupted by politics. But who isn't? To judge an Englishman by his politicians is like judging him by his drunkards.

You suggest that Europe is disappointed in the Englishman. But does Europe hate him? I think not. Where I should think he is most hated is in what he now calls the Commonwealth of Nations. This is not because he is rude to them or contemptuous of them or insensitive to their finer feelings. Not at all. It is because he appears to be patronising.

'He was looking down his nose at us', said an Irishman to me of an Englishman who had spent the evening humbly entranced by the wit, fervour and sincerity of his company. His nose was a snub and he would have had to look up it, but let that pass—except as an instance of the Irishman's faulty observation.

The Englishman quite genuinely pities his relatives who are, through no fault of their own, exiled from the ambit (so to speak) of Bow Bells. He is anxious that they should realise that he thinks none the worse of them for that. He tries hard to put them at their ease.

He inhabits the Mother Country and feels a little paternal. I need not tell you how infuriating this is. Even we have suffered it, for he has some sort of hazy notion that England is the Mother Country of Scotland and, every now and then, clucks pathetically over us like a duck's hen foster-mother. But this is not insensitivity. It is touching to behold how carefully he avoids calling us Scotch, though the description was good enough for Scott and Burns. When he employs this daddified approach to the citizens of the United States, however, there is danger in it. The rage of Canadians, Australasians and South Africans has been curbed in the past by the consciousness that perhaps he is, after all, a sort of a rich uncle. It may not be so curbed when the wealthy relative is bankrupt, but still devastatingly kind and gentle.

I doubt whether the attempt to raise the 'subject nations' to the rank of unfortunate relations will be very successful. If you ask me what Dr. Johnson would have thought, I cannot answer. Probably:

'Sir, if a man is such a fool as to divide his inheritance before he is dead, he need not look for many amenities in his declining years.'

Probably not. At any rate he would not look on the liquidation of the British Empire as an act of sacrifice to compensate for 'arrogant, insensitive rectitude' in the past. Acts of sacrifice are as foreign to the English nature as that arrogant, insensitive rectitude which you have falsely imagined and falsely attacked. I am sorry to tell you that generosity is a much likelier guess; for the Englishman, except in some petty money matters, is very capable of generosity. Dislike of

68

responsibility is another guess, but a poor one, I think.

By the way, if you want arrogance, insensitivity and a conviction that he is always in the right, do have a look at your clear-thinking and logical Frenchman . . . who is also, by the way, a whale for making sacrifices.

God bless you and show you the light.

J.B.

LETTER X

From Moray McLaren to James Bridie

Glasgow, 19th December

My dear J.B.,

It is tempting to take up some of the minor points which you so ingeniously provoke me. I should like to defend myself against any suspicion of under-rating the tremendous and lovable James Boswell, a man up for whom I stand with louder voice and quicker pen than I do for almost anyone else. I should like to quarrel with your limitation of tact as the 'skill in the management of fools'. It is often the skilful easing, by whatever means you will, of an agonising situation which may have arisen from a hundred causes other than folly. I should like to defend Lord Rosebery over the incident of the tenant farmers' dinner—and incidentally the Colonel of the Mess who drank out of his finger bowl to put the Sergeant promoted from the ranks at his ease. I should like to elaborate on the theme that the saving of the situation at the moment was far more important than the *possibility* of uneasy private hours on the part of the man whose face one had saved afterwards—and so on. But I resist these and many other temptations.

Unfortunately, where I am writing now, I cannot refer to our previous letters. I have the impression, however, that it is I who have done most of the narking against the English and that it is you who have urbanely defended them, and pulled my leg and theirs at the same time. It is therefore with gusto that I leap upon a point

70

in your letter with which I can agree, and which allows me to speak nicely of them at the same time.

You speak of the English generosity. It is a facet of that generosity which most appeals to me, which comes so constantly to my mind when I am away from them, and wish to think well of them—their amiability. They are, with the possible exception of the African Negroes, the most amiable people under the sun. As with the Negroes, they grow less amiable the more intellectual they are. A Negro who becomes a doctor of philosophy or a 'celebrated thinker' does not lose his black skin; but he does lose an enormous amount of his unaffected likeableness. The editors of most highbrow English journals do not shed the irritating English qualities about which I have allowed myself to speak, but they do lose their amiability. Which all goes to prove something—I do not, or perhaps dare not, say what it is.

I'm not bothering with dictionary definitions but the quality I mean by English amiability is one which I am sure you know and recognise. Oddly enough, it is a quality which can exist in one person along with insensitivity and tactlessness. So I don't have to withdraw on those two counts. The most appealing thing about it is something that you touched on in your last letter. They don't put on an act about it. If they did they would instantly cease to be amiable.

Mark you, I am prepared to defend some of the people you accuse of putting on acts. I defend some of them on the grounds of the excellence of their acts, others on the grounds that I think you sometimes think that acts are being put on when people are being perfectly natural. I suppose that you and I will always find something to disagree about in the Southern Irish. And I think that you often mistake for 'an act' genuine and natural extravagance of feeling and expression. Still, I will agree with you that the Irish, especially the exported kind, often do put on acts about some of their best qualities. We, in Scotland, are terribly prone to putting on extremely poor acts. It makes me blush to think of the quality and the variety of these acts—so much so that I cannot bring myself to mention any of them; but you know them, my dear J.B., you know them. Have I not watched your face at public dinners and meetings in Glasgow and Edinburgh while you have been listening to speeches? Have I not caught that peculiar analytical gleam of dissecting humour behind your benignant glasses? I once saw it directed at myself across a luncheon table when there was no one else present. I quickly pulled myself up.

The French, the Russians and the Jews I defend mostly on the style of their acting. I will give only one example, and from the French. When a French waiter in France attends upon a young couple obviously in love at the corner table of a restaurant, he makes such a song and dance about it that it is a joy to behold him. He does it so well. You would think he was half in love with love itself. He isn't, of course. Part of him hopes for a good tip from the young man. But the major part of him genuinely likes playing the rôle of the attendant upon Venus. And he likes it so well that he does it well—so well that the always indistinct line between 'an act' and sincerity becomes even more hazy than ever.

However, for the English to put on an act about their

amiability is as unthinkable as their putting on an act about their physical courage. One touch of self-consciousness and not only the bloom but the whole thing is gone. That, and intellectual pride are the only failings that can destroy it. And how seldom the English fall victim to these failings. This is particularly true of the North of England, in the industrial districts of Lancashire and Yorkshire. English amiability is here to be seen shewn up most vividly because it exists alongside not only insensitivity and tactlessness but downright crass rudeness. Compared with Manchester or Bradford, the manners of even a Glasgow crowd on a Tuesday afternoon (when the outer shops close) become cloyingly polite. I wonder if anywhere else on the world's surface there is compressed so much honest-to-God unaffected rudeness as in the small portion of it known as the North of England. Yet the amiability of the inhabitants, untouched by self-consciousness or intellectual arrogance, triumphs. Even J. B. Priestley used to be amiable when he was just writing unpretentious little Stevensonian essays for the old *Saturday Review*, and nothing else.

The cockney, of course, has more charm than the Northerner. The South Country peasant, in so far as he still exists, is much more polite in a pleasingly heavy-footed way. But these qualities are insignificant beside his amiability—the great English characteristic. The West Highlandman is infinitely more courteous than the Englishman but he is less amiable. The Irishman has more charm, but he is less amiable. The French-man, *when he wishes to use it*, has a more delicate sensitivity of manner and style in personal matters, but

73

he is less amiable. The German has a lush friendliness which is, in the urgency with which he expresses it, as pathological as is his cruelty and his love of receiving pain. And he is certainly less amiable than the English. The Americans—but even I can't generalise about the Americans without assistance, so I must use other people's generalisations—the Americans, we are told on all sides, are the most hospitable warm-hearted people on earth. Maybe: but, by God, don't they put on an act about it. For all their *bonhomie*, false or true, they *are* less amiable than the English.

Despite everything I may say about the arrogance, tactlessness and insensitivity of the English (and with which you disagree) you can't help liking them. By 'you' I don't mean the French or the Americans who tend to dislike the English for the wrong reasons. I mean literally you, James Bridie, and myself and Sean O'Faolain and Eric Linklater and a little Scotch commercial traveller I met at Stirling the other day. People near enough to be interested, detached enough to be objective.

You travel much more into England nowadays than I do. When I make my rare visits they are directed as much to the North of England as to London and the South. Yet I never leave even for Manchester (a city of which I have the gloomiest recollections) without tasting in advance upon the tongue of my imagination the peculiar tang of English amiability.

It is impossible to define. It is next door to impossible to describe it except by the vaguest allusions. Each one of us has our own private memories of the places and the people that have transmitted to us this Saxon likeableness. When I think of it in connection with Lancashire there comes first to my mind the so-called 'snug' in a squalid little pub in a peculiarly repulsive little back street in Manchester. I may have had to approach this dim little room jumping over filthy puddles in cobbled streets, buffeted by fat men and even fatter women who never think of making way for anyone passing, whose hoarse catarrhal voices are louder and more hideous than anything you will hear in the Gorbals or in Caithness, the homes of the two worst voices in Scotland. Yet I know that when I get to the 'snug' I shall hear talk and enjoy badinage of a warm, humorous, likeable kind such as I would never get in Scotland or Ireland. Or perhaps, in my thoughts, I shall have the luck to go to Blackpool, mysteriously transported there during 'wakes week'. Here there is no point in struggling to be an individual. One is borne along on a tide of human happiness—not gaiety, nor abandonment, nor graceful pleasure, but just happiness and fun of a kind that I have never seen equalled outside England. One is borne along unresisting into the fun fair, along the pier, on to the squalid beach, into the largest circular pub in the United Kingdom with signposts with hands on them directing you to the sherry bar, the bottled ale bar, the champagne bar, the wine bar and so on. And all the while the screech of fat women laughing, the shouts of fat bowler hatted, or cloth capped men hailing each other over the heads of the crowd, the mass giggling of girls, the hooting and whistling of youths drown the noise of machinery, the music of the record penny in the slot machines, and make a symphony of amiable pleasure all on its own.

F

But if it is to London and to the south I am going, my imagination (always easily excited by the slightest travel) goes ahead of me. I relish in advance my first conversation with a cockney, a waitress in a tea shop, a barmaid, a taxi driver—yes, there are a few real cockney taxi drivers left. I think of the kindly pomposity of the senior porter at my club, or the Sam Wellerish perkiness of his junior. I look forward to the slightly over-hearty mental back slapping in the smoking room or billiard room, the slightly inane conversation. I promise myself a visit to a certain back street newspaper shop where I go for my evening papers, from which I never emerge after less than a quarter of an hour's talk about nothing. It's so pleasant. And there's no act about it.

But it doesn't do for one of our race even to approach sentimentality about London. One is apt to get caught out. Our beloved James Bone of the *Manchester Guardian* has extracted the last drop of romance from the place. In his *London Perambulator* and *London Echoing* he has said all that a Scot should ever say in praise of London. Yet even he had a narrow escape from bathos which I witnessed, indeed, of which I was a part.

He rang me up one evening to say that he was leaving his office in Fleet Street at the unusually early hour of 11 p.m. Would I come and have supper with him at 'Rules'? I would, and did. 'Rules' with its Edwardian setting is a perfect background for our James. I thought it charming of him to ask me, one of his very much younger colleagues, to supper there. But I was a bit taken aback to find when we arrived that two dozen oysters and a bottle of champagne had been

76

ordered in advance, and were ready for us. James is the most generous of men, but he is not reckless. He does not usually act on sudden whims to the tune of oysters and Bollinger. Then, just after the first half dozen, the truth came out.

'You know that they're starting to pull down the Adelphi to-morrow morning?' said James in a voice that I knew to be gloomy even though his cheerful Glasgow stutter somewhat deprived it of the intended effect.

'No, I didn't realise it was as soon as that.'

'They can't wait to get their hands on it. I want someone to come down with me to have a last look at it to-night before it goes. Will you come?'

'Of course I will, James.'

As we walked the short distance from Maiden Lane to the Adelphi, I caught a tinge of infection from my companion's romantic sadness. How much of his London which he had adopted and made his very own since his early twenties had he not seen disappear in just such a fashion? And now the very heart of it all was going to go to-morrow morning. This was its last night. I felt flattered that the London Perambulator should have chosen me as a companion when he went to say good-bye to it.

When we reached Adelphi Terrace it was quite deserted save for ourselves. The Savage Club had moved long since to the late Lord Curzon's house in Carlton House Terrace, where, according to report, the new members were already scribbling rhymes and drawings on the great blank spaces on the walls left by the huge portraits and the tapestries now removed. Other residents in flats or business premises in Adelphi

77

Terrace had gone away in preparation for the destruction in the morning. We looked upon the desolate scene and sighed. The outline of the terrace stood out against the dull red glow projected on the sky by Piccadilly Circus from the north. The eighteenth-century façade was clearly illuminated by the Neon lights on the whisky advertisements from across the river on the south. Having looked our fill in silence, we moved across to the railings opposite. Immediately below us was a space of waste-land between the Adelphi Arches and the river. Here we saw the first sign of human life since we had left the Strand. Amidst the rubble of this waste land there stood, forlornly, a hut. Out of this hut there scurried a rat-like figure, which then retreated again.

'That's an old man who lives down there in that hut', said James. 'I've seen him before. I wonder if he knows that the Adelphi is going down to-morrow.' The nostrils of the old reporter-journalist quivered in anticipation of a 'find'. 'Let's go down and talk to him.'

We did go down by some circuitous way through the Adelphi Arches, and found ourselves on the waste land. Rat-like, the figure of a repulsive old man emerged from the hut and ran forward to meet us.

The following dialogue took place:

James Bone: Good evening.

Repulsive
  Old Man: Evening.

J.B.: D'you live here?

R.O.M.: Yus, for years.

(I knew this for a lie, and I'm sure J.B. did too. The land had only been waste for about eighteen months.)

J.B.: D'you like it here?

R.O.M.: Not so bad. Plenty to laugh at.

J.B.: You know that they are going to pull down the terrace over there to-morrow?

R.O.M.: Yus, and a — good job too.

J.B. (rather startled): Why?

R.O.M.: 'Cos Bernard Shaw lives there.

(At this point I could not help laughing; but J.B. continued:)

J.B.: Why don't you like Bernard Shaw?

R.O.M.: 'Cos he's a — old ——.

(Here J.B. laughed too.)

J.B.: Well, that seems a good enough reason. And what about Sir James Barrie and . . .

R.O.M.: He's a — old —. They're all — old — up there. The sooner that bloody place is pulled down the better pleased I'll be.

Here the R.O.M. let out a volley of oaths and obscenities directed against the inhabitants, the architecture and the mere existence of Adelphi Terrace. We retreated. I was rather more crestfallen than James. I had not had his experience in journalism. I did not yet understand that if you don't find what you expect to find in 'news', the exact opposite may always be a good second best. James murmured something about the old man being like Quilp as we walked away, thus retrieving the situation. Worse was yet to come. We had not gone far before we heard his shuffling feet behind us, and his voice whined through the darkness.

R.O.M.: 'Arf a minute, sir, 'arf a minute. I know what you want to see. I know why you come dahn 'ere. Just you come behind these palings 'ere. I'll let you in for a bob. You can stay as long as you like. You can see 'em through a crack in the wood. You can see 'em lovely and stay as long as you like.

J.B. :   What d'you mean?

R.O.M. : They'll be coming any minute now. You can see 'em fine from 'ere. . . .

(Here he launched in a few brief vivid sentences into a description of what happened on the waste land when the vagrants and the blackmailers and tarts and nancy boys from the embankment and the Strand came down after midnight. We were spared no detail of their pleasures and their habits.)

J.B. :   No, thank you.

R.O.M. : Come on, sir. Only a bob. Stay as long as you like.

J.B. :   No, thank you. Here's a shilling. Good night.

R.O.M. (in a puzzled voice) : Don't you want to stay, sir?

J.B. :   NO.

R.O.M. : You're missing a treat, sir. Really you are. Last night I laughed myself sick, I did. Why, I saw. . . .

J.B. :   GOOD NIGHT.

R.O.M. : Good night.

He shuffled back to his rat hole in the hut or behind the palings. We walked on in silence until we reached the Strand. Here, having emerged into the world of light and life again, we stood for a moment saying nothing amidst the drifting midnight crowds. My path lay westwards, his eastwards. Then James said:

'Well, I suppose that's good-bye to Adelphi Terrace.'

80

'I suppose it is', I agreed.

With that we parted, I with my admiration for James Bone increased, he with his romantic devotion to London undiminished. It was undiminished, as I reflected afterwards, because he had never sentimentalised it.

And so, my dear J.B. (same initials by the way), I end this letter to you with this pleasing anecdote from a distantly echoing London. I tell it to you to shew you that, despite my somewhat vaguely expressed but keen admiration for the amiability of the Londoners and the English, I do not think I sentimentalise it. Indeed, should you give me the chance, I could say something about the drawbacks of this delightful quality in them— the reverse side of the medal.

Yours,

Moray McLaren.

LETTER XI

From James Bridie to Moray McLaren

Drymen
7th January, 1949

Dear Moray,

I have got a cold in the head. I have just torn up the worst letter of the series. Toxic. That was what it was. Your admirable story about the Repulsive Old Man set me thinking of the English poor who lie in the Green Park wrapped in newspapers and hoar frost while the wealthy drive past in their carriages on their way to and from expensive entertainments. So I forgot all about Lord Shaftesbury and Elizabeth Fry and wrote a lot of sentimental drivel. I think I have got the virus under control now, so I shall try again.

Yes, sir, the Englishman is amiable. He is the mildest mannered man that ever scuttled ship or cut a throat. I wonder what you mean by saying that even J. B. Priestley used to be amiable. I know him fairly well and I have seen him fairly recently and I should still advance him as an excellent specimen of English amiability. You yourself are an amiable man but you are not amiable to the marrow of your bones as J. B. Priestley is. Like all truly amiable people he is capable of rudeness and even, I should think, delights in practising the art. But he is a rabbit at it. He cannot get away from the shape of his facial bones which were moulded by generations of good-natured people. Haven't you noticed that the only thing he cannot compass in his stage plays is invective? Come to that, have you ever met an Englishman whose nerves were not shattered by poverty, hard labour and hard drink, who could pejorate for five minutes against a Welshman or a Spaniard?

In print they are occasionally not so bad, but any Irishman would immediately recognise even Swinburne as little better than a talented amateur. I rather think the taste for harsh words came to England with a Scots King James and went out with a Scots King Charles.

Even among the under-privileged insult is often couched in terms of wit. You remember the bargee's remark to the lighterman who broke an oar against his hull—'Still the same old Charlie; and talking of oars, how's your sister?' Nobody can inflict serious pain unless he puts his whole mind to it. He cannot get home if he is contriving a joke at the same time. He is no more successful when he is acting bluff hearty arrogance. The English, as the Mystery Man of *The Times Literary Supplement* says, are ruthless enough; but they are seldom arrogant and only intermittently and ineffectively insulting.

The Mystery Man lays great stress on the Englishman's ruthlessness and proves its existence up to the hilt. The fact that it is combined with amiability need not surprise us. Friends of mine who are interested in menageries assure me that the most dangerous of all animals is the brown bear. He never loses his expression of chubby amiability, even when he is about to crush his keeper's ribs into a mess of spiky bones.

The M. M. has also a good deal to say about the Englishman's love of order and pattern. I sometimes

83

wish that you and I had been infected, if only mildly, with that passion. We began this correspondence, if you can cast your memory so far back, with the idea of contributing something tangible to the study of the English. You were to do the field work and I was to do the correlating and arrangement. I was well fitted to do this, I suggested, because I had had a scientific training in my young days. Something must have gone wrong with my scientific training. Indeed, you seem to be contributing the only orderly part of the correspondence and to be perpetually pulling me into some sort of sequential thought. The correspondence itself is developing into fine confused reading, like the old lady's dictionary, but a wee thing disconneckit. We trot along like French infantry, out of step and singing songs that are far from being correct march time, collecting bird cages and old boots and linen from the cottage doors and hedges as we go along. This is no way to carry out an investigation.

It is never, however, too late to mend. As we are a good deal more than half way through this correspondence, this seems a good opportunity to begin at the beginning. The beginning of an Englishman is when his father falls in love. Perhaps you will sit down soberly and conscientiously and give me your considered views on the Englishman in love.

> *I am,*
> *Yours very sincerely,*
> *J.B.*

LETTER XII

From Moray McLaren to James Bridie

Glasgow, The Western Infirmary
14th January, 1949

My dear J.B.,

The Englishman in love, the Englishman and English-woman in the mood for if not in the act of procreation of the English race—yes, by all means. A fascinating if rather frightening topic. But before I follow you there, there are just one or two things to be tidied up.

Thank you for sending me *The Times Lit. Sup.* pamphlet by the anonymous but perfectly well-known mystery Scot. I don't know why I had, half unconsciously, avoided reading it before. It wasn't, I assure you, because of any of that mean spirit of reluctance to look at anything widely praised, which all of us suffer from at some time or another. No, I knew that I would have to read it sooner or later. I had observed that it had thrown the English literate world into a state of chattering, half-flattered, half-shocked delight. I had noticed that it had provoked of all people, St. John Ervine (that one time Donald Duck of journalism) into a sentimental defence of his view of the English. And finally, I had seen him whom you call the mystery man knock Donald Duck's sentimentality for six right out of the ground. I suppose the only thing that held me back from rushing out and getting a copy was the slight reluctance to read the words of so eminent a Scot on the English while you and I were just engaged on the same task. I suppose I was frightened that he, in a few brief paragraphs, might have settled the whole matter and left us nothing to maunder on about. Having read the brilliant and admirable pamphlet, my fears are dispelled. There is still plenty left for us to maunder on about. His luminous paragraphs are but heartening encouraging shafts of light to illuminate us on our circuitous path—our virtuous spiral.

About Priestley, I know that 'knocking' him is nowadays a general sport of left, right and even centre. No, I wasn't joining in that general game when I mentioned him. It was only that he seemed to me a fairly good example of the Englishman whose intellectual growth has encouraged a kind of self-conscious rudeness quite different from the amiable unthoughtout rudeness of his early days. I still maintain that intellectualism, as distinct from intelligence, destroys, with the English, as with the African Negroes, their native amiability.

The other point I wanted to tidy up was something I mentioned at the end of my last letter. I said that if you gave me the chance I would say something about the reverse side of the medal of the Englishman's amiability. I knew what I meant when I said that, but I doubt if I could have put it into words. Your mystery man, and you, with your analogy of the brown bear, have supplied the words and the concept. It's just plain honest to God, unadorned ruthlessness. It is because it is plain and unadorned that it can combine with amiability. There are no frills on it.

It is not the oriental ruthlessness of the Russian who thinks out, as if it were in a game of chess, the advantages and disadvantages of starving two to three million Ukrainian peasants to death because they won't fit into a scheme. It is not the luscious, disgusting, emotional ruthlessness of the German with his sadistic concentration camps and sexual tortures. No, it is just the jolly, amiable, deathly hug of the brown bear.

Whenever I hear of English ruthlessness in some remote place, I always imagine it being expressed (if it be expressed in words at all) in a homely North of England accent. 'You boogers 'ave asked for it, and by goom, you're going to get it.' Then, with smiling countenance, the Englishman proceeds to lam into his opponent and destroy him, rules or no rules.

One of the Englishman's favourite remarks about himself is that he is a bad hater. I see what he means. He doesn't go in for any of the facial grimaces, the turning deathly pale, the baring of the teeth as practised by the Latin or the Celt. Nor does he bear long memories of a quarrel. He usually doesn't need to, because, up till now, he has come out on top. On the one celebrated occasion on which he did not come out on top—the American war of Independence—his habit of forgetfulness prevailed. It remains even to this day, one of the most infuriating things about the English in the American eyes. The average G.I. during the war was rather more than taken aback when he discovered that all Englishmen who had heard about the war of Independence thought it rather a good thing, and that some of them hadn't even heard about it at all. All this supports the view of the Englishman as a bad hater. But, I can't help thinking that if he were a good hater much of his ruthlessness, his rage, would be dissipated and lost. No, he is more dangerous as he is—amiable and ruthless.

I don't know what your experience of the English was when you were a scientist only, and had not taken up what you describe as the writing of 'libretti'. But since the libretti phase of your life you must have come into contact with many Englishmen of the kind that I have been meeting in my oddly variegated profession during the last twenty years. That is to say, editors, publishers, journalists, producers, poets, musicians, artistic financiers, impressarios and in general the more celebrated of the English midwives of the arts. Two things have struck me about these gentry—by the way our present publisher is half Scottish, half South American, so I can say what I like. Those two things are their overwhelming geniality and amiability upon first meeting them and their ruthless snapping of the jaws if one presumes upon this amiability to go one inch too far. I have had some dealings with the same kind of people in France, in Ireland, and of course at home here in Scotland. But nowhere outside of England have I found quite that combination of slap-you-on-the-back at one moment with kick-you-downstairs at the next. But I confess I am thinking of some years ago when my right foot had to be rather more firmly wedged in the editorial or publishing door than is necessary now. This is only my personal experience, but I take it as one more example of the amiability cum ruthlessness of the English.

However, enough of tidying up divagations—back to sex and the original problem you put to me. The Englishman in love.

I take it that you won't object to the general statement that the average Englishman dislikes women.
He dislikes them even more than the lowland Scot
dislikes them: and that's saying a good deal. The
average Scot, unless he has passed through an Anglican
education, is much more habituated to female society
from early youth than is the Englishman. The average
Scot may sometimes be ponderous in his gallantries,
but he does *try* to be gallant. He does not usually
positively shun female company in the way the Englishman does. He (the Scot) may be heavy footed, or
charming, ponderous or fanciful, lustful or romantic.
Or he may be (and often is, alas!) just downright bad-
mannered in the presence of women. But he does give
the impression that as a sex women interest him, play
a part in his life. Not so the Englishman.

The English dislike of women is not due to low
sexual powers nor to a lack of romantic imagination—
far from it. He can love as violently and devotedly as
any other man under the sun. But he just doesn't like
the company of women when he's not loving them. It
is the English who have invented all the ingenious
devices for escaping from women's company. He
invented that luxurious monastery, the man's club. All
successful clubs outside England are imitations of the
English model. But very few are successful. The men
just don't want to escape so much. It is the English
who first thought of shooing away the women from the
dinner table at the end of the meal for over an hour or
even through all the rest of the evening. For over two
centuries the ceremony of the circulation of the post-
prandial port in purely masculine company has been

regarded by many Englishmen as the most delightful part of the dinner. There are men still living who can remember a time when the men did not re-join the ladies until bed or carriage time.

It is never pushed as far as that to-day. But the ceremony lingers on in the most inappropriate places. We have all dined, have we not, in those minute dining rooms in the minute apartments in those huge ant heaps of blocks of flats in London? We have observed, have we not, the sigh of satisfaction from our host as the two women have squeezed out of the room into the next one. The walls are thin. We can still hear the sound of their voices, and the clink of their coffee cups. But the host as he relaxes and passes round the weak port is obviously at ease for the first time in the evening. The ladies have left the table. You are a man. He is alone with you. He is comfortable. They have left us (so his manner seems to say) at peace.

Despite the fact that the English were one of the first peoples in Europe to suppress the monasteries at the Reformation, they clung to the monastic and purely masculine system of education with extraordinary tenacity. The English public schools, even those founded in the nineteenth century, have always been aggressively anti-feminine. And the two older universities, even nowadays with their women students, preserve a gentler but much more subtle and persuasive atmosphere of antagonism to women. An English public schoolboy upon going up to Oxford or Cambridge enjoys an extraordinary efflorescence of the spirit and the mind which has to be experienced to be believed. Max Beerbohm has said that all the nonsense that was knocked out of his head at Charterhouse was carefully put back again at Oxford. One piece of nonsense, however, that is inculcated at both the English public school and the university is the legend that women are an uncomfortable nuisance. The more juvenile aspect of this attitude as exemplified in the old-fashioned type of public schoolmaster and the more callow or hearty undergraduate is somehow, in a muddleheaded way, mixed up with chivalry. The idea being, I suppose, that if you put women up on pedestals they are put comfortably up out of the way. The more adult aspect of this attitude develops into what is politely known as 'the Greek view of life'—the classical don with his charming backwater of college rooms looking out on to the college gardens, his coterie of select undergraduates, changing year by year, but somehow mysteriously remaining always the same. The name of woman in such surroundings always strikes a jarring and discordant note.

The modern educationalists like the now veteran A. S. Neill (the Scotch schoolmaster who has gone into England to teach little English boys and girls to be natural about sex) are never tired of inveighing against the English attitude towards women. The public schools and universities are, according to them, breeding grounds of repression and psychological peculiarities which make the Englishman (so they say) the most sexually unhealthy man in Europe. What rubbish! Have these critics never been abroad? And, if they have, have they never kept their eyes open? At any rate their criticisms are so shrill and so full of malice, envy and spite that one is forced (however un-English one may be oneself in one's attitude to women) to say a word in favour of the traditional Englishman's approach to the opposite sex.

To begin with, there is the sense of mystery which is one of the most delightful as well as essential elements in the relationships between the sexes. I remember a distinguished old English actor who had been happily married for over forty years saying to me, 'I haven't been away from X' (his wife) 'for more than ten days in our whole married life, but I still don't know what she's going to say next.' Then he added (and here one must make allowance for his histrionic manner), 'As soon as I do know what she's going to say next, I'll know that I'm beginning to fall out of love with her.'

'Does she know what you're going to say next?' I asked him.

The question took him slightly aback. I don't think he'd ever thought of it before. 'D'you know', he said reflectively, 'D'you know, I rather think she does. I think she's always known.'

Though the old English actor had made rather an agreeable pose out of his inability to understand his wife he had stumbled on one of the truths about successful marriage. The mystery of a woman's difference from a man should always continue to puzzle his curiosity however well he knows her, however long he has loved her. Sexual curiosity (mental as well as physical) is an essential ingredient in masculine love. Women (contrary to general belief) are less inquisitive than men. They don't bother about men's difference from them; they just accept it. Therefore they know us better than we know them.

Englishmen are very fond of airing, in a rather touching and ingenuous manner, their ignorance of the female mind and temperament. 'Extraordinary creatures women', you will hear them saying, 'you never know what they'll be up to next', or in another mood they will say something like 'Women have got the most amazing pluck. What they put up with beats me. Just imagine what it must be like having a baby', or 'My wife doesn't mind going to the dentist in the least, but ask her to take a mouse out of a trap and just hear what she has to say—most extraordinary.' And so on.

You will never hear such naïve exclamations of surprise from the Latin or the Celtic males. They don't find women's capriciousness or capacity for bearing physical pain at all mysterious. One reason is that both the Latin and the Celtic males are much more feminine in temperament than is the Anglo Saxon. The other reason is (and this is particularly true of the Latin) that neither of them have been taught from earliest youth to regard the female sex as something quite incomprehensible.

Still, I suggest to you that many a happy and long lasting English marriage has been helped towards success by the innocent but invincible ignorance of the male partner to the union. Lest you consider this a sentimental remark, let me remind you that I believe that that innocent and invincible ignorance owes its existence to the fact that, in general, Englishmen dislike the company of women.

On the other hand they are enormously pleased with each other's company. Englishmen tend to quarrel amongst themselves much less than do the males of any other race that I have come across. Indeed their capacity for emotional friendship has been much commented on and frowned upon by the foreigner and the co-educationalists as being unhealthy. I wonder. There are, of course, aberrations and peculiarities in all societies of men. But what strikes one about the immense body of English literature devoted to emotional friendship or comradeship between men is its ingenuousness, its innocence (that word again), its lack of furtiveness. Just think of Browning's *Waring* for instance. How unlike the French and German literature on the same subject.

One other admirable national characteristic of the Englishman as an amorist is this. When he is properly in the throes of love and if his love is returned, he enjoys himself thoroughly and without any of the introspection and obsession with Time which affects the lovers of so many other races, or if he does think about time it is only in terms of his present enjoyment. 'Now, now, forever now' is the burden of his song.

> 'What is love? 'tis not hereafter;
> Present mirth hath present laughter
> What's to come is still unsure:
> In delay there lies no plenty;
> Then come kiss me, sweet and twenty,
> Youth's a stuff will not endure.'

All, uninhibited, free, not lovelorn but love-loving England is in that song. Compare it with that equally beautiful lyric:

> 'Ae fond kiss and then we sever,
> Ae fareweel, alas for ever.'

Burns is getting just as much pleasure out of saying goodbye as Shakespeare is in saying 'Let's do it now.' Whether there is anything to be deduced about the difference between English and Scottish amorousness in the comparison of these two supreme lyrics, I don't know. I just make the comparison for what it is worth.

To tell you the truth, at the moment I don't feel much like making smart comparisons on the form love takes in various nationalities. There is something going on in the very room in which I am writing this letter to you in bed which makes me wish to hold my peace on such a subject forever.

In the corner of the small ward of the Infirmary in which I am lying, a man is dying of cancer of the throat. They have made holes for him to breathe through, but he can still just speak. He is an Italian. They let his wife come and sit with him all of each afternoon. She is a sonsy fair-haired Scotswoman—of about forty— from the country I should think. They do not speak, nor do they touch each other with their hands except when they meet and part. They just stare into each other's eyes for hours on end.

You, in your profession of mercy, must have seen many such sights. I have not.

Yours,
Moray McLaren.

LETTER XIII

From James Bridie to Moray McLaren

Drymen
23rd January, 1949

Dear Moray,

Most gracefully, most restrainedly and yet most adequately, you have dealt with the Englishman in Love.

It is odd that we Scots (who fornicate, according to Cunninghame Graham, gravely and without conviction) should regard him as a brutal sensualist—many educated Russians to whom I have spoken have the same opinion—and that the Latins think him an oafish sort of neuter. Your contribution puts them all in the wrong, I think.

I often wonder whether all those serious scientists—at least from Havelock Ellis onwards—who concern themselves with sex really understand much about it. Anybody who has read the report of a divorce case must be struck by the fact that everybody in Court, from the Judge to the Usher, places himself or herself in the correct posture for lying. They lie steadily, earnestly and deliberately. They lie to the jury, to the public, to themselves and to God Almighty.

In the common associations of life, men seem to lie continuously to women and women to men. What they say to their children shows not only a disregard for the truth, but a positive hatred for that abstraction. Even the words they speak in terror to their medical men are an obvious tissue of lies. The only meaning

96

one can extract from such evidence can hardly be classed as exact knowledge.

Every civilised and uncivilised group has its own rules and conventions for playing this extraordinary game. They all find makebelieve necessary to a greater or to a lesser extent. The English rules and conventions are, perhaps, characteristic of a gamesome people. Perhaps they have a deeper significance. I don't know and I don't believe there is anybody who does know. So to Hell with that. We can leave it to the intelligentsia, to whom the subject is fascinating. Morbidly fascinating, one would think.

And, by the way, what about the English intelligentsia? It runs in my mind that we mentioned them.

You flatter me when you say that I must have come into contact with many of them. Off and on, in the way of business, I have exchanged a few words or notes with them, and once a friend of mine took me to a party half an hour after it had died and I told a number of mild-eyed bearded men all about the Universe, its purpose and how it worked. I formed the vain impression at the time that, given a dram or two, I could talk the heads off any of them. I was almost certainly wrong. Anyhow, they courteously listened to my nonsense and advanced very little of theirs. I expect they were tired.

I suppose that intellectuals are pretty much the same all the world over. The English variety always seem to me, however, to be less sure of themselves than the others. Their profession is not so highly regarded in their own country as it is in others. Those of them who are not men of genius seem often to be labouring in the rearward of the fashion. Anxious. Afraid of making mistakes. A little dreary. Suspicious. Bent on proving that however advanced and realistic and individual and furious they may be, they are still essentially gentlemen and scholars. There is not much wrong with this last, as many of them *are* either gentlemen or scholars or both.

This puts them at some disadvantage with Irish and Scottish highbrows who are seldom either gentlemen or scholars and see no reason why they should be. There *is* no reason why they should be. In Scotland we no more confuse gentility and scholarship with literature than, in France, they confound intelligence with the gendarmerie. In England literature is somewhat confused with tuft hunting, and, for this, their great public schools and universities must take some responsibility.

In Scotland we have even had a King or two who was a considerable man of letters. In each case, the poet-king hung up his crown on a hook and went at the job of composition in his shirtsleeves. There are few genteel pretensions in 'Fy, let us all to the bridal' or in 'The Gaberlunzie Man'. Yet the author's wife would go in to dinner many and many a yard before the wife of the most socially exalted of any of the Sassenach litteratoors that ever put finger to typewriter.

Mind you, in any trade, politeness, as we say, costs nothing. I must admit that I am astonished at your experience among the English . . . ach, what are we to call them? Gigadibses, eh? They don't like being called intellectuals, and 'highbrow' is a silly and vulgar expression.

I must say that I am astonished a little at your sad

98

experiences among the English Gigadibses. There is a smell of treachery about them and treachery is not very common among the English. Indeed, they don't seem to understand what it means. The word 'traitor' is a common article of abuse among them, and they show no consciousness that it is, or ever has been, a very dangerous word indeed. In Ireland and in France it means something. In Scotland, for the time being, there is very little to be treacherous about; but treachery always horrifies us when we meet it (as we frequently do) in our history. We admire it as a really spectacular department of evil. In England the word 'traitor' ranks with, and considerably below, 'no gentleman'.

Be that as it may, we were talking about Gigadibs and his little ways and how those little ways affected you when you were a young writer. You concede that you are less brutally handled these days.

But surely the acts you describe happen in all rackets, and it is well known that London publicists *et hoc genus omne* are racketeers, and jealous guardians of the exclusiveness of their racket. Until you are one of them, or at least until they get used to the cut of your jib, you must expect to be shoved, elbowed, rabbit-punched or flung out on your ear at every attempt you make to muscle in. It is nonsense to suggest that the same thing doesn't happen in Paris, or New York or Dublin. If there is any difference in the application of the law of tooth and claw in London, it is that the Londoners show more civility than the others, and even a touch of generosity. This is the advantage of being, or pretending to be, well bred.

The Scot, who doesn't see what Winchester, Balliol and Debrett have to do with the Arts, is often uncouth enough in his native land. When he goes to London, he is usually intolerable. Except our mutual friend Bone and one or two others whom we name in our hearts, MacGigadibs, the London Scot, is an ill-mannered and pretentious oaf and exactly the man to slap you on the back at one moment and kick you downstairs the next. Are you perfectly sure that you are not thinking of him when you throw your mind back to your calf days?

I know Gigadibs mainly by what he puts down in print, though the lineaments of an occasional dim figure of fact strays into my memory. I have the impression that neither treachery nor rudeness comes much into his composition. Absurdity, yes. But he is not vicious.

I have the impression also of a sort of ordered society (or racket). In the upper reaches walk such figures as Forster, Eliot, Rebecca West and, perhaps, Charles Morgan. They do not appear to abide anybody's question. They are of the racket but not in it. In the same finer air are the Sitwells; but, although they have some of the stigmata of racketeers, they are allowed remoteness and privacy, probably because they undoubtedly belong to the upper gentry. These names and some others form the aristocracy necessary to an aristocratic state. Shaw and Belloc have already been translated, though, when they die, they will certainly be roughly treated. Remember what Gigadibs did to Kipling, Wells, Bennett and Galsworthy.

There is some sort of priesthood, obviously, though

it is difficult to know which of the thaumaturgists are high church and which low church. The low church-men write just as well as the high churchmen and have often been to the same schools. I suppose I could straighten this out by studying which writers are decried or ignored by which group; but I am afraid I haven't the patience.

The official organs are *The New Statesman & Nation*, *The Spectator*, and *Time and Tide*, the leading remnants of a large number of weekly reviews. The writers in one of these seldom so much as mention the writers in the two others. I suppose *The New Statesman* is high church. Desmond MacCarthy occasionally writes for it. Am I right in supposing that *The New Statesman* is *truly representative* of all that is *best* in *contemporary English literature?* I should like to think so. As a libretto writer on the fringe of the Movement, I naturally study its pages very carefully.

Shaw says that the English Theatre is always from seven to ten years behind contemporary trends of thought. If the *N.S.* is a reliable guide to those trends, it ought to be able to tell me what to write in 1959; but I suppose I shall be past caring by that time. If I were a provincial, Scottish, or B.B.C. critic, I should learn the *N.S.* by heart, lest at any time I should stumble into error.

I find, to my delight, that it is not unfashionable to be an old-fashioned Liberal, or Humanist; but that it is abominable and ridiculous to betray any of the characteristically English traits we are so light-heartedly discussing. There is a column in the *N.S.* called 'This England' which is a mine of information about the English and which holds them consistently up to derision. In the competition section, too, its readers are encouraged to mock the English—even, from time to time, the English Gigadibs. The competition entries are often coyly pornographic, within the limits allowed, say, in the society of advanced English gentlewomen (lavatories are very funny); but they seldom transgress good form.

Take it all over, *The New Statesman* is tolerant of its Philistine fellow-countrymen and amused by them. Nor does it, nowadays, try them too high. As much space is, to-day, devoted to Mrs. Gaskell, Miss Austen or Mr. Trollope as used to be devoted to Kafka, Spengler and Rilke. It appears to be losing confidence in the continentals without regaining, or gaining, much confidence in itself. It still regards Proust as a safe bet.

I should have told you, in case you didn't know, that *The New Statesman* is a journal of the Left. I believe it to be a human tendency to become a little bored and disillusioned after the first few weeks in the Promised Land.

The Spectator is rather more genteel than intellectual. It lives up to Mr. Harold Nicolson who is both and who is respectfully regarded by all but the most severe Gigadibses. *Time and Tide* is the only ladylike newspaper in England, and I am not forgetting *The Queen* and *Vogue*. Both these journals are also Liberal. I mean *The Spectator* and *Time and Tide*—not *The Queen* and *Vogue*.

In a rather sterile literary period, criticism is apt to flourish. An uprush of really good imaginative writers usually blows the critics flat on their backs. The literary critic has not the stamina of his musical and artistic colleagues. An original painter or composer can expect violent attacks. If he is original in one of the stereotyped ways he is certain, too, of some loyal support. Gigadibs knows that the graphic arts and music don't really matter much and nobody knows anything about them anyhow. He can 'get away with it'. Literature, on the other hand, is something he knows about. Stable tips are no use. He is, as I have said, a very good writer himself and only too conscious that he can make mistakes. His best line is to patronise and anatomise great writers when they die—to play them down. While they live, they are dangerous. There are plenty of his equals about if he feels disposed to practise the rough stuff. He is quite extraordinarily diffident with originals.

The Theatre is half and between. I must say for the dramatic critic that he has more courage than the literary critic. He likes, like the late Mr. Harry Quilter, his pot shots at things. A sense of power sustains him in his dismal trade. If he is bored, and says so, he can sometimes ruin a year's work and deprive some worthy tradesmen of several thousands of pounds. He is usually sustained also by ignorance of the mystery he is expounding, and, like most literary persons, he is not a man of great judgment. He is given little time to think, so he cries up and he cries down with great confidence and emphasis. He is moderately honest. He writes, like the rest of them, very well indeed. Some of our best modern writers have been persistent dramatic critics.

When I say that he writes very well, I mean that he

writes good English, not that he writes good criticism. That it is possible for an Englishman to write good dramatic criticism is evidenced by Hazlitt and Montague but we seldom see it nowadays. I think this a pity. Criticism is a minor art, and the practitioner of a major art is entitled to have his work assessed at least by a minor artist. A good essayist is no more entitled to an opinion on a play than a good preacher or a good engineer.

It may be a very dangerous thing to set a good essayist loose on a stage play. He is persuasive and one of his objects is to persuade us that his opinion is worth something. In London many of these men (aye, and women) are very persuasive indeed. I wish they were compelled to show their credentials or that the canons of criticism were better understood among English theatre goers.

Do not think, Moray, that I am complaining about English dramatic critics or that this letter is going to expand into something like Scottish Bards and English Reviewers. If I have been rebuked in the *Sunday Stridor*, I have almost invariably been over-praised in the *Daily Potboiler*—usually, in both cases, for something I never intended. I haven't the faintest idea how I stand with the rackets. This in spite of the fact that I know several dramatic critics very well. So well that I can't generalise about the Gigadibs from them. I may tell you that all the London dramatic critics I know are gents—even if some of them are of Nature's variety. Perhaps this is true of all the English Gigadibses except. . . .

Ah! Did you think you were going to get away with

it? You know all about my King Charles's Head. I hate Roman Catholic Gigadibses worse than any. I don't mean you and Compton Mackenzie. You know how to behave. But I long for the pen of John Knox to deal with those covert sneerers, those roaring bullies, those cashers in on the consciousness of sin who have built up the most powerful literary racket in all London. I cannot trust myself to continue. But remember, for all their Frenchified airs, they are English too—and typically English.

I'm very glad you are better.

God bless you,

J.B.

P.S. Isn't it funny that so many Englishmen believe in the Baconian Theory—or one of the others? They can't believe that their God was a shopkeeper's son—and an actor at that.

From Moray McLaren to James Bridie

Glasgow, 27th January, 1949

My dear J.B.,

The trouble with the English Gigadibses (what a good and onomatopœic word that is! So much better than the odious 'highbrow' or misused 'intellectual'. You must introduce it into a play; I will drag it into broadcasts and articles. But I'm afraid so few people nowadays remember Bishop Blougram, let alone his interviewer)—the trouble with the English Gigadibses is this. They are forced by their circumstances into a little world of their own. This induces in so many of them that spirit of rancid pride which is so lamentable and offensive. Gigadibses all the world over suffer from this failing; but none so acutely as the English breed.

It may be that this bitter, half enforced, half adopted seclusion is due to the social circumstances which you have mentioned. To be just to them they have little control over this. Most English Gigadibses spring, as you point out, from the public school or at least University class. Their Gigadibsianism cuts them off from their own native circle; while their obvious and unconcealed upper middle class manners in speech and in print prevent their access to that free world of the spirit and the intellect of 'the common man' towards which so many of them aspire. Hence their habit of taking in their own washing—and not always washing it.

Our lively compatriot Colm Brogan has ridiculed the English Gigadibses for elevating man's clerkly quality of the intellect to such an absurd extent that it is made out to be more important to be intellectual than to be virtuous. Be clever, sweet maid, and let who will be good. There is a good deal in his mockery. And, as usual, he is very entertaining on the subject. But again, as usual, he has overstated his case. He wouldn't be Colm if he didn't. The weakness of the English Gigadibsian attitude is not that they *elevate* the importance of the intellect but that they seek to make it their own exclusive property. To hear some of them talk you would think it is impossible to be intelligent, or intellectual, or whatever you will, *and* brave and good and God-fearing at the same time. Some of them may be (I am sure they are) brave and, after a fashion, good—though precious few of them are God-fearing. But you cannot help feeling that they tend to hold these virtues of small account just because they are possessed by so many of that native circle from which they have sprung and from which they now consider themselves emancipated.

It is this partly imposed seclusiveness which I think is the reason for much of that thin, high note of sneering denigration which sounds through so much of their able, sometimes brilliant writing. How irritable, how tired, how middle-aged they often sound—even when they are fairly young. An echo of 'Tarantella' floats across my mind—The sneers and the jeers of the old Muleteers.

Yes, I too take in, or buy rather, amongst other English weeklies, *The New Statesman and Nation* and find much of it excellent reading. In their literary columns they have recently descended to our level—

maybe on the principle of the last refuge of the complex being simplicity. But, whatever the impetus may be behind it, their writing is excellent. Still I confess that the main reason that makes my saxpence go bang each Friday is the desire to annoy myself with the reading of their political and social comments. It is not that I always disagree with them (though I usually do), it is the manner of them that gives me something of the wry pleasure that one gets from sucking a raw lemon. It is, I suppose, the same reason that makes my twa bawbees go bang each week-day morning when I buy the *Daily Express*—for all its much vaunted Scottish edition, an English paper. Again, much of the writing is, after its fashion, very good. It is entertaining and sometimes informative. But it is to be annoyed by its canting and yet sensational manner that I buy it. But I can't bring myself to take in by order, either this diurnal or this hebdomadal production of England.

Ah, but enough of this jeering and this sneering on my part. I am but catching a Southern and Gigadibsian infection myself in the act of writing to you. I have attempted satire, and fallen merely into abuse. They are so clever, these fellows, that one can't really be annoyed with them—provided one doesn't meet them outside their own little circle, or, as one occasionally does, find them Gigadibling on away about some subject they know nothing about. Here again one must do them the justice to admit that they usually take the trouble to be well informed. It's the use they make of their information that is the trouble. No, Gigadibs for all his priggish pride is not a malicious or intentionally evil fellow. At best he is informative, skilful and provocative. At worst he is irritating and ridiculous, as he plays with the olive and plum stones round his plate (isn't that what the original Gigadibs did in the poem?—I haven't my Browning with me) while the Great Bishop unrolls his mind.

But, my goodness! How English the Gigadibses are. Some of them would be annoyed by such a statement. Some of them, oddly enough (oddly from their own point of view, I mean), take a pride in it. It flatters their sense of seclusiveness to be that most secluded thing, an English intellectual. And yet, why are they so secluded? Gigadibs, for all his narkiness, often gives the impression that he would like to be liked a good deal more generally than he is. While, as for the ordinary English person, he is very far from having that mass hatred for the intelligence which ignorant foreigners ascribe to him. Indeed, when he does act in the mass he is usually more politically intelligent and adult than is any other race under the sun. What nonsense some Americans and Continentals talk about the English! No, I think that Gigadibs' lonely position in England is partly his own fault, and partly the fault of the ordinary Englishman who allows himself to be put off far too easily by eccentricity of manner and speech. Gigadibs is, of course, a master of such kinds of eccentricity—particularly in speech. As you know, I don't often go into England nowadays, though at one time in my youth I saw a good deal of Gigadibs and grew quite accustomed to the noise he makes when speaking. When I hear him talking out of my wireless box now, however, and over a period of years, I can scarcely believe my ears. He really sometimes sounds like a

music hall turn—though his matter is often excellent.
I can quite understand the ordinary Englishman being put
off by it. But he oughtn't to be allowed to be put off
by it quite so much. Up here, the ordinary listener
just thinks it is the 'English accent'! Good Heavens!
How often have I not leapt to the defence of the
Sassenach on this point. Do our less travelled compatriots really believe that the Sussex or Lincolnshire
yokels with their 'English accents' all talk like Stephen
Spender? But perhaps they do nowadays. It is so
long since I have been in Sussex or Lincolnshire.

Neither in Scotland nor in Ireland do we have this
esoteric form of speech. So our people are not
accustomed to other people speaking in a special way
because they write and think in a special way. We
in Scotland have, of course, nothing like the New
Staggers and Naggers (the name we used to give
to it when we were undergraduates). Apart from
any other reason we haven't a large enough public.
But we do have, for a country of our size, a very
large miscellany of small weeklies, monthlies and
casuals devoted to the extremes of Scottish politics and
art—extreme Nationalist, extreme left and extreme
right. I don't know how many of these productions
you see. I buy nearly all of them. Some of them are
really good. Some of them are partly lamentable;
others entirely. But they all make good reading—or
at least so I find. There is a good deal of very hard
hitting, some of it wild and absurd, but it is all done
with gusto and not with that thin whine of superior
almost well-bred denigration of which I have been
complaining. Mixed with these bouts of hard hitting,

there are gusts of enthusiasm. One may not agree with them, but it is difficult sometimes not to catch the infection of their pleasure. You will remember that even C. E. Vulliamy in that ultra-Gigadibsian sneering book of his about Johnson and Boswell had to admit that Boswell's best characteristic was that he 'catched enthusiasm easily'.

Irish journalism is, of course, a joy. I don't care what your attitude towards the Irish in politics, religion or art may be, you must surely enjoy their journalism. I go down twice a week to a little bookstall near St. Enoch's and come away with an armful of entertainment ranging from the *Irish Times* to the *Ballysomething Weekly*. No paper is too pompous or too securely founded for it to be above a bit of fun in verbal hard hitting. No obscure sheet is too small to feel that it cannot take on the rest of Ireland, the rest of Europe, the rest of the world. One is quite certain that every word, every paragraph of outrageous abuse or extravagant praise is written with pleasure (and sometimes with style). The pleasure is again infectious.

Do you see any of the French intellectual journalistic products—or the American? They occasionally drift my way. Before the war I worked in the same office as a man who must have read more European papers than anyone else in London. He understood some dozen languages: contemporary journalism was his hobby. Recollecting his remarks, and attaching them to my own observations, I believe that there doesn't exist outside England any journalistic Gigadibsianism, or Gigadibsian journalism, to equal the home product. There are papers, monthly, quarterly, weekly, daily, which are (particularly in France) more absurd than even the most extreme of Gigadibs' sheets. There are those (particularly in America and in pre-war Germany) that are more foolish, more pretentious, more inflated, more flatulent than anything for which Gigadibs has been responsible in England. Still, Gigadibs' home product remains unique—English through and through.

No, of course I didn't think that I should have escaped your King Charles's head—the faith of our ancestors. I always enjoy a good tussle with you on the subject, whether I am thrown or throw, but I don't know that a Scottish theological argument even on the Catholic faith would entertain anyone else very much nor would it be germane. I permit myself this comment, however. You are always a very doughty and worthy opponent (sometimes too much for me) on the home ground, i.e., the Marian and Knoxian quarrel. I have fenced with you occasionally on the subject of the Faith in regard to Ireland and on the Continent. But it is only when you cross the border into England that you really seem to lose your rag. What is it that's biting you?— what a metaphor! Is it the teeth of some remote Covenanting ancestor who wished to enforce Pres- byterianism on England? What a fantastic rôle for you of all kindly Scots!

But what about the politicians? You have said that one might as well judge a nation by its drunkards as by its politicians. Well, what about *in vino veritas*? Judging one's friends and acquaintances and enemies when they are tight is one way of getting to know them.

Though released from the Infirmary, I am, like you,

writing from bed. I hope you will be better soon. In a
fortnight I may be going on a most exciting journey—
to England.

Yours,
Moray McLaren.

P.S. We really must make the name of Gigadibs
stick. I have had singular luck with nicknames and
catchphrases. A dramatic critic whose regular emissions
of splenetic bile (is that medically correct?) I know
annoy you, still bears the name (either in its Italian or
English form) which I casually affixed to him in an
Edinburgh public house fifteen years ago. So 'Viva
Gigadibs!' And the New Staggers and Old Naggers.

LETTER XV

From James Bridie to Moray McLaren

Drymen
8th February, 1949

Dear Moray,

I think you can put down my passing attack of bigotry to the influenza virus. I shall put down your outburst of malice and uncharitableness to your bruised and battered Antrum of Highmore. No better excuse could be found. In your heart you love the artful prattle of Gigadibs as much as I do and you are as much a *New Statesman* addict as anybody. My father used to read to an old lady who could never make out what he was reading about, but who liked the monotonous sound o' his voice. These fellows write admirably. I wish you and I could write as well. It looks like nonsense. It smells like nonsense. It tastes like nonsense. I believe it is nonsense. But perhaps that is also a characteristic of the English, that they write nonsense really well. Shaw pointed out that the best of all their writers, William Shakespeare, wrote very grave nonsense indeed; but he had the courtesy to admit that the choice and arrangement of words was superb.

A measure of all this is the skill of the Englishman in writing nonsense when he does it intentionally. He can distil the pure stuff, free of any tincture of sense, in crystalline perfection. And, by the way, what about his love of perfection and his attainment of it, every now and again? I mean, perfection for its own sake. The

114

most perfect things ever devised by man are the sailing ship and the sporting gun. It is true that they are useful objects; but what is the use of the discreet carvings (just enough and no more) on the nipples of the gun, and the scroll work and the figurehead on the bow of the ship? They are not the wild ebullitions of crazy artists. They are the Finishing Touch. The thing is *finished*. It will never be done better.

In writing, it has been done by Sterne, it has been done by Herrick, it has been done by Betjeman and by hundreds more. What these men set out to do was, perhaps, a little thing; but it was done once and for all in the best way in which it could possibly be done. It need never be done again. The English, the Chinese and the Egyptians are the best at that. However fine and free and careless they may pretend to be, the English are craftsmen.

By the way, by the way . . . you may be right about the *Daily Express*—I buy it too from railway bookstalls—but the tone from which you turn in such well-bred disgust is surely dictated by its proprietor, who is no more English than I am. He is Scotch to the bone. Like Barrie, he has a keen sense of what is most vulgar in English taste and sentiment; but, by Gum, he knows how to conduct a newspaper and he can make a good buy on its merits. Remember, please, that he is the *entrepreneur* of Low, of Gubbins, of Giles, of Beachcomber, none of whom is very far from that English perfection of which I have just been writing and none of whom is a fanatical follower of the political and social principles of the *Daily Express* or its proprietor.

Also by the way, this is not a mutual admiration

correspondence, but please let us stick to the 'Old Muleteers' if we have occasion again to refer to *The New Statesman and Nation*. It is a sublimely beautiful description.

I think I said to you that it was as fair to judge a nation by its drunkards as by its politicians. It is also as fair to judge it by its politicians as by its journalists. It is a temptation to go back to the drunkards, and perhaps we shall; but do you know many politicians? Those I know best are mostly Irishmen or Scotsmen. The first English politician I ever met was Byles of Bradford, who was a journalist too. He was a very excellent man.

When I was young, I took my notions of English politicians from *The Eyewitness* and, later, from the Chester-Belloc novels. These prints told me plainly and repeatedly that those politicians were dishonest, cheating, thieving, toadying, blackmailing, lying, hypocritical, dull, cowardly, beastly people. Their principles were dictated to them by sly gentlemen of foreign extraction to whom the regrettable Mr. Sidney Stanley was a babe in arms.

It is only right to say that the few English politicians I have met do not correspond to that description. They seem, however, to lead a very narrow sort of social life. They are very like actors. They live in an insulated sort of workshop and appear to have few interests outside of it. They have a curious air of insincerity when they are talking about anything that is not intimately connected with their trade.

I don't think they are insincere. I think that they are simply not interested and that it is part of their job to be continuously polite. The best Club in London fills their lives and they have little room for anything else.

The people they meet outside that Club are mainly obsessional freaks and busybodies and bores, who must be met with an affable and stony smile and a string of carefully prepared clichés, delivered from the teeth outwards, if the politician's sanity is to be preserved.

It is from such people, however, that they gather their impression of Public Opinion. This leads them invariably to be wrong in their forecasts of such things as general elections. I once had the privilege of taking part in a small sweepstake with a group of really important politicians. We each forecast our figures at the forthcoming General Election and backed our fancy with half a sovereign each. I knew nothing of politics, but I won the sweepstake quite easily. Nobody else was within a hundred seats of me.

What do we learn from this? We learn exactly what I have learned from the Theatre. It is part of the English tradition that the Englishman's servants seldom understand him. An Englishman may not be a hero to his valet, but he is at least a mystery to that official. Servants' Halls are so fascinating, so absorbing in their technique, as to leave small space for the study of the idiosyncrasies of the employing classes upstairs. Some superficial study is necessary, of course; but it is very superficial. There is no time or spare energy for it. This is why butlers are so often monuments of slightly anxious arrogance and vanity and why housemaids occasionally forget their place; and why both are often unconscious of the hatred and contempt in which they are held by their employers. This is why actors are so elated by applause and so cast down by indifference, knowing neither the source nor the mechanism of either.

Politicians, like actors, are simple men. They are very clever, but essentially simple. They live and move and have their being in their own ill-lit, ill-ventilated Heaven and are ill-equipped for the entirely different sort of complexity that informs human existence. At least, that is my experience of them.

Now, what about the English drunkard? We are told that the rolling English drunkard made the rolling English road. This is not true in fact—most English and Scottish roads were made by rolling Irish drunkards —and I doubt whether it is true figuratively. At the same time, the English drunkard is so characteristic that he must have some effect on his country's economy, or, at least, demonstrate some of the qualities that do produce an effect.

Mind you, *in vino veritas* is all nonsense. Whatever truth-compelling drug the Soviets use—and, by the way, it is very English to be shocked at the very idea of a truth-compelling drug; the defendant must retain the right to lie himself out of prison, if he can— whatever truth-compelling drug the Soviets use, it cannot be alcohol. The best lies I have ever heard have been invented under the influence of drink. A drunken man is removed several stages from truth.

Certainly, he may approach a very important person and inform the poor V.I.P. that he is the ugliest little devil he ever met. Those in the neighbourhood marvel at this; but the fact that they marvel is a proof that drink is not a remarkable truth teller. Let us suppose Socrates to arrive at the truths that fire is hot and ice cold. These truths are so obvious that his disciples would suspect Socrates of pulling their legs.

Now, everybody knows that very important persons are often ugly little devils. To do them justice, they know that themselves. There is no virtue in tearing off truth's veil if the veil is transparent anyhow and has been imposed by the censor. Such conduct is not truth seeking; it is bad manners.

If the tag means that the drunkard reveals more of himself when he has drink taken, it is equally a lying tag. The drunkard reveals only a personal phantasy of himself, a picture of himself as he would like to be when his faculty of self-criticism has been knocked out by the drug. Thus, a maudlin drunk will present himself as an ill used person though, in fact, he himself has used ill everybody within his reach and is probably a wife beater and an income tax inspector in private life. The jolly, rough, devil-may-care fighting man is nearly always the most diffident of creatures when he is sober. In fact, he merely drinks to dull the gnawing pangs of cowardice.

In spite of all this there is one significant thing about the English drunkard. This is his tendency to break things. 'I like', said the late Maurice Baring, 'the sound of breaking glass.' There can be little doubt that breaking glass is music to the ears of the Englishman when he is drunk and that this fact is so extraordinary as to be significant. But significant of what?

The Englishman is very fond of glass. No Londoner has looked happy since the Crystal Palace was burnt down. He loves pottering about in greenhouses. He likes to split his windows into little bottle bottom squares and diamonds. He likes huge sheets of plate glass in his streets and when Suffragettes particularly wanted to annoy him they broke his beloved toys with hammers. Glass is a clear, transparent, orderly sort of substance, and the Englishman is fond of clarity, transparency and order.

The Englishman is muddled and confused by drink. In his queer, perverse way he feels that universal muddle and confusion can, itself, be a kind of order. He therefore goes straight to the first symbols of order he can find—glass and policemen's helmets—and reduces them to a tidy level of destruction. This may be the explanation. No sensible man can be bothered with neo-psychology; but it runs in my head that the neo-psychologists would explain the thing much along these lines.

Be that as it may, the Englishman's drinking habits are different from those of his neighbours though they approach perhaps most nearly to those of the Germans in that he likes to stupefy himself with large quantities of weak beer. He does not appear to use alcohol as an instrument for the rapid release of his intellectual faculties as do the Irish and the Scots. He is no doubt wise in this. The Scoto-Irish method means that the drug is taken in powerful doses and that poisoning often supervenes too rapidly. Scottish and Irish drinking are often misjudged because of this. The Irish drunk, for example, quite frequently gives the impression of being insane. This is a correct impression, but it does not cover the whole truth. The poor wretch has merely overdone it and has poisoned himself by mistake. The Englishman, on the other hand, poisons himself on purpose. Hence the publican's kidney of the *fin de siècle* humorists. I remember George Graves playing the part of a millionaire who had bought a Tudor house and fallen asleep in it. Among the characters in his dream was a Tudor jester who flicked him playfully with a balloon full of dried peas. 'Don't,' said Mr. Graves, 'hit me with your publican's kidney.'

Correct me if I am wrong, but I think rural pub conversation is better in Scotland than in England. The slow rumble of 'Ar be the missus, Jarge?' and the 'Oo's' and the 'Ar's' of the English pub are not stimulating but soporific and they are probably meant to be. In Scotland the customers try to be funny and are quite often successful and it is not uncommon to hear philosophy raising its bulging head. This is in spite of the fact that the pubs are usually dirty dispensaries and the customers are by no means the pick of the population. In very many rural districts in Scotland a social stigma hangs over the pub and really serious drinking is done at home by respectable people. This does not apply to the Highlands; but the true local does not exist in the Highlands. Drinking is done in hotels and discreetly through the back door. In the Highlands women do not drink in public. In the Lowlands the publicans are making an attempt to attract respectable women into lounges and olde cocktaile barres. It is still thought a little daring and advanced for a woman to go into a pub. In England they sozzle quietly with the men. This probably explains a good deal.

High-flown drunkenness in England is a thing for occasions. If it gets at all imaginative it is frowned upon.

An enterprising fellow who climbed one of their local idols in Piccadilly Circus was as savagely punished as if he had ill-treated a dog and much more savagely punished than if he had pulled his wife round the back kitchen by her hair after kicking her in the stomach. Such an occasion, however, seldom arises. The Englishman seldom gets drunk in that ridiculous fashion. When he does get drunk he is nearly always a bore. Amiable, persistent and terrible as an army without banners.

. . . . .

When I read this over, I see that I have been thinking chiefly of the under-privileged Englishman; but a good deal of it applies to the over-privileged. During the late twenties and early thirties, indeed, the over-privileged indulged in what I call high-flown drunkenness quite a lot. These drunkards called themselves, I think, Bright Young Things. But then, they weren't very bright, were they? They showed off a good deal, and the woman drunkard was quite a fashionable figure. I don't like women drunkards, do you? They seem to miss the point, somehow.

Then there were the Oxford and Cambridge undergraduates on Boat Race and Inter-Varsity Rugger nights. But there was always a bumped up air about those occasions too. Something theatrical. Your proper drunkard is seldom self-conscious. Your proper drunkard. . . .

But one must be careful, here. One must remember our fellow-countrymen who take their America-tartan bunnets over the Border for Wembley. Your English drunkard may well raise his fish-like eye and ask one who one thinks one is talking to? Does one consider the Scottish Supporters to be 'proper' drunkards?

Well, perhaps not. One might point out that the poor fellows have spent the night standing up in a stuffy corridor train and that fatigue, hunger and excitement have all played their part in the orgy. Indeed, one doubts whether any but the toughest of English drinkers would have got as far as Preston alive. It is not nice drunkenness. But is it any nastier than the depressing absorption at ten shillings a time that goes on in the classiest hostelries in London? There, I am told, devitalised young wretches are provided with a silver rail to assist their feeble wrists to convoy the firewater to their slack and pendent gobs. This is not really drinking, is it?

Wouldn't it be better to shove a hollow needle into a vein and feed them with alcohol by the continuous drip process so valuable in surgery? Then they could stay in bed all the time, instead of getting up at five.

> *I am, Sir,*
> *Yours very sincerely,*
> *James Bridie.*

From Moray McLaren to James Bridie

Glasgow, 2nd *March*

My dear J.B.,

I had hoped to lure you, on the subject of English politicians, into one of those tirades of yours which so please me. I don't know quite why, but I had thought that their particular form of cant (not necessarily humbug) might just touch you off. Instead, you produce, with infinitely well-bred weariness, the perfectly adequate excuse for them that they live in a world of their own. How right you are! The self-absorption, the utter unconsciousness of the feelings, the values, even the existence of the outside world of the ordinary House of Commons man is something beyond the vanity of even the most exhibitionist of the artists, the shallowest of courtesans. And yet, as you imply, he is a simple-minded fellow, and really doesn't mean any harm by it. So much for him—at least for the time being.

I have been recuperating in Edinburgh where the keen February winds operated on my head with all the pain of a surgeon's knife, but with more efficacy. Perhaps it was because they were my native winds blowing away from me the romantic and rheumatic, cloying yet colocynthic and catarrhal accumulations of your Clyde Valley. Glasgow is a much more romantic town than Edinburgh.

I am going back to live in Edinburgh—after three years in Glasgow. They have been amongst the most puzzling years of my life. It is not that I have felt a stranger in Glasgow—for all my years in London I feel much more strange there—it is only that as one coming back to Edinburgh from Glasgow I am continually puzzled by the fact that two places can be so essentially the same yet so different on the surface. I remember a passionate Oxford man who had been a don at Cambridge for twenty years saying the same thing about those two places. 'No country but England', he said, 'could produce them, no foreigner could perceive much difference between them: no native could fail to.'

I feel something of the same about Edinburgh and Glasgow. Of course, any foreigner would see the obvious differences, but he would not see the more subtle ones. Any perceptive Englishman coming to Scotland for the first time would have the skill to pass over the fact that Edinburgh has a theatrical skyline and that Glasgow is a city of romantic canyons. He would disregard these superficial and domestic Scottish differences as small when compared with the vast and deeper differences between both places and any English towns, however varied, that he may know—London, Manchester, Bristol or Nottingham. He would, in both places, see in the quality of our grey stone, in the fact that natural wildness crowds in upon the centre of the towns, in the faces, in the streets something so un-English, so over-riding in its foreignness to him that he would (I am supposing him to be subtle) be impatient with us for our sense of internal difference. 'After all, you're both Scotch', he would say. And I would applaud him for it.

Reaching this point in my reflections on Edinburgh

rather cheered me. For, overcome by my acute sense of the internal gulf between Glasgow and Edinburgh upon return to my native city, I had begun to wonder whether I at least, of the two of us, had in my remarks about the English not been indulging in that finicky perception of the 'difference between things', which can be so delightful when observed by someone like Henry James (or our old friend James Bone for that matter), and so trivial when babbled about by lesser minds. But no. Much though I revelled in my home-coming to Edinburgh, affectionate though puzzled were my backward glances at Glasgow, relish though I did the innumerable points of change all around me, I realised that all this was on the surface. Edinburgh and Glasgow are both 'Scotch'. You from the west, and I from the east have every right to think and speak about the English without indulging in the tortuous subtleties of Neo Henry Jacobeans.

On one of the weekends in Edinburgh, I saw a good deal of drunkenness which set me thinking on your remarks about nationality in drink. The reason for the orgy was the defeat of the Scottish Rugby team by the visiting Irishmen. I agree with you that the Irish have a capacity for going more quickly and completely insane under the influence than have any other race. The scenes of revelry, if they can be called such, were of the kind that would have made me, in my youth, either rush into them or rush away. The fact that I was recuperating, combined with the knowledge that I must be rather more careful with myself these days, made me linger only on the fringes of the crowd alone, palely and objectively loitering. I think I was nearly arrested once or twice for being sober. I have seen nothing like it since pre-war days.

The Irish were, as I have said, quite raving mad. My fellow citizens and compatriots were aggressive or terrifyingly friendly by turns. But I admit, in all that flood of Vino I did not perceive much Veritas— at least I hope it was not Veritas. I didn't even see that half truth of people seeing themselves as they thought they were, or thought they would like to be. But Veritas or no Veritas, how different the crowds were from the drunken English crowds I have seen. The English in such moods betray almost quietly that ruthlessness of which we have both spoken. Their solemn, nearly ritualistic love of breaking things extends even to smashing up some of those lovely pieces of perfection that they have made, which you rightly praise. The destructiveness of a crowd of young English males when drunk is not wanton: it is alarmingly orderly. This is what they seem to say, 'Here is something beautiful, carefully constructed, which we or our forefathers have made, let us smash it to pieces.'

Even I, of the post 1914-1918 generation of undergraduates, have seen some really frightening examples of laboriously smashed boats, yes, their own college boats, windows, glasses, even bits of stone architecture. Before 1914 the destruction was, at Oxford and Cambridge, on a much more massive scale. There are hair-raising accounts of the state of New College (of all correct Wykehamical institutions) about that time. It was at New College, I think, that the MSS and notes comprising years of work of a learned and retiring don were destroyed in the ruthless exuberance of a 'rag'. It was at New College that some of the most wholesalely destructive anti-aesthetic pogroms took place. It was at New College that one of our most successful present-day progressive publishers spent, forty years ago, much of his leisure time in hiding under the recesses of a Minty armchair in the Junior Common Room. To those who have encountered his sleek and well-fed figure in Henrietta Street to-day, the image is, I admit, ludicrous to recall. Still, it was an odd way for the sons of William of Wykeham to practise the adage 'Manners Makyth Man.' Harking back another forty years before that time, it is odd to remember that almost the only recorded instance of an æsthete standing up to the English destructiveness was when the Irish Oscar Wilde pitched half a dozen blue-blooded toughs out of his rooms at Magdalen. It makes one realise how rich the English scene is and was to be able to survive, almost without a sign, the result of generations of such destructive drunkenness. We and the Irish are, God knows, silly and offensive enough in our cups, but we are not silly in that way. Why? Is it because we are so much poorer in material things, and that we know, even with half-deadened consciousness, that we cannot afford such behaviour?

I don't think so. Neither the Irish nor we have been noted for caution. And our drunkenness is more violent in character if not in effect than is the English variety. No, I think it is our old friend ruthlessness again. The mention of that word after my accounts of New College manners of nearly half a century ago puts me in mind of an element in that quality in the English upon which neither you nor I have touched. I mean their savage ruthlessness, until quite a recent date, to their own young—their own young particularly of the upper and upper middle classes. It is not for me to harrow your feelings nor to instruct anyone so well informed as yourself by talking about the miseries of all but the senior boys at any public school in England until well on into the last half of the nineteenth century. These things are to be found in Trollope, Sydney Smith and many others, too frequently corroborative of each other all to be exaggerators. I had a large batch of uncles and great-uncles who were sent into England to be educated at her two most famous public schools. Tales have reached me from them at second-hand, which, if not quite as nauseating as those to be found in Trollope and the celestial Sydney, were bad enough, and quite true sounding enough to support the earlier tales. It was not only that the boys were unspeakably brutal to each other but that the system that flowered in the lovely surroundings of Eton and Winchester permitted and even encouraged such brutality.

No, no, I am not unexpectedly going all A. S. Neill on you. I merely point the fact out as a curious one. I don't believe that 'savage' Scots or Irish, or the 'cruel' Spanish or Italians or even the 'sadistic' and 'masochistic' Germans could, or ever have treated their male children of the 'comfortable' classes in anything approaching the way in which the charming, kindly, sympathetic, and above all amiable English have treated theirs. Of course we all know that that is a thing of the past. Indeed, since the beginning of the century, the old brutal English public school system has softened and mellowed into an almost sentimentally humane tradition, calling the feet from under the ground of many would-be eager educationalist reformers. Still, the past is the past, and not so very distantly the past either. There are old men alive to-day who can remember it. Strange, isn't it?

But, to return to that capacity for producing perfect things and for destroying things which you mentioned in your last letter, I think that both come from something very childlike in the English character. Children can spend hours trying to construct perfect things— toys, sand-castles, secret hiding places and the like. The only reason that they so seldom achieve their desire is because they lack the skill, not the desire. Grown-ups have often acquired the skill but lack the childish impetus to perfection in small things. Sometimes children do manage it in the things they make. It would be silly to try and quote celebrated examples like Marjorie Fleming or the six-year-old Mozart. I don't mean that sort of famous oddity. I mean the kind of perfection which, now and again, once in a hundred times, any child manages to pull off. Anyone who has had anything to do with children must have noticed this occasional capacity on their part. Once in a hundred times their intensity of desire to dream the perfect dream, think the perfect story, arrange the perfect combination of bricks or coloured pieces of paper comes true and they achieve perfection just as your English gunsmith achieves perfection with the decorations on the barrels of his shot-gun. But it is the intensity of their desire that really matters, not their rare achievement. The English who (in the management of their hands and eyes at least) are adult and have achieved skill can make perfect things more often than children can. But, as with children, it is their intense, concentrated absorption in the little, but tremendous task of perfection in the small thing that matters, not their technical ability to do it.

Children, at the same time, simply adore destruction. And it is one of the oddest things about them that they particularly like destroying the things they have themselves made. It is their own sand castles, their own carefully built towers and toys that they smash with such gusto. It is their own fairy tales and dreams that they dismiss so easily and contemptuously, to recall them perhaps, long afterwards and with a touch of sentiment—that very touch that means that their pristine purity and perfection has gone.

Is there not some likeness between this childishness and this Englishness? Is not the Englishman in his love of perfection and poetry and ruthless destruction only a child with a grown-up body? And is not the elderly sentimental Englishman who recalls the poetry of perfection and the dreams of his youth only an adolescent looking back a little regretfully at the enchanted world of his pure childhood? Despite all the one time brutality of the English preparatory and public schools, there is no country in the world where the elderly male population looks back upon its boyhood through more roseate spectacles than in England. English provincial towns are full of retired army men, civil servants and the like who can reel off not only the names but the initials of the boys who were at school with them fifty years ago—a feat not only of sentiment but of perfection in memory.

Lest I should be led into sentimentality myself by merely writing about such things, let me correct myself by recalling that other most childish European or semi-European people, the old-fashioned Russians. Their childishness in emotion and in destructiveness was, of course, famous. It doesn't only come out of novels and plays. In the late 1920's and early 30's I used to knock about a good deal in Warsaw. I met a number of people, particularly restaurant proprietors, who remembered the place when it was under the rule of the Russians. Often and often have I heard the tales of huge mirrors, gigantic candelabras being solemnly smashed to pieces by empty champagne bottles thrown by the Russians at the end of dinner.

'Were you never alarmed that you might lose your property?' I used sometimes to ask.

'No, never. They always came round on the next day to pay for the damage.'

'Like gentlemen?'

'No, like children.' And with a shrug of his shoulders that implied that he did not so much excuse as comprehend, the *Maître d'hôtel* at the Europeski, or some such place, would leave me to cogitate on this recollection of ancient mannerisms. 'How like the English', I used to say to myself (but never aloud) as I thought about it. But I think I was not wholly just to the English in this reflection. Those once young (now mostly dead) Russians were much more savage in both their emotionalism and their destructiveness. They may, in certain moods, have been as amiable as the English, but they were never, to hark back to a word I have used too often to you before, as innocent.

Innocent, amiable and ruthless, long to reign over us. No, I don't mean that last. I was betrayed into it by an echo of the National Anthem in my head which is, at the moment of writing, sounding out on the wireless. But the mere whiff of a political sentiment brings me back to the starting point—politicians. It may sound absurd to say so but I do think that even the politicians in England are more amiable and innocent than are their kind in other countries. You say that in your youth you absorbed the doctrine of, or were at least influenced by the Chester-Belloc school of thought (which may account for your present occasional violent reaction from the modern imitators of that school). I am a little bit too young to remember the Marconi row, but I was turning over some papers about it the other day, and was reading Chesterton's own reflections on it years afterwards in his autobiography.

Looking back upon the row, now that the dust of conflict about the persons concerned in it has settled down, two things strike one. The first is the violence that the shock of the row must have created at the time, *and* the fact that that shock has left its effect. The easy cynical attitude towards English politicians and politics which you will hear so often expressed in all classes in England has its roots in this forty year old dispute. Most of the people who glibly say 'Politics is a dirty game' would not know what you were talking about if you referred to the Marconi scandals. Still, I don't think they would be using the phrase so casually had it not been for the fact of those long dead scandals. The second thing that strikes one is that the row was so violent because it was unexpected and came out of a clear sky—a sky whose clarity may have been absurdly exaggerated by English Victorians, but which, none the less, and by comparison with nearly all other countries in the world, was clear. Chesterton points out that his father and grandfather believed that English politicians were the only members of the community who were utterly unaffected by money. According to their view, an English Minister of the Crown only received his salary when it was forced upon him each month and with a start of absent-minded surprise. It was this attitude that received such a severe shock at the time of Marconi. The shock remains, and rightly: so also does the fundamental attitude which it shocked. Despite the cynicism of facile phrases in talk, the average Englishman looks upon his politicians on the whole as easy, amiable dunderheads or mildly capable men—but *not* dishonest men.

In this I think he is, in the main, right. He does not, I believe, recognise to the full the dunderheadedness of most of them. He does not have any idea of the incredible isolation of the English politician's sense of self-importance. The average Englishman being, in his own way, a man of varied if not wide interests, finds it difficult to believe that men's whole interests, whole sense of values, can be so absorbed in, so confined by, the petty world of Westminster. I mean the petty things in the world of Westminster, not Westminster itself. It would be incredible to the average English voter if he were to be told how much value his local representative placed in the *minutiae* of lobby gossip, of what world shaking importance he considered the results of the most trivial party manœuvres to be and so on. He, the voter, has forgotten his own schooldays when he too may have been elated by being chosen as a reserve for the second eleven, or was given some small post of responsibility. Or, if he does remember them, it would not occur to him that his M.P. should still be animated by such childish conceits.

With all this silly isolation there are two things to be said for the usual English House of Commons man. He is, in the main, honest, and he has some vague feeling for England—yes, England, specifically England. However intensely taken up with his position as reserve for the second eleven, the schoolboy usually has, or thinks he has, some feeling for the school. The school's grandeur indeed only helps to increase his own importance. Not so the Scottish House of Commons man. Of him, with a few shining exceptions, I do not trust myself to speak. It has been the same ever since 1707. Scotland has been but the instrument by which he has levered himself into a petty position in a more powerful foreign country. If he ever does speak about Scotland's needs and Scotland's wrongs, it is only to strike an attitude of false patriotism. He lives ponce-like upon the misfortunes, not of his mistress but of his mother. Yes, yes, I know and repeat that there are glowing exceptions. It would be pleasant to name them. It would be even more pleasant to name the others. But this letter must have some end. So much for my own King Charles's head.

I am leaving soon for Provence (by way of England)

and there is some talk of us going on to Spain later. The almost incredible idea is that my wife is to be engaged to speak some Scottish ballads and I to lecture on them. 'Why does your blade sae drap wi' bluid, Edward, Edward' should sound good in Madrid or Seville. Which reminds me, we Scots are always boasting about our ability to turn up in odd places and peculiar situations. In this we are far outstripped by the English. There is no remote spot that I have ever visited, or indeed heard of, that does not have its Englishman gone native. This is true even of America, where, for instance, Alistair Cooke is even more American than the reddest Red Indian. When I first knew him he was an ordinary starry-eyed English romantic undergraduate. There is no cause, national, political or religious in some obscure spot that is without its English fanatical supporter. They are, by the way, usually murdered by the native adherents as soon as the cause becomes successful. Still the stream of enthusiasts continues to pour from England to the furthest corners of the earth as soon as news comes of someone or something being oppressed, or just possibly oppressed. They are an odd people, aren't they?

However, if you feel inclined, there is still time for you to fire off one more devastating broadside at my generalisations and sentimentalisations before I go. If you can provoke me into a parting effort, I will certainly provide it. I'm sure to have certain thoughts of the *l'esprit de l'escalier* kind. If I do, I shall entrust these to postcards or telegrams.

Yours,
Moray McLaren.

From James Bridie to Moray McLaren

Drymen
14th March, 1949

Dear Moray,

All right. Away you go. I hope you and your wife will enjoy your Spanish trip and I am sure that the Spaniards will enjoy you.

I have a friend who writes to me at intervals saying: 'As I said in my last letter, twenty years ago. . . .' Perhaps this correspondence ought to have been like that; but let us finish as we started, on the spur of the moment.

I have enjoyed it and, if you have, that's two. Whether anybody else will enjoy it is a question to be asked.

A week or two ago, a Sunday newspaper offered me some money and I wrote them a playful article about Scotland. I said this and I said that. I hinted that God, from time to time, had been very lavish in providing Scotland with perfervid and original minds. I suggested that Scotland was waking up, now, in this very year of Grace. I expressed the fantastic wish that some of Scotland's remarkable men should come out of the land of Egypt and sport their kilts of many colours in the land of Scotland, where they were born and where, presumably, they could still flourish. I thought that they were in some measure shackled or hog-tied by being heads of departments in an alien land and that there was space for their creative activities at home.

137

This I said, and a good deal in the same tenor.

The article produced a fan mail of surprising proportions, partly from nationally minded Scots, partly from maniacs and mostly from indignant English men and women. It seems that we are not so popular in England as we fondly believed. One writer said that 'Ballfour', 'Roseberry', 'Cambell-Bannerman', 'Bonnar' Law were more responsible than anyone for bringing the English Empire to its present state. Gladstone wasn't so bad; but he was not in any way Scotch. Only his parents were Scotch.

One lady had a friend who billeted two Scotch soldiers during the war. They complained all the time and were very frightened whenever the sirens went.

More than one thought that I would be interested to learn that they had withdrawn their subscriptions from the paper in which my article appeared. All the English letters spluttered with angry sarcasm. What had principally disturbed their natural equability was Scotland's base ingratitude.

If they had attacked me personally for ingratitude, I should have seen their point. England has given me that respectable livelihood which Scotland has refused me. I don't feel ingratitude, though I may have exhibited something like it. But it seems that it is the Scottish nation which is ungrateful for the benefits bestowed on it by England.

These benefits were not specified. I can think of none that Scotland does not share with the rest of the world. Absolutely none.

Do you think that those letters are at all significant? The English do confer benefits. No other nation—

even the Romans—has ever conferred so many and certainly no other nation has ever conferred benefits so disinterestedly. They are admirable landlords. They do honestly put the interests of their tenants and serfs absolutely first. No better masters have ever been invented. Their difficulties come when they are dealing with peoples who do not admit their mastery. Then they are apt to fall back on clumsy cozenage and even flat brutality. With brutality peoples like the Scots and the Irish know how to deal. They are apt to be outwitted by the other thing.

Be that as it may, any serious resistance to their kindly despotism often brings out the worst side of the English. It puzzles them. It makes them uncomfortable. It outrages their deepest religious beliefs.

I was once a Visiting Physician in a Teaching Hospital. This, as you may know from your recent experiences, is a very exalted thing to be. As the 'Chief' makes his solemn progress round 'his' wards, followed by his tidy acolytes all in white, he is to be forgiven if he feels like some sort of Pope, infallibility and all. At least he has the power of life and death over the supine figures in the beds.

I can still feel the shock of horror that came to me on the very few occasions when a patient called my bluff by 'answering back'. I was doing them good, dammit. I knew what was good for them. I was doing them good for nothing and at great personal inconvenience. My only reward was glory and the polite subordination of my victims. Believe me, I understand how the English feel. To-day they must feel like a Chief visiting a ward full of Christian Scientists,

Nature Healers and Homoeopathists. It must be even worse if the Chief is under the direction of some untutored and uncouth Minister of Health, who has never come near to being initiated into his mystery. England's obligations to the United States of America must be hard to bear. We can forgive some irascibility when an afflicted hospital-lawyer answers back.

To say, 'Sir, I am not your patient. I am your colleague' is to answer back, I'm afraid. It is not less offensive because it happens to be true. I do hope we haven't offended the English in this correspondence. To be perfectly frank, I haven't read back in these letters very carefully. There may be places where you and I haven't been objective. I think we both wish Whitehall in Hell. Even if we have been objective, we may still have been offensive. It is very easy to offend in this matter. In what Professor Gruffydd calls his bewildered intransigence, the Englishman is as sensitive to affronts as a Waverley Gael.

You may say that we have been as fair as we know how to be; that nobody asked us to criticise the English and that what we think doesn't much matter and who do we think we are anyway?

I still feel uneasy. I do not want to be ranged with the hairy Moujiks, the nasty Irguni, the insufferable Wops and Dagoes, the coffee coloured Babus, the exhibitionist Coons, the frantic Frogs, the dull Boches, the zoot-suited Middle-Westerners—in short, with the millions of bloody foreigners who rave and shriek and expectorate upon the English. Give me the stupidest Englishman and you can keep all your bloody

140

foreigners. You can keep your Colonials too; and that goes for the U.S.A.

I have many quarrels with the Englishman. I do not subscribe to his opinion that he is God Almighty. But my quarrels are private, family quarrels. My fighting days (if I ever had any) are over. If it were not so, I should proudly stand back to back with any Englishman in any quayside pub, a broken bottle in each hand, to defend the honour of Queen Victoria or Horatio Bottomley or Ernie Bevin against any bunch of foreigners that ever was littered.

It is my firm belief that beyond the shores of Albion is the sea, and that belongs to Great Britain. Beyond the sea lies the scum of the world. I cannot help it. That is what I feel. With many another Scotch fool, I felt my spirit lift when England and Scotland were left alone to fight barbarism in the days of Dunkirk. That is why I don't want the English to think that we are sneering at them.

I have no other reason. Politically, they have treated my country abominably. They are in many ways a ridiculous people. At the same time, they are the only people in the present-day world with the smallest claims to greatness, and I admire them very much. So do you.

Magnanimity is a greater quality than sportsmanship or a sense of humour, those two qualities on which the Englishman, for some reason or other, prides himself. What sportsmanship he has, he learned from the Scots and the French. What humour he has acquired, he got from the Irish. His native brand is very primitive and is concerned mainly with physical calamities. How sad it is when we observe the great Shakespeare or the great Dickens really trying to be funny.

Who cares whether he has a sense of humour or not? Who cares if his, 'Well played, Sir!' sounds perfunctory and false, now and again? You will notice that he commends his enemy with a sincere 'Well played, Sir', only when he is obviously a beaten enemy. This is not sportsmanship—or love of sport for its own sake. To tell the truth, the only true sportsmen are the rabbits of the game, and the Englishman hates to see himself as a rabbit. I'll tell you what it is, though. It is another manifestation of magnanimity. The Englishman cheers on the beaten, the fallen, the plucky underdog and, if his interests are not too inextricably engaged, lends him a helping hand. He is, in short, a pretty good man.

There are good men in other countries. Candour compels that admission. But nobody could call them typical. The good Englishman is, somehow or other, typical. Even in Scotland, where we are remarkable for many high and distinguished traits, we are not typically good. A solemn thought.

If I am right, and the Englishman is good, it should be possible to by-pass his preconceptions and prejudices and appeal straight to that goodness. It should be possible to convince him that Scotsmen are not a superior kind of 'native', or an inferior kind of Englishman. It should be possible to tell him, without offence, that Scotland prizes her individuality and to explain to him exactly what that individuality means. Methods which include time bombs and sawed off shotguns seem to be abominable methods to use in convincing good (if unreasonable) people how to treat their neighbours and partners. If it is news to England that she is not treating Scotland properly, let us spread the tidings by (as Ramsay MacDonald once powerfully said) this means and that means and the other means. She may in time come to understand Scotland's dilemma between party loyalties and British loyalties and Imperial loyalties and loyalty to herself.

All that is another story. We are not writing letters about Scotland. We have been trying to make a Scotsman called McLaren and a Scotsman called Bridie clarify and arrange their ideas about England and relate those ideas to ascertainable truth. My Conscience, we have made a bonny mess of it, I'm thinking. All I know about the English at the hinder end of it is that if they are not the Chosen People they are rather good candidates for the choice, and I doubt if they have any likely rivals.

I, for one, seem to have left out everything I intended to say to you. Your reference to the esprit of the staircase makes me believe that you are in the same case. Perhaps our very inhibitions have another lesson for us. Perhaps St. George strikes his critics dumb, or the next thing to it, so that when they stand at the bar of justice they can only jargonate. By George, now I think of all the powerful analyses I have read of the English character, I believe that is true. Moscow has nothing on the English in making adverse witnesses talk nonsense. They do it without drugs, or hypnotism or torture, or even the use of mirrors. They do it by magic.

A happy trip to you, and to your lady wife.

As ever, James Bridie.

LETTER XVIII

From Moray McLaren to James Bridie

Glasgow, 15th March.

My dear J.B.,

Your last letter, which I receive upon the eve of going away, is so admirably even poignantly sincere, that it demands a sincere answer. I do not mean to imply that, in anything you, or I think I, have written to each other before, we have been insincere. It is only that when talking about so solemn and tremendous a subject as 'The English' (living as we do under their great shadow) it is almost impossible to avoid expressing certain truths flippantly—none the less they are truths. But you have swept flippancy aside in your last letter. I shall do my best to fall in with your undoubtedly appropriate mood. Herewith the dying fall of our correspondence.

What do I really think of the English? Your letter hints if it does not pose the question. Well, I *like* them better than any other race or country under the sun. I love my own country better. I admire or respect (or a mixture of both) the French more. I enjoy the Irish more. But I like the English best. The nearest runners-up for liking are the Italians. They are the only people who, from their natural manners and mannerisms, can make me laugh sympathetically as do the English. They don't make me laugh at their wit or their cruelty or their intellectualism as do some other people: they make me laugh simply because they are (for the moment) happy children with

144

grown-up manners and habits. The reason I like the English better even than the Italians is that the Italians, childish though they may be in their enchanting behaviour, discover in themselves, to themselves, and to the world, the knowledge that childishness is not enough. They always know that there must be an end to the game. They know, or think that they know, that at some time somewhere Someone will say, *Finita la commedia*. The English do not know this. I really think they don't and I don't think they pretend they don't know. That is why I like them better than the Italians. You will see that I don't enjoy quite so large, so good humoured a xenophobia as you do. So far as other nations are concerned, I have had affections and even vast comprehensive international love affairs with whole peoples. But from out of this welter of extraisolian emotion I return to 'the island' to like the English best. Not even my beloved pre-1939 Poles can claim to be liked by me so much as are the English.

To put it mildly you agree in liking the English. But why do we like them? What is the quality of likeableness? How is it to be found, or at least discerned rather than merely felt in the English? Again, I don't know. It certainly isn't their charm. Charm is a fascinating rather than a likeable trait. Moreover, though many Englishmen possess it, it is unnatural to them. I always distrust an Englishman who has charm just as I distrust an Irishman who hasn't. I also distrust an Englishman who speaks French well. But I don't distrust an Irishman or one of our own compatriots who does. May I say that by speaking French well I don't mean speaking it accurately or even perfectly.

I mean speaking it so that it sounds and looks as if a Frenchman were speaking it. Englishmen who manage this almost impossible feat shock and frighten me. It is, I cannot help feeling, the ultimate perversity for them. Here let me break off to say that I have heard more pedantically correct French from Englishmen than from any Frenchman (No, I don't quite mean that, but nearly). At any rate, I have never heard sentences winding to the ringing and conclusive subjunctive so perfectly thought out and so well phrased as from English lips. But the very minuteness of their perfection is like the decoration on the barrels of the shot-gun, unnecessary, and even ridiculous. '*Auriez vous voulu, Madame, que je passasse?*' I once heard an Englishman say after having waited patiently at a door for a Frenchwoman to go through.

No, it is not such charm as they do possess: nor is it their celebrated sense of justice, nor their slowly accumulated and, as compared with other nations, uninterrupted civilization, nor their amiability of which I have spoken so much. It is not anything so simple as that you know where you are with them—because you don't. Nor is it their straightforwardness— they often aren't straightforward, but never intentionally not straightforward. Nor is it even their indefinable sense of innocence. They are a trifle too conscious of this quality in themselves and trade too much on it. No, one of the reasons I like them is because (like the Italians) they make me feel inclined to laugh with them rather than at them. They are, with all their ruthlessness, the race with the least malice on the surface of the Earth. But then I'm forgetting my friends the unintellectual Negroes. But for the purposes of the argument they don't count. Still, as I think I hinted before, it is strange how many good qualities the English and the Negroes share. Finally I suppose one also likes them for their sense of common, or rather uncommon, decency. A howling platitude, I know, but I can only relieve its howlingness by saying that if you ask me to say what I mean by decency, I can't tell you: I only know what I mean. I know also that we Scots, Irish and Welsh aren't half so decent—and that goes, only more so, for the rest of the world.

I really don't know what would happen if we Scots were more generally 'decent'. Decency being, I suppose, a good thing, it would be a good thing if we were more decent. But, somehow, I think I should regret so tremendous a transformation. I should regret it because we would lose, along with the acquisition of decency, so many qualities that are a part of not being decent. We would lose, for instance, our capacity for going to extremes in so much that we do and feel and are. You have said that 'the good English-man is, somehow or other, typical.' How right you are. Goodness is the norm of the English character. It is not (I cannot help thanking goodness) the norm of the Scottish character. The best people I have ever met in my life have come from Scotland: so have the most detestable. This is particularly true of my King Charles's head the politicians. Those who have followed this extraordinary calling (and have not taken their wages and are dead), who have yet pursued it in this island with the purest lamp of virtue shining are, or have been, Scots. On the other hand, a large proportion of our native breed of politicians are surely the lowest things that crawl between fog and mud. I think on the whole I prefer this combination to general goodness. But that is because I am Scotch. None the less, from afar off, I salute English common goodness. It is a good thing.

You have used a very apt simile when you say that you would always be prepared to fight with the English, broken bottle in hand, and back to back. 'Back to back' is the operative phrase. I would not like to fight with (oh, the vagueness of the English preposition!) with the English face to face. We would certainly be defeated. They always win. And, while it is one of our boasts or excuses, or romantic evasions, that we are more glorious in defeat than in victory, I am getting a little bit tired of this kind of 'There's glory for you'— at least nationally speaking. Still less would I like to fight alongside with them; for that would amount to peeping from underneath one of their oxters brandishing a sgian dhu or dirk while they wielded the great two-handed engine above our tousled and protected heads. No, thank you very much. Back to back or nothing.

Yes, they are likeable. They are also very irritating, much more irritating than most other foreigners. One can turn away from and ignore the nerve jarring qualities of remote peoples more easily than one can those of the English. This isn't only because they are geographically close to us and politically on top of us. No, the very childlike innocence of the Englishman's annoying characteristics make them much more difficult to put out of one's mind. Some of us from the 'Celtic

148

fringe' make a kind of living out of being annoyed with the English. This is silly. And it really only flatters the Englishman's self-contentment to the extent of turning it into vanity which is good for no one. It is also a pity for the annoyed one to admit to suffering from so constant an obsession. Surely it is a trifle absurd for so great a giant as Shaw to have spent so large a part of the major portion of a century being annoyed by the English—and he has never really succeeded in annoying them, which must be very annoying for everyone else concerned. I think you have much more urbanely, in a much more kindly, and therefore more devastating a fashion dealt with what it is that is annoying in the English than have the professional annoyees. You have certainly done it better than I could. So there is nothing for me to add on that score save one more example.

I said somewhere near the beginning of these letters that some English people might find it, at best, an amusing affectation for us to claim to be able to talk about the English objectively. I said that you and I knew better. At the risk of seeming to protest too much I return to this point. I do so because my defence in advance has been justified. Some of my English friends who have called on me recently while playing or appearing in Glasgow had heard from me (quite casually, I hasten to say) that you and I were engaged on this correspondence. As I foresaw, they thought the idea might be good fun, but could contain no serious thought, or at least objective thought. 'Why', they said, 'Bridie and you, despite your occasional manner-isms of expression are soaked in Englishness. You can't look on England from without. If you had been a monoglot Gaelic speaker and Bridie a remote Buchan farmer you *might* have had something to say— but even then. . . .' You see the old idea, the idea that one can only be un-English if one is uncouth or ignorant or tucked away. For that (God pity them) is what they meant by being a monoglot Gael or a Buchan farmer.

I did not, of course, argue with them. I did not refer to an old friend of mine, a member of their own profession, who wrote the most charming, the most devastating yet the most affectionate criticism of the Austrians. He was a Viennese of the Viennese, an actor, a playwright and a journalist. When the Empire collapsed in 1918 he stayed on in Vienna. Yet he was able to write about the Austrians and the Viennese so well, not only because he knew them so intimately, but even more so because he had been a Pole from Cracow when it was still a part of the Austrian Empire. He had got into the Viennese spirit and mind, but had never become of it. Neither you nor I could be described as Londoners in the sense that my friend was a Viennese, but it struck me that he might have been a good example for argument. However I did not argue. Nor did I pedantically refer to history, to past and yet surviving social and national customs and all that sort of thing. Least of all did I dream of talking about Heredity. Never would I raise such a subject under the shadow of you, my old Unsleeping Clergyman.

But it did set me thinking once again on the English habit, and how hard it dies, the habit of amiably, humorously and kindly looking upon the Scot and the

Irishman at home as a kind of privileged foreigner, yet
never considering himself (the Englishman) as a foreigner
within these islands. Incredible as it may seem, this
attitude even now lingers on in the English approach
to the Irish business, and it has been amusing to note
the English indignation when the Irish, with their
perverted sense of logic, have reversed the process and
have, as someone said the other day, changed their
old request of 'Include us out' to 'Exclude us in'.
However, this point of view of the English is only the
old Imperial Roman one: and it really isn't annoying.

It is only annoying in the debauching effect it has
on some of our native politicians and on some of our
native (and Irish, oddly enough) music hall comics and
writers. No names no publishers' proof-drill. But
to you of all people I don't need to mention them.
You have heard them roll those ostentatious and
exaggerated 'r's'. You have heard them, whilst undertaking the conducting of choirs, assuming the bogus
Highland whine of uplifting cant. You have seen them
strike those attitudes of sham, rugged northern grandeur, determination and steadfastness. You have seen
how soon these attitudes collapse when pricked by the
pin of necessity. Worse still, you have seen and heard
our compatriots, and the Irish, blatantly appealing to
the Englishman's capacity to laugh and cry in a condescending manner at the same time. You have seen
us (yes, in this we are worse than the Irish) behaving
like a crowd of Babu Jabberjees at one moment and
Bonnie Prince Charlies at the next. In fact you know
better than I do the whole nauseating business. But
you know, not better but just as well as I do, how to

forgive the prostitute minority of our compatriots who behave in this manner and the majority of well-meaning English people who encourage them.

Your remark about fighting back to back with the English is still in my mind. It has really said what we both feel about them once and for all. I, like you, and unlike the Irish, would be appalled to find our country not fighting on the side (not in the side) of the English in any struggle which they were waging for their existence—however foolishly and wantonly provoked by themselves. In any such event I shall be alongside you, with two broken bottles in my hands, but *back to back with Them*. You have said that you would join in such a quarrel in defence of Queen Victoria, Horatio Bottomley or Ernie Bevin. I would go even further. I would wield my bottles even on behalf of Joad, Harold Laski and Kingsley Martin. Can I say more than that?

Yes, I can. Don't you think that 'Back to Back' might be a good sub-title for the Book? Perhaps not.

Yours,

Moray McLaren.

PALE GUARDIAN

PALE GUARDIAN

A James Asher vampire novel

Barbara Hambly

This first world edition published 2016
in Great Britain and 2017 in the USA by
SEVERN HOUSE PUBLISHERS LTD of
19 Cedar Road, Sutton, Surrey, England, SM2 5DA.
Trade paperback edition first published
in Great Britain and the USA 2017 by
SEVERN HOUSE PUBLISHERS LTD

British Library Cataloguing in Publication Data
A CIP catalogue record for this title is available from the British Library.

ISBN-13: 978-0-7278-8677-4 (cased)
ISBN-13: 978-1-84751-780-7 (trade paper)
ISBN-13: 978-1-78010-849-0 (e-book)

All Severn House titles are printed on acid-free paper.

Severn House Publishers support the Forest Stewardship Council™ [FSC™],
the leading international forest certification organisation.
All our titles that are printed on FSC certified paper carry the FSC logo.

MIX
Paper from
responsible sources
FSC
www.fsc.org   FSC® C013056

Typeset by Palimpsest Book Production Ltd.,
Falkirk, Stirlingshire, Scotland.
Printed and bound in Great
TJ International, Padstow,

For Robin

ONE

'Don't go out there—'

Dr Lydia Asher turned as a weak hand plucked at her skirt.

By the light of her lantern the young soldier's face was drawn with pain and chalky with loss of blood. The single eye that had survived the shrapnel when a German shell had struck the forward trench blinked up at her with desperate intensity.

'It's all right,' Lydia whispered. 'You're safe here, Brodie.' It was astounding how many peoples' names she managed to remember, now that she wore her spectacles full-time. Around them the long tent was silent, the wounded men sleeping. For the first time in nearly a week, the road eastward from the camp was quiet, the surgical tent, across the way, dark. Northward, in the direction of Ypres, she could still hear the guns. It was March of 1915. 'We're all—'

The young man shook his head. 'She's walkin' tonight, M'am. I seen her look into the tent. The *bean sí . . .*'

'Shhh.' Lydia leaned over him, marveling that he was alive at all – she'd assisted Major Overstreet yesterday in removing nearly two pounds of wood and metal fragments from the boy's chest – and gently straightened the blanket; the night was bitterly cold. 'It isn't a banshee.'

'It is, M'am,' insisted Brodie, his voice barely a breath, in his pain still mindful of others who slept nearby. 'I seen her in the trenches, just before the Germans came on. The other men have seen her, too. She wears a nursin' sister's uniform but she's none of them here at the station, her eyes is like a cat's in the dark. Wait till she's gone by, M'am. 'Tis the worst sort of bad luck to see her.'

'I'll be all right.' She made a move to disengage her sleeve from the grasping fingers, but his eye pleaded with her.

'You think I'm off me head but I'm not. I really have seen her, down the trenches, in the dead of the night. Me mates say they've seen her near the aid stations, an' the clearin' stations like this one—'

Quietly, Lydia said, 'She doesn't come into the wards like this one. You and your mates—' her glance took in the other men, shapeless lumps beneath the blankets in the frowsty darkness – 'will go back to hospital tomorrow. It isn't you she comes for.' She pushed up the white cuff of her VAD uniform – the best the Medical Corps could come up with for her, as she was neither a nursing sister nor a surgeon – and showed him the four stout lines of silver chain around her wrist. 'Silver keeps them away, you know. I'll be perfectly all right.'

His eye was slipping closed and his head, in its swathe of bandages, sagged back onto the thin pillow. 'Does she come for the dyin', then? That's a *bean sí*, isn't it? And if I seen her walkin' . . .'

'Just because you saw her,' murmured Lydia gently, 'doesn't mean she's coming for you. You rest now, Mr Brodie. I promise. You'll be all right, and I'll be all right. You'll be moved back to hospital in the morning.' *If they have enough ambulances and enough petrol and enough drivers for the less desperate cases, and if the Germans don't decide to shell the Calais road again . . .*

He slid into sleep even as she stepped away from his cot. When she reached the tent-flaps at the far end of the ward, she lowered the flame on her lantern as far as she could, and adjusted a sheet of tin around the glass chimney, such as the wire-cutting parties sometimes used, or the bearers out searching for the wounded. After eleven days in the gutted village of Pont-Sainte-Félicité Lydia was sure enough of her way around the casualty clearing station to at least not bump into walls or fall into either the gaping cellars of bombed houses or the shelled-out labyrinth of abandoned German trenches that surrounded the town.

She pushed up her spectacles to rub her eyes.

She had swabbed the last of the blood from the fluoroscope table that was her charge, checked to see that the machine itself was disconnected from the generator wires, and put back in their places the clumsy lead apron and gloves that she insisted on wearing (to the annoyance of the surgeons: 'It's not a bloomin' death ray, M'am! We've got men dying in here!'). She'd sent her assistant, a slow-speaking Welshman named Dermott, to bed some hours before, when he'd started making mistakes owing to the fact that like herself he'd been awake since yesterday morning. Everything that was left to do, Lydia was reasonably certain, could wait until daylight.

Except this.

This had to be done while darkness yet covered the land.

The thing that Brodie had seen (*How DARE she come peeking into the tents!*) she didn't worry much about, though nothing living stirred in the camp now except the ever-present rats.

As she had intimated to Brodie, in such proximity to the Moribund Ward, where nearly two hundred men lay irreclaimably dying – not to speak of the lines of trenches to the east – she, and he, and all the men in his ward, were almost certainly safe.

She touched the thick links of silver that protected her wrists, and the further chains that lay over the big blood vessels of her throat, and reflected with a kind of tired irony that she stood in the one place in all of Europe where she could be fairly sure that she was not going to be attacked by vampires.

The silence outside was like death, save for the not-very-far-off thunder of the guns.

With her lantern hooded, her eyes accustomed themselves to the darkness. Those who hunted the night in nearly every city of the world were well used to turning aside the eyes of the living. They would assume that she, too, believed the simple mental tricks that shielded them from human notice – that she was merely making some routine round – and would not slip away when they heard the damp scrunch of her footsteps.

But she was aware of what she sought, and so could sometimes see past their illusions. Over the past week and a half – at least before the mad avalanche of wounded had begun to pour in six days previously – or was it seven? – she had been able to catch glimpses of them, and had kept a list. *Tall dark woman, big nose. Stout man, sleek dark hair. Tall blonde man, square face. Small blonde woman, beautiful . . .*

Those were only the ones she'd seen. She knew there were others.

Hundreds, certainly. Thousands, perhaps.

Would Jamie, her husband back in Oxford with their three-year-old daughter, recognize some of them? *Probably.* He knew more of them by sight than she did, though she was certain that on her second night here she'd glimpsed Elysée de Montadour, the Master vampire of Paris.

At a guess, every vampire in Europe was here in Flanders, or further south along the line of trenches that stretched from the Channel to the Alps. Most of them would be lurking around the hospitals. With far less courage than the stretcher-bearers, they only ventured into no man's land itself in the dead hours of the night, if at all. Men and women who had chosen to murder others rather than face whatever lay on the far side of death weren't about to run the risk of encountering a raiding party, or being caught in a sudden barrage of shells, or becoming entangled in barbed wire that would hold them until the sun rose and ignited their pale and bloodless flesh.

Not when there was easier prey a few miles off.

The shattered walls of a ruined cottage provided her with concealment. Her lantern's hooded glimmer touched broken rafters, charred spills of bricks, gaping cellars. Most of the furniture – and many of the bricks – had been looted within hours of the clearing station's establishment in Pont-Sainte-Félicité (she herself had bagged a kitchen table for Dermott's makeshift developing station). She strained her ears as she moved from room to room, until she heard a flickering whisper and stepped close to one of the blown-out windows.

And there they were. Six feet from the window, themselves taking advantage of the walls of a ruined house to survey the hospital tents which glowed very faintly in the darkness, from the lanterns within. Their reflective eyes caught dim shreds of light that shone through the cracks of the hastily-erected wooden mess huts. The tall, dark woman with the big nose, and two men – the taller man strong-built, with fair, receding hair, the smaller, slender and dark. Both men wore British uniforms; the woman, a black dress that blended with the night. Their flesh was almost milk-white, and they stood so close to the window that she could see the woman's hands were armed with inch-long claws. Were it not for the stillness of the blighted town Lydia wouldn't have heard the wind-whisper voices. Flemish? Italian? Lydia knew that vampires had come to the Front from as far away as Sicily, Edinburgh, Athens.

She blinked – her eyes were aching, she had spent twenty hours out of the past twenty-four either taking x-ray photographs of bleeding men or helping out in the surgical tent – and when she looked back they were gone.

'Bother,' she muttered, and moved on.

Not what she was seeking.

Still her heart quickened with terrified dread.

What she sought, she had seen seven nights ago, the night before the big push at Neuve Chapelle. Every night, every day, in the surgical tent and the fluoroscope room and in her dreams when she'd collapse at odd hours to snatch some sleep, she'd fought recurring dread – *I have to find out what was happening. I have to see if it happens again . . .*

It took her about two hours to circle the collection of medical tents, wooden huts and mule-lines, meticulously careful to look about her as if she were simply checking the area for spies or deserters or for Quartermaster's Storeman Pratt out making deals for the Army rations he stole and sold to civilians on the side. She saw three more vampires: one in the ruined houses of the village – the slim woman with soft cascades of light-brown hair whom she'd seen last week, Lydia recalled – and two down in the caved-in horrors of the deserted German trenches, wearing dark civilian clothes and whispering to one another in German. The language didn't trouble her. Plenty of Swiss spoke German, not to mention French Rhinelanders. In any case, she knew quite well that once a living man or woman crossed into the kingdom of the damned, they generally lost all interest in the affairs of the living.

To the vampire, the war – and the battle zone – meant one thing only.

The deserted trenches around the village were horrible. They swarmed with rats, reeked of the German soldiers buried when English shells had caved in their dugouts. Five months at the Front hadn't cured Lydia of her morbid horror of the vermin. Carrying her lantern low so that its light wouldn't be seen above, she had to hold up her skirts in the other hand as she picked her way down the side of a shell-crater, and into the zigzag pits. The water down there was almost knee-deep and freezing cold, and her feet groped to stay on the duckboards down under the surface. The mud beneath them would be like quicksand.

She didn't see the thing she'd seen the previous week. Stumbling with weariness – *I HAVE to find out . . . What if there's another push tomorrow and it's another five days before I can watch again?* – she scrambled up the broken trench ladder she'd scouted out the week before.

I HAVE to find out . . .

A rung of the ladder snapped soggily beneath her foot. She dropped the lantern, grabbed for support, and a hand came down from the darkness above and grasped hers, cold with the cold of a dead man's. The iron-strong fingers tipped with inch-long claws.

She was drawn up over the parapet of sandbags at the top with the effortless strength of the Undead.

'Mistress,' a voice murmured, 'when first you came to this place, for two nights did you walk thus, but I thought you had given the practice o'er. You shall come to grief at it.'

Lydia shook out her muddied skirts and propped her thick-lensed spectacles more firmly onto the bridge of her nose. 'I thought all the vampires were out making a feast of the wounded.' Her voice cracked a little, at the memory of poor Brodie, of all the men in the ward. She realized she was shaking with weariness. 'Either here or up in the front-line trenches—'

'What would you, Mistress?' returned the voice reasonably. 'When the shelling is done, and the dying lie in the mud of the battleground where the guns have left them, where none will reach them? When men die in their blood waiting for an ambulance that will never come? We feed upon blood, lady. We feed upon death. The whole of Flanders, the whole of the Rhineland, the whole of the Front glows with sustenance such as we are, in time of peace, are obliged to ration, sip by sip, lest our existence be suspected. Can you blame those who exist by absorbing the life-force of the living, for being drawn to such a banquet?'

'Yes!' Lydia tried to pull her arm free of his steadying grip. She staggered in her exhaustion and would have fallen had cold arms not caught her, thin as whalebone and steel, and lifted her bodily. 'I can. I do. It's so unfair . . .'

'You are frozen,' said Don Simon Ysidro's soft voice. 'And spent. And I promised James that I would look after you here in Flanders.'

'He'd never have accepted such a promise—'

'Nevertheless I gave it.' To his near-soundless whisper still clung the accents of sixteenth-century Spain, whence he had journeyed, a living man, to the court of the queen whom the English called Bloody Mary. He had encountered the Master of London among the stones of an English churchyard one dark night, and never returned to his home. 'And you will come to grief not from the kindred of darkness,' he went on, as he bore her toward the tents, 'but from getting your feet wet in cold such as this, or from encountering that pestilent creature who peddles ammunition and food and heating-oil to the local peasants – to the poor Germans, too, belike.'

'Storeman Pratt.' She relaxed suddenly, and rested her head on the vampire's thin shoulder. 'You're perfectly right, Don Simon, he probably *would* kill a nurse who surprised him at it. Or at least make up some frightful crime and then blackmail me about it.'

Beneath her cheek she felt the sturdy wool of an epaulet, and guessed that he, too, had adopted the uniform of a British officer – *Procured from Mr Pratt himself, I daresay!* – which no observer, if they *did* spot him, would dare question. He probably had impeccable papers, too – *Very likely purchased from the same source!* She felt beaten, her anger denied and deflected, lost in the greater rage at the greater deaths about which she could do nothing. Her mind touched briefly on the young Yorkshireman who'd died on her x-ray table . . . *Was that this morning? Yesterday afternoon?* On poor Brodie, whose x-ray had showed her that he would almost certainly have his legs amputated once he reached the base hospital at Calais. On another boy – barely seventeen, he'd looked – she'd checked with Captain Calvert in the surgical tent, sobbing for his mother and so riddled with shrapnel that he'd been set gently aside, so that men whose lives *could* be saved could be operated on first.

You're dying anyway, we have no time to save you . . .

Shuttling desperately between her fluoroscope machine and the surgical tent where every trained hand was needed, she hadn't even had time to go back and see that youth before he died.

Tears that she hadn't been able to shed closed her throat. More than anything else, she wanted to be with Jamie at this moment. To be back in Oxford and out of this place of stink and death and cold. *I'm just tired*, she told herself firmly. *I'll feel better when I've had some sleep . . .*

Don Simon Ysidro was a vampire. There had been times, in the eight years of their acquaintance, when she had hated him – for what he was, for what she knew that he did and had done in the centuries since his non-death. There had been times when she'd felt herself falling in love with him – despite her unswerving love for the tall, leathery Lecturer in Philology at New College, Oxford whom she had adored with the whole of her heart since the age of fourteen.

But Jamie was back in Oxford, still recuperating, slowly, from the pneumonia that had nearly killed him in the first month of the war.

And she was here, in the darkness, feeling the thready pale spider-silk of Ysidro's long hair brush against her forehead, and hearing the guns.

She said, 'Someone else is out there looking for vampires.'

'Are they, indeed?'

The smell of latrines, of the hospital tents, of cook-tent smoke and makeshift stoves surrounded them like a fuggy embrace. Ysidro stooped and canvas brushed her face as they entered the nurses' tent, a barely-visible bulk in the darkness. One of the VAD's she shared with would be on the ward at this hour of the night; the other slept like an unwaking corpse. A tiny flicker of light as Ysidro kindled the lantern next to her bed showed her the vampire's face, thin, aquiline, pale as white silk, framed in a loose mane of colorless hair and illuminated by eyes that had, in life, probably been hazel. They'd bleached now to a cold sulfurous yellow, faintly pleated with gray – he'd told her once that this 'bleaching' occasionally happened to vampires, no one quite knew why. The mental illusion that kept her from noticing his fangs also kept Sister Violet Brickwood from waking, not that the poor woman *would* stir, after twenty hours on her feet . . .

Ysidro pulled Lydia's shoes and stockings off her, and wrapped her feet in the blanket of her cot. Then he dipped water from the jerrycan in the corner and poured it into the kettle, which he placed on the heating-stove.

'I saw her a week ago . . . no, longer . . .' Lydia shook her head. 'The second night we were here.'

'Ah.' She thought he did some mental calculation, placing the night in his mind.

'After I finished setting up the fluoroscope room I walked the perimeter of the camp. When we were back at Givenchy – before the clearing station was moved here – I knew there were vampires all around the camp, every night. I'd glimpse them between the tents, and some of the men have seen them, too. They don't know what they are.'

'Did you look for me?'

'I couldn't imagine you'd let anyone see you.'

A smile touched a corner of his mouth, turned his face suddenly human, a living man's, and young. 'You had the right of it, Mistress. Yet you did not make a practice of such patrols at Givenchy.'

'Once I knew they were there, I didn't really see the point.' Lydia propped her spectacles again. 'I mean, I knew they wouldn't attack the nurses, or the surgeons, or really anyone but the dying. Why cause themselves problems when there are so many easier victims? That sounds horrible, but when I thought about it – and about how few of us there were to take care of the wounded and how terrible the casualties were – that was during the fighting at Ypres – I came to the conclusion that I could probably save more lives by getting a few hours more sleep, instead of chasing vampires whom I knew I'd never catch. I don't . . .' she stammered. 'I don't mean that, exactly, but . . .'

'You chose rightly, lady.' He held up a hand. 'And you did a hero's work at Givenchy, and here. I have watched you.'

She brushed his compliment aside with tears of shame in her eyes.

'There was no right choice,' his soft voice insisted. 'More men lie in the Moribund Ward, and in the trenches themselves, than would suffice to glut the greediest of the Undead, were there five times more of us here than there are. We have no need to trouble even those men who can be saved, ere you load them into the ambulance-wagons. Our business is with the dying. 'Tis not we, these days, who deal out death.'

'I know.' She took off her glasses to wipe her tears. 'It doesn't mean you aren't monsters.'

'The vileness of my condition is old news to me, lady.' He measured cocoa from its tin (*Where would a vampire learn to make cocoa?*) into her mug, and stirred the hot water in. 'I admit, 'tis not the future I envisioned for myself when I studied my catechism with the Christian Brothers in Toledo. Yet you have not told me how you came to resume your practice of walking the night?'

'I just . . . wanted to get some idea of the local vampire population.' The thick pottery was God's blessing against her chilled hands. 'Though I knew they'd followed the clearing station down here. But the second night, in the ruins of the village, I saw another woman, moving about like me with her lantern hooded. I thought she might have been a spy when first I saw her light – I suppose there are local women, who think the Germans ought to own this part of France, or even German women who've been slipped across the lines. I closed my lantern entirely and followed her, and it became pretty clear to me that she was doing exactly what I did the first night: she circled the camp at a distance, and checked the bombed-out German trenches. She – we – glimpsed vampires twice, and she stood off at a distance, fingering something she wore at her neck, a silver cross or something of the kind, I assume. She kept watch around the ward tents of the men especially. A spy wouldn't do that.'

'No.' He settled himself on the foot of Nurse Danvers's empty bed, folded slim hands around his knee.

Lydia frowned across at him in the lantern-light. He was attired, as she'd surmised, in the trimly tailored uniform of a staff colonel in the British Expeditionary Force. 'Have you seen her?'

'I have,' returned Ysidro. 'At all events I have seen a young woman with a lantern, stealing about the ruins of the village, and down in the abandoned trenches. This was ere the battle started: brunette, and smaller of stature than yourself, though broader in shoulder and hip. Her clothes were dark, and she might well have worn a silver crucifix about her neck – something silver, at all events.'

Lydia touched the chains around her own throat again self-consciously: enough silver to burn a vampire's mouth or hands, to give her a split-second in which to wrench free, to scream, to run . . .

As if anyone could outrun the Undead.

And unless the crucifix was of nearly-pure silver, it would have no more effect on a vampire than would any other pendant of similar metal content.

'Did she speak to any of the vampires?'

'Not that I have observed. She has not your familiarity with those who hunt the night, Mistress. She seeks, but cannot find. At least, 'twas so ere the casualties started coming in such numbers. Since the fighting started on the tenth I have not seen her.'

'Have you any idea who she is?'

He shook his head, or came as near to doing so as she had ever seen him, a slight motion more of his eyes than his head, as if in the centuries since his death he had lost interest in communication with the living. 'Yet I saw none but yourself engaging in such behavior at Givenchy. And none of the vampires to whom I've spoken, either here or nearer the lines, have mentioned any like matter. I admit I have not joined the groups that go out into the trenches, or into no man's land in the dead of the night. Peasants.' The two smallest fingers of his right hand flicked in a gesture of concentrated scorn. 'Without manners or conversation, most of them. I shall enquire.'

'Thank you,' said Lydia. 'I appreciate it. I'd like very much to know if others – elsewhere along the Front, for instance – are also trying to . . . to meet, and speak with, vampires, or if this is just something, someone, local. I don't expect, when the battle itself was going on, that the woman I saw could get away from wherever she was. Or possibly didn't dare.'

'Given the likelihood that one side or the other might break through the lines, or that shelling might commence anywhere at any time,' remarked the vampire, taking the empty mug from her hands, 'I myself would hesitate to venture far from shelter. I understand the Venetian nest foregathered in the chateau at present occupied by the Master of Prague and his fledglings, for a session of *écarté* which lasted through three nights.'

'What did they play for?' A dreadful question to ask an Undead multiple murderer, but she really did want to know. 'I mean, do you play for money? Do you *have* money? The Bank of France froze all withdrawals at the start of the fighting.'

Ysidro looked down his highbred nose. 'One of the first lessons one learns, Mistress, when one becomes vampire, is never to let oneself be caught without money.' He came back to her cot-side and drew the blankets up over her. 'The second lesson one learns is how to obtain it – anywhere, and under nearly any circumstances. Those who do not learn such lessons in general do not survive. Thus under ordinary conditions, money means very little to the Undead. The gamblers at the chateau played, I understand, for credit-vowels, much like the surgeons and the orderlies play here. Had I known you sought information regarding this enterprising vampire-seeker I would have arranged to attend: such gatherings are clearing houses for gossip, and do not take place often.'

He tucked the blankets in around her, for the tent, though stuffy-smelling, was deeply cold. 'Sleep now,' he ordered, took her spectacles from her hand and placed them on the up-ended packing crate at her side. 'Morn will come soon enough.'

I shouldn't take comfort in his presence, she thought. *He's going to leave here and go straight across to the Moribund Ward . . .*

I shouldn't feel glad to know that he's near.

She stopped herself from catching at his hand, and only asked, 'Where were you? I mean, why weren't you playing cards and trading gossip—? The Master of Prague has a *chateau*? *HERE*?'

'You would expect him perhaps to sleep in a dugout?' One eyebrow lifted, and through a haze of myopia she saw again – or imagined – that his face for a moment became the face of the man he had been, almost three hundred and sixty years ago. And then, more quietly, 'I was watching over you, Mistress.'

And where were YOU sleeping? During the shelling, and the confusion, and the constantly shifting dangers, any one of which could trap a vampire aboveground when the first light of dawn would ignite his flesh and engulf him in flame . . .

Instead she asked, 'Do you know what this woman wants?'

'I expect—' he turned down the lantern – 'nothing good.'

TWO

Colonel Stewart shut the buff folder on his desk with a little hiss of annoyance, and scowled across at James Asher as if what he'd read there were all Asher's fault. 'Damn medicos won't clear you for service till you can run three times round Piccadilly Circus and shin up the Monument with a rope. Got no idea there's a war on and we need every man.'

Asher suspected that the damn medicos, up to their hairlines in shattered and dying men, were as cognizant of the war as Stewart was and were seeing it a damn sight closer. But he only returned, 'I can't say I'm surprised. Or entirely disappointed. Just coming down here knocked me out. I'd hoped to go back up to Oxford tonight and I'm staying in town instead.'

'You look perfectly fit to me,' grumbled the colonel, rising to show Asher from his office. 'Damnit, man, you'd only be sitting in a cell with a lot of Jerries listening to 'em talk! How hard can it be?'

Asher, who'd had three relapses of pneumonia since his return to Oxford in September – after nearly dying of it in Paris – reflected that the last thing his lungs needed was to be surrounded by forty German prisoners of war, all coughing themselves blue. He made noises of commiseration, shook hands and promised to notify the War Office the minute he was fully recovered, and descended the steps of the rambling labyrinth on Whitehall feeling as if he'd personally swum the Channel after battling half a regiment of Roman gladiators, single-handed and armed with a golf club.

Definitely in no shape to deal with Paddington station and two hours standing in the corridor of an overcrowded railway car, much less a trip to the Front.

A younger man – and on that cold March night, though not quite fifty Asher felt like a septuagenarian at least – would have leapt at the chance, if not for glory then because his beautiful young wife, Lydia, was also at the Front. But seventeen years on Her Majesty's Secret Service had cured Asher once and for all of any possible craving for glory, and of even a moment's belief that if such a thing as glory existed (something he had always very much doubted) it could be achieved in war. And though he would without hesitation – even at his age (or the age which he felt) – have re-swum the Channel and fought those hypothetical Roman gladiators a second time with his seven iron in the hopes of even an hour in Lydia's astonishing company, he was sufficiently familiar with the workings of the War Office to know that were he to volunteer to gather information from captured German prisoners, he would undoubtedly be assigned to do so in Serbia, not Flanders. (Lydia's letters were censored but before her departure last November they had worked out a dot code, so he knew she was in Pont-Sainte-Félicité, near Neuve Chapelle.)

Whitehall was nearly dark. The pavement was thick with foot traffic from the government offices, though it was close to seven. Asher's years of sneaking in and out of foreign countries with information about naval emplacements, border fortifications and orders for new weaponry had given him a permanent watchfulness of all those around him, an awareness of faces and details of dress which, in Berlin or Vienna, could mean the difference between making it back to his hotel safely and being found dead in a storm drain. Thus, despite the swift-thickening twilight, he was very much aware that most of the men hastening to catch the 7:10 from Charing Cross had white or grizzled hair beneath their Homburg hats, and that the home-going crowd – thinner by half than it had been the year before – was at least a third female. Women and older men moved to take up the positions of men at the Front.

Or of the men who'd gone to the Front six months ago and were already dead.

Buildings loomed against the cinder sky like a black necropolis. Since January, when German Zeppelins had rained bombs on coastal towns, the government's orders to black out windows and streetlamps had assumed a new seriousness – Asher had read recently of a movement afoot to drain the Serpentine and the lake in St James's Park, lest the glitter of moonlight on their waters serve as a guide to the night raiders. Though the traffic – both motorcars and horse-drawn – was far lighter these days, Trafalgar

Square was a nightmare of jostling dark shapes swimming through the gloom, and had Asher not known the place like the back of his hand he would not have been able to locate the Underground station. Below ground the lights were bright, but the crowds were such – reduced bus service and an almost total absence of cabs more than made up for the shortage of men in city offices – that Asher had a long wait for a train to Bloomsbury.

By the time he reached the small lodging house near Euston Station his head was swimming with fatigue. He had already telegraphed Mrs Grimes – the cook back at the Oxford house – that he wouldn't be home, and briefly toyed with the notion of sending a second wire to bid Miranda a special good-night. At three, and with her mother now gone, his daughter set great store by good-night kisses, even by remote proxy. But the extreme likelihood that the Oxford Post Office wouldn't deliver the greeting until the following morning put the idea from his mind, and he ascended five flights of stairs to what had been the servants' quarters of the tall, narrow house – rooms of any kind were another thing extremely difficult to come by in London in the spring of 1915 – and dropped onto the cot in the penitential little chamber without undressing.

This turned out to be a fortunate circumstance, because twenty minutes later the landlady's daughter thumped loudly on the door with the news that a message had come from the War Office, and it looked to be important.

It was from Colonel Stewart, begging him to return. Sir Collin Hayward of Intelligence was on his way to Paris first thing in the morning, but having heard that Asher was in town, wanted very much to speak to him about assisting in the vetting and training of agents to be sent to the Continent.

Asher roundly cursed both Stewart and Sir Collin, but resumed his coat, tightened his tie (which he hadn't taken off – tired as he was, he assumed he'd have slept in it), and made his way downstairs and back to the Underground.

He spent the next three and a half hours in conference with Sir Collin, who, to do him justice, looked like he hadn't had more than a few hours' sleep in the past week.

Then because of a breakdown on the Northern line – it was past midnight, and the Underground nearly empty – Asher had

to take the Piccadilly line and walk back to Grafton Place from
King's Cross. And, owing to the completely unlighted condition
of the streets, and a moderately thick fog which had settled over
the city, he found himself, uncharacteristically, lost.

This was what he was doing, wandering among the nameless
streets east of King's Cross Station, when he encountered the
revenant.

The fog confused the way sounds carried from the railway
yards. It was too dark, even, to see the street signs, many of
which seemed to have been taken down or taped over (in an
effort his landlady had told him to thwart German spies). Likewise
it was difficult to determine in which direction Regent's Canal
lay. In places the fog was thick enough – reeking with the smoke
of the munitions factories across the river – that Asher had to
feel his way along the house walls and area railings. He could
only be glad that at this hour, nobody was operating a motorcar,
not that anyone in this neighborhood (if he was where he thought
he was) could afford such a luxury (or the petrol to put in it) . . .

Then he smelled it. Sudden, rank and horrible, like rotting fish
and the urine of rats mixed with the peculiarly horrible stench
that oozes from human beings who have washed neither their
bodies nor their clothing for months on end. Unmistakable.

He had smelled it in Peking, two years before. A thousand
times stronger, for the things had been forty and sixty strong by
the time their hive was destroyed. Don Simon Ysidro had told
him that the only other place where such monsters were to be
found was Prague, where they had spawned and multiplied for
nearly three centuries in the old Roman sewers beneath that city.
The Others, Ysidro had called them, though they were related,
in some way, to vampires. Undead, mindless, nearly impossible
to kill, they would devour anything they could catch, and presumably lived for much of the time upon rats, with whose minds
they had a curious affinity.

Here.

In London . . .

Shock and horror smote him like a physical blow.

Damnit—

Horror chilled him.

In London . . .

Listening intently, he could hear it, a slow soft dragging as the stink grew stronger. *The canal can't be more than a hundred yards off.* The Others hid under the bridges in Prague, when night cloaked that city. Down in the bed of the rivers, and in half-flooded sewer vaults, for their flesh would slowly dissolve from exposure to sunlight.

Their minds – if they could be said to have such things – were joined by a sort of mental telepathy, something the older vampires were adept at, though no vampire, so far as he knew, could control the actions of the Others.

And their condition, like that of the vampires, was spread by 'corruption of the blood'.

The vampires, whose mental powers of illusion were lessened by the movement of running water, kept away from them. Lydia had written to him months ago of the vampires at the Front: *Are these things there as well?*

One could reason with vampires.

Not with the Others.

The Others, one could only flee from, and the thought of such things at large in London iced him to the marrow.

Asher felt his way along the wall – the brick gritty under his fingers – until he reached the corner he knew had to be nearby. The smell nearly made him gag. A faint *plish* of water, around the corner to his left. By the feel of the broken pavement under-foot he guessed this was an alley. A few feet further on he trod in something squishy that smelled of rotten vegetables. Ahead, the slight metallic rattle as the Other brushed a dustbin.

Then the furious squeal of a captured rat, followed by the sudden pong of blood. The rat shrieked again – being eaten alive, presumably – and there was a loud clang as either another rat, or a cat, fled the scene in panic. Yellow light bleared suddenly in the fog with a man's shape silhouetted against it:

''Ere, then, what's . . . *Bloody 'ell*!'

Pressed to the brick of the alley wall, Asher was shocked at how close he stood to the thing, close enough to see it clearly through the fog once the light from the open door streamed out. It was indeed such a creature as had bred in the mines west of Peking, the human face deformed and bruised where the jawbones had elongated and the sutures of the face opened. The mouth, human no longer, was raw where its new-grown teeth had gashed the lips. It held the dying rat in one hand – still thrashing – and blood ran down its arm and its chin. The creature's eyes, as it swung toward the open doorway's light, flashed like mirrors.

It dropped the rat and sprang.

The shirtsleeved and unshaven watchman who'd opened the door let out a yell and tried to slam it again between them, but the creature already had him by the arm. It yanked him through and into the wet murk of the alleyway. Asher caught the lid off a dustbin and struck with its edge at the revenant's face. With a grunting bleat the Other struck it aside, staggered back, still holding the shrieking watchman; Asher slammed at it with the lid again and, when it was knocked away, caught up the dustbin itself and rammed it at the monster like a clumsy battering ram.

The revenant hurled his quarry from him and Asher heard the man's skull crack against the brick of the wall. Then it lunged at Asher, who struck with another dustbin – *Do NOT let the thing's blood touch you, do NOT* . . . The creature made one more lunge at the watchman, who lay crumpled where he'd fallen at the foot of the wall, then doubled like a rat and darted into the blackness. Asher plunged after it, one hand to the wall to guide him, and thirty feet on collided with more dustbins, falling over them as the light of two other doors opened in the murky abyss and men's voices shouted about what the 'ell was goin' on 'ere . . . (Only one of them, the philologist in Asher noted automatically, used a Southern Indian's sharper terminal 'g' . . .)

By the time Asher was pulled to his feet the creature was gone.

'What the hell is that stink?' demanded the white-haired Indian. 'Are you all right, sir?'

'He attacked a man,' panted Asher, pointing back into the solid wall of fog. 'One of the watchmen—'

The men looked at each other – three of them, a sailor and two watchmen in this district of small shops and warehouses. 'That'll be 'Arry,' said the other watchman, a silvered bulldog of a man, and as one they all ran back along the alley, Asher thinking, *What the hell will I do if the victim is alive but infected? What the hell can I say?*

The door still stood open. A fat man, balding, with a publican's apron around his waist was just moving to close it; the stouter watchman called, 'What 'appened 'ere, Tim? This gennelman says as 'ow 'Arry was attacked—'

Tim the publican's heavy-browed face creased in a frown. 'They took him away.' Sharp little blue eyes studied Asher and he added, 'You want to come on round the corner to my place, guv, an' have a sit-down. You look done up like a kipper.'

'Who took him?' Asher leaned suddenly against the wall, trembling in a wash of fatigue.

The publican's frown deepened and he put a steadying hand under Asher's arm. 'Dunno, sir. Looked like a plainclothes 'tec ter me. Skinny little feller. I'd just tied a towel round 'Arry's conk – bleedin' like a pig, 'e was – an' the feller says, "I'll take him. Cut along and get some water, 'fore we have every cat in the neighborhood lappin' at the blood." That's where I was off to now, and to get word to Weekes who owns the shop here.'

'He's right about the blood,' agreed the Indian. 'You take the gentleman inside, Tim, I'll get that water and send off to Weekes.'

Asher was led off down the alley to the back door of the Wolf and Child (which, he reflected, had no business still pouring out brandy at this hour of the night). He glanced back, his heart hammering, and he saw that, yes, the wet, black brick of the wall opposite the warehouse door glistened with a dark smear of blood. More blood was dribbled on the pavement where Harry the watchman had fallen.

I have to find him. Find where he was taken. If the creature too was wounded, and its blood found its way into Harry's open flesh, in a few days he'll begin to change . . .

The Indian guard emerged from Harry the watchman's door with a bucket of water, and doused the blood in a soapy torrent.

When Asher returned to the place on the following morning, slightly light-headed and shaky from the fatigue of the night before, and inquired of Mr Weekes – the owner of the silk warehouse Harry had watched – the shop owner had no idea to which hospital Harry had been taken. Nor had Tim the publican, just washing down the front steps of the Wolf and Child and readying to start the day's business, after seeing Asher back to his room in Grafton Place the previous night. 'No, he's got no family here in town.' The fat man shook his balding head. 'Lives in lodgin's somewhere in Camden Town, I think . . . No, I never did hear the name of his landlady. Not that it sounds like she'd care tuppence if he was brought back home cut to pieces in a sack . . .'

'If you do hear of where he might be found—' Asher handed the man his card, containing his Oxford address – 'please telegraph me here at once. I have reason to believe that the man who attacked Harry suffered from a contagious disease – spread through blood contact – and it's imperative that I at least make sure Harry wasn't infected.'

Which in its way was the truth. Neither Weekes nor Tim had been contacted yet by the police, and when Asher inquired at the Holborn Police Station later in the day he learned that the attack had not been reported. Though it was now four in the afternoon and he felt as if his bones had been ground down to the snapping point with weariness, Asher made his way to the Foreign Office.

Langham, to whom he'd reported in his days of mapmaking and rumor-sniffing in the Balkans in the 1880s, was delighted to see him. He clucked worriedly over his haggard appearance ('They told me you'd dashed nearly gone to join the choir invisible in Paris, old fellow – Stewart's an idiot for saying you should be passed as fit for a listening post . . .'), and poured out for him some indifferent sherry from a cache in the bottom of his office bookcase. He listened to Asher's carefully-tailored account of the events of the previous evening: that there had been an attack in the service alley behind the Wolf and Child in Chalton Street, that Asher had heard repeated rumors of German plans to spread an infectious disease in London, that he had reasons to suspect that the man attacked – Henry Gower – had been so infected.

'The men who work in the same street tell me that someone came, almost at once, and took Gower away, presumably to hospital.' Asher sipped his sherry – it didn't help in the least. The thought of trying to deal with the train back to Oxford that night filled him with sickened dismay. 'But it turns out that as of this morning, neither Weekes – Gower's employer – nor any of the witnesses were contacted by the police, and no report was filed. Yet we must find Gower, and more than anything else we must find the – man – who is potentially spreading the disease.'

'And what are the symptoms of this disease?' Langham spoke calmly, but his weak blue eyes were fixed on Asher's face.

Asher felt himself go perfectly cold, with a chill that had nothing to do with the onset of fever.

'High fever,' he replied promptly. 'Rash and virulent irritation, especially around the mouth. What appears to be bruising of the capillaries of the face.' Keeping his face bland, he observed that his former boss was watching him closely, with an expression of studied nonchalance.

He knows about it already.

'Hm.' Langham folded his ladylike hands. 'I'll get a report out to the hospitals, of course . . . and thank you for reporting this, old man. I'm sure it's nothing – some men are being sent home from the Front with quite gruesome cases of shell shock lately – but would it be asking too much for you to write up a report when you get back home? You are going up to Oxford this evening, are you not? That's good,' he added, when Asher nodded as if the matter were a foregone conclusion. 'You look like the very devil, old man. By all means, go to bed and stay there . . . And don't worry.' He permitted himself a secret, and slightly patronizing, little smile. 'Think no more about it. The matter is in hand.'

Asher felt the hair prickle on the nape of his neck.

'I'm glad to hear it, sir.' He smiled, rose, donned his hat – it took all his remaining strength to do so – and got out of the office, and the building, as casually as he could.

And kept an eye out behind him, all the way to Paddington Station.

THREE

'Well, thank God Jerry's taking a breather anyway.' Captain Niles Calvert dunked his hands in the tepid wash water and chivalrously handed Lydia the only dry towel in the wash corner behind the surgical tent. 'We can get some of this lot mopped up . . . God, I hate doing surgery under lights.'

'I keep wondering what we'd do if the generator went out.' Lydia carefully removed her spectacles to wipe the bridge of her nose. Rice-powder was another thing she'd given up when she'd signed her contract with the Army, and without it she felt like a schoolgirl: a blinky-blind, goggle-eyed golliwog (as the other girls at Madame Chappedelaine's had called her), a carrot-topped skinnybones with a nose like a parrot. On the other hand, it was very nice to see the faces of the men she worked with, to say nothing of not falling into shell-holes.

'And what I keep wonderin',' put in Captain Horatio Burke, straightening his own glasses, 'is how I can be sweatin' when I'm freezin' half to death.' Like Lydia, prior to the war the lumbering, grizzle-haired surgeon had had far more experience with the academic side of medicine, and after a long day of work on men deemed critical – but not violently urgent as yesterday's had been – his features sagged with fatigue.

'Different set of glands,' Lydia replied promptly. 'It's part of the fight or flight reaction.'

'You mean it's to do wi' why I don't run outen here screamin'? Aye?' he added, as a tall figure appeared in the darkness of the tent doorway.

'Message for Dr Asher.' The young man carried a hooded lantern, and by its upside-down glow, and the reflected glare from the surgical tent where the orderlies were cleaning up, Lydia automatically noted the square-jawed earnestness of his features, the brilliantined sleekness of his dark hair and the freshness of his uniform. *From Headquarters . . .*

Her heart turned over in her chest.

Oh God, Jamie . . .

Or Miranda . . .

Her hand shook as she took the note.

It was Don Simon Ysidro's handwriting. *I have found those who have seen the woman.*

She raised her eyes in startled alarm to the face of the messenger – he was taller even than Jamie's six-foot height – and he merely said in the plumiest of aristocratic accents, 'If you'd come with me, please, Doctor Asher.'

Don Simon was sitting in a staff-car some twenty feet from the lights of the camp. The young officer – he wore a captain's uniform but God only knew if he was entitled to it – helped Lydia into the vehicle, saluted the vampire and retreated. Lydia could see his broad-shouldered, slim-hipped figure silhouetted between the car and the soft glow within the nearest tents.

It was a still night. The only shelling was miles away, around Vimy, Captain Calvert had said. Shadows moved within the tents as the nursing sisters saw to their charges. When the night wind stirred it brought the stink from the incinerators where the orderlies were burning amputated limbs.

'Is that young man actually in the Army at all?' Lydia asked, and there was a whisper of amusement in Ysidro's usually expressionless voice as he replied.

'*Dios*, no. John – Captain Palfrey – resigned his commission in the First Dragoons last November, under the impression he was being recruited by a branch of the Secret Service so secret that not even the rest of the Department was aware of it – a hoax which has been embarrassingly easy to maintain. Spare me any expression of indignation on his behalf, Mistress: I have certainly saved that young man's life thereby and most assuredly the lives of at least a quarter of the men who might have found themselves under his command. He is a deplorable soldier. Will you come with me, and speak to those who have had converse with this seeker of the Undead among the Dead?'

'Converse?'

'After a fashion.' The glimmer of lights from the camp had lit the cloud of Lydia's breath when she spoke; no such vapor proceeded from the vampire's lips. 'Seeing them, she called out to them, but any vampire in his senses is wary of overtures from the living. They seldom end well. Will you come?'

'It will take me about half an hour to finish with the fluoroscope room. And I'll need to find something to tell the matron—'

'John will deal with that. Get a stouter cloak. 'Tis cold where we're going, and wet.'

Lydia guessed what he meant, and shivered. Under Captain Palfrey's respectful escort, she swabbed and tidied the x-ray table and made sure the fluoroscope was disconnected and that her own protective garb was laid out where she could find it on the morrow. The lecturers at Oxford's Radcliffe Infirmary had been fairly blithe when demonstrating this new miracle equipment, but Lydia's own researches – including at least one article in an American medical journal – had prompted her to encumber her machine with lead shielding (which made it difficult to maneuver and maddening to move) and herself with a lead apron and gloves. Major Overstreet – who handled the most serious cases – would snarl at her for taking too long, when a soldier's life was at risk on his table, but Lydia was convinced that the dangers of exposure to Röntgen rays were not imaginary.

It was nearly eight o'clock, and pitch-dark, when she finally returned to the staff-car. It made a lurching turn and set off eastward; a moment later the hooded headlamps splashed across the stones of the bridge that crossed the Lys River. After that Lydia could see nothing beyond the ruts of the road, water gleaming in potholes, and the occasional gleam in the eyes of a rat.

Most days, one could smell the trenches from the ruins of Pont-Sainte-Félicité, no mean feat, Lydia was aware, considering the olfactory competition from the camp itself. In time the car stopped, and Don Simon stepped down, helping Lydia after him with a gray-gloved hand. Through a break in the clouds the gibbous moon showed her a tortured landscape of what had been, up until last year, some of the most fertile farmland in Europe. Now it was a wasteland of mud, standing water and shell-holes, slashed across and across with trenches, deadly with tangles of barbed wire. Cold as it was, the stench was terrible. From the muffled sounds around them, Lydia guessed these former German trenches were in use now as Allied reserve trenches, with the front-line trenches and no man's land a few hundred yards further to the east. Ysidro steadied her down a ladder into the maze of communication trenches that connected the reserves with the firing trench: far safer, but hideous with icy water just beneath the half-submerged duckboards. The hands of corpses projected from the mud walls. Once she saw a skull face, flesh entirely eaten away by rats. The rats themselves were a constant scuttering movement, amid a broken debris of battered helmets (both German and British), rusting tins and broken entrenching tools that littered the shadows.

Her companion, with his courtly manners, was a vampire. A creature from horror tales.

4

This was nightmare.

'Ah.' A deep voice spoke from the darkness '*C'est la belle rousse qui patrouille dans le camp.*' A lantern-slide was cracked. Lydia made out, in the black angle of the communication trench, the two men she'd seen last night who'd been talking in the ruined village to the woman in black. The taller, fairer man bent and kissed her hand, and even through her glove his lips were warm on her frozen fingers. *He's fed.* Lydia knew it had been on some poor soldier who was dying in any case – quite possibly a German, whom she knew she was supposed to *want* dead (*Or why else are you here?*).

I shouldn't have anything to do with these people. Any of them . . .

With the preternatural quickness of perception that many vampires possessed, the fair man must have read her thoughts in her face, because when she looked back up she saw understanding in his dark eyes, and pity for the dilemma in her heart.

'We have asked ourselves, my friends and I, what it is that you seek with your lantern each night.' His French lilted with an Italian intonation – *Jamie would tell me exactly what part of Italy he comes from.* 'It is this woman, then? This dark-haired nurse—'

'She's a nurse?'

His nose wrinkled in half-comic distaste. 'She smells of carbolic and vinegar, Madame. Her dark cloak covered her dress, but the greatcoat she had underneath it was brown.'

'She could have borrowed it,' put in the slim dark youth behind his shoulder, whose face reminded Lydia of the statue of the degenerate Roman Emperor Heliogabalus in the Capitoline Museum of Rome. 'Or stolen it. Or bought it from that slippery English clerk at Pont-Sainte-Félicité . . .'

'And in fact,' agreed Lydia, taking a deep breath to steady her nerves, 'I can't see what other woman *would* be wandering about so close to the front lines.'

'Ten thousand pardons.' Ysidro bowed. 'Madame Doctor Asher, may I beg the favor of presenting to you Antonio Pentangeli, of the Most Serene Republic of Venice? And this is Basilio Occhipinti.'

'*Madama,*' murmured the dark vampire, and Antonio bowed again.

'I kiss your hands and feet, beautiful lady. As for this dark-haired nurse, wherever she acquired her greatcoat, she called out to me in French, saying, *I would speak to you.* And when we said nothing – Basilio and I – she called again, *You have nothing to fear. But I need to speak with those who hunt the night. I have a proposition, a partnership, to offer you.*'

Lydia said, 'Drat it.'

'Do not distress yourself, dear lady. Neither Basilio nor I – nor, I think, any of us who hunt the night in this appalling place – are so foolish as to think that such an offer from the living means anything but their desire to lure us into imprisonment and servitude. Don Simon will have spoken to you of the game of fox and geese that children play – and at which he himself cheats like a Greek – and it is true that it resembles the relations between the Living and the Dead. We – like the fox – have the power to easily kill any goose. But let the geese organize themselves to surround us, and it is we who die.'

'Not all of your brethren,' returned Lydia, 'have the wisdom to realize it.'

'What can the living offer us?' Antonio Pentangeli spread his hands. Like most vampires he extended his mental powers of illusion so that Lydia had to look very carefully in order to notice his claws and fangs, and the fact that he did not breathe. 'The moment the shooting began, both sides lost their power over us: the power to give us what we crave. They are like nursemaids trying to bribe a child with a peppermint, when that child stands knee-deep in a pile of sweets.'

'Was that all she said?' asked Lydia after a moment. 'Just that? A proposition – a partnership?'

''Twas all we lingered to hear.'

'Where was this? And what time?'

'Between midnight and morning. The moon was on the wane, and rose late – two nights before the battle started at Neuve Chapelle. This was south of here, near – what is the name of that village, Basilio? Haut-le-Bois?'

The slender vampire nodded, and after a moment, added, in a much thicker accent than his friend's, 'She spoke good French, nearly as good as your own, *Madama*. Yet with some accent.'

'Could you tell what sort?'

He shook his head. And indeed, reflected Lydia, one had to be very fluent indeed in a language to be able to tell whether a speaker had an accent, and where it might be from. (*Damn Jamie . . . HE could probably do it . . .*)

'Would you do this for me?' Lydia raised her eyes to Antonio Pentangeli's face. *A predator*, she thought, her heart pounding. *Who knows how many people he killed in Venice, since he himself was killed by its Master, and brought into the world of the Undead?* 'If you hear of this woman again – if you meet others who have been propositioned by her – might I beg it as a favor, that you tell Don Simon about it?'

By Basilio Occhipinti's grimace he found the idea of taking such trouble grotesque – like her Aunt Lavinnia would look, if one of the scullery maids asked her to pass along love notes to the butcher's boy. But Antonio nodded, his dark eyes grave. 'I will, *bella donna.*'

'*Antonio!*'

'Think, dear heart.' The taller vampire laid his palm to Basilio's cheek, but his eyes, Lydia observed in the lantern-light, were flat and cold, doll-like as a shark's. 'Whoever she is, the little nurse, she has some scheme in mind and we know not what it is. Whoever she finds to help her, it will be someone who wants something that isn't blood. We don't know what sort of bargain will be made.'

He bent again over Lydia's hand. 'We shall keep our ears to the ground, Madame, like cowboys in an American dime novel, and will send you word of what we hear.'

Then they were gone.

They seemed to melt into the shadows, but Lydia was prosaically aware that in fact one or the other of them had simply used the same psychic aura that older vampires developed, to make her not notice them walking off down the communications trench, or scrambling inelegantly up its wall. Jamie practiced, diligently, keeping his mind focused when he was in the presence of the Undead, and could sometimes see them move. Lydia knew she should have done so also but had been simply too exhausted. In any case she knew Don Simon would not permit harm to befall her.

Nevertheless she trembled as the Spanish vampire led her back along the trench in the direction of the motorcar, her head aching and her heart beating fast. They were vampires. Charming and polite and well-dressed . . .

She recalled again the warmth of Antonio's lips on her hand. Stolen warmth. Stolen life.

Creatures of evil . . .

Yesterday she'd received a letter from her Uncle Richard, which had mentioned in passing (after lamentations about the difficulty in obtaining coffee and petrol) that two of the footmen who had enlisted last September – men whom Lydia had known since childhood – had been killed at Festubert. A third – Ned – had been returned, blind and crippled, to his family, who would have to support him for the remainder of his life.

So where lies the greater evil? She didn't know.

A thousand tales and warnings about supping with the Devil flooded to her tired mind, but she honestly couldn't think of any way of quickly tracking this other night-prowling nurse who had a *proposition*, a *partnership*, to offer the Undead . . .

And when she stumbled, there was Simon's hand – cold as marble through his glove and the sleeves of her coat and frock – supporting her arm.

Simon, whom Jamie had sworn he would kill, along with every other vampire who crossed his path . . .

He stopped, swung around. 'What's—'

A man flung himself down on them from the top of the trench. Lydia had an impression of uniform, but his head was bare. He was without rifle or pack, clutching a bayonet like a dagger. He slashed at her, seized her arm to drag her into the blow. She saw the gleam of reflective eyes, gasped at the fishy stench of him as Simon yanked the man away from her, tried to twist the weapon from his hand. Instead the soldier pulled his arm free of the vampire's grip – the grip that Lydia had seen bend steel – and flung Simon against the wall of the trench as if he'd been a child.

Lydia ran, stumbling in icy water and broken duckboards – *There has to be a ladder somewhere . . .*

But the soldier was fast. Hands gripped her waist, the reek of him clogged her throat; as she tried to wrench free she glimpsed the slimy glister of a fanged, deformed mouth gaping to bite.

Then the man jerked, head falling forward, and Lydia yanked free as the filthy stink of her attacker's flesh was drowned in the sharp stench of splattering blood. Ysidro raised the entrenching-tool with which he'd struck the soldier's neck for another blow.

She sprang clear as Simon chopped down again with the metal blade, but soldier was still trying to rise, still trying to come at her. The third blow severed the head.

The body continued to crawl.

Methodically, Simon chopped with the pointed end of the tool into the spine – with all the horrific force of a vampire's preter-natural strength – severing it, Lydia estimated, just below the first thoracic, and again below the first lumbar, vertebrae. The arms and legs were still moving as Simon caught her hand and dragged her along the trench. He kept firm hold of the bloodied entrenching-tool.

There might be others.

She knew from experience that they hunted in packs.

FOUR

'It was a *yao-kuei*, wasn't it?' Lydia whispered the name by which she'd first seen the revenants, three years previously in Peking. She pulled her tent-mate Nurse Danvers's greatcoat more tightly around her nightdress and dressing gown. Despite the small oil-stove beside which she sat, the tent was freezing. 'Jamie says *draugar* is the Icelandic word for creatures like that.'

'James would know such matters.' Don Simon brought her another cup of cocoa, as he had last night. There were times that Lydia felt the whole clearing station lived on cocoa.

Nurse Danvers had been coming off her rounds when Lydia returned, had helped her wash off all trace of her attacker's blood and had reaffirmed that Lydia had no cuts or scratches through which that blood could possibly have entered her system. The moment she'd finished this chore she had inexplicably (to her, at least) sunk down, fully dressed, on her own cot and dropped into Sleeping-Beauty-like slumber. Lydia had just been tucking a blanket over her when Don Simon had appeared, silently, at her side.

'I find it distressing,' the vampire went on, 'that the Scandinavians would *require* a word for, as you say, "creatures like that". Yet neither Antonio nor Basilio – nor indeed, any of the Undead to whom I have spoken, on either side of No Man's Land – have mentioned seeing these Others.'

Lydia set the cup on the tent's wooden floor beside her cot, frowning. 'You're right.' A moment before, her revulsion at the thing that had attacked her, had consumed her – the deeper terror that she might somehow have been infected by the revenant's blood, that her own body might distort into a misshapen horror while her mind disappeared into the collective semi-consciousness of the brutes . Now that revulsion vanished before the puzzle of where this particular revenant had come from.

'I haven't heard the men in the wards speak of them, either,' she added. 'And they *do* speak of the vampires.'

She frowned, remembering poor Brodie (*He goes to hospital in Calais tomorrow, I'll have to bid him good luck before he leaves . . .*). She glanced across at Don Simon, warming his thin hands before the stove. She assumed he'd also examined his own flesh for any possibility of transfer of blood, in the three-quarters of an hour since he'd set her down outside the dim lights of the camp. *Did he make poor Captain Palfrey check his back? How did he explain matters to that well-meaning young man?*

She wondered if Palfrey could see, as she did, the glassy claws that the vampire state caused to grow in place of the fingernails. If Simon had used the psychic skill of the Undead to block from the young man's mind the huge scars that crossed the left side of his face and neck, where the talons of the Master vampire of Constantinople had raked him in a struggle, five years before, to save Lydia's life.

She herself couldn't always see them.

She went on, 'My assistant, Mr Dermott, tells me some of the men say they've seen a ghost ambulance-wagon, or ghost stretcher-bearers . . .'

'That's Antonio and Basilio.' Don Simon's slight gesture was a dismissal. 'They often hunt in an ambulance-wagon.'

Lydia turned her face away, for a moment too shaken to speak.

Tears flooded her eyes in spite of the fact that she knew, as he had said, that they preyed only on those dying already . . .

I should hate them all. I should hate HIM.

Don Simon watched her face without expression, a pale shape in the dark of the tent.

How can he be both things to me? Both friend and monster?

She was well aware how meticulously careful he was, never to let her or Jamie see him kill. *And it works*, she thought despairingly. *If we don't SEE it, part of our minds can pretend it isn't happening.*

Good heavens, maybe we DID see something of the kind and he made us forget it. Can he DO that?

She wouldn't put it past him.

She tasted over on her tongue the words, trying them out. *I don't want your protection. I don't want you watching over me. I want you to go away.*

She guessed that he wouldn't. *I'll just never see him at it again . . . or maybe now and then, a glimpse from the corner of my eye . . .* 'We need to go back there.' She looked back at him once again in the dim glow of the stove. 'Now, before first light destroys its flesh. Jamie says sunlight doesn't burn them as quickly as it does vampires, but it will crumble their flesh and their bones to dust. Is that true?'

'It is, Mistress.'

'Then I need one to study. The blood on my frock is too mixed up with mud to examine clearly, even with Major Overstreet's microscope. And I should talk to men in that part of the trenches.' She opened her locker at the foot of her bunk and brought out her spare uniform (*I'll need to talk to Storeman Pratt tomorrow about another one – I am NOT putting the bloodied one on again no matter HOW many times it's boiled!*). 'Someone else must have seen it. We can at least get some idea of what direction it was coming from. Or, if it was German . . . Even if there were others with it, they'll have moved on by this time . . .'

'It shall be as you command.'

He vanished – or seemed to vanish, momentarily blocking her perception of his movement. Shuddering in the cold, Lydia dressed herself again quickly (*And God bless the woman who invented the brassiere!*) and gathered up the bloodied, mud-slathered garments in an old pillowcase. Handling them gingerly, she took a few minutes to cut swatches from the least-contaminated bloodstains, which she stowed in a candy tin at the bottom of her locker. By the time she checked her watch and buttoned on Danvers's borrowed greatcoat, and slipped from the tent with the incinerator-bound pillowcase clutched at arms-length in one hand, it was quarter past two.

Lydia recognized – vaguely – the place where the staff-car lurched to a stop. The damp night, though windless, was very cold, the far-off crashing of the guns to the north like metallic thunder. The effects of the cocoa were wearing off and Lydia felt tired to death and chilled to the marrow of her bones. She leaned forward to the front seat to glimpse Captain Palfrey's wristwatch – her own was the old-fashioned kind, pinned to her breast under a layer of greatcoat – and saw that it was past three.

'Will you be all right?' she whispered to Don Simon. First light would be in two hours. She estimated it was nearly two muddy, slogging miles from where they halted – in a welter of shell-holes and barbed wire – to the communication trench where they had been attacked.

'John has orders to return you safely to the clearing station, should circumstances separate me from you.' He took her hand in his own gloved one and led her toward the remains of the reserve trench, the glow of the shuttered lantern he carried swinging again across the glisten of mud, shattered steel and the red spark of rat eyes in the dark. As they descended the ladder once again she hoped Simon's sense of smell was more discerning than her own in the quagmire of stench: rotting flesh, old blood, cordite, feces, smoke . . . *A whole pack of revenants could be just around the bend of the trench and I'd never smell them.*

The communications trenches were dug in a series of angles to protect against blast, resulting in the sense of being trapped in a wet, filthy labyrinth. On the walls of the trench boards had been roughly fastened, arrows drawn in chalk or paint with direc-tions written above: *1st Scots*, *2nd Lancs*, or, simply and more prosaically, *Rear. Bogs* . . . Without them, Lydia couldn't imagine how anyone could traverse this maze of head-high walls, zigzagged defiles and caved-in dugouts.

She found herself clinging to Don Simon's hand.

'Did you see his uniform?' she asked. 'Whether he was British or German? If these things are multiplying in the German trenches . . .'

'I would have heard,' returned the vampire. 'Many of us haunt both sides of the lines. In any event, what use would such creatures be? Unless their minds could be directed and controlled the danger would be too great. No general in his senses would take such risk.'

'But that may be why this woman – this dark-haired nurse – is seeking a vampire, don't you see?' Lydia glanced quickly across into her companion's face. 'You've said – many times – that a vampire can govern the actions of a living mind. Can summon at will those whose eyes he has looked into, can . . . can even sometimes put himself literally into another's mind, if his victim is drugged, or insane. They're seeking a vampire . . .'

'Then they are fools,' returned Don Simon calmly. 'An old vampire, whose strength has waxed with time and who has been taught to manipulate the minds of the living, perhaps. A master vampire, or someone like Antonio, whose master instructed him in these ancient skills . . . Not all masters trust their fledglings to that extent. And so old a vampire will have doubtless learned not to put faith in the living – leaving aside the fact that no vampire, of any age, cares the purchase of a button about the wars of the living. We do not care, Mistress. As Antonio told you earlier tonight: *we do not care*. Not about our homelands, not about our families, not about those whom we loved in life. Nothing exists for us but the hunt. We know any other ties to be dangerous, and ties to the living, most dangerous of all.'

He paused for an instant where the communications trench in which they now picked their way branched, then turned right (*Welches*, said the sign), his strength helping Lydia find her feet where the duckboards were broken and the icy, filthy water soaked through her shoes.

'The Master of Prague, where these things have long bred, and the Master of Peking, have both affirmed to me, that even the strongest master vampire has no dominion over the minds of these things. If this nurse you have seen— *Carajo*!' He flinched at the sudden, earth-shaking thunder of an explosion that sounded nearly on top of them. Orange glare filled the sky. Another roar followed, and the splattering of torn-up earth, followed by the shouting and cursing of men.

'We're almost there!' Lydia seized Don Simon's hand again, her heart in her throat but her mind still calculating: *That shell was at least a hundred yards away . . .*

Around the corner ahead . . .

She snatched the lantern from his hand and slammed back the slide – no further need of precaution against snipers, not with what sounded like a full-on barrage starting – and ran, digging in her pocket for the rolled-up empty sandbags she'd brought to carry her prize. The ground jerked and the duckboards underfoot suddenly erupted with fleeing rats, swarming from their holes and pouring in a gray river up the side of the trench, as if the Pied Piper had blown his horn somewhere in the hellish cacophony of the darkness. *If there's a push on I'll lose this thing, or it'll be buried in a barrage . . .*

She heard Don Simon swear in Spanish behind her, and a shell went overhead with a noise like an oncoming train.

Am I being intrepid or stupid?

Her heart in her throat, not giving herself time to think, Lydia whipped around the angle of the trench and her lantern-light fell on the huddled black mass of the revenant, and a smaller form leant over it. A woman.

Lydia stumbled to a halt. A shuttered lantern stood near the revenant's severed head, and by its dim light Lydia saw the woman bend over the hacked and bloody body, doing something she couldn't see. As the figure raised its face, she had a momentary vision of a heart-shaped countenance framed in pulled-back dark hair, a rich mouth twisted in resolution and shock. The gleam of a silver cross, dangling around her neck.

Something else by the lantern, a satchel . . .

Another explosion shook the ground, closer this time, and the woman grabbed for something in her pocket. Don Simon's hand closed on Lydia's elbow and Lydia was dragged back around the protective angle of the trench. She saw the woman rise from beside the corpse – it was still aimlessly clawing around it with one hand – and flee down the trench, turning to throw something . . .

Don Simon yanked Lydia along the trench, and she realized what the other woman had flung instants before they ducked around the next angle and the massive shock wave of noise, oily heat and flying debris almost knocked her off her feet. *Grenade . . .*

Men surged, shouting, out of another communications trench, as the barrage intensified over their heads. Yells of 'Get out of it, boys!' mingled with the screaming whistles of officers and bellowed commands to re-form ranks. Don Simon's arm circled Lydia's waist and he dragged her along, slithering expertly through the struggling bodies. He froze as a shell howled over-head and pulled her back, judging the sound of it, Lydia thought . . . And sure enough, some dozen yards ahead of them the crash of its explosion made her head reverberate, and dirt and mud splattered her as the trenches caved in under the blow.

The noise hurt her bones, and the mud splattered on her glasses made it nearly impossible to see. Men formed up around them again into ranks, which flowed through the communications trenches, Don Simon swimming against the tide. They came into a clear space of trench, the walls broken into craters by shells and the duckboards shattered underfoot. Men clattered past them, bearers carrying rolled-up blankets or the new-style litters, feet sinking – as Lydia's sank – into bottomless mud. Twice she stumbled, and glancing down saw she'd tripped over corpses. But every new explosion filled the air above the trenches with flying shrapnel and splattering bits of red-hot metal – *I hope Captain Palfrey has taken cover somewhere . . .*

He evidently had. His hands reached down from the trench-ladder as Lydia was helped up out of the darkness, and it was he who half-guided, half-carried her toward the road down which men were already rushing toward the trenches, to re-enforce the existing troops against the German 'push' that everybody knew was going to come the moment it was light.

I have to get back to the clearing station. The wounded are going to be pouring in any minute . . .

'I'm afraid the car was commandeered, M'am,' gasped Captain Palfrey, as they stumbled over the broken ground. 'I got their names, and units. The colonel's going to have words to say to their commanding officers—'

'The colonel?' Lydia stumbled, and sought in her pockets for some piece of cloth sufficiently un-soaked to make headway against the muck that smeared her glasses. The shell-fire was somewhat behind them now, except for the occasional strays, and men still raced past them, packs clattering, rifles in hand. Minds focused on what lay ahead.

Four miles back to camp . . .

'Colonel Simon.'

The first threads of daylight had not yet begun to dilute the darkness. Don Simon presumably knew how long it would take him to get to a secure shelter – *God knows where!* Reaction was setting in, and Lydia had to cling to Palfrey's arm to keep from falling as they plowed through the wilderness of mud and old shell-holes, her wet skirts slapping and tangling her feet. Rats still swarmed. Once the fighting stopped, the creatures would stream back, to feed on the dead.

Lydia thought she glimpsed, away in the darkness, the pale shape of an ambulance-wagon jolting, and wondered if it was really an ambulance-wagon or just Antonio and Basilio.

Passionately, cold and exasperation and despair overwhelming her, Lydia cried, 'Don't you know what he really is?'

Captain Palfrey took both her hands in his – warm and strong, like Jamie's, the capable hands of a man who understands horses and guns and tools – and his blue eyes held a gentle understanding. From his pocket he produced a clean – *clean!* – handkerchief, and stood while she took off her glasses and wiped the lenses.

Then with a little smile he tapped the side of his nose and said, 'Well, M'am, it's all a deep dark secret, of course . . . And he's warned me that all kinds of the most ridiculous stories are circulated about him. Nursery-tale stuff you'd hardly credit, like a combination of Count Dracula and Bluebeard. But I've guessed the truth.' His eyes shone in the first whisper of the coming dawn. 'He – and his Department – are probably England's best hope of winning the war.'

FIVE

I n his tidy back room on Grafton Place, James Asher sat on the end of the bed and looked down into the narrow yard, glistening under gray morning rain.

And thought about the Others.

Hideous memories, most of them. Shambling figures in the dark of ravines, in the hills west of Peking. Red eyes gleaming in the tunnels of abandoned mines.

Lydia sitting on the muddy shore of one of Peking's artificial lakes, red hair glinting with the fires that consumed the last of the Peking hive, weeping . . .

Miraculously unhurt.

He'd known she was walking back into danger, just a little over two years later – back in November, four months ago, now. He'd said goodbye to her, his first full day on his feet after recovery from pneumonia. He'd gone to the train station with her, the sixth of November, the gray mists that drifted over the station platform still smelling ominously of leftover gun-powder from Bonfire Night. Lydia in her VAD uniform: the single small trunk beside her wouldn't even have contained her cosmetics before the war. After the porter took it away she'd clung to him, gawky and thin and stork-like, her cheek pressed to his (she had carefully removed her spectacles, as she always did before they embraced). Wordless.

He knew she might never come back from the fighting. Seventeen years on Her Majesty's Secret Service – and another decade and a half of following newspapers and reports – had made him sickeningly aware of what waited at the Front: machine guns, artillery that could kill at a distance of miles. And the White Horseman, Pestilence, more terrible than either.

Danger from the revenants, whom they had last seen in Peking, had been the farthest thing from his mind.

Looking back at their parting he couldn't believe he'd been that naïve. *Of course some government was going to hear about them sooner or later.*

Of course they'll try to make them into a weapon of war.

His studies had unearthed almost as many examples of similar beings in folklore as the study of vampires did: *draugar*, *haugbui*, the Celtic *neamh mairbh*. African and Caribbean zombies. Greek *vrykolak*, Chinese hungry ghosts, the barrow wights of ancient English legend. Things that came staggering out of their graves to feed – insatiably. The vampires of Prague, Don Simon Ysidro had told him, had been trying for centuries to get rid of them, to no avail.

And now one of them was in London.

Mrs Taylor – who rented out rooms in this tall, narrow house near Euston Station – had brought him up tea and bread and butter, rather to his surprise and unasked ('I seen yesterday as you was poorly, sir . . .'). He had spent nearly eighteen hours, since he had returned from his abortive visit to the Foreign Office yesterday afternoon, lying on the bed looking at the ceiling wondering if this was any of his business or not. He ate without much appetite, though he no longer felt feverish. Only deeply fatigued.

What he most wanted to do was pack up his slender belongings, take a cab (if he could find such a thing) to Paddington Station and be in Oxford tonight, playing hide-and-seek with Miranda and deciphering Lydia's latest letter from the Front.

What he would do instead, he already knew, was send another telegram to Mrs Grimes, and then go to the Wolf and Child on Chalton Street, to talk to publican Tim.

Think no more about it. Langham's confidential, between-you-and-me smile. *The matter is in hand.*

Asher moved his hand toward the now-cold teapot to see if there was another cup left in it, but instead lay down again. Two years previously, he had sworn enmity to the vampires of London and had destroyed most of the London nest . . . only to discover that those he had killed were the unreliable members whom the Master of London wanted to be rid of anyway.

Twelve years prior to that, at the end of the African war, he had tendered his resignation to the Foreign Office, being unable to put from his mind the young Boer boy he had killed – a good friend, so far as a spy living under cover is able to make actual friends – in the line of what the Department considered duty. Even then he had known that swearing enmity to the Department would be futile and absurd, though he knew what they were. When he'd left Langham's office on that occasion, his chief had shaken his hand and said – with that confidential little smile – '*Au revoir.*' The words had been deliberately chosen. Nothing about Langham was accidental. *Until we meet again.*

Think no more about it . . .

Go back to Oxford and shout '*A plague on both your houses*!' from the window of the departing train.

A revenant was hunting in London. It was only a matter of time before the infection began to spread uncontrollably.

A knock like a siege engine hammered the door. 'Mr Asher, sir,' trumpeted young Ginny Taylor's adenoidal voice in the hall. 'There's a lady come t' see you.'

Asher levered himself from the bed, astonished at how much energy this took, and slid into his jacket. 'Thank you, Ginny,' he said to the girl – fourteen, clean-scrubbed, with a face that reminded him of the roan cob that used to pull his father's gig – as he stepped out into the corridor. 'Please tell her I'll be right down.'

'Professor Asher!' Josetta Beyerly sprang to her feet from the threadbare chair in the parlor window, strode across to grip both his hands. 'I didn't mean for them to drag you down here—'

'This is a respectable house,' replied Asher gravely. 'As Mrs Taylor would no doubt have told you if you'd even thought about suggesting the possibility of coming up to a gentleman's room. I take it Mrs Grimes telegraphed you with her conviction that I'd taken ill again?'

'Why "good society" leaps to the automatic conclusion that every interaction between a woman and a man is of necessity immodest—' began the young woman indignantly; then she caught herself, and shook her head. 'It's all of a piece,' she sighed. 'A way of making women their own jailers . . . And yes,' she added, with her beautiful smile. 'Mrs Grimes wired me last night. Please.' She drew him back to the chairs by the window. 'Sit down, Professor . . . *Are* you all right?'

Bright brown eyes looked across into his as he took the seat opposite. Even in the blue-and-white uniform of a volunteer at

First London General Hospital, she wore a little rosette of purple, green and beige ribbons that marked her as a suffragette (*And I'll bet she fights every day with the ward sister about it . . .*). He smiled a little, pleased by her stubborn adherence to a cause that many women had set aside at the start of the war because *we must all stick together . . .*

Strident though she was about her politics, Josetta had been Lydia's close friend since 1898, the year his wife had spent at a select finishing school for girls in Switzerland, where Josetta, five years the elder, had been the English mistress. And Josetta had been the gawky, bookish young heiress's only friend. Eighteen months later in England, it was Josetta who had secretly coached Lydia through the examination to get her accepted to Somerville College – an acceptance which had resulted in Lydia being disowned by her outraged father. A small legacy had enabled the one-time English mistress to remain in England, where she took day pupils in French and music to make ends meet, and now, at thirty-seven, she was active in a dozen causes, from votes for women, Irish independence and settlement houses to 'rational dress', the elimination of the House of Lords, and vegetarianism.

'I'm quite well,' Asher reassured her, though her dark brows plunged over her delicate nose at this. Evidently, he reflected, it was obvious he was lying. 'I was kept later than I'd planned by meetings, and in fact I was on my way to the post office to let Mrs Grimes know that I won't be home today either, nor probably tomorrow.'

'Is there anything I can do for you?' she asked. 'Do you have board at this place, or are you eating at one of the frightful cafés hereabouts? Come to dinner with me at my club, if you'd care to – the menu isn't much, but at least it would be an improvement on fried chips and sausage.' She smiled, reached across to pat his hand, still slim as a girl. 'Lydia did tell me to look after you.'

'Thank you.' Asher returned her smile, though he suspected that, to earn even the utilitarian Josetta's disapprobation, the food on offer at the Grosvenor Crescent Club must be mediocre indeed. 'I should like that.'

'Have you heard from her?'

'Not since before I left Oxford. But I know the fighting in Flanders has been heavy, so she may not have had time to write.'

While the former English mistress spoke of her own experiences with the casualties of the spring's first great 'push', and of her outrage against the propagandist posters which plastered the hospital (and indeed, two virulent examples of the genre glared from the wall of the parlor: *Women of Britain say 'Go!'* and *Lend your Five Shillings to your Country and Crush the Germans*), his mind sifted her words automatically. '. . . And of course they don't know any better. Most of those poor boys haven't been outside their own neighborhoods in their lives. The women who'd come into the settlement houses could give you chapter and verse about each others' grandfathers and great-aunts, but would regard Kensington as foreign soil . . .'

'There is something you can do for me,' said Asher, when Josetta finished her account of procuring books and magazines for the wounded men in London General. 'If you would be so kind. Do you still have connections with the settlement house in Camden Town? I have heard—' It was a bow drawn at a venture, but he guessed the query would at least bear some fruit – 'that there's been a . . . a mugger, or a slasher, working along the Regent's Canal. A man who attacks at night, and who stinks of dirty clothes and fish. It would help me enormously if you could ask some of the people down at the settlement house, or people in that neighborhood, if they've heard of such a thug making the rounds.'

Josetta regarded him curiously – like himself, he realized with a smile, sifting what he said, tallying in her mind what his purpose might be. 'And does this have something to do with these "meetings" that are keeping you in town?'

Though Lydia – Asher was fairly sure – never spoke to anyone of his former life as one of Her Majesty's Secret Servants, he guessed also that his wife's concerns for him, particularly in the years since he'd become drawn into the affairs of the vampires, had communicated themselves to her friend. Josetta may well have developed suspicions that he wasn't the retiring Oxford don that he appeared, though God knew what interpretation she'd put on his comings and goings. Exactly as he would have, had he been recruiting a political semi-radical for the Department for one of his networks abroad, he replied, 'It's just a matter of personal interest.' With a raised eyebrow and a look that said, *I know perfectly well you're not fooled, Miss Beyerly.*

She returned his secret smile. 'I'll see what I can find. Dinner tonight at seven?'

'Seven it is.'

The Wolf and Child stood at the corner of Chalton Street and Matilda Court, three doors from Weekes and Sons, Importers of Fine Silk, where the unfortunate Harry had been employed. A woman passed Asher in the doorway of the long, wood-paneled taproom: her electric-blue jacket faded and four years out of style, with the telltale mark pressed into her left sleeve by the frame of a sewing machine. The taproom was as quiet today as it had been the previous morning, with only a couple of neighborhood men consuming a pint and a laborer's lunch of bread and cheese. But the lunchers avoided one another's eye, and there was worry in the face of the old man behind the bar as he watched the woman depart. 'Y' maun excuse us, sir,' he said as he fetched the pint of mild that Asher ordered. 'We're a bit moithered just now. Our man didn't show up to open—'

Asher made a gesture of casual acceptance, though cold stabbed him behind the breastbone, and the shock worse because it was unattended by much surprise. 'I'm in no lather.' He kept his accent rural, Shropshire, as he had yesterday morning when speaking with Tim . . . 'Hard lines on you, gaffer, him droppin' his work on you, though. Must be a chore findin' help with all these lads joinin' up.'

'Nay, Tim's not one to scarper, think on. That was his missus just now—' The old man nodded toward the door. 'Never come 'ome las' night, he didn't, and poor Masie at her wits' end over it. 'Tis not the same,' he added worriedly, 'since the start o' this war.'

No, thought Asher, laying his three-penny bit on the counter and looking thoughtfully toward the street, at least in part to conceal the anger that he knew was in his eyes. *No, things are not the same.*

He dreamed that night of Pritchard Crowell, a man he hadn't even thought of in nearly a decade.

Crowell was something of a legend in the Department. Asher had worked with him only once. In Mesopotamia in the early nineties they'd scouted out opposition to Ottoman rule, and put together a network of sleeper agents in the Caucasus and in the desert country beyond Palmyra. The villagers often worked for German 'archaeologists' who coincidentally searched for their buried cities along proposed railway routes where troops might later be moved.

He recalled a wiry small man in his fifties, dark-eyed and dark-haired and absolutely unobtrusive. A wrinkle-threaded face, a hawk-bill nose and a touch with picklocks that half the professional burglars in London might have envied, and a chilly ruthlessness which, at that time, Asher had sought to make his own. The job, and the job only, existed, and everything else, including one's own survival, merely facilitated whatever one had been ordered to do.

'We are weapons . . .' Asher heard again that low voice – a middle-range tenor and like everything else about him, expressionless and unremarkable – against the Mixolydian wail of voices outside the inn at El Deir where they sat. Even through his dream he smelled the burnt languor of coffee, the stink of dust, camel dung, harsh tobacco and *ras el hanout*. 'If one is in a fight for one's life, one wouldn't thank a knife that turned round in your hand and asked questions. One does what one has to, my lad, and forgets about it afterwards . . . Clean as you go, and don't look back.'

This applied, Asher recalled, to the members of one's own network – one's friends among the Bedu or on the Turkish Army supply staffs in Constantinople. They were warned ('When feasible,' Crowell had qualified, casually) that Higher Purposes might require them to be cut adrift. Asher remembered the occasion on which Crowell had let the population of an Armenian village which had sheltered them be massacred by the sultan's tame bandits, rather than give them a warning which would have revealed that the Turkish Army codes had been broken.

One does what one has to . . .

The pragmatist in Asher's soul had admired Crowell's uncanny expertise in the sheer craft of spying – of getting into places, of winkling shards of information from men and women wholly committed to Britain's enemies. He always had an astonishing plethora of information at his fingertips, and was eerily expert at slipping through shadows to escape and bring the 'goods', whatever they were upon any given occasion, back to Langham and the others at the Department. He was an uncannily brilliant guesser. The patriot in Asher had striven to emulate what he saw, both the cold virtuosity and the single-minded loyalty to his Queen. In his dream now, Asher saw him as he'd seen him in those days: clever, cold, unobtrusive and ruthless.

Forget about it afterwards. Clean as you go.

Someone paused for a moment in the doorway of the little *meyhane* where they sat: Asher caught the shadow out of the corner of his eye, and his glance went to the silver coffee pot on the low table between them to see who it was, so he would not be seen to turn. The man was gone before Asher made out the image in the round belly of the polished metal.

But he thought it was Langham.

And just as he woke he thought he smelled the fishy, greasy reek of the Others, that the visitor had left behind.

Over supper, earlier in the evening, at Miss Beyerly's club – mutton every bit as bad as Asher had suspected it would be – Josetta had told him that yes, she had heard rumor among the laborers who worked nights along Regent's Canal, that there was a bludger afoot, mostly in the hours between midnight and three. So far he'd killed a whore and a seven-year-old pickpocket who'd been sleeping in a doorway and had, so the story went, eaten some of their flesh. Hungry Tom, he was called in the neighborhoods, or Tom the Ogre, though nobody had seen him nor knew whether his name was actually Tom or something else. The police were claiming that no such person existed.

'*The matter is in hand,*' Langham had said, with his sly little secret smile.

Langham wants the thing 'for King and country'. Asher knew it as he knew his own name. *He may not know precisely what it is. Only that it can be used.*

And that its use will redound to his credit.

Looking across the coffee table at Crowell in his dream – though Asher knew that in fact, after a lifetime of hair-breadth escapes and false rumors of demise Pritchard Crowell had succumbed to a lucky shot by a Bosnian merchant's blunderbuss in 1899 – he thought, *Crowell would have put Tim the publican out of the way.*

'Of course the police would rather that such a person doesn't exist,' had sniffed Josetta after dinner, stirring coffee like diesel oil in the old-fashioned gaslight of one of the club's small parlors. 'Both the victims are the sort of people the government has been pretending for years are criminals who deserve what they get, or who no longer live in the up-to-date London of the twentieth century . . . Certainly not worth avenging, with the cost of slaughtering Germans to be thought of. And there are no reliable witnesses . . .'

Except Tim, thought Asher, in his dream of Mesopotamia. *Tim, who saw the body of the creature's most recent victim, in the fog of the alleyway behind the Wolf and Child.*

'It pays to be tidy,' Crowell was saying to him, emphasizing the point with one tiny forefinger: he had hands like an eleven-year-old boy. His wrinkled eyelids puckered. 'You never know who's going to talk to whom; what blithering postman is going to remark to his friend who works in Army Intelligence some day, "Ach, that man who's calling himself Martin and drawing pictures of ships in the harbor, I knew him in Strasbourg three years ago when he was named Schmidt . . ." And then it will be you for the high jump, my lad, and the whole show we've set up here blown to kingdom come. And nobody would ever associate the disappearance of the local postman with some traveling artist who'd scarcely even met the man . . .'

Clean as you go.

Crowell might be gone, reflected Asher, waking in the darkness of his rented lodging. But Langham remained.

He turned the dream over in his mind.

And there were a dozen or a hundred fledgling Crowells in the wings, waiting to take his shape, and continue his business.

After killing his young friend Jan van der Platz, Asher had quit the Department, when he'd realized that he was one of them.

Then he smelled blood, quite close to him, and knew suddenly he was in mortal danger.

His eyes flew open to darkness and a cold hand crushed down over his mouth, almost smothering him, while another had him by the wrist even as he snatched for the knife under his pillow.

The hand released its grip an instant later and Asher heard a curse of pain, and knew that his assailant had been burned by the chains of silver he wore.

Vampire . . .

SIX

L ydia didn't even stop at her tent, just went straight on to the fluoroscope chamber and was setting up the apparatus when Captain Calvert barged in looking for her. 'Good, you've heard, then— Good God, woman, where've you been?' was his only comment on her muddy and disheveled state, and he was out the door and into the surgical tent before she drew breath to reply. 'Brickwood, I'm devastated but I'm going to have to ask you to stay,' his voice went on as his steps retreated across the tent. 'Go in and wake up Danvers, would you? Matron, can you get me . . .?'

The tidal wave of wounded didn't slacken for another thirty-six hours. The Germans had hit the line hard, over a front of two miles: first came the men wounded in the preliminary shelling, then the thousands who'd been mowed down, like standing wheat before a reaper's scythe, as they'd scrambled up out of the trench to meet the onrushing line of the enemy. The situation was not helped when four German shells landed on the village of Pont-Sainte-Félicité itself, turning the marketplace to rubble and killing two orderlies. Colonel St-Vire wired furiously up and down the line for more surgeons, more nurses and more orderlies, and later Thursday morning Lydia found herself administering chloroform at the tables of surgeons she'd never seen before, Captain Glover from the First Lancashire and Captain Bryce-Bayington who looked young enough to be one of Jamie's students back in Oxford. Matron – Sister Flavia – came as close to cursing as Lydia had ever heard her do over the three extra nurses who arrived ('Nurses! I shouldn't hire a one of them to make tea for a proper nurse!'), and just before the Germans started shelling Pont-Sainte-Félicité a second time – as Lydia was on her way out of the fluoroscope tent – Lydia recognized one of the new nurses as the young woman she'd seen in the trenches last night, bending over the corpse of the revenant.

The young woman who had tossed a grenade at the corpse, either to destroy it or because she'd seen Lydia and Don Simon.

The young woman who was looking for a vampire with *a partnership to offer you* . . .

For a moment Lydia only stood in startled surprise. But there was no mistaking the wide forehead, the sturdy shape of the shoulders, the dark widow's peak and snub nose. And like her own, she noted, this younger girl's blue-and-white VAD uniform was blotched and splattered with mud – *She must have been bundled straight into a truck and ordered to come here just as she got back to . . . to wherever it is she's assigned, with . . .*

With what?

The revenant's blood? One of its still-flexing hands?

Then Burke bellowed from within the surgical tent 'Asher! Where t' bloody 'ell's them snaps?' and Lydia dashed to his side with the films that she had been taking between filling in as an assistant in the surgery. A few minutes later she glimpsed Captain Palfrey helping the orderlies carry men in from the pre-operative tent, working alongside the Indian motor-mechanics and the cook. Then German shells hit the village again, close enough that fragments of brick and wood clattered like rain on the canvas walls of the tent.

She sponged the other woman from her mind.

She worked on into the night, existing on hot tea and the biscuits Danvers's grandfather had sent her yesterday, which her tent-mate gamely divided among the surgical staff. It occurred to her that she ought to be terrified, when a shell struck particularly close, but she found that associating with vampires for the past eight years had had the salutary effect of making her less inclined to panic: *I can run away screaming anytime I want, which wasn't the case when I was dealing with that horrid Rumanian count or whatever he was in Scotland . . . and if I get killed here, nobody else is likely to suffer.*

James was safe, wherever he was.

Miranda was safe back in Oxford.

These men need help.

She stepped out once, around two in the morning of the nineteenth, and thought she glimpsed the pale shape of Don Simon, standing in the doorway of what was left of the town church across the green from the surgical tent, like the Angel of Death in his trim brown uniform. *To make sure he's on hand if I need rescuing, if one of those shells hits? Or just waiting for the next man to be moved into the Moribund Ward?*

How many others of them are around, where I can't see them?

Not many, she reflected, *with shells still striking the village . . .*

Bearers passed her, carrying a man from the drop-off point by the road into the pre-operative ward. *I'd better get back.*

When she looked again the vampire was gone, if indeed he ever had been there. She was sufficiently tired now that she wasn't certain of what she saw.

At least the surgeons got to sleep most of last night.

The next time she emerged, toward dawn ('There's tea in the mess tent,' Captain Calvert had said, 'and you *will* go and have a cup and sit down for ten minutes'), she passed the door of the clearing tent, the flap tied open so that bearers could carry men in. She saw the little dark-haired nurse kneeling beside one of the cots, her arms around the shoulders of a man who lay there, freckles starring like spattered ink in his waxen face and covered with mud and blood.

'You're alive!' the young woman cried, covering the man's hands with kisses as he raised them to touch her hair. 'Dear God, I thought I'd never see you again—'

'Tuathla,' he murmured. 'Well you know there's no Jerry livin' that's yet forged the gun that'll shoot the shell that'll end my love for you, *mo chroí,* so don't you be thinkin' it.'

'*Miss* Smith!' Matron materialized like a ghost from the dense gloom of the lantern-lit ward. 'If you will *kindly* come over here and lend us the assistance you presumably volunteered to give to your country—'

The dark-haired nurse scrambled to her feet. 'Yes, M'am. Of course, M'am.'

Educated English. Little trace of the graceful Irish drawl that lilted her red-haired lover's speech. Miss Smith . . . Tuathla Smith . . . or was *tuathla* some kind of County Liffey endearment? Lydia's mind seemed to be turning things over very slowly, and she started as a firm hand took her elbow and Captain Calvert said, 'I told you to get into the mess tent and *sit down* for ten minutes, Dr Asher. Bearers are still coming in and we're in for a long morning of it.'

She and the captain were still in the mess tent – Captain Calvert turning to give orders to Trent, the head bearer, to marshal the walking wounded to help carry from the drop-off point – when a shattering explosion sounded from the direction of the river, and not only fragments of dirt and stone rained on the clearing station, but water, as if it had been flung from buckets. Instants later Storeman Pratt raced in, white-faced – the stores tent stood only a dozen feet from the stream – and cried, 'Bugger it, Captain, Jerry's blown the bloody bridge!'

Calvert said something worthy of neither an officer nor a gentleman and sprang to his feet. The surgeon at the other end of the table – a saturnine French Colonel pulled in from God knew where – cursed quietly in his native language and added, 'What they've been after all along, *en effet*. To cut the medical help off from the lines.'

'Finish your tea,' ordered Calvert, as Lydia began to rise. 'You, too, Colonel Lemoine, sir. Be back in the tent in fifteen minutes. The men can rig a causeway out of the rubble . . . God knows we've got plenty of that,' and went tearing off in quest of Colonel St-Vire.

'At least now they've got it,' added Dr Lemoine – Lydia tried to remember what the collar insignia on his pale-blue greatcoat denoted – 'let us hope they leave off wasting shells on men already incapable of harming them, and let us get on with our business. Before last year,' he went on, holding aside the tent-flap for Lydia to pass through before him, 'I gave thirty years of my life to my country's army. But as I learned more and more about the monstrous "improvements" in weaponry I always wondered in my heart: how can we loose such horrors upon living men? Shells that can reduce men – men with wives and children – to blots of jam from five miles away. Airships to drop bombs on

women and children minding their own business in their own
homes. Battleships to bar food and medicines from our enemy's
country, so that all will starve together – old men, women,
children.'

In the dust-choked morning haze Lydia saw his jaw work with
fury and pain.

'And yet I swear to you, Madame, when I see such things as
they do – shelling the hospitals where the wounded lie, torpedoing
passenger ships when they know full well that the innocent will
perish – I think nothing is too savage to do to them in retaliation.
No action of ours is too horrible, if it but makes them throw up
their hands and cry, *I quit!*'

His dark brows pulled together, a handsome man of about
Jamie's age, with gray flecks in his pencil mustache and the
features of a sorrowing king.

Then he glanced across at her – he was taller than she by three
or four inches – and made himself smile. 'And you, Madame? I
had heard the British Army refused to accept female surgeons—'

'Well, they do. And even if they didn't, I'm not a surgeon,
you know. My research was on glandular secretions, so I just
signed on just as a regular volunteer. But when Colonel St-Vire
heard I knew how to operate a fluoroscope apparatus he had me
reassigned to the unit and put me in charge of the x-ray photo-
`graphy, and they pull me into the surgical tent whenever they
need to. I couldn't remove a splinter on my own, but I do know
how to administer anesthetic, and what all the equipment is for,
and the sight of blood doesn't bother me. Here,' she added sadly,
'that's enough.'

Every spare orderly and bearer, along with the ambulance
drivers and the walking wounded, were streaming down to the
river. In the horse-lines, the animals squealed and milled in panic.
Lydia heard a motorbike roar away into the iron-gray morning,
to get the Engineers from Headquarters. Now that the profile
of the town was considerably flattened she could see the line of
ambulance-wagons – both motorized and horse-drawn – lined up
waiting on the far side of the river, while their drivers scrambled
to pull free the men and horses from those who'd been hit on
the bridge itself. The screams of dying mules mingled with the
brutal roar of the guns.

I was in that. Lydia felt a sort of distant, tired wonder at the fact. *Simon and I. I tripped over a corpse, and the hands of other dead men were sticking through the walls where dugouts had collapsed . . .*

She thought she glimpsed Captain Palfrey in a group of mechanics, black with soot and mud and carrying beams from the ruins.

'And Monsieur Asher?' asked Lemoine gently.

'In England.' Lydia's throat closed at the recollection of the misty train platform: the strength of his arms, the warmth of his body against the gray of that bitter morning. At the thought of Miranda at the nursery breakfast table, solemn with a goodbye that she thought was only for a day or two. ('I'll see you when I come home, darling . . .') It was a moment before she could speak. 'With our daughter. I try not to think of them, at times like these.'

She turned, to go back into the charnel house of the tent.

'And for that—' Lemoine's quiet voice turned grim, 'the Boche deserve whatever we can do.'

By eleven in the morning, when the surgeons finished the last of the desperate cases, the Royal Engineers arrived with planks, beams and struts to repair the bridge. Captain Calvert ordered Lydia back to her tent and to bed. She could see at least a dozen motor trucks, and twice as many other vehicles – horse-drawn farm carts, milk floats, staff-cars – waiting on the far bank and all overflowing with wounded. The drivers, and many of the walking wounded, waded out into the Lys to fasten beams to the broken foundations of the stone bridge's arches. 'When they're done,' said Violet Brickwood, falling into step with her, 'they'll all come across at once and it will be all harry in the surgery again. I hope somebody's making the surgeons rest.'

Once in their tent, Lydia lay down in her clothes and passed out as if she'd had a pipe of opium.

And dreamed of the revenant. Dreamed of being tied to a pillar in that horrible lightless room in Peking, listening to the creatures – the *yao-kuei* – smashing through the doors and windows only feet away from her. Dreamed of whatever-his-name-was, that colleague of Jamie's who'd been infected with the creatures' blood, his eyes gleaming like a rat's in the dark and his grip brutally strong on her arm, gasping *Extraordinary. Never been here in my life but remember it . . .* as the last of his mind dissolved into the dim hive of the revenants' collective consciousness, as he touched her face with his bloody and reeking hand.

Simon, she thought. *Simon came and saved me . . .*

And through her dream she heard his voice, like silk chilled from winter midnight, *Mistress . . .*

In her dream she was back on her cot in the nurses' tent, Simon's hand gentle on her shoulder, shaking her. She sat up, and threw herself into his arms, weeping: wanting Jamie, wanting Miranda, wanting to be back in Oxford researching pituitary secretions and wanting the world to be the way the world had always been. No shell-fire. No terror. No watching young men die under her very hands, no cold calm x-ray pictures of shrapnel lodged in organs that couldn't be mended . . .

She whispered, 'I want Jamie . . .'

The tent was silent. No camp noises, no gunfire. Just afternoon sunlight, indescribably sweet, filtering through the dirty white canvas, and the smell of grass and roses, which told her this was a dream. Don Simon, perched on the side of her cot, wore his colonel's uniform, brass buttons winking in the light.

Does HE dream of afternoon sunlight and the smell of roses, lying in his coffin in the daytime hours?

His grip on her was strong and reassuring, the slender shoulder and steel-hard arm within the sleeve as real as anything she had ever felt. His face, in its frame of cobweb-pale hair, was the face of the living man he'd once been, save for the eyes.

His hand stroked her hair. 'Would you have me set him before you?'

She wiped her eyes. In her dream, though she wasn't wearing her glasses, she saw perfectly well. 'It wouldn't be the same,' she said. 'I mean, I should know it was just a picture . . . a very, very accurate one, since you can walk in his dreams, the way you walk in mine . . . The way you're walking in mine right this minute.'

''Tis the best I can give you, lady.' He moved to put his hand to her cheek and then, as if he had seen the horror of her nightmare, drew it back with the gesture unmade. 'I would fain do more, were it in my power.'

He is in my mind, thought Lydia. *Right at this moment. Asleep in his coffin, wherever it's hidden . . .*

This is how he convinced that poor imbecile Captain Palfrey of his bona fides. I'll bet Palfrey's positive he's seen Don Simon by daylight, positive that he showed him unimpeachable proofs of the genuineness of this Secret Department of his . . . Positive of God knows what else! All because at some point Simon looked into his eyes, and later walked in his dreams – as she knew the old and skillful among the vampires could do – and convinced him that these things really happened. That those dreams were real memories.

I really should hate him.

But he was an old, old friend, and there was infinite comfort in the strength of his arms.

'I just want things to be the way they used to be,' she said at length. 'Living in Oxford, I mean, with Jamie and Miranda, and the worst one would see in the newspapers would be bunfights about who actually reached the South Pole first. I know it can't be that way again.' She sat up a little, and Don Simon handed her a perfectly clean white linen handkerchief, to blow her nose. 'I just – this is so hard.'

'Did you not weep for the dying,' replied the vampire in his soft voice, 'and fear for your life, and curse the stupid uselessness of it all – did you not pray that the world will somehow heal before your daughter grows to be aware of its horrors – you would be no more human than the fools and monsters that let this war begin. I have had centuries of watching war and stupidity, Mistress, and they grow no better, I am sorry to say. Your courage is the wine of hope to the men you work with, as well as to those you save. To James as well, I think, and to your child. It keeps their hearts beating. I am sorry you are in pain.'

She wrapped her hand around his, pretending (*I shouldn't . . .*) for a time that he was the living man he had been . . .

Although goodness knows as a living man he was probably a bigoted Catholic and a friend of the Grand Inquisitor and an enemy of England and a firm believer in the humoral theory of medicine. He probably beat his valet, too.

'Thank you,' she said simply, and raised her head from his shoulder. 'I've seen the woman – the one who was hunting the vampires, and looking for the revenant last night. She's one of the extra VADs who came in last night, her name is Smith – Tuathla Smith, I think . . . Oh, bother,' she added, as the tent-flap opened and Matron came in, and suddenly the light changed and Don Simon was gone and the sound of shelling, though no longer close enough to shake the ground, pounded the air with a constant, terrible roar. She heard men shouting above the grinding roar of a fleet of motors . . .

Lydia sat up, and fumbled for her glasses, on the plank floor beside the cot. By the light it was about four in the afternoon. For one moment she recalled that she'd dreamed about roses . . . roses and sunlight . . . then she picked up her much-creased cap from beside the pillow, pinned it on, and said, 'How many of them are there? Should I go to surgery, or the fluoroscope room?'

'Fluoroscope.' Matron spoke over her shoulder as she leaned over Violet's cot. 'Come on, Miss Brickwood, they've got the bridge fixed and the ambulances are coming in. There's tea in the mess tent, and sandwiches,' she added, as Lydia ducked through the flap.

For the next fourteen hours Lydia alternated between working the fluoroscope and assisting whichever of the three surgeons needed help: dripping chloroform with a steady hand, retracting the edges of wounds so that shards of metal could be fished out, clamping off blood vessels and stitching shut flesh and organs so that Captain Calvert or Captain Burke or Colonel Lemoine could get on with the next man. Well after sunrise on the following day – the twentieth – the last of the urgent cases was finished, though the hammering of the German guns had eased many hours before. A dozen of the last group in the ambulances were German prisoners, muttering confusedly: *Haben wir gewonnen*?

Lemoine retorted, in the same tongue, 'You have lost – as you will lose all in the end.'

But Captain Burke only patted his patient's hand and said, 'Nowt t'worry reet now, lad,' as Lydia signed the orderlies to carry the shattered man into the fluoroscope room to see where the shrapnel was buried.

When they were finished at last Colonel St-Vire ordered the whole surgical staff, save for himself, to their tents: 'And I'd better not see one of your faces for the next eight hours, understand? I hear we held the line and pushed Jerry back. It'll be awhile before they try again.'

'Sir, can you tell the neighbors to keep it down?' Captain Calvert pointed east, in the direction of the Front and the thunder of the guns. 'I can't see *how* I'm to get my beauty rest with that *frightful* din going on . . .'

''Ud take more'n eight hours' kip, think on, to render – hrrm! – *some* people beautiful . . .'

Lydia returned to her tent without the slightest thought for Miss Smith, lay down again, and was asleep within moments, dreaming of arteries and kidneys, of pancreatic ducts and lobules, with a sensation of walking in some wonderful garden without anyone's life being at stake, only to view these wonders at her leisure.

When she woke up, and washed (*finally!*) and brushed her hair and had bacon and porridge and tea in the mess tent, and felt herself again ('Be ready to be on at six, Dr Asher . . .'), she went to the ward tent in quest of the little dark-haired volunteer with the heart-shaped face.

And found that she was gone. Nor was there any sign of the red-haired, freckled soldier she'd sat beside, though two men recalled seeing them ('She bust out weepin' like a babe, M'am, an' cried out his name . . . Danny? Davy? Harry? Su'thin' like that.') While Lydia had been sleeping, trucks and ambulances had been departing steadily, carrying the most stable of the men back to the base hospital at Calais. Hundreds had already gone.

Matron – unsurprisingly – had barely had time to scribble down the names of the men as they were brought in, and the nature of their wounds. She thought the extra volunteers had come in from the Friends' ambulance station at Neuve Chapelle, and possibly – she wasn't sure – from the base hospital.

There was no Nurse Smith listed anywhere.

SEVEN

'**L**ay thy crest,' growled a voice like chains stirred in a pot of blood. 'An' I wanted ye dead I'd have had the throat out o' you ere this.'

Asher sat up in his narrow bed. He could see nothing in the darkness – the room's shutters were fast – but he could smell where the vampire sat, and feel the weight of him on the side of the mattress. A stench of graveyard mold and dirty clothing.

Lionel Grippen.

The Master of London.

The weight shifted and a match scratched. As Grippen turned up the gas Asher saw the familiar form, tall and heavy-built, clothed in a frock coat ruinous with age and a waistcoat of Chinese silk spotted with old blood. Greasy black hair, thick as a horse's tail, spilled from beneath the brim of a shallow-crowned beaver hat and framed a face fleshy and thick, a nightmare of centuries of uncaring murder.

The vampire flexed his hand a couple of times and dug a kerchief from his pocket, to wrap on over the burn the silver had left.

'You're seeking this revenant,' said Grippen. 'What've ye found?'

'That someone's screening his movements.' If the master vampire's aim was to hide the revenant himself, Asher was fairly certain Grippen would, indeed, have killed him – or had him killed by the living men in London whose debts he paid, whose affairs he protected, whose dreams he read and who followed his orders without asking who he was or why he wanted things done.

Two years ago, after Asher had killed most of the London nest, Grippen had broken up the ring of henchmen centered on the East End tavern called the Scythe. Asher guessed he'd put together another.

'Germans, you think?'

'There's a nest of the things in Prague.' Asher reached for the shawl he'd spread over his blankets and dragged it up around his shoulders, for the room, though stuffy, was bitterly cold. 'It's certainly a more effective way of destroying civilian morale even than Zeppelin raids. And it could be easily done, by infecting a man and bringing him across immediately, before he starts to transform. In a way I hope it's that, rather than that the condition has developed spontaneously, for God only knows what reason—'

The vampire growled, with the first display Asher had ever seen from him, of uneasiness or fear. 'That can't happen, can it?'

'So far as I can find out, nobody knows how these things first started. They spread through contamination of the blood, but the original source has to have developed it somehow. Which means, it can develop again.'

Grippen whispered, 'God save us, then.'

'I've been saying that for a long time,' returned Asher. 'However the thing came here, the Foreign Office – or men in the Foreign Office – are hunting it, not to destroy it, but to capture it . . . to use it for their own purposes. If that hadn't been the case already I think my former chief, Langham, would have recruited me, instead of warning me off.'

'Faugh! There's the Quality for you.'

Asher couldn't quarrel with him there. 'When did you first see him? And where?'

'Limehouse. Candlemas, thereabouts.' His English had a flatness strongly reminiscent of American, even after three centuries; as a philologist Asher could not help his mind from marking it as Elizabethan. 'Killed a newsboy that was sleepin' rough. Tore him up somethin' savage. Later I smelled him in the fog, near the hospital in St James Road, and I think he killed a whore in the Canal Road near the Kingsland Basin. Leastwise that's what Gopsall tells me, that runs the Black Dog near there. I never actually seen the thing.'

'And it killed a man in an alleyway behind Chalton Street, between King's Cross and Euston, Monday night. The body disappeared. So did the only positive witness. If German agents were behind it, they'd publicize it. They'd see to it that its victims were found – and they might well see to it that its victims were more than prostitutes and homeless newsboys. The Department is covering its tracks.'

'Faugh,' said the vampire again. 'And you look down on *us*, for killin' a whore here and there. You're not sayin' they're lettin' the thing rove free?'

'I don't think so.' Asher shook his head. 'I think they're hunting it – or someone *in* the Department is using the Department's resources to hunt it, while keeping it quiet.'

'For Christ's sake, why?'

'To avoid panic. And, I suspect, to capture the thing to see if we can use it ourselves . . . And the man who captured it would, of course, get a fat promotion and maybe a knighthood if it turns out to be useful.'

The vampire grimaced in disgust – not, Asher was certain, from any moral objection, but at the unworkable stupidity of the idea. Though susceptible to destruction by the light of the sun, the Others, Asher knew, moved about underground for a few hours longer than could vampires, who fell unwakeably asleep with the sun's rising. Like their cousins the vampires they were tremendously strong, and would devour vampires in their coffins if they found them.

'I've been warned off. Unless the condition *has* somehow developed spontaneously – which I pray to God isn't the case – this creature was brought to this country and somehow got loose, which tells me that whoever brought it here has no idea what they're dealing with.'

Grippen snarled again. 'So what do we do?'

Asher stifled the surge of anger at *we* from a walking corpse that had drunk the blood of the living, that had used their deaths to fuel its unholy powers, for over three hundred years. A creature that had kidnapped his child two years ago. Though he had recovered Miranda safe he had sworn to kill it, and all those like it . . .

I am no more part of WE with you than I am with Langham . . .

But, of course, he was.

That was why he was angry.

The revenants were a plague a thousand times worse than the vampire, for they multiplied without conscious volition. And they could not be negotiated with.

The contagion of their being had to be extirpated before it spread.

And whomever it was who had brought one to England – for whatever purpose – had to be found. And destroyed.

He was aware that Grippen was watching him with cynical amusement. In addition to smelling his blood, the vampire had felt that flush of heat that had gone through him and knew – from centuries of observing humankind – exactly what emotion had kindled it.

'How large a network do you command in London these days?' asked Asher after a moment. 'How many observers can you call on?'

'Pah.' The vampire scowled, a horrible sight. 'Damnéd war. Run by a damnéd crew of rabbit-sucking pimps. Half the men in London have turned their backs on their families and homes, to go slaughter cabbage-eaters in Flanders muck, and for why? Because of lies these pribbling whoresons have conjured about country and King, making a man ashamed to tell 'em he'd rather not go die so England can keep its grip on a passle of colonies oversea!'

'Instead of sending them dreams in their sleep about how worthy of trust *you* are? And how they owe *you* their lives . . .'

Grippen jabbed a clawed finger at him. 'None o' your backchat! You whored for 'em yourself, by what Simon tells me. And pimped others to give you what help you sought.'

'I did,' replied Asher quietly. 'I did indeed. I apologize for my words.'

'Hmph. What help d'you seek? 'Tis mostly women and street brats I command these days, and Papist Irish who refuse to sign up 'cause they're too busy runnin' guns from the Germans to the Irish Volunteers. Scum.' The vampire shrugged, as if he spoke of roaches on the wall.

'I'm surprised to see you here,' remarked Asher, changing the subject, rubbing his wrist where the vampire's grip, however fleeting, had driven the silver links hard into the flesh. 'I thought all the vampires were at the Front.'

'And so they be.' Grippen seated himself again on the edge of the bed. Nearby in the darkness the bells of St Pancras chimed two, and even with the shutters and curtains tightly closed the night smelled of dank fog and the soot of trains. 'The more fools they and bad cess to the lot of 'em, swillin' like piggins at a trough. Those that're masters of the cities they rule'll find their error, when they come back to find some upstart's moved in on Paris or Munich or Rome and set up housekeepin' . . . I thought I'd stay here and watch my patch. And a damn good thing, with this clammy wight that should be in its grave prowlin' about spreadin' its contagion. Fine homecomin' that'd be, to get back and find London eye-deep in the things. Has that sneaking Papist whoreson—'

Meaning, Asher knew, Don Simon Ysidro.

'—got anythin' to say of it?'

Asher shook his head, and the vampire's eyes glinted, as if he guessed where Ysidro was and why.

But Grippen kept his peace, and after a moment Asher said, 'Find out if you can where this thing has been sighted or smelled, where rumor has placed it. If it's staying by the canal it can come and go through fog, and through the sewer outfalls. You say you learned of it first six weeks ago – find if there's any word of sightings before that. And keep your ear cocked for word that anyone else is seeking it, or that any who've seen it have disappeared.'

'There's enough disappear in this city without help of revenants, or them as seeks 'em. Christ, you think vampires could dwell anyplace where the poor was kept track of? Where'll I find you?'

'I'm going up to Oxford in the morning.' The thought of the train journey made his bones creak like an overladen bridge, but if he were to stay in London for any time there were things he wanted to fetch, to say nothing of seeing Miranda. 'I should be back Sunday, I'll be staying—'

He paused on the words, as Langham's jowly face and watery, penetrant eyes flashed across his thoughts and he remembered what his old master Pritchard Crowell had taught him, about making things look like accidents. *The wicked flee where none pursueth*, Holy Writ (and Asher's pious and long-deceased father) declared . . . and, frequently, Asher had found, the same could be said of the deranged. Yet it was a truism in the Department, particularly 'abroad', that in some circumstances it was better to flee and be thought deranged (or wicked) than to stop and be picked up by the opposition and shot as a spy.

In other circumstances, of course, flight could be just what the opposition was waiting for you to do.

'I'll put an advert in *The Times*,' he said. 'You still go by the name of Graves?'

The vampire's smile widened unpleasantly. 'That's me.'

'Mine'll be under the name of Scragger.'

'Dr Asher, M'am.' Eamon Dermott laid aside the film plate and turned to Lydia as she came into the fluoroscope tent, still puzzling over Matron's notes and the absence of Nurse Smith. The murmur of voices and clink of metal on china drifted faintly through the wall from the surgical tent, but held nothing of the frantic note of the 'big push' of yesterday and the day before. Down by the river, the Engineers were nearly finished clearing debris to start properly repairing the bridge. This evening, Lydia guessed, would be what Captain Calvert called 'cleanup'.

Men whose wounds could wait a little. Men who wouldn't die from not being seen to at once.

Outside, vehicles of all sorts were still leaving for the base hospital at Calais with wounded. Constant in the distance, the thunder of the guns continued.

'These orders you had from Captain Palfrey Thursday night . . .'

Oh, drat it! Lydia pushed her spectacles up more firmly onto the bridge of her nose and tried to look like Miranda did when questioned about the disappearance of sugar from the sugar bowl . . . *Oh, that? They merely wanted to consult me about training in the use of the fluoroscope . . .*

'Yes?'

'Did it have anythin' to do with taking German prisoners away?'

'German prisoners?'

Dermott nodded. He was a stocky young man a few years Lydia's junior, a Quaker who'd worked in his father's photography studio and assisted the local doctor in his North Wales village. 'Yes, M'am. I know 'tis not my place to be askin' questions, but some of the prisoners— That is, I speak a bit of

German. And one of the prisoners said this mornin' as how both here and at the Front when they was captured, there was an officer separatin' out some of the men, puttin' 'em in a truck and away they'd go. He said he was captured with his cousin, and looked to see him here, but instead it was this same thing. A half-dozen men separated out from the rest and took away, M'am. And he asked me, was this usual, and how would he get in touch with his cousin again? He was a lawyer, see, this German, and had spent some time in England. He said it wasn't anything the British would do.'

'It's certainly nothing I've ever heard about.' Lydia frowned. 'Not with the wounded, at any rate. Seriously wounded?'

'No, M'am. Mostly walking wounded, he said. I did ask Captain Calvert about it, M'am, and he said he'd never heard of it neither, not here nor anywhere else, but if the officer had papers for it – which he did – it must be pukka. But it didn't seem quite right to me still, and I thought about this Captain Palfrey that came the other night with papers for you, and you going off as you did . . . Well, there might be other things going on that even gentlemen like Captain Calvert aren't told about. But I was only asking, and I wouldn't wish to cause trouble.'

'No,' said Lydia thoughtfully. 'No, it's nothing I've heard of, Mr Dermott. Captain Palfrey was simply relaying a request for me to consult about training in the use of the fluoroscope.'

The vampires Antonio and Basilio, driving their ambulance-wagon all along the trench lines? A shiver went through her: anger, helplessness, frustration. Had some other enterprising ghouls, braver than the rest, started a delivery service for the convenience of those Undead who didn't want to risk getting that close to the Front?

How easy it was, to prey on the helpless. The wounded, and prisoners . . .

She closed her eyes for a moment, sickened. *Every vampire in Europe is here. Feeding at will. Killing at will.*

And nobody notices.

In the momentary silence, the crashing of the guns sounded very loud.

And why would they notice?

She looked at Dermott again. 'Could I speak with this man?'

EIGHT

'Rhinehardt?' Nurse Danvers checked the notebook she carried, close-scribbled with hundreds of names dashed off in a hurry between cleaning, bandaging and the endless ancillary chores of making beds and ironing sheets. Lydia was burningly aware that she herself should be in the fluoroscope tent at that moment, sorting through films of the men waiting for surgery, instead of snooping around the prisoners' compound . . .

'A fair-haired man.' Lydia repeated the description Dermott had given her. 'Broken nose and shrapnel wounds in the face.'

Across the small tent where the wounded prisoners had been kept under guard last night, Matron called, 'Danvers—'

Danvers peered at her notes, turned the book sideways, pale brows crumpling together.

'Danvers—'

'Just coming, M'am! Oh, aye, he's been taken on to Calais. A whole lot of them went this afternoon.'

BOTHER! 'Thank you!' As Lydia hurried from the prisoners' tent – jammed with men last night, nearly vacant now save for a handful of the worst cases down at the far end – she cursed herself for not waking earlier. Yet she was aware she needed the sleep, and by what Dermott had said of this man Rhinehardt's wounds, she doubted whether the man she sought would have been able to talk to her much earlier. A dozen finger-sized fragments of shell-casing and wood from the trench re-enforcements had been taken out of his face, throat and chest last night. That morning, Dermott had said, he'd still have been under morphia.

To her left, by the road that led westward to Calais, a line of soldiers caught her eye, rifles ready, and before them, men in gray-green uniforms, seated on the ground. A big wagon, drawn by two exhausted-looking farm horses, was being loaded under guard.

This afternoon, she said . . . but these things always take forever . . .

Lydia caught up her skirts and nearly ran. 'Excuse me, Sergeant Waller, but is there any chance I might speak to one of the prisoners? There are some details about his injury I didn't get last night before he was operated on . . .'

'Well . . .' The sergeant frowned. A friendly soul, he had several times traded encomia with Lydia about the perfections of their respective children. 'We're not supposed to, M'am. But if it's in the way of medical information . . .'

Sure enough, Captain Rhinehardt lay on a stretcher, waiting for a place on the next wagon or (Lydia did a hasty calculation) probably the next but one . . .

Now if I can just remember enough German . . .

'*Bitte* . . .' she said hesitantly, and the young man turned his head, blinking up at her with his one undamaged eye.

'*Gnädige Frau Doktor* . . .' His voice sounded like dry mud being scraped off tin.

'Do you speak English?' *If he's visited England . . .*

He was haggard with pain and still sleepy from the morphia, but answered her in that language. 'Please forgive me for not rising, Madame . . .'

'Good Heavens, Captain, it's I who should be asking *your* forgiveness, for troubling you at such a time.' She knelt at his side. 'My assistant, Mr Dermott, said you were seeking your cousin, who had been . . . taken away from the other prisoners. Things were so confused for the last few days we're still not certain what happened, but I will try to trace him. Was his name Rhinehardt also?'

An infinitesimal nod. 'Oberleutnant Gleb Rhinehardt.'

'And he was also wounded?'

'Not so badly as I, Madame. How do you say it? Walking wounded. A bullet had broken his arm.'

Lydia flinched. Flanders soil, manured for croplands for centuries, was incredibly virulent in cuts. Even the smallest wounds went septic within hours.

'And men were being taken away from the main group of the wounded?' A glance along the line of the prisoners showed her at once that over a dozen of them were on their feet and able to help their comrades.

'So they were, Madame. A French officer – a surgeon – with

two British soldiers, and a nurse, or a nursing sister – dressed as you are, in light blue with a white apron. Gleb was sitting with me – he could have escaped, fled when the remainder of our unit did, but he was captured when he saw that I could not walk. I heard our officer calling to him to do so and he would not let go of my hand. At the dressing station he asked the sergeant in charge of guarding us, could he fetch me some water, and the sergeant permitted him to do so; there was a water butt nearby. Gleb walked over to it with his cup and this French officer saw him and pointed to him, the two soldiers stopped him and took him away with five others, in a big ambulance-wagon. A long chassis Sunbeam, I think it was. Gleb was a motor mechanic in Dresden, Madame. There was no vehicle in our lines that he did not point out to me and tell me about, inch by inch.'

Something that might have been a smile twitched one corner of his mouth at the memory of his friend, then quickly faded.

'I saw Gleb trying to talk the soldiers into letting him come back to me but they put all six of those men into the ambulance truck. He got one of the regular guards to bring his cup to me with the water. I asked this man, where had they been taken, and he said he didn't know. No one I have spoken to knows anything about it. But one of the other prisoners here told me the same thing: that this French surgeon and his nurse took away ten men, only lightly wounded, from the dressing station where he, and they, had been held before coming here. The French surgeon looked at him – the man who told me this, a sergeant in the Uhlans – but said he was too badly injured and would not do.'

Lydia frowned. This didn't sound like anything Don Simon had told her, but of course considering the other vampires abroad along no man's land, there was no way of telling. However, if this young man had been able to identify the make of an ambulance . . .

'What time of day was this?'

Rhinehardt shook his head. 'The assault started just after sunrise. I was hit before we reached the English lines, and I was unconscious when Gleb found me. I know it was daylight when we were at the English dressing station – an hour, two hours, before dusk began to fall, perhaps? It is hard to judge, Madame . . .'

'Of course,' said Lydia quickly. *Not vampires, anyway. Unless*

*they've got the living working for them – like poor Captain Palfrey
– but why on earth would they want the walking wounded?* 'Thank
you,' she added. 'I'll do everything I can to see if I can locate
your friend . . .'

'*Danke*,' he whispered, and closed his eye.

'Is there anything I can get for you? Do you need more
morphia? Or cigarettes?'

'*Danke*, Madame, but I am well for the moment.'

Lydia started to rise, then knelt again and asked, 'One more
thing, if I may ask, sir. How did you know the French officer
was a surgeon?'

The young captain blinked up at her, his brow tightening as
if the pain were returning, and his voice was a little slurred with
weariness. 'He was here,' he said. 'I saw him pass through the
tent last night, before I was taken to surgery. I was afraid . . .
He and his nurse were both there. I was afraid they had come
to search for others.'

'Was it Nurse Smith?' asked Lydia. 'Short and young, with
black hair and a heart-shaped face, a . . .' What was the German
word for a widow's peak? She sketched a downward-pointing
arrowhead from her hairline, hoping he understood, and he
nodded.

'Yes, this was her,' he murmured. 'The one who loved the
Irishman.' His eye slipped closed again, and after a moment, he
said, 'If it would not be a trouble to you, *Frau Doktor*, yes, I
think I would like some morphia, if I am to go in the ambulance.'

Lydia stopped at the ward tent, and made arrangements with
Matron for a syrette of morphine to be sent to Rhinehardt, on her
way to the fluoroscope room. Subsequent inquiry however, that
night in the mess tent and at intervals the following day, yielded
nothing out of the ordinary about Colonel Lemoine. As far as
anyone knew, Captain Calvert told her, Lemoine was with the
Second French Army somewhere near Nesle. He'd only happened
to be at Haut-le-Bois down the line when word came of the German
attack. Further queries over bully beef and stale biscuits the
following evening elicited only the information that no Nurse Smith
was assigned to the nearest clearing station south of Haut-le-Bois,
at Orchies-le-Petit, at least as far as Captain Calvert knew.

Before bed that night Lydia took a jar of Aunt Lavinnia's

marmalade to the stores hut, and ascertained that Storeman Pratt had never heard of her there, either – and due to his wide-flung network of graft and trade, Pratt knew pretty much everyone on the Front.

'Tell you what, though, Mrs A—' The rangy, curiously angular-looking storeman unscrewed the jar lid, and without breaking the bleached white wax of the seal inhaled the faint scent of oranges and sugar with the half-shut eyes of a connoisseur – 'I'll hold onto this 'ere jar, and ask about a bit, y'know? Tiny Clinkers, what looks after the motors at Headquarters, got a list of just about every woman on the Front, how old they are and if they're pretty and will they or won't they, if you'll excuse my French, M'am. Pretty, you say?'

'I think so. Black hair, widow's peak, short, retroussé nose. What my nephews call a pocket Venus. I heard that young Irishman with the freckles call her Tuathla . . .'

'That's just one of them Irish fairy-tale names.' Pratt shook his head at the entire heritage of Celtic civilization. 'Readin' too much Yeats an' seein' leprechauns, an' handloom weavin' their own skirts. Last couple years, every coal-'eaver's daughter in Holborn been changing 'er name from Nancy and Mary to Eibhlhin and Nuala. I've never heard of a nurse looks like that in this part of the Front, much less one that'd be at Headquarters t'other night when the balloon went up. Home-made, this is—' He gestured with the jar – 'There's men at Headquarters – them as don't have relatives that could afford to stock up on sugar before the war – would trade me any amount of petrol and cigarettes for this, and I'll see you get the worth of it, M'am.'

'Thank you.' Lydia put as much warmth as she could into her voice, though she wanted to stamp her foot at him. The petrol and cigarettes were of course being stolen from motor pools that were to take the wounded to hospital, and the slender rations of comfort that were supposedly being sent to the men. But her mother, and the fearsome Nanna who had reigned over the nursery in her childhood, had drilled her in the art of sounding friendly no matter what she thought or actually felt, and this training served her in good stead now. As she was turning to leave a thought came to her, and she turned back. 'And does Corporal Clinkers have a list of all motorcars on this portion of the Front?'

'Lor' bless you, M'am, we all of us got those. What might you be interested in?'

She had the impression that if she'd pulled thirty pounds from her pocket he'd have sold her Commander-in-Chief Sir John French's personal vehicle.

'A long-chassis Sunbeam lorry ambulance. Can you find who has them, and where?'

'Nuthin' simpler, M'am. Just gi' me 'arf a day.'

The warmth in her voice was genuine when she said again, 'Thank you.' Technically she supposed that getting information from – and fraternizing willingly with – Storeman Pratt was probably less dreadful than getting information from vampires . . . Unless you counted Pratt as a vampire himself.

'Am I on this Corporal Clinkers' list?'

'Oh, absolutely, Mrs A.' Pratt saluted her. 'Right up there with Matron and seventy-eight percent of the nuns at Calais. Under 'D', for *Don't Waste Your Time On It, Boy-O.*' He screwed the jar shut, and stashed it under the counter. 'And if you should 'appen to be sent any other little thing you might want to spare – or if there's anythin' *you'll* be wantin' in the way of sweets or smokes or silk stockin's . . .'

'You are a disgrace.' Lydia did her best to sound severe but couldn't keep from laughing, and his own grin widened.

'I do me best, M'am.'

'No luck, Mistress?'

Without a sound, Don Simon Ysidro had materialized at her side.

The night was now pitch-dark, the tent-canvas once again dimly aglow with lanterns, though owing to a failed delivery (or perhaps, Lydia speculated darkly, theft by Storeman Pratt and his spiritual kin) there were fewer of these than there had been five nights ago. Someone had tried to rig barriers of twine and fragments of bandage, to mark the new shell-holes, and the trees blown out of the ground by the German bombardment now lay strewn about the camp, half sawn-up to fuel the extra furnace that was being constructed (*In the bearers' abundant spare time!*) for the amputated limbs. The air was gritty with smoke, and reeked of spoiling meat.

The smell of someone's cigarette, momentary in the darkness. In one of the tents, someone with a beautiful Welsh tenor was singing 'Keep the Home Fires Burning', against a thready harmonica and a soft chorus of bass.

Jamie . . .

She pushed the thought of her husband aside.

Miranda . . .

'You heard all that?' She nodded back in the direction of the stores hut.

'I know you have been seeking word of this woman we saw in the trenches, as I have been, among those who hunt the night. So far as I have learned, these revenants do not wander at large in the German lines. Nor yet have any seen any such thing in the wasted lands between the lines, nor wandering in the abandoned trenches on either side.'

'They might have.' Lydia removed her spectacles, and polished them with her handkerchief. Her head ached, from an afternoon of concentration in both the x-ray room and the surgical tent. 'If a man had taken a head wound, and was wandering about in confusion; or a wounded man in no man's land trying to make his way back to the lines . . .'

'We are cowards at heart,' said Don Simon. 'Seldom do we actually venture into no man's land. Aside from the issue of shelling, too many men on both sides use cocaine to stay awake at their posts, and there is greater chance that we will be seen and shot at. If any saw such a man, either in the wasteland or in a bombed-out trench, we – my kindred and I – would take him, for such men seldom reach safety in any case. None that I know of have said to me – nor to any to whom I have spoken – "*I saw a man whom I thought merely wounded, and when I went to take him, found he was such a creature instead.*" Personally,' he added, tilting his head in a gesture curiously mantis-like, 'I find this very odd.'

'That means there aren't a great many of the Others about—'

'Yet.'

'Yet.' Lydia resumed her spectacles and frowned. 'How are they created, Don Simon? I mean, the ones Jamie told me about, in Prague . . .'

'I know not, Mistress. Nor does the Master of Prague . . . Who is, I think, vexed and distressed at the news that one such creature has unquestionably appeared here. With all of no man's land a labyrinth of old trenches and buried dugouts and sapper's tunnels, 'twere too easy for these Others to move about. They can cover themselves from the awareness of the Undead, and find us where we sleep, in the crypts and cellars of ruined churches and manors, devouring us in our coffins. And if, like the revenants of Prague and Peking, those breeding here can control rats, the situation is more dangerous still.'

Lydia flinched in disgust. In the mines northwest of Peking she had seen men swarmed by rats, when they'd attempted to invade the *yao-kuei* hive there.

'As I once told James – and as it is also written in the Book of the Kindred of Darkness – the Others first appeared in Prague just after the Great Plague, five and a half centuries ago. But whether it is a virus that transforms their flesh – or if such virus is a *mutation*, as de Vries calls such changes, of the virus that transforms the flesh of a man into that of a vampire – if *that* be a virus – I know no more than do the messenger dogs in their kennels.'

'Has any vampire ever . . . ever killed one? A revenant, I mean. And not just trying to get away from it.'

'Never that I have heard of. Would you drink the blood of such a thing, knowing that to mix its blood with your own might pass its condition along to yourself? How much less would one try to drink its life, the energies of its death? The mere thought appalls.' He put his hand beneath her elbow, and helped her across rough and squishy debris around a shell-crater. It had rained that day, and cloud still veiled the moon.

'But you drink the blood of syphilitics, and consumptives, and drug-takers,' pointed out Lydia, a little diffidently. 'The blood and . . . and the life . . .' She glanced across at him, wondering at the same time why on earth she felt she needed to be tactful: *He's certainly aware of what he is . . .*

''Tis not the same.'

Lydia stumbled on a flooded wagon-rut, and became aware that they were leaving the tents and huts behind them. 'Where are we going?'

'To meet Antonio and Basilio once more. They have seen

this ambulance-truck with the walking wounded, and know now where it went.'

Antonio Pentangeli and Basilio Occhipinti were, as before, in a dugout in what had been a German reserve trench before the English had retaken Pont-Sainte-Félicité, playing picquet – an antique card-game much favored among the older vampires – at a broken-down table to the music of a gramophone with a cracked horn. A couple of candles burned on shelves – Lydia saw the lights flare up as she and Don Simon came around the last corner of the revetment – and, of all things, a small pot of tea sat keeping warm on the makeshift stove: ''Tis a cold night, *bella donna*.' Antonio poured some out for her into a teacup that had to have been looted from the village. 'You seek a long-chassis Sunbeam ambulance with a French officer, who visits the dressing stations in search of the walking wounded?' He brought up a chair for her, cushioned with a folded blanket.

He was dressed, Lydia observed, in an officer's uniform as before; the beautiful Basilio was costumed as a driver, with the armband of the Red Cross. She tried not to think of Uncle Richard's footmen – Charles and William – bleeding in some shell-hole watching the approach of their ambulance-wagon with hope.

'Have you seen him?'

'Twice. Most recently the night before last, when all the German prisoners were brought from their attack. But again before that, three weeks ago, just after the fighting at Neuve Chapelle. This same officer, with the brow of Saturn and the little black mustache—'

'Colonel Lemoine,' said Lydia at once. 'That's what the German prisoners said, too.'

'I know not.' Antonio shook his head. 'But he had papers which he showed to the guards. He selected from among the prisoners, men not badly hurt. I am not, you understand, much concerned about such men, nor do I understand how prisoners are dealt with in this war. In my day the captains simply ransomed them back to one another, if they were gentlemen, or killed them if they were very angry, or hadn't enough food, or if the prisoners were Protestants.' He shrugged. 'And I thought perhaps this was an ordinary thing.'

'It may be.' Lydia propped her spectacles, and sipped the tea. Basilio offered her sugar in a Limoges dish, and, of all things, fresh milk. 'But I've never heard of such procedure. There are several very queer things happening hereabouts: between the revenant we saw, and this nurse whose name isn't Smith offering deals to the Undead . . . and people disappearing whom everyone is too busy and too tired to look for. You told me once—' she looked back at Don Simon, who had resumed his seat, hands folded, on a sort of earthen bench that had once been a bunk, his yellow eyes narrowed – 'that the Undead feed primarily on the poor: on people whom no one will trace and no one cares about. Like that song in *The Mikado*, about, "They'll none of them be missed". And that sounds like a description of those poor prisoners. As if someone wants the living – in reasonably good shape – rather than the dying.'

'Doing in fact with human beings,' remarked Don Simon, 'what the despicable Storeman Pratt does with petrol and cigarettes and morphia, I daresay. As war is waged now, things get mixed up and lost and mislaid all the time, and nobody thinks a thing of it. Where is this Lemoine posted, know you, lady?'

'Nesle, Captain Calvert says. But he's often in the camp at Haut-le-Bois.'

'I think a journey thence might profit us all. I shall arrange for the proper papers to be made out to release you from your duties for a time, and the good Captain Palfrey will call for you in the morning.'

NINE

The casualty clearing station at Haut-le-Bois lay some twenty miles south of Pont-Sainte-Félicité, where an outcrop of the Artois Hills made a long promontory above the farm country around it. In Sussex it would have been considered 'a bit of a rise', but in Flanders it amounted to 'heights.' Rain began just before sunup, and 'Colonel Simon's' staff-car jolted cautiously over roads deeply rutted by military traffic and cratered with shell-holes. 'It reminds me of the fen country, when the floods are out,' said Captain Palfrey, with affection rather than annoyance in his voice which made Lydia inquire, 'Are you from there?'

Rain streamed off the brim of his hat as he looked up – he'd climbed from the car to mend their second puncture of the trip. His smile alone answered her query. 'Can you tell?'

'Well, my husband probably could spot you from the way you pronounce your words – he's an expert at that. But my uncle always says that the only people who really love the fens are those who're born there.'

The young man lifted one hand, ruefully owning his guilt. 'Wisbach. Actually Deepmere, about ten miles from Wisbach; my grandfather's place, really, but I was born there. My grandfather is Viscount Deepmere.'

Lydia said, 'Good Heavens!' having danced in her brief debutant days with several young men who had probably been Palfrey's older brothers or cousins – 'good society' in England being actually rather small. (And the 'good society' admissible to parties in the home of her own grandfather, Viscount Halfdene, smaller yet.)

As they resumed their careful progress, Lydia learned from him, by degrees, the difficult but not surprising tale of the younger son of a younger son, raised on the fringes of 'good society' with no prospects and no greater ambition than to return to Norfolk and raise cattle, horses and sugar beets – a niche already solidly occupied by his elder cousins. 'And Father was in the Twenty-Fourth Bengal Cavalry, so it was the Done Thing that I'd follow in his footsteps. Grandmother put up the money for me to get into the Guards rather than an India regiment. Father was her favorite. When he died Grandmother got it into her head that India's a horribly unhealthy climate – he and Mother both died of cholera – and wouldn't hear of me going there. It's where he met Colonel Simon,' he added, a little hesitantly, and a frown puckered his brow. 'At least I think . . .'

'Tell me about Colonel Simon.'

'Well, a great deal about him falls under the Official Secrets Act, you know,' Palfrey warned her. Shy pride glimmered in his blue eyes, and a trace of hero worship. 'But I think – I *know* –

my father knew him in India. I remember his name in letters father wrote me . . .'

Or he's put it into one of your dreams that you remember . . .

'Father died when I was just six, but . . . I remember the name. Mother, too.' He sounded uncertain, as if sorting clear memories from things he felt he knew from somewhere without being able to quote specifics.

'Wouldn't he be a much older man,' probed Lydia, 'if he knew your father?'

'He is . . . older than he looks, he says. But he must have known Father, because he knew my name when he met me. And he spoke of Father like one who knew him.'

Or like one who has practiced the art of 'reading' people and telling them what they want to hear, for three hundred and fifty years . . .

'He introduced himself to me at the Guards' Club, and said he had a proposition for me, if I were willing to do it. A few nights later we met, very late, and I was interviewed by the chief of his Department—'

'And where was that?' asked Lydia. 'What Department?'

'The Foreign Office.' Palfrey frowned, concentrating on maneuvering the staff-car off the bombed-out road and around an enormous morass of shell-holes. This was an area which had been retaken, Lydia guessed, fairly recently – the whole length of the drive (it was now mid-morning) the booming of the guns sounded very close, and the crackle of rifle-fire. Two or three miles off, Lydia calculated. What had once been farmland lay all around them in a waste of shell-pitted mud, crisscrossed with abandoned trenches and entanglements of barbed wire still bright and sharp in the rain. Once the road had brought them close enough to the reserve trenches that Lydia could see the men piling sandbags along the lip of the cut, and the smoke that rose from the cooking-fires. Twice lines of men passed them, marching in from St-Omer. Stoic faces, empty and sunk into their own thoughts. Supply-wagons followed the men, mules slipping and straining against the sheer weight of the gray mud. Mostly the land was empty, desolate under the pattering rain.

'Somewhere in Whitehall,' the young captain continued, the uncertainty in his voice telling its own tale. 'It was hideously

late at night, as I said – I'd dozed off in my digs waiting for
Colonel Simon to call for me. When I got back it was nearly
morning and I fell straight to sleep when I came in, and woke
up still dressed in my chair. And then, what with the black-out
and Colonel Simon's caution about letting me see where we
were, I'm not sure I could find the place by daylight anyway.'
His eyes sparkled boyishly at being part of such a hush-hush
operation. 'I know the officer I spoke to told me the official name
of the Department, but I've forgotten it. Mostly we just call it
the Department.'

As Jamie does . . .

*Only Jamie's Department is REAL. Not something Don Simon
caused this poor young man to dream about . . .*

Palfrey chuckled. 'It's all rather like a blood-and-thunder novel,
really. My pay just magically appears in my bank account, so I
think they must deposit it in cash. But the officer told me, at
Whitehall that night, that what Colonel Simon is doing in France
is of vital importance to the War. Without his work – and of
course I have not the slightest idea what it actually is – our
armies here might very well be overrun and wiped out by summer.
Colonel Simon has a network of agents in France, and some in
Germany. Mostly what he needs – what he needs *me* for – is as
a bodyguard, a driver, a man to make arrangements for things
when he's called elsewhere. And I've tried to give satisfaction,'
he added shyly. 'I realize I'm a complete fool about the brainy
stuff – I was forever being caned at Harrow for not being able
to learn Latin or history or how many x's you need to make a y
– but I *can* get things done. That's done it,' he added, pleased
with himself, and nudged the car back up onto the crazy road
again. 'I'd feel a complete fool if we went through all that to
avoid a puddle a few inches deep, but on the other hand, those
craters could have been deeper than the top of this car and
quicksand at the bottom, you know, and then where'd we be?'

'And your grandmother wasn't horrified that you quit the
Guards?'

'Well, she was,' admitted Captain Palfrey. 'I told her a little
about Colonel Simon – though he'd warned me not to speak of
his having known Father. She's the only one I've told . . . she
and Aemilia, of course.'

'Aemilia?'

'Aemilia Bellingham.' His fair-skinned face actually blushed. 'We hope – that is . . . I hope we're to be married when the war ends.'

Lydia closed her gloved hands, and looked out across the sodden wasteland toward the reserve trenches. Don Simon had come here, she thought, to watch over her; and because of the terrible fragility of vampire flesh, he had needed a living servant. Like a *'shabbas goy'*, Jamie had once said: the Gentile servant whom pious Jews would hire to open windows or start kitchen fires on the Sabbath, so that their own piety would remain unblemished. She wanted to shout at this young man, *Have you ever seen him by daylight? He's a vampire, Undead . . . he lives on the blood and the energies of the dying . . .*

Only he wouldn't believe her. *He's warned me that all kinds of the most ridiculous stories are circulated about him . . . a combination of Count Dracula and Bluebeard . . .*

Precisely the sort of thing, Jamie had told her, that he – Jamie – had done in his spying days, when he was setting up a network somewhere abroad: German shopkeepers or Syrian peasants or Russian factory workers, who would provide him with information about their country's roads or local rebellions or how many of what supplies were being ordered. Who would cheerfully do so under the impression that they were actually helping their country rather than giving that information to enemies.

If anything went wrong, it was the dupes who would be punished, not the spymaster.

'And here we are!' Captain Palfrey guided the long-nosed vehicle carefully off the main road again, and toward a cluster of tents. 'According to my map, that should be Haut-le-Bois.'

Lydia had been provided not only with papers requesting her presence ostensibly in Arras, several hours further down the Amiens road, but with a convincing story of why they were stopping in Haut-le-Bois (a faulty map and a can of petrol so badly watered that, once Palfrey had poured it into the gas tank, the staff-car barely ran at all). As this portion of the line was fairly quiet at the moment, while Palfrey and the dark-faced, cheerful Algerians of the motor pool drained the tank and replenished the jerrycans, Lydia had sufficient time to walk around the whole of the camp and ascertain that there were no German prisoners anywhere in it, walking wounded or otherwise.

Colonel Lemoine invited her to join him for lunch in the officer's mess, and entertained her – over appalling coffee – with accounts of his various postings in the farther corners of France's overseas empire: Indochina, Algeria, West Africa and the 'concessions' in Shanghai and Peking.

'We were there in October . . . three years ago?' said Lydia. 'Nineteen twelve . . .'

'I had left by then,' said the physician. 'I came up the previous year during the uprising, and left when peace was restored to the city. It must have been in August or September of '12.'

'What was your impression of the hospitals?' asked Lydia, to deflect the man's attention from any possibility that she herself might know that at that time the little hive of revenants had been festering in the coal mines in the arid hills west of the city. She longed to mention Dr Krista Bauer – the German missionary whose account of finding the body of one such 'hill demon' had brought Jamie and herself (and Don Simon) to Peking – to see what Lemoine's reaction would be.

But caution closed her lips.

Only when Lemoine had walked her out to the motor pool, where Palfrey waited for her with the car, did she glimpse, among the other vehicles, a long-bodied ambulance, clearly a converted truck, though even wearing her spectacles she couldn't have told a Sunbeam from a governess cart. She let the colonel help her into the staff-car, and as he walked away turned casually to one of the several motor mechanics still loitering nearby and said, 'Do you think Colonel Lemoine might be here when I come back this way? I had ever such a delightful time.'

'Alas, Madame, that is very much the luck of the day,' replied the man in his singsong French. Lydia had observed that the cook in the officer's tent had been African, and recalled what Captain Calvert had commented some days ago: that the government of France was bringing in more and more men from its overseas empire, both in the Army and in the factories and farms, to free native Frenchmen to join the fight. 'He comes and he

goes, the colonel, and now that this section of the Front is quiet
he is gone more than he is here. Myself—' He tapped the side
of his enormous nose and looked wise – 'I think he is employed
by the government on some other matter that he does not tell us.
The other Big Ones—' he nodded toward the officers' tents –
'make no comment when he disappears.'

Lydia turned the matter over in her mind as the staff-car made
its slow, lurching return journey north to Pont-Sainte-Félicité,
with the rain falling again, and the desultory spatter of machine-
gun fire like the clatter of Death's bones in the gathering
darkness.

Everything innocuous and clear.

Reaching the clearing station, she had to help Dermott clean
up the fluoroscope room and develop films for nearly two hours
before she was finally able to return to her tent.

A letter lay on her pillow, addressed in James's firm, jagged
black writing. Three straggly hearts on the envelope were from
Miranda. A fourth, more firmly drawn, could only have been
from James.

Her eyes filled with tears so it was a moment before she could
read the small news of familiar things – of the sweet stillness of
Oxford during vacation, of rain pattering on the Isis, of her maid
Ellen's shy suitor, Mr Hurley, from down the King's Arms.

She read these innocent tidings first, like a forbidden sweet,
having seen immediately the dots beneath certain letters that told
her of coded matters. Only when she'd pretended to herself for
a few moments that the price of sugar was all anyone had to
worry about did she get out a pencil and decipher what couldn't
be shown to the censors.

One revenant at least in London.

Asher took the train up to Oxford on Friday afternoon, the 19th
of March. He ached in every joint when he woke, and by the
time he reached Oxford his chest burned and his skull buzzed
with fever. Ellen and Mrs Grimes put him to bed, and Mrs Grimes
– in between making blancmange and gruel – told him in no
uncertain terms that this was his own fault for gallivanting off
to London when Dr Hoggett had told him to rest, and that if he
came down with pneumonia again she was going to throw him

out into the road to die and would tell Miss Lydia that he'd run off with a drover's widow from Dorset.

Dr Hoggett – one of Asher's very small circle of intimate friends – when he came to see him on Saturday, added to this that he himself would then marry Mrs Asher, and it would serve Asher right. Hoggett returned Sunday evening, by which time Asher was well enough to beat him in two games (out of four) of chess after dinner: 'But if I hear you speak again of going back up to London tomorrow I'm going to break out my grandfather's phlebotomy knives and bleed you to keep you in bed.'

So Asher remained in the old brick house on Holyrood Street, rereading *Bleak House* and Lydia's letters and reflecting upon how ridiculous it was for a man approaching fifty, with gray in his hair and mustache, to feel moved to sing silly songs (*'Tho' the road between us stretches/Many a weary mile/I forget that you're not with me yet/When I think I see you smile . . .'*) at the sight of his wife's handwriting.

He checked the Personals column of *The Times* daily, but saw no message from Dr Graves. The revenant was lying low.

On Tuesday he was well enough to play hide-and-seek in the garden with Miranda – who was still of an age to believe that if she put her head in a cupboard in the potting shed that she was concealed – and to have tea with the Warden of his college. It was good to talk philosophy and ancient history with the old man, and to forget for a time what they both knew was happening in Europe: when Professor Spooner digressed indignantly on an undergraduate who had 'missed every one of my mystery lectures and was actually caught fighting a liar in the quad!'. Asher, long used to his conversation, merely inquired as to why the young man in question had chosen so public a place to light a fire.

Dr Spooner's kindly and erudite hospitality was a welcome contrast to dinner Wednesday evening with Lydia's Uncle Ambrose, the Dean of New College, who spent the evening complaining about the price of bread (*Who does he think is growing crops, with twenty thousand men a day being slaughtered in Flanders?*) and the influx of female servants at the colleges – 'They've actually hired a woman as a cook in the college kitchens! A *woman*! And I must say the quality of the men they're getting in these days is nearly as bad . . .' remarks which immediately segued into a fussy diatribe about how more men – 'decent, skilled, intelligent men' – should be volunteering for the Army instead of staying home.

'Honestly, between you and me, Asher, I'm ashamed to see who they're getting into the Army these days! I don't mind the Canadians so much, but the Australians . . .! And as for the idea of bringing in a lot of Indian wogs and niggers from Africa . . . How on earth are we going to keep a proper attitude back in the colonies when this is all over, I ask you, when they've been encouraged to kill white men? And for God's sake, when I see them fraternizing with white women here . . .!' He shuddered. 'And as for the officers . . .'

What the hell did you think is going to happen? Where do you think those men are coming from? You spill them like sand into the wind – send them with rifles in their hands against German machine-gun nests – and you think there will always be more?

His one attempt to divert the conversation onto Lydia resulted only in an angry speech about how hospitals were no place for a woman and how Asher should never have permitted Lydia to become a doctor in the first place. 'What's a woman know about medicine, anyway? All that suffragist nonsense . . . God made them women, and they should be content to be so!'

He returned to the dining room after seeing Uncle Ambrose off, to find that Ellen – who took over a footman's job of serving when they had company, now that Mick had joined the Ox and Bucks Light Infantry – just setting a cup of cocoa at his place: 'I thought you might need it, sir. And this came for you this afternoon while you were resting.'

It was a letter from Lydia.

The letter was long, and merely glancing at it, he knew there was something greatly wrong. A moment's mental calculation told him it had been sent before his own letter could have reached her, telling her of the revenant – or revenants – in London. But there were three times the usual number of little code-dots sprinkled over and around the text: some in ink, some pricked with a pin, some looking like flecks of the mud in which the Flanders trenches were drowning.

He carried the letter and the cocoa into his study, put on his reading glasses, turned up the gas and began to decrypt with a cold weight on his heart.

> *P-S-F – A* (The simplest of the code: *still at Pont-Sainte-Félicité, and well.* Sometimes the coded portions of her letters consisted only of that)
> *Other in N-M-L x volunteer nurse seeks vampires x says has proposition a partnership to offer x seen here CCS 16-3 x same nurse sought found body of Other, did ?? then destroyed it x alias Tuathla Smith no such person x German prisoner says Fr officer taking prisoners away not to HQ x Sunbeam ? ambulance no markings*
> *DSY here*

The following morning he took breakfast in the nursery. ('Grown-ups don't eat in the nursery, Papa!' objected Miranda, though delighted with his presence; she was at this time much invested in everything being in its proper place. 'It's my house, best beloved, and I can eat wherever I want.')

He had spent yesterday morning in the garden with her, listening to her explanations of where fairies hid when it rained (which it had, on and off, for several days), and now produced Lydia's letter, of which he read to her the plain text: expurgated of Lydia's weariness, her anger at the war, and some of her more ironic comments, even those she'd deemed mild enough to go through the censors. Miranda, a grave little copper-haired princess, was aware of such things as the war and that Mummy was away taking care of the men who were fighting it. She asked for clarification of things like x-rays and trenches, and made sure in her own mind that Mummy wasn't going to be hurt and would be back for Christmas.

After that he kissed her goodbye and returned to the railway station, stopping at Blackwell's for a large-scale Ordnance Survey map of London. He reached London shortly after noon, took rooms under the name of Edmund Hocking in Pembridge Place, Bayswater – he'd had papers made up for Hocking when last he'd been in Paris and the Department knew nothing of them – and put an advertisement in the papers asking for a meeting the following night with Mr Graves.

The advert was signed 'Scragger' – the old name for the public hangman.

Then he went to the British Museum, where at this time of day he was almost certain to find Osric Millward.

Osric Millward was a vampire-hunter.

Entering the vast, hushed space of the Reading Room's dome, Asher spotted him without trouble. He sat at his usual place at the end of one of the long desks, amid a welter of catalogs, manuscripts and ancient black-letter books on the occult: a tall, thin man whose raven hair was shot now with silver and whose dark eyes peered at the pages before him like those of an Inquisitor probing a heretic's lies.

When Asher had first met him, back in the eighties, Millward already had a reputation of being something of a crackpot, a profound believer in the beings whom Asher at that time had regarded as mere creations of folklore, like broom-riding witches and Miranda's fairies at the bottom of the garden. By the time Asher had returned from his first excursion 'abroad' on the business of the Department, Millward's study and belief had turned to obsession. A respected scholar of proto-Judaic Middle Eastern religious texts, Millward had gradually ceased to publish, and his lectures at King's College were more and more frequently cancelled because he could not be found. He'd be off on unexplained trips to London or Cornwall or Edinburgh, following up clues about vampire nests or suspected vampire kills. Eventually he lost his stipend from King's. In despair, his wife had returned to the home of her parents.

Watching him from the Reading Room's doorway, Asher reflected that Millward was everything that he himself dreaded to become. '*To hunt us would be to hunt smoke,*' Don Simon Ysidro had said to him once. '*You could hunt us down eventually, were you willing to put the time into it, to give your soul to it, to become obsessed, as all vampire-hunters must be obsessed with their prey . . . Are you willing to give it years?*'

I should have been willing, Asher thought. *And I wasn't.*

In the eight years since that night in Harley Street, Ysidro, and Grippen, and those fledglings that Grippen had begotten, had killed who knew how many men and women, the poor whom no one would miss or avenge. Asher didn't know whether, in that eight years, if he'd given his heart and his time and all of his attention to hunting vampires – instead of the hours of his mortal happiness with Lydia and Miranda, with the students he guided and the research into languages that gave him such joy – whether he'd have been able to find and destroy them or not.

And if he had, he reflected despairingly, there would only have been more.

'*We have what you do not have,*' Ysidro had said. '*We have time.*'

Looking at that shabby, graying figure, with his threadbare jacket and his unshined shoes, Asher could not keep the thought from his mind: *At least he has tried to rid the world of evil. While I, like the vampires, have traded the lives of all those unavenged innocents in the London slums for the peace and the joy and the happiness of these past eight years. Knowing they existed, and turning my face away.*

So far as Asher knew, Millward had never destroyed a single vampire.

As Asher circled the space between the shelves and the desks a young man emerged from the shelves carrying a couple of very fat, yellowing volumes that Asher recognized as the 1867 reprints of a Georgian collection of Scots witchcraft lore: there was mention in them, he recalled, of the 'Cauld Lad' that used to walk Graykirk Close in Edinburgh, whom it was considered death to meet. The young man, though shabbily dressed, wore a blue-, brown-and-red school tie from Winchester, much faded, and he bent over Millward with the same fanatic eagerness that the vampire-hunter himself had shown towards his books. His face glowed when Millward showed him something in the pages, and he dove away into the shelves again with the air of Sir Percival on the track of the Grail.

When he was out of earshot Asher approached the desk. 'Millward?'

The scholar turned in his chair. At the sight of Asher his eyes widened for a moment – their most recent meeting had involved Millward breaking Asher's ankle with a rifle butt and leaving him as bait for a vampire in the buried crypt of a Roman temple under Covent Garden – and then slitted in suspicion.

'What do you want?'

'Information.' Beneath Millward's frayed shirt-cuff Asher could see the other man also wore chains of silver around his wrists. 'What do you know about the Regent's Canal vampire?'

'Have you seen it?' Millward seized his sleeve, as if afraid that being questioned, Asher might run away.

'I've smelt it. And I saw the man it killed in Chalton Street, on the night of the sixteenth. I'm trying to track its appearances, to find where it's centered. And most specifically, who's protecting it.'

TEN

Millward had a room in Bethnal Green, near the goods yard. The threadbare curtains on its single window were dingy with soot and even the dried ropes of star-like white garlic blossoms that festooned them couldn't counteract either the stink of the gasworks nearby, nor the smell of mildew that took Asher by the throat.

Cardboard boxes stacked every wall head-high, protruded from beneath the bed and ranged under the cheap deal table. A hob the size of a shoebox accommodated a kettle, and tins of crackers shared the shelf over the table with yet more, smaller, cardboard boxes; the table itself was stacked with newspapers, as was one of the room's two wooden chairs. Millward moved the papers aside onto the bed, poured water from the jar by the door into the kettle, and fetched a handful of newspaper from what was evidently the discard box to kindle beneath a couple of knobs of coal. 'My true work's in the library,' he said as he scratched a lucifer match on the box. 'This place is no more than a pied-à-terre, so to speak.'

His breezy tone made it sound as if he still had his oak-lined study back at King's College, and the comfortable little house on Star Street that he'd shared with his long-suffering wife. Asher said nothing. He'd inhabited far worse, for months at a time, in the course of what the Department called 'cover'. But it had always been with the knowledge that his own rooms at New College were his true home.

To hunt us is to hunt smoke . . . to become obsessed, as all vampire hunters must be obsessed . . .

Since the night he'd lain, half-freezing in the damp, in the crypt where Millward and his disciples had pinned him as bait for the vampire they were trying to trap, he had hated the man – a hatred revived every time his ankle hurt him in winter. Now the hatred washed away in a wave of pity, seeing what the scholar had made of himself. He'd heard – he'd forgotten from whom – that the parents of Millward's wife still made him a tiny allowance.

This was what it was, he thought, looking around him, to be obsessed.

For years he'd seen Millward as an ageing Don Quixote, tilting at windmills invisible to sane eyes. But now, strangely, the person that came to his mind was his old teacher, the master-spy Crowell. The single-minded hunter in pursuit of his prey. A weapon in the hand of the Cause. Everything geared and tuned, like the engine of a motorcar, for one purpose and one purpose only.

And something else . . .

The box that Millward set on the table before him was fairly new, and labeled neatly – all the boxes were labeled – *Regent's Canal*. The clippings – Asher noted automatically the typefaces of *The Times*, the *Telegraph*, the *Sun*, the *Daily Mail* and the *Illustrated London News* among others – were arranged chronologically; among the papers on the table at his elbow he identified *Le Figaro*, *l'Oeuvre*, *der Neuigkeits Welt-Blatt* and several German, Italian and American journals as well.

'It killed first on the thirtieth of January.' The vampire-hunter plucked a clipping from the envelopes within the box. 'A prostitute in Lampter Street near the Southgate Road. People said it was Jack the Ripper returning to his old haunts – if the Ripper's under sixty nowadays he must have been little more than a schoolboy his first time round! – but the details of the crime weren't the same. And the Ripper, whoever he was, never made the attempt to hide his victims. A frightful deed.' He laid the article on the table before Asher – barely two paragraphs, an afterthought to the German submarine attacks in the Irish Sea.

Asher glanced over the specifics of the horrible remains and shivered.

'The body of a man was found – or what remained of one – on February eighth, on Dee Street near the gasworks. Police estimated that he hadn't been dead more than twenty-four hours. An elderly man was reported missing at about that time near Victoria Park—'

'By the Union Canal.' Asher mentally identified the place. 'And Dee Street is where Bow Creek joins the river. Water, both times.'

'I noticed that.' Millward laid out his clippings with a slow flourish, as if proving Asher wrong somehow or vindicating himself. Asher reflected that the man had fought so long to be believed – by his wife, by the police, by the King's College authorities when challenged about his disappearances – that the faint, arrogant look of defiance had become habitual, though Asher was one of the few men in England – or probably in the world – who understood that Millward was in fact telling the truth.

Those windmills really *were* giants.

'I thought it curious,' the vampire-hunter added. 'They usually avoid running water. And it is more savage than the other vampires. They kill, but do not molest the bodies afterwards, even when they conceal them. I can show you—' He turned back toward the stacks of boxes, and Asher lifted his hand.

'You don't need to,' he said. 'I know this one is different.'

Wary contempt gleamed in the other man's dark eyes. *Aye, YOU would know, who consort with such beings . . .*

Asher sorted the little squares of newsprint, moving them around on the tabletop, as he had with the bits of information about the time and place of German so-called 'archaeological' expeditions in Mesopotamia back in the eighties, or where all those extra Legation 'clerks' had been seen, and at what times. Ysidro had surmised that Millward's brother, who had died young and unexpectedly, had been the victim of a vampire (*Carlotta?* Asher wondered. *The Lady Anthea Ernchester? Grippen himself?*) It was this, in the vampire's opinion, which had turned the scholar's already-extant belief in vampires to obsession . . . But sometimes Asher wondered whether it was Millward's belief in vampires that had caused him to probe into matters concerning the world of the Undead – possibly with his brother's help – and thus bring that young man into peril in the first place.

As he himself had brought Lydia. And their daughter.

Enough to drive a man a little mad.

But he was not wrong, to seek those silent killers . . .

He took one of his Ordnance Survey maps from his pocket, and with his pen marked the places where kills had occurred. He marked also neighborhoods where people had been reported missing, often vagrants who slept rough, little regarded by the police. 'Nothing further south than Dee Street,' he commented after a moment. 'Nor further north than Leyton Marsh. Nothing more than a dozen yards from navigable water: creeks, canals, basins.'

'It's where the fog gathers thickest.' Millward sank into the other chair, leaned to look over his shoulder. 'Legend has it that they can summon fog . . .'

'They actually can't.' Asher moved another two-line clipping, put another X on the map. 'But there's waste ground along the canal, and buildings that stand deserted for days at a time: gasworks, the India docks, Hackney Common. The goods yards and tracks of the Midlands Railway. The pattern of this thing's hunting is different. It's an animal we're tracking, not a man.'

'It's a man,' retorted Millward grimly. 'A woman in Canal Road glimpsed it in the fog. Or it was a man once. The Undead—'

'This isn't one of the Undead.' Asher tilted his head a little to one side, still intent on the map. 'The pattern is similar, as the thing itself is similar. It's a revenant, what the early English called a wight: nearly mindless, and hungry. The vampires call them the Others. Like the Undead, it can to some extent fool the perceptions of the living. And like the Undead, it can transmit its condition through contamination of the blood, like a disease.'

'You're sure of this?' The scholar's silver-shot brows drew down. 'How do you—?'

'I'm sure. I have seen them cut to pieces, and the cut pieces continue to crawl about with what appears to be conscious volition. Sunlight destroys them; more slowly than their cousins, I'm told, but I've never seen it. But the thing is alive, and it can be killed. Vampires hunt all over the city – or they did,' he added with a grimace, 'until most of them left for the Front. This revenant – this Other—'

His finger traced the gray line of the Regent's Canal, with its myriad of auxiliary cuts and basins, curving through the East End like an old-time moat among a patchwork of industry and building yards. 'It hunts along here. And I intend to find it – or them. By this time there may be more than one.'

'You will have whatever help I – and those who help me, who believe in this war that we wage against the forces of Evil – can give.'

Asher thought about the young man in the Winchester tie in the Reading Room.

And about Crowell leaving his agents to die.

'But where did it come from?' Millward turned the map around, frowned over the neat X's. Then his sharp dark gaze cut back to Asher. 'And how did you learn of it? Did the Undead create it, then? Do they control it?'

'Not that I know of. I understand the vampires of Prague have tried for centuries to exert mental control over the Others that haunt the crypts beneath that city, without success.'

Millward's silence made Asher glance at him. He read in the dark eyes loathing and distress, tinged with admiration. Almost the same feelings, he reflected, that he himself had felt towards Pritchard Crowell.

'Prague . . .'

'The only city I've heard of so far,' said Asher, 'where these Others nest.'

'How did it come to England, then?'

'That,' said Asher, 'is one of the several things I intend to find out.'

Millward saw him down four flights to the door, through a front hallway whose dirty lino was cluttered with bicycles, coal scuttles and baby prams. The sun had just dipped behind the smoke-grayed line of brick houses opposite. It was a long walk to the nearest bus stop, and Asher guessed few cabs cruised these dismal streets. Dank fog was already rising from the river. On the way downstairs, Millward spoke of the young men who believed, as he did, in the Undead, who worked for him as secretaries and gatherers of information – 'Only Donnie's left of them. The rest are at the Front.' (Presumably Donnie was the young man in the Winchester tie.) 'Donnie isn't strong, but he and I will patrol the canal—'

But when Asher stepped across the threshold and the door shut behind him, he automatically cleared every thought from his mind, and scanned the street: wide flagways bustling with housewives, children running home from school, voices shrill in the air. A woman brought a birdcage and a wicker basket up from a nearby areaway, chirruping to her canary in alternation with some of the most hair-raising oaths Asher had ever heard – *Islands Scots, what's she doing here?* An old man with an elaborate cart and equipment for the repair of umbrellas called 'Brollies to mend!' in a quavering voice. Asher's eye touched the areaways of the houses nearby, the bleared windows across the road, as if he were in Berlin or St Petersburg, seeking anomalies or . . .

There.

He didn't turn his head. His sidelong glance passed across the sunken kitchen entry where he thought he'd seen a man's face, but there was nothing, and he turned away at once. One of the first rules was, *If you think you're being followed, don't let on. Maybe later you can see who it is, and take a guess at what they want.*

He thought he'd seen something, some anomalous shadow, outside the Reading Room.

And now here.

The Department? He trudged down Charlotte Street toward the Great Eastern goods yard where the omnibus would stop on its way to Charing Cross. *Or someone who, like Millward, has his own freelance disciples?*

Someone who thinks Millward may know something . . . About the Other? Someone who, like me, knows that Millward will at least have information about where the Other has been?

If it is the Department, he reflected, taking into account that he'd barely gotten a glimpse of Millward's watcher, *shame on them. If Stewart wasn't lying, and they need every man to gather information in the battle zones, why waste a good agent keeping an eye on a vampire-hunting crank who isn't even aware that every vampire in London is now at the Front?*

Unless of course, Asher thought – without looking back – *I'm the one who's being followed.*

Lydia saw the vampires outside her tent in a dream: Antonio and Basilio, Red Cross armbands pale against the dark rough coats of stretcher-bearers, Don Simon in his British Army khaki. In the gibbous moonlight, their eyes gleamed like the eyes of the bloated trench rats, and Lydia was at once aware that the sporadic gunfire in the distance had stilled.

In her mind she heard Simon's voice whisper, 'Mistress . . .'

Waking, she knew they were there still.

Waking, the sound of the guns seemed very far away. The fretful cluck of the Lys over the remains of the broken bridge came startlingly clear.

In the next cot, Danvers slept like a dead woman. Brickwood's cot was empty. Lydia pulled on as much as she could of her clothing under her nightgown – brassiere, chemise and blouse – before getting out of bed in the freezing cold. Hastily pulling on skirt, boots, petticoat and coat, she put on her spectacles and stepped quietly to the tent's entry, and looked out into the night.

And there they were.

Simon touched his lips for silence, and took her hand. The other two vampires soundlessly following, he led her to his staff-car at the edge of the camp – no Palfrey this time, she noticed – and helped her inside; Antonio took the wheel and drove off in the direction of the Front. Just short of the reserve trenches they stopped, left Basilio with the car and, as they had before, went on afoot, descending first into an abandoned reserve trench and then following the half-flooded mazes of the communications trenches: icy water underfoot, scuttling rats, the stench of death and latrine holes. Sometimes Simon or Antonio would lift her bodily in their arms, with the preternatural strength of the Undead, and carry her swiftly, like being borne by angels in a dream.

The stillness around them was the hush of nightmare. Her arms around Antonio's neck, as Don Simon clambered like a colorless spider up the side of the trench to look over at the hideous wasteland above, Lydia thought, for the thousandth time, *I shouldn't be doing this . . .*

Yet she felt no fear.

And, after a very short time, she understood that it was the silence that lay on this portion of no man's land that had drawn their attention, which had sent them to fetch her. Such absolute tranquility wasn't natural. No crackle of rifle-fire. Not a murmur from the front-line trenches, though they lay within yards. Once they passed a dugout, where half a dozen Indian infantrymen slumped around a makeshift stove and a tin of still-steaming tea. Not dead – she could see them breathing – but dozing. This was often the case with men in the trenches, but she understood that someone had put that illusion of inattention, that haze of sleepiness, on the sentries of both sides, and on the men hereabouts, for a reason.

And that someone has to be a vampire.

Simon scrambled up onto the fire step, looked over the sandbags. Lifted his gloved hand. *Come. Carefully.*

When she cautiously put her head over the sandbags – something that could get one killed, even at night – Don Simon passed her binoculars. The moon was a few days yet from full, but gave enough light to let her see the nurse Tuathla Smith – or whatever her name really was – crouched on the lip of a shell-crater, less than thirty feet away.

Nurse Smith wore the khaki coat of a British soldier, and had, like Lydia, left off her cap. Dark curls twisted into a loose knot at the back of her head, and framed the pale blur of her face as she looked around her. Aboveground in no man's land was not the place to be, even on a quiet night . . . and perhaps she also was aware, thought Lydia, that the silence hereabouts wasn't natural.

That someone had laid this silence on this small portion of the lines for a purpose.

And that purpose was to meet her without either of them getting shot.

And if a vampire were coming to speak to this young woman, thought Lydia, that vampire would be listening, with the uncanny sharpness of Undead perceptions, for the smallest whisper of sound.

And thank goodness that even in the cold like this the whole place stinks so that a vampire can't smell living blood.

She felt rather than saw Don Simon glance sidelong at her, nodded very slightly: *Yes, it's she.* And squeezed his cold fingers: *Thank you.*

Movement in the moonlight. Walking, like the *bean sí* of poor Corporal Brodie's nightmares, as lightly as a ghost over the torn soil of this unspeakable hell.

As Corporal Brodie had said, she wore the uniform of a nursing sister under a dark cloak. Her hair, like Smith's was uncovered, the flaxen hue of raw silk in the moonlight and lying, like silk, loose over her shoulders. Her face was an exquisite oval.

'Meagher,' she said, as the young nurse stood up.

'I'm she.'

'You seek me?'

'If you truly are one of the Undead – one of the vampire kind – I do indeed.'

The vampire looked around her, scanning the ruined landscape with those darkness-piercing eyes. Lydia remained perfectly still, her own eyes cast down, praying Don Simon and Antonio were vampires of sufficient age and power to turn aside this woman's glance.

'I am called Francesca Gheric.' The vampire's voice was a soft contralto, with an accent to it that Lydia guessed would have told Jamie of some other time, some other place. 'By some called Francesca Brucioram, or Francesca the White. And I am what is called a vampire.'

'Tuathla Meagher.'

The vampire merely looked at her extended hand, then back to her face, one butterfly-wing eyebrow atilt. 'That isn't the name your father calls you, when you dream.'

Meagher straightened her shoulders, chin lifted defiantly. 'It's the name I took for myself when I left his house and his chains forever.'

Francesca the White's mouth flexed a little, like a bird-watcher identifying the whistle of some rare species. *Oh, one of those . . .*

'It's true, then,' Meagher went on, 'that you can touch the dreams of the living? Can weave spells in them to control their thoughts, and guide them where you will? That you can control the thoughts of certain beasts – the wolf, and the rat, and the bat – and command the actions of the mad?'

Through the binoculars, Lydia saw the vampire's red lips curve . . . (*Red, she has fed, she has killed once, or several times, tonight . . .*) 'You seek a demonstration, pretty child?'

What Francesca Gheric did then, Lydia didn't see, but Nurse Meagher jerked as if at some startling sound, and threshed the air before her face with her hand. Then she fell back a step, staring at the vampire in shocked respect.

Francesca raised one eyebrow again: *Satisfied?*

'Will you help us?' said Meagher eagerly. 'In return, we can—'

'I know who you are,' the White Lady cut her off. 'And I know who you work for, and what you do in that compound of yours. Don't think I haven't watched you, walking about these deadly lands in the darkness, and speaking to my brothers and sisters of the night. This man Lemoine, this physician, this dabbler in chemicals and blood. I would speak to him.'

'I'm here,' said Meagher, barely able to contain her triumph, 'to take you to him.'

And with a sudden move she raised her hand to her throat, tore loose the silver cross she wore, and cast it away into the mud.

ELEVEN

'Francesca Gheric.' Antonio Pentangeli gazed thoughtfully into the distance as Basilio guided the staff-car down the shell-holed road in the moonlight. 'Well, well.'

He now shared the back seat with Lydia and Don Simon, and spoke barely to be heard over the growl of the engine. Basilio, Lydia guessed, had located Meagher's motorcar while she, Don Simon, and Antonio had been in the trench, and was following it now by the sound of its motor, audible to his Undead senses over the rumble of the guns to the south. *Unless of course he's just reasoned they can't leave the road at this point.* The land on both sides was a pitted ruin, laced with the water that had leaked from demolished drainage canals and stitched across and across with barbed wire.

They were headed south on the Arras road.

It is Lemoine . . .

'What about Francesca Gheric?'

'She dwelt in Strasbourg.' Antonio's dark eyes narrowed as he cast his memory back. 'For years and years, when Arioso was master of that city. Arioso had a network of living servants over the whole of the countryside between Strasbourg and Nancy. Very clever with illusion and dreams, but all said the White Lady was the stronger vampire. She was the elder in any case, and he never could control his fledglings and was forever having trouble with them. I always thought that with little effort she could have taken control of that whole district. But she didn't.'

'Is that so odd?'

'You would think so had you ever encountered Arioso.' Don Simon folded his narrow, gloved hands.

'He demanded absolute control over those he made vampire,' explained Antonio. 'And unfortunately he was drawn to people who lived untidy and dramatic lives. A non-entity himself, he loved the excitement, but then had not the strength to bend them to his will. The Strasbourg nest has always been a snake pit of internal feuds. Francesca quarreled constantly with Arioso, and had she made even a few fledglings she could have driven him and his from the city. But in the end it was she who left. She dwelt for many years in Prague. Later she had a palazzo in Venice, just across the Campo di San Silvestro from Basilio and myself.'

Lydia reflected that should she ever have the opportunity to vacation in that city – or any city in Europe, for that matter – she would consult Don Simon first about potential neighbors.

'Hieronymus – the Master of Venice – tolerated her but never trusted her. She wouldn't obey him, either, but killed as she pleased. I know he feared she would contest his mastery.

'She is not like Simon,' Antonio added, seeing Lydia's sidelong glance at the older vampire. 'Simon has chosen to live like a shadow on the wall. I'm told he dwelt in Rome for two years before the nest there even knew of his presence. Francesca disobeys the masters of the cities where she dwells, forms cliques among their fledglings and networks of servants among the living – Hieronymus was forever killing them. But she would never move to take genuine power.'

'Maybe she preferred just to be a troublemaker?' Lydia recalled girls she'd gone to school with, and debutantes who had come 'out' in the same year as she, who simply delighted in malicious gossip and the stirring-up of trouble between friends, while seeming to lack, it appeared to her, genuine friends of their own.

'She was made vampire by the Lady Chretienne,' remarked Don Simon after a time. 'A master who taught her fledglings the finer arts of the Undead state, and selected them with some care. At the time I encountered them during the Wars of Religion 'twas my impression Chretienne intended Francesca to succeed her as master of that whole region. Then later she made Philip Berengar vampire, who succeeded her, and he made Arioso his fledgling and master of Strasbourg in his turn. I thought it curious, that La Dame Blanche, as Francesca was called, was bypassed. Now she seeks the help of this Lemoine, this "dabbler in blood and chemicals". What know you of this Lemoine, lady?'

'Only what I mentioned before.' She shook her head. 'That he's with the French Sixth Army, and served in Algeria, Indochina, West Africa. He was in Peking in early 1912, where he might easily have heard of the revenants in the Western Hills.'

'More than that, I think.' A tiny line scratched itself between Simon's colorless brows. 'I have made a study of the vampire state over the years, and have read a good many articles on the composition and maladies of the blood.'

On Lydia's other side, Antonio Pentangeli shook his head, with an expression, attenuated as it was, that in a living man would have been an eyeball-rolling wave of exasperation. 'Were you this much of a pedant as a living man, Simon? I keep abreast of the world, but I swear this for the truth, *bella donna*, he writes sonnets about the composition of blood! Never would I bore a beautiful lady into a lethargy by—'

'Oh!' interrupted Lydia, and then, realizing that up ahead of them, Francesca might be listening for sounds of pursuit, she whispered, 'You think Colonel Lemoine might be *Jules* Lemoine, who wrote that article the year before last about viral mutations of red corpuscles?'

'I confess I did not completely understand his argument,' murmured Don Simon. 'Yet something of the way he spoke of blood made me wonder if he had ever had occasion to study the blood of the Undead.'

'And he was in Peking in 1912,' finished Lydia. 'He might have actually encountered the revenants, or someone who had fallen victim to one. He did say when we lunched together on Monday, that he never passed up an opportunity to study the pathologies of the local people, wherever he was stationed.'

The staff-car picked up speed as the road improved and the hammering of the guns faded a little to the east. For long periods now, stands of trees bordered the road, unshattered by shell-fire, and in the darkness she smelled the green scents of early spring. When she opened her mouth to speak again Don Simon gestured her quiet: the drone of a pursuing engine could be lost in the noise of one's own motor, but even the quietest of living voices might easily register to Undead ears. They had passed the turning to Haut-le-Bois some time ago, and in the weak moonlight the low swell of hills that sheltered that clearing station lifted a little against the western sky. Lydia had no idea how long it was until dawn, or if, and where, her three companions had a safe place to go to ground at first light.

Evil mingled with good, she thought, looking from Antonio's craggy profile to Don Simon's aloof, half-averted face. *But can't that be said of all human beings? I should hate them for what they are, for what they do.*

But at least, she thought, they believed her, and would understand the significance of the fact that it was Lemoine who was kidnapping German prisoners of war.

Men who weren't severely wounded, but who legitimately could be restrained. Men who had no power to protest, and no one to protest to. Whose disappearance would be greeted with a shrug: *They must have got the papers mixed up . . .*

Like petrol and cigarettes and morphia.

Basilio switched off the engine, and let the car glide to a stop. Silence lay on the land, save for the intermittent boom of the guns. *We must have swung east again, or the Front curved west . . .*

Antonio climbed out over the door (*So there won't be the sound of it opening, in the stillness of the night?*) and held up his hands for her; Don Simon lifted her over, with the casualness of a man picking up a kitten. Basilio remained where he was, and Antonio touched his hand where it lay on the car door, lightly, as they walked away.

Distantly, Lydia heard an engine start up again. 'A gate,' Antonio murmured, leaning close. 'Guards. French.'

Leaving the road, they climbed a hill's shoulder that gave a view onto the next rise of ground. In ancient times a wide-spread cluster of gray buildings had covered that rise, half of them in ruins now and the whole area studded with French Army tents and a half-dozen rough-built huts. A deep ditch surrounded the whole, fenced on both sides with a hedge of barbed wire.

Old trench works, Lydia thought. The dark slots went right up the slope behind the buildings, and she could see where the woods that surrounded the place had been cut back to let the 'moat' completely encircle the place.

Those buildings that remained whole, though simply built of gray stone, had the look of profound age.

Don Simon's voice was barely louder than the rustle of the leaves. 'The nunnery of Cuvé Sainte-Bride.'

'You know it?'

'Only the name on maps. 'Twas naught to speak of, even when I was in France years ago.'

A few tents glowed from lantern-light within. A window in one of the huts brightened, then dimmed as a shadow crossed it. Breeze brought the smell of latrines and cooking-fires, stinks familiar from the clearing station. And another smell that lifted the hair on Lydia's neck.

Her hand closed hard on Don Simon's fingers.

'Best be gone.' His whisper brushed her ear. 'She'll come out soon, if she's any wits at all. Dawn's coming, and we're twenty miles from Pont-Sainte-Félicité. We shall convey you home, lady, unless you'd wish a few hours' sleep at the chateau of the Master of Prague. You'll be granted little enough rest at your camp.'

'Thank you,' said Lydia. 'I'll take my chances at the clearing station.' She already had a headache from lack of sleep, but the thought of calmly bedding down in a vampire nest – though she knew to the marrow of her bones that Don Simon's influence would keep her as safe – was more than she wished to contemplate.

Both vampires bowed, like courtiers of some bygone world, and guided her back toward the car.

When night was fully come after his encounter with Millward, Asher took a cab from his hotel in Pembridge Place to Paddington Station, purchased a return ticket for Bristol, packaged up his Burberry and hat in the gents' room and paid a porter there to quietly mail them back to Oxford for him. Then he donned the cap he'd had in his Burberry pocket, and slipped down the stairway to the Underground, watching the platform behind him as he stepped at the last minute onto the train for Hammersmith. At Shepherd's Bush Market he got out – again leaving it till the last moment, and still feeling somewhere in the back of his thoughts the prickling wariness that had touched him outside of Millward's – and took the omnibus for the East India Dock, switching to a cab in Oxford Street and backtracking along the Edgware Road until he came – at almost midnight – to Regent's Park.

His meeting with Grippen wasn't until tomorrow night, but he guessed the Master of London knew perfectly well where he was.

Freezing damp rose from the grass as he followed the graveled path toward the boating lake. At this hour the stillness was such that he could listen behind him for the telltale scrunch of a stealthy foot on gravel, the wet squish of someone treading last autumn's dying leaves.

He heard nothing, and didn't think he'd seen that whisper of shadow, that itchy hint of a half-recognized silhouette, since the Underground station.

But he heard nothing – not a thing – in the moments before a heavy hand closed on his shoulder and he smelled stale blood and foulness. 'Mr Scragger?'

'Mr Graves.'

Grippen seemed to form himself out of shadows, congealed darkness in an old-fashioned greatcoat. 'Who's your friend?'

'He still with me?'

'Narh.' Even as a scarce-heard whisper the vampire's voice was harsh as lava rock. 'I turned him aside in Commercial Road. He'll not be back.'

'You get a look at him?'

'Dark coat. Great nose. Winkers and spinach. He was across the street.'

Glasses and a beard, Asher knew, could also be easily wadded into a Burberry pocket. He'd done it himself, more times than he could count. 'Short? Small?'

'A rat in an overcoat. Know him?'

Asher hesitated, then shook his head. 'If you see him again, let me know. I want to know who put him on me.' Although he had a strong suspicion that he knew already.

The vampire made a sound like a dog snarling. 'Crafty cove. I'll swear he saw me, and not many as can do that. You figure him for a beak?'

'Could be,' said Asher. 'He's working for someone, and I think he's looking for the same thing we are. So chances are good we'll meet him again.'

They turned north, to where Regent's Canal bordered the park's wooded fringes in its West End guise.

'Aye,' rumbled Grippen. 'I'll have a word wi' him then, and see what he's got to say for himself.'

They followed the canal into the maze of locks and bridges among the railroad yards, surreal tangles of sidings, sheds, coal bunkers and basins. Moving slowly and without light, Grippen sniffed, probing the darkness with those dark gleaming eyes. Asher listened, and watched for movement within the blackout abysses around them. It was like picking one's way through sightless and jagged Hell.

At one point, near the horrible old workhouse of St Pancras, when they stopped to let Asher rest, he passed along in a whisper what he'd gleaned from Millward's obsessive collection of newspaper clippings: that the revenant seldom strayed far from the canal, and that in the two months it had been at large in London it had killed only half a dozen times. 'It may be living on rats.' Asher perched himself on the bollard of a half-sunk wharf across from the vast blackness of the Midland Railroad goods yard, and wished as he shivered that he hadn't sent his Burberry away. 'The Others have a collective mind – like a hive of bees – but how much mind a single one of them has, away from its nest, I'd be curious to know. Or how far away it can be, and still be under their influence. The nests of them that I encountered in China could summon and command rats to defend their hiding places, or to swarm an intruder . . . or presumably, to let themselves be caught and devoured.'

'Don't speak ill of it,' rumbled Grippen. 'We drink rat blood, at need. It's hot and it's red, and it's living – aye, and there's a little dark sparkle to it of fire, like the fire of a man's death, or a woman's. Many's the vampire that's lived on rats, if he found himself where the living were suspicious, or too few to kill without drawin' down attention. Wolves we can call sometimes, too, and foxes, though precious few o' them you'll find about these days. Aye, and bats, like that silly caitiff Stoker wrote. Small use they are, though, save to flush a quarry from hidin' with a good scare.

'Ye've never thought of it yoursel'?' he added after a moment, with a sidelong glance at Asher.

'Thought of what?'

'Livin' forever.'

The silence lasted a long time after that. Asher found himself curiously unsurprised by the question.

And – he noted this with abstract interest – not in the least offended that the question had been put to him.

He supposed the proper reaction would be *How dare you think I would even for a moment entertain such a notion?* though he couldn't think of a single one of his former colleagues in the Department who would have made such a reply, either. Or who would have meant it, if they had spoken the words.

When at length Grippen spoke again his voice was soft, like a monster's purr. 'Never tell me you haven't wondered, what it'd be like not to get old? Rots you, don't it, that you've had to ask to stop and breathe a bit like a spavined horse after but a mile along the canal? That for all you know, you may never get back the strength you had five years ago? That you may always have that pain in your chest, that weakness in your legs? I need a fledgling, Asher. A good one, a strong one, that's got a brain in his skull; that knows this city and this land as I know 'em. That knows mankind as I know 'em.'

'If you need a fledgling,' Asher reminded him, 'it's because I killed yours.'

Grippen waved the objection aside. 'You was in a flame, and frighted for your brat. Think on it,' he urged softly. 'You get used to drinkin' blood, that's nuthin'. And what 'tis like to take a soul . . . Ahh, the heat of it, and the glory of it . . . And I know you miss it.'

Asher looked sharply sidelong at him.

'Huntin' as you used. The life in darkness, the life beyond the wall. You wouldn't have spied all those years for that cold little snirp of a queen, if it hadn't been in your blood, to see how you could move through the world whilst stayin' outside of it. Teachin' whey-faced rich-boys that Englishmen used to say "fall" when they meant "autumn", an' "ah" when they meant "ay" – tcha! An' havin' tea with them lack-wits at your college.' The dark eyes narrowed. ''Tis no life for a man and you know it.'

The big hand closed, thick black-furred fingers, tipped with inch-long claws pale and slick as glass. 'We could hold London, the two of us.'

'And you would hold me,' returned Asher quietly. 'Having given you my soul, to guide it through the body's death and transformation, you would keep a piece of it, always. If nothing else, I don't want you to have a piece of my soul. I've seen the Master of St Petersburg make one of his fledglings kiss my feet, and Don Simon Ysidro force a fledgling he'd made to remain outdoors as the sun came up. It's not a power I'd hand to anyone on this earth, let alone one who's lived by murder for three hundred and fifty years.'

'Well, that's the trick, i'n't it?' The vampire's grin was a horrible thing to see. 'You pay for what you get. And who knows but that I might run afoul of your little friend Millward some night and wake up with a stake through my heart? Then you'd be Master of London. Why not?'

Why not?

Asher rose from the bollard, not refreshed but at least able to continue; knowing they had the whole of the night yet to walk.

'If I change my mind,' he said, 'you shall be the first to know.'

*   *   *

'We have to go back there, you know,' said Lydia, when Don Simon helped her back into the staff-car. 'I mean, I think we all know what's going on there, and what Colonel Lemoine wants Francesca's help with, though I can't see that he's going to get it. As far as I know, no vampire can control the minds of the Others unless he – or she – has actually been infected with their blood.' She shivered at the recollection of the thing she'd discovered in that hidden vault in Peking, lying like a gruesome worm, laughing insanely in the dark. 'And what could Lemoine offer her that would get her to take that kind of a risk?'

'Lemoine,' murmured Antonio, 'or whoever is behind him.' He shrugged, and glanced over his shoulder – he was in the front seat now beside Basilio – and by the sound of his voice Lydia could tell that the whole matter was to him no more than a means to while away the night. He'd probably taken two lives before he and Don Simon ever came to her tent, when in other times he'd have spent the whole of the night hunting.

Helping her was simply an entertainment, like the opera.

He went on, 'Though surely the French government—'

'The French government is desperate for soldiers,' returned Don Simon calmly. ''Tis now no mere matter of spies and secrets. They seek soldiers to throw at their enemy – men who will walk without question into machine-gun fire. Who better than the mindless, if they can be controlled from afar off? Men moreover who can be taken from the enemy himself and rendered to such a state without consequences and without questions being asked, not even by this Lemoine's own conscience, assuming that he has one. Who has not read a thousand posters on every street corner and hoarding in Paris, on the walls of every hospital and railway station and officer's mess from here to the sea? *Crush the Germans, Destroy This Mad Brute.* Pictures of German nurses pouring water on the ground rather than moisten the lips of wounded British prisoners.' His dismissive shrug was barely more than a movement of one finger. 'Of course they deserve it. Your king has said so, so it must be true.

'What think you then, Mistress? Walking into that place alone puts the White Lady at this Lemoine's mercy. He has but to hold her until sunrise – not far off now, as I have said. Once she sleeps, he can take from her as much blood as he will, upon which to perform his experiments. Or he can inject her with the blood of these revenants, making her one of their communal mind, willy-nilly. For what would *you* put yourself in such peril?'

Antonio, looking over the back of the seat, raised his fair brows, his opinion of the ridiculousness of such a question clear on his face.

To any vampire, thought Lydia, the answer to that question would be, self-evidently, *Nothing . . .*

But she knew that to be not quite true.

Slowly, she said, 'If she is human – if she remained human, through her transformation to the vampire state – she might do such a thing for love. You say she has been a vampire for a long time . . .'

'She had become one not many years before I visited Strasbourg during the great Wars of Religion – 1610, perhaps?'

'So it isn't likely she would be protecting her child, for instance. I know . . . I have met . . .' Her voice faltered and she found she couldn't look at the thin pale figure beside her. 'Some vampires do retain the capacity to love . . .'

Not being able to look at Don Simon, she was gazing straight ahead of her, and saw, at her words, Antonio's gloved fingers tighten, very slightly, on Basilio's shoulder. The fair vampire agreed quietly, 'Some do, indeed. I know not if the Lady is one of them. For all our years of proximity I do not know her well. In Venice, she would carry on long courtships with living men, sometimes for years – alluring them, bedding them . . . For you are no doubt aware, *bella donna*, that while the organs of genera-tion in the male vampire become nonfunctional, a woman can of course receive a living man, provided she feeds beforehand so that her flesh will be warm to his touch. And indeed, this was how these courtships ended, for her. Her favorite sport was to kill her lover in the act.'

'Unlikely, then,' remarked Don Simon, 'that she would put her mind, her life and her freedom into anyone's hand, for the sake of a man she loved.'

'And yet,' mused Antonio, 'the lady has proven herself indifferent to the sweet seductions of power—'

'And whatever her reason for going in there was,' added Lydia, with a frown, 'I expect she *could* get out, as long as it was dark. *Would* barbed wire stop a vampire?'

'We are flesh and bone, lady.' Don Simon spread his hands. 'And that is what barbed wire is designed to catch. A frightened vampire would be less likely to let the pain of the barbs stop him – or her – but they would be able to tear their flesh free only a little more quickly than a living man. And though we can survive the loss of blood better than the living, it renders us – as it does you – weak, and in time unable to flee or seek shelter. Of a certainty barbed wire would hold them, until their captors could come up to them with stouter bonds . . . if capture is the aim of their enemies. Did you see what was in those trenches, which surround the whole of the camp and the convent?'

Lydia shook her head, though the recollection of the smell returned to her, horrible and with echoes more dreadful still.

'They are floored with barbed wire, as well as fenced with it on both sides. From which I can only deduce the presence, somewhere in that camp, of a hive of revenants sufficiently large to permit the formation among them of group-mind, group-thought. A group will be capable,' he concluded, tenting his thin fingers, 'of controlling the local population of rats for their own defense. And I should imagine this close to no man's land, there is no shortage of those.'

Lydia thought that one through, and said, 'Oh, dear.'

TWELVE

26-3
Jamie
Cuvé Sainte-Bride x Former nunnery x Nord x nr Haut-le-Bois x Dr Jules Lemoine infecting German POWs x Others x work w vampire Francesca Gheric of Strasbourg x How ?? x Tuathla (not real name) Meagher x heavily fortified x how get in? x any information x promise I will be careful x you be careful too
   All my love

The letter was postmarked Paris, Friday 26 March, at the Gare St Lazare. The hand was undoubtedly Lydia's, though Asher guessed Ysidro had posted it. It was topped and tailed by addresses and names not Lydia's own, encoded as a rambling complaint about the difficulties in obtaining sugar and decent coffee in Paris, and the cipher it contained raised the hair on his scalp.

He was still working on an innocuous missive whose coded text read *Don't you DARE investigate ANYTHING until you hear from me* (knowing full well that this wouldn't reach her for three days at least) when a brisk rap sounded at his door, which he recognized as belonging to Josetta Beyerly.

Late-afternoon sunlight lay across the foot of his bed from the room's single window. He knew Lydia's friend had pupils, most mornings – French language, or piano – and on those she didn't, she drove an ambulance-wagon from the docks to First London General Hospital. This was just as well, for through the past three nights he had hunted with Lionel Grippen, following Regent's Canal and its ramifications into Hackney Marshes and Hampstead Heath. They sought as much for the places where a revenant might be hiding, as for sight of the thing itself, and so far had found little. Most of those evenings had been foggy, as well as pitch-dark from the blackout, and Asher could feel his energy seeping away from night to night, never returning, after sleep, to quite what it had been before. Hoggett would flay him alive if he knew.

Josetta wouldn't have come to Faraday's Private Hotel like this unless it was important.

'There's something very, very queer happening over in Brabazon Street.'

'His daughter won't call the police,' the teacher explained, when she and Asher stepped from the overcrowded bus at the junction of East and West India Docks Roads. Men – women, too, now – crowded the flagways at this hour, and the bus had been jammed, for the docks, the chemical works and the gasworks all lay nearby. The raw air was rank with coal smoke and the sewery smell of outhouses. The flat-fronted brick rows of two-up two-downs were nearly black with years' accumulation of soot, and Asher had to stop beside a lamppost and cough for some minutes. Josetta took his arm worriedly, and he waved her off.

'I'll be fine.' This was a lie. 'Is there some reason he doesn't want the police searching the house?'

'The neighbors think he receives stolen goods,' she replied matter-of-factly. 'He may well – he owns a pawnshop in the Limehouse Road. But I think the main reason is that he's involved with buying guns for the Irish Volunteers.'

Asher's jaw tightened grimly. On the omnibus from Kensington he'd picked out, as was his habit, the different accents of his fellow-passengers, and ever since they'd crossed the Regent's Canal he'd been swimming in a sea of elongated vowels and dentalized t's. In the shabby jacket and down-at-heels shoes he'd changed into when Josetta had spoken of their destination, he guessed he wouldn't stand out, and the VAD uniform of his companion would pass pretty much anywhere in London. Depending on how deeply the Mayo family was involved with those willing to use violence to obtain independence for Ireland, this probably wasn't a neighborhood in which to be heard asking questions.

Josetta climbed two steps – washed two or three days ago, by the look of the grime accumulated since – and rapped at the door, her sharp one-and-two characteristic knock. The house smelled of cooked cabbage and poverty, the areaway below, of decaying vegetables and piss. *No alley behind.* Areaways usually meant back-to-backs. *In this neighborhood, probably a yard . . .*

The woman who opened the door a crack looked as if she hadn't slept in several nights.

'I've brought someone to see Bert,' said Josetta simply.

The woman closed the door a few inches, her eyes like shuttered windows. 'Nuttin' wrong with Da.'

'There is,' said Josetta. 'You know there is, Katie. This man can be trusted.'

Tears flooded the woman's eyes and she clamped her lips hard. *Grieved*, thought Asher. *And scared for her life.*

'His mouth?' he asked softly, and hardened the final 'th' just slightly, a whisper of the accents of Katie's own land. *You can trust me . . . I'm one of your own . . .* If the danger hadn't been so desperate he'd have been ashamed of himself. 'His teeth?

Bruisin' here—' His fingers traced on his own head where he knew the sutures of the skull would be deforming – 'an' here?'

Katie began to cry, and opened the door.

A younger woman, still dressed for factory work, put her head out of the kitchen door at the back (and yes, by the window behind her there was a yard). From the other door on the narrow hall two tow-headed boys peeked, in their early teens and also, Asher noted, still in the grimed overalls of dockhands. None of them looked like they'd slept.

Katie led them up the stair without a word.

Asher had seen before what greeted him in the tiny rear bedroom. The figure huddled in the room's darkest corner was a man in his sixties, balled together with his arms around his knees and his body leaned against the wall. Sheets and blankets had been stripped from the bed and draped over the single window, packed tight in every cranny in a desperate attempt to shut out all light. He winced and made a sound of protesting pain as Katie lit the old-fashioned gas: 'Da, there's a man come to see you. We'll be needin' a bit of light.'

He made a strangled sound, as if clearing something out of his throat. Then, 'Don't want to see nobody, Kate.'

'He knows what's wrong wit' you, Da.'

Looking at the bruises on the face where the skull was elongating, the bloody smears on the old man's hands and mouth where his teeth were starting to grow, Asher knew exactly what was wrong with him, and his heart turned sick inside him. Sick with pity and dread.

Damn it, he thought. *Damn it.*

And damn whoever brought the first of those things over here. Damn them to the bottommost smoking crevice of Hell.

Gently he took Katie's arm, led her back into the hall and shut the door.

'Does this door lock?' he asked softly. She shook her head. She looked to be in her forties, though hard work and childbearing had aged her face. She stood no higher than his shoulder, thin as a twig-doll. Her hair was streaked with gray and she'd lost several of her teeth.

'You need to get a bolt and lock it,' he said. 'I'll come back—' He calculated times, and of course there wouldn't be a shop in town open at this hour . . . 'I'll come back tomorrow, wit' your permission, and put it on, if you've no one else—'

'Terry'll do it.' Katie seemed to pull herself together a little. 'Kerr. Next door. He's a foreman at Lavender Wharf.'

'Do it tonight, if you can.' He kept his accent the one she'd unconsciously connect with home, South Ireland: those predominantly Catholic counties where resentment burned strong against the Empire which for centuries had shut the Irish themselves out of owning or ruling their own land. 'An' get your boys – them two I saw downstairs? – out of the house, find somewheres else for 'em to sleep. Your da's ill,' he went on, seeing her shake her head, as if disbelieving that such a thing could be happening to them. 'And he's not gonna get better. I'm sorry to be the one tellin' you this, I'm so sorry, but there's nuttin' to be done. He's gonna go off his head soon, an' try to harm anyone he sees. Katie—' He tightened his grip, gently, on her shoulders as her face convulsed with tears, and he glanced quickly at Josetta.

'Reilley,' she mouthed back at him, knowing what he sought.

'Mrs Reilley . . . I'm sorry, but I need to know this. When did this happen, and where? Somethin' attacked him, didn't it? Tom the Ogre? Bit him? Tore him up?'

The woman nodded, clinging now to his arms and shaking with her effort to control her sobs. 'Comin' home. Last Tuesday night. He'd been at the Green King over in Tildey Street—'

On the other side of the Limehouse Cut. He'd have had to cross it, coming back, late and in the fog . . .

'Will he eat? Drink?'

'He ain't all day. He did, up to yesterday—'

'Do you have laudanum in the house? Good—'

'I'll ask Polly for it downstairs.' Josetta clattered off, to return a few moments later with a substantial square black bottle in one hand, a smaller green one in the other labeled 'Infants Quietness Elixir'.

Quietness indeed, reflected Asher grimly. *Will opiates work on one of Them?* They certainly didn't on vampires, not unless they were mixed with some of those ingredients inimical to vampire flesh: silver, aconite, tincture of Christmas rose. He'd seen nothing concerning the Others in the medieval text which seemed the most accurate, the notorious Book of the Kindred of Darkness. From

what Don Simon Ysidro had told him, that volume had supposedly been written in Spain only a few years after the first of the
Others had appeared in Bohemia. As little as anyone knew about
vampires, the knowledge was vast compared with what anyone
knew about these filthy cousins of theirs.

'We're goin' to try to sedate him.' He turned back to the terrified woman beside the shut bedroom door. 'Put him to sleep.
He'll be a danger to you, Mrs Reilley, an' soon. I'm sorry, but
that's what this is, this sickness that he caught from the thing
that tore him up. It spreads by blood, so don't let him bite you
or tear you, don't let one drop of his blood mix with yours. That's
why I'm tellin' you, get your family outen this house. I wish I
could make it different—'

She was weeping again, his hands strong on her arms.

'—but I can't. You got to be strong, M'am. There's nuttin'
can be done for him now but keep him asleep if we can. You
got to be strong.'

Shuddering, she wiped her nose and her eyes. 'I'll be strong.'

'Good lass.'

He glanced at Josetta again.

'I got the rest of the family out of the house.'

'Wait for us—' he turned back to Mrs Reilley – 'down the
foot of the stair. I swear to you we'll do him no harm, but by
the saints, there's nuttin' to be done for him. And I swear,' he
added, turning to Josetta as the little woman slowly descended
the stair to the darkness which had now gathered thick in the
house below, 'I wouldn't ask this of you, Miss Beyerly, if I had
any choice in the world about it.'

'That's a pip of a brogue you've got there, Professor,' she
returned, unruffled. 'Better than the halls.' Then her expression
darkened, and she said softly, 'What's happening to him?
What you were asking about – looking for . . . How did you
know?'

'Don't ask.'

For a moment the young woman stared at him in the dimness
of the narrow hallway, as if she couldn't believe what she saw
in his eyes.

'We have to get him to hospital. I can get an ambulance-
wagon—'

'Let's get him sedated first.' Asher's mind was racing, Langham's complicit smile returning to him: *The matter is in hand . . .*

You bastard. You know that thing is in London and you're watching the hospitals, aren't you? And if you get hold of this poor sod . . . What? 'Infecting German POWs . . .'

Use them against the Germans? And then later against the Irish who demand rule of their own lands, or riot against the threat of conscription for England's war?

Use them against Indians who want independence?

Sick cold went through him, like the onset of fever. (*And maybe it IS the onset of fever . . .*)

First things first.

He signed to Josetta to remain in the hall, stepped into the bedroom.

The gas was out. There was no smell of it in the room, so presumably Bert Mayo retained enough recollection of who and what he was to have turned the gas off rather than just dousing the minimal flame. A weak reflection of light from the hall picked up a red glint from the corner where the man had been huddled earlier, and, near him, the tiny, vicious sparks of the eyes of rats.

Four or five rats, all within a few feet of him.

Damn it . . .

Asher struck a match. Mayo hid his eyes. The rats fled.

So far, so good.

'Get out of it,' whispered the stricken man, the words dribbling from his lips like the mutter of delirium. 'Put out the bloody light. Make 'em shut up. Katie . . .'

'Make who shut up, Bert?' Asher lit the gas and turned it down as far as he safely could.

Bert covered his face with his arms, then scrabbled to the bed and grabbed the pillow to further block the light from his eyes. The walls around him were smeared with blood where his mouth had touched; the mattress, and the bedclothes hung over the window, streaked with it.

DO NOT let that blood touch you . . .

'Rats,' whispered Bert Mayo hoarsely. 'Chatterin'. Voices in me conk. Make 'em shut up!' He lurched to his feet. Seen full-on for the first time his face was a horror, the flesh a mass of bruises where the mouth and jaw had lengthened out like an ape's, blood from his bitten lips stringing into the gray stubble of his chin. Behind him in the doorway Asher heard Josetta gasp, and he reached back and took the laudanum bottle from her hand.

'This'll make the voices shut up, Bert,' he said. 'Then we'll make the rats go away.'

'Rats'll never go away.' Slowly, Bert began to circle toward the door. 'Crawl in an' out o' me skull-bones whilst I sleep. I hear their squeakin' an' it sounds like words.'

'This'll shut 'em up. Guaranteed.' *How many revenants constitute a hive mind? Is he controlled by the colony – good God! – that this Lemoine is growing in France, or by Hungry Tom out in the fog of the canal? Or – Jesus! – is his mind controlled by the rats, rather than the other way around, given that they outnumber him?*

He held out the bottle. 'Drink it,' he offered. 'You'll be the better for it.'

Bert's lips pulled back from the bloodied mess of fangs and he lunged at Asher, clawed hands outstretched. Asher yelled 'Door!' and, thank God, Josetta had the wits to slam it without any wailed vacillation about *I can't shut you in there with it . . .!* If he knew Josetta she had one sturdy shoulder braced against its panels, not that that would do any good—

He flung himself at the window, ripped down the wadded blankets, and hurled them over Bert's head as Bert reached him. The stricken man was strong, but it was still human strength, the strength of a man of sixty who's worked hard all his life, not the hideous abnatural strength of mutated cell tissue and altered muscle. Asher rolled him in the blankets, shouted 'Josetta!' and she was in the room, striding to help him—

'Asher, there's—'

Feet thundered in the stairwell. Men slammed into the room, half a dozen of them, as Asher grappled with the blanket-wrapped thing that had been Bert Mayo. Three of the men – laborers smelling of sweat and beer and very cheap tobacco – grabbed Bert and wrapped him still tighter in the blankets, and in the same instant one of the men seized Asher's arms from behind, pulled him out of the fray, and held him while another whipped from his pocket a weighted rubber sap.

'Get him outta here,' commanded the sixth man, who held Josetta's arms behind her – Asher automatically placed his accent within a few miles of Cork, like his round Celtic face and the thick shoulders in their meal-colored jumper. 'These two—'

That was as far as he got. Josetta stomped hard on the man's instep, dropped her weight, twisted in his shock-loosened grip and gouged for his eyes. In the same moment Asher kicked the man with the sap in front of him, performed the same classic stomp-drop-twist on his own captor before smashing him across the face with the laudanum bottle, grabbed Josetta's wrist – it did not appear to be the time to ask questions – and used the pillow round his fist to smash open the window. There was a shed outside – there was always a shed, in tiny houses like this one – and he swung Josetta out the window and dropped out after her himself, into a yard the size of a dining-room table and choked with rubbish. He pulled Josetta into the outhouse and closed the door. Through its tiny judas he saw two of the men drop through the window, dash to the rear fence of the yard and scramble over it: the logical direction of pursuit.

They stood together, in black and stinking darkness, for nearly ten minutes, long after the house itself grew silent and still.

No light returned to the windows of its kitchen. No one opened its rear door.

Josetta made not a sound, though he could hear her breathing fast and hard and could feel her trembling where her body pressed his.

He himself was shaking, as if his legs would crumple if he tried to walk.

Hirelings of whoever it was – that flickering shadow that he'd thought he'd glimpsed in Charlotte Street? The bewhiskered and bespectacled 'rat in an overcoat' that Grippen had seen? Bert Mayo's pals in the Irish Brotherhood, concerned that Katie had taken a stranger into the house? (*And God knows what was hidden up in the attic . . .*) The local Brotherhood of Light Fingers, if the enterprising Bert was in fact a fence as well as a gunrunner?

Dear God, what were they going to do if Bert tore into them with those bloodied teeth?

The matter is in hand, Langham had said, with a twinkle and a smile.

In time Asher slipped out of the outhouse, crept shakily across the yard – it was now pitch-black – and listened at the back door of the house.

Nothing.

The yard of the house behind the Mayos was tidier, when Asher clambered over its fence. By the feel of the dirt underfoot, and the way plants brushed his groping hands, he guessed the neighbors had a garden (and wouldn't thank his pursuers for trampling it). He went back and fetched Josetta, offered her help (which she turned down indignantly) over the fence, and over three more, moving laterally parallel to (he calculated) Ellesmere Street, the next street over from Brabazon, before finding a house that sounded vacant. With a mental apology to its tenants he broke the kitchen window, and let himself and Josetta through kitchen and hallway and out at last into Ellesmere Street indeed.

Since no cabs ever cruised anywhere near the grimy purlieus of Brabazon Street – and the busses had long since ceased running – they had a walk of nearly a mile to the cluster of pubs around the East India Docks where such a thing could finally, by chance, be obtained.

Lying awake in the darkness, Lydia thought about blood.

She'd dreamed about it, as she often did, especially since her expedition – nearly a week ago now – to Cuvé Sainte-Bride. In her dream she'd seen the vampire Francesca Gheric attempting to flee from the convent of Cuvé Sainte-Bride, getting caught on the barbed wire that half-filled the trenches which surrounded it like a toothed steel moat, trying to tear herself loose from the barbs. (These were longer and far more thickly wound on military wire, Captain Calvert had told her, than they were on the mere stuff that Americans used to pen their cattle.) '*We are flesh and bone, lady,*' Don Simon had said, and in Lydia's dream Francesca had struggled, tearing both flesh and bone in an attempt to get out of the trench before the heaving gray tide of rats reached her.

Blood had glistened on the steel barbs and, standing on the brink of the trench, Lydia had tried to figure out how she was going to obtain a sample of that blood.

She'd eventually decided that the best way was to have

Don Simon transform himself into a bat and go fetch some for her, and they were in the midst of a rather convoluted argument about whether or not this was possible (*'Were it possible for a vampire to transform into a bat, Mistress, the Lady Francesca would not now be in the difficult situation that she is . . .'*) when she woke.

Why did I want her blood? She frowned over the question.

I've already SEEN vampire blood under a microscope. Simon had donated some a few years ago, and had been as curious as she herself, to compare it with the blood of the living.

She had written up her findings, and had handled the sample with the greatest of care, well aware that if the vampire state were in fact connected with some unknown virus – and were related to the hideous pathology of the Others – no chances could be risked of contamination. When finished with her study (which had taken place by gaslight) she had set the sample outdoors, and had been queasily disturbed to see it spontaneously catch fire, and burn up at the first touch of morning sun.

So why did I want HER blood?

A thought, like the echo of her now-fading dream, came at once: *Because the blood is the answer.*

But she had no idea what that meant.

By the sound of the camp it was three or four in the morning. The guns were stilled; there wasn't even the grind of motors from the road, or the hollow rumble of lorries on the makeshift wooden bridge. No sound had yet begun from the camp kitchen, nor was there smell of smoke. In the pitch-dark tent Lydia heard the stealthy scrabble of rats, and bit her lips to keep from screaming: in four months of living daily with the vermin she had never lost her terror of them. She should, by all rights, be sunk in the sleep of exhaustion – keeping company with vampires, on top of her duties in the fluoroscope tent (*And if we have another quiet day tomorrow I'll take the apparatus apart and give it the cleaning it needs . . .*), meant she was constantly short of sleep. *Thank goodness Colonel St-Vire insists on the surgical crews getting all the sleep they need during the quiet times . . .*

When she closed her eyes she felt as far from sleep as she was from a hot bath or Mrs Grimes's batter-cakes. But she saw, as if it were printed on her eyelids, the dreamworld moonlight glistening on Francesca Gheric's blood, dripping from the twisted spikes.

Saw Don Simon's blood under her microscope, the altered, queerly elongated corpuscles motionless and cold.

Her favorite sport was to kill her lover in the act, said Antonio's beautiful, velvety whisper.

And her own hesitant voice, *Some vampires do retain a capacity for love . . .*

She was still awake when first daylight outlined the tent-seams, and above the wasteland of blood-soaked mud and tangled wire, the guns began to pound.

'What happened to that man?' Josetta's whisper barely carried over the rattle of the cab's iron tires on the brick streets of the Limehouse. 'His face . . .'

'Don't speak of it.' Now that Asher was sitting down and more or less warm and in no immediate danger of being killed or worse, waves of exhaustion threatened to drown him. 'Not to anyone. For your life, Miss Beyerly; I'm not joking . . .'

'For my life?' At least she didn't laugh. The moon had set, and the blackness of the blacked-out streets was absolute. God alone knew how the cab driver – the only one to be found in the Wise Child, and arguably not sober – saw to steer . . . *Maybe he has a sober horse . . .*

'I don't know who is behind this,' he said wearily. 'It may be that our government brought those things – that infection – to England as a plan to win the war . . . as a cheap alternative to conscription. To get men to fight who won't ask questions, who won't even know what they're doing or why.'

He heard the harsh draw of her breath. At least, he reflected, having battled Parliament for years over votes for women, she wouldn't automatically assume that the government a) was always right, or b) knew what it was doing.

'Or it may be someone who wants to spread chaos and panic here, so that we can't produce enough food or munitions to effectively keep an army in the field. And I suspect we'd do it to the Germans quick enough. It may be someone who wants to raise a private army, for their own purposes. Someone who knows they'll be outnumbered and outgunned by the police . . .'

'I know one of the men,' said Josetta quietly. 'One of those who took the thing away, I mean. I've seen him at the settlement house. His name's Teague, he's part of the Irish Volunteers. Someone told me he's one of the men who's buying guns from the Germans and smuggling them into Ireland.'

Asher heard the hesitant note in her voice, the admission of the secret she was breaking, and shut his mouth hard on his first, embittered exclamation. With Irish independence tabled 'until the war is over', – and, worse, used like a hostage to lever Ireland into accepting forced conscription – he could understand the anger of those who had waited for years for a political solution to Ireland's self-rule. The fact that armed militias had formed among the Protestants, who didn't want to be governed by the Catholic majority – and were *also* smuggling guns in from Germany to arm themselves – and the Catholics, who in the face of violence in the countryside, were responding in kind, did not help the situation any.

'Thank you,' he said quietly. 'Whoever is behind this – and there's no reason to think this Teague is working for one side or the other in particular – please remember that we have no idea who is passing along information to whom. If you value your life, tell *no one* about what happened tonight. The last man who was a witness to the existence of these things vanished without a trace on the sixteenth of March. Promise me.'

She gripped his hand as if to emphasize what she was about to say, but he was unconscious before her words were spoken.

THIRTEEN

'Is the offer still open,' inquired Lydia, 'for me to pay a call on the Master of Prague?'

Don Simon regarded her for a moment with raised brows. Had he been like any of the men she worked with – both here in Pont-Sainte-Félicité and in fact back in Oxford – he would probably have greeted this volte-face with *And this is the woman who thinks we're monsters?* and similar chaffering, but this was evidently another of the things he'd outgrown (or gotten tired of) in three-plus centuries of being Undead. He merely inclined his head and replied, 'Graf Szgedny will be honored and flattered, lady. Am I correct in my guess that this concerns the Lady Francesca and her bargain – whatever it may be – with Dr Lemoine? Then might I suggest that the visit itself be kept secret?

'E'en in the best of times,' he added, when Lydia almost protested that she'd never in any case mention to Captain Calvert that she was going to tea with a vampire, 'the Undead are frightful gossips. With eternity before us and little enough of each night required for hunting, I do not see how it could be otherwise, given the human material of which the vampire is formed. Caution warns me against bringing your inquiries to the Lady Francesca's attention.'

'I think that's wise.' Lydia glanced back over her shoulder at the lights of the clearing station. The purposeful bustle among the tents would soon die down. Another day was done. A few dozen men had been brought in – even when there was no 'push' on, constant sniperfire took its toll. Shells were always falling, sometimes close enough to the front-line trenches to blow men into fragments on their way back from the latrines. Trench foot, pneumonia, hideous and fast-spreading sepsis from the smallest of cuts . . .

When things grew quiet, did poor Brodie's *bean sí* still walk among the tents? (*And is there a German equivalent, over on the other side of no man's land? I'm sure Jamie would know . . .*)

'What about Antonio and Basilio?' she asked worriedly. 'They know I'm asking questions. And they're friends – or at least neighbors – of Lady Francesca.'

'I spoke to them when we parted Thursday evening. Antonio at least shares my alarm at the Lady's meddling in human affairs: such involvements never end well. Then again, merely the suggestion that someone is experimenting with the Others – let alone producing them – is enough to incline them to my will. The Others shock and repel us as much as they do you, lady. Perhaps more so, for those of us who are aware of them at all recognize a kinship . . . and fear the further connections that may exist. Do not look to them for aid in this matter, but at least they will keep their silence.'

Shouting near the bridge, and the rumble of engines. 'Bother,' said Lydia. 'I'd hoped it would be a quiet night . . .' *Not noisy enough for a push. A local attack . . .*

'I must go.'

He bowed over her hand. 'Until tomorrow, then, Mistress. 'Twere best we pay our call early, while the rest are out. I shall send John in the afternoon with papers, and come for you when darkness falls. 'Tis a dozen miles.'

'I'll be ready. You haven't heard—' She paused, half-turning back from the lights of the camp. 'You haven't heard anything concerning Jamie, have you? Mrs Grimes wrote that he'd gone down to London. The last I heard from him was that one of these . . . these things . . . is in London itself.'

The startled widening of his eyes was the greatest display of shock she'd ever seen from him. But all he said was, 'Is it so, indeed?'

'That means that either someone was infected here – one of Lemoine's assistants, perhaps, or one of those poor prisoners who escaped – and developed the condition when he got to London. Or else someone shipped or carried one of Lemoine's subjects to Britain, and it escaped.'

'Or that the vector of the infection is asymptomatic, and does not manifest the physical changes of the condition himself.' Don Simon folded his arms, and leaned one slender shoulder against the corner of the smashed-in wooden hut that stood between the last of the disused German trenches and the first houses of the village. From its shadow Lydia knew they were nearly invisible to the hurrying figures in the camp. 'Rather like that woman Mary Mallon, who spread typhoid a few years ago in America . . .'

Lydia shivered, and pulled her greatcoat more tightly around her body. 'I've asked Jamie to send me whatever information he has. If I know Jamie . . .'

She looked aside, unable to go on.

'I do indeed know James,' returned the vampire. 'Thus I feel sure that when you do receive a reply to your reports of these creatures – and recall that any letter of yours to him must be forwarded from Oxford – 'twill contain the words *Do NOT pursue this matter*. Lionel is in London still.' He named the Master vampire of London. 'But to attempt to touch his dreams in quest of what he may know of this is like playing the lute before a rooting pig. If you will it, Mistress, I shall seek out James's dreams in the depths of the night, and at least endeavor to learn if he is well.'

Then he was gone, as if he could – as the legends said – dislimn into mist, and melt away.

Feeling rather like the corpse at a funeral in morning dress better suited to London than to Wendens Ambo, James Asher stepped from the first-class railway carriage and handed his companions out, reflecting for the hundredth time on the usefulness of 'connection' with the aristocracy. The son of a Church of England rector, he'd always been aware that the folk up at the 'big house' at Wychford had the power to make life easy or difficult for his parents and sister – interference which Sir Boniface's family seemed to regard as part of 'keeping them in their place'. Four years at Oxford in close proximity to the scions of nobility hadn't much improved his opinion of the breed. But he had discovered at Oxford that the purpose of Oxford was as much to meet people as to actually learn anything. One could learn as much or as little as one chose, depending on the ability of one's parents to keep one there. (Or, in Asher's case, one's diligence at any number of tutoring jobs.) But being in Balliol or Merton or King's would be, ever after, a passport to a degree of acquaintance, rather like sharing a seat in a lifeboat with total strangers.

After four years, men of one's year or one's staircase or one's college were strangers no more. His Oxford connections had certainly been as much of a factor in his employment in the Foreign Office as had been his fluency in Czech and Persian.

And by marrying the granddaughter of a viscount, he had quadrupled the number of people to whom he could acquire an introduction on the grounds of casual proximity. Lord Halfdene's four surviving sisters might look down their elegant noses at the mere New College lecturer their beautiful niece had married, but when push came to shove, one of them at least could be counted on to know the person whom Asher sought to meet.

So it had proved in his quest to locate – and speak to – the Comte de Beaucailles, whose property in the Département du

Nord had included the old convent of Cuvé Sainte-Bride. Once Josetta's suffragette friend in the government purchasing office had found mention of the money Britain had lent to the French to refurbish the place as a research laboratory – after the French Army had acquired it in November – it had been easy to identify the former owner. Lydia's Aunt Lavinnia, though she habitually referred to Asher as 'that person poor Lydia married', wasn't immune to being taken out for a criminally expensive tea at the Northumberland (Lydia's income deriving from American bonds and real estate in four major cities, and not farmland). In the course of consuming two cups of China tea and a single cucumber sandwich, Aunt Lavinnia had divulged the fact that the Comte de Beaucailles had come to England (as Asher had suspected: who in their right mind would remain in Flanders, or even in a Paris shorn of sugar, coffee and entertainment?) and was residing, with his family, as the guest of Lord Whitsedge at Whitsedge Court.

Lydia's Aunt Harriet, while deploring her niece's education, current occupation and husband (her own was the younger son of a duke, and a well-regarded barrister), knew everyone in Debrett's and was sufficiently good-natured as to write to Lord Whitsedge (whose Aunt Claire had married a Halfdene cousin) on Asher's behalf (though she referred to him in the course of a single paragraph as Ashley, Ashford and Ashden). And Lydia's Aunt Faith, who even now shed tears over the way in which her dear sister's child had 'thrown herself away' after being 'the most beautiful debutante of her year' (Lydia still had nightmares about her single 'season'), was so ecstatic at the idea of a weekend away from acting as companion to Aunt Louise down at Halfdene Hall that she had even agreed to accompany Asher (and Aunt Louise's official companion, Mrs Flasket) down to Whitsedge Court and introduce her plebeian nephew-in-law to Lord Whitsedge and his guests.

The Comte de Beaucailles proved to be an elderly, fragile man who took Asher to his bosom on the grounds of the perfection of his French. It was a joy, he said, to listen to after the tomcat squawking of 'ces Anglais', the gesture of his yellow-gloved hand dismissing the hosts without whose hospitality he would have been living on cabbage soup in Hoxton. He nursed a profound hatred of Germany and all Germans, as if the Battle of Sedan (in which he had fought) had been yesterday instead of forty-five years previously, and could still be reduced to shouting outrage over the Dreyfus Case. But he recalled with tender vividness the France of his childhood, the France of the days of empire, and every detail of the convent which had stood only miles from the family chateau.

'The good sisters were still at Sainte-Bride when I was a boy,' he reminisced, to Asher's question after dinner. 'It was much larger in the days before the Revolution – quite a substantial foundation – but my cousins and I were always welcome there. My great-grandfather provided the money for a new chapel in 1773, and many of our aunts and great-aunts had taken the veil there. Its cellars were famous—' He chuckled softly, and made an ironic little half-salute with Lord Whitsedge's indifferent sherry – 'and there had been a healing well there, oh, centuries ago. Standing as it does on a ridge of hills, there is a veritable labyrinth of cata-combs beneath it, far exceeding the present size of the convent.'

The remaining servants had pulled shut the draperies of slightly faded mustard velvet over the Regency drawing room's long windows. One of Lord Whitsedge's other guests was playing the piano, a Mozart dance whose effervescent serenity echoed bitter-sweet in the quiet room. Whitsedge Court was an old-fashioned country seat in which gas had never been installed, let alone electricity; Lady Whitsedge's booming voice could be heard from the card table, bemoaning the absence of the footmen, and the butler's replacement by his venerable and stone-deaf predecessor. In London Asher had been conscious of the number of women hurrying along the sidewalks at the close of factories and shops, and of the hoary heads of bus conductors and ticket clerks on the Underground. Here in the depth of Essex, with the cold spring wind blowing spits of rain from the Channel, the sense of loss, of men missing who would never return, was more poignant, despite Her Ladyship's evident belief that the entire war had been concocted by God to inconvenience her daughter's coming-out.

'*Honestly*, if the fighting goes on for another six months – and *what* those generals are thinking, I can't *imagine* – Alice will be nineteen. *Nineteen!* I could *flay* Mother for talking me into delaying her debut last spring . . .'

'When was the convent abandoned?' Asher inquired.

'Oh, heavens, when I was ten or eleven, I think.' The Comte seemed to bask in the belief that the most casual of acquaintances found his childhood in the long-vanished France of Empire as fascinating as he did himself. 'Yes, because that year I was enrolled in the Lycée Notre-Dame in Lille—'

'I remember there was a sort of ruin across the field from my father's rectory,' reminisced Asher mendaciously. (He'd been packed off to school in Scotland at the age of seven and his father hadn't been a believer in bringing young James home for those few summers before his own death in 1874.) 'I have no idea what the place was – monastery or a small castle or just an ancient inn – but my sister and I found a way into it from the crypt of a sort of little chapel in what had been its grounds . . .'

The old nobleman laughed. 'Nothing nearly so romantic, I'm afraid! The convent at Cuvé Sainte-Bride had in a manner of speaking died by inches, so there was a huge zone of deserted farms, chapels, bathhouses and storage-buildings all round the cloister, even in the days when the good sisters were still in occupation. My cousins and I played hide-and-seek – risking our lives, I'm sure, for some of those old crypts were none too stable, and the roofs were always falling in! – in the unused portions, so as not to disturb the nuns. But after they were removed we ran about them underground like wild Indians.'

The old man's eyes sparkled at the recollection, and he leaned forward, decades melting from his lined face. 'After my cousin Etienne was caught in a cave-in and nearly drowned – because, of course, the deeper crypts flooded in the wintertimes – my grandfather had most of the outbuildings torn down and the ways into the crypt sealed. But still we'd get in. There was a well by one of the old barns, on the hillside behind the convent, and if one of your friends would lower you by bucket to just above the level of the water, there was a little door leading into what I think used to be a drain from the old baths . . . Ah, the smell of that tunnel, all green and damp! And our girl cousins used to stand at the top and cry because none of us boys would let them go down with us. And one of the young men of the district, Henri Clerc his name was, unblocked the entrance that led into what had been the nuns' old wine cellar, and would use the place to tryst with the village girls . . .'

A young footman, walking carefully on a wood-and-metal leg encased in the livery's old-fashioned silk stockings, brought them a tray of drinkables and a soda siphon. At the other end of the too-long, lamp-lit room Aunt Faith meekly nodded while Lady Whitsedge continued her monologue on the shortcomings of maids who would quit and go to work in factories, and Mrs Flasket listened in intelligent silence to Lord Whitsedge's account of his spaniel bitch's latest confinement.

Asher kept the old Comte talking, and, when he finally retired to his small chamber (which looked down on an inner courtyard of the rambling old Court: Aunt Faith, though regarded throughout her family as little better than a paid companion to Aunt Louise, still rated a room in the main part of the house), was able to put together a rough description of five different ways to enter the crypts of Cuvé Sainte-Bride undetected. He spent the remainder of the night encoding a letter to Lydia, which ended with a further admonition not to investigate anything herself. *If Don Simon is there, and willing, he is far more likely to enter and leave in safety than you are. I will put in train arrangements to come there myself to follow up on his reconnaissance.*

The thought of going to Colonel Stewart for the necessary papers – and of the concessions he'd have to make to get himself assigned to that area of Flanders – made him groan, not to speak of the hazards of crossing the submarine-haunted Channel and making his way from Calais to Pont-Sainte-Félicité and Haut-le-Bois. Then there was the issue of leaving his ill-assorted 'network' of information-gatherers on their own in London, seeking for word of this second revenant, and for the Irish gunrunner Teague. *I'll have to brief Grippen*, he thought, *without telling him who's collecting the information.* Josetta and Millward could communicate with the master vampire via newspaper. It wouldn't be the first time he'd run a network in which no member was aware of the identities of the others.

And God knows what Grippen will do with the information when he gets it.

Damn. He leaned back in the leather armchair beside the tiny grate, and drew his dressing-gown – and a paisley cashmere shawl – tightly around his shoulders. Despite the fire, the room was freezing cold and there was no coal left in the scuttle: guest rooms at Whitsedge Court were not supplied with fuel to burn all night. The clock on the mantelpiece chimed a tiny silver reminder that it was quarter to three. Around him the house was silent, with the darkness of centuries.

For eight years I've tried to keep the governments of both sides from employing vampires. He closed his eyes. *And I might as well have saved myself the trouble, since once the fighting started, both sides are giving the vampires, gratis, the only thing they'd have accepted as payment.*

And after swearing to kill them I'm working on their side.

He thought about going back to Oxford. Or taking Lydia and Miranda and emigrating to America, which was quite sensibly keeping out of the war while selling ammunition and supplies to both sides. But he knew there was no question of doing so. If one side or the other – *Or both, God help us!* – found a way to control the revenants, to use them as soldiers, God alone knew where that would end.

Not well.

He made a move to rise to compose a note to be placed in the Personals column to Grippen for a meeting – and the next thing he knew it was broad daylight and a maid was coming quietly into the room to open the curtains.

FOURTEEN

'We who hunt the night have long memories.' Don Simon Ysidro's gloved fingers, grasping Lydia's, were cold as they steadied her over the broken ground; cold as the iron of the unlit bull's-eye lantern she bore. The moon, four days past full, hid behind its bank of clouds, though the rain had stopped half an hour ago. The darkness smelled of wet trees and farmland. Somewhere an owl hooted. 'Yet being human, we are no more comfortable looking back on the road we have travelled than are other men. Among us it is held to be a sign of weakness and advancing age. Most look neither forward nor back.'

They had left the car with Captain Palfrey, in blackness so thick Lydia could only form the vaguest ideas where she might be. Having been taken to vampire lairs before, she had half-expected to be blindfolded – or at least have her glasses taken away, which would have amounted to the same thing – and had formed her protest ready: *What if something happens to you and I'm left out all alone in the dark?*

But the cloud-smothered blackness of the night had made any sort of blindfold supererogatory. Don Simon had taken the wheel ('He's a marvel, isn't he?' had enthused Captain Palfrey, in the back seat beside her), and in addition to driving the staff-car, Lydia suspected her guardian of using his mental influence on both her and her living companion in the back seat. Even now, barely sixty feet from the car, she found she had only the dimmest recollection of the drive: of how long it had been, or of any feature of sound or smell, or of the number of turnings or the condition of the road surface, that might have identified where they were. She remembered chatting with Captain Palfrey, but couldn't call to mind a single word. Had he been likewise beglamored? she wondered. And if so, was he even aware of it?

Damn Simon . . .

'Graf Aloyïs Szgedny, like the Lady Francesca, became vampire in the days of the great Wars of Religion,' the vampire's whispering voice continued, as they walked on through what smelled, and felt, like woods. 'The master who made him – Odo Magnus Matilorum – was a very old vampire, who recalled clearly when first the revenants were seen in the days when plague made its terrible harvest through Christendom. The city of Prague was not hit so hard as other regions, yet it is a pious lie to say that 'twas spared through a vision of the Christ Child. Szgedny does not speak of this matter often. Indeed I am surprised that he has consented to do so to you. Remember when you speak to him that he is a very great nobleman, of ancient lineage, long used to deference.'

Wet leaves rustled in the stirring of breeze, and droplets pattered on Lydia's cloak and hair. She had the dim impression of looming walls ahead, and her feet gritted on what felt like gravel. Then her thought slipped away, to the memory – tiny and perfect, like something in those miniature Austrian snow globes – of walking up to the garden door of her house in Holyrood Street in Oxford, with her shoes crunching on the gravel of the path and James and Miranda standing in the lighted doorway . . .

She found herself, with a sensation of waking up, in a damp-smelling corridor, candlelight ahead of her outlining a partly-opened door. *DAMN you, Simon . . .*

She was aware that her heart was pounding. She was in the house of the vampire, and, for the sake of good manners, had left her silver wrist and neck chains back at the clearing station. *If anything goes wrong . . .*

She caught his sleeve. 'Goodness, I didn't think . . . does the Graf speak English?'

'German, Latin, French and Polish, as well as his native Czech . . . which in his time one only used to address one's servants or one's horses.'

I work and eat and sleep, daily, in a place within range of German guns. They've shelled the clearing station more than once. Why should I worry about paying a call on a deathless multiple murderer?

Her knees were still shaking.

He led her up a short flight of stone steps, and pushed open the lighted door.

'I trust Madame was not chilled on her journey here?'

Like most vampires Lydia had seen, the Graf seemed to be in the prime of life, though his long hair and his abundant mustaches were silvery-gray. His face was heavily lined, and beneath grizzled brows his gray eyes were level and cold, catching the firelight like mirrors as he rose from his seat beside the hearth. When Lydia sank into a curtsey (thanking her governess and the instructors at Madame Chappedelaine's School for the ability to do it properly and with grace) he took, and kissed, her hand.

'Thank you, my lord, I was most comfortable. It's kind of you to ask.'

He conducted her to a chair, and Don Simon took Lydia's cloak (and the lantern), and fetched tea from the small spirit kettle on a marquetry table nearby. Lydia could not help noticing that only one cup stood ready, and beside it, a small plate of chocolate biscuits (*and I'll bet he got THOSE from Storeman Pratt!*)

She was infinitely glad of Don Simon's presence.

'And I'm most grateful to you, sir, for consenting to see me. I appreciate it very much.'

Beyond the reach of the firelight Lydia made out the dim shapes of a long salon: card tables, a harp, the flicker of gold leaf on an elaborate clock. Deep-set windows opened uncurtained to the night. Closer, flame-glow outlined the carving of the hearth-side chairs, the marble angels, lizards, lilies and foxes that twined the fireplace itself.

'Simon informs me you seek information about the Lady Francesca Brucioram.'

Lydia took a sip of tea, and nibbled on a biscuit. After a full day in the fluoroscope tent and the surgical theater she felt she could have devoured the entire plateful without denting either her exhaustion or her hunger. 'In a manner of speaking, my lord. About her, and also about the revenants, the Others, to which I understand you can attest at first hand. Don Simon will have told you what we believe is happening at the old convent of Cuvé Sainte-Bride?'

'He has told me.' The wrinkled lids lowered over eyes devoid of expression: intelligent, cynical, and cruel. His powerful fingers rearranged themselves on his lap.

'Francesca the White is a woman with a great store of anger inside her,' he said at last. 'From what cause I know not.'

The slight movement of his head caused the fire-glow to pick momentarily at the strings of the distant harp: Lydia wondered if it was in tune, and if any of the vampires played.

'In most lamia – as you doubtless know, Madame – the capacity for feeling dwindles quickly. Loyalty, and the affection for one's family, become as the recollection of sugarplums loved in child-hood: an objective awareness that such a craving once existed, coupled with a mild distaste at the thought of gorging oneself now. Given the opportunity to slay one's enemies with near-impunity, one finds no real desire to put oneself to the trouble. They will die . . . and we will not.'

The gray brows pinched slightly over the broken aquiline of

his nose. 'For La Dame Blanche, the hunt is about cruelty. Many enjoy chasing a victim, the game of cat-and-mouse in the darkness: seeing a man piss himself with terror, hearing him squeak and plead at the touch of claws on his throat. The taste of his hope when he still thinks he can get away.' The tiniest smile tugged one corner of his mustache.

'For her the game is more elaborate. More personal. And the pleasure she takes in it has seemed always to me – for she left Prague, as most of us did, when the Prussians attacked under King Frederick – to come not from the kill itself, but from a sort of spite. As if every victim were the one who had done her ill. As if every kill were vengeance. I had many occasions to speak to her, when one of her "games", as she liked to call them, would involve three or four members of the same family or a circle of friends, pursued over a time long enough for word of their misfortunes to spread. In a city barely a tenth the size of London, of older beliefs and different organization, this can cause serious danger to others of the nest.'

'Did she ever try to command your fledglings, my lord?'

His lips compressed in an anger that she hoped wasn't directed at her. 'She did.'

'Forgive me, my lord—' Lydia ducked her head and looked as humble as she could – 'did it ever impress you that she would have taken command of the Prague nest, if she were able?'

His deep, soft voice remained level. 'There were times when I thought as much.'

'Yet she never actually made an attempt to supplant you? Or began a conspiracy to have you killed?'

''Twould have been fairly easy to arrange,' added Don Simon from the shadows. 'In those days, much of Bohemia believed in the *vampìr* more certainly than they believed that the earth circles the sun.'

'Not so easily as you might think,' retorted Szgedny. 'I had – as I still have – eyes and ears throughout the city, among the living as among the Undead. In any case, she did not.'

'Did you ever ask yourself why?' Lydia took another sip of tea.

He sat for a time like a cat watching birds. When he said, 'I did not,' there was, instead of irritation in his deep voice (in so far as it displayed anything), a kind of curiosity at himself for this omission.

'Because it sounds to me,' said Lydia diffidently, 'as if the
Lady Francesca might be incapable of creating fledglings. And
that's what she thinks Lemoine can give her.'

In his dressing-gown and his paisley shawl, before the faint
warmth of the tiny hearth in the room at Whitsedge Court, Asher
dreamed of the echoing vastness of the Liverpool Street Station.
Streaming mobs of people, as he helped Aunt Faith and Mrs
Flasket from the cab, paid the driver, mentally identified the
man's speech as originating from around Shepherd's Bush; his
ear caught the sing-song cry of the girls selling violets around
one of the cast-iron pillars near the platform steps. Two girls and
a woman, in the black of mourning . . . Beyond them, a worried
little man (from Devon, by his accent) fussed with his Scots
servant about the cat he carried in a basket . . .

Faces in the crowd. The smell of smoke from a cockle vendor's
barrow and a child's frightened wailing. Clouds of steam rolling
from Platform One as the express from Norwich ground to a
halt. A flicker of shadow, a characteristic movement near the
bookseller's – a ragged dark mackintosh . . .

When he turned it was gone.

Dreaming, he returned to the scene. Aunt Faith clung again to
his arm – she was the only one of Lydia's aunts who would treat
him with more than chill civility – and prattled in her gentle
voice of the letters she'd gotten from the family of one of the
Halfdene footmen who'd come back, blind and crippled, from
the Front, while his own attention moved like a gunsight, trying
to identify that flicker of a half-familiar shape.

Like spotting Lydia, or Dr Hoggett, or any of his scholastic
colleagues at a great distance off in a crowd . . .

Who was that?

He knew, but the knowledge slipped away.

And in his dream he remembered – not entirely illogically –
Josetta Beyerly, when she'd let him off at his lodgings Tuesday
night after their adventure in Brabazon Street. Exhausted and
shivering a little with what he suspected was a low-running fever,
he hadn't waked until the cab had reached the door and then
he'd been simply too tired to insist that they go round the corner
so that he could slip in through the old mews that had been one

of his reasons for choosing Faraday's Private Hotel in the first place.

When she'd seen him to his door, and walked back down the shallow step to the cab, he'd thought, as her heels clicked on the flagway, *I hope she's keeping safe . . .*

He'd looked up and down the dark street before closing the door behind him, and had seen no one.

''Twould make sense,' said Don Simon at length, 'of her own master's decision to make another her favorite in Strasbourg, lesser in strength by all accounts than the Lady. One does not bequeath one's estates to a gelding.'

For a long time Szgedny said nothing, but Lydia had the impression, almost, of hearing an abacus click behind those colorless eyes. 'And 'twould make sense,' he said at last, 'of her anger. 'Twas clear as day she considered herself a law unto herself, and entitled to be master of Prague in my stead.'

'And if Lemoine is working with the physical pathology of the Undead,' Lydia continued, 'which it sounds like he is doing, from what I've read of his work – she might well trade her assistance in controlling the Others for a cure for her own condition.'

'Children trading pebbles by the seashore.' The Graf's nostrils flared in irritation. 'A thousand imaginary ducats to pay for an imaginary horse. Best of luck to them both.'

'Are you sure?'

She saw Don Simon's yellow eyes move sidelong, to touch the Graf's snow-gray ones.

'I at least am sure,' returned the Master of Prague, 'that the Lady Francesca is incapable of commanding the revenants. Three hundred years I have watched them, and my master before me. Years will go by – decades, sometimes – between sightings of them, beneath the bridges of the Vltava and on the river's islands when the moon has set. But they are there, in the crypts beneath the old city, the forgotten cisterns and drains. The sub-cellars of the old town palaces and the ossuaries under churches ruined and built over and erased from the memory of the town. Never more than a few handfuls of them, living on rats in the darkness.

'My master, Odo Magnus, tried to gain command over them, when first they began to appear. One of his fledglings made the attempt also, Odo believed in order to gain control of the city and to drive Odo out. Or else to kill him and those loyal to him – such schisms, lady—' He inclined his head to Lydia – 'are uncommon but by no means unheard of, among those who hunt the night. This fledgling ended by being torn to pieces and eaten by the Others, who will it seems devour anything.'

'So we have observed,' murmured Don Simon.

'I have myself, like Odo before me, tried to control them as I control the minds of the living.' Stirred to the point of forgetting his calm dignity, the Graf leaned forward, gestured with one powerful hand, and his French became harder to follow as it slid back into the language as he had first learned it, centuries before. 'Looking into their eyes I saw naught: no mind, no memories, no dreams. Not even the most rudimentary sensations of hunger and fear by which one commands the actions of beasts. Meditating—' He glanced at Don Simon, as if making sure that he understood whatever mental technique that was, that each had learned from his master to control the perceptions of men – 'I could touch nothing of their thoughts, either singly or en masse. The effort only revealed my hiding place to them, and I was obliged to flee.'

'And there's no chance, my lord, that you were trying this too close to running water? You said they live in the channel of the river.'

A wolf's smile lifted one corner of the long mustaches again. 'Clever little lady. I was inland, well enough.' The silvery eyes met hers, and Lydia glanced quickly aside. To meet a vampire's eyes opened your own mind to the possibility of its tampering with your dreams. To the danger that one day it would summon you . . . and you would go.

'And the fact that the Lady Francesca didn't take the opportunity to enlist the Others herself, against you,' she concluded, 'seems to confirm that she probably couldn't. If she dwelt in Prague for – how long?'

'Seventy years, or thereabouts. And you are right, Madame.' He sat back, like a bleached cobra recoiling upon its rock. 'I doubt not that she made the attempt, more than once. She would have used them, if she could.'

'But Dr Lemoine doesn't know that.'

'And if her goal be merely to get of him some cure for her incapacity,' went on Don Simon, 'I cannot see her taking any pains to make sure these things remain under control. Lemoine's experiments are sufficiently irresponsible as they stand – God knows how they acquired the first of their revenants, upon which to found their efforts, though I can conceive several ways in which 'twere easily done. But Lemoine at least is a living man, with a living man's loyalties to his own. So far as I can ascertain, the Lady Francesca has none.'

'Tell me one more thing, my lord, if you would,' said Lydia, as Don Simon fetched her cloak and they prepared to leave. It was, by the exquisite goldwork clock, nearly ten, and for several minutes she had seen her escort listening carefully, for the sound of returning feet. By the look of the card tables, there was every chance the Graf's fledglings would foregather in this room, or wonder why they were excluded from doing so.

Whether their fear of her companion would keep the vampires at bay in a group she didn't know, though she was aware that most vampires held Don Simon Ysidro in considerable awe. In any case, the thought of that many of the Undead knowing who she was, and what she looked like, and that she was tampering in their affairs, frightened her a good deal. They gossiped, Don Simon had said, like schoolgirls, and there was no guarantee that one or more of them weren't bosom-bows with Francesca.

'And what might that be, Madame?' Graf Szgedny bent over her hand.

'Has there ever been occasion on which a vampire has tried to make a fledgling of a revenant?'

'The condition of these things is spread by the blood. I know of no vampire, no matter how inexperienced, who would take such risk.'

'But so far as I understand it, at least, it is the *death* – the absorption of the mind at death – that is involved in the transformation to vampire, not the blood itself. Might a vampire take in whatever mind exists in the revenant, and return it to the creature's body after it's dead? And then control it, as a master vampire controls its fledgling?'

'There must be an exchange of blood, lady. The blood is

what transforms the living man into the vampire, once he has passed through death. The risk would be simply too great.'

Lydia heard nothing, but Don Simon turned his head a little, then bowed deeply to the Graf. 'That sounds like Elysée de Montadour's voice, and those execrable fledglings of hers—'

'Flee.' Szgedny made a slight gesture, as though flicking water from his fingertips. 'Your visit shall be as if it never occurred.' For a moment – as sometimes happened with Don Simon's – his face turned briefly human when he smiled. Tired – and amused, perhaps, at being able to step for a moment out of the society of the Undead and provide information to the quests of the living. But the cynical cruelty in his eyes remained.

Asher returned to London on the Saturday afternoon train from Saffron Walden, though Aunt Faith chose to remain at the Court until Wednesday, with Mrs Flasket to bear her company. 'I'm sorry you have to return,' said the Dowager Lady Whitsedge, as she poured out tea for Asher in the bright sunlight at breakfast that morning. 'Thursday night was the first time I've seen the poor old Comte so cheerful. I do quite worry about him, losing his home as he has, and his son and both of his grandsons. I think it quite took him back, to tell somebody about his home, and the way things were when he was a boy.'

Once, on the four-mile drive to the station, Asher caught sight of a bicyclist following the Court's pony-trap at a distance: too far to easily make out details of the rider under the striped shadows of the new-leafed trees. The man was wearing a shabby Fair Isle sweater rather than a mackintosh, but something in his outline, even at that distance, rang alarm bells in Asher's mind.

FIFTEEN

'Is all well, M'am?'

Lydia looked up quickly from the corner of the makeshift table, which, in daytime (and through more nights than she cared to think about) served Eamon Dermott as a workbench.

The tiny root cellar beneath the ruins behind the fluoroscope room was barely large enough for both it and the tin basin he used as a developing bath, its rafters so low that during the daytimes (and through more nights than Lydia cared to think about) she and her assistant had to duck and weave about, to avoid the films hanging as they dried.

It was the only place in the clearing station where she knew she could work undisturbed.

She turned Jamie's letter face down beside her candle, and crossed to the door.

VAD Violet Brickwood stood on the stair. Listening, Lydia heard no clamor of voices and motors in the camp, no rattle of the fluoroscope being moved in the building above.

Only the guns.

She propped her glasses on her nose. 'I'm well. I just—'

The young volunteer's glance went past her shoulder, to the papers that strewed the table. 'I couldn't help seeing, M'am, that that nice Captain Palfrey brought you that letter today. I hope it's nothing amiss with your husband, or your little girl?' The earnest brown eyes returned to Lydia's face in the lantern-light, seeking – Lydia realized – the marks of grief. 'I'll sometimes go read my letters in the stores tent,' the girl added. 'If they're from my sister, about Mama, I mean. I just . . . Please don't think I'm meaning to pry, but you've been down here a long while. I just hoped you were all right.'

Lydia smiled, and gave the younger girl an impulsive hug. 'Thank you,' she said. 'All is well. There's nothing amiss.'

Except for a MONSTROUS scheme to dissolve the souls from out of men's brains, that their bodies may be enslaved because the governments find they're running out of good Frenchmen or good Englishmen or good Russians to kill.

Lydia returned to Dermott's worktable as Violet's shoes patted gently up the stair again, and stared at the letter.

It was on the stationery of Whitsedge Court (*What on EARTH is Jamie doing there?*) and ran to many pages – *It must have taken him HOURS to write it all!* – so that the minuscule dots, blots and pinpricks wouldn't be obvious as a code. Even though the letter had been sent to Don Simon's accommodation address in Paris, Jamie didn't trust anyone. The letter before this one, which she'd received through regular (censored) Army channels, had contained the terse warning *??? home team screening*, after the alarming information that there was a second revenant at large in London.

??? home team screening.

Monsters. She closed her eyes, leaned her forehead on her knuckles. The King's own government – or at least the Department that worked for them – was hiding the existence of those things she had encountered in China. Protecting them.

How that was worse than simply killing those poor Germans she wasn't sure, but it turned her stomach.

And chilled the blood in her veins.

A quick scratch on the door behind her. A whispered voice. 'Mistress?'

She turned in her chair and managed a half-smile. 'Well, you were right,' she said, as Don Simon slipped into the tiny cellar, closed the door without a sound. 'Jamie does indeed say *Do NOT investigate this yourself.*' She held out the decryption to him, her hand shaking with exhaustion. 'He suggests you do it.'

'Does he?'

The vampire scanned it. Four possible entrances to the sub-crypts and drains beneath the convent of Cuvé Sainte-Bride. Heaven only knew where Jamie had acquired the rough map, which according to the plain text of the letter was her Aunt Faith's house in Little Bookham (Aunt Faith had no such thing and had been Aunt Louise's pensioner for decades). One entrance was in the ruins of a chapel near lilac trees; another, thirty feet down the side of a well in a farmyard a mile from the Amiens road. And Heaven only knew if any of the four would still be usable.

'He says he's coming here himself, as soon as he can get the military clearances he needs.' She tried to keep her voice calm and decisive. The labored shakiness of Jamie's handwriting had told its own story. *Don't do it. You'll kill yourself . . .*

'Does he?' The vampire's pale brows lifted.

'It would help things,' said Lydia hesitantly. 'Speed things, if we knew at least whether those entrances are still open or not, or how dangerous they are. Obviously they're difficult of access, since none of the other Undead have spoken of revenants wandering about the back roads and battlefields—'

'Yet one at least got through.' Don Simon refolded the decryption, drew it thoughtfully through his long fingers. 'Whether that was one of ten, or one of fifty, we know not – nor yet why our Nurse Smith would have risked her life getting a sample of its blood or its flesh, when she has access to ample at Sainte-Bride. Curious.' His glance shifted sidelong to her. 'If I read this description aright – and the map also, though 'tis clearly not to scale – the crypts and catacombs beneath the convent at its height extend far beyond the walls as they currently stand, and presumably beneath the trenches that surround it. And given the habit which the living have, of judging situations to be "under control" when they very much desire them to be, 'twould little surprise me if one or more of these things is hiding in the far corners of these crypts, unbeknownst to this Lemoine.'

'Which would mean—' Lydia regarded him somberly by the candle's flickering light – 'that it's only a matter of time before they start to multiply beyond the convent walls. And once they start to spread . . .'

'E'en so.' He folded up the paper. 'Though if they exist in any substantial number, how they are to be destroyed, with the French Army and, it seems, the War Department of England shielding them, 'tis another matter.'

He picked up Lydia's cold hand and kissed it. 'As for James's coming, if I have learned one thing since last September, lady, 'tis the oriental leisure of official conduct with regards to these "military clearances" of which he speaks. I should refer them all to the forgers who work in Montparnasse and Pigalle: 'tis a wonderment to me that none has ever questioned "Colonel Simon", on how speedily he seems to acquire documents.'

And taking up her candle, he followed her up the crumbling stone steps to the ground above.

On the following day the British First Army made a determined probe at the German lines, principally (Captain Calvert opined, spattered bicep-high in blood and cursing like a very quiet and well-bred Australian sailor) to pull potential German attacks from the French around Arras. From first light Wednesday, when the casualties began coming in, until midnight Thursday night, Lydia took x-ray photographs, administered chloroform, held retractors and sponges, and irrigated wounds, in between taking tea out to the men queued up on stretchers outside the pre-op tent where Matron was grimly sorting them into those who would live and those who wouldn't. Lydia saw not so much as the glint of reflective eyes in the darkness on either night, but knew they were watching. She didn't know whether she was more furious at them or General Haig.

Colonel St-Vire finally sent the last members of the surgical crews to bed at three o'clock Friday morning with orders not to stir until teatime.

'Captain Palfrey's been to see you twice,' reported Nurse Brickwood worriedly, coming into the nurses' tent Friday evening while Lydia was sponging down with a flannel. Lydia felt her stomach sink, at the thought of what Don Simon might have found. Nevertheless she finished washing, brushed her hair, dressed and went to the mess tent (*Does this headache have anything to do with not having dinner last night?*), and was picking at a rock-hard biscuit soaked in a bowl of lukewarm Maconochie when Palfrey's voice exclaimed 'Dr Asher!' from the twilight of the doorway.

He dodged between the tables to her, and Captain Burke – with whom she'd been eating and commiserating about the upcoming evening's work – heaved his bulk from the bench and shook a facetious finger at her. 'Any more meetin's wi' that captain, lass, and I'll be writin' Professor Asher of you.' Everyone in the clearing station knew by this time that Lydia was involved in 'something for the brass' – presumably concerning x-ray photography – and had come to recognize Captain Palfrey as the liaison.

She thankfully abandoned the tinned swill before her and rose to meet the young captain, who guided her swiftly from the tent.

But instead of handing her a note – and enough light lingered in the sky that she knew Don Simon hadn't come himself – Palfrey inquired worriedly, 'Have you heard anything of Colonel Simon, Dr Asher? I'm dreadfully sorry to interrupt you, as I know you've had a rough time of it these past two nights – everyone has, all the way up to Festubert . . . But Colonel Simon didn't meet me last night.'

'He is very much a law unto himself . . .'

'I know.' The young man grimaced at his own concern. 'And he'll joke me sometimes about being a mother hen. But . . .

Wednesday we drove down as far as Haut-le-Bois, and he ordered me to wait for him, with the car, in a lane a few miles beyond the village. I had orders, if he didn't return by sunrise, to go back to Aubigny and wait. Aubigny is where we're staying. Where *I'm* staying,' he corrected himself. 'I honestly have no idea where Colonel Simon stays. He had me rent a sort of accommodation address for him there, but he doesn't seem to use it.'

The young man's brisk calm cracked then, and for a moment his mouth tightened, and distress pulled the flesh around his eyes. 'But he . . . He never came to my lodgings last night. I sat up nearly all night for him, and I – in my heart I feel something terrible has happened to him, M'am. Dr Asher. Every time I fell asleep – and I did nod off three or four times – I thought I heard him calling for me. I must have gotten up and gone to the door a dozen times! And I wondered—'

And I was so tired when I finally lay down last night I wouldn't have waked if Miranda had stood next to my cot and screamed. Her heart turned chill inside her. *He went to investigate the crypts under Sainte-Bride.*

Because I asked him to.

And he didn't come out.

Asher told himself, as his train pulled out from Saffron Walden on Saturday afternoon, that the man on the bicycle couldn't possibly have anything to do with the glimpse of what might or might not have been a half-familiar shadow in Brabazon Street Tuesday evening. Nevertheless he changed his own jacket in his second-class compartment and stepped off the train on the last foot or so of platform as it was leaving Epping, and after a considerable hunt for a cab, found one and took it to Pembridge Place. There he paid his bill, changed his jacket and hat yet again, and sought new lodgings in Kensington, after two more cabs and an excursion to Holborn on the Underground, just to make sure that he wasn't being followed. Descending to the Underground troubled him, for its tunnels were the logical place for the Others – two of them, now – to hide.

How long before they added a third to their number?

Does Teague the gunrunner have the slightest idea of the danger of blood contact? Did the man or men employing him?

Tomorrow, he told himself, he'd need to consult both Millward and Josetta, Sabbath or no Sabbath.

After a slender tea at a café, which he was far too exhausted to eat, he composed a telegram to Josetta, another to Miranda (care of Ellen and Mrs Grimes) and a Personals message to 'Dr Graves', then retired to bed, where he lay, shivering with fever, for the next four days. Between bouts of coughing he hoped Mr Fair Isle had been struck on his bicycle by a lorry and squashed flat.

On Thursday he felt sufficiently recovered to venture forth to the British Museum.

Osric Millward was precisely where Asher had found him first, at the end of one of the long desks beneath the great rotunda of the Reading Room. The shabbily-dressed Donnie was still helping him, assisted by another – stooped, a little rat-like, wearing no tie at all, but a kerchief knotted around his throat under a battered frieze jacket – whose intense eyes remained on Millward's face with every word he spoke.

Millward's 'network'. Asher wondered if they had had brothers, sisters, sweethearts, friends who had become victims of a vampire. In their unprepossessing faces he read not only hunger for revenge, but a kind of eager gratitude to have someone who believed them.

The posters Asher had passed in the hallway leading to the great room – garish colors, looming figures – seemed aimed at those two young men, the only men under the age of forty-five in the room: *Come Along, Boys, Before It's Too Late! Will You Answer the Call? YOU are the MAN we want . . .*

How much courage did it take to say *No, I need to stay in London and hunt for vampires*?

Millward sprang to his feet as Asher approached, seized him by the hand. 'When I didn't hear from you I feared they'd gotten you.'

He meant the vampires of London, not their own government departments, but Asher shook his head. 'I had to go down to the country to see a man about a dog.'

The older man studied his face, his brows drawn together in concern. Asher reflected that he probably looked more like someone who'd been attacked by vampires than like one who had an appointment to meet the Master of London in Piccadilly at midnight for a chat. Millward steered him into a chair, murmured to his two acolytes, 'Would you excuse us . . .?' and sat down himself. When the young men had gone he whispered, 'I've found where they're hiding.'

SIXTEEN

'Shouldn't we wait until it gets dark?' Captain Palfrey braked the staff-car to a halt. 'Colonel Simon always does.'

Scanning the description and instructions she had recopied from Jamie's original letter, Lydia wondered how complicated it would be to explain to this young man that 'Colonel Simon' only appeared at night, Palfrey's convictions to the contrary. 'It'll be dark soon,' she said instead. Indeed, sufficient twilight had gathered to make reading difficult, in the shadows of the leafless trees. 'And if anything goes wrong and we get separated and have to run for it, I'd feel much safer trying to do so with at least a little daylight.' She added, 'I don't have Colonel Simon's night-eyes,' and Palfrey, turning in the front seat, grinned understandingly.

'Lord, isn't that the truth! I don't think any man living does.'

You're quite right about that. She went back to studying the paper. Their visit to Cuvé Sainte-Bride two weeks previously had revealed nothing about picket guards, and Lydia wondered how great a staff the French Army was willing to pay for.

How many men could be trusted not to blab about what was going on inside, either from horror and outrage or simply in their cups in the *estaminets* of Haut-le-Bois? Lemoine had a couple of soldiers to help manage the prisoners when they were selected, and certainly at least one man on the gate, but how many more? And how many was too many?

Three people can keep a secret only if two of them are dead. Wasn't that how the old proverb ran?

Lydia propped her glasses on her nose, and took a deep breath. '*Old farm near Amiens road*,' she read aloud. '*Well*. Is there rope in the car?'

'Yes, M'am. I had some Wednesday night, also. Colonel Simon took it with him.'

'*Sub-crypt of chapel . . .*' She lowered the paper, scanned the silent woods around them. They stood a little above the lacerated road, where a lane led to the bullet-riddled shell of what had been a farm. '*Near lilac trees—*'

'There are lilacs two miles down the main road from here, and up the ridge a little. I noticed them because there are lilacs at Deepmere. They're Aemilia's favorite.' Palfrey looked shy at the mention of his sweetheart's name. 'They won't be in bloom for two months yet . . .'

Lydia smiled. *And you probably keep them pressed in your book of the King's Regulations . . .*

'We'll go through the woods.' She turned back to judge how well concealed the staff-car was behind them. 'If we keep the road on our left we shouldn't get too lost. You don't happen to have anything like a tarpaulin or a gun-cover in the boot?'

He shook his head. 'I have a billhook, though. It won't take but a few minutes to cut brush.'

Lydia strained her ears for the sound of another vehicle on the road as she helped her escort pile cut saplings and shrubs of hawthorn over the vehicle ('You might want to not cut them all from one area . . .' 'Oh, right! Excellent thought, M'am!'). They were still, by her calculation, several miles from the old convent, and though the vehicle couldn't be seen from the main road, anyone who *did* see the rough camouflage-job would be bound to guess that somebody was up to something.

Of course, simply the sight of a staff motorcar sitting out here would cause them to guess that.

It was quite clear that fighting had passed over these woods the previous autumn. As they trudged through the shredded rags of undergrowth, the shrapnel-blasted trees, Lydia caught occasional glimpses of weather-faded khaki or gray under the winter's dead beech leaves, and the brown of exposed bone.

Wednesday night. Lydia shifted her grip on the unlit lantern she carried, her heart beating hard. *Did he get in? Was he trapped below ground?* The earth would block most of a vampire's psychic connection with the living. Even had Simon tried to make mental contact with her Wednesday night, she'd been awake, concentrating on taking x-ray photographs and administering anesthetics. Last night she'd slept so deeply she doubted anything could have waked her. *Oh, Simon, I'm sorry . . .*

If he were underground she suspected she'd have to be standing at one of the entrances to the crypts to hear his voice whisper in her mind. Even then it mightn't reach her.

Or will I reach the chapel and find only a heap of ash and bone?

The chapel lay in the center of a zone of shell-craters and scratched-out, makeshift shelters, scrabbled with entrenching-tools by men who had no time to do more than scrape gouges in the earth to lie in and pray. All around the pulverized walls, branches, trunks, shrubs and earth bore the appearance of having passed beneath the teeth of some frightful harrow that had stripped everything in its path. The lilacs of which Palfrey – and Jamie's informant – had spoken had survived only because they lay far enough from the chapel itself to be on the edge of the death zone.

This near the road, any building that could have given shelter would have been bombed out of existence by the other side. She didn't need to slip and scramble into the chapel itself to guess what she'd find there, though she had to check: a pit some twenty feet deep, where bombs had repeatedly fallen on the sub-crypt, caving it out of existence. The graveyard smell of incompletely buried bodies lingered over the ruined earth.

She whispered, 'Drat it,' though it was just as well. The fewer holes for stray revenants to get through the better. 'How far are we from the Amiens road?'

Hiking over the ridge took the remainder of the fading daylight, though there was very little (*Thank Heavens!*) barbed wire in the shell-torn underbrush of the woods. Palfrey led the way, with a map of the area and a compass; full darkness was closer than Lydia cared for, when they finally glimpsed the charred stones of the farmhouse. There had been fighting here as well, but it didn't look as though the shattered cottage had been shelled.

'Mills bombs, it looks like.' Palfrey lowered his map, and frowned through the gloom at the ruin. 'Look how much of the roof is undamaged.'

The well stood halfway between the house and what remained

of the barn. The windlass was gone, as was most of the well-curb. Palfrey found an unburnt section of beam, lit the lantern and laying the beam across the hole, stretched himself out on it to lower the light on his rope. 'We're still fairly high above the local water table here,' he reported, and Lydia, kneeling to peer down, saw the yellow reflection of the light some fifty or sixty feet below.

'Is that a hole, or a door, in the side of the well shaft?' she asked. 'Or just a trick of the shadows?'

The young captain lowered the light as far down as he could, the shadow clearly outlining a roughly rectangular mouth of shadow in the wall.

'Look,' she added, pointing, 'those are iron staples in the wall leading down to it.'

'Good,' returned Palfrey grimly. 'Because there isn't anything to tie this line to closer than twenty feet from the well. It should just get us down to the first of the staples.' He pulled up the rope, untied the lantern and carried the coil to the remains of the barn door. Lydia undid her belt – she wore a holstered Webley service revolver at her waist – and kilted up her stout linen skirt above her knees.

I really should get a man's trousers, to do things like this. They can't be less modest than a pair of bicycle bloomers. She checked the safety and the cylinder of the Webley, actions she'd performed half a dozen times in the car already. *Though it would be impossible to sneak out of the camp unnoticed in them. I wonder if Storeman Pratt would sell me a pair?* Captain Palfrey, returning with the end of the rope in his hands, halted in startled alarm at the sight of her calves and ankles: 'Oh, come, it can't be worse than a bathing costume, surely?' she answered his blush.

'No, of course—' He looked away from her as he dropped the end of the rope down over the edge. 'That'll reach,' he said. 'I'll go first.' He threaded his belt through the lantern's handle, wrapped the rope firmly around his forearms (Lydia watched carefully and hoped she remembered from her schooldays how it was done), and climbed down, leaning out on the rope and bracing his feet on the wall.

I think I can do that . . .

She wondered breathlessly how deep the water was in the well, and if there would be rats in the tunnel.

If there were people at Cuvé Sainte-Bride, there would be rats. *And revenants, of course . . .*

The rope ended a few feet below the first of the iron staples. She saw Palfrey shift over to the staples, and continue the descent, testing each before he put his full weight on it. She saw three of them jar and shift, and heard the patter of bits of stone as they fell into the water below. With the disturbance of the surface the smell of it came up to her, a sickening whiff of rotting meat. *What'll I do if a staple breaks and he falls in? I'll never be able to get him out.*

When he drew near the entry hole she saw that the last few staples had been broken off – *Did they rust quicker because they're closer to the water?* – and Palfrey had to wedge his boot-toe on the tiny stubs that remained. One of these broke, and he swung himself deftly into the narrow slot. Lantern-light outlined the doorway's edges, then dimmed as he moved a little into the passageway beyond. For an outraged moment Lydia thought he was going to go in alone ('This is no task for a fragile little woman . . .') but an instant later he put his head out again, and signed for her to descend.

I have Josetta's word for it that there's scientific proof that women are just as strong and enduring as men . . .

And Simon got himself into this because I asked him.

She took a deep breath, wrapped the rope around her forearms and began her descent.

Jamie . . . Miranda . . . if I get killed I'm so sorry . . .

Oh, dear, which staples were the weak ones . . .?

Rope to staples. Staples – there were nineteen of them – into the blackness, with barely a feather-brush of yellow light on the wet stone against which she pressed her face and body as she descended. The horrible suggestion of the charnel reek below her, like a kitchen garbage pail too long neglected.

Nineteen. Her groping toe extended down, found nothing. Shifting a little sideways, she found the nubbin of the broken staple, but Palfrey whispered, 'I'll get you, with your permission,' and his hand – with that male gripping power that always surprised her – closed firmly around her calf. 'Lower yourself down . . .'

His arm circled her hips and he swung her down into the doorway with him.

Inside in the tunnel, the fishy, ratty stink of the revenants mingled with the acrid whiff of carbolic soap. Lydia was aware that she was terrified and aware also that there was no time for it, and no turning back. And of course, no guarantee that Simon had ever passed this way . . .

Palfrey slid down the cover of the lantern till it was barely a glimmer, and unholstered his own gun. From his tunic pocket he produced a silencer, which he screwed onto the barrel. Lydia observed he'd also brought the billhook from the car, hanging in a leather sheathe from his waist. *As if any of that's going to do any good . . .*

The tunnel was barely five feet in diameter, and went on for what felt like miles, though Jamie's map had assured her it was not quite three-quarters of a mile from the well to the convent's crypts. It dipped and rose, the low places sheeted with water, sometimes knee-deep, that stank like a sewer. A few yards before the end, it dropped off into what looked like another well, and another ladder of iron staples on a sort of pillar led up to what appeared to be the pierced cover of a drain.

The smell from above was almost unbearable.

Revenants.

Lydia held her watch close to the lantern and saw that it was just before eight. The sun had set some forty-five minutes before. The Master of Prague had told her the revenants were awake and moving about well before full dark: some vampires were astir that early also, Don Simon among them, though they could not venture out into the deadly sunlight. Her heart pounding so that she felt nearly sick, she listened, but heard no sound.

Palfrey moved her gently aside, slipping up the lantern-slide the tiniest crack, mounted the ladder and shifted the cover aside. Nothing attacked him, and the next moment he climbed through, and lowered one hand down to her.

The room above had been a chapel; it was a storeroom now. Above the tops of crates (*Lait en poudre* and *Legumes sec*) the walls showed whitewash. To the right an archway had been barred across, and the lantern-gleam flashed on silver. Shapes stirred beyond. Chains clinked; Lydia saw the flash of reflective eyes.

She heard Palfrey gasp and read the shock on his face, but gripped his wrist, bringing him back to himself. Touched her own lips. *Not one sound . . .*

One of them, she thought, *is poor Captain Rhinehardt's cousin, who was captured because he wouldn't leave his kinsman.* Brain gone, soul gone, as casually as students in a biology laboratory would pith a frog.

She wondered how she had ever considered Simon and his brothers and sisters in Undeath the worst monsters at large in Flanders.

And in making those judgments, will I become a monster, too?

She touched her companion's elbow, moved softly toward the chapel's shut door.

A door opened somewhere beyond, and footsteps retreated on a stone floor. Echoes implied a corridor . . .

'—tell her the equipment is ready,' said Lemoine's voice beyond the door. 'And make her understand that we could not set it up in any other place.'

'There's still a little light in the sky,' returned a woman's voice. The footfalls paused upon the words, then started again, and died away.

'You're a fool if you think this will help you,' said Don Simon Ysidro's voice.

Lydia shut the lantern-slide, opened the door a crack. There was indeed a short corridor beyond. Reflected light – the strong glare of electricity (*They must have a generator somewhere*) – flowed through a half-open door a few yards along, showing her the same ruinous medieval masonry, roughly plastered and whitewashed.

'Oh, I think that remains to be seen.' Dr Lemoine, standing in the doorway, turned and re-entered the room behind him as he spoke, a sort of keyed-up cheerfulness edging his voice. Lydia signed for Palfrey to follow, crept toward the lighted door.

'If the Undead could increase their power by killing the Undead, they would have been preying upon one another for thousands of years.' Don Simon's whispering tones held nothing but a kind of tired patience, like a mother pointing out to a child that no matter how much that child wanted to fly, those cardboard wings would not do the job. 'To drink the blood of another vampire only renders a vampire desperately and incurably sick—'

'Ah, but she's not going to drink your blood.' Something in the room ahead clinked softly, metal on metal. 'Only absorb your energies, at the instant of your death.'

'The instant of my death,' sighed Don Simon, 'was in 1555.'

'And how many deaths have you absorbed since then?'

Lydia felt Palfrey halt, threw a quick look back and saw his face, in the reflected glow, transformed with protesting shock. This transmuted to unbelieving horror as they looked around the jamb of the door, to the room beyond.

The laboratory was a small one. Lydia guessed that the straps that held Don Simon to a sort of steel gridiron at one end of the room must be plated inside with silver. Either that, or simple stress and exhaustion prevented him from using any illusion to conceal his true appearance: silk-white, skeletal. His own claws – his own fangs – were clearly visible from the doorway, as were the scars that ripped across his face and continued down onto his throat, to where the open neck of his shirt fell away from it, gouged by the Master of Constantinople six years ago, when Simon had saved her life.

Beneath the grid on which he lay were arranged cylinders of oxyacetylene gas, their valves linked together so that a single switch (so far as she could tell) would ignite them all.

Don Simon's right arm was strapped close to his side; his left was extended to a small metal table – of the type Lydia was familiar with from the surgical tent – and likewise held by a strap at the wrist. The fingers of this hand Dr Lemoine grasped in his excitement, his voice almost trembling with eagerness. 'Your death – their deaths – is what she needs. Not your blood.' He nodded toward a couple of gleaming gallon jars on the floor, and a small array of scalpels on a nearby table. 'We know that draining all the blood from your body wouldn't kill you. But your death, your real death—'

'Will gain you nothing. If alliance with the Lady Francesca is your goal, 'twill thwart you of it, for 'twill drive her mad—'

'No,' insisted Lemoine. 'No, it will simply complete her transformation to the vampire state. Her power is incomplete, it has always been. Once we—'

At that point Palfrey produced his revolver and shot Dr Lemoine in the back.

Even equipped with a so-called silencer, the report was loud in the underground silence – Lydia wondered, as she strode into the little room, how many soldiers were in the crypts and if the weight of the earth and the tangle of the small rooms and chapels would stifle the sound. She'd already seen a small ring of keys on the table with the surgical equipment and snatched them up, Palfrey still standing in the doorway, as if hypnotized with shock, dismay, betrayal.

Good, at least he won't turn on the oxyacetylene himself in a fit of heroism . . .

Would Jamie?

She didn't know.

'There is a guard in the hall above,' said Don Simon, as Lydia unlocked the straps. ''Twill take them a moment, but – *cagafuego*,' he added, as the revenants in the nearby chamber began to howl.

'Can they control rats?' She caught his arm as he rolled off the gridiron, turned toward the door, which was still blocked by Palfrey, staring at him as if he could not believe what he saw.

Don Simon's wrists and forehead, Lydia noted automatically, were welted and bleeding where the straps had touched – a glance confirmed that, yes, the leather was sewn inside with silver plates.

'You knew.' Palfrey's revolver pointed at both of them, perfectly steady though his whole body was trembling with shock. 'Mrs Asher, you . . . you *knew* . . .' The blue eyes turned pleadingly to Don Simon: pleading, anger, disbelief. 'What *are* you?'

Boots clattered on the stair, a man's voice yelled, 'Colonel Lemoine—?'

And against the wall where he had collapsed, Lemoine raised himself to one elbow, blood seeping across the left shoulder of his lab coat. 'Spies!' he gasped. 'Germans!'

Palfrey reacted automatically, ducking back to the door and firing into the passage; Don Simon grabbed Lydia's arm, as she would have taken the moment to dodge past him. A gunshot in the passageway, unmuffled by a silencer, it rang like the crack of doom, and Palfrey buckled and collapsed. There was another unsilenced shot and Lemoine groped his own sidearm from its holster; Don Simon dragged Lydia out the door, stooped to snatch up Palfrey's revolver and fire another shot at the guard – who lay, Lydia now saw, a dozen feet away in a spreading pool of blood.

'Dressing,' Don Simon ordered, ripping open Palfrey's tunic. Lydia whipped her clasp knife from her pocket and cut a four-inch strip from the hem of her skirt (*I couldn't have done THAT if I'd been wearing trousers!*). The vampire tore the tough linen into two pieces as if it had been paper, wadded up the larger piece over the bleeding hole in the young captain's chest and used the shorter to bind it into place, with shouting and the thunder of feet sounding somewhere in the darkness of the stair. 'Stay close.'

'*I have a constitutional dislike of losing those who serve me,*' he had said to her once, and with a single swift movement scooped the taller man up over his shoulder as he rose. Lydia picked up Palfrey's revolver, reached back into the laboratory behind her to switch off the electric light there – Lemoine was on his feet, stumbling towards the door. She heard him crash into something as she caught Don Simon's hand in her own free one. In pitch darkness she followed the vampire at a run down the uneven corridor back to the chapel-cum-storeroom, while the guards shouted and bumbled in the stair.

She felt rather than saw when they passed through the door into the chapel, and heard the revenants howling and baying in their cell, and the clash of their chains. (*Do they chain them to keep them from eating one another?*) Now and then one of them yelled a German word. Iron scraped – the cover of the drain. She groped for the staples on the wall, dropped down into the darkness, and the ice-cold fingers closed around hers again.

'Thank you, Mistress. She'll be in the hunt—'

No need to ask who 'she' was.

'We've a motorcar on the other side of the ridge, up the lane about two miles from the chapel with the lilacs. Did you try that way in first?'

'I guessed 'twould have been a target for artillery.' They were striding along the uneven passageway, Lydia stumbling where the floor dipped, cold, smelly water freezing her feet where the way was flooded. 'Is there a rope?'

'Only near the top. There was nothing to tie it to.'

The vampire swore again. 'Mine I left in the farmhouse, rather than have any man find it hanging down the well. 'Twill be but minutes to fetch it—'

Lydia thought of trying to leap from the threshold of the little doorway in the well's side, up to the first broken stub of iron, and shuddered. Even hanging onto the vampire's neck or shoulders had only to be thought of, to be discarded – vampires didn't weigh much, but she knew the double weight would crumble the rusted remains of the metal. 'All right. How badly is Captain Palfrey hurt?'

''Tis not so deep as a well nor so wide as a church door,' the vampire quoted grimly. 'Can I but bring him to help, 'twill be well.'

Lydia shivered, recalling the young man's horrified face. *You knew . . .*

She said no more, but kept hold of the vampire's hand, and in time smelled the contaminated water of the well ahead of them, and the wet pong of moss on its stones. She listened desperately to the silence behind them, trying to determine if she could hear footsteps or not. And wondered whether anyone there would be smart enough to deduce that they'd have to escape via the well, and be waiting for them at the top.

Or didn't they know about the well?

And did Simon shut the drain-cover in the chapel—?

He stopped, and she felt him put Palfrey down. Holding Lydia's hand, he signed her to kneel, then led her, feeling the floor, to the edge of the doorway, to show her where it lay. Then he kissed her hand and released it, and she felt the sleeve of his shirt brush her cheek as he stood. There was the faintest whisper of scratching as he jumped – she was glad there was no light, for she didn't even like to picture it – and, presumably, seized the broken nubbins of iron above and to the right of the doorway, for she didn't hear a splash. A moment later the faint pitter of dislodged stone fragments falling into the water.

She crawled back to Palfrey, took his hand. It was cold with shock. She put the back of her wrist against his lips, and felt the warm thread of breath. His pulse, when she felt it a moment later, was fast and thready: *He HAS to be got to help . . .*

'*You knew,*' he had said.

And how will I explain to him that vampires can bend and ensorcel human perceptions? Particularly the very old, very skilled vampires

*like Simon? How will I explain – how will I make him believe – that
all those times he thinks he met Simon by daylight, all those 'impressions' he had of reading mention of him in his father's letters – were
only thoughts implanted in his dreams?*

*EVERYTHING – resigning from the Guards, and coming here
to France, and leaving poor Miss Bellingham – EVERYTHING was
based upon a lie. Everything he undertook was only because Don
Simon needed someone to work for him in the daylight hours.*

Her hand tightened involuntarily on Palfrey's, and – a little to
her surprise – she felt the pressure feebly returned.

She listened into the darkness of the tunnel behind them,
seeking again for the rattle of soldiers' boots, the creak of belt
leather. *How much do the guards know? How many of them are
there? And do THEY know the kind of thing Lemoine is up to,
with his enslavement of German prisoners who are stripped of
their own minds?*

*Do they know how deadly it is to come into any contact with
these things that might result in blood transfer? Do they—?*

Something brushed her face.

She realized her thoughts had been wandering an instant before
she smelled blood and cold hands seized her around the waist
and throat.

A woman screamed, cursed, in the blackness beside her – silver
burning a vampire's hands . . .

Lydia tried to wrench free and fell over Palfrey's body, cried
out in pain as those steel hands grabbed her again, around the
waist and by the hair, this time, and a woman's voice hissed in
her ear, *'Rogneux puteresse!'*

She was dragged away into the tunnel's reeking darkness.

SEVENTEEN

A sher knew the place when Millward described it, a vast
zone of waste ground beyond London's East End, where
drab dockside merged with marshes, gorse and woodland. Rough land blotched around its edges by turpentine works,

phosphate plants, varnish factories and sewer outfalls, before one came to the market gardens of Stratford and West Ham. Brown with factory waste, the River Lea and assorted creeks and cuts wound their way toward the Thames, and the bodies of vagrants and outcasts turned up periodically in the dirty margins of those streams, unmourned and not much regarded by the Metropolitan Police.

'There's a pub about two hundred yards from where Carpenter's Road ends in the marsh,' said Millward. They had retreated to the Reading Room's vestibule, with its garish recruiting posters, and the intermittent comings and goings of scholars, journalists, students and cranks. 'A stone's throw from the waterworks reservoir . . .'

'The Blind King.' Asher saw the grimy red-brick box in his mind: nailed-up shutters, padlocked door. The ground was marshy but the steps up to the door, and the narrow window slits at ground level, told him there was a cellar of sorts beneath it. 'It's been shut up for years.'

'Well, the police found a body near the outfall embankment Tuesday morning. Donnie and I went out there—' Millward nodded back toward the Reading Room – 'when we heard about the state in which it was found. A man we met there spoke of some boys playing along the City Mill Creek and in the marshes finding rats . . . You said these things can control rats? Dozens of them, torn to pieces and partially eaten, they said, lying all of a . . . all of a heap, as if they'd been dumped from a basket. He said it wasn't dogs.'

The vampire-hunter's silver-shot brows tugged together, oblivious to a tweed-clothed woman who was trying to get past him with her arms full of notebooks. Millward always planted himself in the center of any room.

'He said he'd seen rats after a ratting, and it was nothing like. Nothing like anything he'd seen. And a man who lives in Turnpike Row said he'd seen a thing, twice, in the fog, late at night, a thing like what you described.'

Asher spread out his ordnance map against the wall and located the Blind King, and then Turnpike Row, City Mill Creek and the embankment of the outfall. His recollection of that end of Hackney Marsh included no other buildings nearby isolated enough to permit concealing any creature that size in a cellar.

'Good man.' He folded his map, gripped the former scholar's shoulder. 'It sounds as if one of them's being kept there and is feeding itself on rats. The other may be lurking near. Any sense that anyone else thinks it might be the Blind King?'

Millward considered the matter, and Asher guessed he had pursued enquiries no further. Guessed that with his instinctive upper-class reticence, it hadn't even occurred to Millward to go down to the nearest pub on Carpenter's Road – the Dolphin – and further his researches. But he only shook his head, and didn't – as many people did when faced with such a question – elaborate or surmise: 'I wouldn't know, no.'

'Good man,' Asher said again. 'I'll go have a look at the place this afternoon.'

'Will you need help?'

'Probably later, yes, thank you. At the moment I think one man will be less obvious than two.' And particularly, Asher mused as he listened and mentally sorted through the rest of Millward's researches and newspaper cuttings from the past five days, if one of those two was as striking in appearance as the handsome raven-and-silver vampire-hunter. Nor did Millward possess the professional spy's quality of what Asher mentally termed *un-visibility*: the trick of blending into a crowd, of making himself look like nobody of importance. All his colleagues in the Department had had it, whether they were dressed as dons or coal-heavers. Pritchard Crowell, he recalled, could 'doze off' so convincingly that village chiefs of police had been known to interview local informers in his presence, and never be able to give a description of 'that fellow in the corner' when the informers (or in one case the village chief of police) later turned up dead.

It was – Asher reflected, as the suffocatingly overcrowded bus clattered its way out to Hackney that afternoon – one of his few reservations about Doyle's Sherlock Holmes tales: the fact that Holmes, though repeatedly touted as a master of disguise, was also described in terms of being a man of distinctive appearance.

But then, there was a streak of actor in many of the best agents, himself, he suspected, included. He stepped from the bus at Old Ford Road, glad of the stick that – with the flour in his hair and mustache, the long, grizzled side-whiskers that formed part of his little disguise kit, and a pair of steel-rimmed spectacles – contributed to the addition of twenty years to his age. And indeed he felt like a man in his sixties, as he hobbled his careful way across the Five Bells Bridge and then along the railroad right-of-way through that grubby world of empty fields and straggly market allotments. The hot rawness in his chest and the swiftness with which fatigue descended on him were whispered reminders of the previous week's fever. *Don't mess about with this, Jimmy!* Hoggett had insisted, the last time – just after Christmas, it had been – that Asher had been felled by low-grade fever, crippling fatigue and paroxysms of coughing. *Once you've had pneumonia it lingers in your body for years . . .*

Like the infection that had been devouring poor Bert Mayo in that tiny back room on Brabazon Street: once contracted, there was nothing that could be done. He was, he knew, lucky.

The most pneumonia would do was kill him.

He reached the Dolphin public house at about three. It was the dead hour in business, before all the local mills and factories let out. The Dolphin was of the old style of public houses, literally a house, with beer and ale served in the front parlor and more private quarters in the back. The place was empty when Asher reached it and he presented himself as a Liverpudlian on the tramp, looking for some kind of easy work, having had pneumonia in the first days of the fighting. The landlady, with a husband and one son dead and another son still at the Front, was sympathetic, and Asher's offer to 'help with the washing-up' to pay for a second glass of beer and a sandwich earned him a full account of the two mysterious heaps of dead rats (one Sunday and the next only yesterday), and the condition of the vagrant's body found in the Lea Tuesday morning.

'Myself, I think it was an accident at the railway workshops, or the mills up past Bully Fen,' Mrs Farnum insisted, dipping hot water from the copper on the stove (the interview had moved into the kitchen) and spreading towels on all but a corner of the kitchen table. 'They're short of men there to work and they push them to all hours of the night – no, Mr Pritchard, I won't have you lugging great buckets of water about, I know how that pneumonia sticks to a man's bones!' (*I should introduce*

you to Hoggett . . .) 'You just stand here by the sink and do
the washing and I'll bring the glasses up to you . . . My father
worked in the Houldsworth Mill in Reddish and had his hand
taken off and all the flesh skinned off his arm – clear down to
the bone! – by the belt on a ring frame, and the company
claimed he was drunk and it was his own fault, but when you've
worked fifteen hours – let alone where you'd even get the liquor
to get drunk on – you're that tired, as the men are, working
now, those that're left—'

But by the sound of it, once Asher had sifted through the long
circumlocutions of her tale, the man had not been ripped up by
machinery, but by a beast.

'Looked like poor Dandy did, when that brute mastiff of Ted
Clavering's tore him up last Michaelmas two years . . .'

A beast, he thought grimly, which had once been a man.

The sightings in the fog by Mr Sawyer of Turnpike Row were
both confirmed as well, and both between the so-called Channel
Sea River (actually a drainage creek) and the equally narrow
Waterworks River – both within a few hundred yards of the Blind
King, Asher estimated – and had been accompanied by a smell.
'I think that was the worst of it, you know,' said the Widow
Farnum. 'Evil, that smell: fishy, and greasy, and ratty – not like
nothing I've smelled before . . .'

'*You've* smelled?'

She nodded with a grimace. 'Near the old boarded-up pub
out past the end of Carpenter's Road. He's lurkin' around
there, whoever he is – You can't get anybody here on the
street, nowadays, to walk out on the marsh at night. Even
them as works in the phosphate plant, they'll walk in groups
back home . . .'

In the late afternoon's harsh chill Asher walked out along
Carpenter's Road itself, where it petered out into the Stratford
Marsh, and hobbled as slowly as he dared along the railway
embankment as if following the Great Eastern line northwest to
the cluster of factories in Hackney Wick. *Always look as if
you've got good reason to be where you are* had been the first
thing he'd learned when working in the Department, and it was
a caution he'd never forgotten. And the Blind King – sitting
like a dropped brick in the midst of those brown wastes of clay

and grass, now thinly filmed with the first of spring green – was the choice of a professional. You couldn't get near it without being seen. But from the railway embankment, Asher identified the path leading to it which continued the roadbed of Carpenter's Road, and noted that the straggly assortment of sheds around the original pub seemed to have been put into some kind of order. They all had doors, and the grass around the walls of the pub itself looked beaten-down, as if there'd been activity there in the two weeks since Bert Mayo had been dragged away from the upstairs room on Brabazon Street.

Wind swept over the marshes, smelling of the estuary. A gull cried, rocking on black-tipped wings. Asher kept moving stolidly, leaning on his stick and prickling with the sensation of being watched – the awareness that the red-brick house wasn't empty. The feeling pursued him, all the long trudge back to Hackney, and on his bus ride home.

The negotiation with Colonel Stewart that evening was a long one, but Asher emerged from it at last with a temporary commission as Major, orders to report to General Finch in Flanders, an ambiguously-worded mandate to 'undertake such independent investigations as will further the war effort, at his own sole discretion', and a place on the Channel steamer *Eleanor* on the fifteenth. Stewart had wanted him to depart on Monday, but there remained the problem of the Blind King, and the thing that dwelt beneath it.

For that, Asher guessed, he was going to need Grippen's help.

He took a circuitous route back to Warwick Place, dropping out of the last bus on Holland Walk amid a beery crowd of pub-goers and walking through the deserted, blacked-out, misty streets to the mews that served all the houses on that block. Since that afternoon on Stratford Marsh he had been plagued with the uneasy sense that Mr Mackintosh had picked up his trail again, though he had never been able to form a clear proof that this was or wasn't so. It was probably this suspicion that saved him. As he counted doorways with his left hand he listened behind him and before him, mind sorting every drip and whisper of the night, and something made him turn even as a cosh cracked a terrific blow on his shoulder. The next second a man's weight slammed him to the pavement and he barely got his hand up in time to catch a garrote slipped around his neck. It cut into his fingers as his attacker dragged it tight, cutting off Asher's breath as he twisted to get some kind of purchase against his assailant.

The man was an expert, grinding him into the pavement with elbows and knees as the silk line tightened. His fingers under the noose distributed the strain but didn't alleviate the pressure; his ears were ringing and he was losing consciousness when he felt the man's grip slack suddenly, greater weight crushing him at the same moment he gasped, and heard a man's hoarse voice behind him curse.

Only half-conscious, he felt rather than heard light footfalls fleeing, and his second gasp filled his nostrils with the stink of old blood and dirty clothing as he heard Grippen snarl, 'Dogs spit your arse, whoreson!' The Master of London continued in that vein for some minutes, using terms that even Asher – a trained etymologist – had never heard, while Asher lay face-down on the wet bricks, trying to breathe through a bruised throat and wishing he had a notebook and pencil.

At length he felt Grippen's coat-skirt brush his hand and the vampire turned him roughly over. 'Live you?'

Asher started to reply, but could only cough, and the vampire dragged him to his feet.

''Twas the suck-arse clot that followed you to the park,' said Grippen. 'Hogs chew his lights— argh! Damn!'

Asher lit a match (*To hell with the blackout*) and saw, to his startled alarm, the whole side of Grippen's face was blistered, one eye welted almost shut and both blood and pus oozing from the skin. 'What the—?'

'The whoreson had silver – a chain of it wrapped round his fingers, or plated onto the back of a glove, devil burn him! Worms eat his—'

'He had it ready?' Asher offered him a clean handkerchief.

'He was too goddam occupied wi' skraggin' you, wasn't he, to go diggin' about for it in his pockets!'

'In other words,' said Asher, 'he knew he might be dealing with a vampire?'

Grippen was silent for a moment, daubing his injuries and thinking that over. Then he said, ''Od's cock.'

Asher said, 'Yes,' quite softly, with the sense of things coming together in his mind: glimpses, like the fleeting sense of a familiar outline half-seen from the corner of his eye, that slowly coalesced into a half-recognized form.

'Will you come with me?' he added after a moment. 'I've found the revenants – and something tells me they'll be moved elsewhere by tomorrow, and all this looking will have to start again. I think it's best we deal with them – and the man who's seeking them – tonight.'

The protesting squawk of chickens rattled in the misty night. A man cursed: Asher placed his vowels within ten miles of Cork.

Teague.

After a moment the faintest creak from the dark ahead of him spoke of a shed door opening. He hoped to Heaven that Grippen was listening behind them, around them, in the salt-smelling blackness for the squishy tread of feet, sniffing for the fishy, rat-piss foulness of their quarry. But like the vampire, he knew that the Others could, upon occasion, conceal their stink and their sound and their presence, until they were on top of their prey.

In a voice that living ears wouldn't have picked up, even had the listener stood – as Grippen stood now – shoulder-to-shoulder with him at the foot of the railway embankment, Asher breathed, 'How many in the house?'

And that bass rumble softer than a gnat's whine murmured back, 'Four above stairs. If the thing's in the cellar no man'll be down with him. I wouldn't be. I smell smoke an' beer.'

Enough thready moonlight pierced the mists to show Asher the vampire's turned head, and the distant, grimy mustard seed of lamplight leaked from the house's shutters caught a reflection in his half-shut eyes. Asher knew what he was doing.

Two years ago, in the spring of 1913, Grippen had stood thus in the alleyway behind Asher's own house on Holyrood Street in Oxford, and had put the household to sleep, so that he could walk in and steal Asher's child. Even retrieving Miranda, safe and unharmed, had not shaken Asher's resolve, taken at that time, that he would kill them: Grippen, Don

Simon, the London nest. Every soul of the cursed Undead who crossed his path.

And here he was at Grippen's side, watching him do the thing that the old vampires, the skilled vampires, the vampires who had absorbed thousands of lives over hundreds of years, could do.

He heard the man Teague, in the shed, mutter, 'Jaysus . . .' in a voice thick with sleep. Then long silence, broken, in time, by the soft, slithering bump of his body sliding to the floor from whatever bench or box he'd sat down on when drowsiness overcame him. The chickens continued to squawk frantically, desperately, and on the still air Asher caught the faintest whiff of blood.

Grippen said, 'He's all yours, Jimmy.' Taking Asher by the elbow, the vampire led him toward the shed, not to risk even the faintest flicker of lantern-light on the marsh until they were within the shed itself. As they approached it, Grippen rumbled, 'You given further thought to my offer?'

To become vampire.

To acquire just precisely those qualities that would be most useful to a spy: the mental power over other men's perceptions, the ability to turn their eyes aside, to cause them to think you looked like someone who belonged where they glimpsed you. In time, to bend their dreams so that they were sure they'd met you before and that you were trustworthy.

To become a thing of illusion and shadow, apart from the world and its pain.

Abilities and qualities he had worked for years to acquire. He had sought to perfect them in himself, having seen them in Pritchard Crowell. 'I've given it thought, yes.'

He edged up the slide on the lantern as they entered the shed, showing two chickens, tied by their feet at the back. Blood made dark splotches on their white feathers. To Undead senses, the smell would permeate the fog for miles. The beam of his light traced wires from their bound legs up the corners of the rear wall and across the rafters of the small loft that covered half the shed's width, to a mechanism that would drop a steel grille, like a portcullis, down over the door. He could see where coins had been welded onto the steel, enough silver to burn the hands of a vampire – or a revenant.

Beside an old milking stool at one side of the shed the man
Teague lay: Asher recognized him from the confused struggle in
Brabazon Street. A heavy pug chin and a broken nose, the tight,
nearly lipless mouth sagging open like a child's in stuporous
sleep.

Asher climbed to the loft and found rope there. Rope, and a
dozen long crates labeled Ludwig-Loewe, one of the largest arms
manufacturers in Berlin.

Grippen stood just outside the shed door, barely more than a
shadow. Asher guessed that if the grille had fallen and trapped
them both inside the rickety roof wouldn't have held out against
the vampire's strength. But wariness was the core of the vampire's
soul – they understood themselves to be both predator and prey.

He dragged Teague to one of the supports that held up the
loft, tied his hands together and then sat him up against the beam
and tied him to it, in such a way that he could cut him free, and
drag him from the shed, without loosing his bonds. He roped his
ankles together as well – the man didn't stir – then crossed to
the terrible shadow by the door. 'Anything?'

'Narh. But you don't always hear 'em. Or smell 'em, much
as they stink.'

Nerves prickling with watchfulness, Asher shut the lantern,
slung the remainder of the rope over his shoulder, and followed
Grippen to the shut-up pub itself. Unlike the Dolphin, the Blind
King had been purpose-built as a pub, with a large taproom facing
the road and kitchen, storeroom and private parlor behind. The
four men dead asleep in the parlor, with drinks before them on
the table and cigars smoldering in a cracked Queensware dish,
were those who'd helped drag poor Bert Mayo from his daughter's house on Brabazon Street – it had for years been part of
Asher's business to remember even faces glimpsed once and
under trying circumstances.

Even through the dusty fetor of a building shut up for decades,
and the heavy odor of cigar smoke, the smell of the revenant
stained the air. Asher found the cellar door in the kitchen,
re-enforced with makeshift metal, and triple-locked. His ear to
its panels, he could hear a kind of groaning bleat down below.

Not just 'a revenant', he thought. *Not just 'one of those things'*.
A man named Bert Mayo, whose daughter loved him enough to

take care of him and shelter him though what was happening to him terrified her.

Every one of the revenants started out human.

As did, he reminded himself, every one of the vampires.

Grippen came in and listened, too, then looked around the kitchen by the light of Asher's lantern, and grunted. 'Whoreson cullions.' He nodded toward the crates stacked around the walls, more long boxes of rifles, and smaller metal containers of ammunition, likewise bearing the mark of German manufacture. 'The Papists, is it, taking the chance of this greater war to rise up 'gainst the King?'

'It could actually be either side,' returned Asher quietly. 'Either those who seek to free Ireland from English domination, or those who don't want to be ruled by a Catholic majority. Who want Ireland to continue as a part of a greater Empire. And are willing to stamp out anything they consider rebellion.'

'I've no quarrel wi' killin' Papists.' Grippen's fangs glinted in the shadows, and he shrugged. 'Either way 'tis naught to me. But they're fools an' worse than fools if they think making revenants'll gain 'em anything. As well loose a cage full of wolves and tigers onto a battlefield. They'll kill your enemy, sure, but devour as many of your own in doin' it.'

'They think they have someone who can control them,' said Asher. 'For the sake of humanity I hope they're wrong. Does the name Francesca Gheric mean anything to you?'

'The White Lady?' The piggy dark eyes narrowed. 'What of her? A troublemaker in every city she's dwelt in, I hear tell, but when all's said she's proved no great threat to any.'

They passed through the taproom on their way out, the four men lying, bound hand and foot by Grippen, on the floor. 'When I give the word,' Asher added, 'get these men out of here. Is the revenant in the cellar chained?' He found he couldn't use Bert Mayo's name.

'Aye.'

He couldn't say, *Good*, either, knowing that a bullet wouldn't kill the thing that that poor old Irish fence had become. That the only way out for him – and for any future victim of his insane hunger – was through fire. Fire, or the burning corrosion of the sun.

All he could say was, 'Let's do what we have to do, then.'

EIGHTEEN

Teague was awake when Asher and Grippen returned to the shed. The chickens still chattered and clucked, though softer, resigning themselves – as animals do – stoically to their pain. The Irishman, Asher noticed, hadn't cried out, and it interested him that the man had enough on his conscience to keep him quiet even in a pitch-black shed on the Hackney Marshes with a revenant somewhere out in the darkness . . .

And the smell of fresh blood close by.

Asher unhooded the lantern. 'So is this something you're being paid for, or were you the ones taking delivery on that first package from France when it got away in London?'

Teague spit at him. Asher sidestepped the wad.

'We know about that French doctor trying to cook these things up for their army, and it doesn't really make a lot of difference whether it was the French who sent that poor Fritzy over here and he went astray, or whether one of your people lifted him from them, either on-site in France or on the way. What I need to know is, who are you working for, and do they – or do the French – have some way of controlling these things?'

'Sod you.'

'I see you mistake me for someone in the Department.' Asher slipped one of his knives from his boot, set the lantern down and slashed the buttons from Teague's shirt, then ripped the garment back over his shoulders. With precise care he cut a large, shallow X in the Irishman's chest, only deep enough to bleed. Copiously.

Teague's eyes flared in horror. 'Damn it, you can't . . .'

'I told you I'm not in the Department.' Asher wiped the blade on Teague's shirt and replaced it in his boot. 'Even if I were, I suspect you underestimate them. I think the smell of that'll carry more than those poor chickens.'

He stepped back, and watched his prisoner thrash in a violent effort to twist free of the ropes. The man didn't curse, as he would have, Asher thought, had he been less utterly terrified.

At length Asher said, 'That's not going to help you, and it is wasting your time. I think you know none of your men is in any state to help you and I think you know what's going to happen when that revenant gets here. Even if you do manage to break free and get away during its attack, I think you know what happens to those whose blood gets mixed with Fritzy's. So why don't you—'

He turned his head sharply as, from the door, Grippen said, 'It's out there.'

'You're lying—' Teague's voice was hoarse with shock. 'I been setting chickens out here three nights now—'

Asher retreated a step or two up the ladder to the loft, his eyes warily on the door.

'I don't know anythin'—'

'Too bad.'

'I swear it!'

Asher said nothing. He'd been perfectly prepared to have Grippen impersonate the revenant – the night was coal-sack dark and the vampire perfectly capable of imitating the random, bleating groans that had come from the cellar – but he knew this wasn't the case.

Damn it, he'd better not hold out . . .

He dropped from the ladder, walked to the door to listen, to breathe the damp air— *'Don't!'* Teague screamed, clearly thinking he was going to go through the door and keep on going.

Outside in the blackness Asher neither heard nor scented a thing. But the whole night seemed to whisper of it.

He turned back, his face a calm blank.

'They got one they say'll be able to command 'em—'

'Name?'

'I dunno. Some woman.'

'*Would* or *does* command them?'

'I dunno! She said *would be, will be . . .*'

'Who said?'

'Meagher. Oonah Meagher. Calls herself Tuathla. Let me out of here, for the Lord's sake—'

'I thought finding these things was the thing you most wanted in the world, Teague. Bringing them over to England, so they could walk about—'

'For the love of God, man, it's business! Meagher and her friends, they heard talk of a risin' against John Bull, while England's army's away in France an' half the Ulster volunteers with 'em! Meagher works over there for this Frenchie, says he's come up wi' a scheme to make soldiers out o' nuttin', men who'll walk straight into machine-gun fire an' won't care. I dunno the whole of it, they just hired me an' my boys to meet 'em on the Calais beach in a motor launch: two hard Armagh lads an' a Fritzy that just huddled under a blanket an' shivered. We put 'em up in a safe house in Brunswick Road an' that's where he broke out from . . .'

'Names of the friends?'

'For God's sake—!'

He could still smell nothing, hear nothing, but backed from the doorway toward the ladder. Grippen was nowhere to be seen, and Asher knew better than to think that the master vampire would tackle a revenant. Keeping his voice expressionless, he replied, 'No. For the sake of the men – and women – who won't be either killed by these things or transformed into them; who won't have to be killed like murrain cattle to keep this plague from spreading. For the sake of this country – of the world, if you will – if these things start roving at large. And for your own, of course.'

'Jimmy Darcie, Nan Sloan, Joey Strahan . . .' He almost babbled the names. 'Uh— Jerry Dwyer . . . Ned Mulready . . .'

'Any of them hurt when the thing broke out?'

'No! 'Twas down the cellar, an' broke a window. I'm to tell 'em when we catch it – then we heard it got Bert . . . Please, man, please, what d'you want me to say? If it's comin'—'

Asher heard – or thought he heard – the soft crunch of a step on the wet gravel outside, and his heart turned sick with shock. 'Any more of them come over, or just the one?'

'Just the one – dear God—!'

'Who else is in on this?'

'Nobody— Just us! Meagher, an' Joey—'

'Safe house, bunch of hard lads,' mused Asher. 'That's a lot of money invested, for just a couple of rebels.'

'Nobody else knows!' Teague screamed the words. 'Not a livin' soul, I swear it—'

Asher tested the ladder that led up into the loft, made sure that it wasn't attached and could be pushed down easily. He pulled the knife from his boot again and mounted a step or two, to check whether the cord that would release the trap on the shed door could be easily cut. It could. He mounted another step and Teague shrieked, 'Butler, a chap named Butler! He paid for it all! Sets up deliveries of the guns wi' the Germans! We told 'em we had a way to get fighters is all! He gave Jimmy Darcie a hundred pounds and paid us besides! I swear that's all! I swear it!'

Asher sprang down from the ladder, bent to cut the cord that held Teague to the beam, and in that instant was surrounded by the stink of the revenant: blood, rats, urine, filth. He swung around, aghast to see that it was inside the shed with them, coming at them in the dim glow of the dark lantern, *How could I not have seen it? Not have heard it . . .?*

With a hideous crash the steel-and-silver grille dropped over the shed door, but the revenant didn't slow its rush by a second. Asher made to dive to cut the rope on Teague's feet, but like a nightmare darkness surrounded him, and he had a vague awareness of being dragged literally off his feet. The next second, it seemed, he fell with a crash on the plank flooring of the loft and by the lamplight reflected from below saw Grippen hurl the ladder down into the shed beneath them.

Teague screamed.

'You've more bollocks than brains,' snapped Grippen, and ripped open the lid of one of the crates. 'Could have got yoursel' killed, an' who knows how many of these godless things yet to deal with.' As Asher had guessed, the crate was full of rifles, brand new and still thick with factory grease. The vampire pulled one out and used it to smash a hole in the flimsy wood of the roof between the rafters. 'Don't bother,' he added, as Asher moved toward the edge of the loft. 'The man's dead.'

Teague was still screaming, but Asher knew what the vampire meant.

Grippen sprang lightly up to the hole and pulled himself through it, reached down – brutal, strong hands in their black gloves – to draw Asher up after him, then slid down the roof to the edge and dropped off, a bare eight feet to the ground. Asher followed, and walked with him to the boarded-up pub, where, more by touch than anything else – for no gas was laid on in the building and Asher guessed, now, that it would be deadly dangerous to light a lamp – they dragged Teague's compatriots out and into one of the other sheds.

'There's paraffin in the kitchen,' said Asher.

'Stay here, then,' growled the vampire. 'I'll make sure the place is good an' doused – an' you look like hell.' He shoved Asher down onto something – it felt like a barrel – in the smaller shed, and turned back, a dim shape of black in the blackness, toward the pub.

Realizing that he was, in fact, almost too tired to stand, Asher caught the dirty wool sleeve of his coat. 'Did you ever hear that thing coming?'

'Nary a peep.'

'Did you hear anyone else? See anyone?'

The vampire turned back, stood over him, a dark presence more sensed than seen. 'There's someone out there, aye,' he said. 'One of these Irish or one of your lot, I don't know. Followin' old Hungry Tom in there—' he jerked his head toward the larger shed – 'I'm guessin'.'

'The Department knew one of their subjects had been taken,' said Asher wearily. 'They had a man looking out for him, the moment he landed in England. Trying to trace him – and trying to keep those who'd stolen him from recapturing him before they did.' He rubbed his throat, where the bruises of the garrote still smarted. 'By whatever means they could.'

The matter is in hand, Langham had smiled . . .

And somebody in Germany was doubtless saying the same thing to his superiors, and basking in anticipation of promotion.

He added, 'Thank you. That's twice tonight you've saved my life.'

'Huh.' The vampire set his hands on his hips. 'I ain't given up hope you'll come round to my way of thinkin', Asher. I need a man like you. And you're a natural for it. But I warn you now. I'll kill you mesel', ere I let that Papist whoreson Ysidro make you a fledgling of his.'

*   *   *

Grippen scattered paraffin over both the Blind King and the shed where the first revenant – Hungry Tom, Tom the Ogre, some poor nameless German soldier picked at random from among prisoners in a war he might never have wanted to have anything to do with – gouged and tore at Teague's body. Then Asher and the Master of London sat down to wait until it was almost sun-up, Asher to make sure that neither revenant would escape the flame into night's darkness, Grippen listening for 'our little pal' in the darkness, though Asher was, by this time, fairly certain of who it was out there. Certain, and a little disgusted with himself for not having guessed it sooner.

Shortly before the first whispers of daylight, Asher became aware that Grippen had gone, and tossed burning screws of paraffin-soaked newspaper through the broken windows of the pub, and the hole in the roof of the shed. Then he went back into the smaller shed, to inform Teague's henchmen that the police would be on their way. With the first stains of light, he discovered that the smaller shed also contained boxes of German rifles.

And that it now contained only two bound Irishmen, when he knew that there had been four, asleep around the table in the pub.

Grippen had brought them out to the shed in darkness.

Grippen, who'd had a severe burn from the silver wielded by Asher's attacker earlier in the night; a burn that vampires had only one way of healing.

He closed his eyes. Yes, the men had been smuggling guns from Germany to Ireland, a hanging offense in time of war. And yes, they'd been part of a plan for even greater horror: greater still, had the plan progressed to the point where Germans could get involved. And yes, they'd have killed him two weeks ago if he hadn't gone through that window and gotten away.

But they'd been prisoners. And bound.

And the house would burn over their bloodless bodies and no one – not the police, not Osric Millward and his hunters – would know how they died.

And Grippen wants me to become part of that world. Because I'd be a useful fledgling. A good vampire.

He walked away from the burning buildings, back toward the

railway embankment. With the destruction of the two revenants he was fairly certain that he was now safe from further attack – Langham certainly wouldn't care about the fates of a couple of Irish rebels – but frizzling in any case with the sense of being watched as he went.

But if I'm right about who it is who's been watching me—

The thought snagged at his mind as he started the long trudge across the Marshes toward St Paul's Road, where the busses would begin running for the city.

—why doesn't Grippen try to recruit HIM?

NINETEEN

'**M**y dear Madame Asher!' Lamplight bobbed on the stone of the walls. On the other side of the archway – filled in with bars which gleamed with tarnishing silver plate – the revenants muttered and jerked at their chains, their eyes catching the light. Lydia's cell had been, she guessed, a burial chapel built off the long catacomb that had been adapted for the revenants. One archway – the one barred with silver – opened into it. Another, also barred, led back into the main round chapel that served as a storeroom.

When the Lady Francesca had dragged her back up out of the tunnel to the well and had thrown her in here, she'd left the cover off the tunnel. In the ten or fifteen minutes that Lydia had been in the cell, with only one of her pocket candles for light, she'd seen half a dozen rats emerge, either from the tunnel, or from the hall which led to Lemoine's laboratory, and trot straight into the catacomb where the revenants were chained.

There they were torn to pieces, and devoured raw.

So thirteen revenants constitutes a community large enough to have a hive-mind capable of controlling rats.

Lydia was fascinated, despite her horror of the rats and her fear that the next person who entered the storeroom would throw her into the catacomb as well.

I am wearing silver but how long would I be able to stay

awake even if three chains' worth is enough to get them to back off?

Palfrey, bleeding to death back in the tunnel . . .

Unless Francesca went back and finished him?

Poor Palfrey—

Colonel Dr Jules Lemoine strode into the chapel, his left arm in a sling (Palfrey's aim, Lydia now saw, left a great deal to be desired), pale in the light of the lantern he carried in his good hand. This he set down, and drew a key from his pocket.

'What are you doing?' Nurse Meagher appeared from the shadowy hallway at his heels. 'You can't mean to let her out, sir! She tried to kill you!'

'Nonsense.' Lemoine held up Lydia's Webley. 'This weapon hasn't been fired. It was her companion – like her,' he added gravely, 'under the delusion that the vampire we took was their friend.'

'She is the pale vampire's *mignonne*.' Lydia didn't see her enter, but Francesca Gheric now stood beside the chapel door.

Seen closer, and in the lantern-light that was marginally better than the shreddy moonlight of no man's land, she was indeed beautiful. But maybe that was only a vampire's illusion. Like Meagher, she was dressed as a nurse – *In case any of the guards sees her?*

Any Matron on the Front would tell her to put her hair up . . .

Facing the three of them, with the revenants stirring and growling on the far side of the silver bars, Lydia had to struggle to keep her breathing steady.

She clutched at the bars of the smaller archway that separated her from Lemoine, made her expression as earnest as if she were trying to convince her Nanna that she'd only been seeking a book of sermons in her father's library, and cried, 'He is indeed my friend, sir! He has long ago given up preying upon humankind, and has pledged his loyalty to the British crown!' *Which I'm sure was precisely what he told poor Palfrey . . .*

The colonel's gaze melted from sternness to pity. 'Madame, Madame, do you truly believe that?' and Lydia let her eyes fill with tears.

'Who told you about the passageway that you used?' Meagher walked up to the bars, planted herself at Lemoine's side.

'Colonel Simon.' Lydia took off her spectacles, wiped her eyes and tried to sound as if she were struggling against the inner suspicion that she had indeed been betrayed. 'He said the fate of Britain depends on his mission here—'

Meagher rolled her eyes impatiently. 'Of course that's what he told her! And probably his driver as well.'

Lydia reached timidly to clutch Lemoine's sleeve, and threw a glance of terror toward the darkness beyond the silver barrier. 'Colonel, what *are* those . . . those *things*? Captain Palfrey wouldn't tell me anything, only said things like, "Dark forces are at work . . ."'

'Why did he bring you?' demanded Meagher.

'He said he might need a second person to drive the motorcar, if he were injured.' She sobbed, and bit her lip in what she hoped was a touching display of wan and ignorant courage. 'I wanted to help—'

'It's all right.' Lemoine put a strong hand over hers. 'You've gotten mixed up in things that are no business of yours, Madame. Deeply secret things. And you *can* help.'

Meagher's blue eyes flared wide and she grabbed the edge of Lemoine's sling, dragged him from the bars to the far side of the little storeroom chapel. Francesca watched them for a moment with cynical cerulean eyes. *Probably telling him he can't trust me and that Don Simon's going to read my mind first thing, if they let me go . . .*

Then the vampire turned her mocking gaze back to Lydia.

Lydia hastily looked away, and fumbled in her pocket for a handkerchief. But she felt the tug on her mind of cold power, power from outside herself. James had told her that picturing a door shutting, or a blank brick wall, worked, but she remembered also that both Antonio and the Master of Prague had described Francesca Gheric as overwhelmingly powerful – *Can she see through that brick wall?*

What will she see if she does?

And will thinking of it tip her off that I'm not as ignorant as I pretend?

Lydia called up images to her mind of what it would feel like to be swept into Simon's arms, passionately kissed (*What about those teeth? Never mind . . .*), overwhelmed by a torrent of ecstasy

(*Was that Mr Stoker who'd said that? Or Mrs Radcliffe in* Romance of the Forest*? Or was that someone else . . .?*). Hoping for the best, she yielded meekly to that terrible cold grip on her will, and raised her eyes timidly to the vampire's. (*And I hope this works . . .*)

(*Oh, wait, if I were passionately in love with Don Simon why would I be wearing all this silver . . .?*)

Francesca's lip curled again at whatever she saw in Lydia's thoughts, and she put her hand through the bars to pat her cheek, patronizing as a duchess handing a farthing to an orphan while her friends are watching.

Lemoine jerked from his conversation with Meagher and reached the bars in a stride. 'You will not touch her!'

Francesca raised her brows – *YOU'RE saying this to ME?* – and the physician hurriedly collected himself.

'It's clear she's only this Colonel Simon's dupe,' he amended. 'She has nothing to do with either the Germans or the British government, or my own.' He turned back to Lydia. 'I'm very sorry, Madame,' he said, 'but you're going to have to stay here for a time. And I'm afraid you'll have to remain underground—'

Drat it, Simon won't be able to speak with me in my dreams—

'—since the men on guard in the compound know only as much as they need to know, to accomplish their duties.'

'I wouldn't say a word to anyone.' Lydia gazed up at him with brimming eyes. 'It's just that—' She glanced at the revenants in their long, niche-lined cell. 'Those things . . . And . . . And the rats—'

'The rats won't bother you.' Lemoine thought hard for a moment. 'I'll have you moved as soon as a place can be readied for you. You have nothing to fear, Madame. Our work here – our work with these . . . these men—' He nodded toward the cata-comb – 'is nearing its conclusion. In a day or two I may ask you to help us—'

Meagher's nostrils flared, like a horse about to kick.

'We need trained personnel, and I can promise you, Madame Asher, that whatever this Colonel Simon told you, the work we're doing here will indeed make the difference between victory over the Germans, and defeat.'

Behind her, Lydia heard one of the revenants speak, in a dazed mumble yet completely comprehensible: '*Wo bin ich? Welcher Ort ist das?*'

Where am I? What is this place?

Her heart clenched in rage and grief, *Dear God . . .*

'*He could have escaped,*' Rhinehardt had said of his cousin. '*Fled when the remainder of our unit did . . . but he would not let go of my hand . . .*'

Without waiting to hear what Lemoine had to say next, or plan her own strategy, she pulled away from him, stumbled to the farthest corner of the cell, curled up on the floor and wept as if her heart would break.

Lemoine put her in a storeroom off the laboratory, formerly the cell of some anchoress, Lydia assumed, since it had a judas window in the door. The bars of that little window had been wrapped in silver wire, and a hasp and padlock hastily screwed onto the door. Both, Lydia saw, were plated with silver.

'I am truly sorry for the crude amenities, Madame,' said Lemoine as he led her in, past boxes of laboratory glassware and light bulbs, spools of wire and packets of silver chain now stacked up in the hall. 'Please understand that my hesitation to release you stems from the desperate importance of what we do here.'

There was a cot in the cell, an empty box for a table, a tin pitcher of water and a chamber pot behind a screen. When he'd locked her in and crossed the lab, Lydia heard Meagher say, 'That's all very well, Colonel, but the fact remains that thanks to that girl, we've lost the vampire. God only knows how long it'll be before we trap another! That puts our work back two days, three days, maybe a week—'

What Lemoine replied Lydia didn't hear, but after his footsteps had died away down the hall, Francesca's voice said, very softly, 'Don't trouble yourself, my sugarplum. He'll come back for her.'

It was a long time before Lydia could sleep. The electric bulb burned permanently in the laboratory: dragging the lightweight screen from the chamber pot to cover the judas in the door only dimmed the glare. For many hours (specifically, from 3:10 until 6:25 by her watch) she could think of little but poor Captain

Palfrey, lying in the tunnel on the lip of the well in the darkness: deluded, dying, dreaming perhaps of Don Simon's lies about aiding King and country. *I'll have to write to Aemilia Bellingham*, she thought at one point . . . *But say what? That he was chosen because he was stupid, and died because he tried to do his duty to a hoax?*

And what makes me think I'll live to see daylight again?

She wondered if Francesca had gone back through the tunnel to finish him, before Don Simon could return.

She wondered if the man who'd cried out in German – whether it was Gleb Rhinehardt or some other poor soldier – had done so because he actually had some dying flicker of his own mind left, or whether it had been merely a spasmodic firing of the nerves in the brain, the equivalent of the galvanic twitching of a frog's severed legs in the laboratory.

She wondered if Tuathla Meagher was planning to kill her the moment Lemoine's back was turned, and what would happen to her if Lemoine's gunshot wound – which seemed to be in his shoulder – turned septic.

Not as long as Francesca thinks she can lure Don Simon back here, using me as bait.

Cold comfort.

One thing Dr Lemoine was right about was that there were no rats. Presumably all were lured into the catacomb of the revenants – a frightful thought, considering how many rats swarmed every shell-crater and trench in no man's land.

'As you've seen, they're not mistreated in the least,' Lemoine told her, when he returned later in the day (10:15, by Lydia's watch) with a tin mess kit top holding a quarter-cup of bully beef, two rock-hard biscuits and a sloshy quantity of Maconochie, the ubiquitous tinned stew of the field kitchens. 'Nor are the other German subjects we're still keeping above ground. Those who have been—' he seemed to hesitate over a euphemism for *infected* '—*converted* are fed quite well, but half of them refuse real food and kill and eat rats instead.' (Lydia felt inclined to take issue at his definition of Maconochie as 'real food', but didn't.) He had locked the door of the laboratory behind him, and opened that of Lydia's cell, to allow her to eat at one of the laboratory tables. He had gained some of his color back, and the slight difference of his tone told her he'd injected a little morphia for the pain.

'They're only kept chained because I'm afraid they'll attack one another.'

'But what *are* they?' asked Lydia again, guessing that such a question – whose answer she already knew – would not only add to the impression of ignorant harmlessness she was trying to give, but tell her how many people above Lemoine in the French Army and government were in on the secret.

??? home side screening, Jamie had written.

So at least someone in the British government might know of this hideous scheme as well.

And probably – like Colonel Lemoine – thought it was going to be perfectly safe.

And that it was perfectly acceptable to mind-strip, enslave and kill German soldiers for the purpose. They had, after all, asked for it.

She widened her eyes and kept her mouth shut. Men, she had learned back in her days as a debutante, loved to explain things to women. And Lemoine especially wanted to make sure she understood how right he – and the French Army – was in undertaking this terrible project.

'Hundreds of thousands of men have died.' Lemoine leaned across the corner of the table, the tea he had made for them both on a Bunsen burner forgotten before him. He hadn't taken enough morphia to be dopey, but the impression Lydia had was of a man after two glasses of wine.

'Hundreds of thousands more are dying daily in a bloody stalemate that cannot be broken. Already France struggles to fill its ranks. You've seen the colonials, the native troops of Algeria and Senegal and Indochina, fighting white men whom they should be taught to respect. You've seen them in Paris, learning to treat white women as they treat the whores of their own countries. And they have not the courage, the *élan*, of the white race! The men of France – yes, and of Britain, too! – bleed away their lives in the mud, and what kind of world will we win, if this goes on? What sort of world can we bequeath to our children? There must be some other solution.'

Lydia nodded, with an expression of shaken horror. 'But where

does the Lady Francesca come into this?' she asked timidly. 'And
what were you going to do with . . . with Colonel Simon? He
said you were going to kill him . . .'

Gravely, Lemoine asked, 'You know what Colonel Simon is,
do you not, Madame?'

She turned her eyes away as if distressed, and rotated her tin
cup of now-cold tea in her hands. 'He – I – It isn't how it is in
all those silly books,' she stammered. 'He told me that . . . that
people like him . . . They only need to drink a little bit of blood
to survive. Just a sip . . . mostly those they . . . they *take from*
aren't even aware of it . . .'

She had no idea whether this was something Francesca had
told Lemoine, and if it was, whether Lemoine had believed it or
wanted to believe. But he looked troubled, and nodded. 'But the
fact remains that many of the Undead do in fact kill their victims,'
he replied gently. 'I have made a study of them for some years,
Madame. At first – like yourself, I daresay – I was unwilling
even to believe in their existence. Later, as I studied them further,
I came to realize that these revenants, these Half-Dead, are, as
it were, cousins of the true vampire, and that like the vampire
they have a psychic – a mental – component of their state.'

Lydia nodded. 'I know that Colonel Simon can . . . can
communicate with me in my dreams.'

'Even so, Madame.' Lemoine would have grasped her hands,
she thought, in his eagerness that she should believe and agree,
had she not been married. 'I believe – and I shall very shortly
accomplish it, I hope – that vampires can learn to control the
minds of these revenants.'

Lydia forcibly stopped herself from protesting *Not according
to the Master of Prague, they can't*, and only exclaimed, 'Oh,
my goodness, how?'

'By absorbing the mind – the life – the soul – of one of the
revenants, before his mind entirely dissolves into the group-mind
of their kind. Once she – the Lady Francesca – can control the
mind of one of them, she can participate in, and guide, as it
were, the whole of the group.'

'And she's agreed to do this?' Lydia hoped she sounded
wondering rather than totally disbelieving, or completely aghast.
'Isn't it terribly dangerous?'

'Not if there is no blood exchanged. The disease – the state
of the revenants – is in the blood,' the Frenchman assured her.
'The control is in the mind.'

'And she'll do this for you?' Lydia gave an exaggerated shiver.
'She seems so . . . so *sinister* . . .'

'She will do this,' agreed Lemoine. 'For a consideration.'

TWENTY

B y Lydia's later estimate, it was two days before the next
stage of the 'project', as Lemoine called it, could be
undertaken. Both Meagher and Lemoine saw her daily,
Meagher tense – *screwed*, as Lady Macbeth would have it, *to
the sticking-place* with frustration and dread that something would
go wrong – Lemoine dreading likewise but quiet and calm. Lydia
saw no one else, and gathered by degrees that, as Lemoine had
said, none of the fifteen guards aboveground knew what the
project was nor why a dozen or so German prisoners were being
kept in the upper area of the compound . . . nor what had happened
to the further dozen who had disappeared into the catacomb.

In the face of Meagher's sharp-tongued impatience, Lemoine
increasingly turned to Lydia, vastly to the Irish nurse's irritation.
Lydia bit her tongue and pretended that she was her Aunt Faith –
book-learned intelligent but absolutely uncritical and accepting
– and by nodding and unconditionally agreeing with whatever
the Colonel said, gathered that no one in the French High
Command knew the exact nature of the means by which the
hemato-bacteriologist (for such was Lemoine's area of study)
proposed to 'convert' German prisoners of war to men who would
fight for France. 'Most of them assume I'm using a combination
of drugs and hypnosis,' he confided, one afternoon while Lydia
was helping him sweep the laboratory. 'I cannot reveal the true
nature of my work until I have something to show for it – until
the Lady Francesca is actually able to demonstrate her control
over the revenants. The British government paid for much of this.'
He gestured around him with his good arm at the whitewashed

crypt, with its line of electric bulbs hanging from the ceiling and the grinning, horrible apparatus of the burning-grille to which Don Simon had been lashed.

Lydia plied her broom and looked fascinated.

'I understand they've been putting pressure on Commander Joffre for information,' Lemoine went on. 'I am curious as to how much our High Command will disclose, even as we prepare to mobilize our new weapon. It is one reason for my concern about this Colonel Simon of yours, provided he was telling you even a little of the truth: the British do not even yet appreciate how desperate things are here in France.'

'Is that why you're keeping me here?' Lydia paused in sweeping, and straightened up. Lemoine was always careful to keep the door of the laboratory locked, and even with his injured shoulder she wasn't at all certain she'd be able to overpower him and take the key. And if she did, if she'd be able to find her way out. But in the meantime her body craved exercise, and she swept and washed tables and – with the hot water Lemoine brought her – washed her own chemise and linen when he, rather shyly, presented her with a second set, almost certainly borrowed from the grudging Meagher. Anything to keep moving.

'It isn't that I mistrust your intentions,' the Colonel assured her. 'But Nurse Meagher is right. At this point we cannot afford even the smallest whisper of rumor regarding what we do here.'

In addition to food and hot water, in those two days Colonel Lemoine brought her reading material: issues of the *Lancet*, containing his own articles on disorders of the blood and their effect on the brain and other tissues, volumes of several Russian occult publications which contained his articles on the nature of vampires, the Ossian Poems (Meagher's – her name was in the front cover), Yeats's *Fairy and Folk Tales of the Irish Peasantry* (from the same source) and four numbers of the *Irish Literary Review*. Between reading all of these works cover to cover, Lydia paced her cell, back and forth, aching with inaction, and when she slept, her dreams were broken and troubled.

Once, waking, she saw Francesca looking in through the judas at her, a speculative smile in her heaven-blue eyes. And once, jerked from sleep by some noise in the laboratory outside, she went to the judas and saw two revenants there, slimed and filthy and smelling of sewage and rats. The laboratory door stood open. By the stillness outside, it was clearly deep in the night.

Some of them have got away, and are hiding in the crypts.

Lydia withdrew to the farthest corner of her cell, almost ill with terror. They came to the door of her cell but drew back in pain from the silver lock. The incident expanded, horribly, the possibilities of what might have become of Captain Palfrey in the tunnel. *Dear God, poor Palfrey . . .*

If something went wrong – if Lemoine and all his men were arrested or killed or pulled out of their barbed-wire fortress of Cuvé Sainte-Bride – would the revenants in the catacomb break free in hunger and find some way of tearing through the door? The thought returned to her in nightmares.

Escape – if and when the opportunity presented itself – would be horribly dangerous, and the chances that Don Simon would come back for her – if he had managed to get away at all – dwindled to almost nothing.

When she told Lemoine of the revenants' incursion the next day he looked shocked and troubled – though the outer door actually hadn't been locked properly – and asked her several times if it might not have been a dream. 'Because we've been very thoroughly over the crypts below the convent, right down to the foundation vaults, and haven't found any evidence whatsoever that any of them have gotten away . . .'

Lydia knew it hadn't been a dream.

She felt safer sleeping during the day, and that evening was just finishing cleaning the laboratory after supper and tea with Lemoine, when the lab door rattled on its hinges, and Meagher's face appeared in the judas window that led to the corridor. 'Colonel!' she shouted, her voice jubilant, 'Colonel, we've got him! Lock that bitch up, Colonel, and open the door—'

Lydia lunged for the door and Lemoine caught her arm. She whispered, 'Simon—' as Meagher called out again, triumphant,

'Francesca got him! Get the gridiron ready—'

Lydia tried to pull free of his grip but as she'd guessed, even one-handed, Lemoine was strong. 'I'm sorry, Madame – but you do understand that he was deceiving you? He was deceiving you all along—' he insisted, as he pulled her, as gently as he could, to the door of her storeroom, thrust her inside and slammed it.

If I call out his name I'll give myself away . . .

She threw herself against the door, face pressed to the silver bars of the judas, as Lemoine unlocked the door of the laboratory and both Meagher and Francesca entered, their prisoner borne slung over Francesca's shoulder.

Lemoine gasped, 'Good God! What did you do to him?'

'Broke every bone in his body,' returned the vampire calmly, and flung her prisoner down on the grille above the gas cylinders. 'This time there'll be no running away.'

The captive vampire sobbed in agony as Meagher and Francesca dragged his limbs straight, and screamed as they buckled the straps over his arms, his ankles, his forehead. When Francesca stepped aside, Lydia saw that the man's hair was black, not white.

It wasn't Don Simon.

It was the beautiful Basilio.

She rapidly calculated the number of people that the handsome vampire must have killed – between thirty and sixty thousand, not counting the dying whose lives he had devoured since the start of the war – but it didn't make what she watched less horrible. Francesca bent over him, held the left hand that was fastened away from his body, at a ninety-degree angle to his side, gripped his chin in her other hand, forcing his eyes to meet hers. Basilio began to sob, '*Prego, prego, per favore—*' and Francesca smiled, and kissed his mouth, like a lover, murmuring in whatever Renaissance form of Latin or Italian that both had learned, centuries ago. On the other side of the grille, Lemoine stepped close, and cut Basilio's throat with a scalpel, catching the blood – which oozed slowly rather than spurted, Lydia observed (*of course it would, if his heart doesn't beat*) – in a glass laboratory jar.

He had no pity on any of his own victims . . .

Her eyes still locked on Basilio's, Francesca stepped back, gripping his hand, and with her free hand signed to Meagher. Lemoine turned a switch and the roar of jerry-built fans in the old air-passages filled the room.

Basilio screamed, 'Antonio!' as flame engulfed him.

Francesca's head snapped back, her face convulsed with ecstasy. Greasy black smoke rolled up under the low vaults of the crypt, but the fans could make little headway against the hideous stench.

Basilio screamed for ten minutes and thirty-five seconds (Lydia timed him). It was another eight minutes before Francesca released his hand – still jutting from the flame and still, as far as Lydia could see, attached to the bone of the arm – and stepped back. Her eyes were shut, her face transformed, like Bernini's statue of St Teresa in the Vatican. Across the flame that still swathed the blackening corpse (*If it IS a corpse – how long WOULD it take a vampire to die in flame?*), Meagher and Lemoine watched the White Lady with shocked and fascinated eyes.

Then – and this interested Lydia almost more than all the rest – she saw both colonel and nurse lose the focus of their gaze, and stand as if in trance as Francesca walked to the door and left. She knew this was what vampires did – put people in that half-dreaming state of inattention, so they couldn't see the vampire move – but it was the first time she'd seen it done, Francesca obviously having forgotten that Lydia was present on the other side of the storeroom door.

I'll have to write all this down for Jamie.

Under the grille the gas cylinders still spouted flame, the vampire's singularly tough tissues slowly dissolving into ash. Smoke choked the whole of the room, as if the underground chamber were in fact Hell. Lydia realized she was trembling.

If I get out of this alive . . .

The train from Calais to St-Omer was vile. Even the corridors were crowded with men coming off their leave or shipping in from their training, tense, harried, half-drunk or dog-tired, and all of them, it seemed to Asher – in a first-class compartment with a dozen officers – smoking like chimneys. He'd acquired the uniform of a major in the Second Army as a matter of convenience – everyone would look askance at civilian mufti – and dozed most of the way, wrapped in his army greatcoat. But his dreams were troubled.

He had, after all, taken passage yesterday, as Stewart had originally wished. He'd turned in the names of the Irish Brotherhood clique who had been in on the revenant scheme, and that of Butler, the German agent who'd bankrolled them;

had wired both Josetta and Millward to watch for further sign of new revenants. So far as he could tell, British participation in Lemoine's project was financial – at a guess the French Army hadn't told them where they were getting their 'special troops' and possibly didn't know themselves. But with a man like Langham sniffing for a way to take over the project 'for the good of the Empire' – and given the agent he was using – that situation could alter in less than a day to something far more deadly.

How many times, Asher wondered wearily, had he heard men say, 'It's perfectly safe,' or, 'It's actually much safer than it looks,' preparatory to destroying themselves and everyone around them? Including the idiots who'd gotten Britain mixed up in the war to begin with. *It's perfectly safe*, in Asher's mind, ranked right up there with *I don't really see what else we can do*, and *It will all be over by Christmas*.

His own experience of serving the Queen had been that most things were a great deal more dangerous than people wanted to think – or say – they were, and that anything could go wrong.

Even in twilight, the streets of the medieval town of St-Omer teemed with men in uniform. VAD nurses in blue and white brushed shoulders with British khaki, French blue, men in the darker 'hospital blues'. Horse-drawn ambulance wagons and drays of supplies rattled from the train station: tinned beef, crates of biscuits, box after box of ammunition, rumbling field guns. Asher had the horrible sensation of seeing goods going in at one end of some nightmare factory – men, food, weapons – and coming out at the other, discreetly bundled in bandages and dribbling blood. Did vampires haunt the railway station, he wondered, silent in the shadows behind the volunteers who brought hot tea to the men on stretchers being loaded for Calais?

Or are they all at the Front?

At Divisional HQ Asher presented his papers, pointed out the 'at his sole discretion' and 'please render all and any assistance requested' clauses to a harassed clerk and then to an equally exhausted colonel. The colonel ran a jaundiced eye over the letter and said drily, 'You're another one of them, then, are you?' and Asher raised his brows.

'Has he come through, then?' he asked. 'I heard he would.'

The colonel's mustache bristled irritably and he rubbed a tired hand over his eyes. 'Don't ask me. Didn't see him – didn't read his papers – don't know a thing about him . . .'

'Small chap?' Asher put a note of sympathy into his voice. 'Silver hair, though of course he may have dyed it . . . beaky nose. Face like a raisin and a voice you can't hear across the room. Hands like a schoolgirl.'

The officer's grimace answered his question and Asher thought, *He always did get across men in authority . . .*

And he wondered at himself that he wasn't surprised to have his suspicion confirmed.

'And I suppose,' Asher went on, 'he bagged the best of the motorcars in the pool, didn't he? Always does.'

'Not my business.' The colonel sniffed. 'Good as told me so. And where'll you be off to, with your precious "at his own discretion"? I suppose you'll want it first thing in the morning? And a driver?'

'If you'd be so kind.' Asher inclined his head, and took the requisition the colonel shoved at him across his desk. 'I'll be going to Pont-Sainte-Félicité.'

Because of the weight of the earth that surrounded the crypts of Cuvé Sainte-Bride, Lydia guessed that whatever psychic outcry had poured from Basilio's mind at his death had gone no further than the stone walls of the laboratory.

The following night they took Antonio Pentangeli as well.

TWENTY-ONE

'**B**e careful out there.' Captain Niles Calvert touched Asher's sleeve, staying him in the doorway of the wooden hut designated 'officer's mess'. 'Jerry's getting ready for something – you've been hearing that since you landed at Calais, haven't you? But every wire-cutting party, every listening post, up and down the line as far as Langemarck, reports the same thing: fresh troops coming up, supplies laid in, artillery moving about behind their lines.' He glanced out past the dim glow of lantern-light through tent-canvas, the glimmer of illumination leaked between cracks in the rough board shanties that had been built over Pont-Sainte-Félicité's shattered foundations. A machine gun chattered – a German MG-04, by the sound – for the sixth time in an hour, and the rumble of the guns vibrated the ground under Asher's boots. 'Can't tell when they're going to hit.'

'I'll be careful.'

The surgeon's eyes narrowed as he studied Asher's face, as if he'd have preferred a reply more along the lines of, *Heavens, perhaps I'd better stay indoors . . .*

'Mrs Asher goes out like that as well – as I'm sure you know. And she won't be told either. It always worries me sick,' he added, 'even before . . .' He hesitated, then lowered his voice. 'I don't ask you to tell tales out of school, but . . . I take it you're from Headquarters?'

'I passed through Headquarters, yes.'

Like the colonel in St-Omer, this foxlike little surgeon clearly had his own opinions about people who moved about the battle zone with things like 'at his sole discretion' and 'please render all and any assistance requested' written on their papers. His mouth twisted a little and he drew a last breath of smoke from his cigarette – the air in the mess behind them was blue with it.

'You didn't happen to hear anything about these . . . these whatever-they-are. Madmen—' His red-gold brows dived down over the bridge of his nose. 'Only they're not . . .'

'Not mad?' Asher felt cold to the marrow of his bones.

Calvert's voice was a whisper. 'Not men. Not mankind, though they seem male enough. You haven't heard tell of 'em?'

'Tell me.'

For a moment Asher was afraid Calvert would balk. It was clear from his eyes that he read absolutely no surprise in Asher's face, and was angry at it, and no wonder.

Then he said, 'Night before last a lone Jerry attacked a listening post near Loos. Didn't even seem to feel the barbed wire. They shot him, but he wouldn't die, they said. Just hung there in the wire sort of bleating at them like a dying goat, and the smell of him – *it* – was something fearful, they said, something the like of which they'd never smelled, and after six months in this section, believe me, Major, that's something. They doused their lantern and didn't dare put their heads up for fear of his *kamer-aden*, but two of them – good men, I know them, and not easily funked – swear his face was more like an ape's, or a dog's, than a man's. By daylight he was gone. There was blood all over the wires, and over the ground. Their bullets had hit him, all right.'

Calvert shook his head. 'Then yesterday Trent, the head of the stretcher-bearers, came to me saying they'd been attacked out in no man's land, just before dawn. They go out then, if there's been a dust-up; less chance of Jerry potting at them. They had a hooded lantern with them. Trent said—'

He winced, and seemed to back himself up on his tracks: 'Trent's a good man. Conchy, and steady as a rock. Trent said they'd found a . . . they'd found a dead Tommy in a shell-hole, and with him what he first thought was a dead Jerry, crumpled up where a shell fragment had hit him. But when they got close, Trent says the Jerry sat up, and came at them – crawling because he'd been blown nearly in half, and his face, when he described it, was like this other thing that Guin from the listening post had seen: ape-like, dog-like, and smelling like Hell doesn't have words to describe. Trent and his boys were about to go after this . . . he called it a Jerry . . . with clubs, when another of 'em came over the lip of the shell-hole. They shot it, but it just got back up again, and I can't blame 'em for running for it.

'*What is it?* What's out there?' Calvert's face had such intensity that Asher almost felt the surgeon was about to grab him by the shoulders and try to shake the truth out of him. 'Trent and his boys went back just after daybreak – and got shot at by snipers for their trouble – and found the wounded Jerry . . . not just dead. Half-burned-up, Trent said. He said his sister used to work in a match factory, and had got burned once by the phosphorous there. He said these burns looked like that. He said that by the look of him, the dead Tommy had been torn open and partly eaten.'

'Did you report this?' *Shit, bugger, damn . . .* Had Asher not been blessed with ears that didn't turn red with anger, he knew he would have been scarlet to his hairline. *Bastards . . . BASTARDS . . .*

Calvert's mouth twisted. 'Oh, aye.'

'*The matter is in hand . . .*'

When Asher said nothing, Calvert pitched his cigarette stub to the mud and ground it with his heel. After a time, in a calmer voice, the surgeon asked, 'Did Mrs Asher see any of these things?' He held up his hand, as if to stay Asher's reply of *I don't know*, and said, 'I just wondered. The way she started getting these "special orders" to come and go, and drivers taking her off down to Arras and Amiens, and I never did quite believe it was all about teaching others to use a fluoroscope, although God knows we need that, too . . . And I know you can't say. But looking back, she'd take these walks late at night, like you're off to do. So I just wonder.'

Keeping himself outwardly calm, as he had long ago learned to do, Asher felt, inwardly, that he was shaking in his whole being like a plucked guitar string. *They're getting out . . .*

What the hell did those idiots THINK was going to happen, if they started farming these things, growing them like a Hell-crop of monsters . . . ?

'I wonder also,' he said. 'And I don't actually *know* anything. But tell your stretcher parties – and tell your surgeons – that if they encounter one of these things again, *do not* make contact with its blood. The condition is transmitted by blood contact, and is irreversible. Those who are infected lose their memories and their minds, and yes, they will eat not only the dead but the living.'

Calvert stared at him: hardened at everything he had seen and done on the Front since the previous autumn, he was still knocked aghast.

'I hope to catch up with Mrs Asher in Amiens,' Asher went on. 'And to find out – I hope – a little more about what's going on. She may in fact be teaching fluoroscopy.' He pushed his hat back, and rubbed his face. The thought of fifty miles over the shell-holed roads tomorrow was already a nightmare. 'If she's already on her way back – if we miss each other – please let her know that I'm here and I'm searching for her. Don't let her go off on another of these "special assignments" before she talks to me. And in the meantime,' he added grimly, 'I think I need to have a look at whatever she saw out there in the dark.'

The man they got – the revenant they got – had just begun to turn. Looking through the judas into the lighted laboratory, Lydia thought he looked barely twenty, desperately trying to keep his fortitude in the face of his captors and clearly on the verge of vomiting with terror. She saw him reach up repeatedly to finger his face, his mouth, the sides of his skull where the sutures would be just beginning to deform. He looked wildly from Lemoine's face to Francesca's, horrible in their absolute impersonality, as if he were indeed nothing more than the chicken they were going to have for dinner, once they'd wrung its neck.

Had Lydia had a gun she'd have cheerfully shot them both.

It was worse, she thought – as the young man balked at the last moment, at the sight of the gas cylinders beneath the grille – knowing that even if he did escape, even if both Lemoine and the White Lady were to drop dead (*and go straight to Hell!*), he was doomed, damned, infected already with the condition that would eat his brain into nothingness, that would turn him into a walking appetite that spread its horror into any that it wounded but did not kill. *Even if I shot them, and Nurse Meagher* – who was absent from the laboratory and whom Lydia had not seen all day – *I would have to kill him, too.*

She leaned her head against the edge of the judas, and discarded the idea of going to hide her head in the pillow of her cot. *Jamie's going to need to know exactly what happens and how long it takes. And I want to know, too.*

I'm so sorry, Hans or Gleb or Heinrich – even if you were the person who shot Uncle Richard's poor footman Ned, I am so sorry . . .

She timed it. Nearly seventy seconds elapsed from the moment that the White Lady took the young soldier's hand – gazing into his eyes, whispering to him in German – and the moment that she signed Lemoine to turn on the flame. Longer, Lydia thought, than it had taken for poor Basilio to surrender his mind into hers. But it was less than a minute before he ceased screaming, and only two and a half, before Francesca let go. Her shoulders relaxed just before she did, and her head dropped back a little, as Josetta's sometimes did when she'd sipped really, really good champagne.

Nothing of the paroxysm that had shaken the whole of her body, with Basilio's death.

'How do you feel, Madame?' asked Lemoine.

Francesca looked at him, and smiled. 'Not bad at all.' She moved her shoulders, as if readjusting to the decrease in tension. Ran a hand through her flaxen hair. 'Certainly I'm not hearing voices in my mind, if that's what you mean. To be honest,' she added, ''twas a concern of mine as well. Let me—' Her smile widened. 'Let me adjust . . . digest . . . contemplate . . .'

'Of course.' Colonel Lemoine's stiffness spoke worlds for his own impatience, his own barely-concealed apprehension that something might still go wrong with his mission, his project—

He turned his head, regarding the burning corpse on its bed of blue flame. 'And there will be no trouble – no danger – in destroying these things, once the fighting is over?'

'Mmm . . . I shouldn't think so.' She made a little rippling movement of all her muscles, like a cat stretching, as if feeling for some change within herself. 'If I am able to control them – as I feel, I think, I must be . . .' Her velvety voice was barely audible over the roaring of the ventilator fans. 'What can be simpler than ordering them all into a walled enclosure open to the sunlight, and waiting for dawn? If in fact,' she added casually, 'you *want* to get rid of them when the fighting is done. Someone in your government might want to keep them around a little—'

Lemoine's eyes flared wide. '*Never!*' By the horror in his voice the idea – obvious to Lydia – had never crossed his mind. 'These creatures – these *monstrosities* – will be used for one thing only! When we have achieved that victory, we shall ask you to destroy them – all of them!'

'Oh, peace!' She lifted one clawed hand. ''Tis your endeavor; I'm only your . . . *condottiere*. Your helper. You have paid me . . . *amply*.' Smug satisfaction oozed like cream from her words. 'I am in your debt, I am indeed, Colonel. And I am – agog – to see if in fact your supposition about how these things can be controlled is in fact correct.'

'Tomorrow night?' The voice of a man who is trying hard not to nag.

'Tomorrow night.'

'I don't suppose—'

And Lydia, incredulous, realized that the issue of whether or not someone in the government would want to keep a mob of tame revenants when the war was done had already dropped completely out of his thoughts. As if he truly imagined that saying *Never* and *You must destroy them* was going to be the end.

As if the truly important thing – the only thing – was victory over the Germans, and not other uses to which such a horror might be put.

He really is thinking no further than that.

'No.' The Lady smiled to take the sting out of the word, and reached with a forefinger – with its long, glass-like claw – to flick the surgeon's cheek. Lydia saw – and she was positive the Lady saw as well – Lemoine stiffen, as if he would have twitched away from the contact, detesting the woman even as they bargained for the victory of France. 'I will return tomorrow. Ah,' she added, practically purring as she turned toward the laboratory door. *'There's* our wandering girl!'

Meagher stood in the doorway.

She'd become a vampire.

Lemoine turned his head, saw her, startled . . . then Francesca glanced at him, that eternal, pleased smile still broadening her lips, and he relaxed. 'Would you finish up here, Nurse Meagher?' he asked, and Lydia realized, shocked, *He doesn't see it. HE DOESN'T NOTICE.*

And he hasn't noticed that she's probably been missing since last night.

No wonder Graf Szgedny, and poor Antonio, and Don Simon said she was strong . . .

Lemoine left, probably, thought Lydia, to write up his notes. Francesca and Meagher stood looking at one another in the electric glare and stinking smoke of that charnel house crypt, the light of the dying flame playing across their faces.

'Is it done?' Meagher asked, as if she were no longer certain of her voice,

'Well, *he's* done, at any rate.' The White Lady shrugged peerless shoulders. 'As for whether I'll be able to control the whole swarm of them . . . truly, it remains to be seen. I certainly feel no ill effects. But as for coming to Ireland with you . . .'

'I wouldn't ask you to.' Meagher put up her hands, to push her black heavy hair from her face, then looked at them, turning them over in the light. Her nails had already grown out to claws. She opened her lips a little, ran her tongue over her fangs. 'Thank you,' she added. 'I can . . . if you will but teach me how . . .'

Francesca Gheric regarded her, hugely amused. Like an adult, thought Lydia, listening to a four-year-old's plans to slay dragons or find buried treasure.

Does Meagher really think she isn't this woman's slave now?

Or that, having been deprived of the ability to make a fledgling for the whole of her Undead existence, Francesca's going to let her new-wrought fledgling go?

'In time,' purred Francesca. 'In time.'

'When you do,' said Meagher, her speech still a little fumbling, 'perhaps we can – we should . . . The revenants are getting out, you see. I've counted them, and . . . I knew there were a few, hiding in the foundation vaults below the wine cellars, and the drainage passages. But now . . . I think they're finding ways outside. Will we be able to . . . to summon them back?'

The master vampire chuckled. 'Old Stiff-Rump will have a seizure if we don't, won't he?' She shrugged again. 'They come back ere daybreak, you know. 'Tis where their hive is. In the meantime—' She put out a hand, and stroked her fledgling's cheek. 'Let me look at you. My pretty, pretty child . . . You do know that our condition, our state, is one of perfection, don't you? Physical perfection. The prime of life, if I may so term it. The prime of health.' She reached up to finger the girl's black, curling hair. 'Your handsome soldier – whatever his name is – won't be able to keep his hands off you when he gets here—'

Meagher shook her head uncertainly, and stepped back from the caress. 'It's not . . . It's not important what I look like.'

'Oh, but it is, my sugarplum.' Her voice turned warm and crooning. 'We look as we always knew in our hearts that we look – as we look in our sweetest dreams. And we gain strength – we maintain our strength – by the kill. How are you going to get anyone to walk up a dark alley with you if you aren't the prettiest thing he's ever seen in his life? We maintain our ability to make the living see what we wish them to see, only by the lives we drink.'

'I know that.' The girl spoke unwillingly, as if bracing herself for a horror – like Lemoine facing the burning of that young

German alive – that must be got through, to attain the goal. 'And I will do whatever I need to do, pay whatever price needs be paid—' The words stammered, learned by rote in another lifetime, and Francesca laughed again, and again patted Meagher's cheek.

'And so you shall, my blue-eyed angel. So you shall. But right now, how do you feel?'

Meagher's eyes met hers at last, and she whispered, 'Hungry.'

'I, also.' Her smile turned dark, gleaming and terrible, and she put a caressing arm around her fledgling's shoulders. 'Let us go forth, then, sweet child. And I'll teach you how to hunt.'

TWENTY-TWO

Moving among the charred ruins of what had been a small French village, a willow pole in one hand like a blind man's cane and a lantern, sheathed down to its tiniest thread of yellow light, in the other, Asher was aware of the Undead. Since the night in 1907 when he'd come home to find the household in near-coma slumber and Don Simon Ysidro sitting at his study desk, he had dealt with enough vampires to spot them in the darkness. There were techniques of mental focus that improved one's chances, though this didn't always help, and he had the bite scars to prove it. Revenants were abroad, and some at least shared their vampiric cousins' ability to go unnoticed until they were almost on top of their victims.

By what Grippen had told him in London, he guessed himself almost safe from the vampires here.

But the reeking network of old trenches, gaping cellars and shell-craters – black as the abyssal pits of hell – could conceal any number of revenants.

Still he walked, whispers of moonlight glimmering on the ruined land.

If Lydia had received 'special orders' to go down to Amiens – and he guessed that Amiens wasn't her actual destination – she was almost certainly with Don Simon Ysidro, and curiously, the thought brought him comfort. He had for years watched the relationship between his wife and the vampire and was virtually certain that Ysidro would not let harm come to her. *'I will keep her safe,'* the pale vampire had said, on the night before Lydia's departure for France: the night Asher had waked to see a light burning in the upstairs hallway of their house on Holyrood Street, and had gone down in his dressing-gown to investigate, nearly certain what he would find.

He had been, at that time, barely three weeks recovered from his most recent relapse of pneumonia and had just begun to be up and about for a few hours a day, readying himself to begin teaching the Hilary term. The weather had turned cold at the start of November; the house was freezing. As Asher had expected, the vampire Ysidro had been sitting in Lydia's green velvet chair before the banked ashes of the study grate.

'Will you be going to France?' Asher had asked him, wanting to hate him and not able to do so; and the vampire had inclined his moonlight-colored head.

'Look after her.' It was as if they continued a conversation already begun, and the vampire nodded again.

'I came here tonight on purpose, James, to reassure you that I would.'

'Have you told her this?'

Ysidro made the slight movement with his eyes that passed for a headshake, even as his nods were barely perceptible. *'Best not. Yet I thought you would wish to know—'*

Movement in one of the half-caved-in trenches; a fugitive glint of the feeble moonlight in animal eyes. The scrabble of rats among the bricks of a fallen chimney. Beyond the shattered stumps of what had been an orchard, past the makeshift bridge, the ruined country swelled, plowed by shell-fire into a sodden wasteland of darkness, barbed wire and wrecked wagons, stinking of the carcasses of horses and mules. Asher stopped, heart beating hard. Then, after a moment, moved on.

'Promenading oneself', Ysidro called this. Vampires did it, when newly arrived in the territory of a nest not their own, to ask permission of the master vampire to hunt on his or her grounds. Vampires always knew who walked their domains of darkness. If they wanted to speak to you, they would.

A white flicker in the bitter night.

The glint of eyes.

Asher kept walking, old instinct forbidding him to let any adversary know that he was capable of detecting them. He even made himself start when she laid a soft little clawed hand on his arm and said, 'James!' in a pleased voice.

'Madame.' He bowed. Lydia had told him she thought she had seen this woman, among the many who haunted the vicinity of the hospitals behind the lines. 'A long way from Paris.'

Her French was modern, though it slipped now and then into the old-fashioned idiom of Napoleonic times. Moonlight made her green eyes nearly transparent. Scorning disguise, she wore a simple white dress, her black hair loosed about her shoulders in thick curls. Blood and mud spattered her hem and her sleeves, but this he only noticed later. It seemed to disappear from his consciousness as he spoke to her, even as he was only intermittently aware of her claws and fangs. She appeared to him to be the most beautiful, most desirable woman he had ever seen.

'Dare I surmise you have come out in the hopes of a rendezvous?'

Elysée de Montadour was insatiably curious and vampires were the worst gossips in the world. She'd have accosted him if he'd had a whitethorn stake in one hand and a silver crucifix in the other.

'The merest recollection of your name in one of my wife's letters was enough to bring me forth.'

'Brave soul.' The next moment, the green eyes narrowed. 'As for your wife, she's gone off with Don Simon . . . and when you meet her again, tell her for me that spectacles *never* improve a woman's appearance! *Outré*!' She gave a theatrical shiver. 'Like a great bug! Not that I mean to disparage—'

Of course you do, you witch. 'No, no . . .'

'Purely for her own good, as woman to woman—'

'Of course.' He kissed her hand. Warm. Even in the wasted moonlight there showed a flicker of color in her cheeks. 'Do you know where they've gone? The surgeons tell me she had orders for Amiens.'

She made a sly little moue. 'Maybe after they left Cuvé Sainte-Bride, they did. I hear that's where Simon was seen, five nights

ago, Johanna tells me . . . You know Johanna Falknerin, that
horrid harpy from Berlin?'

'We've met.' Asher had no desire to encounter the hawk-nosed
Rhineland vampire – or indeed any of the Berlin nest – again.

'Dreadful woman! And tells tales . . .' Elysée shook her head.
'And speaks French like a goat! One can barely understand a
word she says, not that one would wish to . . . Disgusting. But
she says she saw Simon emerge from Cuvé Sainte-Bride with
his minion – I presume your pretty little wife – and go off in a
motorcar. So they may well have gone to Amiens for all I know.'

She shrugged, the gesture extravagant, as if playing to some
far balcony packed with admirers. 'So they're not back yet? Only
to be expected. Simon is the most *extraordinary* creature in his
taste for the company of the living.'

'What about the revenants?'

She startled, swung about and swept the shapeless landscape
with those darkness-piercing eyes. 'The Boche,' she said softly.
'Only cabbage-eaters, gone off their heads . . . They have to be,
don't they? Oh, I know about those awful things that are supposed
to exist in Prague, but how could they get here? Even the Germans
can't be such fools as to—'

'I doubt there's anything,' returned Asher, softly and from the
bottom of his heart, 'that either side in this wretched war would
consider too foolish to contemplate. Have you seen them?'

'Not close.' She drew nearer to him, like a frightened woman
seeking comfort in a male embrace; Asher retreated a step. Her
glance flickered at him, half-reproachful, half-amused. 'And not
near here. South, five, perhaps six miles, towards Arras. I saw
one the night before last, shambling among the shell-holes in the
moonlight. Looking for wounded, I suppose. And I have seen
the bodies of the wounded they have found and fed upon. Last
night I came on – I don't know, I suppose one had got himself
caught in barbed wire, and the flesh burned away off his bones
when the sun came up. But it could have been a living man, you
know, caught too close to a bomb-blast.'

'It could.'

'These things . . .' Elysée looked over her shoulder again, her
beautiful face taut with dread. 'I have heard – from the Prague
vampires, I have heard – that they devour the Undead in their

coffins. That they live in the sewers, and the crypts below old churches . . . I have thought of fleeing back to Paris, but what if these things come to Paris? What if they make their nests there, like rats, like wood beetles that no one can ever quite root out? Who among us would be safe?'

'Are there any of you, left in Paris?'

She waved, as if to chase away a subject unpleasing to her. 'There isn't a city in Europe, where we who hunt the night linger. The cities are full of soldiers, and spies, and people looking for spies, and for what sort of pickings? And my boys – dear boys . . .' She smiled at the mention of her nest of fledglings, chosen – in Ysidro's opinion – for their looks rather than their brains. 'On their own, without me, they'd get themselves killed inside a week.'

'And is there another man,' Asher asked, 'a day ago, maybe two, who has promenaded himself as I did? A smallish man, and slender? Large nose, gray hair, dark eyes? Possibly – probably – in uniform?'

The delicate brows puckered, and again she shook her head. 'None save you and your wife, and that little fool of an Irish nurse . . . Whom I haven't seen, now that I consider it, in weeks . . . Did she ever meet with the Undead, do you know? Did the pretty Lydia encounter her?'

'I sincerely hope not.'

'And this man—' Elysée, who had once been an actress, made a mime of mocking a man with a large nose. 'He too is seeking us? La, so popular as we have become . . . Is he a friend of this Irish *poule*?'

'I don't think so,' replied Asher. 'But I suspect they have acquaintances in common.'

In the deep of her dreams, Lydia heard the lock click.

Simon, she thought. *Simon came back for me . . .*

She struggled to shake off sleep, to surface from a black well fathoms deep. *Why can't I wake up? I sleep so badly in this place . . .*

To the very walls, the blanket on her cot, clung the stink of charred flesh.

I shouldn't be asleep anyway. It's night. It's dangerous to sleep at night. But if Simon just unlocked the door of my cell, it HAS to be night.

It can't be Simon, the lock is silver . . .

Fear jolted her awake. A bar of the laboratory's electric glare fell across her face. The cell door stood open, about an inch.

Beyond it, the laboratory was tomb-silent. Even the constant, distant groaning and yowling of the revenants in the crypt was stilled.

Simon?

Lydia got cautiously to her feet. She was still dressed – *It IS still night, I DIDN'T go to bed.* Heart hammering, she tiptoed to the door and looked through the judas.

Nothing. The lab was empty. The burning-grille, steel-bright where Lemoine had scrubbed it that afternoon, gleamed under the harsh string of bulbs. The door to the corridor stood open, like this one, an inch or so.

This is a trap.

She knew it to the marrow of her bones.

But what kind of a trap? They've already GOT me.

A trap for Simon? She remembered Basilio screaming as the flames poured over him. Remembered Antonio crying in that thundering bass voice, *'Oh, God, oh God, have mercy on me, a sinner . . .'* The look of shuddering ecstasy on Francesca's face.

DON'T GO NEAR THAT DOOR.

Slowly, the gap in the outer door widened, and the reek of the revenants flowed into the lab.

Oh, dear God . . .

Even before the door opened sufficiently to reveal them Lydia knew they were there, and they were. She ducked back into her cell, looked desperately for some way to lock it from the inside – there was neither keyhole nor handle on that side of the door, and the door itself opened outward. Slowly the things shuffled into the lab, half-crouched and unbelievably hideous in the too-bright glare of the electric lights. Faces still bruised where the jaws had grown forward, mouths bloody from the unaccustomed length of new tusks. Eyes blank. The nostrils of their deformed noses flared, sniffing; heads thick with matted, uncut hair swinging back and forth; the remains of their uniforms stinking of bodily waste unregarded.

(*Why on earth don't they die of their own infections? They must after a time . . . CAN they die in this state?*)

At the same time the other half of her mind screamed in panic *NO! NO!* as they suddenly turned, sniffing, toward the cell door. *NO!*

Get past them? The door was narrow and there were four of them in the lab.

The cell was barely six feet by ten. *I can use the cot as a shield . . .*

She unfastened the silver chains from her wrists, wrapped them around her hands. *How badly will that amount of silver burn revenants? Enough to let me get past them?*

The cot weighed something over twenty pounds and she was barely aware of it as she up-ended it, flattened against the wall beside the door, holding it in front of her body. *The legs are going to tangle in the door so I have to wait till they all get—*

The reek smote her like a hammer as the door was yanked open. Lydia shoved the cot at them, slithered past and out the door and almost into the arms of two more revenants that had entered the lab behind the first group. She flattened back to the wall, threw a fast glance at the door . . .

And saw Francesca standing, smiling, against the dark of the corridor.

Lydia twisted, dodged to another corner as the revenants came at her. One of them, still more man-like than bestial, sprang at her like a panther; she looked for something loose to throw and there was nothing. *If I strike at it and miss, it'll grab me—*

She dodged past and the other four emerged from the cell, surrounding her—

'Stop this!' Lemoine's voice shouted from the hall. 'What the hell are you doing?'

The revenants stopped in their tracks.

Stood swaying, scratching themselves, looking about them as if she, Lydia, had suddenly become invisible and odorless.

Francesca's smile widened. She stepped out of the doorway, angelic eyes glittering with delight. 'We're only having a little test.'

Lemoine pushed past her into the laboratory, in shirtsleeves, clutching his aching arm. *He must have been in bed and asleep.*

Lydia began to shake so that she could barely stand. She felt as if she would vomit, as much from sheer terror as because the six revenants stood only a few feet from her – even Lemoine hesitated to approach her, his eyes darting from the creatures to the White Lady, still standing beside him in the doorway. Lydia could almost see his struggle, knowing he should stride over to her and bring her out of the circle of the things and not daring.

Meagher slipped into the lab behind him, blue eyes sparkling with the mischief of Hell. 'And here we thought you'd be pleased,' she teased, and Lemoine swung around to face her. This time he saw what she was, and his eyes bulged with shock.

He whispered, 'What have you done?'

'Well, I was hardly going to risk touching those things—' Francesca gestured toward the revenants – 'before I'd made sure you were paying me in genuine coin.' She put an arm around Meagher's shoulders, and the Irish vampire stepped into the embrace like a cat asking to be stroked. Like sisters. Like school friends. 'And I'm pleased to say your procedure passed the test, dear man, with flying colors. You should be well pleased.'

She turned her attention – Lydia didn't see how exactly she did it, more than just looking at the revenants – back to the creatures, and they shambled into one corner of the lab.

'It is . . . an extraordinary sensation,' the White Lady went on. 'Feeling their minds. Look.'

She fixed them with her gaze. After a moment a huge gray rat emerged from behind the boxes in one corner of the lab, then another. They ran toward Lydia, who stepped back with a sickened cry. Lemoine said again, 'Stop that!' and the rats stopped.

'Go ahead,' said Francesca after a moment. 'Hit one. It won't run away.'

Lemoine stood still for a long moment, then looked around him for something to strike the rat with, but as Lydia had observed a few moments before, there was nothing loose in the lab to use for a weapon. With a laugh, Meagher stepped forward, picked up the rat – which made no move to resist – and grabbed it by head and body, and with a twist broke its neck. In the brightness of the laboratory lights, Lydia could see the rosy pinkness of the Irish girl's face, the red of her lips: only by the reflective gleam of her eyes, by the fangs that showed when she smiled and the long claws that tipped her fingers, could anyone have said she was vampire. She'd clearly fed.

Meagher turned her mocking eyes on Lydia. 'Why don't you go back into your cell now, dear?'

'They won't hurt you,' added Francesca, when Lydia tried to step past the revenants without touching any of them. It wasn't possible to do, but Francesca was right: they didn't even turn their heads when Lydia's shoulders brushed against them as she slipped by.

'You see,' said the White Lady to Lemoine, as Lydia closed the cell door behind her. 'Everything you wished to achieve. I stand ready to complete your plan.' She curtsied elaborately.

Lemoine drew a deep breath and let it out slowly. Accepting – Lydia could see the shift in his shoulders. Accepting that sometimes evil must be done that good may come . . .

'I am . . .' he began, and then paused. 'This is astounding. First we must test— How many of these creatures can you control, and at what distances? Not,' he added warningly, 'with a test such as this, which, if you will permit me to say so, was inexcusably cruel—'

'And I am *inexcusably* sorry.' Francesca curtsied, without an atom of contrition in her voice. 'I assure you, it will not happen again.'

Even from the judas of her cell, Lydia could see the White Lady and Meagher exchange a wink.

A wink which Lemoine didn't even see. *Isn't he even aware that they can tinker with his perceptions? That they're altering them – blinding him – even now? Making him see what he wants to see?*

Or doesn't he even need a vampire's delusion for that?

'When we have tested – when we have documented what is possible – I will inform the Ministry,' Lemoine went on, as the revenants filed from the laboratory. 'No one – NO ONE – knows the extent of what I have sought here: the Germans have spies everywhere. And not the Germans only,' he added darkly. 'Even the British poke and pry, and try to find out what isn't their business—'

He started to follow the revenants from the lab, when Meagher touched his arm and said, 'Lock?'

'Ah.' Lemoine crossed to the door of Lydia's cell. In one quick stride Lydia was huddled in the corner, knees drawn up to her forehead, arms wrapped around her shins, shaking and sobbing.

'Madame,' said the French surgeon urgently, and hurried to her side. 'Madame, be calm. You must be calm. You can see – you *have* seen – that these creatures are now completely under control. Believe me, I swear to you that what we do here, shocking as it may seem to you, is necessary, for the defeat of Germany and the salvation of France . . . and of your own country, of course.'

He knelt on the floor before her, grasped her hand in his. 'Sometimes one must use shocking methods, to bring about the good of all,' he said. 'Germany *must* be defeated. France – the French people – *must* prevail. Once this war is won, these things will be utterly destroyed, never to be used again—'

If I go on shuddering like this he'll give me a sedative.

And does he actually believe that seeing what I have seen, the French government is going to let me go and tell people about all this?

Lydia looked up and straightened her glasses, and tried to give him an expression of dewy-eyed trust. 'Do you . . . do you swear it?' she managed to whisper – *Not bad*, she thought, considering how badly she wanted to scream YOU IRRESPONSIBLE WRETCHED IDIOT!!!

'Upon my honor, Madame,' said Lemoine. 'And upon my honor, as soon as it is safe to do so, you will be released . . .'

Lydia gave a sniffle or two (*Do NOT scream . . .*) and, a little to her own surprise, succeeded in forcing herself to her feet, and crossing the cell to pick up and right her cot. 'I just want to go home,' she whispered, like a beaten woman, and, spreading pillow and blanket back into place, lay down with her back to the door. 'I just want to go home.'

She heard the click of the silver padlock, and the creak of the laboratory door.

Rising swiftly, she crossed to the judas in time to see Francesca leave the lab in Lemoine's wake. Meagher turned, and with a casually savage stomp, broke the back of the surviving rat that still sat in the midst of the laboratory floor.

TWENTY-THREE

'**M**istress . . .'

Lydia jerked awake, as the voice whispered, like a thread of pale mist, at the edge of her dreams.

She immediately checked her watch. Four thirty. The first threads of light would not yet have begun to stain the sky outside. She hadn't meant to fall asleep that early and, given the events of the night, hadn't thought she would. But the fact that Simon's mind could touch her dreams meant that he was somewhere close by, underground as she was and near enough that he could read her dreams.

Damn it, she thought. *Damn it, revenants or no revenants, I have to sleep . . .*

Her heart was hammering and she debated about getting changed for sleep – she had fallen asleep again fully dressed – and then decided against it. *If he's down here it may be that he has a plan to escape now, before sunrise*, and she wasn't about to undertake it in a pair of French Army pajamas.

She lay down again, closed her eyes, tried hard not to see the laboratory door opening, the circle of revenants closing around her. Tried not to see the tickled delight in Francesca's eyes, like a child at the cinema waiting to watch Ben Turpin get a custard pie in his face. '*There was a kind of spite to her*,' Szgedny had said . . .

Fall asleep! Simon will have to retreat, will fall asleep himself soon . . .

Miranda sleeping in her tiny cot back on Holyrood Street, silk-fine red hair spread over her pillow. Princess, the nursery cat, sleeping at Miranda's feet. Jamie asleep . . . Jamie . . . the recollection of waking somewhere in the deeps of her wedding night and lying there looking at the shape of his shoulders in the moonlight, the way slumber smoothed the lines of his face and left it like a young boy's . . .

'Mistress . . .'

In her dream (*Do NOT wake up . . .!*) she sat up (*Aunt Lavinnia would FAINT if she knew I dreamed about Simon standing at the foot of my bed . . .*) and caught him against her as he perched on the cot's edge, cold and skeletal in uniform trousers and braces, the sleeves of his shirt wet with dirty water: 'Simon, where *are* you?'

'Hush – near. Near enough to see what happened tonight. Forgive me, lady – I would have come from hiding had things gone any further. But I heard Lemoine coming and gambled that he'd be able to stop her. Had I shown myself—'

'Don't be silly,' said Lydia. 'We would both have been killed, and you at least have to get out of here and warn somebody – Jamie, if you can do it—'

'Hush,' he said quickly, and the cold, clawed fingers pressed her lips. 'I'll sleep soon. Have you still your picklocks?'

She nodded. 'I can't use them on the padlock . . .'

'Do you still aid this Lemoine in the cleaning of his workroom? Good. Leave them behind the storage boxes where the rats came from tonight. The Irishwoman has a key to the laboratory but regards it little now that she has ceased helping him with his work. I can take it from her room when all have gone out to this test of theirs tomorrow. Revenants—'

His head nodded suddenly, and the thin white brows buckled over his nose.

'Revenants haunt the crypts.'

'Simon—' *Good Heavens, don't fall asleep before you can get yourself hidden—!*

She was sitting up in bed, alone.

His voice whispered, like an ectoplasmic scratching at a dark windowpane: 'Can't get out . . .'

True waking came then, and the clammy stuffiness of the underground. The smell of the revenants, and of greasy smoke, absorbed into blankets and walls.

It was late afternoon when Asher reached Army Headquarters at Amiens. The road south of Pont-Sainte-Félicité had been shelled Monday night, and was blocked with supply-trains waiting for the digging parties to get duckboards on the surface. Beyond Haut-le-Bois it was impassable, necessitating Asher's driver to backtrack half a dozen miles and take a muddy track over a shallow range of hills, to a more protected route.

Before they reached that point, Asher was able to get a glimpse of the old nunnery of Cuvé Sainte-Bride.

He didn't dare stop, but the state of the road and the heavy traffic of mule-drawn wagons allowed him ample time to train his field glasses on the square gray buildings on the slope above the road, the dense snarls of barbed wire that rimmed the trenches around it, the lone sentry at its gate. According to the records unearthed by Josetta's friend at the War Ministry (*Who could easily have been interred under the Official Secrets Act for her trouble*, he reflected), there were five French soldiers and five British assigned to the place, as well as Lemoine and five members of 'staff', some of whom were almost certainly local cleaners and a cook. But the requisitions for rations were too high, and even without Lydia's messages Asher would have deduced its use as a prison of some kind by this time. Presumably Lemoine had the French equivalent of 'at his sole discretion' and 'please render all and any assistance'.

I wonder what he told them back in Paris?

The truth?

Or just, I have a plan to win the war.

He wondered how far Lydia and Ysidro had gotten into the place before they'd slipped out again, and what they had discovered. Was a coded letter even now lying on his desk in Holyrood Street?

Two miles down the wider road after crossing the hills, the car broke down.

'I don't blame you for wanting to get a shift on, sir,' confided the young captain in charge of Field Artillery Battery Twelve, while Asher waited in the makeshift hut for horse-drawn transport to be arranged. Asher had given him a cigarette and expressed his genuine admiration for the battery – four BL-60s that dated back to the Boer War and a number of Woolwich Mk-IX naval guns mounted on railway carriages. Beneath a careful public-school English, the glottalized t's and disappearing l's of the West Country still lurked through. 'There's weird stories going about this countryside at night – things people see in the woods just lately, or things they've found. It's not some form of shell shock, sir, or nerves. There's not a man in the battery'll venture past the perimeter when the light goes.'

'An' I don't care what Colonel St-Vire says,' added Asher's driver, 'beggin' your pardon, sir, I'm sure, an' no disrespec' an' all . . . But it's Jerry. It's got to be. Nick Frampton – my mate back at Félicité – 'e swears the thing 'e saw shamblin' about the old trenches one night, wi' a face on it like God's nightmare, 'ad on a Jerry uniform, an' eyes glowin' like a cat's. The men are spooked, sir.' He drew on the Woodbine Asher had given him. 'I'm glad that axle went out 'ere, an' not further on down the road where we might be stuck when it was growin' dark.'

'Have you reported this?' asked Asher. 'How long has this been going on?'

'A week?' The driver glanced inquiringly at the captain. 'Ten days?'

'A week,' said the captain. 'And I think it's growing worse. As for reporting, what can we say, really? Things somebody says he saw – the state bodies are found in, or that poor horse the lads found in the woods, torn to pieces by God knows what . . .'

'Me dad's a gamekeeper,' put in the driver. 'An' I never seen an animal what could do that. But beyond that . . .' He spread his hands.

'You write a report, you send it to your colonel,' went on the captain, 'who's got his own plate full of grief just keeping shells coming for the guns and food for the men, and he sees it an' thinks, *Hrm, well, somebody going a bit shell-shocked, this'll wait.* But if you were to know anyone, sir . . .' His casual finger brushed the War Ministry papers, which, Asher was well aware, had 'Spook' written all over them.

'I might have a friend or two who'd be interested in this.'

'I'd appreciate it, sir.' The captain touched his hat brim. 'Because God's honest truth, sir, it's giving me the jim-jams.'

A corporal came in then, with word that transport had been found, and Asher did the last ten miles to Amiens in a wagon-load of wounded drawn by two of the beautiful copper-bay Shire horses that a year ago – like their owner, Asher reflected – had been peacefully plowing some Shropshire rye field. Conscripts who would lay their faithful bones in foreign earth. As they jogged toward the great cathedral city Asher turned the problem

over in his mind, reflecting that the young captain of Battery
Twelve was right. '*You write a report, you send it to your colonel
. . .*' and the revenants slipped from the crypt beneath Sainte-
Bride, a danger not because of who they killed, but because of
those that survived an encounter.

And say Lydia and Ysidro did find something, some proof
utterly damning, in their visit to the half-ruined convent – proof
that presumably had sent them hotfoot to Amiens . . . What then?
What if he himself added to the report the contention that the
Irish Brotherhood – and who could tell what other groups within
the Empire, or what other groups they'd talked to – once means
of controlling them was found – were seeking to breed up their
own? Would that stand up against Langham's bland assurances
that 'everything is in hand'?

Would everything lock up in some committee or other until it
was too late? Until some wounded survivor of an attack was
simply sent home to Britain with the infection in his veins?

No, thought Asher.

Simply, *No*.

No one at Headquarters in Amiens had seen or heard anything
of Lydia, with or without a companion whom Asher was fairly
certain was masquerading as a British officer. (*If the Undead can
tamper with human perception he can probably make them believe
he's Sir John French and none of them would think to question
the impression . . .*) As a major rail hub and supply depot immediately behind the front lines, the ancient cathedral town was
swollen with troops and short on everything: coal, food, petrol,
transport and most especially housing. Nevertheless, Asher's
papers got him a somewhat elderly Silver Ghost (plus driver) for
the following day, and a garret room on the Rue des Tanneurs
near the cathedral, to which he repaired after a sketchy dinner
of bread, charcuterie and what he privately suspected was mule
meat in the officer's mess.

Coming down the steps of the mess, he was just reaching for
the handle of its outer door when the door was opened and
Pritchard Crowell came in.

Asher was in the act of putting on his cap and didn't pause
or turn his head, simply brushed past the man who was a legend
in the Department – the man who had supposedly died in 1895

– the man who had instructed him in the finer points of running networks 'abroad' – stepped out into Rue des Trois Cailloux, and ducked into the blackness of a shop doorway where he waited for ten minutes. When he was fairly certain that Crowell wasn't going to emerge and follow him, he made his way – cautiously – to his lodgings, but wasn't terribly surprised, an hour later, to move his blackout curtain aside and, after long waiting, glimpse against the darkness on the far side of the canal a flicker of movement, a suspicion of moon-glint on uniform buttons.

Crowell had been in uniform at the mess.

Pritchard Crowell.

Why did it never occur to me years ago that the man had to be working with a vampire partner?

Probably because I'm not insane, he reflected after a moment's thought. *It's the sort of conclusion Millward would have leapt to immediately. When I knew the man – extricating himself from impossible situations, slipping past sentries and guards like a combination of Leatherstocking and Bulldog Drummond – I disbelieved in vampires, though I had studied their lore for years. And by the time I came to understand that the Undead were more than legends, Pritchard Crowell was – supposedly – dead.*

And I had rebuilt my life in Oxford.

Is Crowell a vampire himself?

A flicker of dark mackintosh in the corner of his eye, a shadow seen from the railway embankment on Stratford Marsh . . . A half-glimpsed figure on a bicycle on an Essex lane. *Grippen would know.*

Or is that why Grippen tried to recruit me?

He recalled the night Ysidro had recruited him, to search for the day-killer that was slaying the vampires of London in their coffins – after first drinking their blood – eight years ago: *We need a man who can move about in the daylight.* Twice since then, he'd encountered attempts by governments to recruit vampires, back in the days of that intricate chess game of information and preparation, before war had shattered all schemes.

Crowell was working with a vampire. He's been hiding, for twenty years, waiting . . . for what?

Yet it's HE who's watching ME. It's he who tried to kill me back in London. Not his vampire partner.

What does that mean?

Is he waiting, tonight, for a vampire partner to appear at his side, so that he can direct him or her up here to make sure of me?

Or is he waiting for me to come out, so he can follow me to Lydia?

Lydia, who's the one who knows . . . whatever it was she and Ysidro had found out about Cuvé Sainte-Bride.

Damn it . . .

And of course, rooms in Amiens being scarce as hen's teeth, he had been forced to take one in a building that had only one way out – a room that had only one window, so he couldn't even take the expedient of leaving over the roof. Not that that was anything he wanted to try at the moment. Exhaustion made him feel as if he were wearing the lead-imbued apron Lydia had rigged up to protect her from the supposed danger of invisible rays from her fluoroscope; his lungs felt on fire and all he truly wanted was to lie down and sleep.

Not possible, he told himself. He simply hadn't the strength. *Think of something else.*

A fingernail scratched at the door of his chamber. Like the gnawing of a mouse, barely to be heard.

He slipped up the shade on his lantern the tiniest fraction, and crossed to the door.

'Simon?'

'A friend of his.'

Asher unhooked the silver chain from around his wrist, wrapped it round the fingers of his right hand. Opened the door and stepped to the side, fast – though that, he knew, would make no difference against a vampire's attack.

The vampire standing in the dark of the attic corridor had the curious appearance of an old man. A seamed face framed with long gray hair; eyes that had probably once been dark gleamed on either side of a broken hook of a nose. Like most vampires at the Front (according to Lydia, anyway) he wore a uniform, this one French. But his face, like Ysidro's, was not a twentieth-century face. Pale gloves hid the clawed hands, one of which he extended to Asher.

'Permit me.' His French was eighteenth-century, but kept

slipping back to an older form. 'I am the Graf Szgedny Aloyïs, of Prague.' He stepped into the garret, like a Slavic god, and handed Asher a card. The address lay near the Charles Bridge in the Bohemian city, almost certainly an accommodation. 'And you are the *Anglus* – the English – whom Simon has made his friend? From him I understand that you and I have another acquaintance in common, Solomon Karlebach, the Jew of Prague.'

'Did Simon send you?'

'I have not seen Simon since he escorted the most charming Madame Asher to visit me for the purpose of learning about the woman Francesca Gheric, who has now taken employment with this French madman, Lemoine. It is on that subject that I have sought you out, *Anglus* – that we must speak.'

At Asher's gesture he took the room's single chair, and Asher seated himself on the end of the narrow bed, and unapologetically refastened the silver chain on his wrist. Szgedny's odd, dust-gray eyes followed his movements, and one corner of the long gray mustaches lifted in an ironic half-smile. 'Elysée de Montadour tells me you seek to destroy the things that breed in Cuvé Sainte-Bride. Evil is being done there – I see you try not to smile, to hear me say such a thing . . . An evil I do not fully understand. But Hieronymus, Master of Venice, tells me that three nights ago his fledgling Basilio Occhipinti perished, in horror and in flame – this he felt, he knew, as masters sometimes do feel the deaths of their get. Yet afterwards he said he felt the young man's mind, his awareness, still stirring, in a way that he had never encountered before. As if thought and brain had been pulped, Hieronymus said, and yet the soul were trying to speak out of the bleeding mush.'

Like Ysidro, the vampire showed little expression or change of tone in his deep voice, yet his eyes burned somberly. 'Basilio and his lover, Antonio, slept in the crypt of a ruined church, ten miles from Cuvé Sainte-Bride.'

'Mrs Asher wrote me of these two.'

'But ere Hieronymus reached me with this tale, Antonio had come to me in great consternation saying Basilio had not returned to the crypt the night before. Yet, he said, he knew his friend was alive – if you will excuse my use of the term. After Hieronymus's visit I sought for Antonio, for whom I cherish great respect, but could not find him. He had not taken the ambulance-wagon in which he usually hunts. Then, on this Wednesday past, Hieronymus came to me again saying he had experienced, the previous night, the same sensations concerning Antonio: first the horror of death by fire – only it was not death, exactly. Fragmented dribbles of his thought, his self, remained somewhere, weeping and screaming . . .'

He shook his head, deeply troubled. 'It is Sainte-Bride,' he said at last. 'The evil there. It is breeding these things, these revenants . . . And in my bones I feel that it has taken both Basilio and Antonio. This Lemoine – or rather his minion, the Irishwoman Tuathla – has sought for many weeks to find a vampire willing to work with him, willing to become his partner in some enterprise. It can be nothing but to give him a way to control the revenants whose numbers have grown so quickly of late.'

Asher said, 'I agree.'

The vampire considered him beneath the long gray brows, as if waiting for him to add, *But what has this to do with me?*

When he did not, Szgedny went on, ''Twas the White Lady who came forward at last and entered this man's service. When your beautiful lady spoke of her to me, she surmised that the White Lady was incapable of getting fledglings. The reward, she surmised, that La Dame Blanche asked of Lemoine was that he find some way to alter her condition. To permit her to pass along her own condition to others: to beget fledglings of her blood.'

'Slaves, you mean.'

'Children are – or should be – slaves to their begetters. E'en the Commandments so order it.' The gray vampire inclined his head. 'But this . . . This is an abomination. I am convinced she has drunk the lives of Basilio and Antonio – and indeed used those bleeding fragments of Basilio's thought to call Antonio to her. Whether this will give her what she seeks—'

Asher thought, *Ah*, with the sensation of seeing the pieces of a puzzle drop into place. No great cry of triumph, but an awareness of what had been before him, like a half-filled-in decryption of a cipher, all along.

'Can she control the revenants?'

'As I told your lady, I have never found it possible. But who knows what means this Lemoine has found?'

'According to Mrs Asher, who has read his work, he has studied the vampire state for many years,' said Asher thoughtfully. 'And he had the chance to observe them in China, where for a short time a hive of them flourished near Peking.'

'They must be stopped,' said the vampire. 'This Lemoine must be stopped. Say what you will, *Anglus*, of me and of my kindred – and yes, I know you have made a vow to destroy us, as your master Karlebach has vowed. But though the revenants hunt us in our crypts, through the brains of the rats that seek out our scent, in this you must aid us. For the sake of all the living, as well as the sake of the Undead, these things cannot be permitted to spread. Though they would kill us all, yet the harm that would come of making them your slaves – if you can do it – would be an ocean, a cataclysm, compared to what little harm we do when we hunt the night.'

Asher closed his lips on the observation that 'little harm' was a generous way of looking at the matter. But he remembered that small band of furious Irishmen, who thought they had found an unstoppable weapon to make their land free. And Lemoine, who similarly believed that he had found a way to defeat the Germans before the war could shred away the willing manhood that had – in his eyes – made France great. And Langham who doubtless believed the same, when Crowell went to him with the information that such a useful creature had gotten itself loose and could be captured and put in British hands . . .

In exchange for what?

Protection? Another 'letter of instruction' like his own, to carry him here to France?

And meanwhile each night brought closer the moment when a wounded man would be sent home from the Front, with the infection in his veins.

He left the lantern on the corner of the dresser, and walked back to the window to peep out.

Cloud had shifted across the moon, but even had the light been a little better, he doubted that he could have seen anything in the blackness below. 'Is there anyone there?'

Behind his shoulder, close enough to the back of his neck to make his flesh creep, Szgedny's deep voice replied. 'I see none.'

Which doesn't mean he isn't somewhere near. And doesn't

mean that he won't dog me tomorrow, if he thinks I'll lead him to Lydia . . .

'Aid us.' The vampire's hands rested on his shoulders. 'Simon speaks of you as a man capable of such a feat.'

'I hope I am,' said Asher slowly. 'But I will need your help.'

TWENTY-FOUR

The clink of a chain.

The flat, grunting '*Unnh . . .*' of a revenant – a creature, thought Lydia miserably, who had once been able to say things like *Take care of Mother* to a younger brother, or *Whatever happens, I will hold you always in my heart* to a weeping fiancée.

For two hours she had heard the thing moving around in the laboratory on the end of its short chain. 'Devil on you, you stupid gobshite,' said Meagher disgustedly. 'Ain't you got brain enough to hear through dirt?'

Lydia could have told her that any mental instruction that the White Lady might have given, in the ruined trenches just north of the old convent compound, would be unlikely to penetrate the depth of earth that surrounded the convent crypt, but didn't. And in fact she wasn't certain of this. Lying on her cot feigning sleep, she was profoundly curious as to whether Francesca's commands to the rest of the group of revenants *would* be perceptible to an isolate chained in the lab.

So far, to judge by Meagher's *sotto voce* cursing, as she sat on a lab stool with a pocket watch in one hand and a notebook (*time-synchronized commands?*) in the other, it didn't look promising.

'*Bitseach*,' added the Irishwoman, something Uncle Richard's head groom had occasionally called Aunt Isobel's high-strung mare.

'Eleven,' said Meagher. 'Time for dinner, and let's see if the *raicleach* upstairs can teach you some manners.'

Lydia's heart lurched within her, at the terror of last night's 'experiment', but the next moment she heard the soft clang of a wire cage, and a rat's frantic squeaking.

Simon is out there somewhere, she thought desperately. *Waiting for the moment to come in – please, God, don't let Meagher start poking about and find the picklocks! – and with all the revenants out of the crypt, this one remains.*

And Meagher.

A hoarse grunt from the revenant, and the rat's squeals turned to shrieks. Meagher said, 'Ah, you disgusting maggot!' and there was a metallic rattle, as if she'd dropped the cage. The revenant howled, clashing its chain. If exposure to food had been scheduled for eleven, followed immediately by the command to desist from pursuing it, Lydia guessed that poor Gobshite had failed the test.

Or Francesca had.

And if that were so, and her control of the revenants wasn't complete (*Why not?*), would they simply scatter in the trenches, rove the battlefields, until one of them managed to wound a man but not kill him? Wound him badly enough to return to England or Paris with the contagion growing in his veins . . .

I have to get out.

What would Jamie do?

Poison them? Burn the place down? Blow the place up . . .?

'Tuathla!' The voice outside was a hoarse cry. Lydia heard the legs of the stool scrape, and risked the vampire's distracted attention to roll to her feet and cross the tiny cell in one long stride. A soldier stood in the lab doorway, staring into the room – yes, the revenant was standing over the torn-apart cage, greedily devouring the rat – and Meagher had sprung down from her chair . . .

I know him . . .

It was the freckled soldier Meagher had been bending over in the pre-op tent, on the night of the big push.

'Joey—!'

He won't be able to keep his hands off you, Francesca had predicted.

Joey's eyes were stretched wide, seeing her for what she was – changed, Undead, vampire – and trapped, aghast, fascinated, literally enchanted by what he saw. He whispered, 'Dear God in Heaven . . .'

Meagher crossed to him, slid her arms around his waist – he was over six feet tall and her head barely topped his breastbone – and as if against his will he bent to receive her kiss. Lydia heard him groan, in ecstasy and grief.

'You did it,' he breathed, separating his mouth from hers at last. 'Oh, *mo stór, mo chroí*, I never thought . . . I prayed and hoped another way could be found. For freedom . . . for Ireland . . .'

He shook his head, stunned, and Meagher put one small hand up to stroke his red-brown hair from his brow. 'Goose,' she murmured. 'Silly lamb.'

'And is it true?' He pulled himself together with an effort. 'This creature . . . She can control these things? You've found a way? A way you can learn now? I got word from Teague in London, they got the thing again, got it chained up good now, with silver as you said. Is there anythin' I can—?'

She said, 'Poo,' and waved her hand. 'Teague's a fool. And Francesca's a bigger one.'

He put up his hand to her cheek, but she turned away with a shrug.

'To do this,' he whispered, tears in his voice. 'To make yourself into such a creature, for the sake of our country . . . When can you—?'

'Don't be an imbecile,' Meagher snapped. 'I'm not going to do anything of the kind. To spend my time with those things?' She nodded toward the revenant, tugging at its chain and reaching now and then toward Joey, whose face convulsed with pity at the sight of it. Dirty, bestial, blood-smeared and stinking, it still wore the remains of a German uniform, a dim reminder that it had once been a man. 'Even if I could do it, without goin' mad myself—'

'Goin' mad?'

The girl laughed shortly. 'Isn't that a joke on her, with all her petting ways, and speaking to me as if I was a child? And her just hugging herself, that she can bid these things come and go: it's enough to make a cat laugh. She took one of those things into her mind, *mo chroí*, so she could get a grip on the minds of them all. And now it's *their* minds that are getting a grip on *hers*. I can see it in her eyes.'

She looked back at him, twinkling with delight, and saw the look on his face as Lydia saw it in the glare of the laboratory lights: heartbroken, disappointed, shocked, crushed.

'But what are we to do?' he stammered. 'There must be some way you can get control of these things, without . . . without riskin' of yourself. Are you sure? Teague's got the creature, and others can be made from it: *and* the thing's hand you sent along! We can't let this go now! We're so close! We can't let what you've done – my darling, my darling, how you've become – we can't let it go all for nothing . . .'

'Goose.' She stretched out her arms to him, and Lydia saw the change in his face as desire swamped all his horror, all his desperation at the shattering of their long-held plan – a desire whose insane intensity confused him all the more. Her husky voice was a caress as she stepped close to him, wound her arms once more around his waist. 'Silly goose.'

She put her palm to the side of his face, stroking ear and cheek and neck. Then with a flick she brought her hand down, and with her claw-like nails slit the veins of his throat.

Joey Strahan stepped back with a gasp but Meagher had him fast. Lydia saw him thrusting, struggling with all his strength to break her grip. She sprang up on him, literally climbed him so that her mouth could fasten on the squirting artery, and he sobbed and cried incoherent pleas and prayers as his strength gave out and he fell to his knees. Meagher dropped with him, his hair locked in one hand and the other arm still round his waist, ignoring the blows he rained on her back – by the time he realized he had to strike with all his strength, Lydia guessed that his strength was half gone.

The revenant jerked its chain, groaned and howled, smelling the blood. Lydia flinched when the young soldier started to convulse, as the blood drained from his heart and organs. His hands flailed helplessly; Meagher's dark head bent low over him as he slipped to the floor. A final spasm arched his back like a landed fish and he made a thin, protesting noise, and went limp.

Meagher sat back on her heels, her head tilted back, mouth glistening with gore. Lydia reached her cot in a soundless rush and lay down, her back to the door, and took care to breathe deeply, mimicking the rhythms of sleep. Whether the vampire came to the judas or not, Lydia didn't know – and she breathed a thousand thanks for the silver plating on the lock and bars. But she heard Meagher laugh, the thick chuckle of sated lust.

Count down from sixty ten times . . .

Fifty-nine, fifty-eight, fifty-seven . . .

A clash of chain, and the revenant's howling moan, followed by thick noises that could only be tearing flesh.

Meagher had shoved Joey's body into its reach.

. . . fifty-six, fifty-five, fifty-four . . .

'Mistress . . .'

She rolled off the cot and was by the door as Simon, in shirt-sleeves as he had been in her dream, his hands wrapped in three laboratory towels and clumsy as a drunken man's, bent gingerly to the silvered lock.

'Watch behind me—'

The door was open behind him, into the blackness of the corridor. There wasn't the slightest hope that she would hear the approach of either Meagher or Francesca before it was too late for Simon to flee, but she watched nevertheless.

Has he been hiding down here . . . for how long? If there were escaped revenants still wandering in the crypts – and how far do the crypts extend? – they must sleep in the daytime, as he did, but the risk was hideous . . . Not to speak of the rats . . .

Was that a sound in the corridor?

The lock clicked. Doubling and trebling the towels around his hand, Simon pulled the padlock loose and Lydia plunged out, and into his arms. The revenant howled again, poor Joey's blood covering its hands and chin. Simon steered her, not in the direction of the round chamber where the well was (*They must have blocked it after Simon's escape . . .*) but further up the corridor, to a narrow door and a stair that led down, barely wider than Lydia's shoulders. The darkness stank of rats, excrement, decaying flesh and the fishy reek of the revenants; cold water slopped and squished under their feet. Simon held her right hand in his, his left arm around her waist, guiding her in absolute blackness.

'They're in the vaults of the foundations,' he murmured in her ear. 'Half a dozen. They move in a group, and seem to have disregarded the Lady's summons to their brethren to go out to military exercises this evening—'

'Meagher says – Meagher told Joey—'

'The young gentleman whose liver Corporal Schultz was devouring back in the laboratory?'

'Meagher told him Francesca is beginning to – to be absorbed into the mind of the revenants. That may be the reason . . .'

'Is she, indeed?' He stopped, placed her hands on what felt like a pillar some eighteen inches in diameter, then gripped her waist in a firm hold. 'Pardon me while I execute a gavotte of joy. Keep your hands on the pillar, just as they are, while I lift you. You should feel handholds and footholds. There's a loft about five feet above the first of the footholds. Watch your head as you go through the trapdoor. The loft contains bones, but there's room to sit and to lie. *Hop-la!*'

He boosted her up as if she'd been a bunch of daisies. Lydia felt the holes in the pillar, scrambled up, as he had said, and felt the rough wood of a square trap around her, then damp wooden flooring as she pulled herself through. Her hand encountered something hard that rolled when she touched it: a human skull. She slid herself out of the way of the trap and the next moment Don Simon's sleeve brushed her as he came up through.

'Bone loft.' Lydia heard the slight grit of a cover being slipped over the trap. 'I judge 'twas formerly used for the store of food. The roof of the natural cavern is but a few feet above our heads, were we to stand. The wine vault was below us.'

'Is the way out through the well blocked?'

'With a great tangle of barbed wire. From the wine vault beneath us, a passage leads—'

'What about poor Captain Palfrey?'

'I brought him up out of the well and stanched his wound as best I might. I then put him in the motorcar, which I left at the edge of the camp, where he would be found. And I told those that loitered about the Moribund Ward, to stay away from the car and tell the others so as well. 'Twas near dawn then. I returned here the following night to find the tunnel from the well already blocked.'

'And you've been here since?'

'Where else would I be, lady? Hush,' he added softly, as she threw her arms around him again. 'Hush, lady. James will call me out, should harm befall you – or should you go on clinging to me in this fashion.' But his hands grasped hers, strong and cold. 'Listen to me now. 'Tis deep night still, and the Others still wander the crypts, in such force that 'twere peril to try to get out through the old chapel above the Arras road. There are sufficient among them that they can summon and control rats, at least some of the time.'

One hand let go of hers, and a moment later two candles, and a brass tube that rattled with the dry sound of matches, were put into hers.

'At daybreak I shall sleep. Wait a little time after that – for the Others move about longer than we – then climb down from here. From the pillar you can move in any direction and soon or late will find the wall of the wine vault. Follow this until you come to what was the great door of this place; the door itself is gone, and the stair beyond nearly filled in with rubble. You can climb past the rubble, squeezing against the wall to your right. 'Tis a short climb to another crypt, in whose floor you'll find a trap with an iron grille over it, an old drainage conduit. 'Tis wet and nasty, but leads to the caved-in crypt of the chapel, at a distance of something over a mile. Do not wait for me. Make your way back to Pont-Sainte-Félicité as quickly as you might. If James wrote two weeks ago that he was seeking military clearances to come here he might well be at the clearing station now. Tell him all and see if he can come upon a way to destroy this place utterly. Knowing James—' she heard the slight, chilly smile in his voice – 'I place great faith in his ability to do so.'

'Oh, yes,' breathed Lydia. 'Jamie's very good at that sort of thing. But you—'

He put fingers like Death's over her lips. 'I've no intention of making a martyr of myself for the good of humankind. There are other ways yet, out of this place. Now tell me of what this *Irlandésita* had to say of our fair Francesca . . . and speak soft. The Undead cannot hear so clearly through the weight of earth as they can in the night overhead, yet their ears are sharp.'

In an undervoice she related all that had taken place in the laboratory that night, not only Meagher's words to Joey, when she had casually turned her back on the scheme for which, it seemed, they had both come to the Front, but the fact that

Francesca's signals to the revenants under her control had evidently not worked on the creature chained in the lab. 'It might just be the thickness of the earth, as you say,' she whispered. 'Or the distance – I don't know where exactly they've taken the revenants for this test. But if what Meagher said is true, and Francesca is becoming *absorbed* into their minds, from taking the mind of that single revenant into hers . . . *Would* one of her fledglings be able to sense this?'

'Without a doubt. No master vampire I've ever heard of has made the attempt, to take the mind of one of the Others – with or without the pollution of their blood. I am indeed curious as to whether this pollution of the mind – the influence of the hive of the revenants themselves – will spread from Francesca's to Meagher's, through that link alone.'

'How horrible!'

'Horrible indeed,' murmured the vampire, 'if the mind and strengths of the Undead come to be added to the hive. As Graf Szgedny told you, we who walk the night conscious and aware know surprisingly little of our unspeakable cousins. If either of us be so fortunate as to emerge from these crypts undevoured, we must add this information to that store of knowledge concerning the Undead – and the Unliving. As for Mistress Meagher, it surprises me not that after going to the pains of sending one of these things to her rebel compatriots in Ireland she would abandon the whole scheme, once she became vampire herself. 'Tis what most vampires do.'

'Forget the things they loved?'

'Lose their capacity to love.' There was long silence, and when he spoke again his voice seemed barely louder than the scratch of an insect's foot passing over bone.

'Love, as I understand it, is founded in hope, and in the faith that one's soul can at length be at peace in the embrace of another soul. For the damned, there is neither hope nor faith – nor any reason not simply to take one's pleasure in the kill, which is what gives pleasure to the highest degree.'

'Not all of them,' said Lydia, remembering Basilio, screaming his friend's name.

'No,' returned the vampire. 'Not all.'

*   *   *

Light drifted from below, lantern-glow almost painfully bright after hours of utter darkness. Lydia saw that indeed she and Don Simon were in a sort of loft built over what could have been storage space below. Francesca said, 'Brainless *putain*,' and Lemoine, 'It matters not whose doing this was. What we must do is find her, before she encounters revenants down here—'

'I thought there *were* no revenants down here,' jibed Meagher.

'In the event that there are,' amended Lemoine quickly. 'And it may be that there are some that have broken free.'

Lydia worked her way, flat to the floor and soundlessly pushing herself with her toes, to the edge of the loft, and looking down, saw that thin spots had developed in the White Lady's shimmering primrose hair. The color of the hair itself had faded, streaked with the hue of dust. Through it the scalp showed rough and slightly warty. By the way Francesca's hands moved, restlessly fingering her jaw and her elbows, Lydia guessed that physical changes were beginning to overtake her as well.

We look as we always know in our hearts that we look – as we look in our own sweetest dreams.

And her dreams were being devoured, as she had devoured the souls of how many thousands over the centuries . . .

She can still use her skills of illusion to keep Lemoine from noticing – maybe even to keep Meagher from seeing changes. Maybe she's still telling HERSELF that what she feels is only her imagination. Or some effect of controlling the revenants that doesn't really matter.

Her hand closed around Simon's, as the lantern-light bobbed back the way they'd come, up the narrow stair to the corridor outside the lab. After a short time, Lydia heard the wet *splash* of shuffling footfalls, and smelled revenants, moving through the chamber below.

When Don Simon fell asleep, his hand still in hers, Lydia estimated that it must be close to six in the morning, but dared not strike even the light of a single match to check. Revenants had come into the chamber below, and for a time Lydia had heard the shriek and squeal of the rats they summoned to their hands, and the horrible noises of the revenants feeding. *I'll have to tell*

Jamie that there seem to be TWO hives down here, one under Francesca's control, and one independent.

Bother! I don't suppose I'll EVER get access to Colonel Lemoine's notes, to see how that might have come about . . . Maybe one is the German prisoners and the other is guards they might have infected? Or soldiers from the front-line trenches? Have the lines moved while I've been down here? They were only a few miles away . . .

And what do the uninfected guards up top think about all this? What do they think is going on?

The noises below died away. Lydia began to count.

When she reached sixty for what she hoped was the sixtieth time – she got distracted, retracing Simon's instructions and what she remembered about the road back to Pont-Sainte-Félicité – she lit a candle, opened the heavy trapdoor, and peered down to make sure there wasn't a revenant sleeping directly at the bottom of the pillar. Then she turned back, and took a long look at Simon, lying on his back with his neck pillowed on a femur, a great heap of brown bones rising behind him: skulls, pelvises, long bones, with ribs and vertebrae scattered about him like dried flowers. His face was peaceful, a young man's face, white eyelashes lying on the fine-grained white skin of his cheek like a child's.

He chose to be what he is.

If he hadn't, I would never have met him.

Or have met the thing he's become.

She propped her spectacles more firmly onto her nose, blew out the candle, and first climbed – then slid – down the pillar.

At the bottom she lit the candle again (*I do NOT want to trip over a revenant . . .!*) and made her careful way around the wall. She found, as Simon had said, an archway and the first two shallow steps of a wide stairway whose next step was buried in rubble. The narrow space to the right of the rubble was barely visible, even at close inspection, and thin as she was, scarcely admitted her body. Had she not had the vampire's assurance that it was indeed the way which led to the surface she would not have dared to squeeze herself in, for fear of getting stuck further in. But even when it narrowed to a crawl space, she could see the faint movement of her candle flame with the current of air, and this kept her going.

Jamie, PLEASE be at the clearing station when I get there . . .

She tried to calculate the days since Francesca had caught her in the tunnel by the well. Jamie's letter from Whitsedge Court had been dated the second of April. How long would it take him to convince the Army to give him transport to France? And if he was assigned to go to some specific place far from Flanders, how long would it take him to wangle his way out of it, acquire a motorcar (*I HOPE he isn't going to cadge a ride on a train!*) and reach Pont-Sainte-Félicité . . .

I should have left a message for him . . .

Oh, God, what if they start shelling the chapel again before I get out?

The blackness around her opened out. The dank air smelled of rats and death and revenants, but more faintly; she saw none in the low crypt into which she wriggled from the caved-in doorway. It took all her strength to wrestle the iron grille from the drain in the floor, and the stink of the old passageway beneath – it was ankle-deep in water, and too low even to stand in upright – made her queasy.

The thought of encountering a revenant down there was enough to make her understand, to the marrow of her bones, why Don Simon had put off the escape until daylight.

'*There are other ways yet, out of this place,*' he had said.

She wondered whether he'd been telling the truth.

Something over a mile, he had said. The thought was horrible, but there was no going back. She tucked her skirt more firmly up under her belt, lowered herself down and dragged the grille back into place.

The last five yards were the worst. The tunnel had been caved in, choked with rubble and mud; had she been attempting the escape by night Lydia wasn't sure she wouldn't have simply put her head down and wept. But the candle flame still leaned toward the scraped, narrow crack in the mess, and, more glorious still, pallid daylight leaked through, so Lydia simply shoved her head and shoulders into the gap between two boulders, and began to wriggle and push her way. She was conscious that the stones around her were actually stones, not earth. They'd been cut. Once she even saw the broken remains of a carven saint's face.

The daylight was almost painful.

The smell of the fresh air, when she crawled forth from a hole in the steep bank of rubble that rimmed what seemed like an enormous shell-crater, made her want to fall to her knees and weep.

She had emerged at the bottom of what seemed to be a cellar, whose vaulted roof had been shattered. Fragments of stonework littered the brick floor, and a huge spill of rubble hid the whole of one end of the chamber. Clambering up this, with much slipping and backsliding, she reached a second crypt, above which, she saw, rose the remains of the church itself. It was the same chapel near the lilacs she and Palfrey had visited – *How many days ago was it?* – and had ruled out as impossible.

Exhausted, shaking and dizzy with thirst, she scrambled up a half-ruined stair to the pounded remains of the chapel itself, and from there into a caved-in labyrinth of trenches and sandbag walls. *Just get to the road*, she thought. *SOMEBODY should be along, and I'll come up with some tale to get a lift back to the clearing station.*

German spies? Black-marketeers? She glanced down at her clothing, gray with mud and torn from two long crawls through rubble*: I came to be buried in a caved-in dugout and have no recollection of how I got there . . .*

An ambulance-wagon came rattling from the direction of Arras and Lydia stepped out and waved. *Colonel Simon and I were on our way back from Amiens and were attacked last night by a German reconnaissance party . . .*

The ambulance-wagon pulled up and a slender man in a dark mackintosh sprang from the cab: civilian trousers and shoes. At the same moment two French soldiers leaped from the back, hurried toward her. They had almost reached her when Lydia realized that the vehicle was a long-chassis Sunbeam.

Oh, damn . . .!

The civilian produced a pistol and even if he hadn't, Lydia knew she simply hadn't the strength to run away. She staggered, put one hand to her forehead, and collapsed in what she earnestly hoped was a convincing faint.

TWENTY-FIVE

'She's shamming,' said the little man in the mackintosh as the ambulance-wagon lurched into gear. Even with her eyes shut Lydia could tell he bent over her, and she caught the whiff of smelling-salts as he uncorked the bottle of them. By the nearness of Lemoine's voice, the colonel pulled the little civilian away from her cot.

'Can't you see she has been through hell, man?' Then, closer and more gently, 'You'll be all right, Madame Asher.'

'Asher?'

'Madame James Asher.' By the sound of Lemoine's voice he – and his companion – had taken a seat on the opposite cot. Very sensibly, Lydia thought, since it was pretty clear that the Arras road had been shelled again, and the ambulance-wagon bucked like a Wild West bronco. 'Her husband lectures on folklore and linguistics at New College.'

'Her husband—' Mr Mackintosh's soft, slightly nasal voice sounded amused – 'worked for seventeen years for the Foreign Office, if it's the same James Asher I worked with in '93 in Mesopotamia. And her husband, so far as I could tell when I was back in London, knows perfectly well what's going on in your research station, Colonel – which I think answers all those questions you had about how she'd gotten mixed up with the vampires. These days he works for the London nest.'

Oh, damn . . .

'I . . . She . . . *What?*'

'This woman,' sighed Mr Mackintosh patiently, 'has been lying like Ananias. You didn't even search her for picklocks, did you?'

'Of course not! And in any case, there is no lock on the inside of that door.'

Mackintosh sniffed. 'I'd say then that the woman Meagher let her out – having killed that young idiot Strahan, the kill might easily have gone to her head. Or she had some idea of shoving Mrs Asher into the arms of that abomination chained in the lab, to test her own control over it, since that's obviously been the plan from the moment Nurse Meagher figured out what you were doing with these things.'

'Nurse Meagher has been selflessly loyal! Even after she . . . she was transformed . . .'

'Cock. One of your prisoners was smuggled to London by a group of Irish gunrunners, with the intention – I should think – of holding him somewhere safe until Nurse Meagher figured out how these things can be controlled. I understand she's also been pinching tissue, which is less conspicuous to send. I have no idea what instructions she sent about safety precautions but obviously her boys botched it, because the thing got away – something a detached hand wasn't about to do. My friends at the FO got wind of it and asked me to bring it in—'

?? home side screening . . . Evidently Jamie was right . . .

'Probably put two and two together with what they may have already guessed about your show here. Whether Asher – his name was Grant, when I worked with him – is also working for the Department or for someone else, including the Irish Brotherhood, I don't know, but he clearly knows all about you. He's in Amiens now. I lost track of him last night, but I'd suggest you send one of your young ladies to make sure of him. He killed three gunrunners and the revenant in London, and his vampire partner near as dammit killed me.'

'Does anyone else know?' Lemoine sounded utterly aghast. As well he might, thought Lydia, considering how much of a secret he thought this was.

Jamie, she thought in the same moment. *Jamie here . . .*

'God knows.' Mr Mackintosh didn't sound terribly concerned about it. 'I'm only here to . . . *assist* . . . the Lady Gheric. But if I were you I'd finish that assessment of the Lady's abilities to control your little pets quick smart, and put the whole thing on an official footing. Otherwise you're going to find the entire circus taken away from you, and everyone shaking their fingers and telling you how naughty you were even to think of it. I'd also have a little chat with Nurse Meagher, as soon as she's up. And not believe a single word she says.'

*   *   *

Asher spent Friday in the cellar of a house in St Acheul, close enough to the old church there that he suspected the building's third-century crypt was one of Szgedny's daytime hiding places. The cellar was so jammed with sacks of wheat and sugar, flitches of bacon, packets of coffee, cans of petrol and boxes of cigarettes that there was barely room for a cot for Asher to doze on. His hosts – three of the biggest, toughest women he'd ever seen – cheerfully fetched him bread, cheese, pâté, tea and clean linen: 'From which army would be your preference, sir?'

Arriving in company with the Master of Prague shortly before dawn, he slept most of the day. If Lydia was in Amiens, he guessed that to hunt for her would only serve to give Crowell – if he was still in the town – time to find (and attempt to kill) him. Or, worse, would lead Crowell to Lydia. He studied again the Comte de Beaucailles's descriptions of the old convent's crypts, and with the aid of a prewar map of the Département du Nord, worked out the exact coordinates not only of the convent, but of the farthest extent of its crypts.

It would be, he guessed, a long night.

His hostesses fetched him upstairs after dark, where a handsome staff-car waited in the little courtyard ('From which army would be your preference, sir?'). 'The Boche, he's getting ready for a big push,' one of them said to him, and offered him a cigar. 'All up and down the line they're saying so. We've given you an extra pistol – there in that box on the seat – a flask of coffee, some chocolate biscuits and two Mills bombs.'

'It is as well to be prepared,' added her sister kindly.

Szgedny appeared shortly after that, paid off Mesdames and rode at Asher's side as he drove back through the dark countryside, the hooded light of the headlamps barely flickering on the desolation of mud, torn-up railway tracks, broken carts, dead horses and bombed-out villages. Again and again the car was held up by lines of wagons, struggling through the mud. Asher tried both staying on the road (deep mud and the necessity of levers and duckboards to pry the wheels clear) and veering carefully off the road through the fields (deep mud and flooded shell-holes).

It was nine o'clock before they reached Field Artillery Battery Number Twelve.

'You sure about that, sir?' The young captain in charge looked like he had neither slept nor shaved since Asher had conversed with him the day before – certainly not changed his clothing, possibly not eaten either. On the road outside the half-repaired cottage a shouting match had developed in the darkness between men driving wagon-loads of food and those offloading crates of ammunition; the guns sounded far off, a distant thunder broken by rifle-fire like lightning. 'I've heard there's some kind of Frenchie hospital station up there.'

'Our men will be cleared out by morning.' Asher touched his own orders – *sole discretion, all and any assistance* over some very formidable signatures – and the neat table of coordinates. 'The Germans have been running their own show in the crypts, using the boffins there as a blind. Believe me, it's devilish clever and I wouldn't have believed it myself if I hadn't seen it with my own eyes. This is our only way to eradicate them.'

It sounded gossamer-thin to him, but the captain frowned, looked from Asher to Szgedny. The vampire met his gaze, held his eyes quietly for a time. 'I—' the captain stammered. And then, as if remembering earlier orders, turned smartly back to Asher and saluted. 'Of course, sir. Just at sunrise.'

'Will you keep an eye on the place?' said Asher, when he and the vampire stepped out into the night once more. 'On the off-chance that the man who was waiting outside my lodgings in Amiens will appear and try to stop it? Which I wouldn't put past him,' he added, when Szgedny lifted his gray brows. 'Crowell was always an uncannily good guesser. When he realizes I gave him the slip he may work out that my next move might be—'

'*Crowell?*' It was the closest Asher had seen to the Graf looking truly surprised.

'You know the name?'

'Dear me, yes. He went by others – Jourel was one, Grassheart another. Thirty years ago, forty years ago, he was very much La Dame Blanche's minion, much as you are to Simon, and to others of the London nest. It amused her—' And his own eyes glinted as Asher opened his mouth to protest that he worked neither for Ysidro nor Grippen.

When, after all, Asher did not speak he went on, 'I think she

loved the game as a form of hunting, though she hadn't
the slightest interest in your Empire nor mine. There was a time
when I wondered if she meant to make him vampire, to serve
her. He would have been a dangerous one. So that was he?' A
corner of the Graf's long mustache lifted in his one-sided grin.

'Forty years ago.' *She must have been lurking somewhere in
the background all the time we were in Mesopotamia.*

'He's old now,' observed Szgedny. 'I begin to think your lady
wife correct in her surmise that the White Lady's bite is sterile.
She can kill, but cannot give the semblance of life in death. Like
those rare queen bees whose eggs produce only drones. Well,
well . . .'

'Will you watch for him?'

'I can remain until an hour before first light. This young man
will sleep before then—' He nodded back to the captain's rough
shelter. 'That I shall see to. Spent as he is, it should be no trouble.
I will speak to his dreams a little, to hold by your orders with
good will. By sunrise, all the revenants should be in the crypts.
And where do you go?'

For Asher had turned toward the staff-car again.

'Cuvé Sainte-Bride. I suspect if I handed in a note at the front
gate, when light is in the sky,' he added, seeing the vampire's
silvery eyes widen, 'that will give Lemoine and his staff just
enough time to run for it, and to evacuate any uninfected prisoners. But it will be impossible for any of the Undead – or the
Unliving, as you call them – to follow.'

The vampire's brow clouded. 'They will be far more inclined
to clap you in irons—'

'It's a risk I'll take. Don't fear that I'll go there a moment
before there's enough light in the sky to destroy a vampire,' he
added, seeing thought and suspicion flicker across the Graf's
face. 'I must – we must – see those things destroyed. But I won't
have the innocent destroyed with them.'

'I would hardly describe this Lemoine as innocent.'

'His guards are. Without Francesca Gheric, and the revenants
themselves, Lemoine can do no harm.'

Szgedny's eyes narrowed. For a moment Asher wondered if
the vampire had enough power of illusion to kill him in front of
half the men of the battery and every mule-driver in the British

Expeditionary Force. But the Master of Prague only gestured toward the black east, and the red flashes of fire over no man's land: 'He can do no harm until the next thing he thinks up; or someone else thinks up. There are no innocent in this war, Professor. Not Lemoine, not me, not you.'

That night Mr Jourel – which was what Dr Lemoine called Mr Mackintosh, though Lydia suspected that wasn't his real name either – came and took Lydia from her cell at gunpoint, and led her to a smaller room deeper in the crypts. Deeper underground, she thought, and more thickly insulated by the weight of the earth: *So Simon won't know I'm still down here? (Does he guess that Simon's still hiding somewhere in the crypts?) Or so Francesca won't know?*

As Jourel was leading her from the laboratory he paused in the doorway, and Lydia needed no threat from his gun, to stand quiet beside him. The first of the revenants bound for the surface passed them, stinking to heaven and walking without looking around them, or seeming to notice their surroundings. Those Lydia had seen elsewhere – in the crypts, in the Peking mines, or, horribly, in the laboratory two nights ago – had moved with a peculiarly shuffling gait, heads swinging from side to side, nostrils flaring as they sniffed for prey.

These weren't looking for prey – or for anything. They had almost the movement of marching men.

Francesca Gheric walked among them. Her awareness sharpened by years of discreet cosmetic use, Lydia noticed the White Lady's carefully powdered cheeks and chin, through which faint bruises still showed, where the shape of her face was beginning to alter. The Lady's head had begun to have that slight characteristic side-to-side movement, and once or twice she could not keep herself from picking at her own collarbone and wrists.

And more than anything else, there was an indefinable change: in her posture, in her step, in her eyes.

Maybe if she hadn't been among the revenants, it would have been less obvious.

Lydia counted twelve revenants, each an ambulatory reservoir of further infection.

There had been thirteen in the long crypt.

Lemoine followed, notebook in hand. He was making notes as he walked, keeping a sharp eye on his charges, so that he – no more than had Francesca – didn't see his guest and Lydia, standing in the laboratory door. Jourel's childlike left hand, resting on Lydia's shoulder, tightened slightly and she wondered if Lemoine knew she'd been taken from her cell and what the old man beside her would do if she cried out.

But the thought of what the revenants might do if Francesca's concentration on them broke closed her throat. Without a sound she watched them pass along the corridor and ascend the stair into darkness.

The lower level of the crypts, entered through a winding stair at the far end of the reeking chamber in which the revenants had been kept chained, was flooded a few inches deep in water that reeked of soured decay. A small lantern hung at the bottom of the stair, its light just sufficient to show her rats: living ones crawling along the stonework, chewed carcasses littering the stair and bobbing in the dirty water. Thirty feet away, among the squat arches of the convent's deepest foundations, a chair stood ready, with a larger lantern on a goods box beside it and two pairs of handcuffs locked, one on either side, to the chair's frame. Lydia wondered in panic if she could kick Jourel and flee, but she knew from the stink, and the floating carrion, that revenants hid here.

He's going to ask me about Jamie . . .

She hadn't seen Meagher with Francesca and Lemoine, and wondered when she'd put in an appearance. Was Meagher still asleep? It was early. Did Francesca, like the revenants, now wake a little earlier than sunset?

They can't kill me. Lemoine will be furious.

But Lemoine isn't here NOW.

But when they reached the bottom of the steps, Jourel pushed her back against one of the niter-crusted archways, turned her roughly to face him and demanded, 'What's happened to Francesca?'

'She took the mind – the soul – of an infected man into her own.' Lydia was astonished at how calm her own voice sounded. 'That's how she's controlling the revenants. It's how she gained access to the . . . the group-mind, I suppose you'd call it. Control of the revenants was the price Lemoine asked, you see, to help her make fledglings. But now *it's* starting to control *her*.'

'You're lying. She'd never have touched the blood of those things.'

'She didn't.' Lydia tried to sound matter-of-fact, as if there were no gun digging into her left seventh rib. 'She absorbed its soul without drinking its blood, at the moment of its death. I was there. They burned it up in acetylene flame, the same as they did the two vampires whose deaths – whose souls – she absorbed, in order to let her make fledglings in the first place.'

His bead-black eyes narrowed, though the lined features remained expressionless – as Jamie could go expressionless when he was thinking – in the dim glow of the smaller lantern near by them. 'You know a great deal about it, young lady.'

'Well, as you said yourself,' she pointed out reasonably, 'my husband and I have been dealing with the London vampires for the past eight years. Think about it,' she added. 'Vampires look how they think they looked in life. That's why most of them look young, you know. But it seems to work both ways now. She's starting to *think* she looks like a revenant. She is becoming one in her own mind. Becoming what they are: appetite, with the mind that controls it eaten away. And maybe the minds of the two vampires she devoured are still alive, after a fashion, within hers. Alive and welcoming the revenants in, as a way of destroying her. Maybe that's why vampires don't devour their own kind. She didn't drink their blood, either. Ask Meagher,' she began to add, but her captor's eyes had shifted past her, gazing into the blackness of the sub-crypt.

In a voice hoarse with rage he whispered, 'Bitch.'

His hand tightened painfully over Lydia's arm and the barrel of his pistol pressed into her side. But it was not of her, she realized, that he spoke.

'Stupid, lying bitch. All these years of waiting—'

The black eyes snapped back to her and he said, 'What does your husband know of this?'

Nothing, not a thing . . .

How much can he reasonably have learned?

'He knows about the revenants,' she said, hoping she still sounded as if she weren't making this up as she went along. 'I don't know whether he knows about this place or not.' *Has this man deciphered my letters to Jamie?* 'He knows Lemoine has been using German prisoners—'

'How did you know how to get inside here?'

'Don Simon – one of the vampires – showed me.'

'Who is your husband working for?'

'I don't know,' said Lydia simply. 'I haven't been home since November.'

'How did—?' He turned his head sharply at a noise. Movement in the blackness of the crypt and the faint, almost soundless whisper of stirred water. Then eyes gleamed in the lantern-light. Lydia's heart was in her throat at the thought of a revenant, but it was Tuathla Meagher, her nurse's uniform damp and dirty now but her face deathlessly beautiful, framed in the blackness of her hair.

Jourel shook Lydia roughly, demanded, 'Is what this bitch says true? About Francesca?'

'You've noticed, have you?' The jewel-blue eyes smiled briefly, amused, into Lydia's, like a child speaking to a puppy. Then her glance returned to the old man. 'And noticed a great deal more than that, I see. You must be Crowell. I'm Meagher. She's spoken of you.'

'Has she, now?' Jourel – Crowell, and Lydia hoped that actually was his name – gave a single, snickering laugh. 'The one who was going to raise an army of revenants and free Ireland?'

Meagher waved her hand, like a coquette dismissing the recollections of a schoolroom passion. 'Guilty as charged, my lord.' Lydia remembered poor freckled Joey, whispering of freedom for their homeland. 'I calculate – at the rate she's deteriorating – it's going to be about two more days before she loses the ability to keep Lemoine from seeing anything's wrong. Another beyond that for her mind to disappear. Nasty *cailleach* . . . I'd have left last night,' she added, with the sidelong, alluring grin she'd given poor Joey, 'but I heard you were coming.'

Their gazes locked, and held.

Understanding one another.

Meagher went on, 'She planned to go to Paris. The master there's weak, she said. A fool. Moreover, the Master of Paris is *here*, someplace on the Front.'

'That's what she said to me,' returned Crowell. 'That she and I would rule Paris, forever, between us. But as for laying my life into the hand of a woman I've just met two minutes ago . . .'

'What choice do you have?' Meagher stepped closer, sinking her voice though there was no one (except herself, Lydia noted nervously) to hear. 'Whatever contamination she avoided in her blood, it's in her brain now. If she made you vampire, it would pass to you. You'd be scratching in a corner eating rats and liking it inside a week. She said you were the best, Crowell: clever and strong and ruthless. With you, she said, she could rule half Europe.'

'And she would rule me.' Crowell's voice was equally soft. 'But I knew her. We knew each other, worked together, for long, long years. I knew what I'd be getting, as her . . . partner. And so I waited, while she sought for a way to overcome her barrenness, like a biblical matriarch rooting for mandrakes. But you . . .'

The vampire smiled again, and shook her head. 'What choice have you, *mo grá*? All those years of waiting . . .' Her voice teased, as if savoring his bitterness. 'And now 'tis gone, because of her impatience for it . . . Or was it yours? How many more years would you have waited? *Could* you have waited? How many more years before your own brain started to go, along with your eyesight and your bowels and the heat in your loins?' Her fingers brushed his body as she spoke of it. 'How many years till you were too weak to hold onto the hand she stretched out to you, to carry you across Death? She put you at that risk, remember, for the off-chance of having you be *her* servant and no other's.'

Crowell said nothing, and they stood like lovers, hesitating before a kiss from which each knows there will be no going back. But, Lydia noticed, his grip on her arm did not slacken one bit. Nor his grip on his revolver.

'And when she comes back,' whispered Meagher, 'she'll want you. She slapped me like a housemaid, only for looking hard at the bruises on her face, where her jaw's growin' out into a snout. She wants you for her own fledgling and if you don't go to her of your own you know she'll take you. Then the pair of you can sit and eat rats together.

'This is your last chance.' The vampire swayed closer to him,

blue eyes glowing like sea jewels into his. 'And you know it. Or
do you know another vampire, whom you trust more than me?'

'You're something of a *cailleach* yourself,' murmured Crowell,
'*acushla*. Here?'

'I've been through the whole of the vault. Even the strays and
runaways are gone out; they won't be back till near dawn. You'll
fall asleep for a few hours . . .'

Her glance went to Lydia, and her smile widened.

'And wake hungry.'

TWENTY-SIX

From the hillslope above the Arras road, James Asher could
look east across to the ruined land where the French Second
Army had driven back the Germans in January.

He'd hiked these roads as a young man, tramping through
Picardy during one of his vacations from Oxford, picking up
strange old legends and half-forgotten words, tales of Celtic gods
or of peasant girls who achieved good fortune from fairies by
woodland wells. The well and grotto – the *cuvé* in question – at
Sainte-Bride had long been sacred to the goddess who had later
been adopted into the Catholic church as a saint, and Asher
recalled the scene before him as it had been back in the early
eighties: lush meadows dotted with black-and-white cattle, fields
hip-deep in growing wheat. Lines of elms, an echo of the back
lanes of Kent in his boyhood. Birdsong, and the whisper of wind.

A ghastly wasteland of mud and shell-holes and caved-in
trenches under the sickly moon. And – not clearly visible from
the road that ran along the feet of these low hills – a hideous
suggestion of movement in the abyssal shadows of those trenches.

The Front lay three miles to the east, but the supply-routes to
the firing line did not cross these lands. There had been no traffic
on the road for hours. A glance at his watch showed Asher that
it was a quarter to four. An hour until the first glimmerings of
light.

He trained his binoculars on the two figures at the side of the

road. A broad-shouldered man in the gray-blue uniform of a
French officer, his left arm in a sling. A pale-haired woman in
white, like a spirit in the moonlight. He saw her raise her arms,
and the man looked out with his own field glasses, over the
mud and the darkness.

All along the line of one trench, shadowy forms emerged from
the earth. As they shambled toward the road in a ragged line
Asher saw movement around their feet, as if the earth squirmed,
and he shivered at what he was pretty sure that was. In a way,
he thought, Lemoine scarcely needed the revenants, if through
them Francesca the White could achieve control over the rats.
While he watched, one of the revenants stumbled, staggered and
fell, entangled in the remains of the barbed wire that both sides
had stretched across no man's land. Like an insect caught in a
spider's web it thrashed, kicked, and the creatures nearest it
swung around, converged, almost certainly at the smell of its
blood. But at the roadside Francesca the White raised her hand,
and the revenants turned away, and kept moving in the line of
their march.

Asher estimated the distance. A good half-mile – *Can she
operate out of line-of-sight?*

Can she see through their eyes? Their minds?

Vampires could walk in the dreams of the living. Could, under
certain circumstances, control their bodies, ride them like rented
horses, see through their eyes, speak through their mouths. Single
individuals, but what about the collective mind, formed of individual consciousnesses whose self-awareness was gone?

A sound in the trees behind him. Momentary as a thought, the
filthy smell that disappeared almost at once . . .

So not all of them were down across the road. Some, at least,
escaped her control. An effect of distance? Or was her control
not absolute? Asher listened behind him, heard nothing.
Nevertheless, he began to move down slope, to where he'd left
the motorcar, concealed by the broken ruin of what had once
been a farmhouse.

He moved carefully, knowing he'd be visible to someone
across the road in the flatlands, if they happened to look his
way. The rise of land where he'd stood had commanded a view
of the convent, on the next slope of ground. What little remained

of the moon was sinking in the sky, and even shot to pieces and winter-barren, the woods would be pitch dark. He could only hope that Francesca the White and Dr Lemoine were too preoccupied with their observations – and their control – of the revenants to see him.

How much of her mind does she need, to control them? he wondered. *And how is Lemoine going to phrase this, in his report to the French High Command? 'I have turned German prisoners into mindless monsters which I'm paying a vampire to control for us. They're cheap to feed and don't mind being killed and oh, by the way, be very careful about contact with good Frenchmen . . .'*

And how long is it going to be before we run out of prisoners and start looking for 'volunteers' in our own ranks? He could think of a couple of his scholastic colleagues – not to speak of Marcellus Langham, hungry for his promotion – who'd be perfectly happy to see 'niggers' from India or Algiers pushed into the ranks of mindless cannon fodder. *Ah, well,* 'dulce et decorum est' *and all that, old boy . . .*

His mind briefly conjured the fifth year of the war, when the Germans had adopted the same method of fighting – *and surely there's a German vampire who wants something badly enough to strike the sort of bargain the White Lady struck* – and no man's land had spread across half the world, revenants mindlessly fighting revenants in the shell-cratered ruins of Paris, London, Berlin . . .

The revenants broke from their line, and began to move toward the road.

Damn it.

He'd been seen.

He left off the cautious smoothness of his walk and ran for the car, weakness clutching his chest and limbs like a leaden shroud and terror searing him. *Do NOT let yourself be caught, do NOT . . .*

He stumbled, scrambled up, dizzy and gasping – the foremost grabbed his arms and Asher shucked out of his greatcoat, turned, and fired his pistol point-blank between the creature's eyes. The thing stumbled and Asher didn't look back, knowing it would be on its feet and after him but blind. He reached the car with ten revenants from across the road lumbering toward him – two emerged from the woods behind the car: no thoroughfare in that direction, it would take too long to turn . . .

He snatched up one of the Mills bombs and flung it at those in front, far too close to the front of the car but he was past caring; crammed himself behind the dashboard and felt the car jolt in the blast, fragments of steel (and of revenants) spattering against the vehicle's sides. *Now if only there's enough left of the road to drive on . . .*

He came up from behind the dash, yanked the self-starter and got nothing. Half a dozen revenants were only yards away and even those that had been shattered by the blast were crawling in his direction. He turned with his pistol as those behind the car scrambled onto its back . . .

Then they sprang off, as if the metal were hot.

At the same moment those in the road before him stopped, and turned away. As if he'd suddenly become invisible, or someone had blown a magic whistle.

They started to stride off down the road, in the direction of Cuvé Sainte-Bride.

Asher looked back, automatically, toward where Francesca had stood beside the road, some fifty yards from the car, pale in the moonlight. She was still there, Lemoine grasping her arm – Asher heard him shout something at her but could not make out words. He saw the woman pull against the Frenchman's grip, with a curious, swaying movement that reminded him eerily of the revenants themselves. Lemoine jerked his hand towards Asher – *Asking something? Ordering something?*

Francesca lunged at him, twisting her arm free and seizing the officer around the neck. Lemoine was taller than she, and built like an old-time warrior; still she twisted and shook, in a single, vicious gesture, and Asher saw the colonel's body spasm and his knees buckle, and knew she'd broken his neck.

Then she was running across the road in a swirl of white: ivory gown, pale hair flowing like a cloak. She moved with the curious light swiftness, faster than any human speed, which the vampires usually hid from living eyes, and the remaining half-dozen revenants stampeded around her.

The roar of a motorcycle made him swing around. . . .

Chest burning, knees shaking with exhaustion, Asher was too flattened with weariness even to feel surprise at the sight of Don Simon Ysidro on a dispatch rider's 550 Model-H Triumph. 'Get on,' said the vampire.

Asher obeyed, though Ysidro showed no sign of turning the bike around and evidently proposed to head straight past the last of the revenants. 'Where's Lydia?'

'She has to be at the convent. I felt no trace of her when I woke—' They were already careening up the road, weaving past the gore-littered crater left by the Mills bomb, gaining on the revenants – 'but she's not at the clearing station—'

Asher didn't ask what the hell Lydia had been doing at Cuvé Sainte-Bride in the first place, when Ysidro and his '*mignonne*', as Elysée had said, had been reported getting clear of the place . . .

Unless he has another living assistant that he was seen leaving with . . .

They swept past the revenants. Francesca had outdistanced them, and was now nowhere in sight.

'They're going to shell it out of existence at sunrise.'

'Good,' said Ysidro. 'Then we'll have to hurry.'

When Meagher came down the narrow stair again Lydia knew it must be shortly before first light.

The small lamp by the stair arch had gone out: Lydia knew they burned for about six hours on one filling, but had no way of knowing how long it had been kindled before the man Crowell had dragged her down to the vaults. Sick horror filled her at the thought that the larger lantern at her side would go out before Crowell woke, leaving her to listen in the darkness.

For revenants. For Crowell. For rats.

For death . . .

Oh, Miranda, I'm sorry! Jamie, I'm so sorry . . .

They'd left her handcuffed to the chair while they'd gone upstairs again, to fetch down a cot and a chain. Lydia thought, given time, she could have done something to break the chair – which was a common, wooden kitchen chair – before Crowell woke, but they'd fixed the handcuffs to the chain and the chain around one of the squat Romanesque pillars that held up the groined roof, and she knew there was no getting out of that.

Meagher had drunk Crowell's blood, and he, dying, hers, as she'd laid him down on the cot a few feet from Lydia. Then Meagher had smiled, and with the old man's blood on her lips had come over and given Lydia a playful kiss, enjoying her dread, before disappearing up the stair into the darkness. Lydia had wiped the blood off on her shoulder the moment the vampire was gone.

Then for several hours – as nearly as Lydia could estimate it – she had alternately pulled and twisted at the handcuffs, to utterly no avail, and had watched, with a deep interest that at times overcame her dread, the changes passing over Crowell's dead body.

His eyes didn't settle, as the eyes of corpses do after about thirty minutes. In between bouts of digging and scratching and scraping at the chain where the handcuffs were attached (and which she could not quite reach owing to the chain's tautness around the pillar), she tried to see whether Crowell was developing hypostasis on his shoulders, buttocks and the back of his head. *Probably not*, she thought. *And of course he won't develop rigor either, even in this cold.* She wished the light was better, and that she could examine him more closely. (*And while I'm wishing, I wish that I could run away . . .*) His face had gone the horrible, bleached, waxy yellow of a corpse's face, and his mouth had dropped slightly open.

His mind, Lydia was well aware – while wondering what that was actually like – was alive, tucked in some corner of Meagher's consciousness.

Some part of it would always stay there.

There's got to be SOME way out of here . . .

Does Simon know about this sub-crypt? She didn't know. *I don't see how he could. While he's awake the revenants have been down here, and when they're asleep, he's asleep.*

Because they are of the same order of being. Unliving and Undead. Terrifyingly similar . . .

Now and then she'd lash with her foot at exploring rats, but she noticed that the rats – which, she had observed in the clearing station, were very quick to ascertain when a human being was helpless – went nowhere near the vampire.

In time, even the waxed leather of her stout shoes grew wet, and her feet got numb from cold.

Miranda, she thought, and to her mind came again her last sight of her child, by the nursery fire. Smiling, thinking her mother was only going down to London for a day. *Oh, my poor baby, I hope Jamie gives you all the love I would have done . . .*

Then Meagher was there, standing on the edge of the lantern-light at the bottom of the stair.

She gave Lydia a smile and stroked her cheek as she passed; her hand, Lydia observed, was warm. She'd fed, either out in no man's land or in the trenches, scavenging the deaths so freely harvested by war. Looking back at Crowell as Meagher crossed to his cot, Lydia observed that the wrinkles had all but disappeared from his face, and that his hair had darkened, from white to a deep, sable brown. A young man's face. The nails on his child-like hands had become glassy and thick, lengthened to half an inch or so beyond the fingertips. In his half-open mouth Lydia glimpsed the fangs. Meagher stood for a moment looking down at him, smiling, and her smile wasn't one of tenderness.

It was a smile of triumph. Of pleasure, and the anticipation of pleasure to come.

He was the best, according to Francesca. The living man who would make a very, very good vampire. Lydia had the uncomfortable feeling she'd met others who fit that description – her stepmother leaped to mind. What had Meagher said? *Smart, strong and ruthless . . .*

Appetite that cares about nothing but itself.

Francesca had worked with Crowell, for years, evidently, in something of the same way Simon had worked with her and Jamie . . . *Is that what Simon would say of Jamie? Is that what he'd see in him?*

Exhausted, terrified, it was hard to tell, or to think clearly.

You'll wake hungry . . .

Meagher knelt in the shallow water at Crowell's side, and bent over him, her black hair framing his face as she pressed her lips to his. Lydia shivered, but couldn't look away. Couldn't mentally keep herself from taking notes. For some reason she thought of the vampire-hunter Osric Millward – *He'd want to know this kind of thing . . .*

And I'll need to tell Jamie . . .

But I won't be seeing Jamie again, ever. Or Simon. Or my child . . .

Crowell's hand twitched, and Meagher covered it with her own. His whole body shivered, and he pulled his hand free, grasped her arm, clung to her for an instant. Their lips still locked, as she released back into him the consciousness, the soul, that she'd carried in her own mind while his body died.

Released it back . . . but not all of it. She kept part of it within herself.

Then Crowell turned his head, as if denying that his first instinct had been to seek protection, and opened his eyes. They caught the lantern's reflection, like a cat's.

Lydia thought she should probably pray for her own soul but couldn't come up with any words.

'Pritchard?' said Meagher softly, and his hand returned to her arm, stroking this time. '*Mo chroí . . .*'

'Forty years,' he murmured. 'Forty years I've waited. I always wondered what it would be like. She made me wait . . . Just so that I would be hers, and not someone else's.'

'And now you're mine.' She nodded toward Lydia, without taking her eyes from Crowell's. 'Are you hungry? Will you play for a bit? Unchain her and blow out the lantern? They're still out with the Others, we have a little time. They won't be back till just before—'

'Whore—' The word came out of the darkness of the stairway like an animal's bleat, hoarse and bestial, as if formed with difficulty and pain. 'Swill-bellied stinking whore—'

Meagher and Crowell swung around like guilty lovers, staring into the darkness.

A white blur shimmered beyond the lantern-light. A huge clawed hand grasped the lintel of the narrow door as Francesca Gheric lurched into the glow.

'You dared. You *dared*—'

Crowell rolled off the cot and darted away into the darkness; Meagher sprang in the opposite direction, as Francesca lunged at her, snatching with her claws. *And now Crowell can get up the stair and away . . .*

It's what Jamie would have done . . .

If the woman he was leaving behind wasn't me.

A flicker near the stair – *Yes, that's him, all right . . .*

Crowell froze with his foot on the lowest step, light and thin and active, a young man again. In the dark of the stair above him, eyes gleamed. Stench rolled into the room like the black exhalation of Hell.

In the darkness Meagher shrieked, and Lydia had to shut her jaw hard to keep from screaming, too. She flattened back against the pillar, watched in terror as the revenants piled into the room. Six of them, mouths stretched open, howling and reaching—

—and running right past her as Francesca shouted, 'Kill them! Kill them!'

Water splashed, dashing about in the blackness as Meagher had moments ago suggested as a game. Meagher screamed again—

The next instant another pair of eyes flashed in the stairway and Simon and Jamie were beside her. Lydia choked back her husband's name as Simon made short work of the chain with a pair of bolt cutters. Behind them Crowell and Meagher screamed, but the two men ran her to the stair and scrambled up the slippery, crooked steps. *If I say anything Francesca will hear me—*

Will she care if we get away?

Probably not – she seemed MUCH more interested in making sure the revenants chomped up Meagher and Crowell – *but let's not take chances . . .*

She clung to the arms that held her in the darkness, Jamie's lanky with muscle, Simon's like a dancer's, leading the way through the abysses. She was aware of it when Jamie stumbled – *Good Heavens, he shouldn't be running around breaking into vampire lairs anyway . . .*

Through a doorway and into the storeroom with the drain in the floor, and the electric light of the laboratory pouring from the corridor. Jamie – as sheet-white as a vampire but looking far less healthy – rushed her along that hallway toward the stair and Lydia straightened her glasses and gasped, 'What about the guards?'

'Gone,' he panted. 'The prisoners, too. The Twelfth Field Artillery Battery is going to start shelling this place in eight minutes— Sunrise—'

Lydia looked back in panic, but Simon was gone. Stumbling,

Jamie dragged her up the stair, through an old stone room and then through a modern wooden one, and out into a courtyard gray with misty dawnlight. *If they shell it as they did the chapel by the lilacs even the deepest vault will be laid bare. The light will consume Francesca, destroy the revenants . . .*

Burn Simon to ashes . . .

NO . . .

There was a motorcycle in the middle of the courtyard and Jamie flung himself onto it, Lydia straddling the carrier *à l'Amazone* and clinging around her husband's waist. The morning air was freezing and she barely felt it. Rooster tails of liquescent mud splattered up around them in all directions as they roared toward the open gate, between the lines of barbed wire and the defensive trench, past the empty guardhouse and along the rutted track toward the Arras road.

Simon, she thought. *Simon can get to the tunnel that leads to the well, hidden in the darkness . . .*

Will that be protection enough?

She knew she shouldn't hope that it would be. Pressed her cheek to Jamie's back, and hung on tight.

Distantly – five miles at least – heavy guns began to sound, and in moments she heard the shattering freight-train roar of shells overhead. The road beneath them lurched, making the motorcycle jerk like a terrified horse, and even at this distance Lydia felt the shock wave of the first explosions, and the vicious spray of rocks and hot dirt pelting her back.

By the time they stopped to breathe, four or five miles down the road toward Pont-Sainte-Félicité, Lydia had stopped crying.

TWENTY-SEVEN

Lydia got two weeks' leave, to go back to England. Jamie didn't.

'This is what I traded to Stewart,' he said, 'for that "at his sole discretion" and "any and all assistance" on my papers.'

Against the glowing lights of the clearing station's tents

shadows moved, preparing men for surgery, ascertaining how much damage had been done, writing tickets for the next stage of care. Now and then, in one of the wooden buildings – or the additions built onto the charred ruins of Pont Sainte-Félicité – a door would open, and men's voices would be heard. Storeman Pratt walked by the bench where they sat, outside the officer's mess, with what looked like an entire crate of cigarettes casually tucked under his arm.

The wet, grievous stink of mud and smoke and decaying flesh mingled with the smell of the river, and the April green of a few ruined trees.

'The understanding was that I'd have a free hand – a *completely* free hand – in gathering information, even if it meant shelling a French Army research project on the grounds that it was actually being used by Germans. I had to commit myself to gathering information.'

He coughed, deeply and painfully. He'd spent forty-eight hours in the Isolation Ward with a low fever and Lydia thought he still looked haggard and shaky. It was good only to sit beside him, to hold his hand.

Near the makeshift bridge, ambulance-wagons rumbled in and bearers clustered around with their lanterns, and from the corner of her eye Lydia thought she saw two shadows – the dark woman with the big nose, and a gray-haired man like a Slavic god – flit in the direction of the Moribund Ward.

Far off, the guns boomed like thunder.

'Is that what you told them? That it was really the Germans behind that project?'

Jamie had spent most of the afternoon – when he should have been sleeping – writing up a report about why he'd instructed the men of Field Artillery Battery Twelve to shell Cuvé Sainte-Bride into a crater of sunbathed dust.

'With Colonel Lemoine dead I could say anything I wanted. I said that the whole project was a German plan to spread plague among our troops. I wasn't that far from the truth.'

'He meant well.' Lydia shook her head. 'So did poor Meagher. I wish I could feel towards them something other than horror at the means they proposed to use. At their blindness to the devastation it would cause.'

'They meant well,' agreed Jamie quietly. 'And too often, people who mean well find it hard to believe that the thing that will win them their victory is too dangerous to use, or might have consequences that they don't foresee. And don't want to hear arguments to the contrary.'

He lifted his hand to return Captain Palfrey's salute as that young man walked past in hospital blues. It was Palfrey's first day on his feet; the young man had asked Lydia, daily, when she'd gone in to visit him, if she had heard word of 'Colonel Simon'. He clearly had not the smallest recollection of the scene in the laboratory. Or he recalled it quite differently.

Jamie had surmised – when he and Lydia had talked it over – that it was Don Simon bringing Palfrey out of the well that Johanna of Berlin had seen and told Elysée about. With the woman's bad French it was not surprising that Elysée had mistaken the sex of the reported 'minion'. He had also filled in for her his recollections of Pritchard Crowell: 'Had I still been working with him, once I came to know the London nest, I think I would have spotted at once that he had a vampire partner. At least I like to think I would.'

'And your Mr Langham covered for him, when he faked his own death . . . What was it, twenty years ago?'

Jamie had nodded. 'I suspect if I'd continued much longer in the service I'd have been obliged to do the same,' he said. 'It isn't uncommon in the Department. You go into hiding, you make a new life, where those you've wronged and those you've betrayed and those whose loved ones you've killed won't find you. But the Department knows. And the Department can always come calling, if they need you.'

As Simon had, thought Lydia, eight years ago, when the London nest found itself in need of a day man.

'Or members of the Department,' he'd added, 'who have some little scheme of their own going, in hopes of a promotion or a knighthood.'

Lydia hoped that in time Captain Palfrey would return to his grandfather's estate and 'wait for orders' that would never come. That he'd marry his lovely Miss Bellingham and live happily ever after without ever returning to Europe again.

Now she asked softly, 'Will you be all right?'

Jamie nodded, and coughed again. 'Mostly what I'll be doing is listening,' he said. 'Dressing up in German uniform and sitting with prisoners. Finding out about troop movements, and conditions in the Fatherland. Looking at pictures and newspaper articles, deducing the conditions of their economy from toffee wrappers. Letting the boffins back in England guess where we need to apply pressure, and what kind of inducements to hold out if they ever get round to negotiating for truce.'

'Will they make you go to Germany?'

He was a long while silent. Then: 'I don't know.'

'I'm committed to another year here,' she said after a time. 'Ellen writes me that Miranda is well and happy with Aunt Lavinnia, but asks after us. I think when my year is up I'll ask for my papers, depending on where you are in your work. It must have been hard for you,' she added, 'signing up . . .'

Another silence. James, Lydia had learned, was a man who didn't speak easily of could-be's or might-have-been's. Like herself, he dealt with the world as it came at him. At length he said, 'They had to be stopped.'

He'd spoken to her of getting help from the vampire-hunter Osric Millward. In times past they'd made the man a figure of fun, but she knew that in his heart Jamie understood him. And understood that he was right.

'It's all very well to talk about doing evil that good may come, best beloved,' he went on. 'But the problem about evil is that the line is seldom clear, how evil is evil. And how much evil will bleed into the good you're trying to do – like the virus of the revenants, spreading in one's veins.'

'Not to speak,' added Don Simon Ysidro's soft voice, 'of the difficulty one can have in distinguishing when evil is masquerading as good.'

He stepped from the darkness, his uniform new and trim and looking as if he'd never gone crawling through old drains or cut his way through barbed wire, or done whatever he'd done to get himself to safety. He took Lydia's hand in his own gloved one, and bent over it.

'I am glad to see you well, Mistress. And yourself, James.'

With an ironic twist to his mouth, Jamie saluted him, which the vampire calmly returned.

'You will be pleased to hear that the matter of the shelling of Cuvé Sainte-Bride is being hushed up under the Official Secrets Act,' he reported. 'And that those of us who hunt the night have passed across no man's land for two days now, and have encountered no sign of revenants. I understand Colonel Lemoine's body was recovered after the destruction of Cuvé Sainte-Bride, and returned to his family, with no stain on his record.'

'Thank you,' Jamie said quietly. 'That means a great deal, to families.'

'It did to mine.'

The vampire turned to Lydia, and again took her hand. 'And you are returning to England, lady?'

'For two weeks.' She spoke around a sudden tightness in her throat. 'I'm taking the evening train from St-Omer Thursday. I'll return to finish out my year—' She fought back the grief she felt, the concern about all those young men in the surgical tent, the hundreds – thousands – who had passed beneath her hands since November. 'But I don't want you watching over me when I return. Nor ever again.'

He said nothing, and there was neither grief, nor question, nor surprise in his yellow eyes.

Beside her, Jamie was silent also, though she felt his eyes touch her.

'I don't care how much trouble I get in,' she made herself go on. 'Or what's happening around me, or whether I need help or not. I can't . . .'

He inclined his head. 'As you will, lady.'

'And I release you,' added Jamie quietly, 'from whatever promise you made to me, Don Simon.'

'I understand.' His glance returned to Lydia, and she knew that he did.

She turned her hand in his, and holding it, drew off his silk-fine, gray kid glove, and felt his fingers, clawed like a dragon's. They were warm. He'd fed.

Probably over in the Moribund Ward . . .

With the others of his kind.

Fed on young men dying, men she'd cared for that afternoon. She remembered their faces. Their wounds. The names they'd whispered in delirium, friends and sweethearts and children they'd never see again.

She couldn't speak.

'I chose to be as I am,' said Simon quietly. 'Not the best decision in my life, but one from which there is no going back. No more than these men—' He nodded towards the soft glow of the tents – 'can go back from the choice they made. I can be nothing but what I am, lady: a killer who devours the lives of others. I do not ask you to forgive me either my choice, or my current state.'

She couldn't look at him, either. Only sat, looking down at the long, slim hand in hers.

A demon's hand.

He saved my life at the risk of his own. And . . . She shut her mind on the further thought: *And I care for him* . . .

How can I go on accepting that he kills people, regularly, for his own benefit?

There could be no condoning what he was – what he did, and the side of his existence that he hid from her – no matter how convenient it was for her.

Gently he withdrew his hand, and she was desolate at the thought of never hearing his voice again.

Asher and Lydia got a ride on an ambulance-wagon to St-Omer the following afternoon. They had dinner in a small *auberge* near the cathedral, then walked to the station in the damp cold of the spring night: Lydia had some twenty minutes to wait for her train to Calais; Asher's, to Amiens, would leave in an hour. They were standing together, handfast, marveling in one another's presence, speaking softly of Oxford and Miranda and what codes they'd use to defeat the censors, when shouting started around the telegraph offices at the end of the platform: Asher heard someone yell, 'Ypres!'

Another Jerry push, he thought. The one everybody had been expecting.

People crowded in that direction. Military police and railway officials began to work their way along the platform, stopping people from getting on the trains.

''Strewth!' exclaimed a young man in a sapper's uniform close by, to a friend on a stretcher. 'They fookin' better not be confiscatin' these trains—'

Lydia's eyes widened in protesting dismay, and yes, the officials were getting on the trains, herding people off, soldiers mostly bound for leave, a few civilians complaining vociferously that they had their papers, by God . . .

The crowd mobbed tighter around the telegraph office, and Asher heard someone shout, 'Poison gas—'

He caught the arm of one of the military police as the man moved toward Lydia's train. 'What is it?'

'Jerry's hit Ypres. Chlorine gas – four miles of line – thousands of the French dead in minutes—' The man's voice shook a little. 'Most of 'em drowned in the fluid in their own lungs. Or had their eyes burned out. We're gonna need every train.'

The shouting was growing louder, as crowds of soldiers jostled on the platforms. Bearers were already coming to carry the wounded back to waiting rooms. People called questions, cursed, groaned. A delicate little VAD, bringing tea to the waiting men on the stretchers, swore like a sergeant of the Marines.

'—still fighting – Canadians holdin' the line, some of the Frenchies as well. Damn bloody bastards—'

Asher didn't mention that the French had also experimented with poison gas.

Behind her thick spectacles, Lydia's eyes filled with tears.

She said quietly, 'I have to go back.'

'I know.'

'Please . . .' She stayed the sergeant, as he would have gone on. 'Transport back to the Front . . . I'm an expert at fluoroscope. I should get back to my unit . . .'

'Bless you, M'am.' The man saluted her. 'Where'll that be?'

'The clearing station at Pont-Sainte-Félicité.'

'There'll be a convoy of ambulance-wagons outside the City Hall at ten. But they may take you on up to Ypres instead . . .'

'That's all right. Thank you . . .'

She turned back to Asher. 'If they cancel your train—'

'I'll find another.' He took her in his arms, kissed her gently. 'And I'll wire Ellen, and your aunt—'

Her arms tightened hard around him, pulling back only a moment to remove her spectacles before pressing her face to his shoulder. 'I'm sorry—'

'Go.' He kissed her temple, then, when she raised her face

to his, her lips. 'I'll write to you there, and let you know where I am.'

It was ten minutes to ten. He watched her walk away along the platform, tallish, skinny, her gray nurse's cloak billowing slightly around the carpetbag she carried, her red hair screwed tightly up under her nurse's cap and already working itself loose from its pins . . .

The most beautiful woman in the world.

And the flame that had warmed his heart back to life, from beneath the cold ash that the Department had left of it. With lucid certainty he knew that she was the reason he hadn't turned into Pritchard Crowell.

'*Why not?*' Grippen had asked.

There was the reason.

As she disappeared into the darkness outside the station's doors, he thought he saw a slim figure in a British colonel's uniform – a flicker of pale hair like cobwebs – follow her into the night.

I'M STILL HERE

I'M STILL HERE

BLACK DIGNITY IN A WORLD MADE FOR WHITENESS

AUSTIN CHANNING BROWN

virago

VIRAGO

First published in the United States in 2018 by Convergent Books
First published in Great Britain in 2020 by Virago Press

1 3 5 7 9 10 8 6 4 2

This book is a work of memoir, however, occasionally the author
has altered the chronology of events for clarity and changed the
names of people and places and organisations in order to disguise
their identities. Any resulting resemblance to persons living or
dead is entirely coincidental and unintentional.

The chapter 'Why I Love Being a Black Girl' was originally published
in a different form at austinchanningbrown.com, in 2015.

A CIP catalogue record for this book
is available from the British Library.

Hardback ISBN 978-0-349-01487-6
Trade paperback ISBN 978-0-349-01486-9

Printed and bound in Great Britain by Clays Ltd, Elcograf S.p.A.

Papers used by Virago are from well-managed forests
and other responsible sources.

Virago Press
An imprint of
Little, Brown Book Group
Carmelite House
50 Victoria Embankment
London EC4Y 0DZ

An Hachette UK Company
www.hachette.co.uk

www.virago.co.uk

I dedicate this book to

G. Jacqueline Holley, my grandmother,

who is the personification of

Black dignity and love.

CONTENTS

I'M STILL HERE

1

White People Are Exhausting

White people can be exhausting. Particularly exhausting are white people who don't know they are white, and those who need to be white. But of all the white people I've met—and I've met a lot of them in more than three decades of living, studying, and working in places where I'm often the only Black woman in sight—the first I found exhausting were those who expected *me* to be white.

To be fair, my parents did set them up for failure. In this society where we believe a name tells us everything we need to know about someone's race, gender, income, and personality, my parents decided to outwit everyone by giving their daughter a white man's name. When I was growing up, they explained that my grandmother's maiden name was

Austin, and since her only brother didn't have children, they wanted to make me the last Austin of our family line.

Sounds beautiful, right? Well, it is. It just happens to be half the story.

How did I discover the other half? Through my exhaustion with a white person. We were in my favorite place—our local library, built in a square with an outdoor garden at the center. At seven years old, with books piled high in my arms, I often had to be reminded how many I had already checked out when it came time for our next visit. I am certain my family singlehandedly kept our library funded. We checked out so many books at a time, we would find them under the car seat, between the cushions of our couch, or hiding under the mail on the table.

On this sunny Saturday afternoon, as I stepped up to the front desk to check out my books, I remember the librarian taking my library card and scanning the back as usual. I braced myself, expecting her to announce the fine I owed for the week.

Instead, she raised one eyebrow as the other furrowed and asked, "Is this your card?"

Wondering for a split second if I'd mixed up my card with my mother's, I nodded my head yes, but hesitantly. "Are you sure?" she said. "This card says Austin."

I nodded more emphatically and smiled. "Yes, that's my card." Perhaps she was surprised a first-grader could rack up such a fine. But when I peered over the counter, I saw that she still hadn't opened the book covers to stamp the day when I should bring them back (emphasis on *should*). I waited.

"Are you sure this is your card?" she asked again, this time drawing out *sure* and *your* as if they had more than one syllable. I tilted my head in exasperation, rolling my eyes toward the popcorn ceiling. Did she not see all the recent books on my account? Surely this woman didn't think I didn't know my own name.

Then it dawned on me. She wasn't questioning my literacy. She was another in an already long line of people who couldn't believe my name belonged to me. With a sigh too deep for my young years, I replied, "Yes, my name is Austin, and that is my library card." She stammered something about my name being unusual as her eyebrows met. I didn't respond. I just waited for her to hand my books back to me.

My check-outs in hand, I marched over to my mother, who was standing in the VHS section with my little brother. I demanded that she tell me why she named me Austin.

By then, I had gotten used to white people

expecting me to be male. It happened every first day of school, at roll call. The boys and girls automatically gravitated to opposite sides of the room, and when my name was called, I had to do jumping jacks to get the teacher's attention away from the "boys' section." So how did I know this wasn't more of the same? The woman's suspicion. Because, after I answered her question about my little library card, I still was not believed. I couldn't have explained it at the time, but I knew this was about more than me not being a boy.

"Why did you give me this name?" I demanded, letting my books fall loudly on the table next to us. My mother, probably wondering how she'd managed to raise a little Judy Blume character of her own, started retelling the story of my grandmother and the Austin family. But I cut her off. "Momma, I know *how* you came up with my name, but why did you choose it?"

She walked me over to a set of scratchy green armchairs and started talking in a slow, soothing voice. "Austin, your father and I had a really hard time coming up with a name that we both liked. One of us thought to use your grandmother's maiden name—her last name before she married your grandfather." I already knew this part of the story. I swung my legs impatiently, waiting for her to tell me more.

"As we said it aloud, we loved it," she continued. "We knew that anyone who saw it before meeting you would assume you are a white man. One day you will have to apply for jobs. We just wanted to make sure you could make it to the interview."

My mother watched my face, waiting for a reaction. My brain scrolled through all the times a stranger had said my name but wasn't talking to me. In every instance, the intended target had been not only a boy but a white boy. I didn't quite understand my mother's point about job applications—to that point, the only application I had filled out was probably for the library card in my hand. But one thing became clear. People's reaction to my name wasn't just about my gender. It was also about my brown skin. My legs stilled. That's why the librarian hadn't believed me. She didn't know a name like Austin could be stretched wide enough to cloak a little Black girl.

As I grew older, my parents' plan worked—almost too well. To this day, I receive emails addressed to "Mr. Austin Brown" and voice mails asking if Mr. Brown can please return their call. When I am being introduced to new people, there is often an attempt to feminize my name ("You mean Autumn?") or to assign my name to my husband. And though I usually note that I am a Black woman in my cover letters, I nonetheless surprise hiring committees when I show up to the interview in all my melanin glory.

Heading into the meeting, I'm dressed up and nervous. Typically I have made it beyond the essay-writing stage, the personality test, or the phone interview with HR. This in-person group interview is usually the final step. I sit in the lobby waiting for someone to collect me. An assistant comes around the corner and looks at me, wondering if I could possibly be the next candidate. A little tentative in case a grave mistake has been made, he asks, "Are you Austin?"

I reply with an enthusiastic yes, pretending I didn't notice the look of panic that they'd accidentally invited a Black girl to the interview. The tension eases for him as it grips the muscle under my right shoulder blade. I silently take a couple deep breaths as I follow him to the conference room. "Everyone, this is Austin . . ."

Every pair of eyes looks at me in surprise. They look at the person next to them. They blink. Then they look down at my résumé. Every. Single. Time.

The person who walked me into the room is still talking, but no one is listening. They are all combing my résumé looking for clues. Should they have known? Am I now more impressive or less impressive? What does this mean for the position? For the partners? For the team? They weren't prepared for this. They were expecting a white man.

It would be comical if it wasn't so damn disappointing.

Thanks to the progressive circles I usually travel in, most people want to be excited by the "mistake" and ignore all the thoughts, the questions, the change that happened when my body stood before them. But that moment cannot be ignored. The thoughts and questions may dissipate from the interview but never from the mind, the heart. For this becomes the unspoken question for my entire time with an organization: *Are we sure she will be a good fit?* Or, said another way, *Since we didn't vet her knowing she is a Black woman, are we sure she'll fit in with our* [white] *culture? Or should we have hired the white person who came next?*

I cannot speak for every Black woman navigating white culture, but this is how being hired usually unfolds for me:

First, I am given a promise, usually from a

supervisor, co-worker, or member of the hiring committee, that she is a safe person for me to talk to if anything racist happens. To make the promise of safety feel genuine, she admits that the organization isn't perfect and assures me that I can share if there is ever an inappropriate comment, a wrong word. That way, the problem can be addressed. Second, I am given a brief account of the organization's imperfections, a series of stories involving elusive people who no longer belong to the organization. The stories usually concern examples of "missteps"—the time a white person "misspoke" in a board meeting or when a racist email was intercepted by leadership—but they end on a note of hope, expressing how the organization reacted. *We invited* [insert name of famous Black person] *to speak at our annual lunch. We launched an eight-week discussion group on* [book by Black author].

But within my first few weeks of working there, the organization's stereotypes, biases, or prejudices begin to emerge. Comments about my hair. Accolades for being "surprisingly articulate" or "particularly entertaining." Requests to "be more Black" in my speech. Questions about single moms, the hood, "black-on-black crime," and other hot topics I am supposed to know all about because I'm Black.

So I bring up the incidents with my safe person—the one who said she wants to know about these encounters—but the response is some version of "Perhaps you misunderstood" or "I'm sure he didn't mean it like that." Oftentimes the responsibility to extend compassion falls on me. "You really ought to go back to talk to him. Perhaps if you were more patient, you could see his heart." So I move on. Rather than dwell on individuals, I speak about the system. About white boardrooms and white leadership teams. About white culture and the organization's habit of hiring people who perpetuate that culture rather than diversify it. But the white consensus doesn't want me to point out these things. I was only supposed to name the "bad apples," so now whiteness has a few names for me. *Divisive. Negative. Toxic.*

I feel disappointed. I had hoped that this organization, this group of people, might be different from the last one—that they would understand what it means to embody an organization's diversity in more than numbers. But instead of giving up, I take a step back. I return to pointing out the "bad apples," hoping that my doing so will lead others to see the systemic. I talk about the woman who touched my hair without permission, and the man who called me "colored" in the hallway. I talk about how when I walk into our church, people still ask me if I am looking for the food pantry. How they greet me as a newcomer every Sunday, even though I have not changed my seat in two years.

I am not interested in getting anyone in trouble; I am trying to clarify what it's like to exist in a Black body in an organization that doesn't understand it is not only Christian but also white. But instead of offering empathy and action, whiteness finds new names for me and offers ominous advice. I am too sensitive, and should be careful with what I report. I am too angry, and should watch my tone when I talk about my experiences. I am too inflexible, and should learn to offer more grace to people who are really trying.

It's exhausting.

White people who expect me to be white have not yet realized that their cultural way of being is not in fact the result of goodness, rightness, or God's blessing. Pushing back, resisting the lie, is hella work.

It's work to be the only person of color in an organization, bearing the weight of all your white co-workers' questions about Blackness.

It's work to always be hypervisible because of

your skin—easily identified as being present or absent—but for your needs to be completely invisible to those around you.

It's work to do the emotional labor of pointing out problematic racist thinking, policies, actions, and statements while desperately trying to avoid bitterness and cynicism.

It's work to stay open to an organization to learn new skills without drinking in the cultural expectations of body size, personality, interests, and talents most valued according to whiteness.

Quite frankly, the work isn't just tedious. It can be dangerous for Black women to attempt to carve out space for themselves—their perspective, their gifts, their skills, their education, their experiences—in places that haven't examined the prevailing assumption of white culture. The danger of letting whiteness walk off with our joy, our peace, our sense of dignity and self-love, is ever present. But it doesn't have to be this way. Togetherness across racial lines doesn't have to mean the uplifting of whiteness and harming of Blackness. And even though the Church I love has been the oppressor as often as it has been the champion of the oppressed, I can't let go of my belief in Church—in a universal body of belonging, in a community that reaches toward love in a world so often filled with hate. I continue to be drawn toward the collective partici- pation of seeking good, even when that means cri- tiquing the institution I love for its commitment to whiteness.

This book is my story about growing up in a Black girl's body. There is nothing profound about where my story takes place. I didn't grow up in an- other country, in the Deep South or the hood. I grew up around white people in a family-friendly middle-class neighborhood. There was neither dev- astating poverty nor incredible wealth, and the dem- ographics of my neighborhood and schools often mimicked America as a whole—mostly white, but never exclusively so.

I also grew up in the late eighties and early nineties, the height of America's supposed com- mitment to racial color blindness. At my Christian elementary school, we sang, "Jesus loves the little children . . . red and yellow, black and white, all are precious in his sight." In alignment with this song, white people often professed, "I don't even see color," reassuring me that I would be safe from racism with them. And yet, I learned pretty early in life that while Jesus may be cool with racial di- versity, America is not. The ideology that white- ness is supreme, better, best, permeates the air we breathe—in our schools, in our offices, and in our country's common life. White supremacy is a tradition that must be named and a religion that must be renounced. When this work has not been done, those who live in whiteness become oppressive, whether intentional or not.

I learned about whiteness up close. In its classrooms and hallways, in its offices and sanctuaries. At the same time, I was also learning about Blackness, about myself, and about my faith. My story is not about condemning white people but about rejecting the assumption—sometimes spoken, sometimes not—that white is right: closer to God, holy, chosen, the epitome of being. My story is about choosing to love my Black femaleness, even when it shocks folks who expected someone quite different. It's about standing before roomfuls of Christians and challenging them to see Blackness without the baggage of racist bias. It's about surviving in a world not made for me—where my parents tried to arm me with the cultural cash of a white, male name.

I offer this story in hopes that we will embody a community eager to name whiteness, celebrate Blackness, and, in a world still governed by systems of racial oppression, begin to see that there's another way.

2

Playing Spades

I had to learn what it really means to love Blackness. I hate to admit it, but it's true.

My parents' home was a Black family's home. Framed posters of Alvin Ailey dancers were suspended on the walls and the words of Alice Walker, Toni Morrison, Langston Hughes, and other Black authors occupied every inch of space on maple-colored bookshelves. On Saturday mornings, Luther Vandross crooned from our record player as we completed our chores. Afterward, as a reward, Mom and Dad twirled us around the family room, practicing the Cleveland hand dance. At the dinner table they stuffed us with stories of Black achievement and wondered aloud about the color barriers we would break when we got older . . . But how-

Playing Spades

ever hard my parents worked to instill in me pride in being Black, their arms weren't long enough to reach beyond the walls of our family.

My elementary school was predominately white. From pre-K all the way through eighth grade, I was always just one of a handful of Black students in my classes—but because I had attended that school longer than most of the teachers had worked there, I walked the hallways like I owned the place. Not that I didn't notice differences between myself and the white girls in my classroom. I wondered why their ponytails swung side to side but mine bounced up and down. I wondered why all the characters in my school's library books seemed obsessed with camp-fires and playing the guitar on a beach, and I also noticed that none of my teachers looked like me.

But rather than my race being the elephant in the room, it seemed instead to be my secret knowl-edge. I knew all about the world of my white teachers and peers, but they didn't seem to know a thing about mine. Teachers never referenced televi-sion shows my family wouldn't miss—*A Different World*; *Sister, Sister*; or *Moesha*. Our school praised the music of Amy Grant, DC Talk, and Michael W. Smith, but never mentioned gospel artists like Babbie Mason, Helen Baylor, Fred Hammond, and

25

Kirk Franklin. Conversations that filled the air in my household never would've happened with my teachers.

For example, I remember one Christmas weekend when I was eleven or twelve, my family gathered in my grandmother's home in Cleveland. My grandparents, aunts, uncles, and cousins sat around two tables—one for the adults, one for the kids—separated by a short open bookshelf filled with vintage bells my grandmother had collected over decades. From my folding chair at the kids' table, I peered through the gaps in the shelves, trying to follow the adults' conversation as my mom went toe-to-toe with the men sitting across from her.

"I'm just not sure integration has actually helped Black Americans," she said. Her hands danced in front of her as she continued the impassioned monologue, her afro nodding in agreement.

"Well, what was the alternative, Karen?" one of my uncles retorted. "Remaining in segregation?"

Her eyes flashed. She knew she had them. "Of course not. I'm just saying that *segregation* didn't have to be followed with *integration*. Surely relegating us to the back of the bus could have stopped without us having to give up all the businesses that died because we started going to white folks. Think about all that we lost—the doctors' and dentists' offices, the grocery store owners and auto mechanics. I mean, could we have kept a great number of Black teachers if we had demanded equal funding for our schools rather than busing ourselves to theirs?"

The debate continued, deep voices rising and falling, conceding and breaking away. Conversations like this were normal with this crew, but my white school was different. There, we weren't supposed to question history. We were expected to learn the names of Rosa Parks and Martin Luther King Jr., thank God that we could all share an integrated classroom now, and move on to another lesson with hearts of gratitude.

But we weren't always grateful to be with the white kids.

I think I was in the fourth grade when it first happened. My classmates and I were lining up to leave for gym class or perhaps art or music class. I was standing toward the back of the line when a short white boy, Zach, stood in front of me and mumbled something about monkeys and bananas, looking at no one in particular.

"What?" I responded, genuinely confused. I glanced at the bulletin boards around the room, searching for a good reason he would be talking about monkeys.

Zach turned all the way around to stare up into my eyes. "Nigger," he said.

Everything stopped. The twelve kids in front of him disappeared as my eyes narrowed. My stomach lurched. I had always thought of myself as a nice kid, the kind who gets along with her classmates. But in this moment I had a feeling I was about to surprise myself. I don't remember exactly what I retorted, but I do know that I wasn't silent, and I know it was mean, because Zach never tried that shit again.

My parents never sat me down to tell me what I should do if a white person called me a nigger, and I was too young to know the history of that word at the time. But there was one thing I knew for sure. My anger was justified. And though I never got "The Talk" about the n–word, my parents did give me plenty of other examples about the ways a white person might try me.

Following my dad through the toy section of the party store, I picked up a little trinket that caught my attention. "Don't even think about it," he said, shooting me down before I could debate whether or not to ask him to buy it. I sighed, put the trinket back, and stuffed my hands in the pockets of my overalls, willing myself not to be tempted again.

My father glanced back at me, but when he noticed my little fists bulging from my pockets, he stopped in the middle of the aisle and turned all the way around. "Don't do that," he said sternly.

Do what? I wondered to myself. I had long ago learned to tame my smart mouth with my dad. Was he now reading my mind?

"Don't ever do that," he repeated more softly this time, bending his six-foot-two frame toward me to let me know I wasn't in trouble. But I was still confused. What had I done wrong?

"Even if you put it back on the shelf, Austin, you can't touch store products and then put your hands in your pockets," he explained as his large hands gently removed mine from their denim hiding place. "Someone might notice and assume you are trying to steal."

I nodded. It took some time, but eventually I trained myself not to touch my pockets—and nowadays, my purse—when walking through store aisles.

Then there was the moment when my mom took me to the mall to buy my first CD. I spent far longer than I should have combing through the thin boxes, deciding between new releases from Boyz II Men, Aaliyah, Mariah Carey, Tevin Campbell, and SWV. I chose Mariah Carey's *Music Box,* took it to the front of the line, and paid for it with the little cash I had. On our way out of the store, I tore into the plastic, opening the CD liner, where artists kept photos and lyrics.

"Whoa, Daughter," my mother warned. I looked at her quizzically, wondering if I had shown too much excitement. Even the cashier paused for a moment, surprised by her sudden forcefulness.

"You never open an item in the store, and always have the receipt in your hand if you do," my mother said. "You always want to be able to show someone you paid for your things." It's funny how in these little life lessons, I always knew that "someone" was white people.

My parents made sure I knew that at any moment when I wasn't paying attention, when I was just being a person, everything could be interrupted. *Be careful with white people* was the message I received loud and clear. But strangely enough, it was being around Black kids that turned out to be harder for me . . . at first.

It happened when I was ten. My parents got divorced, and my little brother and I started spending summers in Cleveland with my mother. Cleveland was only two hours away from my home in Toledo, but the move from a mostly white setting into one that was all Black made our new neighborhood feel like a different planet. It was the first time I had ever walked into a public sphere where the majority of people looked like me. The culture shock was glorious and terrifying.

At first, I didn't understand the culture I had landed in. I wasn't prepared for the loudness, the playfulness. I didn't know about dance competitions and talent shows, and I didn't know there were more line dances than the Electric Slide. (The Tootsie Roll was a complete takeover that summer.) Kids and adults here cursed on a regular basis. There were no games reciting the books of the Bible at the day camp our mother enrolled us in; I had to learn to play Spades in this joint.

It was hard to keep up. When the popular song "Weak" by SWV came on the radio, our entire bus started singing it on the way to the community pool. I had never heard the song before, so I attempted to lip-synch the whole thing, praying that the girls around me would continue singing with their eyes closed instead of noticing me. I listened to the Black radio station all summer after that, trying to learn the popular songs. But no matter how hard I worked to pretend this new world made sense to me, there was so much I didn't know. I had no idea who Bobby Brown was, or why Whitney Houston shouldn't marry him. And I didn't know why the girls at day camp dared me to say "Candyman" five times in the bathroom mirror. On the fifth time, they all screamed, so I screamed, too. I had no idea what I was supposed to be afraid of. The only thing I feared was being discovered.

Here in Cleveland, other Black children called me Oreo and were curious about why I "talked white." I didn't know what to say the first time someone told me that. *Well, I only live here during the summers . . . I actually live in Toledo with my dad and go to a school that looks nothing like this neighborhood . . . All my teachers have been white and most of my classmates, too . . . So I guess that's why I talk white?* Kids didn't have time for all that, and I wasn't mature enough to question the question. But still, it hurt. I was working so hard to hide the culture of whiteness, only to discover that it was dripping from my body, pouring from my throat. All I wanted was to fit in, but everyone knew I was pretending.

It was draining—to the point where I sometimes feigned being sick. I would find a table as far from everyone as I could and put my head down. When a counselor came to check on me, I would squint as if the light was hurting my eyes and explain that I just didn't feel good. It wasn't exactly a lie. I knew I would never fit into whiteness. That was okay. But the loss of Blackness? I didn't know how to handle that. I was too white for Black people, and too Black for white people. I had a boy's name and bad acne. It was terrible.

Then, just when I thought I'd never fit anywhere, Blackness created space for me. I finally found a friend. Her name was Tiffani. She lived four houses down from my mother. We were the same age, but that and being Black were about all we had in common. She was short and spunky, self-confident and playful. I was tall but quiet, working hard at blending in. She was loud and cussed and taught me a few things about boys. She was everything I was not. She was everything I needed.

Whether she knew it or not, Tiffani became my teacher. She taught me about music and dances. She taught me about Ebonics and pop culture. She taught me about playing with neighborhood kids and running around outside until the streetlights came on. She danced with me. She played with me. And she vouched for me. She believed in my Blackness. And because she did, I could, too. To paraphrase the poet Ntozake Shange, there were no white girls in our hopscotch games.

Tiffani didn't just teach me about Black culture. She also taught me that I could embrace new things about Blackness without being stripped of my identity. I learned how to do the Butterfly—I almost won a dance contest that year, I'll have you know—but I also learned it was okay if I still preferred to read while everyone else played neighborhood kickball. I easily fell into Ebonics but never mastered the most popular slang, like *You buggin* or *Let's bounce;* it always sounded funny escaping my throat. I didn't see *Candyman* until I was grown.

Tiffani was my bridge to understanding that Black is beautiful whether it looked nerdy like me or cool like her. I could choose what felt right for me without needing to be like everyone, or needing everyone to be like me. Black is not monolithic. Black is expansive, and I didn't need the approval of whiteness in order to feel good in my skin; there was no whiteness available to offer an opinion. It was freedom.

I couldn't hear it when I first landed in Cleveland, but Blackness had been screaming (rather harshly, I'd thought), "There is another way." Another way of speaking, of thinking, of being that did not need white affirmation to be valuable. My way of speaking sounded like a hybrid of my white classmates and my Black parents, but that was not the only way to communicate. In fact, among the neighborhood kids, it wasn't the most valuable way to communicate. There was more than what I knew or could learn from a textbook; more than what whiteness said was right.

Lesson learned.

Summers in Cleveland weren't the only change I experienced as a result of my parents' divorce. Two years later, my dad remarried and my brother and I welcomed a new little sister into the world. Our family of five was creating new traditions, and on Sunday mornings we started going to church—a Black church in Toledo. Until this moment, all I knew of worship services were our school chapels on Friday afternoons. These usually consisted of [white] Christian contemporary songs, a passage read from our [white] illustrated Bibles, a [white] speaker sharing some sort of testimony, and finally accepting [white] Jesus as our Savior.

It was assumed by faculty, staff, and ultimately by most of the students that everything taking place in these chapel services applied to all bodies equally. I had no idea that when I walked into my dad's new church, I would be meeting black Jesus. I fell in love.

On that first Sunday, as we wandered down a fluorescent-lit hallway toward the sanctuary, the air was filled with the smell of perfume. I didn't know what to expect. Along the way congregation members welcomed us, the women in elaborate hats and dark stockings, the men in suits, ties, and snakeskin shoes. Everyone we passed greeted us with a warm *good morning* as if they already knew us. We waited a second at the wooden doors outside the sanctuary, because the people inside were in the middle of prayer. But soon, an "Amen" in unison filled the air, and the double doors swung open. Sunlight poured in from the stained glass windows lining the far wall. Pea green carpet stretched the length of the sanctuary. The organ had already started playing and everyone was standing on their feet, swaying the same direction. Hands clapped to the beat of the song.

I looked up into the choir stand, filled with brown faces like mine. The choir director moved her hands up and down in unison. Every member paid close attention to what she was doing. I later learned that this was because we rarely sang any song the same way twice. She wasn't just conducting prewritten music; she created a new song for us every time. We rewarded her with shouts of "Sing, choir!" and our own melody of "Hallelujahs."

That day, I fell in love. I fell in love with the soaring voices and the songs that moved us to tears and then chased the blues away. I fell in love with peppermint-dealing church mothers and hymn-singing deacons. I fell in love with fiery preaching that moved so deep, it would undergird you and push you to your feet in praise. I fell in love with a Jesus who saw the poor and sick and hurting, a Jesus who had bigger plans for me than keeping me a virgin, a Jesus who loved and reveled in our Blackness.

Sunday after Sunday, what grabbed my attention more than anything was the pastor. In sermons he preached, Jesus sounded like a Black person, dealing with familiar hardships of life—injustice, broken relationships, the pain of being called names. Pastor would read a passage of Scripture filled with *thees* and *thous* as beautiful as poetry. But then he would take the time to restate what happened to sound like the present day. He was incapable of standing still behind the pulpit—by the end of the service, he usually needed a face towel to wipe away the sweat from his forehead. But any given Sunday, the message was clear: *God was with us.*

We were a family. Sometimes dysfunctional, for sure. But we were constantly reminded of our connection to one another. We referred to each other as *brother* and *sister.* As we grew closer, those titles changed to *Auntie, Uncle,* even *Momma.*

I had to wait till adulthood before I heard the name James Cone or read about Black liberation theology. But by the time I learned of Black Jesus and his liberating power, I knew I had already met him at ten years old, in a Baptist church where the Spirit moved us every week. There Jesus cared about my soul, but he also cared about the woman who didn't have transportation or couldn't pay the light or water bill. Jesus cared about the folks who were addicted to drugs or alcohol, who wanted to save their bodies from the poison and their hearts from pain. And for those whose families hurt us, or significant others had left us, or supervisors didn't understand us—all these things were taken very seriously, but every Sunday we were also reminded that trouble don't last always. Heartbreak and struggle weren't the end of our story. We learned that God had some expectations for us, too, to resist sin and temptations of all kinds, but even these were offered contextualized—embodied, real in ways that the sermons from my school chapel services hadn't been.

The Black church gave me the greatest sense of belonging I had ever experienced. There was still much to learn: speaking in tongues, being slain in the Spirit, prophetic announcements and praise dances. (Not to mention, I hadn't realized that you could be in such a large group and everyone could clap in time on the two and four. Like, everyone . . .) It was an adjustment, but none of this made me nervous or uncomfortable like I'd been in school or during those first weeks in Cleveland. I loved the Black church and she loved me.

Slowly, over time and in layers, Blackness had found me. It found me and it changed my life.

3

The Other Side of Harmony

Much like my elementary school, the Catholic high school I attended was predominately white, but by then there were enough students of color to fill multiple tables at lunch, form a gospel choir, and generally make our presence known. To tell the truth, I don't remember any major racial incidents happening in any of the four years I was there. No swastikas on bathroom stalls, no fistfights prompted by an overconfident white boy using the n–word, no blackface parties or inappropriate Halloween costumes. For the most part, we all existed in harmony, but there were a few key moments in which I learned that *harmony*—the absence of outright conflict—often leaves deeper complications untouched.

Ms. Phillips's classroom was a favorite for students. She was short with a square frame and a foul mouth, which was intriguing since she taught our religion class. She mostly donned mom jeans and oversize shirts. She had a big laugh and told big stories, and as she taught from behind her podium, her energy filled the room.

Ms. Phillips gave us life lessons right alongside the curriculum (and sometimes *instead* of her curriculum). She told us about living in community with other single women, sharing resources, prioritizing friendships and intimacy. There was nothing we couldn't ask her. One day, after Ms. Phillips told us about her fear of ghosts, we stole the remote to the classroom TV and spent the class period turning it off and on. At first Ms. Phillips had us made, convinced we had figured out a way to control the television. But as the class wore on and the TV continued turning on and off, she started testing it. "If you are my uncle, turn off now," she countered. Off went the TV. She turned to us, eyes wide, and kept testing it by calling out the names of dead relatives. Minutes later, when we burst into laughter and revealed the truth, she wasn't mad at all. In fact, she dubbed us the best class she had ever had.

One day it was Ms. Phillips who caught us

off guard. As we filed into her classroom, she announced she would no longer use a seating chart. For the first time we scanned the room, deciding where we wanted to sit. Once we were settled, she informed us that she wanted to share why we suddenly had been given permission to choose our seats. There was something uncharacteristically soft about the way she spoke.

"Every year I use a seating chart," she began, "deciding where each of you will sit. Earlier this week I realized that my tendency to do this is racist." I froze. This was another classroom in which I was perhaps one of three students of color. I had no idea what was coming next, but I suddenly became very aware of my body.

"You see," she continued, "I have been using a seating chart to separate Black students. I didn't fully realize it until I failed to separate two Black young women in one of my classes. When I saw them together I panicked, thinking, *Great, now they are going to laugh and talk through the entire period.*"

She paused. She was clearly overwhelmed, yet making an effort to be as forthcoming as she would be about anything else. She did not mince words or sugarcoat any part of her thinking.

"That's when I realized what I was doing was racist. I have never ever wondered if any of my white students were going to be disruptive. I've never been nervous to find two white girls sitting next to one another. I am so disappointed with myself, and from now on, you all will sit where you want to sit."

She took a deep breath, and so did I. I'm guessing there were plenty of classes in which Ms. Phillips had to separate two white students for being disruptive. However, by her own admission, this tendency toward disruption was never attributed to their race. Only when the disruptive students were Black did race become a defining factor.

While I was grateful that she'd had an epiphany, or at least wanted to be grateful, the revelation made me incredibly self-conscious. I thought so much of Ms. Phillips; I wasn't prepared to hear what she had thought of me, of my body. The stereotype about sassy, disrespectful Black girls was not lost on me—but until then, I had thought it was just a convenient movie trope. I didn't realize it could be used against me.

I looked around the classroom to gauge the response of the other students. No one had much to add; I think most of them were just glad to be able to sit wherever they wanted. But I was having an entirely different experience. Should I have been glad for my teacher's aha moment? Did it make me safer in her classroom now that she was aware of her bias? What about the other teachers at my school? Were they—even the ones I liked—watching me, judging me?

It was the first time I saw beyond my own perception of the racial harmony at my school. I was grateful that I didn't have to deal with overt acts of racism, but was it better to know that teachers silently believed I would be a nuisance unless I proved otherwise? How could I know if beneath other amicable interactions, the stereotypes and biases of those in power were operating against students who looked like me?

This moment of disappointment made me even more determined to assert agency over my academic life. For the most part, my defiance manifested itself in demanding the right to explore Blackness. Book report due? I was choosing a Black author. History paper assigned? Black history was the only option for me. Like many Black students in predominately white schools, if I wanted to see myself reflected in the curriculum, I had to act on my own behalf.

Resisting an education built on a white worldview meant constantly having to evaluate the risks of telling the truth or furthering the myth. Would I write that Christopher Columbus "discovered" America? Would I do the report on Malcolm X instead of Mark Twain? My parents left the decision to me. I could choose the better grade or I could choose to affirm Blackness. It's a decision many students of color have to make. Sometimes I just stated the truth, "Christopher Columbus sailed the ocean blue in 1492, but the land he 'discovered' was already inhabited." Other times I would give the answer the teacher wanted with a disclaimer, "Our textbook states that . . ." I won't lie; I kind of enjoyed being more right than my teachers, even if it cost me half a letter grade.

So it was a rare gift when I could walk into a classroom that didn't require this kind of work from me. Mr. Slivinski's class was like that.

Mr. Slivinski was my freshman English teacher and the first to expose me to the power of an intentionally diverse curriculum. He was short, white, and full of energy—whether natural or from coffee, we couldn't tell. (He kept a warm pot in his classroom at all times.) On the first day of class, Mr. Sli informed us that his goal for the year was to give us a headache from thinking so hard. And he often succeeded. There were passionate discussions of Richard Connell's "The Most Dangerous

Game," line-by-line readings of Shakespeare, and assignments to analyze the character development in Daphne du Maurier's *Rebecca*. Through all of this, Mr. Slivinski inspired us to interrogate the assumptions we held about culture, ethics, laws. He wanted us to color outside the lines of our black and white thinking.

Mr. Slivinski's lesson plans would follow our textbook for a few weeks, and then break away for the sake of diversity. One of those breakaways was a unit on poetry. Each day, Mr. Slivinski printed out poems he'd selected, instructing us to read them and mark up the page. What words stood out? What did we notice about the structure? How did the content make us feel?

One day, Mr. Slivinski passed out a poem entitled "We Wear the Mask." I started reading immediately. The author's name, Paul Laurence Dunbar, was familiar to me. My stepmom worked as a high school English teacher and was always eager to recite Black poetry to me, so I knew we were about to read a poem about the Black experience. Still, my eyes widened as I read the words:

Why should the world be over-wise,
In counting all our tears and sighs?

Nay, let them only see us, while
We wear the mask.

A mask. My mind raced, wondering how often I did this without much thought. Were there parts of me that I kept buried from white people—even the ones I counted as friends? Things did feel different when I was the only Black girl in the class, versus when I was surrounded by Blackness at the lunch table or in our gospel choir. When I finished the poem, I felt both relieved and saddened. I looked up at Mr. Slivinski, wondering, *How do you know?*

When I realized he was about to open up the floor for discussion, I folded myself into the chair, trying to make my body smaller, trying to disappear. *Will you make me explain this? Will you ask me to tell this all-white class about the masks Black people wear?*

I was surprised by own reaction. It felt deeply gratifying to have my own experience named, lifted up, discussed, considered worthy of everyone's attention. And yet, I had no desire to be the Black spokesperson. It felt too risky. I wasn't sure that my classmates had earned the right to know, to understand, to be given access to such a vulnerable place in my experience. For me, this was more than an educational exercise. This is how we survive.

It's a common conundrum for Black children navigating mostly white classrooms. It is often expected—both by the other students and by the teacher—that Black students will have no problem acting as the race experts for their classrooms. Eventually, though, we begin to question whether we'll be safe when the subject comes up—or if we even have the right to speak on behalf of all Black people. I mean, it's not like we have a committee meeting every Wednesday night to decide what we think about any given issue. But my first reaction in this moment possessed none of these thoughts. I simply wasn't interested in taking off the mask.

Fortunately, Mr. Slivinski didn't call on me to respond to Dunbar's words. Though we had not exchanged one word since the exercise began, I sensed that he respected my decision to keep my thoughts private. I listened in amusement as white students—many of whom possessed an intellect and creativity that I sincerely admired—attempted to interpret the poem. No matter how well reasoned their responses, they just couldn't *know*. But that didn't stop Mr. Slivinski from challenging them.

I was grateful that my teacher was equipped to navigate that conversation without making me the momentary substitute teacher. Mr. Slivinski already had my respect, but that day, he also gained my trust. He was able to redraw the boundaries of our comfort zone. Breaking the social policy of just ignoring race didn't have to end badly. I wished he could steer discussions in every classroom.

I remember a religion class toward the end of my senior year when our teacher asked the students about our future plans. Most of us were bound for college in the fall, so the conversation gravitated toward talk of applications, scholarships, and possible majors—a discussion that led one white classmate to air her grievances about not being accepted to the University of Michigan. Rather than chalking it up to the sheer number of applications U of M must receive in any given year, she had a different explanation: A Black person must have taken her place. And not a Black person who perhaps had above-average test scores, who'd completed more hours of community service, or perhaps had written a stronger biographical essay on the application. Had this been her assumption about the Black people who earned spots at the university, I probably could have forgiven her. But alas, her explanation was short: "Because of affirmative action, Black people took my spot."

Her spot.

Or, if I were to add all that was left unspoken in her sentence: "If the University of Michigan hadn't let unqualified Black people in, I, who am obviously deserving and qualified above and beyond those people, would have easily been accepted."

My blood boiled. I really wanted to hurt her feelings. I wanted to suggest that perhaps she was not as qualified as *any* of the students who were let in—Black or otherwise. I wanted to tell her that if I was one of the applicants, I knew for a fact I would get in before her, and it had nothing to do with my skin color. I wanted to tell her that no one stole anything from her; that's what made it an application.

My reaction surprised me. I had not applied to U of M, and yet her words stung as if I had personally offended her with access to the coveted university. In my mind, she wasn't just talking about a specific group of Black students. She was talking about Black people, all of us. That's why I wanted to hurt her feelings. She was telling me exactly what she thought about Black people, and I was ready to tell her about herself in return.

Back then I didn't have all the terminology I have now to process awkward interactions with white people. I didn't have phrases like *white tears* or *white fragility,* and I'm not sure I had even explored the term *white privilege* at that point in my life. But I was learning about these things all the same—not from theory, but from life.

Our teacher completely froze as the tension climbed. But more concerning was that four years at a racially diverse school hadn't been enough to challenge my classmate's belief that whiteness, on its own merit, made her more deserving. Our school's "racial harmony" might not have created that assumption, but it didn't help her unlearn it either. A lack of confrontation had done her no favors. As high school came to an end, I took this lesson with me and became determined always to question what looks like unity at first glance.

4

Ain't No Friends Here

By the time I went off to college, Chicago seemed like the perfect place to practice adulthood. The city took my breath away. The fast pace, the gorgeous architecture, the diversity at every turn. It seemed to me that important things were happening here.

When I walked onto campus my freshman year, my first surprise was Crendalyn McMath. She was my first Black teacher, a marketing professor, and she took command of every classroom she stepped into. Tall with shoulder-length black hair, she wore suits that seemed only to elongate her frame. She was a brilliant teacher who brought stories from her professional experience into the classroom. I was so proud that she was a Black woman, like me.

The gift of Professor McMath's presence went

beyond the fact that she looked like me, though that was special all by itself. The true gift was that I didn't have to create my own sense of belonging in her class. In every previous classroom, I had been responsible for decoding teachers' references to white middle-class experiences. *It's like when you're sailing . . .* or *You know how when you're skiing, you have to . . .* My white teachers had an unspoken commitment to the belief that *we are all the same,* a default setting that masked for them how often white culture bled into the curriculum. For example, when teachers wanted to drive home the point that we should do something daily, they often likened it to how you wash your hair every morning. It never occurred to them that none of the Black girls in the class did this. Knowing it was true for white people, and having gotten used to white teachers' assumption of universality, we would all nod our heads and move on. Who had time to teach the teacher?

But Professor McMath was different. One day, while illustrating a point regarding business planning, she decided to use the example of opening a beauty shop. Our conversation moved along as usual until Professor McMath made an analogy to "getting a relaxer." My head snapped up in recognition, but all the white students looked toward the lectern completely baffled. I was the only one who understood the reference. I smiled at Professor McMath while she feigned surprise at the other students' confusion. "Come on, you all. You know what a relaxer is, right?" They continued to stare blankly at her until she explained that some Black women choose to get a relaxer, which is sort of the opposite of what happens when white people get a perm. "Relaxers make black curly hair straight . . . they relax the curls." She winked at me, and I grinned from ear to ear.

I relished the sense of belonging I felt in her classroom. Suddenly I wasn't content to feel like I was attending a college made for someone else. I paid tuition like every white student. Something was stirring inside, and there was one particular experience that caused it to burst out in full.

That spring, my roommate invited me on a trip called Sankofa. Sankofa was a three-day journey down South exploring Black history in partnership with another student. There were about twenty pairs of us, mostly comprising one Black and one white student. We traveled all night long from Chicago to Louisiana, arriving at our first stop: a plantation. We had come prepared to witness the harsh realities of slavery, but the real revelation was how ignorant and self-congratulatory our guides from the plantation could be. For the entire tour, we were told about "happy slaves" who sang in the fields, who worked under better conditions than most other slaves, and whose fingers never bled despite the massive amounts of cotton they picked. The guides' presentations were filled with misconceptions and inaccuracies, and at the conclusion of the tour, they even gave us the chance to pick some cotton ourselves.

Black students. Picking cotton.

The anger of the Black students and the confusion of the white students was palpable. As we climbed aboard the bus to roll to our next destination, our conversation quickly moved beyond superficial niceties. We took turns speaking into a microphone at the front of the bus. The Black students were livid at the romanticism displayed at the plantation. The white students listened politely but seemed unmoved as they weighed our information against the "experts" at the plantation. They responded with questions like "What about the Holocaust or the potato famine? Don't most people groups have some trauma in their history?" We did our best to correct the misconceptions, but the tour had driven a wedge in the group. And our next stop would drive that wedge even deeper.

Our bus pulled in to a museum consisting of only one exhibit—a history of lynching. Every wall was filled with photographs of dark-skinned human beings swinging by their necks. A mother and son hanging over a bridge. Burned bodies swinging over dying fires. White children staring in wide-eyed wonder while their parents proudly point to the mutilated body behind them. The cruel smiles of white faces testifying to the joy of the occasion. We came across newspaper stories that advertised lynchings as community events. In another case we saw a postcard. On the front was a photo of a mutilated man still hanging from a rope. On the other side, a handwritten note: "Sorry we missed you at the barbecue."

There was no sound as we walked through the exhibit. We could barely breathe, let alone speak.

When we climbed back on the bus, all that could be heard were sniffles. The emotion was thick. It was as if no time had passed between the generation in the pictures and the one sitting on that bus. It was all so real.

The first students to break the silence were white. "I didn't know this even happened." "It's not my fault; I wasn't there." They reached for anything that would distance themselves from the pain and anger of the moment; anything to ward off the guilt and shame, the shock and devastation.

The Black students had passed beyond any need to appear polite. We shared personal stories of pain—lynchings that happened to our own families—trying to make real those bodies from the photographs. But we weren't just interested in focusing on Black bodies; we were going to focus on white ones, too.

A tall Black woman, a senior that year, peered at us all as she spoke evenly, almost disarmingly in the heat of the moment. "I just want to say that I'm having a hard time even being mad at you white people anymore. I think I've just been convinced that white people are innately evil. You can't help it. You steal and kill, you enslave and lynch. You are just evil." Then she handed the microphone back to the next person and calmly took her seat. The white students hadn't appreciated her words, but the Black students on the bus could have kissed her feet. She had done what social convention and re-spectability politics said not to do—she had spoken her truth even if it meant hurting the feelings of every white person on that bus.

The tension climbed. Black and white grew further and further apart with each new speaker. The white students defended their family histories as the Black students searched for the words to express how it felt to stare at ours in those photos from the museum. Then, as we pulled into a parking lot to break for lunch, another white student stood to speak. But instead of a different variation on "Please don't make me responsible for this," she took a deep breath and gave in to the emotion of it all.

"I don't know what to do with what I've learned," she said. "I can't fix your pain, and I can't take it away, but I can see it. And I can work for the rest of my life to make sure your children don't have to experience the pain of racism."

And then she said nine words that I've never forgotten: "Doing nothing is no longer an option for me."

Those words changed the air on that bus. She acknowledged the depth of our pain without making excuse for it. And in that moment, I knew her words were true for me as well. Something shifted inside me on this trip. Something powerful and unmistakable. Doing nothing was no longer an option for me.

Sankofa was the first time I felt the distance

between history and myself collapsing. The black-and-white photos I had grown used to were now filled with color, associated with real places, places I had now walked. The inspiration to be part of their legacy was palpable, and the ways Christianity had been used to uphold all the evil of this history was not lost on me. Somehow, I just knew it was time to devote myself to the struggle.

After many more stops, discussions, tears, and prayers, we returned home. But before we got off the bus, our leaders had one final task for us. We all had to share one way in which we would become change agents as a result of the trip. I don't remember what I said that day, but my commitment was genuine.

I was no organizer, like many of my girlfriends on that trip. But I did start showing up. I helped challenge our college's administration to hire and retain Black faculty and staff. I attended race-related events like movie discussions and conferences, lending my voice to the cause. I started small gatherings where diversity could be practiced—prayer groups and worship services. Unlike in high school, where I noticed racism but kept my thoughts to myself, in college I started speaking up.

Our college was white, so most students of color

found themselves constantly teaching white folks about racial justice. For the most part we embraced this role. Finally, people saw *us* as the experts in the room. We enjoyed asserting ourselves, our history, our culture, in a space that was dominated by the normalization of whiteness. In our minds, we were fighting the good fight. But I must confess: These first collegiate attempts at seeking racial justice were a little unhealthy.

Somewhere along the way, I picked up the unspoken belief that I was made for white people. That might sound weird, but it's true. Much of my teaching (and learning) managed to revolve around whiteness—white privilege, white ignorance, white shame, the things white folks "needed" in order to believe racial justice is a worthy cause. Movie discussions on *Do the Right Thing* or *Crash* often focused on the white characters, and "privilege walks" focused on making white people recognize the unearned advantages they'd gotten at birth.

I worked as if white folks were at the center, the great hope, the linchpin, the key to racial justice and reconciliation—and so I contorted myself to be the voice white folks could hear. It's amazing how white supremacy even invades programs aimed at seeking racial reconciliation. Just when I was about to lose myself to whiteness in an entirely different way, along came the second Black teacher of my life.

Dr. Simms taught courses in African American and Mexican American history. Brown, bald, and bespectacled, he wore clothes from Phat Farm and had a small leather pouch that he strapped like a messenger bag across the front of his chest. Standing no taller than five foot seven, but commanding a gravitas that many students found intimidating, the man was an intellectual powerhouse and possessed a wealth of experience that kept him grounded in real life. Many of the white students avoided him like the plague, but I didn't know a Black student who would dare graduate without taking at least one of his classes. Dr. Simms believed in the power of Black history and Black culture. He believed it could change our lives.

Dr. Simms was right.

He began each class period with a list of new terms written on the chalkboard—one of which was usually spelled incorrectly. We often teased him for being so brilliant that he didn't have space in his brain for such trivial matters as spelling. For a class period focusing on slavery in America, we would arrive with Dr. Simms's terms already on the board: *chattel, Middle Passage, slave codes, rebellion, Dred Scott,* and five or six more phrases. He would then spend the period defining each one in narrative form, making us feel like we'd witnessed events of the past.

As he taught, Dr. Simms spoke softly and repetitiously, making sure we understood his point. But he also wanted to know what we thought. "Tell me, Kate, what do you think about that?" Dr. Simms would ask. If someone spoke too softly or too hesitantly, he would extend his index and middle fingers together, twirling them in the air as he encouraged the student. "Speak up. We want to hear what you have to say. Speak up so those in the back can hear you." It didn't matter whether our insights were profound or middling—Dr. Simms always found a way to incorporate our ideas into his lecture. His gentleness did not stop him from demanding that we think deeply.

Dr. Simms wanted us to be suspicious of the language of America.

He taught us to analyze the news. Did anyone notice how only the faces of Black criminals were shown in this segment? In the next segment, the anchor said there was a crowd—could you tell if the camera angle made it seem larger or smaller?

That whole story was on immigrants, but why did it focus only on immigrants of color? He wanted us to pay attention. I remember him often bringing in multiple newspapers—one the English-language *Chicago Tribune* and the other *Hoy,* the Spanish-language paper headquartered in the same city. He would have us read two stories on the same topic, then ask, "How are these two stories different? What details did the *Trib* leave out or *Hoy* include?"

He also encouraged us to question everyday "patriotic" language. When referring to the drafters of the Constitution, Dr. Simms refused to call them the Founding Fathers. "Those aren't my Fathers!" he would state matter-of-factly. His declaration invited the question for the rest of us: *Are they mine?*

We always told Dr. Simms that he ruined our lives. He made us so aware of racial bias, we could no longer watch the news as leisure. We analyzed movies for accuracy like we never had before. Newly conscious that the literature we read carried an angle, we now couldn't help but seek it out. We thought critically about everything, and it was all Dr. Simms's fault.

Dr. Simms didn't just make us recite names and dates. He taught us to care about the past. When he spoke of Martin Luther King Jr.'s assassination, his eyes would fill with tears. It was like he was hearing the announcement all over again. He wept so hard after showing a documentary on the work of Cesar Chavez, he had to dismiss class that day. Dr. Simms wanted us to be emotionally connected to our learning, to sit in the pain, the horror, the absurdity of America's racist history, and to humanize those who dared stand against the system. Dr. Simms made us believe that we could follow that legacy of resistance, but one piece of his advice stood out to me more than all the others.

"Ain't no friends here."

Whenever Dr. Simms said this—in a lecture on Lincoln's true views on race, or while talking about the mainstream media's mixed track record in covering social movements—it always made me laugh. Dr. Simms wouldn't hurt a fly. He exuded gentleness and softness, and he relied on knowledge and humor when responding to critics. I never heard him raise his voice to anyone except to shout "Friends! Friends!" when our discussions became incomprehensible with passion. So hearing him say anything that could be perceived as an overgeneralization or inherently suspicious of others seemed like a departure. And yet, we all knew he was not joking. We already had plenty of examples in our history books and on our college campus, but it would take some time to figure out how deep and wide his life lesson would stretch.

For the rest of undergrad, my professor's words would come back to me whenever white people acted a fool. When they wrote in our newspaper that the Black students should just leave if we weren't happy. When I overheard racist comments in the cafeteria, or explained to the residence director for the millionth time that our lobby isn't suddenly "scary" when Black football players happen to be occupying it. Any time something like this happened, Dr. Simms's voice would sound in my head: *Ain't no friends here.*

Professor McMath, Dr. Simms, and a handful of additional faculty and staff members helped me define what it meant to be a Black student in white spaces. They helped me demand what I wanted. They made it safe for me to explore my own voice. Though I was often surrounded by whiteness, they reminded me that I was capable of responding to racist white people, and encouraged me to seek comfort in Black history and the healing of Black community. They pushed me to rethink what whiteness had taught me about myself, about my personhood, about my vocation, about my place in the world. They were teaching me to speak up until those in the back could hear me.

School was over. Time for the real world. Turned out Dr. Simms was right, even when I didn't want him to be.

5

Whiteness at Work

Confession: By the time I graduated from college, I thought I was the white culture whisperer. I was fearless. I thought any future encounters of racism would rear their ugly heads like purple dragons, and I had no doubt in my ability to slay racist nonsense wherever I found it. I was so wrong. Far from an imposing beast, I found that white supremacy is more like a poison. It seeps into your mind, drip by drip, until it makes you wonder if your perception of reality is true.

Being a Black woman in the professional world of majority-white nonprofit ministries was far more difficult than my younger self could imagine. In school I had been surrounded by whiteness, but colleges often encourage students to question authority, to navigate cultural conflicts, to be creative in starting alternative organizations and clubs. While every school certainly contains boundaries for students, at some basic level it is expected that students push those boundaries, that they learn not only through books but through new experiences. The professional world, I soon discovered, is altogether different.

Companies love talking about their "diversity and inclusion efforts," but I remember one unusually frank conversation with our organization's board of directors, in which I learned how those efforts often work. Less than a year into the job, I was seeking approval for a new racial diversity training program. I knew the meeting wasn't going well when the treasurer said, "Just to play devil's advocate . . ." and then posed a series of questions, speaking gently so as to preserve an air of innocence. "Why don't we want assimilation? Isn't that the point of an organization's culture? Don't we want to bring in people of diverse backgrounds and then become one unified organization?"

My mouth dropped open, but the rest of my body froze. I had no idea how to speak truth to the person who held my program in his hands. How could I possibly explain that the unity he desired always came at my expense? I had worked for a number of organizations that struggled to create meaningful opportunities for people of color, but I had never heard anyone make an overt case in favor of assimilation—particularly at an organization that promoted diversity in its mission statements and messaging. Granted, many people of color on our team had grown suspicious of those statements, suspecting that the organization wanted our racial diversity without our diversity of thought and culture. I just never imagined someone with his influence would say it aloud and with positivity.

It's so easy to believe the pretty pictures on the website filled with racial diversity, to buy in to the well-crafted statements of purpose, to enjoy being invited into the process of "being part of the change." The role of a bridge builder sounds appealing until it becomes clear how often that bridge is your broken back.

It usually begins with the job interview.

Overcompensation is hard to resist in this moment. When you need a job, and are genuinely drawn to the work described in the job posting, it's tempting to sit in that seat and say all the right things, laugh the right laugh, extend all the right jokes. The goal, after all, is to impress. Do I make myself more likable? Do I use references to movies, music, books that I know the folks around the table would appreciate—references that would imply *I am just like you?* Sometimes I just want to prove I can do it. That I can make them comfortable, make them believe. But the question is always, *Is it worth it?*

White institutions are constantly communicating how much Blackness they want. It begins with numbers. How many scholarships are being offered? How many seats are being "saved" for "neighborhood kids"? How many Black bodies must be present for us to have "good" diversity numbers? How many people of color are needed for the website, the commercials, the pamphlets?

But numbers are only the beginning. Whiteness constantly polices the expressions of Blackness allowed within its walls, attempting to accrue no more than what's necessary to affirm itself. It wants us to sing the celebratory "We Shall Overcome" during MLK Day but doesn't want to hear the indicting lyrics of "Strange Fruit." It wants to see a Black person seated at the table but doesn't want to hear a dissenting viewpoint. It wants to pat itself on the back for helping poor Black folks through missions or urban projects but has no interest in learning from Black people's wisdom, talent, and spiritual depth. Whiteness wants enough Blackness to affirm the goodness of whiteness, the progressiveness of whiteness, the openheartedness of whiteness. Whiteness likes a trickle of Blackness, but only that which can be controlled.

Here's how all of this plays out if you're a Black woman trying to survive in a culture of professional whiteness:

8:55 A.M.: I arrive at work and walk through the lobby to get to my office. On the way, I am asked three times if I need help finding the outreach center. My white co-worker, whose footsteps I hear behind me, is never asked this question. *The message: I am a Black woman, so I must be poor and in need of help.*

8:58 A.M.: I set my purse down in my cubicle. The white co-worker who was walking behind me stares in shock. She has never seen me with my hair in a pineapple fro. She reaches out to touch my hair while telling me how beautiful it is. When I pull back, startled by the sudden act of intimacy, she looks hurt and isn't sure what to do next. *The message: I am different, exotic. Anyone should have the right to my body in exchange for a compliment.*

9:58 A.M.: An hour later, I am asked to see my supervisor. When I get to her office she asks me to shut the door. She tells me she received a note saying that I made someone uncomfortable when they were just trying to be friendly and kind. She suggests that I work on being more of a team player, and not being so closed off. I look at her incredulously. I now wonder if this is just about the one co-worker, or if my supervisor gets emails about me every week from awkward white people. *The message: I am responsible for the feelings of white people, and my boss will not defend me from these accusations.*

10:05 A.M.: I attempt to respond, but before I can finish, my supervisor asks if I don't mind changing my tone a bit. I sound angry and she was trying to be helpful, trying to make sure I can stay here long-term. I mumble something about my own frustrations, but they are dismissed with a wave of her hand and a promise to work with me. *The message: My tone will be interpreted as angry, even if I'm just feeling hurt or misunderstood. My actual feelings are irrelevant and could be used as reason to fire me.*

12:00 noon: It's lunchtime now, and I desperately need to talk to my girlfriends in another department. I find a seat among this group of women of color who use the lunch break to offer support and encouragement to one another. After talking with them for a little bit, I feel like I can breathe again. Even though we don't work in the same departments, they are the reason I've survived here this long. I return to my office.

1:00 P.M.: I have a project due at the end of the week, so I put on my headphones to block out the office noise while I work. Another team member comes to my door. "Austin, can I talk to you for a second?" "Sure," I respond. "I noticed that you wear your headphones a lot in the office," she says. "It sometimes feels like you don't want to be around us." I take a deep breath. Because we work in cubicles, many of us wear headphones when we need to focus. Mine aren't on more often than anyone else's. *The message: My body is being scrutinized in ways that others are not subjected to, and the worst is being assumed of me.*

1:05 P.M.: I respond to the co-worker but quickly turn the conversation to the project we're working on together, hoping to discuss the changes I made that morning. Thirty minutes into this conversation, I realize I am answering questions about Black music, a news segment on "urban violence" she saw the other night, and something her adopted Black nephew said the other day. She emphasizes the word *black,* clearly not used to saying the word. I am tired. I am not sure what led us here. *The message: I am here to educate my white co-workers when they are confused about a racial issue in their lives.*

1:40 P.M.: I take a deep breath. "Hey, I need to stretch my legs. I'm going to get some coffee, you want anything?" I don't like coffee, but I will get some anyway if it helps end this conversation.

1:50 P.M.: Standing in line at the coffee shop next door, I quickly notice a man who stopped me in the hallway and referred to me as "colored." He had come to one session of my Tuesday night class on race and thought it appropriate to pepper me with questions about Blackness (well, "colored-ness") since he'd decided not to continue coming. Rather than answer his questions on the spot, I'd told him he should come back to the class. But now here he is behind me. Maybe he won't speak up, or maybe he'll think he has me confused with an-other Black person. He doesn't say anything, but my body is stiff with anticipatory tension.

2:07 P.M.: As soon as I get my coffee and turn toward the door, it happens. Someone I have never met insists that she emailed me and can't wait to chat more. She is right that we work at the same or-ganization, but I've never seen this woman. "I think you have me confused with someone else," I say.

She insists I am wrong. "Oh no, don't you re-member . . ." I stare at her blankly, my warm coffee reminding me that I am not in the sunken place.

I let her finish, then I repeat slowly, "I think you have me confused with someone else." The explanation continues until I am given enough information to know which Black person she has me confused with. "Nope, that's not me. You're talking about Tina in the communications department. She is amazing, you two will have a good talk, I'm sure." Her eyes grow wide, embarrassment climbing her face. "I'm so sorry, I have to run!" I say, before the apologies get messy. *The message: My body, my person is not distinct; I am interchangeable with all other Black women.*

2:17 P.M.: I'm back in my office; preparing for an afternoon staff meeting in which I will give a short presentation. I feel good about my content—I've worked hard on it, knowing my perspective is often different from my co-workers'—but my heart still beats fast. How will I be received by my team?

2:30 P.M.: I'm in the staff meeting. I give my eight-minute spiel. There is a pause, and then some pushback. I knew this was a possibility, so I hear them out, trying not to form a response as they speak. Another co-worker pipes in before I can respond: "I think what Austin is trying to say is . . ." Suddenly everyone is nodding in agreement even though I'm pretty sure she repeated me almost word for word. *The message: I need white approval and interpretation before my idea will be considered good.*

3:30 P.M.: The meeting has closed, and some co-workers race back to their cubicles. Even though I am behind on emails, I know that I must stay and chat. If I race back to my cubicle it will be interpreted as me being antisocial. I stick around and make small talk, leaving with another co-worker so that my body doesn't stand out.

3:40 P.M.: I'm back in my office. I glance at the clock. There are still two more hours in the day.

These are the daily annoyances, the subtle messages of whiteness. But we bear other scars, too. Over and over I have seen white men and women get praise for their gifts and skills while women of color are told only about their *potential* for leadership. When white people end up being terrible at their jobs, I have seen supervisors move mountains to give them new positions more suited to their talents, while people of color are told to master their positions or be let go. I have been in the room when promises were made to diversify boardrooms, leadership teams, pastoral staff, faculty and staff positions, only to watch committees appoint a white man in the end. It's difficult to express how these incidents accumulate, making you feel undervalued, unappreciated, and ultimately expendable.

Over the years, I have grown used to hearing the response "Well, why don't you just leave if you don't like it here?" As if this experience is a unique phenomenon, or specific to only a handful of delinquent organizations. Even if it were unique, it's highly privileged to believe that Black women can just quit and find another place to work without missing paychecks or losing benefits. Just changing jobs is rarely that simple. So Black women come up with life hacks.

These life hacks don't involve nifty uses for egg cartons or finding unique ways to use paper clips. They involve helping one another write emails to our supervisors or coworkers, which we know will be scrutinized for tone. Our life hacks include keeping folders in our in-boxes where we place every single email that praises our project, attitude, or giftedness. This is not for our self-esteem; it's an insurance policy, because we know there are emails being sent to our bosses that say the opposite. Our life hacks include finding a cohort, a girlfriend, an ally—someone who is safe. Someone to have lunch with who doesn't need an explanation of our being. Our life hacks include secret Facebook groups where we process awkward interpersonal microaggressions and suggest ways to tackle them in the future.

But for many of us, life hacks can't stop the inevitable. They can slow it down, yes. But eventually, those of us who work for white Christians are asked the question *Are you sure God has really called you . . . here?*

And then I know just how invisible and dispensible I am.

Rather than having a conversation about policy or assumptions or interactions, I am asked what God thinks about me. This is convenient, because it allows the people in charge to wash their hands of the conflict. But the suggestion that I assimilate doesn't always come passive-aggressively, or with ill intent. Sometimes it sounds loving.

It's been a hard week at the office. Because I work at a Christian organization, my co-workers ask if they can pray for me. I am moved that they've noticed my emotional distress. They gather round, lay their hands on my shoulders. I close my eyes and breathe deeply, listening to their words. But before I know it, the prayers take a turn. They are no longer about my circumstances but about me. They ask not that I would be understood but that

I would find it within myself to give more grace. The prayers don't ask that doors would open for me; they ask that God would gift me with skills they wish I had. These prayers aren't for me. The prayers are that I would become who *they* want me to be. "Lord, make this Black person just like us."

I'm not sure my co-workers even realize the difference; they've been praying the prayer for so long. In this way whiteness reveals its true desire for people of color. Whiteness wants us to be empty, malleable, so that it can shape Blackness into whatever is necessary for the white organization's own success. It sees potential, possibility, a future where Black people could share some of the benefits of whiteness if only we try hard enough to mimic it. The initial expectation is that I simply code-switch, conforming to the cultural communication of white people when I'm with them. But in the end, this is never enough. The ultimate expectation is that I will come to realize that white ways of thinking, behaving, communicating, and understanding the world are to be valued above all else.

Rare is the ministry praying that they would be worthy of the giftedness of Black minds and hearts. So we must remind ourselves. It's the only way to spit out the poison. We must remind ourselves and one another that we are fearfully and wonderfully made, arming ourselves against the ultimate message of whiteness—that we are inferior. We must stare at ourselves in the mirror and repeat that we, too, are fully capable, immensely talented, and uniquely gifted. We are not tokens. We are valuable in the fullness of our humanity. We are not perfect, but we are here, able to contribute something special, beautiful, lasting to the companies and ministries to which we belong.

Interlude:

Why I Love Being a Black Girl

As a Black woman working in white spaces, my perception of racial dynamics has been questioned, minimized, or denied altogether. Over time, the experience of not being believed, especially by people I thought were my friends, wore away my sense of self. As I entered the professional world and sensed this happening to me, it became vital to remind myself daily of why I love being a Black girl:

I am enlivened by our stories of survival. Even though white folks tried to steal our histories—our lives, our labor, our culture, our origins—we recover the records. We find the census, the photos, the certificates, the inscriptions. Thanks to my grandmother, I am filled with stories of triumph over slavery, over lynching, over Jim Crow, because our dignity was too strong to crush. I have felt the cast-iron pot of my grandmother and held the Bible of my great-grandmother. I sit at the feet of my elders and listen to them honor our shared past.

When I begin to doubt myself, I remember that we are creators. We are pioneers of language itself. We invent new words and kill old ones. We smash syllables together and watch them reverberate across the nation. We have a language we share with one another. Though our words are stolen and often misused or misapplied, we know the depth of our vocabulary when used among ourselves. Our conversations are call-and-response. Someone uncolored might assume we are cutting each other off, interrupting—but all we did was move church outside the building walls. We will shout "Yes, amen" and "You better say that" in affirmation of one another.

When my body stands out and I am tempted to forget my own beauty, I close my eyes and remember the feel of my father's fingers against my scalp, braiding each perfectly parted row while telling me I am not tender-headed so stop squirming. There was the cooling sensation of Blue Magic and Pink Lotion and the smell of hot curling irons as I learned about all the special things my hair can do.

Natural or relaxed, braided or dreaded, twisted or knotted, cornrowed or weaved—our hair believes in being free to do what she wants. When I rub cocoa butter into my skin, I remember the warmth of my mother's hands when she used to tell me to get all the hidden spots—behind my ankles and around my knees. The memories of her care for my body are a reminder of the care my body deserves.

Black women are the backbone and muscle of every church I've attended. They are prophets speaking a word when it seems God is silent. They are hospitality, welcoming with food and kindness, with a seat at the table, with a place you can call home. We are capable of building community anywhere—not just at church or at work, but also in the "ethnic" hair care section of stores, in elevators, and other random places where we take the opportunity to simply say, "I see you."

I love being a Black woman because we are demanding. We demand the right to live as fully human. We demand access—the right to vote, to education, to employment, to housing, to equal treatment under the law. And we do it creatively: Sit-ins and die-ins, signs and songs, writing and filmmaking. We demand because our ancestors did. We demand because we believe in our own dignity.

I could go on and on. I haven't touched the poetry of Nikki Giovanni, Lucille Clifton, and every southern grandmother who ever urged her children to keep on keeping on. I haven't covered the hugs and head nods and compliments from strangers; the Black cool of our photographers and dancers, politicians and teachers, and the everyday folks we love. There is so much beauty to share. But my point is this: I love being a Black girl.

6

White Fragility

A lot of white people have never sat under the authority of a Black teacher, pastor, professor, or supervisor. The person who's in control, setting the standards, handing out the grades, making the moral commands, is usually someone who looks like them. As I grew into my career and found myself in positions of relative authority, I learned that being the first Black woman authority figure in a white person's world can be . . . intense.

I'll never forget the day when one white man in particular made it clear for me how combustible white folks can be. I had just finished teaching a class called Race and Faith. We spent the class period discussing common racial stereotypes, where they come from, how they are reinforced, and what we can do to combat them in ourselves and others.

Toward the end of our time together, I pointed to the far wall, still covered in Post-its from the activity, recounting the aha moments of our discussion. The participants sat in a large circle in folding chairs, but I noticed one man sat with his arms crossed, sinking down into his chair, clearly brooding over the content of our class. As I spoke, he attempted to interrupt me, but I asked him if he wouldn't mind waiting until the class was over. I could tell by his body language and the heat in his voice that he was not interested in engaging so much as fighting, but I hoped listening to one of my co-teachers end the class with Scripture and prayer would help him calm down. It didn't work.

Minutes after my co-teacher said amen, officially ending the class, the man stood across a high-top table, screaming at me. His face had turned entirely red. He stood a head taller than me, and his eyes were wide as he waved his outstretched hands in my face. His voice alternated between passionate debate and outright exasperation.

I looked at the faces of my co-teachers to make sure this scene was as over the top as it felt to me. "Trayvon Martin is not a victim," he yelled. He then pointed to the Post-its on the wall where the other participants had confessed their association of the word *thug* with Black people. He attempted to school me. "Black boys just need jobs. That's it. Do you know the jobless rate of Black boys?" As he circled through these points again and again, I struggled to understand what any of this had to do with me. All we knew was that I had become the object of his anger. The eyes of my co-teachers, wide with disbelief, said it all, "Yep, this is unreal."

I placed my hands on the table between myself and the man, willing myself toward emotional stability. The louder his voice became, the more I dropped mine. Still, for the next twenty minutes, he raged at me, teaching me everything he thought he knew about Black boys in the hood. When it became clear that I was already pretty familiar with the topic, he pivoted. "Who is really in charge here?" At last, we had arrived at the true source of this conflict: my incompetence. Surely someone else, someone occupying a different body, would understand him.

A white male co-worker, offended at this question, stepped in. "Austin is in charge here. This is her class. But would you mind talking with me over here, if that's okay with you, Austin?" I nodded, appreciating the request for permission. The pair walked to the other side of the classroom, while

I attempted to regroup from the onslaught of the man's temper.

His wife—small and quiet—happened to be in the group that was listening. "I'm so sorry," she said to me. "He came in late, missing all the setup, the activity, and half the discussion. When he came in, you mentioned Trayvon Martin and he saw the Post-its from the activity on the wall naming the stereotypes faced by Black boys. The combination just set him off."

Well, that's annoying. And sadly, it's all too common for qualified Black women to find themselves facing off with white ignorance. White men have yelled at me in defensiveness, challenged the entirety of my talks during open Q and A sessions, and simply ignored me as if I don't exist, gathering all their privilege like a shield. White women have dismissed me completely, crumbled into tears, or launched into stories that center on That One Time Something Bad Happened to Them. Beneath the volatility, the combativeness, white people become disturbed because they often can't fathom Black people have something important to teach them about themselves and about the world.

That day I cried. I knew I had done nothing wrong, but my body was still processing the onslaught of anger and condescension. I willed my body to relax, removing my hands from the table and crossing them in front of my chest, a feeble attempt to stop from shaking. I knew more than that man did about all the things he considered himself an expert on—Black boys, the hood, the nonprofits working on issues of crime, poverty, and education. But instead of recognizing that I am flesh, blood, emotion, real, a human, he had taken all these things for granted, speaking to me in a way that he wouldn't have to anyone who looked like him.

This is partly what makes the fragility of whiteness so damn dangerous. It ignores the personhood of people of color and instead makes the feelings of whiteness the most important thing. It happens in classes and workshops, board meetings and staff meetings, via email and social media, but it takes other forms, too. If Black people are dying in the street, we must consult with white feelings before naming the evils of police brutality. If white family members are being racist, we must take Grandpa's feelings into account before we proclaim our objections to such speech. If an organization's policies are discriminatory and harmful, that can only be corrected if we can ensure white people won't feel bad about the change. White fragility protects whiteness and forces Black people to fend for themselves.

The day after the man raged at me, I was pulled

into a meeting by a staff member. Several of my co-teachers, both Black and white, started by rehashing the events. But before I knew it, the conversation became about the feelings of the white man and what I could have done to calm him down. Perhaps if I had let him walk it off or traveled to a different location in the room. Perhaps if I had used a different, friendlier tone. Perhaps if I had done something magically obvious, something simple—something they surely would have done— maybe the white man would have been less irate, less threatening toward me.

This conversation was not about my safety, my security, my authority. Not about my feelings, but about his. About how I should have taken care of those feelings, changed those feelings so that I would have been safe.

No one was yelling or threatening me physically. In fact, everyone present loved me, yet white fragility was undergirding this conversation, too. I was pretty sure that if the man had treated a white woman this way, we'd be having a different discussion. This meeting was not for my support; it was a critique. But just when I was starting to wonder if my own co-workers would indulge my humanity, someone spoke up. "Wait a second," she said. "This conversation seems to have moved away from the reality that this grown man is responsible for his own feelings. And there is no circumstance under which his behavior would be tolerated if used against any other teacher or speaker. Austin did nothing wrong."

The group began to backtrack, looking at me in horror as if I'd been the one who'd chided them. But the conversation shifted. They stopped focusing on what I could have done differently and began discussing how the church could protect me and the other women leading the class. Feeling emboldened, I made it clear that a class on race, led by a Black woman, would likely draw similar reactions in the future.

I am grateful the conversation moved forward, but it reminded me how easy it is to center white feelings without thinking twice. And there are other times when white fragility is so self-obsessed, so over the top that the damage it inflicts on marginalized people becomes immediately apparent.

For a year I worked for a short-term missions site on the West Side of Chicago. Our program was located in a Black neighborhood and intentionally brought students to learn about all the amazing ways God was already working in Black neighborhoods through Black people. We hosted about fifty people each week of the summer, and smaller

groups through the year. Most of the white participants were a little nervous when they climbed out
of their vans, having never spent time in a predominately Black community. But my staff of college
students would quickly win them over and before
long the groups would be traipsing around the city,
hopping on and off the El like pros as they learned
about our hood.

One group, however, couldn't get over their fears
about the neighborhood—or the fact that Austin,
the director of the program, was not a white man.

I sensed something was wrong as soon as the
group pulled up. Typically, young people would
pour out of the bus, eager to stretch their legs after
being cooped up for the hours-long drive. Their excitement would turn into a flurry of bright colored
bags, blankets, pillows, and matching T-shirts. But
this group was different. They just sat on the bus.
It was almost eerie. After a while, my staff went to
greet them, and somehow managed to coax them
off the bus and into the room where we held the
opening service.

There were worship songs, icebreakers, introductions, and a tour of the church to get everyone accli-
mated to the new space. Usually this would last for
about an hour, after which I would steal away the

parents for an orientation of their own. But right in the middle of the icebreakers, the youth pastor asked me if she could speak with Austin, the director. When I informed her that I, in fact, was Austin, her eyes grew wide. She looked away from me toward her group, then back at me again, her eyes still bulging. I had a sinking feeling that the shock wouldn't pass with an awkward laugh.

She finally spoke. "Oh." Though she hadn't asked me anything, I responded as if she had. "My name is Austin and I am the director of this program."

She exhaled. "Could the rest of the parents and I have a word with you? It's important."

I nodded and asked one of my staff members to take them to the conference room where I always led the adult orientation. I needed a second. I knew from the woman's reaction that this was going to be awful. It was.

When I walked into the room, all six of the parents gave me the same shocked look. I repeated what was becoming a mantra that evening: "My name is Austin, and I am the director of this program." What came next was an onslaught of questions rooted in their fears of Blackness. They started with a desire to know who was "really" in charge, as if a white person would suddenly make an appearance. Thirty minutes later they ended with questions about the possibility of being killed by Black gang members. The message behind their questions was clear: My neighborhood was untrustworthy, and so was my Black female body.

The end of the parent meeting was usually when I would share about the amazing work happening in our community and hand out the schedule of nonprofits I'd prepared for them to visit. But I didn't trust this group enough to stick to the schedule. I informed them that in light of their clear discomfort, I wanted to make their group a little larger—allowing them to travel as ten to twelve, rather than four to five people. I would need time to talk with the directors of our partner programs and confirm everything.

The parents were so grateful to be able to travel in larger groups, they didn't mind the last-minute change in plans. Little did they know, my first priority was protecting the nonprofits. I refused to allow their toxic ideas and offensive assumptions anywhere near the organizations, the people, I loved. Instead, I arranged to send them to a massive homeless shelter, one with strong religious underpinnings that this group would appreciate. I knew the bulk of their time would be spent on a tour of the facility, leaving very little time for the group to interact with actual folks who were experiencing homelessness. They went on the visit, and many people in the group came back from their trip genuinely moved by the experience. But it wasn't enough to salvage the situation. An hour or so after returning from the shelter—twenty-four hours into a planned weeklong trip—the youth pastor informed me the group was leaving. The parents' fear of a Black neighborhood had won out in the end.

As the youth group packed their things, the mothers ducked into an empty conference room to talk with my staff. With eyes downcast, the mothers began to tearfully confess their fears. They wanted to thank my staff for opening their eyes to their own racism. My staff listened patiently. But just as they started to approach something close to forgiveness, another white parent, a father, entered the room. He immediately took over the discussion. He shared that the first thing he had done when they arrived in front of our building was call the local police department and ask if it was safe for white people to be here. He then noted his disappointment that there was no "welcoming committee" offering them safe passage for the fifteen feet between the bus and the building. As he continued to list his grievances, he started referring to me in the third person as "the director" though I was sitting two feet from him. "You mean Austin?" one of the apologetic parents interrupted. "Who is Austin?" he replied, and then continued to list all the other things "the director" had done wrong.

At that point I'd had enough. "This conversation is over," I said. "It's time for you all to leave."

I was livid. But I also knew this was my job—dealing with white people. How far should I have gone to manage their fears? At what point did the group become not only a nuisance but a detriment to the community I love? What would I have done if they'd stayed? What was my responsibility to my white student employees—to believe in the possibility of the group's transformation, or to give them the reality that not everyone is interested in change? And how did I hold that up against my Black student employees, who had to listen to this racist nonsense? What would my supervisor think? What would the board of directors think? How much would this episode cost the organization?

I was making decisions on the fly, and I did the best I could. But I still wonder if I should have waited even twenty-four hours. The first sixty minutes had been damaging enough.

Thank goodness, that group wasn't the only one we hosted that week. Another one showed up a few days later, completely ready to confront their biases as they volunteered at urban gardens, shelters, group homes, and food pantries. This group was more homogenous than the other, but they came prepared to learn.

At the end of the week, this second group sat down with my staff to process their trip. Five or six of the teenagers had gone to a group home that kept an urban garden to supplement groceries in the house. The youth group spent the day working in the garden, and then learned how to cook the proceeds from teenage boys who lived in the home. As they told me how it went, one girl spoke up. "I had a really good time working alongside the guys, but my biggest lesson came after we left." She then recounted how upon their leaving, some of the guys from the home followed them out the door on their way to work.

The girl's father, who was accompanying the group, asked his daughter to turn around. "What would you think of those guys if you hadn't just spent the afternoon with them?"

It only took her a moment to tell the truth. "I would have looked at their skin color and tattoos, the way they dress and their playfulness and assumed they were gang members." She paused for a moment, then declared, "I realized today that I can be racist."

Though she was the first to say it aloud, many members of the youth group had a similar moment by the end of the week. Their confessions were no burden to me or my staff because they took full ownership of what it meant to face their own racism.

It was a painful week, but it taught me that I cannot control expressions of white fragility. Each group was responsible for their own reaction. One indulged their fragility, the other resisted it.

To stay committed to this work, I have learned to accept the constant experience of entrenchment and transformation. On the bad days, when entrenchment is lashing out, tearing down, pretending you don't have a name, this work feels soul crushing, dehumanizing. But on the good days, you witness transformation, openness, a willingness to change one's worldview. And for a brief moment, I can believe in the possibility that we are still inching toward justice.

7

Nice White People

We were on a working retreat. Earlier that day, the seven of us had left the safety of the diverse city and traveled north to a quieter, whiter town. After working for a couple hours, my group decided to take a break from the hotel conference room. We spent the rest of the morning sailing—we'll get to that in a second, but let's just say it didn't go well for me. After departing the boat, we ended up at a restaurant bar with a distinctly nautical theme for lunch.

We were waiting for our drinks when a co-worker walked over to me. "Are you doing okay?" she asked. I thought she was referring to the reason our sailing trip had ended early. I was not used to being on a boat. Out on the water, my stomach had felt like it was moving around as much as the waves. While everyone conversed and laughed on deck, wearing big sunglasses and leaning against the walls of the boat, I was practicing deep breathing techniques and weighing which would be more embarrassing—throwing up or asking the captain if we could return to shore.

But that's not what she meant. "I noticed you're the only person of color here and I know that can be uncomfortable," she said with great concern.

She meant well, and part of me was really proud of her for noticing. I was pretty sure this was a moment of growth for her to walk into a room and realize it's white. But truth be told, I was equally perplexed by the timing of her question. She was right. I was the only person of color in the bar that day. But I had also been the only person of color on the bus we drove up in, in the conference room we occupied for our work, on the boat we had just disembarked. And when we returned to our workplace, I would often be the only person of color in the room again.

I smiled, thanked her for noticing, and told her I was fine. To point out that I am always aware of my color, even with her and our fellow co-workers, would have been too much for that moment. I would have been telling her that her whiteness is not fundamentally different than the whiteness of the space we currently occupied. It would have threatened her sense of goodness—of being a "good white person," the kind who notices when we are in a restaurant with no people of color. In my experience, white people who believe they are safe often prove dangerous when that identity is challenged.

This is in part because most white people still believe that they are good and the true racists are easy to spot. The true racists wouldn't have hired me, wouldn't have brought me on this trip, wouldn't have noticed the homogenous environment. My colleagues were much too nice to be racists.

I don't know where this belief comes from, but I do know it has consequences. When you believe niceness disproves the presence of racism, it's easy to start believing bigotry is rare, and that the label *racist* should be applied only to mean-spirited, intentional acts of discrimination. The problem with this framework—besides being a gross misunderstanding of how racism operates in systems and structures enabled by nice people—is that it obligates me to be nice in return, rather than truthful. I am expected to come closer to the racists. Be nicer to them. Coddle them.

Even more, if most white people are good, innocent, lovely folks who are just angry or scared or ignorant, it naturally follows that whenever racial tension arises, I must be the problem. I am not kind enough, patient enough, warm enough. I don't have enough understanding for the white heart, white feelings, white needs. It does not matter that I don't always feel like teaching white people through my pain, through the disappointment of allies who gave up and colaborers who left. It does not matter that the "well-intentioned" questions hurt my feelings or that the decisions made in all-white meetings affect me differently than they do everyone else. If my feelings do not fit the narrative of white innocence and goodness, the burden of change gets placed on me.

When this narrative of goodness is disrupted by the unplanned utterance of racial slurs, jokes, rants, or their kind, whiteness has perfected another tool for defending its innocence. I call it the Relational Defense. It happens in the media all the time. A government official, teacher, pastor, or principal is caught on tape saying something that is clearly racist. But rather than confess and seek transformation, the person defends their "goodness" by appealing to the relationships of those who "know" them.

"I am not racist! Just ask [blank]. She knows me."
"My family and friends know my heart. They
    will tell you I couldn't be racist."
"I have a Black spouse/child/friend. I don't have
    a racist bone in my body."

PR-challenged politicians and celebrities aren't the only ones who use the Relational Defense, and white people are often willing to extend this defense to one another. Once, after inviting me to lead a diversity training session for volunteers at a food pantry, the organization's director explained why she thought the training was necessary. She told me a story about a committed volunteer, a white woman, getting into an altercation with an older Black female shopper. Though I hadn't been there when the argument happened, the details didn't surprise me. The director admitted that the volunteer had treated the shopper like a child, using a condescending, paternalistic tone. It wasn't long before the shopper had had enough. Things escalated from there until the pair were yelling back and forth.

The director then cut to the white volunteer's reaction. "She marched into my office after the shopper left, shouting about how ungrateful the woman was. She said she wanted to go home early because she was afraid the woman would come back with

her gang friends and blow her head off just for trying to help her."

The director summarized, "So you can see, we
do need more diversity training. But the volunteer
isn't racist. I know her—she has Black friends, just
not *poor* Black friends. Her problem, and maybe
other volunteers', too, is their class privilege."

I had only just met this well-meaning director,
so I wasn't sure how to point out the false dichot-
omy. It implied that if a person is nice (as evidenced
by the fact that they have Black friends), then they
couldn't possibly be racist or bigoted. Never mind
that the woman had blatantly employed racial
stereotypes to demean the character of the Black
woman; if the volunteer was nice to rich Black people, it meant she couldn't possibly be racist.

White people desperately want to believe that
only the lonely, isolated "whites only" club members are racist. This is why the word *racist* offends
"nice white people" so deeply. It challenges their
self-identification as good people. Sadly, most white
people are more worried about being called racist
than about whether or not their actions are in fact
racist or harmful.

But the truth is, even the monsters—the Klan
members, the faces in the lynch mob, the murder-

ers who bombed churches—they all had friends and family members. Each one of them was connected to people who would testify that they had good hearts. They had families who loved them, friends who came over for dinner, churches where they made small talk with the pastor after the service. The monster has always been well dressed and well loved.

But I suspect that white people really don't want to believe that we (people of color) know them, too. They want to believe their proximity to people of color makes them immune. That if they smile at people of color, hire a person of color, read books by people of color, marry or adopt a person of color, we won't sense the ugliness of racism buried in the psyche and ingrained in the heart. White people don't want to believe that we sense the discomfort, hear the ignorance, notice the ways they process race, our bodies, our presence. We know them; we know they are racist.

Entertaining a discussion about race with someone who believes in white innocence often feels like entering the twilight zone. This is largely because those who believe in white innocence don't have enough of a knowledge base to participate meaningfully in the discussion. They haven't educated themselves through books or courses. They are unfamiliar with the lexicon on race, not realizing their words have particular meanings. Their understanding of both America's racial history and current racial landscape is lacking. But this does not prevent them from being convinced of their rightness and need to reassert dominance.

White people are notorious for trying to turn race conversations into debates, and then becoming angry or dismissive when people of color won't participate. White people believe this is because people of color haven't thought it through or are stumped by a well-made point. But the truth is, oftentimes people of color don't have the time, energy, or willpower to teach the white person enough to turn the conversation into a real debate. To do so would be a ton of work.

Even on the occasion when a conversation actually proves itself productive, Black folks still have to be on the lookout for white fragility's cousin: white guilt.

I don't have much use for white guilt anymore. I used to interpret white guilt as an early sign of a change in heart, a glimpse that a movie, program, or speaker had broken through and was producing a changed mind. While that may or may not be true, for those on the receiving end, white guilt is like having tar dry all over your hands and heart. It takes so much work to peel off the layers, rub away the stickiness, get rid of the smell. Unsolicited confessions inspired by a sense of guilt are often poured over Black bodies in search of their own relief.

I experienced this self-indulgent desire for relief after a church celebration for MLK Day. During the service, my friend Jenny and I stood on the church stage, recounting the story of our friendship—formed during the Sankofa trip, back in college. We weaved together our personal stories, ending with specific details from the conversation on that bus. She chose images that would play on the screen behind us as we spoke, hoping those in the congregation would feel some sense of sitting on the bus with us, experiencing what we did. We talked about the first time someone called me a nigger, the disrespectful plantation tour, the horror of the lynching museum. It worked. Sort of.

By the time we stepped off the stage, white people were lining up to offer their racist confessions. A man who looked to be in his thirties: "I once called someone the n–word, and I am so ashamed." A white woman in her early twenties: "My parents wouldn't let me date a Black man, and it only just occurred to me." A forty-ish woman who told me she prided herself on spending time with the Black worship leaders of the church but went on to share, "At my workplace, there is an Indian woman who is often discussed behind her back, but I've never stood up for her."

On and on the confessions went, but none was healing to my soul. Clearly the congregation had been moved by our story. They were thinking through their personal histories. But the stories of hate—only minor incidents in the lives of the confessors—reminded me of the ease with which racism is practiced on a daily basis.

After half an hour of this, I checked in with Jenny. "Is anyone making their confessions to you?" I asked.

"No," she replied. "No one." But it turned out I wasn't alone. The most prominent Black female worship leaders on stage that day were hearing confessions left and right, too. Black women were bearing the brunt of these stories as white attenders sought relief from guilt over the ways they had participated in racism. None of them seemed to consider how their confessions affected the people hearing them.

The same happened when I spoke at a conference in South Carolina just a few months after the

Charleston shooting. The room was predominately white, and the murders at Mother Emanuel AME were still very much on the minds of the people gathered.

My talk was really well received. The audience cried and laughed in all the right places. They *amen*ed and *hhhhmmm*ed just when I had hoped they would. But then the confessions began.

For the final two days of the conference, I was treated to stories of racist parents at holiday dinner parties, Confederate flags adorning homes, and passive church pastors who think the answer to racial justice is just being nice to all people. None of these confessions involved me. No one was apologizing for not listening to me, for being mean to me, or judging me unfairly. But after I had heard all of those confessions, it felt personal. It felt like I was sitting at the table when the racist joke was made and the confessor said nothing. It felt like I was in the home with the Confederate flag that bothered no one else but me. It felt that way because for every confessor, my body had become the stand-in for the actual people who had been harmed in those situations. I was left with the weight of these moments I hadn't experienced. I was expected to offer absolution.

But I am not a priest for the white soul.

The more tired I get, the more I have to un-glue myself from these offensive, painful stories for which white people expect an absolution I cannot give. They want me to tell them "it's okay" and give them a handy excuse for their behavior. Youth, ig-norance, innocence—anything to make them feel better. White people really want this to be what reconciliation means: a Black person forgiving them for one racist sin. But just as I cannot make myself responsible for the transformation of white people, neither can I offer relief for their souls.

So I don't accept confessions like these any-more. Nowadays, when someone confesses about their racist uncle or that time they said the n–word, I determine to offer a challenge toward transfor-mation. For most confessions, this is as simple as asking, "So what are you going to do differently?" The question lifts the weight off my shoulders and forces the person to move forward, resisting the easy comfort of having spoken the confession. The person could, of course, dissolve into excuses, but at that point the weight of that decision belongs to them, not to me.

I once received a heartfelt apology from a con-ference planner who felt bad for making purposeful decisions that uplifted white women above women of color as presenters. She explained her thinking at that time, spoke a little about her reflection on the moment, and shared vulnerably about the difficulties of being a conference planner. I was intrigued—not by the confession itself but by the potential that her change of heart could lead to changes in the conferences she oversaw.

And so, rather than accept her apology and close my computer, I asked her to think about how those decisions could be prevented in the future. I offered a couple suggestions: "Perhaps in the future, people of color could receive the most airtime during the conference. Or perhaps you could make a powerful statement by making people of color the highest-paid presenters—a nod to their value, expertise, and the emotional labor of discussing race and justice." I don't know if anything I suggested will go beyond that email. But I enjoyed the imaginative process of making suggestions to someone who professed a desire to change. Whether or not anything I proposed manifested itself was not my responsibility—not my weight to carry. She could decide the significance of her own confession and determine what it would take to fulfill her own reflection on the moment. That was work I was happy to leave between her and the Holy Spirit.

8

The Story We Tell

Not long ago, I was sitting in a diversity training for a new job. Our group slumped into folding chairs beneath the almost blue fluorescent lights. We were halfway through the three-day workshop, doing an activity that left the white women in our group rather emotional. Our facilitators tried to coax our group into discussion, but after giving them short and to-the-point answers, we descended into the kind of silence workshop facilitators hate—the silence that feels so warm and comfortable, it could last forever. And then it came.

Our collective silence was shattered by a trembling white female voice: "I just can't believe it. This is so much to take in. I mean, I had no idea." Inhale. "This is just unbelievable. Why didn't anyone teach us this? I feel so cheated, deceived. I mean, really." Inhale. "This is going to sound crazy. I know it sounds crazy, but I really didn't know that slavery happened on purpose. Like on purpose." Inhale. "I don't know. I just kinda thought that it just . . . happened." Inhale. Her sobbing then filled the room as she grappled for the first time with our country's real history.

Slavery was no accident.

We didn't trip and fall into black subjugation.

Racism wasn't a bad joke that just never went away.

It was all on purpose.

Every bit of it was on purpose.

Racial injustices, like slavery and our system of mass incarceration, were purposeful inventions, but instead of seeking to understand how we got here, the national narrative remains filled with comforting myths, patchwork time lines, and colonial ideals. Like the sobbing woman in the workshop, many Americans try to live comfortably in ignorance of America's racial history.

We have not thoroughly assessed the bodies snatched from dirt and sand to be chained in a cell. We have not reckoned with the horrendous, violent mass kidnapping that we call the Middle Passage.

We have not been honest about all of America's complicity—about the wealth the South earned on the backs of the enslaved, or the wealth the North gained through the production of enslaved hands. We have not fully understood the status symbol that owning bodies offered. We have not confronted the humanity, the emotions, the heartbeats of the multiple generations who were born into slavery and died in it, who never tasted freedom on America's land.

The same goes for the Civil War. We have refused to honestly confront the fact that so many were willing to die in order to hold the freedom of others in their hands. We have refused to acknowledge slavery's role at all, preferring to boil things down to the far more palatable "states' rights." We have not confessed that the end of slavery was so bitterly resented, the rise of Jim Crow became inevitable—and with it, a belief in Black inferiority that lives on in hearts and minds today.

We have painted the hundred-year history of Jim Crow as little more than mean signage and the inconvenience that white people and Black people could not drink from the same fountain. But those signs weren't just "mean." They were perpetual reminders of the swift humiliation and brutal violence that could be suffered at any moment in the presence of whiteness. Jim Crow meant paying taxes for services one could not fully enjoy; working for meager wages; and owning nothing that couldn't be snatched away. For many black families, it meant never building wealth and never having legal recourse for injustice. The mob violence, the burned-down homes, the bombed churches and businesses, the Black bodies that were lynched every couple of days—Jim Crow was walking through life measuring every step.

Even our celebrations of the Civil Rights Movement are sanitized, its victories accentuated while the battles are whitewashed. We have not come to grips with the spitting and shouting, the pulling and tugging, the clubs, dogs, bombs, and guns, the passion and vitriol with which the rights of Black Americans were fought against. We have not acknowledged the bloodshed that often preceded victory. We would rather focus on the beautiful words of Martin Luther King Jr. than on the terror he and protestors endured at marches, boycotts, and from behind jail doors. We don't want to acknowledge that for decades, whiteness fought against every civil right Black Americans sought—from sitting at lunch counters and in integrated classrooms to the right to vote and have a say in how our country was run.

We like to pretend that all those white faces who carried protest signs and batons, who turned on their sprinklers and their fire hoses, who wrote against the demonstrations and preached against the changes, just disappeared. We like to pretend that they were won over, transformed, the moment King proclaimed, "I have a dream." We don't want to acknowledge that just as Black people who experienced Jim Crow are still alive, so are the white people who vehemently protected it—who drew red lines around Black neighborhoods and divested them of support given to average white citizens. We ignore that white people still avoid Black neighborhoods, still don't want their kids going to predominantly Black schools, still don't want to destroy segregation.

The moment Black Americans achieved freedom from enslavement, America could have put to death the idea of Black inferiority. But whiteness was not prepared to sober up from the drunkenness of power over another people group. Whiteness was not ready to give up the ability to control, humiliate, or do violence to any Black body in the vicinity—all without consequence.

Ultimately, the reason we have not yet told the truth about this history of Black and white America is that telling an ordered history of this nation would mean finally naming America's commitment to violent, abusive, exploitative, immoral white supremacy, which seeks the absolute control of Black bodies. It would mean doing something about it.

How long will it be before we finally choose to connect all the dots? How long before we confess the history of racism embedded in our systems of housing, education, health, criminal justice, and more? How long before we dig to the root?

Because it is the truth that will set us free.

Sadly, too many of us in the church don't live like we believe this. We live as if we are afraid acknowledging the past will tighten the chains of injustice rather than break them. We live as if the ghosts of the past will snatch us if we walk through the valley of the shadow of death. So instead we walk around the valley, talk around the valley. We speak of the valley with cute euphemisms:

> "We just have so many divisions in this country."
> "If we could just get better at diversity, we'd be
> so much better off."
> "We are experiencing some cultural changes."

Our only chance at dismantling racial injustice is being more curious about its origins than we are worried about our comfort. It's not a comfortable conversation for any of us. It is risky and messy. It is haunting work to recall the sins of our past. But is this not the work we have been called to anyway? Is this not the work of the Holy Spirit to illuminate truth and inspire transformation?

It's haunting. But it's also holy.

And when we talk about race today, with all the pain packed into that conversation, the Holy Spirit remains in the room. This doesn't mean the conversations aren't painful, aren't personal, aren't charged with emotion. But it does mean we can survive. We can survive honest discussions about slavery, about convict leasing, about stolen land, deportation, discrimination, and exclusion. We can identify the harmful politics of gerrymandering, voter suppression, criminal justice laws, and policies that disproportionately affect people of color negatively. And we can expose the actions of white institutions—the history of segregation and white flight, the real impact of all-white leadership, the racial disparity in wages, and opportunities for advancement. We can lament and mourn. We can be livid and enraged. We can be honest. We can tell the truth. We can trust that the Holy Spirit is here. We must.

For only by being truthful about how we got here can we begin to imagine another way.

9

Creative Anger

In 1961 James Baldwin, perhaps the greatest American essayist of the twentieth century, stated the following in a recorded panel discussion:

> To be a Negro in this country and to be relatively conscious, is to be in a rage almost all the time. So that the first problem is how to control that rage so that it won't destroy you. Part of the rage is this: it isn't only what is happening to you, but it's what's happening all around you all of the time, in the face of the most extraordinary and criminal indifference, the indifference and ignorance of most white people in this country.

Baldwin wasn't lying. I have become very intimate with anger.

It is rage inducing to be told that we can do anything we put our minds to, when we work at companies and ministries where no one above middle management looks like us. It is rage inducing to know my body is being judged differently at every turn—when I am late to work, when I choose to eat lunch alone, when I am expressing hurt or anger. I become either a stand-in for another Black female body—without distinction between our size, our hair, our color, our voices, our interests, our names, our personalities—or a stand-in for the worst stereotypes—sassy, disrespectful, uncontrollable, or childlike and in need of whiteness to protect me from my [Black] self.

These indignities follow us home, too, when we open the newspaper or turn on the TV. Gross references to Serena Williams's body as animal-like. The reinforcement of Black inferiority as when *The New York Times* publishes a piece saying Viola Davis is not "classically beautiful." The media often seem gleeful when given the opportunity to tear down Black women, and if not careful, these attacks can chip away at our self-esteem. But words are hardly the worst of it. If we look at statistics and standards of living, we find a host of racial disparities that have persisted over decades—wages, home ownership, job accessibility, health care, treatment by law enforcement, and the list goes on. For us, these aren't just statistics—they are the facts of life for us and our mothers, our sisters, our friends and neighbors.

Meanwhile, whiteness twiddles its thumbs with feigned innocence and shallow apologies. Diversity gets treated like a passing trend, a friendly group project in which everyone takes on equal risks and rewards. In the mind of whiteness, half-baked efforts at diversity are enough, because the status quo is fine. It is better than slavery, better than Jim Crow. What more could Black people possibly ask than this—to not be overtly subject to the white will? "Is there more?" white innocence asks before bursting into tears at the possibility that we would dare question its sincerity.

It's hard to be calm in a world made for whiteness.

I've met a number of white people who adamantly resist thinking of themselves as a community, but I cannot imagine resisting my identity as a member of the Black community. I feel kinship and responsibility, pride, belonging, and connection with people simply because of a shared racial and cultural background.

When I pass a Black person being pulled over by the police, I wonder if they are innocent. I wonder how often this happens to them, and I wonder if they need help. Even in my childhood years, when I thought police officers pulled over only guilty people, I would think, *Shoot! Why does the Black person have to get pulled over?* I am not proud of this, but it speaks to how even when the feeling was shame, I still felt connected to random people I didn't know and would never meet, simply because of Blackness.

> When we win the award, I feel something.
> When we get the promotion, I feel something.
> When we break barriers, I feel something.

But I also feel something when we are dying in the streets. When we are derided for our bodies even as white women try to imitate them. When feminism is limited to the needs of whiteness, or when Blackness is used for profit without acknowledging the brilliance of the creators.

I feel something when a white woman mocks the body of Serena Williams by stuffing padding in her skirt and top. When First Lady Michelle Obama is called a monkey. When nine men and women are murdered in a church because they are Black.

I feel anger.

Even more frustrating, there are so few acceptable occasions for my rage to be expressed. Because I am a Black person, my anger is considered dangerous, explosive, and unwarranted. Because I am a woman, my anger supposedly reveals an emotional problem or gets dismissed as a temporary state that will go away once I choose to be rational. Because I am a Christian, my anger is dismissed as a character flaw, showing just how far I have turned from Jesus. Real Christians are nice, kind, forgiving— and anger is none of those things.

Though I knew these interpretations to be ludicrous, dealing with these reactions to any hint of my anger was enough to prevent me from speaking it. The boldness I possessed in school melted away in the face of supervisors, performance reviews, benefits packages, and the backlash that came from expecting more out of my Church.

In moments when I was angry, I used to wish I was *that* Black girl. You know the one. The one who snaps her gum. Who claps out every word when angry. The one who rolls her eyes and you feel it in your bones. The one who always says what she thinks—who begins her sentences with "First of all . . ." and then lists what you ain't gon do. I wanted to be the Black girl who white people are afraid of making angry.

But that Black girl wasn't me. I longed for the immediate release of rage, but my mild-mannered nature would not allow me this luxury.

I wished I was Zora Neale Hurston, genuinely confused by any white people who would deny themselves her company. I wanted to be Nina Simone, quick to check anyone who would underestimate the beauty of her Blackness. I wanted to be Angela Davis, intellectual and bold, speaking truth to power about society's treatment of Black people.

I wanted to be anyone but mild-mannered me.

And so my anger would boil, below the surface. I was launched right back into Dunbar's poem. *Austin wears the mask that grins and lies.*

Instead of anger, I would try to communicate other emotions that I thought might receive an audience—pain, disappointment, sadness. I would roll up my sleeves and reveal the scars, cut myself open and hope the blood that emerged would move my listeners. I believed that I was taking Baldwin's advice, that I was working to not be destroyed by my own rage. I thought I was getting to the bottom of it, but really I was denying it, covering it. All those years ago, on a bus in the South, I had watched a young Black woman state her rage with clarity and calm, despite how anyone else on that bus felt. But I couldn't do it. I was more afraid of my own rage than I realized.

I tried to be the wise, patient teacher, the composed one. I tried to wear an air of unbotheredness, standing on something akin to moral superiority. But ultimately, these were attempts at self-restriction. I left my humanity at the door.

Then Audre Lorde saved me. In her book *Sister Outsider,* Lorde wrote an essay entitled "The Uses of Anger." She writes that anger is not a shortcoming to be denied, but a creative force that tells us when something is wrong.

> Every woman has a well-stocked arsenal of anger potentially useful against those oppressions, personal and institutional, which brought that anger into being. Focused with precision it can become a powerful source of energy serving progress and change . . . Anger expressed and translated into action in the service of our vision and our future is a liberating and strengthening act of clarification.

A sense of freedom fell over me as I read her words. Anger is not inherently destructive. My anger can be a force for good. My anger can be creative and imaginative, seeing a better world that doesn't yet exist. It can fuel a righteous movement toward justice and freedom. I don't need to fear my own anger. I don't have to be afraid of myself. I am not mild-mannered. I am passionate and strong and clear-eyed and focused on continuing the legacy of proclaiming the human dignity of Black bodies.

Once upon a time I was mad that I wasn't *that* Black girl. But I am not her. I am not the gum-snapping, head-rolling, don't-think-I-won't-make-a-scene Black girl. So who am I? That is the question I had to ask in order to make use of my anger.

I am not Zora, but I can decide not to measure my effectiveness in the ebbs and flows of white affirmation. I am not Nina, but I can defend Black dignity through writing and preaching. I am not Angela, but I am learning to speak truth to power in ways that are equally invitational and challenging.

It was hard at first, trusting my voice of anger. But Black life is full of opportunities to practice. And so I did. I wrote. And I spoke. And I engaged with others, and then I wrote some more. Just like Lorde promised, my anger led to creativity, to connections with others who were angry, too. My anger didn't destroy me. It did not leave me alone and desolate. On the contrary, my anger undergirded my calling, my vocation. It gave me the courage to say hard things and to write like Black lives are on the line.

It shouldn't have surprised me. I serve a God who experienced and expressed anger. One of the most meaningful passages of Scripture for me is found in the New Testament, where Jesus leads a one-man protest inside the Temple walls. Jesus shouts at the corrupt Temple officials, overturns furniture, sets animals free, blocks the doorways with his body, and carries a weapon—a whip—through the place. Jesus throws folks out the building, and in so doing creates space for the most marginalized to come in: the poor, the wounded, the children. I imagine the next day's newspapers called Jesus's anger destructive. But I think those without power would've said that his anger led to freedom—the freedom of belonging, the freedom of healing, and the freedom of participating as full members in God's house.

How to Survive Racism in an Organization That Claims to Be Antiracist

10. Ask why they want you. Get as much clarity as possible on what the organization has read about you, what they understand about you, what they assume are your gifts and strengths. What does the organization hope you will bring to the table? Do those answers align with your reasons for wanting to be at the table?

9. Define your terms. You and the organization may have different definitions of words like *justice, diversity,* or *antiracism.* Ask for definitions, examples, or success stories to give you a better idea of how the organization understands and embodies these words. Also ask

about who is in charge and who is held accountable for these efforts. Then ask yourself if you can work within that structure.

8. Hold the organization to the highest vision they committed to for as long as you can. Be ready to move if the leaders aren't prepared to pursue their own stated vision.

7. Find your people. If you are going to push back against the system or push leadership forward, it's wise not to do so alone. Build or join an antiracist cohort within the organization.

6. Have mentors and counselors on standby. Don't just choose a really good friend or a parent when seeking advice. It's important to have one or two mentors who can give advice based on their personal knowledge of the organization and its leaders. You want someone who can help you navigate the particular politics of your organization.

5. Practice self-care. Remember that you are a whole person, not a mule to carry the racial sins of the organization. Fall in love, take your children to the park, don't miss doctors' visits,

read for pleasure, dance with abandon, have lots of good sex, be gentle with yourself.

4. Find donors who will contribute to the cause. Who's willing to keep the class funded, the diversity positions going, the social justice center operating? It's important for the organization to know the members of your cohort aren't the only ones who care. Demonstrate that there are stakeholders, congregation members, and donors who want to see real change.

3. Know your rights. There are some racist things that are just mean, but others are against the law. Know the difference, and keep records of it all.

2. Speak. Of course, context matters. You must be strategic about when, how, to whom, and about which situations you decide to call out. But speak. Find your voice and use it.

1. Remember: You are a creative being who is capable of making change. But it is not your responsibility to transform an entire organization.

10

The Ritual of Fear

A lot of people know the names Trayvon Martin, Eric Garner, and Michael Brown, thanks to the three Black women who coined the phrase Black Lives Matter and launched a justice movement to address the needs of Black America. But for me, personally, there was another precipitating event. One life that forced me to ask the question *Do all Black lives matter?*

My cousin Dalin was a big guy. He stood about six feet tall, with a muscular frame that gave him the illusion of having another two to three inches in height. He always dressed his best—bright-colored, oversize shirts and designer jeans made for Black men. His shoes were what we would have called crispy back when we were kids. I sometimes wondered if he kept shoe cleaner in his back pocket.

More than his style, though, Dalin was known for his laugh. If Dalin was six feet tall, his laugh was twelve. He had a short chuckle for when things amused him, but if he really thought something was funny, you'd hear him around the block. It was a deep, bellowing laugh that sounded too old for his young body—more like the laugh possessed by grandfathers who've lived a thousand lives and need to invite the whole neighborhood into their joy.

Like many Black men, Dalin was funny as hell. At family gatherings, where he had more competition for the center of attention, he usually stayed pretty quiet. Or so you thought, until you sat next to him and heard his side comments and sarcasm. Dalin knew the quirks of every person in our family, and his loving, easy quips contained too much truth to not elicit a laugh.

Despite being my first cousin, Dalin always seemed just a little out of reach. He was a boy, and I was a girl. He was a cool and confident sixteen when I was still a self-conscious and shy eight-year-old. His family lived in Akron, and mine in Toledo. We moved around each other in concentric circles, only occasionally occupying the same space.

One year during Christmas break, my aunts and uncles, cousins and friends, had crammed into the warm, creaky house in Akron where my father was raised. While the adults gathered in the kitchen, I snuck upstairs to my grandmother's room, where she lay in bed under warm blankets, watching her twenty-inch tube television with the squiggly lines and long antenna. I was eight years old and didn't often get my grandmother to myself, so I happily sat on the floor, talking about the commercials and laughing at the silly characters on the screen.

All of a sudden, a commotion downstairs broke the calm. The front door slammed—*bang!*—and Dalin's voice shot through the floor, more high-pitched than usual and frantic in sound. His mother's voice responded, matching in cadence but three octaves higher. "What? Oh, no you're not!" she started to say before Dalin cut her off. The noise grew steadily. My grandmother and I only caught snatches of words and phrases, but the one that stood out was the word *gun*. My grandmother and I looked at each other with eyebrows raised. She didn't move, so I didn't either.

The yelling stopped as footsteps pounded on the stairs, heading up toward us. I could tell my grandmother knew it was Dalin. She turned toward the door before he reached it. "What's going on?" she asked as he came into view.

My cool cousin had disappeared. This teenager, lit only by the glow from the small TV, was shook. "I was out with my friends when some dude took my shoes," Dalin said, cracking his knuckles.

My grandmother's confusion mirrored my own. "Took your shoes?" she asked.

Dalin explained that he had just bought a new pair of sneakers. After leaving the store, he and his friends were held up at gunpoint. His crew didn't carry weapons, so Dalin had no choice but to hand the bright white shoes over. And he was pissed.

"So what are you going to do now?" our grandmother asked, clearly looking for an honest answer. Dalin didn't hesitate. "I'm looking for a gun to go get my shoes back." His knuckles cracked again.

My grandmother and I stared at him in horror. I wonder if her mind was doing what mine was. I was so afraid he would go outside and never come home—but even at a young age, I knew this wasn't about his shoes. This was about his pride. Not the icky, arrogant kind. I mean the pride inherent in being human. The kind that flares when a stranger believes your life is worth less than a pair of shoes. I could hear the desire not quite for revenge but for the righting of a wrong. A desire to rearrange the world and go back to being in control, being safe, being in charge of what happened that night. And since Dalin was a teenager who'd just paid a lot of money for those tennis shoes . . . I'm thinking he also wanted the shoes back.

I can still see his face, a troubling mix of anger and sadness. I'm not sure it even registered for him that I was there. But that was the moment when I understood the rules governing my cousin's life were different than those governing my own. I knew going to the police wasn't a viable option for him. But if the same had happened to me, not only was I unaware of where I could possibly get a gun in my world but I wouldn't even have known who to ask. Dalin lived in a world I knew only through headlines. So I believed him. I believed his description of his world, and I was afraid for him. I wanted him to live.

It's a fear I came to know well as I got older. Fear that my father won't make it home when he travels through white rural Ohio for work, or that my brother's deep intellect won't stop someone from assuming he's a criminal. It's the fear that my husband will be mistaken for someone else, or that I won't be able to protect my little boy when my womb no longer hides him. Fear that my own body will be violated by the state.

Sometimes the fear is debilitating. As I write this, my husband has left to visit his parents. He must drive two hours across the state of Michigan to get there and two hours back. I am actively trying not to imagine him being pulled over, frisked. I am actively trying not to imagine his anger rising, his tongue getting the best of him. I am actively trying not to imagine. I don't want to pass my anxiety to him.

So when he left this morning, I gave him a hug. I told him to be safe. I said, "Promise you will come back to me," and he knew I was not joking.

He looked me in the eyes. "I will be fine. I'll call you when I get there." I nodded and smiled and pretended to feel better.

Sometimes when I'm hanging out with my white friends, they notice that I call my husband, Tommie, whenever I arrive, and then call him again when I'm leaving. They've never teased me outright for this, but I have seen the looks of amusement pass between them. I know they think Tommie and I do this because we are inseparable, or because he is demanding. For a moment my feminist card is revoked in their eyes. But these are our rituals for staying safe when we're out in the world. This is how we beat back the fear.

I first felt it with Dalin. And even though he didn't go back into the night thanks to our uncles' intervention, I have felt that fear ever since. So have countless other Black parents, Black siblings, Black couples, Black communities. We fear the overreactions of white people who clutch their purses in elevators and lock their doors when we walk by. We fear the overreaction of police who assume they are in danger when they have the wrong suspect or when we are unarmed. We fear that appearing guilty means incurring the repercussions of being guilty. We fear that any public imperfection of our children will lead to extrajudicial, deadly consequences. Even when our babies aren't perfect, even when they are rude or disrespectful, even when they make mistakes or fail, even when their sixteen-year-old brains tell them to do risky, stupid things, we still want them to live. We want them to make it to another day.

But until then, we find ourselves repeating this all-too-familiar ritual of fear.

11

A God for the Accused

After college, I moved to Michigan and enrolled in a master's program for social justice while working full-time. Toward the end of the program, we were required to read *A Place to Stand,* Jimmy Santiago Baca's bracing memoir of life in prison. That book knocked the wind out of me. I had heard stories about innocent men going away and their harrowing experiences of life behind bars. But even though Baca did in fact commit the crime that sent him to prison, I couldn't stomach the life he described. As I read about the violence, the abuse, the pressure of always being ready to defend oneself, all I could think about was Dalin.

Dalin and I never became close over the years. He was pursuing a rap career, and studio time required a lot of money, so in order to fund his passion, he sold drugs. It was a bad time to start that kind of a career. Around the time my cousin was emerging from teenager to adult, President Clinton signed an act that called for mandatory minimums for multiple drug offenses, and police departments around the country started cracking down on nonviolent crime. In Black neighborhoods, it was impossible to be a young man of Dalin's build and not get pulled over by the police on a regular basis. He was strip-searched in the streets. He was assaulted by officers who enjoyed his humiliation. And he was arrested . . . a lot.

When I came back to town for the holidays, it was not uncommon to hear Dalin was behind bars. But in years when he could join in the festivities, he was a doting father, thoroughly enjoying the spunky antics of his daughter, who was just learning to walk and talk. When Dalin was home, nothing else mattered—we bowed our heads and thanked God that we had one another.

When I heard Dalin received his third strike, I wasn't sure how to take the news. This wouldn't be just a short stint. This meant a mandatory ten years away from us—the equivalent of my entire high school and college career plus two more years of adulthood. How could anyone process spending that much time in prison for a nonviolent offense?

By the time I enrolled in my master's program and read *A Place to Stand,* Dalin had already been away for a few years. As I turned the pages filled with solitary confinement, violence, and hallucinations, I kept asking myself: *Is this what Dalin is experiencing? Is my cousin learning these rules, fighting to survive the politics of prison? Does he spend his days trying to avoid violence from fellow inmates or guards? Does the staff keep his mail from him as punishment? What is happening to him? Is this what it's like for everyone inside?*

I hadn't reached out to Dalin since he went to prison. I wondered about him, but I wasn't sure how to ask about his incarceration. I knew my cousin's crime wasn't violent, but I didn't know if we were going to talk about it. Could I ask my aunt how he was doing? Did people visit him? Was this a family secret, or was it okay to talk about openly? Every now and then I got up the courage to ask my father about Dalin, but the answers were usually short. I let the subject drop. I think my father knew more than he was telling me.

After reading *A Place to Stand,* though, I decided I wasn't waiting anymore. I would reach out and try to start a relationship with Dalin. I wasn't going to wait for his release, or keep my childhood hope that one day life would bring us together. I would step into the chasm between us and hope he would join me there.

I researched how to send a letter to someone in prison, and then wrote it painstakingly. My handwriting has never looked better. I told Dalin about life since the last time I had seen him. I was married now and living in Michigan. As a hobby, I had started researching our family history, so I told him the things I had discovered about our grandparents and great-grandparents. How our great-grandfather was missing a big toe; how even though he could have passed as white during the war—with light skin and blue eyes—his draft card listed him as "colored." I told Dalin I was thinking about him, but I didn't include the words *I love you*. I was afraid he would laugh. I knew I deserved it.

Even as I sealed the envelope, I wondered if the note would reach him. Then I wondered if he'd bother to respond, since I hadn't talked to him in years. I didn't know, but I had to try. I put it in the mail and waited. I waited so long, I almost missed his reply.

Weeks later, the post office clerk set the letter

on the counter between us. My hands trembled as I picked it up and walked to my car. What if he was offended and just wrote a one-word response? What if the letter was just a monologue handing me my ass for not writing a long time ago? My eyes watered as I read the first line. "Yo, Cuz. Yeah I was surprised to get your letter, but we family so its all love." And then, having absolved me, he went on to respond to everything in my letter, concluding with details about his life inside and hopes for his future after his release. Turned out he already knew about our great-grandfather's missing big toe. Apparently he'd asked about it when he was a little boy, but no one had ever satisfied his curiosity. I smiled, imagining tiny Dalin boldly asking about this missing body part and being completely dismissed by the adults. That sounded accurate, but also like an era that was long gone.

I don't think I've ever felt more overwhelmed by another person offering me mercy and love. I was so excited. I would finally get to know my cousin. I sat down and immediately started the next letter.

I don't know if he ever got it. He died in prison just a few weeks later.

It took hours of calling the prison officials through tears before they told my family what happened. Dalin and some of his friends had been in the yard one day when rain and thunder broke out above them. The men were residing in an honor program, in a separate part of the facility. Though the general population had received the warning about the impending storm, those living in the honor program had not. As the storm grew worse, turning into heavy rain, the men tried to come back inside, but it was too late. Lightning struck and Dalin was gone.

A few days later, we sat waiting for Dalin's wake to officially begin. Pictures from his childhood scrolled across large screens, and I placed my hand on my Bible with his letter tucked into the front. To this day, it is a constant reminder of who my cousin really was—funny, merciful, hopeful, connected to our family history, and wanting to come home. I glanced at his handwriting and cried.

Seven days later, I was standing in church when the anger hit me. The pastor was "opening the doors of the church"—the moment in a service when the minster invites people to become members of the church or recommit their lives to Christ. The Sunday after Dalin died, a young man, about thirty years old, came down front. He spoke with a minister for a couple minutes, then, as was customary, the pastor shared a little bit with the congregation. The young man had just been released from prison. He'd learned about Christ while inside but wanted to make another commitment to God as he started his life again. The church roared in approval, and the man's ten-year-old daughter raced down to the front and into his arms. It was so beautiful. And it pissed me off.

I didn't understand why Dalin hadn't gotten another chance. Just days earlier I'd watched my aunt tell her granddaughter that her father had died, that he was never coming back home. She would never race into her father's arms again.

As the rest of the congregation rose to its feet, praising God and encouraging the family, my legs started to give way. Fury flooded my body. All I could do was lean into the wooden pew and cry. *God, why did you take him?* Who else was I going to blame? My cousin hadn't been killed in a fight; he was struck by lightning, and I believed in a God who controls nature. A God who could have saved his life. What the hell?

My anger didn't scare me. The Bible is filled with stories of God handling anger from people far more important than me. I needed to let someone have it. God was there.

But when I was done fuming at God, having cycled through my grief, I still had some questions: What was the state's responsibility to those who are incarcerated? How many unjust interactions with police had Dalin experienced? How did I feel about laws like mandatory minimums? The questions kept piling up. As I began to study the criminal justice system in relationship to the Black community, I was forced to ask one more question: What did my theology have to say about Black lives that don't look like mine?

Dalin's death challenged me to expand my understanding for racial justice. I could talk all day long about the injustices within the Church, but I needed to be able to speak to the realities of Black life beyond my own privileged experiences—my private white Christian education and ministry life. Most of all, I had to reject the notion that my cousin's life was somehow less valuable because he did not meet the "Christian criteria" of innocence and perfection.

Even as I write these words, I am bracing myself for the reaction of those who will not care, those who will tell me that Dalin's death is his own fault. They will spit out the words *drug dealer,* just as they spit out the word *criminal.* Maybe they'll call him a thug, a nigger, or tell me that the world is better without him in it. But the one word that will go unspoken is the word *black*. Underneath all the other hurtful words, this is the one that whiteness really wants to spew.

Whiteness has never needed much of an excuse for our deaths.

Accused of looking at a white woman. Resisted arrest. Scared the officer. Thought he had a weapon. Had a criminal record (that the officer knew nothing about). Looked suspicious. Looked like someone else.

It doesn't really matter. At the end of the day, Blackness is always the true offense. Whiteness needs just a hint of a reason to maintain its own goodness, assuring itself that there's no reason to worry, because the victim had it coming. He was a drug dealer. A criminal. A thug.

We don't talk about white drug dealers this way. We don't even talk about white *murderers* this way. Somehow, we manage to think of them as people first, who just happened to do something bad. But the same respect is rarely afforded to Black folks. We must always earn the right to live. Perfection is demanded of Blackness before mercy or grace or justice can even be considered. I refuse to live this way.

All those years ago, I learned in church that Jesus understood the poor. Because of Dalin, I realized that Jesus also understood the accused, the incarcerated, the criminals. Jesus was accused. Jesus was incarcerated. Jesus hung on a cross with his crime listed above his crown of thorns. It doesn't bring Dalin back. But it matters to me that my God knows what Dalin's body endured. Suddenly racial justice and reconciliation wasn't limited to Black and white church members; it became a living framework for understanding God's work in the world.

12

We're Still Here

For millions of people—white and Black—the election of Barack Obama was a sign that America had become a postracial society. Even in those early years of optimism, I knew better than to expect so much. I do not want to dismiss the deep meaning I felt watching the Obama family wave at the crowds in Chicago after his victory speech, a feat I myself had called an impossibility just a year before. And yet, beneath the celebration, most of us (Black people) were still afraid. Given America's history of murdering Black civil rights leaders, in our bones we worried that someone would assassinate him for this accomplishment of winning the White House. We were aware of the protests not about his policies but about his race. We saw the signs and the nooses, the comic strips and the billboards, the essays and the articles, the constant condescending language that President Barack Obama simply *"didn't understand"* an issue, a policy, a law, or America itself.

Though it bothered me to no end, I had braced myself for the backlash to Obama's race, at least on the part of average white citizens. The stupid signs, the offensive comics . . . In my mind these were to be expected. The election of Barack Obama had not suddenly ushered in a postracial America. And yet.

What I didn't see coming was Ferguson. Like that moment in the lynching museum years earlier, the gap between history and present closed once again, this time on my living room TV.

It took a while for the mainstream media to realize news was being made in this suburb of St. Louis, but the residents of Ferguson knew. Days later, once cable news caught up, the images began appearing on our television screens nightly. Police faced Black residents as if ready for war. They donned riot gear, held dogs by the leash, threw tear gas, and confronted residents with tanks in front of the damn McDonald's. If all you could see were the police officers, you would've thought these images were from another country, or that the police were staring down folks armed with rifles and bulletproof vests. But in the widened camera lenses, we saw that the standoff was with our parents, our aunts and uncles, our cousins and children. All of them dressed in shorts and T-shirts demanding that an officer be held accountable for the shooting of an unarmed teen.

The parallels to the photos from my history book could not be ignored.

By the time the era called Black Lives Matter began, I was already familiar with the theory that racism never went away; it just evolved. But as I stared at my screen in horror and sadness, watching Black residents being treated like enemies of the state, it seemed to me that racism hadn't evolved at all. Instead of confronting Black residents on horseback with nightsticks, police now showed up in tanks with automatic rifles strapped to their backs.

I was frustrated and sad—and yet it all seemed so familiar. Like I had been here before. Like my parents had been here before. Like my grandparents had been here before.

White people often want me to be grateful for America's so-called racial progress. When I lead trainings, discussing America's history, they want me to praise America for "how far we have come." This is where they want me to place my hope—in the narrative that says things are getting better.

But I cannot.

Don't get me wrong. I am eternally grateful to my ancestors who carried the unbearable weight of slavery. I am grateful for those who lived and loved and worked and played before there was any talk of a national movement to secure equal civil rights. I am grateful for my great-great-great-grandfather, who escaped slavery to join the Union army. For my great-great-grandmother, who refused to ride in the back of the train when traveling to visit her sister in Arkansas. I am grateful for my ancestors' struggle and their survival. But I am not impressed with America's progress.

I am not impressed that slavery was abolished or that Jim Crow ended. I feel no need to pat America on its back for these "achievements." This is how it always should have been. Many call it progress, but I do not consider it praiseworthy that only within the last generation did America reach the baseline for human decency. As comedian Chris Rock says, I suppose these things were progress for white people, but damn. I hope there is progress I can sincerely applaud on the horizon.

Because the extrajudicial killing of Black people is still too familiar.

Because the racist rhetoric that Black people are lazier, more criminal, more undeserving than white people is still too familiar.

Because the locking up of a disproportionate number of Black bodies is still too familiar.

Because the beating of Black people in the streets is still too familiar.

History is collapsing on itself once again.

On Sunday, September 15, 1963, a bomb tore through the walls of the Sixteenth Street Baptist Church in Birmingham, Alabama. Inside, Black congregation members had been preparing for their Sunday service, unaware that members of the Ku Klux Klan had laid sticks of dynamite under the church's stairs. Twenty-two people were injured in the planned attack, and four little girls were killed: Cynthia Wesley, Carole Robertson, and Addie Mae Collins—all fourteen years old—and eleven-year-old Denise McNair.

Just two weeks earlier, Martin Luther King Jr. stood on the steps of the National Mall and gave his famous "I Have a Dream" speech. In the following days, Alabama began integrating high schools and elementary schools for the first time in its history.

The world was changing, and segregationists who worshipped at the altar of white supremacy could not contain their hatred and frustration. This was the third bombing in just eleven days since the integration order—but the first to prove deadly. White folks were making clear that they would rather see Black people die violent deaths than attend school with their children.

Though I grew up hearing this story about the Four Little Girls, there was a lot I didn't know. I didn't know that bombings had been a regular form of intimidation, or that the famous March on Washington had taken place only eighteen days before. What I knew was this: White people had been willing to bomb a Black church, right in the middle of Sunday school, and kill four Black girls. These weren't just words in a history book. I was a teenager who loved being in church. What if I had been born in another day and time?

I stopped wondering when the distance between past and present closed yet again one evening in June 2015, when a white supremacist walked into Emanuel African Methodist Episcopal Church and took as many lives as he could with a Glock 41 handgun. I was just about to turn over and go to sleep when I saw a tweet from an MSNBC anchor announcing that there had been a shooting in a Black church. With only 140 characters to spare, the tweet was short and declarative, yet my heart sank. The chances that it wasn't racially motivated seemed nil. I turned on the TV and watched the news for as long as I could stomach. My heart grew heavy as my eyes took it in. My beloved Church had been attacked again.

I've never stepped foot in Mother Emanuel, the loving nickname for that Charleston church. I don't know any of the congregation members, and I had never heard the name of its beloved pastor, or of any of the people killed that night. And yet, despite the geographical gap, it felt as if my own home church had been violated. The goal of terror attacks, after all, is to inspire fearfulness beyond the target.

It worked.

Until June 17, 2015, I had never been afraid of walking into a Black church. Black churches are gracious and hospitable, loving and welcoming, filled with people who like hugs and can't wait for the opportunity to speak goodness into your life. Even the shooter, on the very night of the rampage, had been a recipient of this love. And while many Black churches have members and pastors who are politically active, I had never carried the fear of church bombings or that local heroes would be victims of political assassinations—these were fears my parents, my grandparents, and my great-grandparents had known. That was all past, or so I thought, until the terror gripped my heart.

My fear lasted through the night, while the shooter remained at large. What if he went to another church? Would there be more death that night? Was the shooter working alone, or had a group of white terrorists spread out across the city—or, God forbid, the country? When I fell asleep that night, I still didn't know. And even when I woke up the next morning and discovered he'd been captured, the fear remained. What if the shooting inspired copycats? I deeply resented that the next time I walked into my own church, I would be afraid to sit with my back to the door.

That resentment turned into anger, and anger into defiance. I got up, got dressed, drove to a quiet church, and cried.

I cried for the lost lives of Cynthia Graham Hurd, Susie Jackson, Ethel Lance, Depayne Middleton-Doctor, Clementa Pinckney, Tywanza Sanders, Daniel Simmons, Sharonda Coleman-Singleton, and Myra Thompson. I cried for the family members and friends who would miss them.

I cried for the survivors who watched people they love die in front of them. I cried for the congregation members who would never be the same.

But I also cried for me. I cried not because I felt sorry for myself but because—in spite of all I had witnessed in the previous year—I still wanted to believe that America had become better than this. *Ain't no friends here,* I heard Dr. Simms's voice in my head, and the tears could not be stopped. I had wanted to believe that some things were now off-limits. But I was wrong. I underestimated the enduring power, the lethal imagination, the insatiable desire for blood of white supremacy. And I felt stupid. I should've known better. Had I not spent the last year writing about the persistence and deadliness of hatred for the Black body? It hurt to know America could still hurt me.

For all their talk about being persecuted, white Christian Americans don't know this kind of terror. Generations of Black Americans have known nothing but this kind of terror.

Allowing the reality of the moment to settle around me, that the past is still present, that racial hatred can still take our bodies in mass, I had to return to Black writers who understood the pain of societal hatred. Ntozake Shange wrote the following in her exquisite choreopoem, *For Colored Girls*

*Who Have Considered Suicide When the Rainbow Is
Enuf*:

> *i thot i waz but i waz so stupid i waz able to be*
> *hurt*
> *& that's not real*
> *not anymore*
> *i shd be immune*

In this particular poem, Shange writes in the
voice of a woman who can't believe love has crushed
her once again. But for me, this poem puts words
to my relationship with America. I know the surreal feeling of believing I have achieved immunity
from racial hatred only to feel the sting once again.
I ought to be immune by now; I know too much
about our racial history to be surprised. I've learned
about slavery and lynchings, about white riots and
bombings. It's not fair that my knowledge doesn't
save me, that I can still be hurt. But I am human. I
am human. And I am still alive.

Even when the world doesn't believe that Black
bodies are capable of love. Even when it doesn't believe that I survive on intimacy, that I need other
beings for love. Even when I would prefer to be immune, I am human. I demand intimacy. I demand
tomorrow. I demand love.

As I cried and prayed and sang in an empty church sanctuary that afternoon, I knew what I needed to do next. For the first time in years, I needed to return to my childhood church with the green carpet and giant double doors. I needed to be with my daddy. I needed to go back, and that Sunday I did.

Turned out the carpet was no longer green—but all the important things were still the same. We still held hands while praying at the altar. Pastor still wiped his forehead with the same white towels after preaching. Church mothers still sat on the front row, and ushers still passed out fans with MLK on one side and a funeral home advertisement on the other. The choir still sang.

How excellent! How excellent! How excellent!
iiiiiis your naaaaame!
Jesus, is the sweetest name I knoooooow.
My soul is anchored. My soul is anchored. My my
my my soul is anchored in the Lord.

Our voices grew stronger with each song. We would not let our generations of worship be halted by terror. Like so many times before, we found safety in one another and discovered that the Spirit delighted in who we are: in our praise, in our proclamation, in our prayers—but also in our person. The Spirit moved through our brown hands lifted in surrender, our hips swaying to the organ, our rich voices lifted in song. The Spirit moved among us. The Spirit was with us, just as she had always been. We would go on.

That Sunday also happened to be Children's Sunday, when the kids of the church prepared Scripture readings to deliver before the congregation. There was not a dry eye in the place as those little brown faces recited words of hope—some with bold confidence and others shyly repeating the words of the children's pastor. It didn't matter. They were here. We were here. We would go on. God would be with us.

I cried all the way through that service and many times in the days that followed. America had reawakened me to the power of its devastation. I recognized that history is still on repeat. Four little girls in 1963. Nine Black parishioners in 2015. But I also experienced again the love of other beings. I was surviving on the intimacy of the Black community—online, in real life, in the Church and outside of it. I was baptized again into the tradition of Black love—love for self and love for one another when the world deems us unworthy of life itself. We would stand and declare that our lives mattered. And as the days went on, and we kept protesting, organizing, marching, writing, and creating, I knew I could face tomorrow.

Interlude:

A Letter to My Son

My sweet son,

Even as I type this, you are tumbling around in my belly. You are only two pounds in weight, so your kicks feel like flutters, like butterflies in my stomach. You are my butterfly.

   I often wonder if you will be as active as you feel. Will you play basketball or join the swim team? Will you climb trees and jump in puddles? Will you beg your daddy to learn karate and scare me to death by jumping off tables and couches and shopping carts and playground bars? Or will you prefer to stay inside? Will you forever have your head in a book? Will you be like your uncle and have an obsession with computers? Or will you be more like your aunts, with a flair for the artistic? I wonder about your developing personality. I wonder what the church mothers will prophetically declare about your future.

Your daddy and I talk about you all the time. He can't wait to show you all his favorite films, and he hopes you will like horror movies as much as he does. I think about taking you to the park, and indulging in my own childish sense of curiosity at the world, seeing it through your eyes anew. We wonder about the shape of your eyes, the sound of your laugh, the feel of your toes. We wonder how much you will cry. Your daddy is already dreaming of the day when you will join him in the barbershop for your first taper.

And though you are still being formed in my tummy, your father and I are slowly turning into parents—wondering more about your future than about our own. While we delight in these conversations about who and what you will become in life, we have been avoiding other conversations.

We have avoided talking about the first time someone will call you a nigger. We have been avoiding talking about the first time you will be pulled over by a cop because you look suspicious. We have been avoiding talking about the many assumptions people will have of you simply because God kissed your glorious skin and it blushed at the attention. We have avoided discussing how we will tell you about the world.

Of course we will. But we don't like to think of it yet. We would rather wonder if you will be precocious or subdued, bold or shy, funny or serious, adventurous or introspective. We would rather wonder about your humanity than ruminate on the ways the world will try to take that away from you. They will first think you are beautiful, innocent—and you will be. But as your baby fat disappears and your height comes to match ours, they will start to see you as dangerous—but we will be here to refute the lies. We will be here to remind you that you are worthy of joy and love and adventure.

In our house, there will be dancing. There will be laughter. There will be love. In our house, there will be the smell of soul food and the sound of Stevie. We will teach you all of Michael Jackson's moves, and we will let you stay up late to watch the NBA finals with your dad. There will also be tears. It won't be all joy all the time, and yet you, too, will be inducted into this blessing called Black love. It will undergird you and push you. It will envelop you and warm you. It will remind you of who you are. And we will be the first to welcome you into this divine community of hope.

For now, you keep tumbling around and around in my tummy. (Maybe consider taking a break at night.) I will never be able to protect you as I can now. So, you stay safe and grow strong. Though we are crazy scared, stupidly excited—we can't wait to meet you when the time comes.

Love,

Your Momma

13

Justice, Then Reconciliation

Racial reconciliation has become something of a buzzword in Christian circles. Churches refer to themselves as "multicultural" and uplift their missions work as evidence that they are making a difference in the world. But though the term has powerful implications for how Christians should pursue racial justice and multiracial community, you could be forgiven for thinking *reconciliation* is just a churchy-sounding catchall for any kind of diversity effort.

It's worth being clear; *reconciliation* is not a fancy word for any of the following:

- There are lots of [insert ethnicity here] people in my church.

- A multiethnic church
- Sharing a building with another, more diverse congregation
- Having one or two people of color and/or women on your leadership team
- Diversity that's represented only in custodial positions
- Asking lots of racial questions over a cup of coffee
- Celebrating various ethnicities and cultures every month
- Missions work
- Outreach work
- Urban ministry

Too often, attempts at reconciliation go no further than the items on this list—and when this happens, the word becomes commonplace, drained of its extraordinary power. In its true form, reconciliation possesses the impossible power of the lion lying down with the lamb; the transformative power of turning swords into plowshares. But instead of pushing for relationships that are deep, transformative, and just—instead of allowing these efforts to alter our worldview, deepen our sense of connectedness, and inspire us toward a generosity that seeks to make all things right—we have allowed *reconciliation* to become synonymous with *contentedly hanging out together.*

Reconciliation is not a magic word that we can trot out whenever we need healing or inspiration. Deep down, I think we know this is true, because our efforts to partake of an easy reconciliation have proved fruitless in the world. Too often, our discussions of race are emotional but not strategic, our outreach work remains paternalistic, and our ethnic celebrations fetishize people of color. Many champions of racial justice in the Church have stopped using the term altogether, because it has been so watered down from its original potency.

In their book *Radical Reconciliation,* Curtiss DeYoung and Allan Boesak unpack why this happens. They write, "reconciliation is revolutionary, that is, oriented to structural change." Which means, reconciliation can never be apolitical. Reconciliation chooses sides, and the side is always justice.

This is why white American churches remain so far from experiencing anything resembling reconciliation. The white Church considers power its birthright rather than its curse. And so, rather than seeking reconciliation, they stage moments of racial harmony that don't challenge the status quo. They organize worship services where the choirs of two racially different churches sing together, where a pastor of a different race preaches a couple times a year, where they celebrate MLK but don't acknowledge current racial injustices. Acts like these can create beautiful moments of harmony and goodwill, but since they don't change the underlying power structure at the organization, it would be misleading to call them acts of reconciliation. Even worse, when they're not paired with greater change, diversity efforts can have the opposite of their intended effect. They keep the church feeling good, innocent, maybe even progressive, all the while preserving the roots of injustice.

When an organization confuses diversity or inclusion with reconciliation, it often shows up in an obsession with numbers. How many Black people are in the photo? Has the 20 percent quota been met, so that we can call ourselves multicultural? Does our publication have enough stories written by people of color? Are there enough people of color on the TV show? But without people of color in key positions, influencing topics of conversation, content, direction, and vision, whatever diversity is included is still essentially white—it just adds people of color like sprinkles on top. The cake is still vanilla.

When this happens, people of color in the organization get saddled with the task of constantly fixing the harm done by halfhearted diversity efforts. We find ourselves challenging hiring decisions that don't reflect the company's stated commitment to diversity, pushing allies to speak up in rooms where marginalized voices aren't represented, responding to events or sermons that didn't go far enough (or worse, sermons that perpetuated harmful ideas). But must we always be the prophetic voice, the dissenter, the corrector, the fixer? Organizations would be wise to tap Black women in helping to craft the direction of the organization, the vision of the publication, the purpose of the ministry. When our voices are truly desired, numbers will cease to be the sole mark of achievement.

Here's another misconception. A great many people believe that reconciliation boils down to dialogue: a conference on race, a lecture, a moving sermon about the diversity we'll see in heaven. But dialogue is productive toward reconciliation only when it leads to action—when it inverts power and pursues justice for those who are most marginalized. Unfortunately, most "reconciliation conversations" spend most of their time teaching white people about racism. In too many churches and organizations, listening to the hurt and pain of people of color is the end of the road, rather than the beginning.

I am convinced that one of the reasons white churches favor dialogue is that the parameters of dialogue can be easily manipulated to benefit whiteness. Tone policing takes priority over listening to the pain inflicted on people of color. People of color are told they should be nicer, kinder, more gracious, less angry in their delivery, or that white people's needs, feelings, and thoughts should be given equal weight. But we cannot negotiate our way to reconciliation. White people need to listen, to pause so that people of color can clearly articulate both the disappointment they've endured and what it would take for reparations to be made. Too often, dialogue functions as a stall tactic, allowing white people to believe they've done something heroic when the real work is yet to come.

Fortunately, dialogue isn't the only way to participate in the creative work of justice and reconciliation. In fact, I suspect that other actions—marches and protests, books and Scripture, art and sermons, and active participation in coalitions seeking change— are equally transformative. But when white organizations rest on their laurels and demand that people of color only express gratefulness for past change, these creative efforts stall. They tell us we should be happy to be onstage, singing or playing those drums. We should be happy to have our staff position, or happy that they *gave us the chance* to write that book, lead that program, teach that class, or speak at that conference at all. And when we suggest that justice might require greater representation in leadership, greater access to funding, greater influence over mission or strategy, people of color find themselves hitting a wall. *Ain't no friends here.*

When white people stop short of reconciliation, it's often because they are motivated by a deep need to believe in their own goodness, and for that goodness to be affirmed over and over and over again. These folks want a pat on the back simply for arriving at the conclusion that having people of color around is good. But reconciliation is not about white feelings. It's about diverting power and attention to the oppressed, toward the powerless. It's not enough to dabble at diversity and inclusion while leaving the existing authority structure in place. Reconciliation demands more.

Reconciliation is the pursuit of the impossible—an upside-down world where those who are powerful have relinquished that power to the margins. It's reimagining an entirely different way of being with one another. Reconciliation requires imagination. It requires looking beyond what is to what could be. It looks beyond intentions to real outcomes, real hurts, real histories. How just, how equitable can our efforts be? What would it take to enact reparations, to make all things right?

Reconciliation is what Jesus does. When sin and brokenness and evil tore us from God, it was Jesus who reconciled us, whose body imagined a different relationship, who took upon himself the cross and became peace.

> Therefore, if anyone is in Christ, he is a new creation. The old has passed away; behold, the new has come. All this is from God, who through Christ reconciled us to himself and gave us the ministry of reconciliation; that is, in Christ God was reconciling the world to himself, not counting their trespasses against them, and entrusting to us the message of reconciliation.

> 2 CORINTHIANS 5:17–19

Reconciliation is ministry that belongs to Jesus. Jesus, who left the comfort of heaven and put on flesh, experiencing the beauty and brutality of being human. Jesus, who died on a cross and rose from the grave, making a way for all humanity to be joined in union with God. Through this divine experience of death, life, and reunion, we find the capacity for the work. In this, we see why reconciliation can transform not just our hearts or our churches but one day the whole world.

Fortunately, Jesus doesn't need all white people to get onboard before justice and reconciliation can be achieved. For me, this is freedom. Freedom to tell the truth. Freedom to create. Freedom to teach and write without burdening myself with the expectation that I can change anyone. It has also shifted my focus. Rather than making white people's reactions the linchpin that holds racial justice together, I am free to link arms with those who are already being transformed. Because at no point in America's history did all white people come together to correct racial injustice. At no point did all white people decide chattel slavery should end. At no point did all white people decide we should listen to the freedom fighters, end segregation, and enact the right of Black Americans to vote. At no point have all white people gotten together and agreed to the equitable treatment of Black people. And yet there has been change, over time, over generations, over history.

The march toward change has been grueling, but it is real. And all it has ever taken was the transformed—the people of color confronting past and present to imagine a new future, and the handful of white people willing to release indifference and join the struggle.

14

Standing in the Shadow of Hope

Christians talk about love a lot. It's one of our favorite words, especially when the topic is race.

> If we could just learn to love one another . . .
> Love trumps hate . . .
> Love someone different from you today . . .

But I have found this love to be largely inconsequential. More often than not, my experience has been that whiteness sees love as a prize it is owed, rather than a moral obligation it must demonstrate. Love, for whiteness, dissolves into a demand for grace, for niceness, for endless patience—to keep everyone feeling comfortable while hearts are being changed. In this way, so-called love dodges any responsibility for action and waits for the great catalytic moment that finally spurs accountability.

I am not interested in love that is aloof. In a love that refuses hard work, instead demanding a bite-size education that doesn't transform anything. In a love that qualifies the statement "Black lives matter," because it is unconvinced this is true. I am not interested in a love that refuses to see systems and structures of injustice, preferring to ask itself only about personal intentions.

This aloof kind of love is useless to me.

I need a love that is troubled by injustice. A love that is provoked to anger when Black folks, including our children, lie dead in the streets. A love that can no longer be concerned with tone because it is concerned with life. A love that has no tolerance for hate, no excuses for racist decisions, no contentment in the status quo. I need a love that is fierce in its resilience and sacrifice. I need a love that chooses justice.

But I have learned that when I expect this kind of love for my Black female body, it means inviting hopelessness to my doorstep.

Hopelessness and I have become good friends.

When Ta-Nehisi Coates released his landmark book *Between the World and Me,* a stunning memoir of Black life in America, much of the talk in both secular and Christian circles revolved around the question of hope. Was Coates being too cynical by describing race relations to his son in such bleak terms? Why write such a depressing book? Is Coates that hopeless in real life? People read his words about America—about its history, about its present, about the realities of living in a Black body—and then demanded hopefulness. It boggles the mind.

For me, Coates's words contain relief in that they were spoken aloud, in public, with the forcefulness history demands. But talking about race in America is not usually a hopeful experience if you're Black. It brings no pleasure to speak of the hatred inflicted on our souls, the stories of discrimination and pain and injustices large and small that populate our lives. At the same time, we are barraged by society's reinforcement that we are less than. I may be grieving the murder of Trayvon Martin and at the same time dodging the inquisitive fingers of a white woman reaching to touch my hair. I may be angry over the events in Ferguson and in the same moment attempting to respond with dignity to a white man who treats me as his verbal punching bag. I may have just heard about the latest racist words spewed by a white talk-show host, actor, or politician on the same day when I'm trying to claim my space in the classroom or on my college campus. The persistence of racism in America—individual and societal—is altogether overwhelming. It doesn't lay the best fertilizer for hope to grow.

And so hope for me has died one thousand deaths. I hoped that friend would get it, but hope died. I hoped that person would be an ally for life, but hope died. I hoped that my organization really desired change, but hope died. I hoped I'd be treated with the full respect I deserve at my job, but hope died. I hoped that racist policies would change, and just policies would never be reversed, but hope died. I hoped the perpetrator in uniform would be brought to justice this time, but hope died. I hoped history would stop repeating itself, but hope died. I hoped things would be better for my children, but hope died.

So I have learned not to fear the death of hope. In order for me to stay in this work, hope must die. I do not enjoy the tears that come from these great disappointments. I do not look forward to future racialized traumas. I don't really want to recount all the ways that hope has let me down; it's so damn painful. But all of this comes with living, with struggling, with believing in the possibility of change. The death of hope gives way to a sadness that heals, to anger that inspires, to a wisdom that empowers me the next time I get to work, pick up my pen, join a march, tell my story.

The death of hope begins in fury, ferocious as a wildfire. It feels uncontrollable, disastrous at first, as if it will destroy everything in the vicinity—but in the midst of the fury, I am forced to find my center. What is left when hope is gone? What is left when the source of my hope has failed? Each death of hope has been painful and costly. But in the mourning there always rises a new clarity about the world, about the Church, about myself, about God.

And in this there is new life. Realignment. Rediscovery.

And on the really good days: renewal.

I cannot hope in whiteness. I cannot hope in white people or white institutions or white America. I cannot hope in lawmakers or politicians, and I cannot hope even in pastors or ministries or mission statements. I cannot hope in misquoted wisdom from MLK, superficial ethnic heritage celebrations, or love that is aloof. I cannot hope even in myself. I am no one's savior. The longer this list gets, the more elusive hope becomes.

And so, instead of waiting for the bright sunshine, I have learned to rest in the shadow of hope.

Shortly after the publication of his book, Ta-Nehisi Coates was asked if he had reason to hope that racism in America will one day change. He responded:

> Slavery in this country was 250 years. What that means is that there were African Americans who were born in this country in 1750/1760 and if they looked backwards their parents were slaves. Their grandparents were slaves. Their great grandparents were slaves. If they looked forward, their children would be slaves. Their grandchildren would be slaves. And possibly, their great grandchildren will be slaves. There was no real hope within their individual life span of ending enslavement—the most brutal form of degradation in this country's history. There was nothing in their life that said, "This will end in my lifetime. I will see the end of this." And they struggled. And they resisted.

This is the shadow of hope. Knowing that we may never see the realization of our dreams, and yet still showing up. I do not believe that I or my children or my grandchildren will live in an America that has achieved racial equality. I do not believe this is a problem that America will fix within any soon-coming generation. And so I stand in the legacy of all that Black Americans have already accomplished—in their resistance, in their teachings, in their voices, in their faith—and I work toward a world unseen, currently unimaginable. I am not enslaved, and yet I look back and see centuries of creative evolution of the hatred for Black bodies. I look at the present—police brutality, racial disparities, backlash against being "politically correct," hatred for our first Black president, the gutting of the Voting Rights Act, and the election of a chief executive who stoked the fire of racial animosity to win—and I ask myself, *Where is your hope, Austin?* The answer: It is but a shadow.

It is working in the dark, not knowing if anything I do will ever make a difference. It is speaking anyway, writing anyway, loving anyway. It is enduring disappointment and then getting back to work. It is knowing this book may be read only by my Momma, and writing it anyway. It is pushing back, even though my words will never be big enough, powerful enough, weighty enough to change everything. It is knowing that God is God and I am not.

This is the cool place from where I demand a

love that matters. In this place, I see the sun setting behind me, its light as far away as the stars, and I let the limitations of hope settle over me. I possess not the strength of hope but its weakness, its fragility, its ability to die. Because I must demand anyway. It is my birthright. It is the culmination of everything my ancestors endured, of all that my parents taught me, of the Blackness that rescued me. How dare I consider surrender simply because I want the warmth of the sun? This warmth has not been promised to me. My faith does not require it.

When the sun happens to shine, I bask in the rays. But I know I cannot stay there. That is not my place to stand. So I abide in the shadows, and let hope have its day and its death. It is my duty to live anyway.

ACKNOWLEDGMENTS

There are so many people who have supported me on this journey in so many ways; I am not sure how to make these words convey the amount of gratitude I feel.

First, I want to thank everyone who literally made this book possible. Thank you to my agent, Rachelle Gardner, for all the phone calls, meetings, and notes (and for making me practice saying "I am a writer" until I believed it). Thanks also to Derek Reed, my editor, for putting up with my firm belief that grammar only exists to make the sentences sound the way I would want them read aloud. Thanks to Convergent for taking a chance on this new author and giving yourselves to this book. To David Kopp, Tina Constable, Campbell

Wharton, Carisa Hays, Megan Schumann, Nick Stewart, Ayelet Gruenspecht, Ashley Hong, Jessie Bright, Norman Watkins, Ada Yonenaka, and Songhee Kim, my deepest gratitude for your time, energy, and creative brilliance.

Next I must thank the family members and friends who lent me their memories when mine failed. I am so honored to be able to call, text, DM, email and tweet you without ever wondering if I will hear back from you. Your responses to my questions, the sharing of memories, made this a less lonely writing project.

To my early readers, you made this book better. Thank you for your honest feedback, critique, questions, and suggestions.

There are a host of mentors who introduced me to the publishing world, supported my writing early on, and regularly encouraged me throughout this process. I could not have done this without you all.

Thank you to my parents whose excitement has never waned over the long life of this project. Thank you for your support, from teaching me the ABCs to listening to me when I am all out of words.

Lastly, I must thank my wonderful husband, Tommie Brown. Years ago, with tears in my eyes and the blanket pulled over my head, I asked you if writing was just the dream of a teenage girl—a dream I needed to let go. I fully expected you to tell me it was time to grow up and stop trying. But you held my hand, wiped away the tears, and believed in me when I was too scared to hope anymore. Thank you for taking such good care of my heart, that day and every day since. I love you.

Get **more** out of libraries

Please return or renew this item by the last date shown.
You can renew online at www.hants.gov.uk/library
Or by phoning 0845 603 5631

 **Hampshire**
County Council

The Secretary's Bossman Bargain

RED GARNIER

MILLS & BOON®

All the characters in this book have no existence outside
the imagination of the author, and have no relation
whatsoever to anyone bearing the same name or names.
They are not even distantly inspired by any individual
known or unknown to the author, and all the incidents
are pure invention.

First published in Great Britain 2011
by Mills & Boon, an imprint of Harlequin (UK) Limited,
Large Print edition 2011
Eton House, 18-24 Paradise Road,
Richmond, Surrey TW9 1SR

© Red Garnier 2010

ISBN: 978 0 263 21708 7

Harlequin (UK) policy is to use papers that are natural,
renewable and recyclable products and made from
wood grown in sustainable forests. The logging
and manufacturing process conform to the legal
environmental regulations of the country of origin.

Printed and bound in Great Britain
by CPI Antony Rowe, Chippenham, Wiltshire

RED GARNIER

is a fan of books, chocolate and happily ever afters. What better way to spend the day than combining all three? Travelling frequently between the United States and Mexico, Red likes to call Texas home. She'd love to hear from her readers at redgarnier@gmail.com. For more on upcoming books and current contests, please visit her website, www.redgarnier.com

This book is dedicated to the fabulous Desire editors, who provide endless wisdom, advice and inspiration. Krista, Charles, and Shana—
Thank you for the
gift of writing for your line.
And to Diana Ventimiglia, who believed in me since the beginning.
You're fondly remembered.

One

She was ready to beg him.

Virginia Hollis shuddered. She wrapped her arms around herself and stared out the back window of the sleek black Lincoln as it wound along the darkened streets of Chicago. People strolled down the block, hands in their pockets, chins neatly tucked to their chests to shield their faces from the biting wind. Men held cell phones to their ears; women struggled with their shopping bags. One glimpse made it seem like such a regular evening. An ordinary night.

But it wasn't ordinary. It couldn't be.

Because Virginia's world had stopped turning. The men who'd knocked on her door this morning had had a message for her, and it had not been a kind one.

She inhaled deeply and glanced at her simple black dress and the delicate strappy heels on her pink-toed feet. It seemed important for her to look nice—not just respectable, but sophisticated, noble—because the favor she was to ask was anything but.

And she could think of no one else to ask but *him*. God. Just thinking of humiliating herself like this in front of *him* made her stomach churn.

Nervously, she tugged on the pearl strand draped around her neck and tried focusing on the city again. The pearls were smooth under her fingers, genuine and old, the only thing Virginia had been able to salvage from her mother's belongings.

Her father had lost it all.

Bet by bet, he'd lost the cars, the antiques, the house. Virginia had watched with a combination of helplessness and rage. She'd threatened, screamed, pleaded with the quickly aging man, all to no avail.

There was no stopping him. No stopping the gambling.

There was nothing left now.

Nothing but her.

And she could not, *could* not, turn a blind eye to those men—to the threat they posed. To the threat they had succinctly delivered. No matter how much she frowned upon what her father did, and no matter how many times she'd promised never again to speak to him about it and he continued gambling anyway, he was her father. Her only family.

Once he'd been a businessman. Respected, admired even. Now it saddened her to think what she'd become.

Virginia didn't know how much he owed. She'd rather not know. All she knew was the deal she'd struck with those three surly men that morning. She had a month to come up with one hundred thousand dollars, during which time they would leave him alone.

In her wildest dreams, Virginia had never imagined coming up with that amount of money, on such little time. But while *she* couldn't, Marcos Allende could.

The little hairs on her arms pricked to attention at the thought of him. Her boss was a quiet, devastatingly handsome man. Some said he was gifted; his touch was that of a Midas. While

Virginia had only been his assistant for a year—his third of three assistants, because it seemed one alone couldn't handle the daunting task of having him as boss—in that length of time, she had seen enough of him to agree.

The man was out of context.

He was bold, ruthless and proud. Single-handedly, he'd spotted, bought and righted troubled companies, and he'd created an empire. He inspired respect and admiration among peers and fear among his enemies. Judging by the overwhelming number of phone calls he received from the female population of Chicago, Virginia could tell they adored him. And in Virginia herself, the man inspired things she dared not consider.

Every morning when she stepped into his office, he would study her with that dark, compelling gaze and disturb every inch and atom of her body with the hot intimacy in his eyes. She would always try to act professionally, to look away when his stare became inappropriately long. But his eyes had a way of undressing her, of speaking in silence, of summoning visions in her mind about him and her and skin and sweat. Yet tonight she was on her way to him for one purpose only, and she reminded herself that her visit to his lair at such a late hour might not be welcome.

With his assistants he was always the firm, quiet boss, but Marcos Allende was reputed to have a hell of a temper, one she might witness tonight for the very first time.

Her stomach clenched when the car pulled into the ample driveway of one of the Windy City's most luxurious apartment buildings, situated on the heavily trafficked Michigan Avenue. A uniformed valet opened the door.

She mumbled a quick "thank you" and stepped out of the car, walking into the sumptuous apartment building with an eerie calm that belied every one of the roiling emotions inside her.

She made no eye contact with the people milling around the area, but instead focused all of her attention on the polished bronze doors at the far end of the lobby.

"Mr. Allende is expecting you."

An elevator attendant waited for her. He slipped a card into the top slot inside the confined elevator space and lit the top *P* before stepping out with a bow. "Good evening, madam."

The doors closed and Virginia stared at her blurry reflection.

Oh, God, please let him help me. I'll do anything. Anything...

Long seconds later, the doors rolled open to reveal the penthouse—a vast room with black granite floors, dimly lit and lavishly furnished. The walls could've been covered in crisp green bills and screamed the owner's net worth just as loudly. To a mortal, his place seemed as inaccessible in price as the owner was claimed to be in character.

Virginia stepped inside. A pair of elegant, willowy bronzes flanked the entry and a massive oil painting with vibrant black brushstrokes hung at the end wall. Before she could absorb the rest of the opulent area, as though drawn by some unknown force of nature, her gaze landed on him. He stood next to the bar at the far end of the living room. He was as elegant and unmoving as the designer furniture surrounding him. Dark, tall, detached. He faced the window, his broad back filling the shoulders of his jacket. Her heart thumped as she took a step forward, the click of her heels on granite magnified in the silence.

"I trust you had a fine ride."

Her flesh pebbled at the hum of his voice. So husky. So mellow. As though he were no threat to anyone. The crackling energy around him dispelled the notion fast.

"I did. Thank you for sending a car, and for seeing me on such short notice," she said quietly.

Starting to shake inside, she advanced toward the living room, stepping lightly across a plush Persian rug. He didn't turn. Virginia wasn't certain she even wanted him to. Every time their gazes met, a bolt of electricity would shoot through her. Sometimes he didn't even need to speak. His eyes did it for him. And in her mind, he said the wickedest things to her.

Now here she was, in his apartment, ready to face that bold, virile man she'd fantasized about. Ready to beg him.

Never mind Virginia had her modestly successful life, which she'd tried to live by the book. Never mind she'd paid her bills on time and tried first and foremost to stay out of trouble. Never mind anything but what had to be done. Saving her father. Doing anything she had to, to make him safe again.

She could've sworn Marcos read her thoughts just now, for he whispered, "Are you in trouble,

Virginia?" While still gazing out the window as though mesmerized by the tiny flicker of city lights.

She swallowed, eyeing his back. "It appears I am."

"And you came to ask for my help?"

A ball of unease settled in the pit of her stomach, and the words seemed to be wrenched from her throat. "I do need your help, Marcos."

He turned, and she was rendered motionless by the sheer black power of his stare. "How much?"

Her heart pounded faster. His face was so exquisitely masculine, and there was something so naughty about him—his attitude, his dark good looks, his accent—that a dormant part of her found thrilling and frightening at once. Every inch of his Latin blood showed in his bronzed skin, the very masculinity oozing from his pores.

His inquisitive gaze traveled with interest down the length of her body until she could bear no more. She lifted her chin with pride, though the way she wrung her hands before her wasn't all that convincing. "I—I don't expect anything for free. I wanted to see you about an advance. A loan. Perhaps I could do more work for you. Special projects."

His eyelids dropped as he sighted her lips. "You're very pretty tonight, Virginia."

The low seduction in his words made her heart clench in a fistful of thrill. She fought the thrill, telling herself he was a sexy, virile man—and that he must look at all women this way. Which was why they called him. All. The. Time! When those eyes were on her, he made her feel like the sexiest woman alive—like the only woman alive.

"I'm trying to raise…" She paused, summoning all her courage. "I'm trying to raise one hundred thousand dollars. Can you help me?" she asked him then, lowering her face. As she spoke, she felt so…so cheap…so humiliated to be asking for money…

"Is that all you need?" he asked softly. As though it were nothing. A paltry sum. And to him, with all his billions, of course it would be.

He surveyed her in silence. "May I ask why you need it?"

Her gaze flicked up to his, and she shook her head. She couldn't bear it.

His lips twitched and the corners of his eyes crinkled, almost—*almost*—managing to make him less threatening. "You won't tell me?" he prodded.

"If you don't mind," she mumbled. She tugged the hem of her dress to her knees when his gaze ventured to her legs and lingered. "So there's nothing I could do for you? In exchange for this… incredible salary?" God. She couldn't even say the amount it seemed so out of reach.

He laughed, and Virginia didn't think she'd ever heard him laugh before. The sound resembled the roll of distant thunder.

He set his glass on the nearby bar and signaled to the twin leather couches. "Sit."

She sat. Her back was stiff and straight as she tracked his lithe moves around the room. How could a big man move with such grace? How could—

"Wine?"

"No."

He poured two glasses nonetheless. His hands moved skillfully—too skillfully not to notice— and brought one to her.

"Drink."

She grasped the fluted glass and stared at a faraway bronze sculpture, trying not to breathe for fear of what his scent might do to her. He smelled so amazingly good. Earthy and musky and male. She drew in a shaky breath until he dropped onto the couch across from hers.

When he stretched his arms out behind him, he made the couch appear small, his wide frame overwhelming the bone-colored leather designer piece. Under his jacket, the dress shirt he wore was unbuttoned at the top, gifting her with a view of smooth, bronzed skin and a polished gold cross.

She wanted to touch him. She wondered what that bronze skin would feel like under her fingers, if his cross was cold or warm…

Suddenly sensing his scrutiny, she raised her chin and smiled.

Lifting one black brow, Marcos opened his hand and signaled to her. "You're not drinking."

Virginia started, then obediently sipped. "It's… good. Very…um, rich."

"Have I ever bitten you?"

She almost choked on the wine, blinked, and then, then she saw the smile. A prime smile. Rare, like everything valuable, higher on one end than the other.

"I can see this is difficult for you," he said, with a glimmer of warmth in his eyes.

"No. I mean, yes. It is." He had no clue!

He set his glass aside, crossed his arms over his chest, and snuggled back as if to watch a movie. "You don't trust me?"

Her heart skipped a nervous beat.

Trust him? She respected him. Admired him. Was in awe of him and, because of his power, even a little afraid of him. And maybe, she realized, she trusted him, too. From what she'd seen, Marcos—quiet, solid, heart-of-gold Marcos— had proved to be nothing but a champion for his people. A lion protecting his cubs. When Lindsay, assistant two, had been weeping for months after her twins were born, Marcos had hired an army of nannies and sent her off to a second honeymoon in Hawaii with her husband.

Lindsay was still talking about Maui.

And when Mrs. Fuller's husband passed away, the overwrought woman had cried more tears reminiscing about all that Marcos had done to support and aid her family than she had cried at the funeral.

No matter how humiliating this was, how awful her situation and having him know it, she knew, like nothing in her life, he was as steady as a mountain.

Holding his gaze, she replied in all honesty. "I trust you more than I trust anyone."

His face lit in surprise, and he scraped his chin between two blunt fingers. "And yet you don't tell me what troubles you?"

The thought that he—the man she most honored, esteemed—would know her life was in such shambles squished her heart like a bug. "I would tell you what I need the money for if I thought it mattered, and I would tell you if that is the only way you'll give it to me."

With an expression that would befit a lone hunting wolf, Marcos rose and strode over, then pried the glass from her fingers. "Come with me."

Unnerved that she couldn't even begin to guess the thoughts in that unique, labyrinthine mind of his, Virginia followed him down the wide, domed hallway of his penthouse, becoming acutely aware of his formidable frame next to her.

And she couldn't help but wonder if maybe she wasn't a little bit the fool for trusting him after all.

Predatorily, Marcos studied her profile, her nose, the untamed, unruly bounce of her curls. She bit her lip in nervousness. Where was he taking her?

Visions of a bedroom flicked across her mind, and her cheeks flamed hot.

He opened the last door for her, and Virginia entered the darkened room, shamed at her own quickening pulse.

"Your home office?" she asked.

"Yes."

He flicked on the light switch, and the room burst to life. Bookshelves lined three of the four walls. A Turkish rug spread across the sitting area. Five glossy wood file cabinets formed a long, neat row behind his desk. No adornments. No picture frames. No distractions. As fine in taste as the rest of his apartment, with a state-of-the-art computer perched atop a massive desk, his office screamed two words: *no nonsense.*

"I like it." She strode inside, the knowledge that this was his private, personal space making her blood bubble. Her fingers itched with the over-whelming urge to organize the stacks of papers on his desk.

"I know about your father, Miss Hollis."

Dread sunk like a bowling ball in her stomach. "You do?"

She spun around, and when he stepped into the room, Marcos achieved the impossible: he made it shrink in size. "You do not exist in the world I do without being cautious about everyone who comes into your inner circle. I have a dossier on everyone who works in close proximity with me, and I know every detail of their lives. Yes, I know about his problem."

"Oh."

What else did he know?

He passed her as he crossed the room, and she stifled a tremor as if he'd been a cool hurricane wind. "Why didn't you come to me before?" he asked, matter of fact.

"I'm here now," she whispered.

Halting behind his desk, he shoved the leather chair aside and leaned over the surface. His shirt stretched taut over his bunched shoulders and his eyebrows pulled low. "How bad is it?"

"It… The gambling comes and goes." Flushing at his scrutiny, she turned to busy herself with the books on the shelves, and then said, as if he'd expertly unlatched a closed door which had been near bursting with secrets, "He's out of control. He keeps betting more than what he has and more than I could possibly earn."

"Is that the only reason you're here?"

His voice grew so textured, a jolt of feminine

heat rippled through her. She spun around—shocked by the question. Shocked by the answering flutter in her womb.

Her breath stopped.

His gaze. It was open. Raw. Revealed a galvanizing wildness, a primitive hunger lurking—lurking *there*—in the depths of his eyes, like a prowling beast.

Pent-up desire rushed through her bloodstream as he continued to stare. Stare at her in a way no man, ever, should look at a woman and expect her to survive. "Is that the only reason you're here tonight? Virginia?"

As if in a trance, she moved forward on shaky legs, closer to his desk. "Y-yes."

"You want nothing else? Just the money?"

How to talk? How to think? Breathe? Her heart felt ready to pop from the pressure of answering. "N-nothing."

In the back of her mind, she vaguely realized how simple and unassuming her needs sounded as she voiced them. When they were not. They were tangled. They had grown fierce with his proximity. Out of reason, out of context, out of *control*.

"Will you help me," she murmured as she

reached the desk, and somehow the plea sounded as intimate as if she'd asked for a kiss.

"I will." Deep and rough, the determination in his answer flooded her with relief.

He was going to help her.

In her soaring mind, Marcos was mounted on a white charger holding up a flag that read "Virginia."

And she…well, hers might be a banner. A neon sign. A brand on every inch of her body and possibly her heart. Marcos Allende. God, she was a fool.

"I don't expect something for nothing," she said. Her voice throbbed even as a tide of relief flooded her.

It was as if some unnatural force drew her to him, pulled her to get closer and closer. Did the force come from him? From her? If it weren't for the desk—always the desk between them—where would she be?

No. The obstacle wasn't a desk. It was everything. Everything. Nothing she could ever arrange or fix or clean.

Marcos raked one hand through his hair, then seized a runaway pen and thrust it into an empty leather holder. "I'll give you the money. But I have a few requests of my own."

"Anything," she said.

His gaze was positively lethal. His hands—they made fists. "There's something I want. Something that *belongs* to me. Something I must have or I'll lose my mind with wanting it."

A shiver ran hot and cold down her spine.

He wasn't speaking of her—of course he wasn't—but nonetheless, she felt something grip inside her as though he were. What would it feel like for Marcos to want her so fiercely? "I...understand."

"Do you?"

He smiled bleakly at her, then continued around his desk.

He swept up a gemstone globe from the edge and spun it around, a lapis lazuli ocean going round and round. "Here." His finger stopped the motion, marking a country encrusted in granite for her eyes. "What I want is here." He tapped.

Tap tap tap.

She stepped closer, longingly lifting a fingertip to stroke the length of the country he signaled. Travel had seemed so far down the line of her priorities she hardly gave any thought to it now.

"Mexico," she whispered.

His finger slid. It touched hers. He watched. And she watched. And neither of them moved. His finger was blunt and tan, hers slim and milky. Both over Mexico. It wasn't even a touch, not even half a touch. And she felt the contact in every fiber of her lonely, quivering being.

He turned his head, their faces so close that his pupils looked enormously black to her. A swirling vortex. He whispered, as though confessing his every hidden desire and sin, "I'm after Allende."

She connected the name immediately. "Your father's business?"

"The business he lost."

He set down the globe, and again, his finger. This time the back of it stroked down her cheek. Marcos touching her, Marcos looking so strangely at her, oh, God. He smelled so good she felt light-headed.

"And you believe I can help?" she asked, one step away from him, then two. Away from his magnificent, compelling force, away from what he made her want.

He scraped a restless hand down his face. "The owner has managed it poorly and contacted me for help." A tiny muscle ticked at the back of his jaw. "I'm usually a sucker for the ailing, I admit, but things are different in this case." Disgusted, he shook his head. "I do not intend to help her, you understand?"

"Yes." She didn't understand, exactly, but rumors around the office were that *no one* mentioned Allende to Marcos unless they wanted their head bitten off.

He paced. "I'm taking it hostilely if I have to."

"I see."

"I could use an escort."

Escort.

"I need someone I can count on. Most of all—" he crossed his arms and his enigmatic black gaze bored into hers "—I need someone willing to pretend to be my lover."

Lover.

Her hands went damp and she discreetly wiped them at her sides. "Lover." When his long steps brought him over to her, she instinctively backed away until her calves hit a small ottoman.

Unperturbed, Marcos headed over to the bookshelf, his strides sure and unhurried. "Would you be interested in doing this for me?"

Her head whizzed with unwelcome, naughty thoughts. Thoughts of Mexico and Marcos.

Martinis and Marcos. Mariachis and Marcos. "Yes, definitely." But what exactly did he mean by *pretend?* "So what would you expect of me, for how long?" An unprecedented thrill was trickling along her veins.

He rummaged through the books, moving tome after tome. "A week as my escort in Monterrey, and perhaps some work after hours until I'm able to close. I'll be sure to handle your…little problem."

"That's all?"

He shot her a look of incredulity. "That's not enough?"

She just smiled. And waited.

And watched.

The muscles under his shirt flexed as he reached the top shelf and pulled out a huge leather volume.

"Maybe your company at the Fintech dinner?" he continued, winged eyebrows flying up. "Would you mind? Going with me?"

She fiddled with her pearls, unable to stop fidgeting. "You… I can always arrange a date for you."

His lips curved upward as he waved the heavy book in her line of vision as easily as if it were a mere piece of paper. "I don't want a date, Miss Hollis. Here. You can take this—a bit about Monterrey, if you'd like." He set it on the otto-man. He had a lovely, lazy kind of smile, and she felt it curl her toes.

"I feel like I'm robbing you blind," she said, lifting the shiny book.

He paused in the middle of the room and stared at her with his deep gypsy eyes. "If I allowed it, it wouldn't be robbery, would it."

She saw his cool, brief smile and flattened the book tight against her breasts when they pricked. Traitors. But he'd smiled three times tonight. Three. Or more? Three or more just had to be a record.

"You're an asset to my company," he contin-ued in an unnaturally husky voice, stalking back around the desk. "A week of your time is valuable to me. You're hard-working, smart. Loyal. You've gained my trust, Virginia, and my admiration—both difficult feats."

A feathery sensation coursed along her skin. She was certain he used that same self-assured tone in his meetings, but she wondered if it had the same thrilling effect on the members of his board.

When she couldn't seem to find anything useful to do other than ogle stupidly, she automatically did what she always did to cure herself. She set the book aside and began arranging the papers at the edge of his desk—from a messy pile to a neat pile. "T-thank you for the compliments. I enjoy working at Fintech very much. And for you...of course. Which is why I don't want to jeopardize my position."

She continued arranging, aware that he was doing nothing—nothing—but towering a few feet away and watching her. Like he did in the office sometimes. He would stop what he was doing and watch with those black, exciting eyes.

"What will we say at the office?" she rambled.

Gossip could be ruthless at Fintech. To think Lindsay or Mrs. Fuller might believe she'd done something unprofessional to land a business trip with Marcos gripped her with unease.

When Marcos didn't reply, she looked up and caught the wicked sparkle in his eyes. She had the strangest sensation that he'd been staring at her bottom. "We will say that I ordered you to accompany me, of course. You are my assistant, after all."

His brows drew together and he peered at her hard, as though daring her to argue with him.

But a pang struck her right where it hurt; she knew she could never be more than an assistant to him. He was Marcos Allende. He could be Zeus himself, he was so unattainable.

Virginia was dreaming if she wanted more than a seat outside his office. Dreaming if she thought the desire in his eyes was for her. Dreaming to think that, even if it were, he'd do something about it and she'd dare let him.

No. She could not, would not allow herself to continue harboring those foolish nightly fantasies about him. The daily ones had to go, too. It was hopeless, and it was hurtful, and it was stupid. He was offering her an assignment.

When the pile couldn't be a more perfect tower, she straightened it with as much dignity as she could muster. "I'd be happy to be your escort."

He nodded slowly. "Good. Great. Excellent." His voice was strangely terse, so utterly rich it seemed to sink into her body until it pulsed inside of her. "I knew we'd come to an agreement, then."

Dealing with a tumult of emotions without betraying herself proved difficult. Excitement warred with worry, gratitude with desire.

One week with him in Mexico. Playing his escort, his *lover*—a role Virginia had slipped into plenty of times in her mind. But this would be real, a real pretense, where she—inexperienced and naive in the ways of men—would pretend to be lover to a hunk, god and legend. Where she could even seize the moment, do something reckless she would no doubt come to regret and plant a kiss on the lips of the man who was unknowingly responsible for Virginia not wanting others. Did she dare? Did she fly? Did she have magic powers?

Was there even the possibility of being a good pretend lover to him after he'd dated actresses, duchesses, centerfolds?

Growing more and more unsettled at her new assignment, she picked up the book, *Monterrey: Tras el Tiempo,* and headed for the door, stealing one last glimpse of him. "Thank you, Marcos. For…everything. Good night."

"Virginia." When she was halfway down the hall, he caught up and seized her wrist, urging her around. His clasp sent a shiver skidding up her arm. "It's a five-hour flight. I mean to leave tomorrow afternoon. Can you be ready by then?"

Ready, she thought wildly.

She could be a virgin Mayan princess prepared her whole life for this ultimate sacrifice, be an Anne Boleyn laughingly led to her beheading, and she would *still* not be ready for Marcos Allende.

But she smiled. Her nod came out jerky.

He seized her chin and raised it slightly. She sucked in a breath at the contact, and the tips of her breasts brushed against his chest. "Will you be ready, Virginia?" he persisted.

Her legs quivered. All kinds of things moved inside her body. His breath was hot and fragrant on her face, and his lush, mobile mouth was so close, a moan rose to her throat, trapped there. Like the wanting of a year, trapped there.

How would he *feel* against her? His mouth? His hands?

He was so hard all over, so unlike any other man she'd known. He made her feel safe and protected and special, but he also made her burn, frightened her with the way she needed *something* from him more than she could possibly bear or understand.

She suppressed a shiver. "I'll be ready," she assured, a nervous excitement flourishing in her breast as she took a healthy step back. "Thank you. I know…I know you could ask someone else to do this for you. And I doubt you'd have to pay for her company."

His eyes smoldered, and his face went taut with some unnameable emotion. "Yes, but I want you."

I want you.

A ribbon of hope unfurled inside her. It feathered from the top of her head down to the soles of her feet. She didn't trust it. Marcos didn't mean the words the way they had sounded to her ears. Ears starved for anything he ever said to her.

She told herself, firmly, until it was embedded in her brain, that Marcos wanted someone trustworthy, someone biddable, and his lionlike instinct surely prodded him to help her.

And, oh, how she had wanted to be different. To him. Not charity. Not like his stepbrother, a reckless playboy Marcos had to rescue time after time—not like all the strangers and friends who called him every day, seeking his counsel, his power, his help.

Everyone wanted something of Marcos Allende, for underneath the hard exterior lay a man with a strong, solid heart of gold. His faith in people was inspiring, his ruthlessness rivaled only by his mercy. Marcos…took care of you. And those early mornings when Virginia had stepped into his office to find his broad shoulders bent over the desk, his shirt rolled up to his elbows, his silky black hair falling over his forehead, his voice husky and his eyes tired from lack of sleep, her heart had ached with wanting to take care of that big, proud warrior. *Who gives you back what you give, Marcos Allende?*

Is there anyone out there who takes care of you for a change?

Now she determined that whatever he wanted, she would give. "You won't regret it, Marcos," she softly promised. "Helping me, I mean."

His lips twitched. That amused smile did things to her stomach, but it didn't seem to reach his eyes. Those remained hooded, unreadable. He ran the back of one finger down her cheek, the touch sparking fire. "It is I who hopes you never regret this visit."

Two

"Your new lover?"

Silent, Marcos stood at the living room window and broodingly watched the car pull away with Virginia inside it. From the penthouse, the Lincoln looked like a sleek black beetle, slipping into the intermittent traffic before the apartment building.

The pressure in his chest mounted with the distance.

His blood still pumped hot inside his veins and his head swam with a thousand thoughts, all of them X-rated.

"Or a mistress maybe?"

Twisting around, he faced his newest guest,

the inquisitive Jack Williams—ex-corporate spy and now self-made millionaire. He was helping himself to a bag of nuts he'd obtained from the bar.

"My assistant," Marcos said tonelessly, swirling his newly poured Scotch in his hand. The cubes clinked in the glass.

Jack had arrived promptly at eleven as promised—the tall, blond Texan was never late, and, like a golden retriever listening to a particularly silent whistle, he had cocked his head when he spotted Virginia almost in Marcos's arms. As she whispered goodbye, Marcos's own instincts had flared to life and whispered that she wanted to stay.

But when "Williams the Bastard"—as the press had dubbed him—said he'd deliver, he delivered. And unfortunately what Marcos expected couldn't wait.

Still, he couldn't allow his friend to get the wrong impression of her, so he lifted his glass in a mocking toast. "She makes good coffee."

Jack popped an almond into his mouth and munched. "Aha. In bed?"

Marcos crossed the living room and headed back into the office, Jack trailing behind him.

Cranky, frustrated and exhausted, he set the glass atop a stack of papers on his desk and sank into the high-backed leather seat. "I'm not that man, Jack. Never mix business with pleasure, remember?"

But Virginia's sweet, fragrant scent lingered in the air. A torment to his straining body. A mockery to his words.

He respected his employees, took pride in being regarded as a man with moral fiber. And yet when it came to Virginia Hollis, it seemed he was reduced to the instincts of a caveman.

His friend's smooth, easy chuckle coming from the threshold somehow cranked up his frustration. "I remember. But the question is: do *you?* Should I have fetched a spoon, buddy? You looked ready to eat her."

Marcos would have scoffed. He certainly didn't welcome the canny twinkle in Jack's eye. But then he remembered the desperate urge he'd had to kiss Virginia…the exquisite scent of her skin, so close to his…the surprisingly fine feel of her in his arms, stirring and enticing beyond belief…

His chest cramped with emotion as he dragged a hand down his hot face. "Perhaps the old adage is true, and some rules are meant to be broken—especially if you're the moron living by them."

"Don't go there, Marcos." Jack pushed away from the door, dead serious. "I've been there. Not fun, man. Not fun for you, definitely not fun for her. Office affairs always end badly—no matter how well you plan them when you begin."

Marcos pondered the massive, crowded bookcase on the wall across from him. A near bursting sensation was lodged in the pit of his gut. He didn't want to hurt her. Hell, he hadn't wanted to *want* her.

Diablos, but he'd been sexually frustrated since the day he'd hired her. She was demure, desperate and determined, and Marcos had feared she'd be a distraction. But he hadn't counted on the fact that his primitive response to her would reach such a fever pitch.

"I've never gotten involved with an employee in my life—but she's different, Jack. And yes, I am aware of how that sounds."

Reclining in his seat with a grimace, he opened his cuff buttons and rolled up his sleeves.

He was actually considering, perhaps he was even past considering and had already made up his mind, giving them both what they'd wanted for months.

He was a man, flesh and blood like all the others. There was only so much he could stand. And Virginia…no matter how energetically she tried to conceal her reactions to him, she responded. Viscerally, primitively—a woman underneath the tidy assistant after all. A sweet, lovely woman who knew instinctively when a man wanted her. No, not wanted—Marcos *burned* for her.

And now he'd asked—practically demanded— she spend a week with him. Pretending to be his lover. At a time when all his energies, all his attention, needed to be on the one prize he'd sought to gain for so long.

Allende.

He hadn't been certain whether to ask her as escort. She was too much a temptation to play lovers with, and in order to successfully achieve his goals, focus was key.

But tonight the lovely Virginia—alone and financially abandoned by her family, something Marcos could identify with—had turned to him for help.

Tonight, as he'd gazed into her bright, fierce eyes, he couldn't deny himself any longer.

He wanted her.

He'd offered her a position for a week, true, but that was merely a guise for what he really wanted to do.

Her powerful effect would linger with him long after he left his office at night. He thought of her continually, every hour. He relived their encounters in his mind sometimes, enjoyed hearing her laugh at Lindsay's antics when his office doors were parted. He could not push her image away at night and loathed to see her in trouble when she seemed to seek so little of it for herself.

He'd made a mental list long ago with plenty of valid reasons to leave her alone.

She was an innocent, he was not. She was vulnerable, he could hurt her. She was his employee, he was her boss. There were dozens of reasons to stay the hell away from Virginia.

The ways she'd looked at him tonight pulverized them all.

"Here. I have just the thing to cheer you up." Jack stepped outside and returned rummaging through his leather briefcase. He yanked out a manila folder and held it out. "There you go, big man. Your wish is my command."

Marcos plucked the file from his hand and immediately honed in on the name printed across the tab. Marissa Galvez.

He smiled darkly. "Ah, my rainmaker. Everything here, I assume?"

"Everything on Marissa and her sleazy little deals. She's quite a busy little bee. You'll find it to be riveting reading. Took me a while, as you can see—but I did give you my word to have it ready by tonight."

Marcos skimmed through the pages, not surprised that the file was as thick as the woman was scheming.

Marissa Galvez. A shaft of anger sliced through him. The lady had hopes of a reconciliation before discussing numbers?

Of course she did. She read *Forbes.* Was smart enough to realize the son was worth more than the father she'd left him for, not thousands or millions, but billions. She knew the company, which should have rightfully been *his,* was prime for takeover and it wouldn't take much but a few savvy connections to learn it had been Marcos who'd been buying the outstanding stock.

Unfortunately, insulting Marissa's renewed interest in him wouldn't do to accomplish his goals. But a beautiful, smiling lover would slowly and surely take care of her dreams of reconciliation—and let them get down to the real business at hand.

Allende. *My company.*

"Mind telling me how you're going to convince the delectable woman to sell? Without succumbing to her request for some personal attention before discussing numbers?" Jack queried.

Marcos lunged to his feet, waving the evidence in the Texan's face. "With this. It's my game now, my rules." He met his friend's sharp, blue-eyed stare and his lips flattened to a grim, strained line. "Allende is in a vulnerable position. Sooner or later, she'll have to sell."

"Not to you, she doesn't."

Marcos shrugged disinterestedly. "She knows she's game for a hostile takeover. And she knows I'm the shark after her. She wouldn't have called if she didn't want to get on my good side."

And I've got my pretty, green-eyed "lover."

"Will she?"

And her pretty little mouth. "What?"

"Get on your good side?"

"When you start wearing a tutu, Jack. Of course not."

Distaste filled him as he recalled her phone call. Dangling Allende up to him like bait, proposing they discuss it in her bed. She'd played with him as a naive, noble, seventeen-year-old boy, but it would be an ice age in hell before she played with the man.

"She called because she wants you back," Jack pointed out.

"Fortunately, I have an escort," he said and headed to the window, a part of him somehow expecting to see the Lincoln. "Being I will be conveniently taken, we'll have to forego the personal and get down to the numbers."

"I see now. So the lovely lady is key."

Those eyes. Big, bright, clear green, and so expressive he thought she'd pummeled his gut when she'd looked at him so adoringly. She made him feel…noble. Decent. Desperate to save her ten times over in exchange for another worshipful gaze.

When she'd called to request a moment of his time only hours ago, he'd allowed himself a brief flight of fantasy. He fantasized she'd been ready to succumb to him, ready to admit what already threatened to become inevitable. Even as he allowed himself the luxury of the fantasy, he knew she was too cautious and respectable for that.

It was up to him now. What was he going to do?

He shot Jack a sidelong look. "Marissa will get what's coming to her." And Virginia…

Jack swept up his briefcase with flair. "The devil on a Falcon jet, yes." He saluted from the threshold and flashed his signature I'm-Jack-the-Ripper grin. "I'll let you pack, my friend."

"My gratitude to you, Williams. And send the bill to Mrs. Fuller this week, she'll take care of it."

When Jack said an easy "will do" and disappeared, Marcos swallowed the last of his Scotch, his eyebrows furrowing together as he thought of the demure strand of pearls around Virginia's neck tonight. His woman wouldn't wear such little pearls. She'd wear diamonds. Tahitians. Emeralds.

With a swell of possessiveness, he brought to mind the lean, toned form of her body, watched countless times across his office desk, countless times when it had been by sheer determination that he'd forced his scrutiny back to his work.

A size six, he predicted, and promptly pulled his contact list from the top drawer and flipped through the pages.

If she was playing his lover, then one thing was certain: Virginia Hollis would look the part.

In the quiet interior of the Fixed Base Operator which specialized in servicing company jets, Marcos stood with his hands in his pockets. He brimmed with anticipation and gazed out the window from the spacious sitting area while the Falcon 7X jet—a sleek, white dove and one of his faster babies—got fueled.

He'd like to blame his simmering impatience on the deal he was about to negotiate. But the truth was, his assistant was late, and he was impatient to see *her.*

Now a door of opportunity was wide open for them. An opportunity to interact outside the busy, hectic pace of his office. An opportunity to step out of their roles and, if they chose to, temporarily into a new one.

She'll pretend to be my lover.

That she had accepted to aid him in this manner made him feel heady. For how long would they be able to pretend and only pretend? Three days, three hours, three minutes?

In the back of the room, the glass doors rolled open. The sounds of traffic sailed into the building and Marcos swung around. To watch Virginia stroll inside.

A balloon of protectiveness blossomed in his chest.

The only thing untidy about his assistant today was her hair. Wild, windblown and uncontrollable. The ebony curls framed a lovely oval face and eyes that were green and clear and thicklashed. Hauling a small black suitcase behind her, she paused to store a bag of peanuts in the outside zippered compartment. The mint-green V-neck sweater she wore dipped sexily to show the barest hint of cleavage. His mouth went dry.

She straightened that agile body of hers and swiped a wave of ebony curls behind her shoulder. The scent of citrus—lemons, oranges, everything that made him salivate—wafted through the air as she continued hauling her suitcase forward. Christ, she was a sexpot.

"Virginia," he said.

Her head swiveled to his. "Marcos."

He smiled. The sight of her face, warm in the

sunlight, made his lungs constrict. She wore no makeup except for a gloss, and with her curls completely free, she was the most enchanting thing he'd ever seen.

Licking her lips as he came forward, she pulled the suitcase up and planted it at her feet—a barrier between their bodies. "You got a head start on me," she said. She spoke in a throaty, shaky voice that revealed her nervousness.

He eyed her lips. Burnished a silky pink today, inciting him to taste.

"I apologize, I had some last-minute work out of the office."

Dragging in a breath, he jerked his chin in the direction of the long table down the hall, offering coffee, cookies, napkins—all that Virginia liked to toil with. "Fix yourself coffee if you want. We'll board in a few minutes."

"You? Coffee?"

Somberly he shook his head, unable to prevent noticing the subtle sway of her skirt-clad hips as she left her compact black suitcase with him and walked away.

He was fascinated. By the sweet-smelling, sexy package of Virginia Hollis. Five feet four inches of reality. Of *pretend* lover.

Cursing under his breath, he snatched her suitcase handle and rolled the bag up to his spot by the window. The pilots were storing his luggage, consisting mostly of shopping bags from Neiman Marcus.

He crossed his arms as he waited for their signal. The file the infallible Jack Williams had given him last night provided him with more than enough ammo to persuade Marissa to sell, yet even the knowledge of emerging victorious didn't make this particular task any easier. You could crush a bug in your fist and it still didn't mean you would enjoy it. But Allende—a transport company on its last breath, flailing for help—had his name on it.

It was his. To resuscitate or to murder.

Virginia drew up beside him and he went rigid, inhumanly aware of her body close to his. She was a subtle, scented, stirring presence.

Without so much as moving his head, he let his eyes venture to the front of her sweater. The fabric clung to the small, shapely, seductive swells of her breasts. A wealth of tenderness flooded him. Virginia had come dressed as his assistant in the sweater, her typical knee-length gray skirt, the simple closed-toe shoes with no personality. "I'm afraid this won't do," he murmured.

A smile danced on her lips as she tipped her face up in bewilderment. She seemed animated today, no more the worried siren begging for his assistance last night. "What won't do?"

Virginia. With her perfect oval face, creamy, elegant throat and bow-shaped morsel of a mouth that invited him to nibble. It really seemed easier to stop breathing than to continue saying *no* to those marshmallow-soft lips. "The sweater," he said quietly, signaling the length of her body with his hand. "The skirt. The sensible shoes. It won't do, Miss Hollis."

She set her coffee cup and napkin on a side table, then tucked her hair behind her ear. "I did pack a few dresses."

"Did you." His eyebrows furrowed together as he surveyed her pearls. "Designer dresses?"

"Why, no."

He raised his hand to the pearl necklace. "How attached are you," he whispered, trailing his finger across the glossy bumps, "to wearing these?"

She watched him for a moment, a telling wariness in her voice. "They were Mother's."

"Pretty. Very pretty." The pent-up desire that blazed inside him textured his voice. "You see, my lover…might wear something else." He was playing with fire. He didn't care. "My woman—" he plucked a pearl between two fingers "—would wear Tahitians. Diamonds. Emeralds."

Her eyes danced. "Are you afraid I won't look presentable?"

He dropped his hands and shot her a dead-serious look. "I'm afraid you will look too much like my assistant and not my lover."

But she kept on smiling, kept on enchanting him. "I see."

He frowned now. "Understand me, Virginia. If I'd wanted to be seen with my assistant, I'd have brought Mrs. Fuller."

This made her gasp, and the gasp did not make his scowl vanish. He nodded towards the Falcon. "Your new wardrobe is in the plane. There's a room in the back. Change."

Three

Of all the highhandedness, of all the *arrogance,* of all the bosses in the world—she had to be in debt to *Marcos*. Undoubtedly the most complicated.

While the jet motors hummed in the background, Virginia slipped into the slinky patterned dress inside the windowless little room at the back of the plane. Damn him. She had agreed to his request, but how was she supposed to reply to his autocratic commands? Worse, the clothes were divine. She couldn't in her right mind stay annoyed at a man with such exquisite taste. Her knight in shining armor.

Enthralled by how slight and satiny the dress

felt against her body, she ran three fingers down the length of her hips, wishing there was a mirror to let her visually appreciate the dress's exquisite, plunging back. *And how is this necessary to his plan?* she wondered.

Gathering her courage with a steady intake of breath, she forced herself to step outside.

Throughout the tasteful wood and leather interior, the air crackled with the suppressed energy of his presence. His head was bent. His powerful, well-built body overwhelmed a cream-colored, plush leather seat, and his hair—abused by his hands during the flight—gleamed in the sunlight as he read through a massive leather tome. He was clad all in black, and the short-sleeved polo shirt he wore revealed tanned, strong forearms corded with veins. Watching him, big and proud and silent, completely engrossed and unaware of her gaze, she felt like sighing.

With a quick mental shake, she walked down the wide plane aisle, noting the screen embedded in the wood-paneled wall behind Marcos's seat. The electronic map showed the plane just three red dashes away from the little dot of Monterrey. At least one more hour.

As she eased in between their seats, intent on

taking her place across from him, one huge hand shot out and manacled her wrist. She was spun around, and she gasped. Then there was nothing to pry those glimmering eyes away from her, no shield from the scorching possessiveness flickering in their depths.

"No," he rasped, his voice hoarsened by how little he'd spoken during the flight.

A melting sensation spread down her thighs, his accent too delicious to not enjoy. *No, don't sit yet,* she thought he meant, but she couldn't be sure. No one could ever be too sure of anything with Marcos. Maybe it was *no* to the dress!

Aware of her chest heaving too close to his face, she tried to pry her wrist free but failed miserably. "I changed. Wasn't that what you wanted?"

He cocked his head farther back and stared, his grip loosening slightly. "You're angry at me."

"I…" She jerked her chin toward the book on his lap, wanting, needing him to remove his hand. "Please. Read."

For a woman who'd strived to become invisible for years, the last thing she felt now was unseen. The filmy Issa London dress hugged her curves subtly, the wrap-around style tied with a bow at her left hip. The fabric felt so feminine she became utterly conscious of her body—and how he peered at it in interest.

"You approve of the clothes I bought you, *amor?*" he said huskily.

Amor? A jolt went through her at the endearment. Panicking, she tugged with more force and whispered, halfheartedly, "You can let go of me now."

His gaze pierced her, his unyielding hand burning her wrist. By the way his touch spread like a wildfire, her boss may as well have been touching her elsewhere. Where her breasts ached, where the back of her knees tingled, where her nerves sparkled and where she felt hot and painfully aware of being empty.

He released her. So abruptly she almost stumbled.

Still reeling, Virginia sank into her seat like a deflated balloon. Her pulse thundered. Her hands shook as she strapped on her seat belt.

His intense regard from across the aisle became a living, breathing thing. "Does a man's interest offend you?" he asked silkily.

Blushing furiously, she propped her purse on her lap. "Did you know Monterrey has over five million people now?" She shoved the maps she'd printed at the office and lists of Spanish words back in her purse.

He slapped the book shut and let it drop with a resounding thump at his feet. "Would *my* interest offend you, Virginia?"

She squinted at him, expecting a laugh, a chuckle, a smile at least.

He was perfectly sober. Excruciatingly handsome and sober.

Oh, no. No, no, no, he wouldn't do this. She was prepared to do a job, but she was not prepared to allow herself to become a man's…plaything.

No matter how much she fantasized about him in private.

With a nervous smile, Virginia shook a chastising finger at him, but it trembled. "Mr. Allende, the closer we've gotten to Mexico, the stranger you've become."

Silence.

For an awful second, her blatant claim—part teasing and part not—hung suspended in the air. Virginia belatedly bit her lip. What had possessed her to say that to her boss? She curled her accusing finger back into her hand, lowering it in shame.

Sitting in a deceptively relaxed pose, he crossed

his arms over his broad chest and regarded her with an unreadable expression. Then he spoke in that hushed, persuasive way of his, "Do you plan to call me *Mr. Allende* when you're out there pretending to be my lover?"

Self-conscious and silently berating herself, Virginia tucked the skirt of her dress under her thighs, her hands burrowing under her knees. "I didn't mean to insult you."

"I'm not insulted."

She racked her brain for what to say. "I don't know what came over me."

He leaned forward with such control that even a glare might have been more welcome by her. "You call me Marcos most of the time. You call me Marcos when you want my favors. Why now, today, do you call me Mr. Allende?"

She looked away, feeling as if her heart were being wrung. He spoke so quietly, almost pleadingly, that he could be saying something else to her—something that did not smack her with misery.

Because I've never been alone with you for so long, she thought.

She hauled in a ragged breath and remained silent.

The plane tilted slightly, eventually coming in for a landing as smoothly as it had flown. Its speed began to ease. If only her hammering heart would follow.

They taxied down a lane decorated with large open plane hangars, and she fixed her attention on the screen behind him, resolved to smooth out the awkwardness. "Do you believe Allende will be a safe investment for Fintech?" she asked. She knew it was all that remained of his past. His mother had passed away long before his father had.

"It's poorly managed." He extracted his BlackBerry from his trouser pocket and powered it on. "Transport vehicles have been seized by the cartels. Travel is less safe these days in this country. For it to become successful, strict security measures will need to be put in place, new routes, new personnel, and this will mean money. So, no. It isn't a safe investment."

She smiled in admiration as he swiftly skimmed through his text messages. He oozed strength. Strength of mind, of body, of purpose. "You'll make it gold again," she said meaningfully, still not believing that, God, she'd called him *strange* to his face!

He lifted his head. "I'm tearing it apart, Virginia."

The plane lurched to a stop. The engines shut down. The aisle lit up with a string of floor lights.

Virginia was paralyzed in her seat, stunned. "You plan to destroy your father's business," she said in utter horror, a sudden understanding of his morose mood barreling into her.

His hard, aquiline face unreadable, he thrust his phone into his pocket and silently contemplated her. "It's not *his* anymore." His face was impassive, but his eyes probed into her. "It was meant to be mine when he passed away. I built it with him."

This morning, between phone calls, coffee, copies and errands, she'd gotten acquainted with Monterrey from afar. Learned it was a valley surrounded by mountains. Industrial, cosmopolitan, home of the wealthy and, at the very outskirts of the city, home of the poor. Indisputably the most prominent part of northern Mexico. Conveniently situated for Allende Transport, of course, as a means to import, export and travel—but also conveniently situated for those who imported and exported illegal substances. Like the cartels.

Allende wasn't a bouquet of roses, she supposed,

but she'd never expected Marcos willingly to attempt to destroy it.

"You look as if I'd confessed to something worse," he noted, not too pleased himself.

"No. It's only that—" She checked herself before continuing this time. "That's not like you. To give up on something. You've never given up on Santos no matter what he does."

His intense expression lightened considerably. "My brother is a person—Allende is not."

Mightily aware of how out of character this decision was, Virginia ached to remind him he'd dedicated his life to helping companies in crisis, had taken under his wing businesses and even people no one else had faith in but Marcos, but instead she rose to her feet. Unfolding like a long, sleek feline just awakened to the hunt, Marcos followed her up. And up.

"Virginia, this isn't Chicago." He loomed over her by at least a head. His face was impassive, but his eyes probed into her. "If you want to sightsee, you'll be accompanied by me. Too dangerous to be alone here."

Dangerous.

The word caused gooseflesh on her skin.

Remembering her research on the city,

she peered out a window as two uniformed *aduanales* and twice as many armed *militares* marched up to the plane. She'd heard military men customarily accompanied the Mexican customs agents but she was still floored by the intimidating sight. The copilot unlatched the door up front and descended to meet them.

She couldn't see much of the city at this late hour, but what she'd read online had mesmerized her. She would have even thought the setting romantic if his careful warning weren't dawning on her. "Dangerous," she said. "What must it be like for the people who live here?"

"Difficult." He rammed his book into a leather briefcase and zipped it shut. "Kidnapping rate has risen alarmingly during the last couple of years. Mothers are lifted outside the supermarkets, kids out of their schools, members of both government and police are bribed to play blind man to what goes on."

A rope of fear stretched taut around her stomach. "That's so sad."

She took one last look out the plane window. Nothing moved but the Mexican flag flapping by the customs building.

"It looks so calm," she protested.

"Under the surface nothing is calm." As he stood there, over six feet of virile overpowering man, he looked just a tad tired, and human, and so much sexier than behind his massive desk. He looked touchable. *Touchable.*

Under the surface nothing is calm. Not even me.

"Mrs. Fuller said you grew up here," she remarked as she eyed the fruit assortment on a table near the front of the plane.

"From when I was eight to eighteen," he answered. He stared, mildly puzzled, as she grabbed two green apples and slipped them into her purse.

"In case we get hungry," she explained sheepishly.

His eyes glittered with humor. "If you get hungry, you tell me and I'll make certain you're fed."

"What made you leave the city?" Leave a place that was beautiful and deadly. A place that gave out the message: Don't trust. You're not safe. And the one that had built a man like Marcos Allende, with an impenetrable core.

He braced one arm on the top wood compartment, waiting for the pilots to give them leave to descend. "Nothing here for me. Nothing in España either."

She loved the way he pronounced that. España. The way his arm stretched upward, long and sinewy, rippling under his black shirt before he let it drop. Somber, he gazed into her eyes, and the concern she saw in his gave her flutters. "Are you tired?"

"I'm fine." *You're here,* she thought.

The look that came to his eyes. The way he appraised her.

Virginia could've sworn there could be no flaw in her entire body. Nothing in this world more perfect to those dark, melted-chocolate eyes than she was.

His eyes fell to her lips and lingered there for an electric moment.

"Virginia." He closed the space between them. One step. All the difference between breathing or not. All the difference between being in control of your senses and being thrust into a twister.

He leaned over as he pried her purse from her cramped hands. His fingers brushed the backs of hers and a sizzle shot up her arm.

"Why are you nervous?" The low, husky whisper in her ear made her stomach tumble. She felt seared by his nearness, branded, as though he were purposely making her aware that his limits extended to breaching hers. She felt utterly...claimed. "You've fidgeted all day."

So he had been aware of her?

Like...a predator. Watching from afar. Planning, plotting, savoring the prey.

Why was this exciting?

His breath misted across the tender skin behind her ear. "Because of me?"

Her muscles gelled. *Because I want you.*

She took a shaky step back, singed to the marrow of her bones but smiling as though she was not. "I always get a charge after being rescued."

"Ahh." He drew out the sound, infusing it with a wealth of meaning. "So do I. After...rescuing." He swung his arm back so her purse dangled from one hooked finger behind his shoulder.

When the pilot announced they were clear, he signaled with an outstretched arm toward the plane steps. "Ladies first."

She warily stepped around his broad, muscled figure. "I admit I'm not used to your silences still."

His gaze never strayed from hers as she went around. "So talk next time," he said. "To me."

Right. Next time. Like he inspired one to make intimate revelations. And like he'd have another company to take over with the help of a "lover."

As both pilots conversed with the customs officials, Virginia stopped a few feet from the gaping doorway. Warmth from outside stole into the air-conditioned cabin, warming her cool skin. But she found she couldn't descend just yet.

She'd do anything to get her father out of his mess, yet suddenly felt woefully unprepared to play anyone's lover. Especially Marcos's lover. No matter how much she ached for the part and planned to get it right.

She pivoted on her heels to find him standing shockingly close. She craned her neck to meet his gaze. "Marcos, I'm going to need you to… tell me. What to do."

He wore an odd expression on his face, part confusion and part amusement. The smile he slowly delivered made her flesh pebble. "You may step out of the plane, Miss Hollis."

Laughing, she gave an emphatic shake of her head. "I mean, regarding my role. I will need to know what you suggest that I do. I'm determined, of course, but I'm hoping to get some pointers. From you."

His lids dropped halfway across his eyes. He lifted a loose fist and brushed his knuckles gently down her cheek. The touch reached into the depths of her soul. "Pretend you want me."

A tremor rushed down her limbs. Oh, God, he was so sexy. She was torn between latching on to his tempting, unyielding lips and running for her life. "I will, of course I will," she breathed.

A cloak of stillness came over her—so that all that moved, all she was aware of, was his hand. As he trailed his thumb down to graze her shoulder and in a ghost of a touch swept a strand of hair back, he swallowed audibly. "Look at me like you always do."

"How?"

"You know how." There was so much need in his eyes, a thirst she didn't know how to appease, which called to a growing, throbbing, aching void inside of her. "Like you care for me, like you need me."

"I do." She shook her cluttered head, straightening her thoughts. "I mean, I am. I *will.*"

She shut her eyes tight, fearing he would see the truth in them. Fearing Marcos would realize she'd been secretly enamored of him all along. Since the very first morning she'd stepped into his office, she had wanted to die—the man was so out of this world. So male. So dark.

And now...what humiliation for him to discover that, if he crooked his finger at her, Virginia would go to him.

He chuckled softly—the sound throaty, arrogant, male. "Good."

His large hand gripped her waist and urged her around to face the open plane door a few feet away. She went rigid at the shocking contact. Longing flourished. Longing for more, for that hand, but on her skin and not her clothes, sliding up or down, God, doing anything.

Dare she dream? Dare she let herself long just a little, without feeling the remorse she always did? Like she could indulge in a healthy fantasy now and then?

She wiggled free, sure of one thing: dissolving into a puddle of want was not what she should be doing just now.

"But...what do you want me to do, exactly?" she insisted, carefully backing up one step as she faced him. His eyebrows met in a scowl. He didn't seem to like her retreating. "This is important to you, right?" she continued.

"Señor Allende, pueden bajar por favor?"

Spurred to action by the voices on the platform, Virginia descended the steps. Marcos quickly took his place beside her.

They followed two uniformed officials toward a rustic, one-story building rivaled in size by Marcos's jet. A small control tower, which looked abandoned at this hour, stood discreetly to the building's right. A gust of hot, dry wind picked up around them, bouncing on the concrete and lifting the tips of her hair.

Virginia grabbed the whirling mass with one hand and pinned it with one fist at her nape. Marcos held the glass doors open for her. "No need to pretend just now, Miss Hollis," he said. "We can do that later."

His eyes glimmered dangerously with something. Something frightening. A promise. A request.

Her heart flew like the wind inside her, bouncing between her ribs, almost lifting the tips of her feet from the ground. Warily she passed through the bridge of his arm, one word's haunting echo resounding in her mind. And for the dread that began to take hold, it might have been a death sentence.

Later.

* * *

Fifteen minutes later, after a brisk *"Bienvenidos a Mexico"* from the *aduanales*, they were settled in the back of a silver Mercedes Benz, their luggage safely tucked in the trunk.

"A Garza Garcia, si?" the uniformed driver asked as he eased behind the wheel.

"Por favor," Marcos said.

His palm tingled. The one he'd touched her with. The one that had reached out to cup the lovely curve of her waist and caused Virginia to back away. From his touch.

Frowning, he checked his watch—it was ten past midnight. Wanting had *never* been like this. You wanted a watch, or a house, or money, but wanting this particular woman was no such whim. It was a need, something pent-up for too long, something so valued you were hesitant to have, or break, or tarnish, or hurt.

The car swerved onto the deserted highway and Virginia tipped her face to the window, lightly tugging at the pearls around her neck.

"You had a decent trip, Señor Allende?" their driver asked.

"Yes," he said, stretching out his legs as far

as he could without bumping his knee into the front seat.

Miles away, the distant core of the city of Monterrey glowed with lights. The sky was clear and veiled with gray, its shadow broken by a steady stream of streetlights rolling by.

"It's lovely here." Virginia transferred her purse to the nook at her feet then tapped a finger to the window. "Look at the mountains."

Her skin appeared luminous upon every brisk caress of the streetlights, and in the shadows her eyes glittered uncommonly bright. They sparkled with excitement.

He felt a tug at his chest. "I'll show you around tomorrow in daylight," he said curtly.

Her eyes slid over to his, grateful, alive eyes. "Thank you."

A heroic feeling feathered up his chest, and he pushed it aside.

During a lengthy quiet spell, the driver flicked on the radio and soft music filled the interior of the car. Virginia remained way over on the other end of the seat.

Not near enough…

He studied her figure, becoming fixated on the rounded breasts swelling under her clingy dress, the curve of her thigh and hip and small waist. Swirly black bits of hair tickled her shoulders. Her long, shapely legs had a satin shine to them, inviting him to wrap them around his body and spill days and weeks and months of wanting inside her.

He whispered, in a low murmur that excluded the driver, "Are you afraid of me?"

She stiffened. Pale, jade-green eyes rose to his for a second before her lashes dropped. "No. Why would you ask?"

Her shyness brought out the hunter in him, and it took effort on his part to keep under control. Go slowly with her... His heart began to pound. He patted his side. "You could come a little closer."

Ducking her head to hide a blush, she smoothed her hands along the front of her dress. Then she flicked a tiny knot of fabric from it. "Just haven't traveled in ages."

"You cringe at anyone's touch, or merely mine?"

She blinked. "Cringe? I'd never cringe if you... touched me."

The words *touched me* hovered between them like a dark, unleashed secret, an invitation to sin, and when Marcos at last responded to that, the thick lust in his voice was unmistakable. "You moved away when I urged you out of the plane. And when I helped you into the car."

"I was surprised." Her throat worked as she swallowed. Her eyes held his in the darkness. "I told you to tell me what to do."

She was whispering, so he whispered back.

"And I asked you to come closer just now."

A tense moment passed.

In silence, Marcos once again patted his side, this time more meaningfully.

After a moment's debate, Virginia seemed to quickly make up her mind. Thrusting out her chin at a haughty angle, she began to edge toward him. "If you're thinking I'm not good at this, I'll have you know I can pretend just fine."

Her scent stormed into his lungs. His nostrils twitched. His heart kicked. His temperature spiked.

Cautiously, as though petting a lion, she turned his hand over and set her cool, small palm on his. She gingerly laced her fingers through his. Lust kicked him in the groin at the unexpected touch. His head fell onto the back of the seat, a groan welling up in the back of his throat. Crucified by arousal, he dragged in a terse, uneven breath, squeezing his eyes shut.

She inched a little closer, tightening her grip. Her lips came to within a breath of his ear. "Does that satisfy you, Your Highness?"

He didn't let it show, the emotion that swept through him, but it made his limbs tremble. He said, thickly, "Come closer."

He wanted to jump her. He wanted all of her, right here, right now.

He inhaled deeply, his chest near bursting with the aroma of her. Clean, womanly, sweet. "Closer," he said, hearing the growl in his own words.

When she didn't, he glanced down at their joined hands. Hers was tiny and fair, nearly engulfed by his larger one. He ran the pad of his thumb along the back of hers, up the ridge of her knuckle, down the tiny smooth slope. She felt so good. And he felt eighteen again. "Soft," came his trancelike murmur.

Transfixed, she watched the movement of his thumb, her breasts stretching the material covering them as she inhaled. He dipped his head and discreetly rubbed his nose across the shiny, springy curls of her hair. Christ. Edible. All of her. He could smell her shampoo, wanted to plunge all ten fingers into her hair, turn her face up and kiss her lips. Softly, so he could savor her breath, go searching deep into her mouth.

Ducking his head so the driver wouldn't hear him, he whispered, "You might try to appear to enjoy my touch."

Their bodies created a heat, a dark intimate cocoon in the confined car interior, enhanced by the warmth of their whispers. "Marcos..."

His hand turned, capturing hers as she attempted to retrieve it. "Virginia."

Their gazes held. Like they did across his office, over the tops of people's heads, in the elevators. Those clear, infinite eyes always sought out his. To find him looking right back. Their fingers brushed at the pass of a coffee mug, a file, the phone. At contact their bodies seemed to flare up like matches—tense, coil, heat up the room. Even with a wall separating them, his awareness of her had escalated to alarming levels. And she'd been more fidgety with him than she had in months.

"We're pretending, remember?" he said, a husky reminder.

Pretend. The only way Marcos could think of

that wouldn't involve her feelings, or his. The only way they might be able to—hell, what was this? It had been going on so long it felt like surrender—without anyone hurting in the end. Without their lives changing, breaking or veering off in separate ways because of it.

"Yes, I know."

"Then relax for me." Lightly securing her fingers between his, he delved his thumb into the center of her palm with a deep, intense stroke, aware of her audible intake of breath as he caressed. "Very good," he cooed. "I'm convinced you want me."

"Yes." Her voice was but a whisper, hinting at how the sinuous, stroking circles of his thumb affected her. "I mean…I'm trying to…appear that I do."

But she seemed as uncertain and startled as a mouse who didn't know where to run to, and Marcos was very much taking to the cat's role. He wanted to play, to corner, to taste.

He glanced up. "Don't tax yourself too much, hmm."

Her warm, fragile fingers trembled in his. The excitement of a new country had left her eyes, replaced by a wild, stormy yearning. "I'm trying not to…get bored."

His thumb went deep at the center then eased back. "Hmm. Yes. I can see you're fighting a yawn." His eyes ventured up along the top of her head, taking in its gloss. "You have pretty hair. Can I touch it?"

He did. It felt soft and silky under his fingers, tempting him to dig in deeper, down to her scalp.

She made a sound in her throat, like a moan. A hunger of the worst, most painful kind clawed inside him. She had a way of staring at him with those big eyes like he was something out of this world. It was a miracle he'd resisted her this long.

"A man," he gruffly began, massaging the back of her head as he greedily surveyed her features, "would be lucky to make you his."

Her eyes sealed shut so tightly she seemed to be in pain. She squirmed a little on the seat and, unbelievably, came nearer. "You don't have to convince me. I'm already pretending."

Her breasts brushed his rib cage, and the heat of her supple body singed his flesh through their clothes. He intensified the strokes of his fingers. "A man would be lucky to make you his, Virginia," he repeated.

Her lashes fluttered upward, revealing her eyes. Pale green, ethereal. Distrustful. "What are you doing?"

His gut tightened. *What does it look like I'm doing?* He wanted to yank her onto his lap, feel his way up her little skirt, and kiss her mouth until her lips turned bright red. Her face blurred with his vision. With his need. He had to force himself to leave her hair alone.

She exhaled a string of broken air, then relaxed somewhat, shifting sideways on the leather seat. Facing him. Her smile faded. "Who are we fooling, Marcos, with this charade?"

"Marissa Galvez, Allende Transport's owner." *And maybe you. Definitely me.*

He retrieved her hand from where it had gone to wring the hem of her dress and secured her wrist in his grip as he raised it. He turned it over and set a soft, lingering kiss at the center of her palm. A tiny, breathless gasp came from her.

"We must practice," he murmured, gazing into those deep, bottomless eyes.

"Oh." She shivered. Not moving away, and not moving closer, she allowed him to drag his lips along her open palm. She watched him through her lashes, her lips shuddering on each uneven breath.

"And why must we fool her?" Her question was a silky wisp.

"Because she wants me," he huskily answered. She tasted divine. Her skin was smooth and satiny under his lips, and he predicted every inch of her body would feel just like it. Perfect. "It wouldn't do to insult her." Against his mouth and lips, he felt the vibrant tremor that danced up her arm. Emboldened by her response, thirsting for more, he opened his mouth and gently grazed his teeth at the heel of her palm. "I happen to want some-one else."

"I'm sure—" she began, swallowing audibly. "I'm sure you can have anyone you want."

"If I want her bad enough and put myself to task, yes." His lips closed and opened against her hand. Before he could restrain himself, he gave a lick at her palm. Pleasure pummeled through him. "And I've grown to want her...bad," he strained out, swallowing back a growl.

"Oh, that was..." Her hand wiggled as she tried prying it free. "I don't think..."

"Shh."

He held her wrist in a gentle grip and raised

his head. He watched her expression soften, melt, as he whisked the pad of his thumb across her dampened palm, getting it wet. He lifted the glistening pad of his thumb to her lips, his timbre coated with arousal. "Pretend you like it when I do this."

A sound welled in the back of her throat as he stroked. She nodded wildly, her lips gleaming at each pass of his thumb. "Yes, yes, I'm pretending," she breathed.

He'd never seen a more erotic sight, felt a more erotic sensation, than playing with Virginia Hollis's quivering pink lips in the back of a moving car. "Umm. Me, too. I will pretend… you're her."

"Aha."

"And I very much want her." God, he enjoyed her unease, enjoyed seeing her pupils dilate, her breath shallow out.

"O-okay."

His thumb continued glancing, whisking, rubbing, right where his mouth wanted to be. He bent to whisper, to conspire together, just him and her. "Let's pretend…we're lovers, Virginia." His voice broke with the force of his desire, came out rough with wanting. "Pretend every night we touch each other…and kiss…and our bodies rock together. And when we find release—"

"Stop!" She pushed herself back with surprising force, sucking great gulps of air. "God, stop. Enough. Enough pretending tonight."

He tugged her closer. They were breathing hard and loud.

"You should kiss me," he said gruffly.

"Kiss you." She absently fingered his cross where it peeked through the top opening of his shirt. He went utterly still—the gesture too sweet, too unexpected, too painful.

Her fingers reached his throat, then traced the links of the thick chain.

Too aware of this now, he dropped her hair and squeezed her elbow meaningfully. "Virginia. Your mouth. On mine."

They'd had foreplay for a year—with every glance, every flick of her hair, every smile.

She drew back and laughed, a choked, strained sound. "Now?" She couldn't seem to believe her eyes and ears, seemed stumped for words to deny him.

The car halted at a stoplight. A few cars drove up beside them. Marcos went still, glancing at her quietly until their car continued.

He had never wanted to feel a body as much as he wanted to feel hers.

And her mouth—he'd give anything to taste that mouth, was being for the first time in his life reckless, selfish, for that very mouth. A mouth that promised all the innocence he'd never had, trust, beauty, affection he'd never had.

Without any further thought, he pulled her close. "One kiss. Right now."

"But you're my boss," she breathed, clutching his shirt collar with a death grip. But her bright, luminous green eyes gazed up at him. And those eyes said yes.

Her lips were plush, parted, eager for his. He brought his thumb back to scrape them. "Just pretend I'm not him."

"But you *are* him—"

"I don't want to be him, I want to be…just Marcos." Their relationship had been wrapped in rules, limited by their roles. What if Virginia had been just a woman? And he just a man? She would have been his, might still be his. "Only Marcos."

The passing city lights caused slanted shadows to shift across her face—she looked splendid, wary, wanting.

"A kiss is harmless, Virginia." His vision blurred with desire as he stretched his arm out on the seat behind her and dipped his head. Their breaths mingled, their mouths opened. "People kiss their pets. They kiss their enemies on the cheeks. They kiss a letter. They even blow kisses into the air. You can kiss me."

"This is a little unexpected."

"God, I'd hate to be predictable." His arm slid from the back of the seat and went around her shoulders, loosely holding her to him. His fingers played with the soft, bouncy curls at her nape. His accent got unbearably thick—like his blood, a terse string of lust flooding his veins. It took concentration to give her a smile meant to disarm. "Stop thinking about it and kiss me."

Her curls bounced at the shake of her head. "We don't have to kiss to pretend to be...together. I can pretend convincingly without kissing."

No kissing? Christ, no. He had a fascination with her mouth, the delicate bow at her upper lip, the ripe flesh of the bottom one. He'd been kissing that mouth for days, weeks, months, in his mind.

"You're wrong, *amor*." He bussed her temple with his lips, aware of his muscles flexing heatedly under his clothes, his skin feverish with pent-up desire as she continued clinging to his shirt. "We must kiss. And we must kiss convincingly."

"I— You didn't mention this before."

He caressed her cheekbone with the back of one finger and noted the frantic pulse fluttering at the base of her throat. Christ, once again she was fixated with his mouth, and he wanted to give it to her. Now. Right now. Slam it over hers, push into her, taste all of her. "Kiss me, Virginia. Kiss me senseless." He barely held himself in check with his ruthless self-discipline.

She hesitated. Then, in a burdened breath, "Only a kiss."

His heart rammed into his ribs at the realization that she had agreed. To kiss him. *Ay, Dios.*

He urged himself to ease back on the seat and stifled the impulse to take matters into his own hands. He was a second away from losing his mind. A second away from tearing off her clothes, the necklace at her throat, his shirt, everything that separated them. Still, he wanted to be sure, sure she wanted this. Him. Them.

He groaned and said, "Kiss me until we can't breathe."

"I… The driver could see us." She sounded as excited as he, and the breathless anticipation in her voice plunged him even deeper into wild, mad desire.

"Look at me, not him."

"You're all I'm looking at, Marcos."

He didn't know who breathed harder, who was seducing whom here. She laid her hands over his abdomen. He hissed. The muscles under her palms clenched. His erection strained painfully.

Her hands slid up his chest, a barely there touch. *Fever.* She cradled his jaw with two cool, dry palms…and waited. Hesitant, inexperienced. In a ragged plea, she croaked, "Close your eyes."

He did. Not because she asked, but because her fingers lovingly stroked his temple, down his jaw. Her hands drifted lower and curled around his shoulders, rubbing along the muscles so sensually he gritted his teeth. This was murder.

She had to stop. She had to go on.

"Do it. Do it now." The helpless urgency in his voice startled him as much as the other emotions coursing through him. Arousal ripped through him like a living beast.

Then he felt the warm mist of her breath on his face, sensed the nearness of her parting lips, heard through the roaring in his ears her tremulous whisper. "I'm a bit out of practice—"

He didn't let her finish. He reached out and slipped a hand beneath the fall of hair at her nape and hauled her to him. "Virginia," he rasped, and slammed her mouth with his.

Four

Virginia had meant for a quick kiss. Only a taste. A taste to satisfy her curiosity. Her need. A taste because she could not, could never, deny this man. But when he pulled her down and his mouth, so strong and fierce and hungry, touched hers, there was no stopping what came over her.

They'd been panting, laughing; he'd been teasing her, had pulled her onto his lap. Pretending had been so easy, but now…now this mouth, this man, the hands gripping the back of her head, were too real. Rough. Raw. Devastating.

She moaned helplessly as he slanted his head, murmuring something indiscernible to her, and his warm, hot tongue came at hers, and his hard need grew larger and stronger under her bottom, and the realization that he really *wanted her* barraged through her.

He began to take little nips, and those lush, sure lips moving against hers set off the flutters in her stomach, the fireworks in her head. *"Sabes a miel."*

He spoke in an aroused rasp against her lips. She clung to his neck and tried not to moan as his warm breath slid across her skin, heating her like a fever.

"Te quiero hacer el amor," he murmured, running his hands down the sides of her body, his fingers brushing the curves of her breasts, his chest heaving with exerted restraint. *"Toda la noche, te quiero hacer el amor."*

She had no idea what he said, but the words pulsed through her in a wave of erotic pleasure. Her breasts swelled heavy, her nipples in such pain she pressed them deeper into his chest and she opened her mouth wide, moving instinctively against him, and she knew this was wrong, so wrong, would not happen again, which surely must be why she incited it. "What are you saying to me…" she murmured into him.

His breath was hot and rapid against her. "I'm

saying I want to make love to you. All evening, all night." He groaned and twisted his tongue around hers as their lips locked, the attachment intense, driven, absolute.

She sucked in a breath as his palms engulfed her straining nipples, felt his desire in every coiled muscle, in the rough way his palms kneaded, the thrusts of his tongue as his mouth turned ravenous on hers.

He groaned, appearing decidedly out of control for the first time since she'd known him. He stroked the undersides of her breasts with his thumbs and whisked his lips along the curve of her jaw, and she cocked her ear to his nibbling lips, shuddered when he murmured to her. "Your gasps tear me to pieces."

"Marcos…"

She was hot and burning inside.

He made a grinding motion with his hips, and her thighs splayed open as he desperately rubbed his erection against her.

His tongue plunged into her ear, wet, hot, sloppy. "Stop me, Virginia." One determined hand unerringly slipped through the V of her dress and enveloped her breast. "Virginia. Stop me, Virginia."

He squeezed her flesh possessively, and when his palm rubbed into her nipple, her eyes flew open in shock. The feel was so delicious, so wrong, so *right,* she hid her heated face against his neck and almost choked on the sounds welling at the back of her throat. Sensations overpowered her body, her mind struggling to comprehend that this was really happening with Marcos Allende.

"That's your hotel up ahead, sir."

Swearing under his breath, Marcos gathered her closer. His ragged breaths blasted her temple. He squeezed her. "We'll finish this upstairs."

Virginia pushed back her rumpled hair. Upstairs? God, what were they even doing?

Chuckling at the look on her face, Marcos bussed her forehead with his lips as his gentle hand stroked down her nape, trembling slightly. "I should've known we'd be combustible," he murmured.

The Mercedes pulled into a wide, palm tree-lined hotel driveway and Virginia fumbled for her purse while Marcos stepped out and strolled to her side, reaching into the car and helping her to her feet.

His glimmering, dark gaze didn't stray from

her face, not for a second. *We kissed,* his dark eyes said. *I touched you. I know you want me.*

And for an insane second, all she wanted was to forget why she was here and who she was and be swept away by this one man, this one night, in this one city.

As though discerning her thoughts, Marcos cupped half of her face in his warm palm, and his eyes held something so wild and bright it almost blinded her. "Upstairs," he said again.

The promise plunged into her like a knife as he moved away to discuss something with the chauffeur, and Virginia stood there like someone in a hypnotized state, watching his big, tanned hands at his sides. Hands she'd felt on her.

She gritted her teeth, fighting the lingering arousal tickling through her. He was playing with her. He was *pretending*. He was a man who'd do anything to win—and he wanted Allende.

Marcos seemed oblivious to her frustration when he returned, slowly reaching behind her, his fingers splaying over the small of her back as he led her up the steps.

She followed him and no, she wasn't imagining him naked, touching her, kissing her in the exact way he'd just done—no, no, no. She studied the beautiful hotel and the potted palms leading to the glass doors with the intensity of a scientist with his microscope.

The lobby and its domed ceiling made her lightheaded. It was so…so… God, the way he'd touched her. With those hands. As if that breast were his to touch and his hand belonged there. How could he pretend so well? He'd been so hard he could've broken cement with his…his…

"Do you like it, Virginia?" he asked, smiling, and signaled around.

She gazed at the elegant but rustic decor. "The hotel? It's beautiful."

His eyes twinkled, but underneath it all, he wore the starved look of a man who'd hungered for a very long time and intended to feast soon. He looked like a man who could do things to her she didn't even imagine in fantasies, like a man who would not want to be denied.

And he would be. He had to be.

"It's very…charming," she continued, anything to steer her mind away from his lips, his mouth, his gaze.

They wound deeper into the marbled hotel lobby. A colorful flower arrangement boasting the most enormous sunflowers she'd ever seen sat on a massive round table near the reception area.

Virginia could still not account, could not even fathom, that she'd just kissed him. Her!—woefully inexperienced, with her last boyfriend dating back to college—kissing Marcos Allende. But he'd been cuddling her, whispering words so naughty she could hardly stand the wanton warmth they elicited. No matter how much resistance she'd tried to put up, he was the sexiest thing on the continent, playing some sort of grown-up game she had yet to put a name to, and Virginia had been close to a meltdown.

It had all been pretend, anyway. Right?

Right.

Trying to compose herself, she admired his broad back as he strolled away, the shoulders straining under his black shirt as he reached the reception desk and leaned over with confidence, acting for the world as if he were the majority stockholder of the hotel. The two women shuffling behind the granite top treated him as if they agreed.

Virginia quietly drew up to his side, her lips feeling raw and sensitive. She licked them once, twice.

A lock of ebony hair fell over Marcos's forehead as he signed the slip and slid it over the counter. "I requested a two-bedroom suite—it would appease me to know you're safe. Will this be a problem?" Facing her, he plunged his Montblanc pen into his shirt pocket, watching her through calm, assessing eyes.

She saw protectiveness there, concern, and though her nerves protested by twisting, she said, "Not at all." Damn. What hell to keep pretending for a week.

"Good."

In the elevator, as they rode up to the ninth floor—the top floor of the low, sprawling building—his body big and commanding in the constricted space, the silence whispered, *we kissed*.

In her mind, her heart, the choir of her reason, everything said, *kiss kiss kiss*.

Not good, any of it. Not the blender her emotions were in, not her tilting world, not the fact that she was already thinking, anticipating, wondering, what it would feel like to kiss again.

Freely. Wildly. Without restraint.

She would have to stall. Abstain. Ignore him. God. If she did something to compromise her job, she would never forgive herself. And nothing compromised a job like sex did. And if she compromised her heart? She stiffened, firmly putting a lid on the thought.

Mom had loved Dad with all her heart—through his flaws, through his odd humors, through his drunken nights, through all the good and bad of which there was more of the latter, her mother had loved with such steadfast, blinded devotion Virginia had secretly felt…pity.

Because her mother had wept more tears for a man than a human should be allowed to weep. Appalling, that one man could have such power over a woman, could take her heart and her future and trample them without thought or conscience.

Even on her deathbed, sweet, beautiful, dedicated Mother had clutched Virginia's hand, and it seemed she'd been hanging on to her life only to continue trying to save her husband. "Take care of Dad, Virginia, he needs someone to look out for him. Promise me, baby? Promise me you will?"

Virginia had promised, determinedly telling herself that if she ever, ever gave away her heart, it would be to someone who would be reliable, and who loved her more than his cards, his games and himself.

No matter her physical, shockingly visceral responses to Marcos, he was still everything she should be wary of. Worldly, sophisticated, ruthless, a man enamored of a challenge, of risks and of his job. The last thing she pictured Marcos Allende being was a family man, no matter how generous he'd proven to be as a boss.

Down the hall, the bellhop emerged from the service elevator, but Marcos was already trying his key, allowing her inside. He flicked on the light switch and the suite glowed in welcome. Golden-tapestried walls, plush taupe-colored carpet, a large sitting area opening up to a room on each side. *"Gracias,"* he said, tipping the bellhop at the door and personally hauling both suitcases inside.

Virginia surveyed the mouthwatering array of food atop the coffee table: trays of chocolate-dipped strawberries, sliced fruit, imported cheeses.

A newspaper sat next to the silver trays and the word *muerte* popped out in the headline. A color picture of a tower of mutilated people stared back at her.

Marcos deadbolted the door. The sound almost

made her wince. And she realized how alone they were. Just him. And her.

And their plan.

Suddenly and with all her might, Virginia wished to know what he was thinking. Did he think they'd kiss again? What if he wanted more than a kiss? What if he didn't?

Feeling her skin pebble, she shied away from his gaze, navigated around a set of chairs and pulled the sheer drapes aside. The city flickered with lights. Outside her window the hotel pool was eerily still, the mountains were still, the moon still. She noted the slow, rough curves and the sharper turns at the peaks, lifted her hand to trace them on the glass. "Do you come here frequently?" she asked quietly—her insides were not still.

"No." She heard the sunken fall of his footsteps on the carpet as he approached—she felt, rather than saw, him draw up behind her. "There wasn't reason to."

He could be uttering something else for the way he spoke so intimately. Inside, a rope of wanting stretched taut around her stomach and she thought she would faint. The proximity of his broad, unyielding hardness sent a flood of warmth across her body, and the muscles of her tummy clenched with yearning. His body wasn't touching hers; there was just the threat of the touch, the presence that created a wanting of it.

In the darkness of her bedroom, very late at night, she'd wondered if Marcos was as ruthless when he loved as when he did business. And if his kiss…was as dark and devastating as his eyes had promised it would be.

It was. Oh, God, it was.

The air seemed to scream at her to turn to him and *kiss.*

The close contours of his chest against her back, the scent of him, were an assault to her senses. He laid his hand on her shoulder, and the touch was fire on his fingertips. "This is a safe neighborhood—I won't lose sight of you, Virginia."

But outside the danger didn't lurk. It was in her. It was him. She locked her muscles in place, afraid of leaning, moving, afraid of the magnetic force of him, how it felt impossible not to turn, touch. "What was it like for you when you were young," she said, softly.

His hand stroked. Fire streaked across her skin as he drew lazy figures along the back of her arm. "It wasn't as dangerous back then. I grew up in the streets—I kept running away with my father's workers, looking for adventure."

Did he move? She thought he'd grown bigger, harder, nearer. She sensed his arousal, the thundering in his chest almost touching her back. Or was it her heart she heard?

He lowered his lips and briefly, only a whisper, set his mouth on her neck. A sharp shudder rushed through her. "Now even bodyguards aren't safe to hire," he whispered on her skin. "Wealthy people have armored cars and weapons instead."

She closed her eyes, the sensations pouring through her. "No-man's-land?" Just a croak. A peep from a little bird who couldn't fly, would willingly be lured in by the feline.

He made a pained sound and stilled his movements on her. "Were you pretending just now when you kissed me?"

Oh. My. God. They were actually discussing it.

Her nod was jerky.

Marcos hesitated, then huskily murmured, "Do you want to…?"

She sank her teeth into her lower lip to keep

from saying something stupid, like yes. "To what?"

His whisper tumbled down her ear. "You know what."

"I don't know what you mean." But she did. Oh, dear, she did.

"Kiss…" Thick and terse, his voice brimmed with passion. "Touch…"

Shaking like a leaf in a storm, she wiggled free and walked around him, her insides wrenching. "I told you I could pretend just fine."

Heading for the couch and plopping down, she surveyed the food once more, but her eyes didn't see anything.

Was she supposed to stay strong and resist what her body and heart wanted when she had a chance to have it? Was she supposed to say no and no and no?

Marcos plunged his hand into his hair. "That was *pretense?*"

"Of course." He sounded so shocked and looked so annoyed she might have even laughed. Instead, her voice grew businesslike. "So you left. And your father stayed here? In this city?"

For a moment, he released a cynical laugh, and when he gradually recovered, he roughly scraped the back of his hand across his mouth as if he couldn't stand remembering their kiss. Reluctantly, he nodded. "You're good, Miss Hollis, I'll give you that."

"What made you leave here?" she asked, blinking.

One lone eyebrow rose and this time when he laughed, she knew it was at her attempt at conversation.

"Well." Propping a shoulder against the wall and crossing his arms over his chest in a seemingly relaxed pose, Marcos exuded a raw, primal power that seemed to take command of the entire room. "Allende Transport was taken. By my father's...woman. It was either her or me—and he chose her. But I promised myself when I came back...the transport company would be mine."

His voice. Sometimes she'd hear it, not the words, just the bass, the accent. Marcos was larger than life, large in every single way, and Virginia could pretend all she wanted but the fact was, she'd be stupid to forget her position. And she had to make sure the car incident would never again be repeated.

"Marcos, what happened here and in the car was—"

"Only the beginning."

She started. The beginning of what? The end? She ground her molars, fighting for calm. "We were pretending."

"Aha."

"Yes," she said, vehemently. "We were."

"Right, Miss Hollis. Whatever you say."

"You asked me to pretend, that's what I'm here for. Isn't it?"

His silence was so prolonged she felt deafened. Was she here for another reason? A reason other than what he'd requested of her? An intimate, wicked, naughty reason?

She could tell by the set of his jaw that if he had a hidden agenda, he wouldn't be admitting to it now.

Walking off her conflicting emotions, she fixed her attention on the food. The scents of lemon, warm bread, cheeses and fruit teased her nostrils, but her stomach was too constricted for her to summon any appetite. Usually she'd be wolfing down the strawberries, but now she wiped her hands on her sides and put on her best secretarial face. "At what time should I wake up tomorrow?"

"We have a late lunch, no need to rise with the sun," he said.

She signaled to both ends of the room, needing

to get away from him, wishing she could get away from herself. "And my room?"

"Pick the one you like."

She felt his gaze on her, sensed it like a fiery lick across her skin.

She went over and peered into a room: a large, double-post bed, white and blue bedclothes. Very beautiful. She went to the other, feeling his eyes follow. The lamplight cast his face in beautiful mellow light. He looked like an angel that had just escaped from hell, like an angel she wanted to sin with.

"I guess either will do," she admitted.

She smiled briefly at him from the doorway, and although he returned the smile, both smiles seemed empty.

And in that instant Virginia was struck with two things at once: she had never wanted anything so much in her life as she wanted the man standing before her, and if his lips covered hers again, if his hands touched her, if his eyes continued to look at her, she would never own her heart again.

She said, "Good night." And didn't wait to hear his reply.

The room she chose was the one with coral-pink

bedding and an upholstered headboard. She didn't question that, for appearances, he would wish him and his "lover" to appear to share a room. But she quietly turned the lock behind her.

As she changed, she thought of what she had read about Marcos and Monterrey. She arranged the clothes in the large closet, each garment on a hanger, and eyed and touched the ones he'd bought her.

She slipped into her cotton nightgown, ignoring the prettier garments made of silk and satin and lace, and climbed into bed. Awareness of his proximity in the adjoining room caused goose-flesh along her arms. A fan hung suspended from the ceiling, twirling. The echo of his words feathered through her, melting her bones. *I'll pretend...you're her.*

She squeezed her eyes shut, her chest constricting. *It's not you, Virginia,* she firmly told herself.

She touched a finger against her sensitive lips and felt a lingering pleasure. And in her heart of hearts, she knew she was. She was her, the woman Marcos wanted. She'd dreamed of him in private, but dreams had been so harmless until they came within reach.

Marcos Allende.

Wanting him was the least safe, most staggering, worrying feeling she'd ever felt.

And one thing she knew for certain was that to her, Marcos Allende was even more dangerous than his beautiful, deadly city of Monterrey.

Sleep eluded him.

The clock read past 1:00 a.m. and Marcos had smashed his pillow into a beat-up ball. He'd kicked off the covers. He'd cursed and then he'd cursed himself some more for thinking one kiss would be enough to rid himself of his obsession of her.

Then there was Allende.

He had to plan, plot, leave no room for error. He had to stoke his hatred of Marissa, to be prepared to crush her once and for all.

But he could not think of anything. Memories of those kisses in the car assailed him. The fierce manner in which his mouth took hers and her greedy responses, the moans she let out when he'd touched her. How his tongue had taken hers, how she'd groaned those tormenting sounds.

He lay awake and glared at the ceiling, his mind counting the steps to her room. Twenty? Maybe fewer. Was she asleep? What did she wear to sleep? Was she remembering, too? Jesus, what a nightmare.

He shouldn't have asked her there.

He'd thought nothing of Allende, nothing of tomorrow, but had kept going over in his mind the ways she'd kissed him and the ways he still wanted to kiss her.

He sat up and critically surveyed the door of his room. He wanted her to give in. Wanted something of hers, a stolen moment, something she hadn't planned to give him, but couldn't help but relinquish. She was cautious by nature. She'd fear ruining everything, all she'd worked so hard for, all she'd tried to achieve. A steady job, security, respect. Could he guarantee this would remain solid when they were through? Could they even continue working together—flaring up like torches like this?

Their kiss had shot him up into outer space; obviously he still couldn't think right. In his drawstring pants, he climbed out of bed and slipped into his shirt.

He meant to review his numbers once again, ascertain that the amount he planned to offer for Allende was low, but fair enough to secure it.

Instead he ignored his files and found himself

standing outside his assistant's bedroom door, his hand on the doorknob, his heart beating a crazy jungle-cat rhythm.

He turned the knob, smiling at his certainty of her, her being always so…orderly, having locked it against him.

His heart stopped when he realized Virginia Hollis's door was unlocked. Now all that kept him from Virginia Hollis were his damned scruples.

Five

"Sleep well?"

"Of course. Wonderfully well. And you?"

"Perfectly."

That was the extent of their conversation the next morning over breakfast. Until Marcos began folding his copy of *El Norte*. "A favor from you, Miss Hollis?"

Virginia glanced up from her breakfast to stare into his handsome, clean-shaven face. *A kiss,* she thought with a tightness in her stomach. A touch. God, a second kiss to get rid of that haunting memory of the first.

With her thoughts presenting her the image of him—Marcos Allende—kissing her, she flushed so hard her skin felt on fire. She toyed with her French toast. "Nothing too drastic, I assume?" she said, some of the giddiness she felt creeping into her voice.

"Drastic?" he repeated, setting the morning paper aside.

She shrugged. "Oh, you know…murder. Blackmail. I don't think I could get away with those."

Eyes glinting with amusement, he shook his head, and his smile was gone. His elbows came to rest on the table as he leaned forward. "What kind of boss do you take me for?"

One I want, she thought. *One who kissed me.*

Those broad, rippling muscles under his shirt could belong to a warrior.

God just didn't make men like these anymore.

She'd lied. She hadn't slept one wink.

If she'd been camping out in the dark, naked, within ten feet of a hungry lion, maybe she'd have been able to sleep. But no. She had been within a few feet of her dream man, and her lips had still tingled from his kiss, and her body seemed to scream for all the years she hadn't paid attention to letting someone love it.

After lying on the bed for what felt like hours,

for some strange reason she had bolted to her feet and rummaged through the stuff he'd bought... and slipped into something sexy. A sleek white silk gown that hugged her like skin. Heart vaulting in excitement, she'd unlocked the door. Returned to bed. And waited. Eyeing the door.

The knob had begun turning. Her eyes widened, and her pulse went out of orbit. She waited minutes, minutes, for the door to open, and yet the knob returned to place again. Nothing happened. He changed his mind? Her heart sped, and then she flung off the covers and stepped out of bed.

The living room was empty—silver in the moonlight. And then, torn between some unnamable need and the need for self-preservation, she'd quietly gone back to bed.

Now, looking like a well-rested, sexy billionaire, he asked what kind of boss she took him for.

"One who's never bitten me," she blurted, then wished to kick herself for the way that came out sounding. Like an invitation. Like...more. Damn him.

He chuckled instantly, and Virginia pushed to her feet when she totally lost her appetite.

He followed her up, uncurling slowly like he always did.

"I like the dress," he said, studying the fabric as it molded around her curves. It was a very nice dress. Green, to match her eyes, and one from a designer to please His Majesty.

"Thank you, I like it, too."

His gaze raked her so intimately she felt stripped to her skin. There was a silence. Her heart pounded once. Twice. Three times. Virginia couldn't take a fourth.

"Name your favor," she offered.

Eyes locked with hers with unsettling intensity, he wound around the table, and his scent enveloped her—not of cologne and definitely not sweet—but so intoxicating she wanted to inhale until her lungs burst inside her chest.

Gently, he seized her chin between his thumb and forefinger, tipping his face back to hers. An unnamable darkness eclipsed his eyes, and an unprecedented huskiness crept into his voice. "Just say, 'Yes, Marcos.'"

Her breath caught. His voice was so ridiculously sexy in the morning. Virginia pulled free of his touch and laughed. "You," she accused, tingles dancing across her skin. "I don't even know what I'm agreeing to."

His arms went around her, slow as a boa constrictor, securing her like giant manacles. "Can't you guess?"

Something exploded inside her body, and it wasn't fear.

Lust. Desire. Everything she didn't want to feel.

His breath was hot and fragrant on her face, eliciting a little moan she couldn't contain. Oh, God. He felt so hard all over, so unlike any other man she'd known.

His voice was gentle as he tipped her chin up. "Yes to my bed for a week, Virginia. Say yes."

Was he insane? "Wow," she said, almost choking on her shock. "I've never had such a blatant come-on."

The determination on his face was anything but apologetic. "I don't want to play games with you." He studied her forehead, her nose, her jaw. "I intend to please you. I've thought of nothing else. Tell me," he urged, caressing her face as he would a porcelain sculpture. "Are you interested?"

Interested? She was on fire, she was frightened,

confused and scared, and she hated thinking, realizing that she was no match for him.

She should've known that if Marcos ever made
a move for her, he'd come on like he always
did—strong, like a stampeding bull charging to
get his way. Her breasts rose and fell against his
chest as she labored to breathe. Her legs were so
weak they couldn't support her, and she remained
standing only by her deathly grip on his arms.
"One week?"

"Seven days. Seven nights. Of pleasure beyond
your imagining."

"A-and what if I can't give you this pleasure
you want?"

"I will take any pleasure you can give me,
Virginia. And you will take mine."

There was no mistaking. His deep, sexy voice
was the most erotic thing she'd ever heard. "A-and
if I say I'm not interested?"

He chuckled softly—the sound throaty, arrogant, male—melting her defenses. "If that is what
you wish." His gaze pierced her, as though searching for secrets, fears. "You haven't wondered
about us?" He lowered his head and skimmed
her lips lightly, enough to tease and make her
shiver when he retracted. "You unlocked your

door last night, and I was so close to opening it, you have no idea."

"Oh, God," she breathed.

His lips grazed hers from end to end. "You wanted me there, you wanted me in your room, your bed."

"I—I can't do this."

His hands lowered to the small of her back and pressed her to his warm, solid length. "You can. Your body speaks to me. It feels soft against mine, it molds to me. Say it in words."

There was no escaping his powerful stare, no escape from what raged inside her. "I can't, Marcos."

Growling, he jerked free and for a blinding second she thought he was going to charge out of the room, he seemed so frustrated. Instead he carried himself—six feet three inches of testosterone and lust and anger—to the window and leaned on the frame. "The first moment I set eyes on you, you planted yourself in my mind. I'm going insane because once, Virginia, once I was sure you were crazy about me. So crazy. You can't help the way you look at me, *amor*. Perhaps others don't notice, but I do. Why do you fight me?"

Her eyes flicked up to his and she was certain her anxiety reached out to him like something tangible. His muscles went taut. "Do I get an answer?" he demanded.

She smiled, shaking her head in disbelief. "You're proposing we mix business and pleasure."

He wanted her desperately, she realized. Like she'd never been wanted before. And she might enjoy allowing herself to be wanted like this.

So, with a pang of anticipation in her left breast, she said, "I'll think about it over lunch."

The floral arrangement in the lobby had been replaced with one chock-full of red gerberas and bright orange tiger lilies bursting amidst green. They navigated around it, Marcos's hand on her back.

"If you want everyone to know you're nervous, by all means, keep fidgeting."

"Fidgeting? Who's fidgeting?"

He grabbed her trembling hand and linked his fingers through hers, his smile more like a grin. "Now no one. Smile, hmm? Pretend you like me."

Her pulse skyrocketed at the feel of his palm against hers, but she did not reject the touch and held on. *This should be easy. Easy,* she told herself. One look at her and everyone would think she was in love with him.

Impulsively she breathed him in, feeling oddly safe and protected. They'd had a wonderful morning, talking of everything and nothing as he accompanied her to the shopping mall across the street. The morning had flown by in casual conversation, which had been a good thing particularly when the night had seemed endless to her.

Now they entered the restaurant. Past the arched foyer entrance stood the most beautiful woman Virginia had ever seen. Tall and toned, blonde and beautiful. Her lips were red, her nails were red. She was clad in a short leather jacket teamed with a white miniskirt and a pair of heels Virginia was certain only an acrobat could walk on. Her face lit up like a sunbeam when she saw Marcos, and then it eclipsed when she saw Virginia.

She swept to her feet and came to them, her walk as graceful as the swaying of a willow tree. All other female eyes in the restaurant landed on Marcos.

"You're bigger." Her eyes became shielded,

wary when they moved to her. "And you're…not alone."

In one clean sweep, Marissa took in the entire length of Virginia's knee-length emerald-green designer dress.

Marcos drew her up closer to him and brought those inscrutable eyes of his down on Virginia, his gaze sharpening possessively. "Virginia Hollis, Marissa Galvez."

He gave Virginia such a male, proprietary look she felt stirrings in all manner of places in her body. Nervous, she offered the woman a nod and a smile. Marissa's hand was slim and ringed everywhere. They shook hands and took their seats.

The awkwardness had a strange beat—slower somehow, and heavy like lead.

Over the sunlit table, Virginia tentatively slid her hand into Marcos's, sensed him smile to himself, then felt him give her a squeeze of gratitude which Marissa might have taken as affection. A silence settled. Every minute was a little more agonizing. Marcos's thumb began to stroke the back of hers, causing pinpricks of awareness to trail up her arm. Sensations of wanting tumbled, one after the other. What would it be like if this were real? Sitting here, with such a man, and knowing the name of the shampoo he showered with and the cologne he wore?

Marissa's blue eyes shone with a tumult of emotions. "Why didn't you come to him? He begged you to."

Virginia's spine stiffened. Whoa. That had been quite a hostile opening line. But then what did she know?

Marcos answered coolly, reclining easily in his upholstered chair. "I did come."

"A day too late."

The corners of his lips kicked up, but the smile was hard somehow, and it didn't reach his eyes. The air was so tense and dense it was scarcely breathable. "Perhaps if he'd really sent for me, I'd have come sooner—but we both know it wasn't him who summoned me."

Surprise flickered across the blonde's face. "Why would he not call his son on his deathbed?"

"Because he's an Allende."

She made a noncommittal sound, rings flashing as she reclined her chin on her right hand. Her eyes dropped to Virginia and Marcos's locked hands over the table, and finally the woman shrugged. "He died with his pride—but I could see him watching the door every day. He wanted to see you. Every time I came in he…" She faltered, pain flashing across her face as she lowered her arm. "He looked away."

Marcos was idly playing with Virginia's fingers. Did he realize? It seemed to distract him. Comfort him, maybe. "He didn't want to see you, Marissa?"

Her eyes became glimmering blue slits. "He wasn't himself those last days." She smiled tightly. *"No se que le paso, estaba muy raro."*

Even as Marcos replied in that calm, controlled voice, Virginia sensed his will there, incontestable, allowing for nothing. "You ruin your life for a woman—I suppose you're bound to have regrets. And to be acting strange," he added, as though referencing the words she's said in Spanish.

A waiter dressed in black and white took their orders. Virginia ordered what Marcos was having, wishing she could try everything on the menu at least once but embarrassed to show herself as a glutton. When the waiter moved on, Marissa's eyes wandered over her. She tapped one long red fingernail to the corners of her red lips.

"You don't look like Marcos's type at all," she commented matter-of-factly.

Virginia half turned to him for a hint of how to answer, and he lifted her hand to graze her knuckles with his lips, saying in a playful murmur that only she seemed to hear, "Aren't you glad to hear that, *amor?*"

She shivered in primal, feminine response to the smooth touch of his lips, and impulsively stroked her fingers down his face. "You didn't see your father before he died?" she asked quietly.

His eyes darkened with emotion. "No," he said, and this time when he kissed the back of her hand, he did so lingeringly, holding her gaze. Her temperature jacked up; how did he do this to her?

The moment when he spread her hand open so her palm cupped his jaw, it felt like it was just them. Nobody else in the restaurant, the hotel, the world.

"You'd never abandon your father," he murmured as he held her gaze trapped, pressing her palm against his face. "I admire that."

Her chest moved as if pulled by an invisible string toward him. Had she ever received a more flattering compliment? His pain streaked through her as though she'd adopted it as hers, and she ached to make him feel better, to take the darkness away from his eyes, to kiss him… kiss him all over.

She stroked his rough jaw with her fingers instead, unable to stop herself. "Perhaps he knew you loved him, and he understood you kept to your pride, like he did," she suggested.

"Marcos? Love? He wouldn't know love if it trampled him," Marissa scoffed and frowned at Marcos, then sobered up when he swiveled around to send her a chilling look. "It's my fault anyway. That you left. I've paid dearly for my mistake, I guarantee it," she added.

He didn't reply. His gaze had dropped to where his thumb stroked the back of Virginia's hand again, distracting her from the conversation that ensued. He seemed to prefer that touch above anything else. He kept stroking, caressing, moving her hand places. He put it, with his, over his thigh, or tucked it under his arm. Longing speared through her every single time he moved it according to his will. He genuinely seemed to… want it. Was he pretending? When his eyes came to hers, there was such warmth and heat there.… Was he pretending that, too?

Marissa mentioned Allende, and Marcos, prepared for the discussion, immediately answered.

His voice stroked down Virginia's spine every time he spoke. Her reaction was the same: a shudder, a quiver, a pang. And she didn't want it to be. She didn't want to have a reaction, she shouldn't.

While the waiter set down their meals, she thought of her father, of how many times he'd disappointed and angered her, and she thought of how hurt she'd have to be in order not to see him again. Sometimes she'd wanted to leave, to pretend he didn't exist to her, and those times, she would feel like the worst sort of daughter for entertaining those thoughts.

Marcos wasn't a heartless man. He stuck by his brother no matter what he did. *My brother is a person, Allende is not,* he'd told her. But his father had been a person, too. What had he done to Marcos to warrant such anger?

She had her answer fifteen minutes later, after she'd eaten the most spicy chile relleno on the continent and swallowed five full glasses of water to prove it. She excused herself to the *baño* and was about to return to the table when she heard Marissa's plea from the nearby table filter into the narrow corridor. "Marcos…if you'd only give me a chance…"

"I'm here to discuss Allende. Not your romps in my father's bed."

"Marcos, I was young, and he was so...so powerful, so interested in me in a way you never were. You were never asking me to marry you, never!"

He didn't answer that. Virginia hadn't realized she stood frozen until a waiter came to ask if she was all right. She nodded, but couldn't make her legs start for the table yet. Her chest hurt so acutely she thought someone had just pulled out her lungs. Marissa Galvez and Marcos. So it was because of a woman, because of her, that Marcos had never spoken again to his father?

"You never once told me if you cared for me, while he...he cared. He wanted me more than anything." Marissa trailed off as if she'd noticed Marcos wasn't interested in her conversation. "So who is this woman? She's a little simple for you—no?"

He laughed, genuinely laughed. "Virginia? Simple?"

Virginia heard her answering whisper, too low to discern, and then she heard his, also too low, and something horrible went through her, blinding her eyes, sinking its claws into her. She remembered how difficult it was as a little girl to cope with the whispers.

The father is always gambling...they say he's crazy...

Now they talked about her. Not about her father. About her. She didn't hear what he said, or what she said, only felt the pain and humiliation slicing through her. Her father had put her in this position once more. No. She'd put herself in it. Pretending to be lovers with a man she truly, desperately wanted…and then looking the fool in front of someone she was sure had really been his lover.

Jealousy swelled and rose in her. She had no right to feel it, had never been promised anything, and yet she did feel it. Their kiss yesterday had been glorified in her mind and she'd begun to wishfully think Marcos had wanted to be with her this week. Silly. She'd even told herself she might like sharing his bed for a week.

She felt winded and strangely stiff when she reached the table. She sat quietly. She focused on dessert, tried to taste and enjoy, and yet her anger mounted, as if she really were his lover, as if she had anything to claim of him.

When he reached for her hand, it took all her

effort, it took her every memory of having gone to beg him for help that evening, not to pull it away.

If she weren't sitting she'd be kicking herself for being so easy. She sucked in air then held it as he guided that hand to his mouth and grazed her knuckles with his lips.

Her racing heart begged for more, but Marcos's kiss was less obvious than last night, more like a whisper on her skin. Every grazing kiss he gave each knuckle felt like a stroke in her core.

A slap in the face.

They say her father's crazy...

By all means, Virginia would pull her hand away in a few seconds. She just wanted...more. More hot breath and warm lips on the back of her hand. More fire between her legs. A place so hot and moist it could only be cooled by—

Something moved.

His phone.

His lips paused on her for a breathless second before he set her hand back on her lap and whispered, "It's the office. I have to get this."

Virginia made a strangled sound which was supposed to be an agreement and clearly sounded more like a dying woman. She watched his dark silhouette move between the tables and disappear down the hall so quickly. She already missed him. She scanned her surroundings. Everybody was eating, carrying on conversations. The world hadn't stopped like she'd thought because of those tiny kisses on her knuckles.

She sank back in her seat, agitated when Marissa watched her. She brought her hand to her mouth, the one he'd kissed, and closed her eyes as she grazed her lips in the exact same places his lips had touched.

Eyes popping open to meet the other woman's canny gaze, she straightened, readjusted the hem of her knee-length dress, and mentally cursed this pretense from here to Alaska and then to Mars. Was he seducing her? Or was this all for Marissa's sake?

"So," Marissa said. "You love him."

Virginia was about to jump in denial, frantic to save herself from this accusation, which of course implied that she was stupid, needed therapy and more, and then she realized he was counting on her to pretend that she did.

Love him.

"I..." Her lips couldn't form the words *I love him*. Her tongue seemed to freeze. Seemed to want to say only one thing, and that was *I hate him.*

She hated him and this stupid plan and how he touched her and how well he pretended to want her.

So instead she nodded, and let Marissa think what she would.

His powerful scent reached her long before he sat down beside her again. Virginia stared straight ahead like a horse with blinders. And just to prevent any more stoking of the staggering anger building inside her, she tucked her hands under her thighs. There. See if the man could touch her knuckles now.

She remained quiet the rest of the meal.

She heard Marissa invite them to a party the next day while she considered Marcos's offer.

She told herself she didn't care to know what kind of offer he'd made.

Six

Something had changed.

Virginia had changed. She was different, and yet, it was all the same with him. The twisting sensation in his gut, the demented beat of his heart, the itch in his hands, the coiling want in his body.

Alert, clever, perceptive and spirited…now his assistant seemed to be struggling to comprehend what she'd witnessed as they reached their rooms.

They'd had such an enjoyable time this morning, he'd been certain he knew where they were heading tonight.

He wasn't sure anymore.

He wasn't sure of anything—very unlike an Allende.

He took her to the middle of the living room and just stood there, his jacket in one hand, looking at her. His every muscle felt stiff and pained, his hard-on merciless, and when he moved the slightest bit, arousal lanced through him. He set his jacket aside and felt as if the air was being squeezed out of his lungs. She was disappointed he'd been such a bad son to his father? He'd lost her admiration? Her respect?

His insides twisted at the thought. He stepped forward, toward her, his thoughts congested, tangled like vines. The heat of her angry breaths made his insides strain in his want to drink it, feel it, appease it. It sent him teetering into an aroused state he couldn't fathom, much less understand. Eyeing her in silence, he tugged at his tie, stripping it from his neck, breathing harshly.

"I'd say that went well."

She tilted her head, her eyes fierce, something there marking him as loathsome. "She didn't believe us for a moment, that we…" She turned away as if disgusted. "She didn't buy it."

He narrowed his eyes—watching the tantalizing

rise and fall of her chest. How would they feel to the touch? Soft. Yes, God, soft and small. Perky? Yes, that, too. His mouth watered. "Whether she believes it or not is of no consequence now."

Her eyes flashed a glittery warning. "You wanted to make her jealous."

"Jealous," he repeated, puzzled by the accusation. "Is that what you believe?"

She shoved her hair back from her forehead. "Yes, it is. And I'm sorry I disappointed, Marcos."

His blood raged hot and wild. He'd never seen her like this. Almost out of control, begging for… something he wanted to give her. Suddenly he'd give anything to hear her utter his name in that same haughty, do-me tone. He'd do anything to just…bury this ache inside her.

"I look at her and feel nothing—not even anger anymore. I didn't want her jealousy, but I didn't want her insinuating herself into my bed either."

"Because you want her there. Otherwise you wouldn't need me standing between you!"

He grabbed her arms and jerked hard, spurred by every ounce of pent-up desire in him, harbored for too long. "Listen to you!" She slammed against him with a gasp. Her eyes flamed in indignation and his body roared to life, singed by her lushness, her mouth so close. "There's only one woman I want in my bed—one. And I've wanted her for a long, long time."

"Then go get her!"

He backed her toward the bedroom. "Oh, I will—and I'll have her right where I want her." He dragged her closer and pulled her dress beneath her breasts and her scent, sweet and warm, washed through his senses. He seized a nipple with two fingers and pushed her breast up to his mouth and sucked.

He paused briefly to say, "The thought of you has me tied into knots. I want to taste you. For you to give me your lips, feel my body in yours. I want you coming with my name on your lips, coming over and over, with me."

She caught his head and moaned. He could see the needs, the emotions, rising in her and darkening her eyes to storms. His hands caught her wrists and pinned them over her head and tightened. "Share my bed."

"Marcos…"

A throbbing sensation pulsed through him, aching in his erection, his chest, his head. His voice grew hard, fierce as his cheek pressed against hers and he murmured in her ear. "I won't beg, not even for you, I won't ask again, Virginia. I have a craving for you…it's running wild and out of control. You share this craving. You crave me, you crave me so much you tremble with the force of it. Don't deny us. Don't deny me."

His breathing was ragged, hers wild. The gleam of defiance died out in her eyes as she gazed at his lips. He groaned and pulled her head to his as he swept down. His kiss was bred by passion, rampant with lust. The raging desire threatened to consume his mind, his sanity. He was undone by her kiss, her taste. His mind raced, his thirst for her sweeping through him. Her response was wholehearted, fiery, and it almost sent him to his knees. Her mouth sipped, her hands took what he wanted to give her. He called upon restraint but there was only passion here. Over and over he thought of being gentle, over and over her answer was to intensify, demand more.

He grabbed her and thrust her onto the bed, bouncing, and he was ripping at his shirt.

She climbed to her knees, her hands on her dress, fumbling to unbutton.

He whipped his shirt off, meeting her glimmering green gaze, stripping naked. "Do you want me?"

"Yes."

He unbuckled his belt and sent it slapping to the floor. "Lie back."

His heart thundered as he waited for her to, aware of the erection straining before her, listening to her sharp inhale. She backed away, her dress riding up to show her blue panties. And she was... There were no words. That lacy blue stuff looked delicious on her.... He wanted to use his lips to pry it off, his teeth... No, he couldn't wait; he needed to feel her skin.

He fell on her and trapped her under him, yanking her arms up, his pelvis arching into her. "You'll take what I can give you, all of it, *amor*."

"Yes."

She struggled against him, but he tamed her with his mouth, pinning her with his weight, stretching out naked on top of her. He grabbed her hair and held her still, and it felt like silk between his fingers. "I'm going to love doing this with you."

She sighed and rubbed against him like a cat. "I'll pretend to like it."

Her voice was husky, full of longing, inviting him to do things to her. He cupped the full globes of her lace-covered breasts, dragging his teeth across that delectable spot of skin, licking the curve between her neck and shoulder. "Oh, you will. I'll make sure you do." Her nipple puckered, and he pinched to draw it out even more. "This little nipple pretends very well."

She lay back, all skin and hair and woman, drawing him to her warmth. Her arms were around him, her hands on his back, kneading the bunched-up muscles. He shuddered. He could lose himself in those eyes, in that body, in her, and he demanded, "Say 'Marcos.' Whisper my name to me."

"Marcos."

She wasn't sure from what part of her had come this determination, this courage or this desperate want, she only knew she needed him. He annihilated her mind, her senses. She hadn't realized what she'd do, how she'd fight to be with this one man until she'd seen Marissa.

She hadn't yet finished saying his name, a word that echoed the passion roaring through her, and he was there already, growling "Virginia" and taking her mouth in a fierce kiss. A flock of butterflies exploded in her stomach when their lips met. Her head swam as the flames spread, his tongue thrusting precisely, strongly, fiercely inside, emotion hissing through her, weakening her, overwhelming her.

Growling, he deepened the kiss as he tugged the bow loose at her hip, and she felt the fabric of her dress unfurl until it opened and hung at her sides. "It's important your body becomes familiar with my touch. All of it. You want Marissa to believe us, don't you? If you want others to believe it you have to believe it yourself. Your body has to know to respond when I touch it."

A strangled sound echoed in the silence and in the back of her mind Virginia realized it came from her. He cupped one lace-encased breast. Oh, it was so wonderful. So bad. So everything. She'd stop him in a minute…in one more minute…no, she'd not stop him, not tonight, maybe not ever.

Utterly possessing her lips, he slid his free palm down the flatness of her stomach and below. "It's important I know your curves…the texture of your skin…"

She could feel every sinew of his muscles against her. His fingers…sliding downward. Deep, forgotten places inside her clenched in waiting for his touch. Opening her mouth, she flicked her tongue out to his. "Marcos."

"Here you are. Soaked."

His voice grew husky. Desire trembled there. His hand between her legs began to slide under her panties. She arched involuntarily when he feathered a finger across the soft, damp spot at the juncture of her thighs. Every pink, throbbing part of her pinged at his touch. She moaned in her throat and sank back deeper into the bed as he caressed more deliberately.

She'd never known a touch could feel like fire, spread through her until every inch throbbed and burned. Involuntarily she moved her hips, filling his palm with the dewy softness between her legs.

"Marcos…" It was a plea, and it carried in it the fright she experienced in what he made her feel.

"Shh." His lips grazed her temple. "Open up to me." His free hand tugged at her bra and bared her left breast to him. Her disbelieving gaze captured the instant the rosy peak of her nipple disappeared between his lips. A thrilling jolt rushed through her as the moist heat of his mouth enveloped her. Her head fell back on a moan.

Instinctively she reached up to cup the back of his head, cradling him with the same gentle care he used to suckle her breast. He groaned profoundly in his throat and continued to fondle her with his mouth, lips nipping, tongue swirling, mouth suckling.

His hand moved lightly, expertly, his fingers unerringly fondling her through her panties. Hot little shivers rushed through her.

One long finger began to stroke her dampness. Open her with little prods of the tip.

She squirmed in shock, a little in agony, seeking ease for the burn growing inside her. "I hurt." Blindly, her parted mouth sought more of the warmth of his lips. He penetrated her. With his tongue. His finger. She arched and cried out, shocked by the sensation. An explosion of colors erupted behind her eyelids. His mouth melded to hers harder. Skin, heat, ecstasy.

Her skin felt damp while every cell in her body felt hot and tingly. With a low growl, he delved a hand into her hair and pulled her head back, moving his mouth up her neck. It was damp and velvety on her flesh, licking as though her skin were his only sustenance. In her ear he rasped, "I'm filling you."

"Yes." Against his throat.

"You crave me to fill you." His finger was thrusting, possessing—his body incredibly hard against hers. "You need me to take away the hurt."

Pleasure ripped through her, and her back arched helplessly as she moaned. "You make me reckless, Marcos, you make me…"

"Burn." He opened his mouth. Giving her the mist of his breath. "I can't believe how ready you are. How slick. Are you pretending? Are you, *amor?*"

"No."

He gave her his tongue. She could hear the soaked sounds his touch caused and felt embarrassed and aroused all at once. "Shh. Take my finger," he huskily murmured, the graze of that finger so bare and fleeting across her entry she mewled with a protest to take it in again. "Soon I'll give you two. Do you want two?"

"No," she lied. Her body ruled now, screamed, shivered against his.

"Hmm." He inserted the first, then the second deeply. "I'll pretend that was a yes."

Her thoughts scattered. "Marcos, please…"

"My God, you're responsive." His hands continued to work their magic as he looked down on her. "You were jealous for me."

The burn intensified. The clench in her womb unbearable. "Yes," she breathed, closing her eyes.

His groan sounded like a growl. "I like that."

"Marcos."

He was watching her, the effects of what he did to her. Every time she gasped, or let go a little moan, his face tightened with emotion—and alternately, something clenched tightly in her. She'd never known the extent of her passion, was surprised at how shamelessly she took pleasure from him.

Gently, he pried her fingers away from his neck and brought her hand between their bodies. "Touch me."

"Where? Where do I…"

"Here." He shifted over her. The sheets slid well below his hips and their every inch, shoulder to hips, became perfectly aligned. The very hardest part of him pushed against her hand. "Feel me," he strained out. "Feel how I want you. This isn't for her, Virginia, this is for you."

He ground his hips against hers unapologetically. When she let go, his rigid length grazed her moistness through her panties. They groaned at the contact. He pressed closer, ground himself harder, wide and long against her. She wanted to die.

By the erratic heaves of his chest, Virginia suspected even though he was larger and more powerful, he was as defenseless to their chemistry as she was. Under her fingers, his skin was warm and slightly damp. Shyly, she continued to explore him, sifting her fingers through the dark hair at his nape, amazed at the soft texture.

His hands covered her breasts. The calluses on his palms were palpable through the lace, and her breast swelled ripely under his kneading.

Turning her cheek into the pillow, she let her eyes drift shut as she fought the intimacy of it all, the swelling tenderness that washed over her as he touched her. It was difficult to imagine that he was not her lover and she wasn't entirely, completely, indisputably his.

Burying his face between her breasts, he gnawed at the tiny bow at the center of her bra. She felt the unmistakable graze of his teeth on her skin. He used them to scrape the top swell of her breast and a very startling whimper escaped her.

His mouth shifted to the peak, pointy and obvious under the fabric, and he licked her. The hot dampness of his tongue seeped into her skin. She shuddered. A thrilling heat fanned out from her center.

He reached around her and unhooked her bra. When he peeled it off her, she instinctively covered herself with her palms.

"I want to see." He pried her hands away and placed them on his shoulders. His dark, heavy-lidded eyes regarded each of her breasts with interest. His breath fanned across one exposed nipple. "So pretty."

She drew in a ragged breath as he brushed the little bud with the pad of his thumb. It puckered under his finger. If possible, his eyes darkened even more. "Do you want my mouth here?"

"I d-don't know."

He swiped his tongue across the tip. "Yes, you do." He closed his eyes and nuzzled her with his nose. "Do you want my mouth here?"

"Yes."

He licked gently. "Like that."

"Yes."

He grazed with his teeth. "Or like that."

She squeezed his shoulders, staring to shiver. "B-both."

He nibbled using his lips then drew her fully into his mouth. "Hmm. Like a raspberry."

Her eyes shut tight. The sensation of being devoured entirely by his mouth had her melting.

Could he say something wrong, please? Could he not lick her...like that? Could his hands be smaller, less thorough, less hot, less knowing?

Turning to suckle her other breast, he delved one hand between her legs and slipped into her panties. "I want my mouth here, too," he murmured, searching her pliant folds with strong, deft fingers.

She gasped and thrashed her head, seized by a mix of shame and pleasure as he unerringly found, opened, invaded that most intimate part of her. "N-no...no mouth there."

"But I can touch?"

Quivering and warm, she sensed him watching her as he gently eased one finger into that moist, swollen place that craved him.

She gulped back an enormous clog of emotion. "Yes."

"Chiquita." It was a reverent whisper, full of wonder as he stretched her. *"Chiquita mia."*

She arched, shamelessly offering herself. As

he continued his foray inside her, a marvelous pressure gathered at her core.

His nostrils flared. "One minute," he rasped as he searched under her dress for the silken string of her panties. She was weightless on the bed when he tugged them off her legs. "And I put us both out of our misery."

His chest gleamed bare when he leaned over her, his shoulders bunched with tension as he grasped her calves. He stared into her eyes, his expression tight as he guided her legs around his hips. "Hold on to me. Don't let me go."

The way he asked to be held made her think she'd never let him go, she'd make him love her, she'd hold on to him.

He pulled her to his hips and she felt him, hot and thick and rigid, pressing into where she was pliant and damp. A wildness raged inside her when he ducked his head to suckle a breast— suckle hard the instant he pushed in. She bucked up to receive him, urging him in with her hands and legs.

They moaned in unison when he entered, their breaths mingling as he angled his head to hers, their lips so close that all he had to do was bend his head an inch to capture her mouth and the whimper that followed when he was fully inside her.

"Yes," he growled.

"Yes," she breathed.

A fullness took her, bringing the discomfort of being stretched more than she could bear, and then he was moving inside her and the unease transformed to pleasure. Waves and waves of pleasure.

And in that instant she loved what he did to her, how he brought her every cell and atom to life, how he offered her ease. Ease for this wanting.

She'd longed for that ease more than anything.

As he moved in her, touched and kissed her, she gave encouraging sounds that seemed to tear out from within her—and he continued. Taking. Giving. Expertly loving her.

Braced up above her, his arms rippled with tension, his throat strained, his face was raw with the semblance of pleasure. All were memorized in her mind.

Vaguely, in her blanked, blissful state, she knew sex would never again be like this. Would a man ever live up to this one?

A sound that was purely male vibrated against

her ear as he placed his mouth there to whisper, "Come for me."

Moving deftly, he pushed her higher and higher, murmuring carnal, unintelligible words in Spanish that melted her bones like the silk and steel thrusts of his body. *Mia. Suave. Hermosa. Mia. Mia. Mia.*

All Virginia could say was "Marcos." In a plea, a murmur, a moan. *Marcos.* Over and over again. *Marcos* as he increased his pace, driving faster, more desperately into her. Vaguely she felt the warmth of him spill inside her, the convulsions that racked his powerful body as ecstasy tore through them both, the pleasure consuming, making him yell, making her scream, scream "Marcos."

"Marcos" as he kissed her breasts, her lips, her neck. "Marcos" as the pressure spread. "Marcos" as she shattered.

Seven

Darkness: it was hard to leave it. But a strong, familiar scent wafted into her nostrils. Tempting. Tantalizing. Beckoning her awake. Coffee. Yes. Strong and rich and ready. Virginia stirred on the bed. She stretched her arms first, then her legs, sighing when it hurt pleasantly to do both.

"...in an hour...yes...we'll be there..."

Virginia bolted upright on the bed when she recognized that particularly deep baritone voice. Her head swam. *Lips tugging at her nipples, fingers pinching, touching, pleasuring...whispers...* A throb started between her legs. She squeezed her eyes shut and swung her feet until her toes touched the carpeted floor. *Calm down.* She would not, could not, panic.

Sunlight glowed in the living room, making her squint as she entered. He stood by the window in his shirt and slacks. His raven-black hair looked damp from a recent bath. He held one arm stretched above his head, his tan hand braced on the windowsill. His was a solid presence in the room. Sturdy as an ox, that was the way he looked. That was the way he was.

"Good morning," she muttered.

He turned, smiled.

She set her coffee on a small round table beside the desk and lowered herself to a chair, Marcos coming forward and kissing her forehead.

"Did you order the entire kitchen contents up here?" she whispered.

He stroked her cheek. "I wanted to be sure I ordered what you liked."

A blush was spreading up her neck because she remembered cuddling against him after she'd gone on and on saying *please.* God, no.

His eyes were full of knowledge, of satisfaction of having loved his lover well and hard for a night. Her skin pebbled with goose bumps as she realized he was remembering everything they'd done through the night: the kissing, the laughing, the kissing, the eating cheese and grapes on the carpet, the kissing.

They had made love until Virginia thought she'd pass out from bliss.

And hours before waking up, when she had cuddled in and draped one leg across his hips, he had made slow, lazy love to her again, and whispered words to her in Spanish she could only dream of finding the meaning of.

He lifted her chin, studying her. "Did I hurt you last night?"

With a small smile, she tugged on the collar of her pajama top and showed him his bite. His forehead furrowed.

"That has to be painful."

"Only in the most pleasurable way."

Settling down, she took a healthy sip of coffee, then set the cup back down. "What?" she pressed.

He was looking at her strangely.

"What?"

"You begged me to take you last night."

"And?"

"And I liked it."

Her stomach muscles contracted. Suddenly her

lips felt puffy and sensitive as she remembered just how thoroughly he'd kissed her. "Marcos, this will be very complicated in Chicago."

"It doesn't have to be."

A thousand butterflies fluttered in her chest. "You expect we can keep this up?"

"We touched. We made love four times in one night. Do you expect we can stop by Monday?"

They'd touched. His tanned, long hands had been somewhere in her body, and hers had been somewhere in his. She couldn't bear to remember. "What do you…suggest?"

"Nobody has to know about us. And my suggestion is to continue."

Her body trembled. Little places zinged and pinged as though reminding her just, exactly, where his hands had been. "Continue."

He leaned against the window and his hand slowly fisted high up on the windowsill. "I swear I've never seen anything lovelier than you, naked. Your breasts."

She closed her eyes, sucking in a breath, willing herself not to remember what he'd done there. How he'd squeezed or cradled or…

"Marcos…"

"You cried out my name when I was inside you."

Oh, God. Yes, she had, yes, she had. Had she no honor? No pride when it came to him? No digni—

"I couldn't sleep for wanting to take you again." He smiled sadly. "You kept cuddling against me and I kept growing hard. I had to…shower."

Wrapping her arms around her shaking frame, she asked, "Do you want to?"

"To what?"

"Make love to me again."

And he said…

"Yes."

Her stomach exploded. He wanted her. Still. More than yesterday? Marcos still wanted her. But they couldn't continue in Chicago. They couldn't.

His arm fell at his side as he spun around and pinned her with a smile. "Eat up, though. We're going sightseeing."

She set down her coffee mug before she spilled it all over herself. "Really?"

"Of course. Really. We're flying over the city on a chopper first. Then we'll lunch downtown."

"A chopper."

"Are you concerned?"

"Actually, no. Excited."

She dug into the eggs, the waffles and the tea.

Marcos was piling his plate as though he hadn't been fed since his toddler years. "Would you like a tour of Allende," he asked casually.

Allende. She grinned. "I thought you'd never ask."

It occurred to her she had never imagined she could ever have one of these mornings with Marcos. Such a lavish, elegant hotel suite and such a clear, sunny day outside, a beautiful morning. Like husband and wife. Talking. Smiling. Laughing as they enjoyed breakfast. But they were boss and assistant, embarking on what had to be wrong. The air around them was charged with sexual tension. Really, it could very well be lightning in there.

"Did she…agree to your bid?" Virginia asked, breaking the silence. This watching him eat was a little too stimulating to her mind.

He popped a grape into his mouth. "She will."

"She didn't seem interested in even discussing business."

"It's a game." His eyes skewered her to her seat. "She wants me to demand Allende and I won't."

"So you'll play this for the entire week."

"Not likely." He spread cream cheese atop his bagel. "I'll leave with an offer and let her think it over."

Were he any other man, Virginia was sure a woman like Marissa could handle him. But he was Marcos. Nobody could think straight with him near and he was as manageable as a wild stallion to a child. "If she rejects your offer?"

He diverted his attention from his tower of gluttony and selected a newspaper among the three folded ones, calmly saying, "She's not getting a better one, trust me."

He yanked open *El Norte*. "What angered you? Yesterday?"

The cup paused halfway to her lips then clattered back down on the plate. "I heard you… discussing me. I've always found that annoying."

Slowly he folded the paper and set it aside. The intense stare he leveled on her made her squirm. Those gypsy eyes, they did magic in her. Black magic.

"You're blushing."

"I'm not."

But her face felt hot and so did other parts of her.

His jaw tightened and a muscle in his cheek flexed. "Is it the attention? You do not like this?"

She drew in a deep breath because unfortunately there was no brown bag she could cover her face with. She had to pretend he was hallucinating. "It's the whispering behind my back."

"You cannot control what people whisper." He popped a piece of his bagel into his mouth and then picked up the paper again.

"You are wrong." How could he think that? "You can control your actions. You can give them no cause to…to whisper."

"You'd let gossip hurt you, Virginia?"

His voice was full of such tenderness she actually felt it like a stroke. "You've never been hurt by words before?"

Once again, the paper was lowered. This time his eyes burned holes through her. "I said words to my father. I'll bet my fortune that yes, they hurt."

Something distressed her. His gaze. His tone. "You wish you took them back?"

He considered with a frown. "No. I wish he'd

have taken them for what they were. The words of a wounded boy determined to break him."

She had never known Marcos to be cruel. But he could be dangerous. He was predator, and he had been wounded. "You could never make amends with him?"

His smile was pantherlike, almost carrying a hiss. "Because of her."

"Marcos," she said again after a moment, even more alarmed at the harsh set of his jaw and ominous slant of his eyebrows. "Marcos, why do you want to destroy the company? You could make amends with it. Save it, mend it."

"It would take too much effort." He waved her off with a hand, went back to the paper. "Eat up, *amor,* I'm eager to show you the city."

"You're eager to get back and have your way with me," she quipped.

He threw his head back and gave out a bark of laughter, his expression so beautiful her heart soared in her chest. "So we understand each other, then."

He couldn't tear his eyes away from her.

She was the same woman he'd wanted for so long, and yet she had become someone else. A sexy woman who was comfortable in his presence, smiling, laughing, open to speaking her mind.

Eyes sparkling as the helicopter touched the ground, Virginia pulled his headphones down to his neck. "That's Allende?" she yelled through the rotor noise.

He glanced out the window, squeezing her fingers with his. Impossible, but her excitement was rubbing off on him. "That's it, yes."

Once they climbed out of the helicopter, Marcos surveyed the vast industrial building that sat on two hundred acres of land. It was smaller than he remembered it—but then he'd been so much younger.

The sun blazed atop their heads. Virginia's raven mane gleamed. And in that moment Marcos didn't see how aged the building appeared, or notice the grease on all the trucks and carriers that were parked in endless rows across the parking lot. He saw his father and himself, discussing the delivery schedule. A strange heaviness settled in his chest, weighing him down.

"Are we going in?"

Pulled from his thoughts, he looked at his assistant. How she managed to stand there—sexy and innocent—while he felt so unsettled was beyond him.

Bracing himself for whatever greeted him inside, he led her toward the double glass doors beneath a metal sign that read *Transportes Allende*.

Within minutes the two guards unlocked the door and ushered them in. Marcos and Virginia were free to roam the old wide halls. An attractive blush tinted her cheeks as she eagerly drank in her surroundings.

There was nothing to say about the structure, except that it was bare bones, obsolete and old. *Horrible*.

New installations were a must. A more recent fleet of carriers to strengthen their position as a link to the U.S. market. New—

"This is terribly spacious," she said, leaning a hand on a red brick wall that served as a room division.

Marcos reined himself back. What in *the hell* had he been thinking?

He didn't want to restore the company to its former glory; he wanted it gone.

He frowned darkly while Virginia swayed her hips and went peeking from room to room. All were vacated for the morning under Marcos's instructions. An encounter with Marissa was the last thing he'd wanted today—and thankfully she was smart enough to have obliged.

Virginia tucked her hair behind her ear, her forehead creasing as she peered up at the rafters on the ceiling.

Rather than notice the paint was peeling off the walls and making a list of fixing that—Miss Hollis was probably already cataloguing that for him, in any case—Marcos focused on her reactions.

Something warm and fuzzy stirred in him. Virginia would be a pitiful poker player. Her expressions were too untrained for intrigue—and her father's past had given her a loathing for the game.

"My first office," he said then, without tone.

She spun around in the doorway as he spoke, wide-eyed. "This one? With the view of the front gate?"

He followed her into the small space and tried to see it through her eyes, old and dirty and cluttered, but then it just appeared like what it was: a promising place in need of some attention.

Marcos could've kicked himself for mentally volunteering to give it some TLC. No. Hell, no.

He wouldn't.

All he wanted was to eliminate it, like wiping out his past in one fell swoop. Swoosh. Gone. Presto!

But judging by the interest that swam in Virginia's eyes, she approved of the place, too. "It fits you somehow," she said. "Rough around the edges."

They shared a smile.

The fuzzy feeling inside him grew to incredible proportions.

"How many transport units does it have?" she asked. "Approximately?"

He watched her sail to the window. His eyes tracked her progress for a moment and then he followed her.

She was peering through the blinds, scanning the vast loading area, when he came up behind her.

He buried his face in the side of her neck and enveloped her in his arms, biting back a groan. "There are two thousand and forty cargo car-riers—plus hundreds of smaller units for simpler deliveries."

She smelled of a soft, powdery fragrance, her hair scented with his travel shampoo. The combination flew up to his head like an aphrodisiac.

He'd never imagined the days they spent together would be like this. Lust and desire constantly had him on edge, true, but there was also the delightful peace and pleasure of her company.

Gently, he guided her around to face him. "As soon as we land in Chicago, I will have the funds transferred to your personal account. I want those men out of your and your father's lives so you can be at peace. Agreed?"

A shadow descended, veiling her eyes. Inch by inch, her smile disappeared.

He cupped her face between his palms. "Something wrong with that?"

Clearly something was. She averted her gaze and gnawed on her lower lip. "Thank you, no, it's all fine. That's our arrangement, right?"

Pretend, she didn't say. But his mind supplied it.

When Marcos did not deny this, Virginia lowered her face and drew away, suddenly looking very young and very vulnerable. She hugged herself tight. "I'd forgotten I'm being paid for this, that my father's bad habits brought me here."

Marcos knew that a woman like her didn't easily fall into a man's bed. Was she regretting that she had? Or only the circumstances that had brought her there?

A host of male instincts assailed him, urging him to embrace her, take her, appease her, seize the instinctive role of a man and protect her.

With a surge of dominant power, he grasped her shoulders and gave a gentle clench. "You're worried he won't stop gambling—that this will only be a temporary relief from your problem."

She nodded. "I am."

Virginia had been calling her father every day. His insides wrenched in protest at the knowledge of her suffering because of a reckless old man on a suicide mission. "How long since your father had a real job?" They strolled back into the hall, side by side.

"Since Mother died. Several years ago."

They came into the last office—his father's old office. Virginia probably didn't know it had been his because of its ample size, or maybe she suspected, Marcos didn't know. All he knew was that he couldn't bear to look around but at the same time couldn't leave it.

He crossed the wood floor, now covered with

a shaggy white rug, and touched the window as he gazed outside. "He's been like this ever since? Your father?"

"It's gotten out of control recently."

Circling around the desk, he stroked the blunt edge with his fingers—he used to sit there and listen to his father talk on the phone. Thoughtfully, he asked, "Has he tried to even get a job?"

"He did. He's tried, but of course he's found nothing. At least that's what he says, but I suspect his pride won't let him accept the kinds of jobs that have been offered to him."

He frowned. "Sometimes you have to take what you can get."

"I agree." She toed the plush ends of the rug with the tip of her high heels. "I just feel he was hoping for someone to give him a chance at what he used to do. He was a good manager except he spoiled his chance."

Second chances, Marcos thought. People spoke of them all the time, but in reality nobody offered them.

His father hadn't offered it to him.

Nor had he offered one to his father.

Gradually, he allowed his surroundings to filter

into his mind. A snapshot of Marissa beside the dormant computer. Frilly female things atop the desk. And he realized with a sinking heart that Marissa had taken possession of his father's office.

There was no picture of the old man who'd raised him. The soccer posters—vintage ones that his old man had collected—were no longer on the walls. She'd taken everything, that heartless witch. *Everything!*

"This is your father's office?" Virginia watched him, and the pity in her eyes made him desperate to eliminate it.

"Not anymore." He smiled tightly, snatching up her hand. "Come on, let's go. The office staff is coming in later."

He escorted her outside. Thinking of how it was too late for his father and him—but maybe not for hers. Marcos's old man had not been a gambler, but his quest for a woman had trampled his own son.

It seemed unfair a child should sacrifice their happiness for a parent. Marcos had not been willing.

He'd *never* accept as a stepmother a woman who'd months before been his lover, *never* accept as a stepmother a woman who was so obviously playing his father for a fool. After numerous heated arguments where Carlos Allende refused to admit his son's view as true, Marcos had packed his bags and left. But Virginia?

When her father fell into that dark gambling pit once more, what was this generous, loyal creature going to do? And what would he be willing to do to help her?

She loved Mexico.

There was something deliciously decadent about the time they spent during the following days poking around little shops, eating in restaurants, walking the city.

This afternoon, as Virginia's heels hit the marbled floors of the awe-inspiring MARCO museum, she drew in a deep, reverent breath. This was a luxury she'd never allowed herself before. She'd rarely allowed herself outings to relax or to stimulate the mind; she'd always been so consumed by worry.

Now she wove through the paintings on exhibit, feeling Marcos's presence next to her, and felt like she'd stepped into an alternate reality.

Every painting that caught her eye, every

sculpture she viewed with the eyes of a woman who had suddenly acquired sight. And hearing. And touch. The colors were vibrant, and the themes were all passionate. Even death seemed passionate.

At night, Marcos took her out to eat in a small café just blocks away from the city plaza. After salad, tacos and fries, they walked arm-in-arm through the throng of people.

She'd never felt so safe.

She was in a dangerous city, surrounded by a language she did not understand and among unique, intriguing people, and she felt utterly safe. Her world felt so distant. Her father's debts, the threats, the fact that things could get worse. Nothing mattered when these long, sinewy, rock-hard arms were around her.

She felt, for the first time in her life, protected. *Secure.*

During their ride back to the hotel, she caught Marcos watching her with those eyes and that knowing smile, and a sneaky little voice whispered to her. It accompanied them to their rooms, nestling somewhere deep inside her.

This is as real as real gets, Virginia Hollis. Can you make him see it?

No, she doubted that she could. He viewed the world with the eyes of a man. While she, with those of a woman.

As she struggled to tame her welling emotions, Marcos grasped her chin between his thumb and forefinger and tipped her head back. "Who does he gamble with? Do you know?"

It took a moment for her to grasp his train of thought. She shook her head. "I don't know."

Marcos hadn't dropped the subject of her father for days. It was as though he were intent on avoiding the topic of his own parent and was focusing instead on fixing the troubles of hers.

Shrugging off his shirt, his eyes held hers in the lamplight, his voice a mellow rumble. "You said his gambling put you in this position. In that bed right behind you. My bed. Did you mean it?"

She considered the question at length, and though she'd needed to save her father no matter what, she also softly admitted, as she pulled off her short-sleeved sweater, "I think I brought myself here."

She tossed her sweater aside, then her bra. Even in the flickering shadows, she caught the tightening flex of his jaw and throat. That her nakedness affected him made her smile and move close to him. Her palms hit the smooth velvet of his chest and her fingers rubbed upward. "What do you say about that, Mr. Allende?" she whispered.

With slow deliberation, he turned his head toward hers. As his fingers ventured in a languorous caress up her back, his mouth grazed her cheek and his sweet, hot breath coasted across her skin. "I say you're the sexiest little thing I've ever seen. Miss Hollis. And I want you to promise me—whatever happens between us, you're coming to me if your father's ever again in trouble."

"No, Marcos."

"Yes. You are. I'd make you give me your word you'll not pay debts that aren't yours, but I know that'd be unfair to ask of you. You feel responsible for him, I respect that. Now please understand I feel responsible for you."

Her toes curled at the proprietary gleam in his eyes. "But you're not."

"You're my employee."

"You have thousands of employees."

His knuckles caressed her nipples, and her body flared to life at the touch. "But only one who's been my lover."

The words lingered in the air for a heated

moment. She was ready to give up. Just wanted to kiss. Could almost hear the seconds ticking as their time together ran out.

"No contest?" he queried then, sensing his victory.

She yielded, shaking her head, wrapping her arms around him. "None."

By the time their lips touched, she was holding her breath, parting her lips for his smiling mouth to take. He seized them softly and began to entice and torment her with nips and nibbles and gentle little suckles she felt down to the soles of her feet.

When he lowered her to the bed, his mouth became more demanding, spreading fire through her veins. And as his tongue forayed hard and hot inside her, one hand traveled up her ribcage to knead one waiting, throbbing breast with long, skillful fingers. *"Chiquita."*

He scraped his whiskers across her chin, and she sighed.

She was his lover for a week.

She was nothing more and she would never be more.

Braced up on one arm, he used his free hand to unbuckle her slacks. He pulled the zipper low and pulled them off her. His thumb touched the elastic of her panties and made slow, sinuous circles before he eased it down.

Lover for a week. That's all.

Discarding her panties, he urged her down on the bed and rained haphazard, unexpected kisses across her torso. On her shoulder, her tummy, then feasted on the tip of one breast. Virginia dropped her hand and absently caressed the back of his satiny black head as it moved, imagining what it would be like to suckle a baby. Their baby.

She'd always wanted a family.

Virginia, lover for a week!

As he kissed a path down her belly, it struck her with a sweet wrenching pain that she had never sensed her dream of a family so far out of reach. At first the desire had been tucked aside to help her father resurface from his grief. Now it had come to the forefront of her mind and it mocked her.

Because she had become lover to this man.

This enthralling black-haired Spaniard.

And every man in her future would always be compared in her mind to Marcos Allende. Every bed she slept in would not be this one. And she dreaded, doubted there would be a man in this world to kiss her the way he did. Touch her like this, just like *this*.

Realizing his mouth was approaching somewhere dangerous, she squirmed under him. "If you knew what I was thinking," she spoke up at the ceiling, "you'd leave the room."

He lifted his head and met her gaze, his voice frighteningly solemn. "Don't give me your heart, Virginia."

Oh, God. She squeezed her eyes shut. *Don't fall in love with him, don't fall in love with him,* don't fall in love with him. She scoffed, yanked her arm free as she sat up. "What? You think you're all that and then some? That I cannot resist you? I'll have you know…my heart…was not part of our bargain. You're the boss and I'm the…employee and this is…an arrangement."

One callused palm ran up and down the side of her leg. "And yet it's easy to forget who we are here, isn't it? Easy to get confused."

She frowned over the concern in his voice and grabbed his head, defiantly pulling his lips to hers.

Lovers. That was all.

This is as real as real gets, Virginia Hollis. Can you make him see it?

* * *

They came to understand each other. Too well, maybe. They talked, but not of the future. They talked, but not of themselves.

They pretended, as they'd agreed to do.

"Did you enjoy yourself this week?"

Riding to the airport in the back of the Mercedes, Virginia sat curled up against Marcos's side and laid her cheek on his shoulder. It was strange—how instinctively she sought this place, and how instinctively Marcos wrapped his arm around her shoulder to offer it to her.

She didn't care if she shouldn't do this, only knew within hours she wouldn't dare. So she did it now.

"It's been wonderful," she admitted and trailed off when he brushed his mouth across her temple and placed a soft, almost imperceptible kiss there. "Unexpected and...surreal and wonderful."

He held her so tight, so intimately, and whispered against her hair, "We should've done this before."

Going pensive at the note of lingering lust in his voice, Virginia played with the buttons on his shirt while Marcos checked his phone and made a call to the office. As he spoke into the receiver, she stole a glance at him.

His voice rumbled in her ear, and his arm around her was absently moving up and down her bare arm. She'd been unable to keep from staring at him all week, and had been secretly delighted that most times he'd been checking up on her, too.

When he hung up, he gazed out the window at the passing car lights and said, "You'll wire yourself the money from my account and take care of your problem straight away. Promptly, tomorrow morning."

A command. As an authoritative man and, also, her boss.

"Understand?"

She hadn't noticed she'd flattened her hand on his chest until his own big one came to cover hers. She watched their fingers entwine. Lovers' fingers.

God, she'd done the most reckless thing. Look at her—draped all over her boss. Imagine if this ever got out? If people knew? Worse of all, her tummy was in a twist because she loathed for it to stop. And it had to—tonight. "Yes, I'll take care of it right away," she murmured, and on impulse took a good long whiff of his familiar scent.

"I've been thinking." Marcos turned her hand around for his inspection and his thumb began to slowly circle the center of her palm. "I'd like to offer your father a job."

"A job?"

"I figure if he realized he could be useful, he'd break the cycle of vice he seems to be stuck in."

She thought about it, still resting her cheek against his chest, feeling utterly contented and yet dreading tomorrow when that feeling could be replaced with unease. "Why?" she asked then.

He quirked an eyebrow, then narrowed his eyes. "Why what?"

She fingered the heavy cross at his throat. "Why…him?"

"Why not?"

She shrugged, but her heart began to flutter at the prospect. "Maybe he's just hopeless." As hopeless as she was. How would she bear Monday at the office? She was terribly in lust with the man. He was an extraordinary lover, made her feel so sexy and wild she wanted to take all kinds of risks with him, and now he offered her father this incredible lifeline?

"Maybe he is hopeless," Marcos agreed, chuckling.

But no, he was not hopeless, no one was. A smile appeared on her face. "Or maybe he will want one more chance." And maybe she could handle Monday after all.

She'd survived so far, had feigned not to want Marcos for days and weeks and months. Now she'd act as though nothing had happened. As though when he looked at her, her insides didn't leap with joy, and when he smiled at her, her stomach didn't quiver.

He smiled at her then, causing all kinds of happenings in her body, and stroked her cheek with his warm hand. "I've looked into him. He was a smart, dedicated man, and he could be one again."

Virginia contemplated his words, pleased that Marcos was smart enough to look past her father's mistakes and see the hardworking man underneath. And a plan formed in her mind. Her father had managed a large chain store so successfully that, if everything hadn't gone downhill after her mother's death, he'd be CEO by now.

"You know, Marcos," she said quietly, straightening on a burst of inspiration, "I think he might enjoy coming to Mexico."

Silence fell. The car swerved to the left and into the small airport driveway. Virginia remembered the look of grim solemnity in Marcos's face during their tour of Allende and she plunged on.

"He might even enjoy working at Allende," she said. She tossed the bait lightly, hoping to plant some kernel of doubt in him so he'd reconsider his decision regarding the company's future. But he went so still, she almost regretted it.

He stared at her with a calculating expression, then gazed out at the waiting jet. "Maybe."

Neither said another word, but when he pulled her close, ducked his head and kissed her, she fought not to feel a painful pang.

This was where they'd first kissed.

It only made sense it would be where they had their last.

<u>Eight</u>

She was tidying up his office the next morning when Marcos halted at the doorway. The sight of Virginia fiddling with the coffeemaker froze him, then heated up his blood.

As she poured a cup—black, as he liked it—the plain buttoned-up shirt she wore stretched across her breasts in a way that made watching feel like purgatory.

"Good morning."

She glanced up with a soft gasp. "Marcos— Mr. Allende." And there went her breasts again, swelling, pert and lovely as she took a little breath.

His heart thudded as they stared at each other, the words lingering in the air. *Mr. Allende.*

A word meant to erase everything that had happened in Monterrey, Mexico.

Having never expected she would make it this easy, he stepped inside and pulled the doors shut behind him. "Good morning, Miss Hollis."

He really could do this.

They'd pretended to be lovers before.

Now they would pretend they never had been.

Black coffee mug cradled against her chest, Virginia stared at him with the glazed wariness of a woman who feared that a man knew her secrets. "Can I get you anything, Mr. Allende?"

You.

He bit off the word, pulled off his jacket and tossed it onto the L-shaped sofa before he started for his desk. His head buzzed with thoughts of her. Her, smiling up at him from her place on his lap. She had an obsession with tidiness, and it showed. His office was pristine. She was a tidy little box, his Miss Hollis. Who would've known she'd be such a wanton in bed? So uninhibited? So sexy? So addictive?

"I hear you arrived home safely," he said, his

groin stirring at the memory of their lovemaking. *Dammit, don't go there, man.*

"Yes, thank you." She flashed him one of those smiles that made his thoughts scramble. "And I caught up on my sleep a little."

"Excellent. Excellent."

His body clenched at her admission, for *he* hadn't had a wink of sleep since their return. He kept remembering her, innocent, cuddled up against him.

Diablos, he had never imagined he'd once again look at Monterrey with longing. Now he did.

He longed to be there with his assistant for another week where he knew exactly what to do with her.

Lips thinning in disgust at his own erotic thoughts, he took the coffee cup from her hands when she passed it to him and dismissed her with a wave. No use in delaying their parting. "That will be all. Thank you, Miss Hollis."

And with a painful wrench of mental muscle, he tore his eyes away and pushed her from his mind.

He had a business to take over.

Chicago felt different. The wind was the same, the noise, the traffic, and yet, it felt so different.

She'd had to face Marcos at the office again today. Yesterday, their nonchalance toward each other had been so borderline pathetic she'd felt nauseated by the time she got home.

This morning, unable to stomach coffee, she made her way down the hall. The door to the extra bedroom where her father had been sleeping for the past couple of months was shut, and Virginia pressed her palm against it for a long moment, wondering if she should wake him. Let him know she was leaving for work. That everything had been taken care of and his debt absolved.

She decided she would call later instead and carried her small black duffel bag outside where the taxi waited, remembering Marcos's offer to give her father a job.

It had been easy then, to accept anything he'd wanted to give her. They'd been…involved. Now, Marcos Allende could calmly forget about it, as he'd forgotten the rest.

Worst of all was it hurt.

Even when she'd expected it.

As she stepped onto the amazingly busy Fintech nineteenth floor, Virginia hoped every employee would be in their usual flurries of movement and therefore too busy to notice she was fifteen minutes late.

But notice her they did.

The very moment her heels hit the carpet, a quiet spread throughout.

For the second day in a row, people glanced up from the copy machines. Behind their desks, heads lifted. The fact that everyone, everyone in the vast open space, knew and had probably discussed the fact that she had spent a week with Marcos in Monterrey became brutally evident. Deep inside, where all her fears were kept in a tight little bundle, she heard something.

They say she's his lover...

Had someone spoken that? Was she putting words and thoughts into their mouths because of her own regrets?

Dragging in a calming breath, she crossed the sea of cubicles, then went down the art-packed hallway. At the far end, to the right of the massive carved doors that led to Marcos's office, three identical rosewood desks stood. She slid in behind hers. The savvy Mrs. Fuller, who'd been with Marcos "longer than his mother has," was quick to make her way around her own tidy work place and greet Virginia. "He's very strange today," the older woman said, wide-eyed. "He smiled at me and he said 'thank you.'"

The words didn't diminish the kernel of fear settled in the pit of Virginia's stomach. If she so much as stepped out of her boundaries this week and onward…if she was fool enough to even remind him of Mexico…she dared not think of who would be sitting behind her desk next week.

"Then the deal must be going in his favor." Virginia attempted a teasing smile as she turned to get settled.

Lindsay, a young redhead near Virginia's age who'd also become her friend, drew up next to Mrs. Fuller. Their expressions were those of genuine excitement. "How was Mexico?" the older woman asked as Virginia sank into her chair and gazed at the top of her desk. A picture of her mother. A fake orchid. Her yellow markers sticking out of a silver can.

"Was it hot? I hear it's sweltering this time of year," Mrs. Fuller insisted. Virginia hadn't seen the woman yesterday since they'd reached Fintech later than normal.

"Yes," Virginia said, having no other answer

to give a woman who was known through the entire building as levelheaded and kind.

As Mrs. Fuller's concerned gray eyes bored into the top of Virginia's head, she wished she could have been spared this encounter with even more fervor than she'd wished to avoid her last one with the dentist.

"He's been gazing out the window all morning, and with so much to do, that is so unlike him," Lindsay confessed under her cinnamon-scented breath. "And he asked me where you were."

Virginia was spared having to reply when the phones began their usual music. Struck as though by lightning, both Lindsay and Mrs. Fuller were spurred to action. They jumped behind their desks and began tackling the calls.

Ignoring the telephone ringing equally obnoxiously on her desk, Virginia tucked the duffel into the nook under the computer. She would not, could not, think of his mood meaning anything. Their deal would be over soon, after the Fintech dinner, and they would forget Mexico. He had promised it would not affect her job.

Inspecting her drawers and taking out her personal notepad and the colored clips she'd bought in a burst of secretarial enthusiasm, Virginia felt her throat close at the sudden memory of her mother. That hopeful light always in her eyes. Her warm, caring smile. She had always had a saying to cheer Virginia up. Would she have one for Virginia today? One about there always being something better out there? Better than Marcos?

"Miss Hollis, I hear you were out with the boss?"

She started in surprise. Fredrick Mendez, one of the youngest accountants, had propped his hip onto the corner of her desk and was eyeing her with a combination of amusement and mock despair.

"For a week," she stressed as she straightened in her chair.

"That's too much, Miss Hollis. Too much time without you. So, did you bring me a key chain?"

"Did you ask for one?"

"All right, at least show us some pictures," Fredrick insisted. But when Virginia's usual friendly smile just would not come, he fell to his knees and clutched a hand to his chest. "Oh, Virginia, thy eyes shalt truth reveal—"

"Am I running a circus here, Mendez?"

The deep, clear voice, but most of all, the distinguished accent, struck Virginia like a cannon blast.

Her eyes flew to locate the source. Inches away, exiting the conference room and on his way to her, Marcos Allende was a sight to behold. Power and sophistication oozed from his every pore. His stride was slow and confident, his expression perfectly composed. And his every step kicked up her heartbeat. Six of his top lawyers followed.

Upon realizing who'd spoken, Fredrick's pale complexion turned in the space of a second to a tomato-red. He jumped to his feet and smoothed a hand along his polka-dot tie. "No, sir. I was just welcoming Virginia back on our behalf."

"Our?" He said the word as though Fredrick had no right to include himself in something he hadn't been invited to.

Turning to where Virginia sat with perfect poise behind the desk, Marcos thrust his hands into his pockets and silently contemplated her. "Don't you have work to do other than hound Miss Hollis," he said softly, and there was no doubt whom he addressed.

Fredrick took off with a mumbled "Yes, sir."

Without removing his eyes from her, he also

said, "Brief me on the new stipulations when they're in."

In unison, the lawyers expressed their agreement and dispersed.

Without the buffer of their presence, there was nothing to pry those jealous black eyes from hers, no shield from the scorching possessiveness flickering in their depths.

Suddenly breathless, Virginia wondered if the blouse she wore today might be too white, or a little sheer? If her skirt was too short, her hair too unruly, the silver hoop earrings inappropriate for Fintech?

Meanwhile Marcos was the epitome of the worldly businessman.

He filled his black Armani like it had been tailor-made for those broad, square shoulders, which tapered down to his lean waist and narrow hips.

God! She could not believe the dark, breathtaking creature before her was her lover from Mexico.

Suddenly, as their gazes held, their eyes screaming with something dark and sinful, Virginia was certain the entire room thought she had slept with him. *They say she's his lover...*

Please, God, let no one ever know.

"Marcos," she said, moderating her tone. "I'm sorry I'm late, but I—"

Hands planted on the desk, Marcos stretched his arms out and in a single fluid move leaned forward. As his face neared her, Virginia saw Mrs. Fuller's eyes turn to saucers, and Lindsay almost fell back in her chair.

When the tip of his nose almost touched hers, she could focus on nothing else but six feet three inches of Marcos Allende. He ducked his head.

"Do you remember our deal?"

The murmur couldn't have been heard by anyone else. But she felt as if the clock, the world, stopped.

The feel of his breath on her face sent a torrent of warmth through her singing veins. "Yes, of course, I remember."

He leaned back a bit, regarding her as though he expected the same illumination he seemed to have experienced to have struck her, too. "After-work hours were included, weren't they?"

She couldn't explain the thrill she experienced, this inspiring and overwhelming happiness. He was asking for more, more from her, and not until this moment when she had his full attention had she realized how thirsty she'd been for it. "They were. Why do you ask? Is it that you need some assistance?"

His smile, slow in reaching completion, was meltingly sexy. "I do."

They say she's his lover...

She was plunging into a bottomless pit where surely there was nothing but heartache, and still, her blood was thrilling in her veins. "I'm always happy to be of assistance."

He gazed directly at her—the intent in his eyes unmistakable. "Be certain you present yourself at my apartment this evening. There's much to do."

She flushed beet-red, and scribbled in a yellow Post-it, *Is this what I think it is?*

He read it and tucked the note into his jacket, not before stroking her thumb with his, and sent her a look of such emotion and longing she almost wept. "Six p.m. sharp, Miss Hollis. I'm afraid it's an all-nighter."

He'd already started for his office when she blurted, "I can handle all-nighters."

"Good. This one's particularly hard."

When the doors closed shut behind him, whispers erupted, and Mrs. Fuller jumped to her feet and raced toward her in a flurry of mortification.

"Virginia. Please don't tell me this is what I think it is."

Heart pumping irregularly, Virginia grabbed her notepad. "I'd better go. The sales projections start in a few minutes and Marcos will want my notes." Oh, God, they had seen and heard all that, hadn't they?

Virginia, like putty in his hands. Marcos, suggesting she go to his place to…to…behave wickedly.

But the woman caught her by the shoulders and clenched tight with her fists, her face stricken. "Oh, sweetie, please say it isn't so!"

"Mrs. Fuller," Virginia said in a placating voice, patting one of her hands for good measure. "I don't know what you mean, but there is nothing going on here, *nothing!*"

"Yes, there is. I've seen the way you look at him. You're a sweet young girl, an innocent little lamb, and Marcos is…a wolf! He's emotionally detached and you can't possibly—"

Virginia turned her head to hide her blush only to catch half the office staring at them. But Lindsay was smiling in glee behind her desk and sticking her thumbs up as though Virginia had just won the lottery.

Lowering her voice to a whisper, Virginia confessed, "I can handle wolves. I can handle a pack of them, I promise you. And this is nothing like what you think."

"Vee. Sweet, sweet Vee." Mrs. Fuller's hands trembled when she framed her cheeks between them. "I adore Marcos like a son. He has been a kind boss to me, and when my poor Herbert died…" She sighed, then shook her perfectly coiffed head and got back on track. "But he is not the kind of man a woman like you needs. There hasn't been a single woman in his history he's kept around for more than a month. You'll end up with a broken heart and even lose your job."

That her last comment struck a nerve was a given.

"I'm not losing my job for anything." Virginia forced a smile to her face and much needed courage into her heart. She wanted him. She wanted him so bad she had to have him, would seduce and remind him. "He's my boss, and he wants me to assist him, and so I will. Please don't worry, Mrs. Fuller, or your heartburn will act up. I'll be fine. And be sure everyone, *everyone* knows there's nothing going on here."

But even as she stepped into the projection room, she couldn't help wondering how well they'd be able to hide it for as long as it lasted.

And what would happen to her when it was really, truly finished.

Nine

After the longest work day of his entire life, and one during which he'd gotten exasperatingly little work done, Marcos arrived home to find her waiting in his living room.

Of course. His assistants had his key code—why shouldn't she be here?

With the sun setting behind her, her feet tucked under her body on the couch, and a book spread open on her lap, Virginia Hollis was a welcoming sight.

When he stepped out of the elevator that opened into the penthouse, she came to her feet, her hands going to her hair—to her rich, curly black hair, which was deliciously tousled as though she'd been running her fingers through it all day.

He fisted his hands at his sides, his mouth going dry. Good God. She wore drawstring pants and a button-up shirt with little ice cream cones. The colorful, almost childish pattern was also stamped all across the pajama pants. And on her, that weathered, warm-looking thing was the sexiest garment he'd ever had the pleasure of gazing upon.

He hadn't intended to sleep with her. Or had he? He'd wanted to see her, damn it. And now he could hardly believe what she was so obviously offering to him.

When he finally spoke, his voice came out rougher than he'd anticipated. "Have a good day?"

She set her book on the side table. Nodded. Then, "You?"

God, this was so domestic he should be climbing back into the elevator right about now. And getting away from there as fast as he could.

Why didn't he?

Because his hands itched to touch her. His guts felt tight and he was hot and hard with wanting her. He'd wanted to drag her into his office today, feel his way up her little skirt, kiss that mouth until her lips were bright red. He couldn't stay away, had now determined he was a fool to.

She wanted him, too.

Removing his jacket, he draped it across the back of a chair, nodding, as well.

"I brought my notes," she said quickly. "Just in case."

He gazed into eyes that were green and bottomless, and slowly advanced. "Good. Notes are important," he offered in return, and because he had missed the enticing, arousing sight of her all day, he gruffly added, "What else did you bring me, Miss Hollis?"

The soft smile that appeared on her lips trembled. Her hands smoothed her pajamas all along her hips and his eyes greedily swept up and down the length of her. "I like that…thing you're wearing." More than that, he was warming up to the idea of tearing it off her and licking her like vanilla ice cream.

"Thank you." She signaled at his throat. "I—I like your tie."

He wrenched it off, tossed it aside, then closed the space between them. "Come here," he said quietly, wrapping an arm around her waist and drawing her flat against his body. "Why are you so shy all of a sudden?"

She set her hands lightly on his shoulders, barely touching him. "I—I don't know. I shouldn't have slipped into my pajamas."

Lust whirled inside him. She had a way of staring at him with those big eyes, like he was something out of this world. And she felt soft and womanly against him, her scent teasing his lungs as he buried his face in her hair. "I've wanted this, Virginia. God, how I've wanted this."

As she tipped her head back to him, he covered her lips with his.

Employing every ounce of experience and coaxing power at his disposal, he began to feast on that little mouth, drink of her honey.

Hesitantly she dipped her tongue into his mouth and a pang of longing struck in his core at how sweet she tasted, how entirely she succumbed and fitted her body to his.

In his need, he didn't hear himself, the way his voice turned hoarse with longing as he spoke to her, cupping the back of her head gently. *"Delicioso...besame...dame tu boca..."*

She tasted of warmth and hunger, and responded

like a woman who'd thought of him all day—
wanted him all day.

Just as he had thought of ways of devouring
her, too.

The kiss went, in the space of three seconds,
from a hard quest to a need that left no room for
finesse. While he took thirsty sips of her mouth,
his hands went places, one to cup a plump but-
tock, the other to work on her shirt.

Her eager hands tugged his shirt out of the
waistband of his pants and slipped inside, making
him groan when her cool, dry palms caressed his
chest up and down.

He imagined lifting her, wrapping her legs
around him and taking her, and she jumped as
though she were thinking the same thing, kissing
him like no woman had ever kissed him before.
She curled one shapely leg around him, and his
hands went to his zipper.

"Damn." He halted, then set her slowly on her
feet. Restless, as he drew back, he rubbed the
straining muscles at the back of his neck.

They were breathing hard and loud.

Her hand flew up to cover her moist, glistening
lips. "I… I'm sorry. I didn't mean to bite you."

That little bite had made him want to bite

her back, in every place imaginable. Damn. He rubbed his face with both hands, his blood thrumming in his body. He'd undone three buttons of her pajama top, and the flesh of one breast threatened to pop out.

Marcos regarded the creamy flesh while an overwhelming urge to dip his fingers inside the cotton and weigh that globe in his hand made him curl his fingers into his palm.

"Marcos?"

He jerked his eyes away, stared at the top of her head. "I had a long day." *And I thought of nothing but this moment.*

He'd been out of his mind with jealousy at the sight of her flushed cheeks, that clown Mendez begging at her feet. How many men had stared at her, wanted her, like Marcos did?

Oblivious to the rampant storms of his thoughts, Virginia followed him down the hall and into the bedroom. He was a mass of craving and thirst and he'd never felt so perilously close to losing control before.

Crossing the length of the room, he braced a hand on the window and gazed out at the city. If she ever dared make a fool of him…if she ever dared so much as look at another man while she was with him…

"Marissa was after me for years."

A quiet settled, disturbed by the rustle of her clothes as she moved around. "I'm sorry."

Yes. Well.

So was he.

Such humiliation, the way she'd played him. "I didn't know my father wanted her," he said, unable to conceal the disgust in his voice, "until they were already…involved."

When he turned, she was standing by the bathroom door. She'd grabbed a brush and was pensively running it through her hair. The lights shone on the satin mass.

Entranced, Marcos watched the curls spring back into place after a pass, and he wanted to plunge his fingers through that hair and wrap it in his hands.

"Don't do that."

She stopped. It took him a moment to realize the hoarse, ragged plea had come from him. She lowered her arm.

"Do what?"

The cotton molded to her chest, rose and dipped in the most attractive places. Aware of how hard he was, how hot under his clothes, he feared his own instincts when she set the brush on the nightstand and directed her full attention on him.

"I'm not Marissa," she said, coming toward him.

He liked how candid she was. How she smiled with her eyes. How she walked. Talked. No, she was not Marissa.

Getting a grip of his thoughts, he shook his head. "I didn't say that." But it would be worse with her. If she ever hurt him. Deceived him. Betrayed him. He'd never trusted so fully, had never felt so many things at once.

"Marcos," she said softly. Her eyes were examining his stiff shoulders, the stony mask on his face, as she halted before him. He was shocked at the raw emotion shining in her eyes. Not only desire. But tenderness. Concern. Caring.

Caring that tugged at some little strings inside him.

Caring that begged him to care, too.

Damn.

She was his lover. He had a right to touch her, take her, come with the pleasure of being inside her. It was all this was. Lust.

Lust lust lust.

"Never—" He could hardly speak as he lifted a hand to her silky, raven hair. She gasped at the touch, went very still.

"—ever—" he said gruffly, and tangled his fingers, fisted that lovely hair in his hand, using his knuckles to push her head up to where his lips waited "—lie to me."

He took her gasp, rubbed her lips farther apart, and traced their seam with his tongue. They were flavored with toothpaste and mint, and they were wet and hot. "Never lie to me with this mouth."

He licked into her, and she moaned. "I love this tongue, never lie to me with this tongue."

She inhaled a ragged breath and his tongue followed its path inside her, searching deep. In one instant her hands curled wantonly around his wrists, went higher up his arms, opening around the width of his biceps. Her fingers bit into his shirt and skin.

It was instinct, need, something fierce he couldn't understand, that pressed him to slam her back against the wall, take her, make her his mistress. It was so consuming to him, this passion, he was afraid if he followed it, he would break her apart. Or maybe he would break apart, feeling this—for her. With her.

Was this what his father had felt for Marissa? Was this why he'd given everything for her, everything to her? Let her slowly finish him off… so long as she kept on kissing him, looking at him, touching him like this?

When a cell phone rang, he tore his mouth away and she fumbled in a purse she'd left by the nightstand to answer. "Yes?"

His hand flicked the buttons of his shirt as she walked away and softly spoke into the receiver.

His heart rammed into his ribs, his blood a thick, terse boil in his veins. He was losing his head—and he didn't like it. He considered retiring to his study to work, put distance between them. No. No. He wanted her. He walked forward, shrugging off his shirt.

"Yes…yes, I didn't want to wake you…and yes, I'll see you…um…I'm working late and I don't know how long I'll be—" Silence. A soft, very soft, "Good night."

She came back, smiled.

"You're spending the night," he said, rendering it a statement when in fact he wanted confirmation. She was seducing him—in her pajamas, brushing her hair, staring with those green, green eyes.

Gritting his teeth against the flaring lust, he readied himself briskly, his erection springing free.

He grabbed her hand and put it on himself. If that didn't tell her, show her, how far gone he was, then he didn't know anything anymore. Still, he recalled Monterrey, all those nights with her, the days, and gruffly spoke. "You're staying the night here—with me."

She nodded and met his gaze, her eyes bright and fiery. She stroked his chest with soft, fluttering hands, dragging her lips across his jaw, his chin. "I want you in me, Marcos."

A primal hunger had overtaken his mind, his senses, until he felt as instinctive as an animal. An animal tantalized by the nearness of his mate. "You came to seduce me, didn't you? You like being at my beck and call. You came to please me, service me."

Smiling, she stepped back, and her hands went to her shirt, and Marcos watched as she began to unbutton it farther. Her fingers pulled another button free, then the next, and his eyes flicked up to hers. "I'm crazy about you," he rasped.

Virginia didn't seem to hear the truth in his

words, the worry they carried. He felt out of control, and he didn't like it.

"C-can I try something with you?" she asked hesitantly, easing her top off her shoulders.

He nodded, mute with desire and anticipation.

"Would you stay still, please?" she asked.

"What are you going to do to me, Miss Hollis?" he asked in a guttural voice. He fisted his hands at his sides, watching her hands like a man about to die under them. He stood utterly still, admiring her flesh as she revealed it. His voice was barely audible, his eyes on the gentle curves of her breasts as she stepped out of her pants and at last stood as naked as he.

"Just don't move, okay?"

So he waited, his chest expanding on each breath. She trembled when she stepped closer. "Can I touch you?"

He swallowed thickly. "Please."

He sucked in a breath when she set her hand on his chest and began kissing his neck, his ear, his jaw. His breathing became a wild thing. He was motionless as her hands began to roam down his chest. She hesitated at his waist.

His jaw clamped, his nostril flared, when she wrapped her hand around him.

"Is this okay?"

Ecstasy surged through him in a tidal wave. His breath made a strange whistle. "Yes."

"Do you want—"

His head fell, forehead against hers. "Just keep touching me."

She eased her fingers between his parted thighs, to gently cup him in her palm. She began to rub.

He hurt under her stroking hand. His mind spun with images of her and him, losing themselves in his bed like he'd wanted to. His hands idle at his sides, he softly, so softly, said, "You're not pregnant, are you, *amor?*"

She tensed for a moment, and he frowned. He reached down and pried her hand away.

"Are you? We didn't use protection the first time, and I'd like to know if there were consequences."

Ignoring him, she took his shoulders in her little hands and urged him down on the mattress. "The only consequence is this, Marcos. Me. Wanting more."

He sat there, on his bed, like a man in hypnosis, and watched her straddle him.

They kissed.

Marcos was dying with pleasure, his body

rocking as he feasted from her lips, lips that were soft and warm against his, lips that were wide open for his tongue to search in deep, so deep. Her sex cradled his hardness, her legs twined around him as tight as her arms while he ran his hands up her sides, into her hair, groaning at the way she whimpered his name. Marcos. All he could say was, "Virginia." Oh, Virginia.

He pulled roughly at her hair.

"Why?" His voice was a cragged sound.

"I…I don't know what you're talking about."

"Why do you look at me like this? What are you playing at?"

Watching him through heavy, sooty lashes, she kissed his nipples, his abs. She was smiling—teasing him with her teeth. Her tongue. Driving him out of his mind. Out. Of. His. Mind. "Must it be a game for you to enjoy it, Mr. Allende?" she purred. "Must we play at another pretense for you to let me in?"

He snatched her hair to halt her wandering mouth, suddenly trembling with thirst for not only her body, but for something else. Something he'd always, always, seen and sensed and tried to grasp in her eyes. "Are you trying to drive me insane?" he demanded.

She pulled free and lovingly cupped his jaw, kissing him softly on the lips. "I'm trying to make you remember."

He framed her face, engulfing it between both hands, and before he took her lips in the hard, hot way his screaming soul demanded, growled, "I'm trying to *forget*."

Ten

"With luck, the negotiations will advance, then my lawyers will fly down to..." Marcos trailed off as Virginia strolled into his office the next morning, bringing those long legs with her, her raven curls bouncing with each tiny step her tapered, knee-length skirt allowed.

She stopped to check discreetly on the coffeemaker—directly in Marcos's line of vision. A bolt of lust arrowed to his groin. *Marcos, oh, please, more, more.*

Her gasps of last night echoed in his head.

This morning they'd gone at each other like—hell, like two wild animals—before they'd separately headed for the office. He'd asked her to buy something special to wear to the Fintech dinner, to splurge. She hadn't seemed to be impressed. He wanted to please her, to give her something, and yet the only thing Virginia Hollis seemed to want was him.

Damn, he was totally taken—in a way not even Marissa had taken him before. Virginia's moans, her body, writhing against his, with his. It maddened him. Heated him. Excited him. Appalled him.

Aware of the abrupt silence in the vast carpeted space, a quiet that magnified her noises as she innocently fiddled with spoons and cups, Marcos jerked his eyes back to the open proposal and tapped his Montblanc pen against the sales projection chart. He cleared his throat. "Where was I?"

"Allende. Marissa Galvez. Negotiations," Jack said, sprawling on a chair across from his desk.

"Of course." He dropped his pen and lounged back in his high-backed leather chair, stacking his hands behind his head. He met the Texan's electric-blue stare. "As soon as negotiations take on a serious note I'll call in the cavalry and we—"

Virginia leaned down to refill Jack's coffee,

and her proximity to the man made Marcos's jaw clamp in anger. He felt ridiculously jealous. Yes, *diablos,* he was totally had.

"We'll close," he finished tightly, and slapped the proposal shut. She had no idea, no idea.

Or was she doing this on purpose?

The sunlight that streamed through the floor-to-ceiling windows of the Art Deco building shone over her loose hair. But she was frowning, he realized then, somehow worried, and the noose tightened around his neck.

"Miss Hollis," he said. Last night's seduction? That ridiculously simple but mouthwateringly sexy outfit? Was all this some sort of plan of hers?

She spun, shocked as if from out of her thoughts. "Yes?"

He reclined in his seat and crossed his arms. She was pale this morning. Guilt assailed him. He hadn't let her sleep much, had he? "I was telling Mr. Williams about Monterrey."

She spared a fleeting glance at Jack's lean, jeans-clad figure, and he shot her one of his disarming grins. "How nice," she said absently, and lifted the glass coffeepot to Marcos. "More coffee?"

He shook his head, searching for warm emotions in her expression, all of which usually showed on her face as she experienced them. There were none this morning either.

Her desperation last night, her need, her wanting…he'd felt them all. He'd throbbed with every one of them. Today she looked distant. Why?

I'm not Marissa…

His body clenched. No. No. She was not. Virginia was even more dangerous.

"Marissa Galvez is flying in this weekend," he then offered. Why did he offer this information? Because deep down, her words continued to pull at his heartstrings. *Mend Allende. Make it gold again.*

Did he dare? Did he even want to?

"Oh. How nice. I'm sure she'll be more agreeable this time."

The reply was so noncommittal and so lacking in generosity of feeling that he frowned. When the carved oak doors shut behind her, Jack murmured, "I see."

"Hmm?" Marcos took a long, warm gulp of coffee.

"I see," Jack repeated, propping a shiny lizard boot atop his knee.

He drank again, savoring the scent, the warmth of her coffee. Was she sick? "Mine, Jack."

"Yes, I see."

Marcos grunted. Jack wouldn't even begin to comprehend the pain of his sexual frustration. The looks she gave him—tenderness, desire, admiration, respect. When would he tire of her? He'd expected to tire within the week, and yet it had been over a month now. He could not get enough of her. Was she tiring of him? Good God, was that a possibility?

His friend's dry chuckle wafted in the air. "I assume your plan worked with Marissa. She no doubt thought you were taken with Virginia."

Marcos pushed to his feet and headed to the wide bay window, his coffee cradled against his chest. "My bid has been rejected, Jack."

Silence.

His chest felt cramped with anger, frustration. "She controls the board and somehow made sure they declined."

"Ahh. Then I assume we're getting hostile? Why are we even discussing Allende if not?"

"We are getting hostile." He spun on his heel. "If we could."

Jack made a scratching noise. "Meaning?"

Damn Marissa and her sneaky ways. Marcos had discussed for the tenth time the purchase of her shares, and she still held off selling to him. In the back of her warped mind, she no doubt believed she could bend Marcos like she'd bent his father—who else would save her company but the son? What else would ensure her continued ownership but marriage?

No. She wouldn't get away with it, not anymore, and yet even in the midst of this surety, the fact that a woman would have power over his future made his blood boil.

"Meaning I must pressure her to sell, Williams. She's flying to Chicago this weekend—I invited her to the Fintech dinner. As long as she owns the majority of the shares, a hostile takeover is close to impossible. She must sell, and she must sell to *me*."

"Pardon my slowness, but you invited her to Chicago?"

"I want Allende, Jack."

"You want to kill it," Jack added.

Marcos absently scanned the busy sidewalks below. "And if I don't?"

Jack's usually fast retorts seemed to fail him this time.

Marcos's mind raced with every new discovery he'd made about Hank Hollis today. The man had lost his way—not unusual after the heartache of losing a beloved wife, Marcos supposed. But he'd been visiting AA meetings, seemed to be struggling to get his life back on track. He'd been a risk-taker on the job, and ruthless when it came to disciplining those beneath him. Years ago, he'd pushed his chain of stores, every single one of them, to be better, more efficient, and the admirable numbers he'd produced for them didn't lie.

"What if I told you," Marcos began, "that I'd save Allende. What if I told you I've found a man to do the dirty work—one who's driven and who's thirsty to prove something to someone?" *Maybe he'd enjoy coming to Mexico.*

"Marcos, I'm on your board as a professional, not as a friend. The same reason you're on mine."

"Of course."

And Virginia would be free of the pain her father had been causing. She would be free to be with him. Marcos.

"Well, as both, I have to tell you," his friend continued in a thickening drawl. "It's that damned prodigal apple. Any opportunity man *or* woman has to get a bite out of it, ten out of ten times, they *will.*"

"Amen."

"I'm serious."

He swung around. "All right. So we get to play gods and kick them out of the kingdom. New management, new rules, no thieving, no blackmailing, no mafia."

"I agree. But who's heading new management?"

His eyebrows furrowed when he realized there was no clear space on his desk to set down his cup of coffee. The last fifteen years of his life—hard, busy years—were in this desk. A heavy oak Herman Miller, the first expensive designer piece he'd bought after his first takeover. It was old—he was superstitious—and it was a keeper and it was *packed.* The surface contained no photo frames, no figurines, nothing but a humming computer and piles and piles of papers that would later go into a roomful of file cabinets. He planted the mug over a stack of papers. "You are," he flatly repeated.

Jack's gaze was razor sharp. "Me."

His lips flattened to a grim, hard line as he nodded. "You. And a man I consider may be hungry to prove himself."

Jack hooked his thumb into his jeans pocket. "Go on."

Marcos folded into his chair, grabbed a blue pen and twirled it in his hand as he contemplated. "I negotiate for Marissa's shares and agree to allow her to stay in the company temporarily, while you and Hank Hollis will get the ropes and start a new team."

"Hank Hollis." His eyes narrowed to slits. "You're not serious."

He smiled the very same smile the Big Bad Wolf might have given Little Red Riding Hood. "Oh, but I am."

Hank Hollis would redeem himself in Virginia's eyes, right along with Allende. Marcos would make sure of it.

If Virginia had had any worries regarding her poor emotional state for the past twenty-four hours—other than having stupidly, blindly, foolishly fallen in love with Marcos Allende—she now had more proof for concern.

Pale-faced, she walked into the long tiled bathroom to stare for the twentieth time at the sleek white predictor test—the third one she'd used today—sitting next to the other two on the bathroom sink.

Pink.

Pink.

Pink.

All three were *pink*.

Of course. Because when it rained, it *poured*. Because when one thing went terribly wrong, *everything* went wrong. Because when your world collapsed on top of your head, really, *nothing* you could do would stop the crash.

Letting go her breath while the sting of tears gathered in her eyes, she leaned back on the white tiles lining the bathroom walls and slowly, weakly, dragged her body down its length until she was sprawled on the floor.

She was very, undeniably pregnant.

With Marcos's baby.

There could be no more solid proof of her naïveté. She'd walked into his penthouse one evening with little in the way of emotional shields, without protection and without standing a chance. She might as well have torn out her heart and offered it in her hand. What had she expected would come out of it? Of all those pretend kisses, the laughter, the moments she could not forget?

Did she think he would say, "Step into my life, Virginia, I want you in it forever?"

Did she think he would say, "Marry me, *amor,* where have you been all my life?"

Oh, God. Covering her face with her hands, she considered what he would do when he found out about this.

A vision of him suggesting something bleak made the bile hitch up in her throat. She choked it back and shook her head, wrapping her arms around her stomach, speaking to herself at first, then below at the tiny little being growing inside her.

"I have to tell him." And when a wealth of maternal love surged through her, she ran a hand across her stomach and determinedly whispered, "I have to tell him."

Maybe she was more of a gambler than she'd thought. He might be furious, and he could turn her away, but still she found herself righting her hair and her clothes in front of the mirror, preparing for battle. Gathering up all the tests in the plastic bag from the drugstore and stuffing it in her purse, she once again headed back to Marcos's office.

She knocked three times. "Mr. Allende?"

His friend Jack seemed to have left already, and now, as she entered, Marcos pulled up a file from a stack on his desk, studied it, set it back down, rubbed his chin then finally stared at her.

"Close the door," he said, all somber.

She couldn't read that expression. She tried for flippant and saucy. "I'm under orders to spend a lot of money on anything I fancy."

"Are you now." He frowned. "Who is this man who orders you around? Seems to me you should run far and fast away from him, Miss Hollis."

The unexpected smile he shot her made her grin. "Did I mistakenly put whiskey in your coffee?" she asked, nearly laughing.

His eyes sparkled. "You might want to sit on my lap while you investigate."

She approached his desk, thinking about the baby, his baby, growing inside her body. "I was wondering if you were busy tonight. I'd like for us to talk."

"Virginia." He leaned forward and gently lowered her to his lap. "You have me. I'm at your disposal every night."

"Marcos…" The words *I want more* faltered in her throat.

He must have misinterpreted her concern, for

Marcos dropped his hands to his sides and sighed. "Nobody knows about us, Virginia, please don't fret. I'm trying to keep things running smoothly. My office won't be abuzz with gossip, I won't allow it."

Gossip. Could everyone be gossiping? Whispering? Her stomach clenched in dread. "But you keep stealing touches and people are noticing." That much was true. And soon…how would she hide a pregnant belly?

Marcos boldly raked her figure with his gaze, reclined in his seat and said, "Then I should give these people something more to do."

She blinked, then realized he was teasing her, and she forced her lips into a smile. But it wasn't funny. Soon they'd notice she was pregnant. Soon she'd be waddling around.

He scraped two fingers across his chin as he studied her. "You look worried."

She couldn't do this here—she felt as emotionally stable as a compass gone berserk. "Maybe the Fintech dinner isn't such a good idea," she suggested.

"It was part of our arrangement, Miss Hollis."

She swallowed and snatched up his files, deciding to postpone this for…tonight. Tomorrow. Never. "The projection room is ready."

"You have your notes?"

"Of course. And yours."

He stormed down the long hallway with her, and as people smiled at her in a "Yay, you" kind of way, her unease grew tenfold.

During the meeting, Virginia tried to concentrate on the images flicking on the projection screen. Sales charts with numbers. But Marcos sat unbearably close.

"Is it the dinner?"

She stiffened. "What?"

"Why you're worried. Is it?"

"I… No."

"The outfit? You're afraid you won't find one you like?"

She shook her head. "No."

He leaned forward. He tapped her pad. "Reading your notes here. 'Colorful charts.' Very observant, Miss Hollis. Now why are you worried? Tell me."

She attempted to take more notes but her mind was elsewhere.

"Now, you see the hedge fund study we just

passed?" he said when she, apparently, was not going to talk. "We lost a little, but the fund was heavily invested in metals, as well, and the gold price has been rising, so we closed with a positive number nonetheless."

"Yes, I understand. You lose some and win some. Like…gambling."

He chuckled. "Indeed. It's all a game of risk, Miss Hollis. You weigh the benefits against the risk. And decide how to move forward. You may lose, but at least you played the game. Or you may win…and the prize is exquisite."

She did the exercise in her mind. Risk—her job, her self-respect, her body to a pregnancy, her heart…no, it was too much to bear to even think it. Benefit—save her father, who didn't deserve saving, and share a wonderful week with the most wonderful, wonderful man.

She would have liked to think that if she remained cool and aloof, she would not be risking anything. If she behaved like her usual self, there was no reason the office would speculate. If she ignored his scent, his lips and his eyes, and the fact that she'd fallen in love with him, then she could settle for the benefits. Eventually.

Except already, there was a child.

Their child.

And she wouldn't be able to hide his growing presence much longer.

Eleven

"That's supposed to be a dress?"

She sensed Marcos at the doorway, actually heard a whoosh of air as though the sight of her had stunned him, and she continued tugging the fabric down her hips, her legs, carefully avoiding his gaze as she stepped into it.

"Hello? Fintech dinner? You said buy something to dazzle them. Splurge. Buy the dress of your dreams." *Before I blow up like a balloon and have your bastard baby.*

"The key word was *something*," Marcos growled, "That is nothing."

In the middle of his spacious, carpeted closet, standing before a mirror in a satiny green dress that was making her smile and Marcos frown, Virginia flicked her hair and scoffed at his words.

His glare deepened. "I'm not taking you looking like this."

"Excuse me?"

"I'm serious."

"This is all I have, I spent a fortune on it. You told me—"

"I don't care what I said. I am saying right now, I'm not taking you…into a party with half the city…in that…that scrap."

"Don't be absurd, it's perfect."

A muscle ticked in the back of his jaw. He grabbed her arm and pulled her close. "Do you have any idea what a man thinks of…at the sight of you in that dress?"

"I thought it was elegant, but seductive, if I'd thought it was—"

He grabbed her by the waist and pressed her to him, and the shock of feeling every lean, hard inch of him against her made her gasp. "He thinks of peeling it off with his teeth. He imagines your breasts without the satin over them, and he imagines you, wrapped all around him, with your hair all across his bed."

Her bones melted inside of her.

Marcos, in a tuxedo, was easily the sexiest thing she'd ever seen. She wanted to beg him to peel the dress off her fevered body with his teeth and to wrap her limbs around him with his weight crushing her on the bed.

She tipped her face back, remembering an entire month of making love to Marcos.

In the morning. At midnight. Evenings when he got home. Coupled with those memories, she had others of him with the morning paper spread across the table, coffee cup in hand. Him shaving. Him taking a shower. With her.

She could not remember a thought that didn't make her tummy constrict.

Feeling her thighs go mushy, she stroked her fingers up his cleanly shaven jaw. "You're so handsome," she whispered.

His eyes roved her face, cataloging her flushed cheeks, the telling glaze in her heavy-lidded eyes. "I want you." His hands tightened, and she became excruciatingly aware of his erection biting into her pelvis. His eyes were so hot they were like flames. "I want you every minute of every godforsaken day and it's making me grumpy."

When she gasped, he let her go. A muscle

flexed in the back of his jaw as he clenched hard. He shook his head. "Damn."

It took an effort to stand on her own two feet while quietly nursing the sting of his rejection, but she thrust her chin up with a little dignity. "This is all I have to wear."

God, she had turned into a wanton. She only wanted to touch and touch and touch him. To be kissed until her breath left her.

Flushing, she pulled open the carved-wood closet doors and began to rummage through the shoe rack.

Marcos paced the area and raked a hand through his hair. "The pearls have to go."

She straightened, a hand coming to stroke a smooth pebble at her throat. Her father had stripped out every material memory of her childhood, of her mother, the life they'd once had. He'd pawned her mother's engagement ring. The pearl earrings to match the necklace she always wore. He'd sold off the nice clothes, even the locket they'd given Virginia as a little girl.

"Are they too old-fashioned?"

"They're not you."

He pulled out a box from a drawer, and she blinked. The box was sky-blue in color, with a silken white bow on top. As his long, tanned fingers tugged the edges of the bow and the shimmering ribbon unfurled in his hand, the unmistakable words *Tiffany & Co.* appeared.

Within seconds, he'd opened a velvet box and held up the largest, most dazzling diamond necklace Virginia had ever seen. Its sparkle was blinding. Its sheer magnificence just made her breath, her brain, her everything scatter.

The piece was worthy of old Hollywood, when the women would wear their finest evening dresses and most impressive jewels for the night. A large, oval-shaped green pendant hung from rows and rows of large, brilliant diamonds that fell like curtains and lace in the most exquisite workmanship Virginia had ever set eyes on.

"I… It's lovely."

"It's yours."

She shook her head. "I can't."

But he stepped behind her and began to fasten it around her neck. His lips grazed the back of her ear as his fingers worked on the clasp. When he was done, he turned her around to face him. "You're mine to spoil. It's yours. Tomorrow. Next week, next month, next year. It's yours."

This was him, announcing, in a way, that he

was sleeping with her. No one who saw her would have any doubt. Why would he do this tonight? Why would she allow it?

She experienced a horrible urge to touch him, an even more intense one to ask him to hold her, but that would only bring the tears gathering in the back of her eyes to the forefront. She didn't understand these tears, or the desperate sensation of having lost before she'd even fought for him.

Her eyes dropped to his chest as she felt a blush creep up her cheeks. His cross lay over his chest, glinting bright gold against the bronzed skin. His breath stirred the hair at the top of her head. The warmth of his body enveloped her.

His hands framed her jaw, lifting her face to his. "I bought you earrings and a bracelet, too."

As he seized her wrist with his long, tanned fingers, she watched the thick cuff bracelet close around her. Oh, God, no wonder mistresses were always so sexy and smiling, when all their men treated them just like this!

"I can't," she still said. Because it felt so wrong. So intimate. So personal. It made her mind race with thoughts she did not—should not—think of. She was lying to him, or at least, withholding something important.

And it felt so odd, the weight of the diamonds and the forest-green emerald on her. It felt like a chain around her neck—Marcos's chain on her. And her baby. And her future.

You're mine to spoil...

"I insist, Virginia," he sternly said, and drew her at arm's length to take in the visual.

Self-conscious, Virginia dropped her gaze and tugged at a loose curl on her shoulder. The dress hugged her body like a lover's embrace, the jewels refracted thousands of little lights and for the first time in her life Virginia felt like a fraud. A woman desperate to be anyone, anyone, that the man she loved could love.

"I don't know what to say."

His chuckle was full of arrogance, but it made her melt all the same. "Then get over here."

When he drew her close and kissed her with a passion that buckled her knees and had her clinging to his shoulders, she didn't say anything at all. But her mind screamed, "We're having a baby!"

"Marcos, I'd like to talk to you, tonight."

He fixed his powerful eyes on her, his face unreadable. He seemed to have forgotten about the dress, and she wondered if he'd been jealous.

Marcos wasn't surrounded by the aura of relaxation of a man who'd spent an entire night feasting on his lover, but with the tension of one who wanted more. The air felt dense between them. "I have other plans for tonight," he admitted.

She could not even smile at that. "Still, I'd like for us to talk."

He cradled her face, forced her to meet his gaze. "What is it?"

The concern in his eyes, the gentleness in his voice, only made her crave his love with more intensity. She did not want to crave it with such intensity, did not want to feel the emptiness growing inside her, realizing she lacked his love at the same time as their baby grew bigger.

Their agreement was over once she accompanied him to the Fintech dinner. And maybe they would be over, too.

She drew in a tremulous breath. "After the party."

"All right," he said, smiling. "In fact, there's something I'd like to speak to you about, too."

Inside the lavishly decorated lobby of the glass-and-steel skyscraper smack in the center in Michigan Avenue, Marcos guided Virginia through the throng of people, nodding to a few. "That's Gage Keller, he's a developer. His company, Syntax, owns half of Las Vegas now. The young woman with him is his wife."

"Second, I presume?"

He grinned. "More like sixth."

He brought her around to where a group of men and women stood by a spectacular ten-foot-tall wine fountain. "The woman drowning in jewels over there is Irene Hillsborough; she owns the most extensive collection of Impressionist art in the States. Old money, very polite."

"Very snotty?" Virginia added when the woman lifted her head to stare at her then promptly glanced away.

An appreciative gleam lit up his eyes as he smiled down at her and patted her hand. "How perceptive."

"Allende." A bearded middle-aged man Marcos had presented her to just moments ago—Samuel...something—came back to slap his back. "Haven't seen much of Santos lately. What is that troublemaker up to?"

"I wouldn't know," Marcos said with a rather bored intonation, then uncharacteristically offered, "You can ask him later if he shows." He steered Virginia away, and an immediate image of Santos—surely gorgeous and bad, so bad—made her ask, "Santos is coming?"

"If only to be a pain in the ass, yes." He said it so decidedly, so automatically, her eyes widened in surprise.

He then urged her around, and a woman with silvering hair and an ecstatic look on her face was fast winding her way toward them.

"That would be Phyllis Dyer," he continued, "the director of donations and—"

"Marcos," the woman said, lightly laying her hand on his shoulder as she kissed one cheek, then the other. Her voice quivered with excitement. "Marcos, I can't thank you enough for your generosity. I heard from the Watkinson Center for Children today and they were all wondering why the early Christmas. It was so kind of you, as usual."

Marcos gave her a curt nod. He then brought Virginia forward. "May I present Virginia."

The woman's soft gray eyes went huge. "Oh, well, how lovely to meet you. I believe this is the first time I have had the pleasure of meeting one of Marcos's girls." To her, she leaned forward to whisper, "This one's a keeper, darling, if you know what I mean."

"Oh, I'm not his… I'm actually his—"

After a bit more small talk, Phyllis left with an encouraging pat on Virginia's shoulder, and Virginia ventured a glance at him. "Why didn't you tell her I was your assistant?"

Tucking her hand into the crook of his arm, he guided her toward the sweeping arched doors that led out into the terrace. He didn't answer her.

Stepping past an elegant trellis, he led her across the terrace, illuminated with flickering gas lanterns that lined the perimeter.

When he loosened his hold on her, Virginia stepped forward and leaned on a cement banister and gazed out at the fountain. A breeze stirred the miniature trees in the nearby planters, the chilly air making her flesh pebble with goose bumps.

Unconsciously, she rubbed her arms up and down, listening to the soft piano music audible through the speakers. Somehow, the notes couldn't completely mute the faint rustle of water.

She drew in a steadying breath. "Aren't you up for a speech soon?"

Through the corner of her eye, she followed

his movements as he set his wineglass on the flat surface of a stone bench. "Yes."

She gasped at the feel of his hand, warm and strong, curling around hers, tugging her forward. In a haze, she found herself slowly but surely gravitating toward him, captivated by the play of moonlight on his features and the gentle, insistent pull of his hand.

"I want us to dance, and I had a feeling you'd say no if I asked you in there."

"Dance," she parroted, mesmerized.

He smiled. Manly appreciation sparkled in his eyes as he curled his arm around her waist and pulled her even closer. *"Te ves hermosa, ven aqui."*

Anything Marcos told her in Spanish Virginia did not understand, but she felt the words so deeply, as though he were telling her a secret her instincts knew how to decode.

Both arms enveloped her and their bodies met in a visceral move, seeking a fit of their own volition. Surrounded by the piano music, feeling the cool breeze on her skin beside the fountain, Virginia suddenly wondered if she would ever experience this again. Everything. What he made her feel. The flutters inside her when she became the sole focus of those pitch-black eyes.

"Marcos," she began to protest.

"Shh. One dance."

Her involuntary squirms only made him tighten his grip on her, press her closer, urge her to move against his tall, hard body in a very slow, sensual dance. He trailed one hand up her back and delved into her hair, his fingers caressing her scalp in a light, hypnotic massage.

His hands shifted on her back, splaying wide, keeping her flat against his solid length. Virginia remembered when they had been sweaty and hot and needing each other last night. She trembled at the memory and he tightened his hold on her. She knew, sensed, felt, that he also remembered.

His eyelids drooped suggestively as he ran his knuckles down her cheek. His lips hovered over her mouth and lightly skimmed side to side. "I can't wait to take you home with me."

A feeling unlike any other bloomed inside her. She trembled down to her knees as she fought to quell it, afraid of what would happen if she set it free.

"Take me home…like a stray?" she ventured. Was this the full-moon fever? Her hormones?

She'd never thought love could feel like this. So total. So powerful.

Marcos let go a rich, delicious chuckle. "More like the loveliest treasure."

She guided her fingers up his taut, hard-boned face, not daring to hope that he might…

"What is it you wanted to tell me tonight? You said you wanted to speak with me, too?"

His smile didn't fade, but a soft tenderness lit up his eyes. "Can't you guess, *chiquita?*"

"Can you give me a hint?"

He nodded, calmly explained, "It's about us."

The tender but possessive way he held her, the warm, admiring way he gazed down at her, prodded her on. "Is there…an us?"

A tingle drummed up and down her body where they touched.

His eyes went liquid, hot with tenderness as he tipped her face back. "You tell me."

I'm pregnant with your baby. She could not say it, needed to know what he had to say first.

He stroked her cheek with one knuckle. "I know what a woman like you wants," he said softly. "I can't give it to you, Virginia, but I'd like…" He trailed off when they heard a sudden noise.

Virginia's stomach tumbled with the need to

hear the rest. What had he meant to say? For a single disconcerting moment, she worried he'd sensed the sudden, alarming, fragile emotions she was struggling with and this made her even more determined to hide them.

Next she heard the echoing footsteps of someone approaching. Virginia trembled when Marcos released her, her heart gripping when she spotted Marissa. Her hair streamed behind her, and her smile was provocative. And suddenly Virginia felt very small and very pregnant.

To Marcos, with wry humor, Marissa handed her arm as though he'd asked her to dance, and slyly purred, "I hope I'm interrupting something."

Bad form. Bad, bad form.

Marcos couldn't make his proposition to Virginia here. *Diablos*—where was his head? On Allende? No, it was not even there, and Marcos was shocked at the discovery.

Somewhere during the past month…somewhere between a headache, when Virginia had smoothed his hair off his brow and "knew the perfect thing to take care of that headache" for him…somewhere between one morning and another, when they sipped coffee in silence…

somewhere between the sheets, when he was lost inside of her in a way he'd never thought humanly possible…somewhere between one of her million kinds of smiles…somewhere between an exchange of files…something had happened.

Marcos had let down his guard. He'd allowed himself to trust a woman, fully and completely, in a way he'd sworn he'd never trust another human. He'd allowed her to filter his mind, his thoughts, to the point where his goals had shifted…shifted and shifted until he no longer knew if they were his or hers.

"I need your help."

Marissa's soft, pleading words registered out on the terrace, and yet his eyes followed Virginia's lovely figure as she glided back into the crowded room. He'd noticed the frustration in her jade-green eyes when she stepped away, saw her struggling to hold her temper in check. She was a curious one, his Virginia. No doubt she craved to know what he'd planned to say. He smiled to himself as she wound her way away from him, into the room, her bearing as regal as a queen's.

She was wearing the most amazing, breathtaking, heart-tripping dress he'd ever seen, and he was dying to take it off her.

"Should we talk inside?" he asked curtly, shifting his attention back to Marissa, who in turn was eyeing him speculatively.

"Of course."

He led her into the decorated space. An orchestra played. Couples danced in harmony to the tune. Amongst the round tables, people mingled.

Heading toward the conference hall at the south end of the lobby, they crossed the room. He greeted several acquaintances, nodded his head at a few more and kept a close eye on Virginia. Her hair fell down to cover part of her face. Her profile was exquisitely feminine, like a doll's.

Taking in her visage, he felt a slow, throbbing ache spread inside of him, and contrary to most of the aches she gave him, this one had nothing to do with physically wanting her.

When he secured Allende, he could mend it, and he could mend her father along with it. He could give her safety and peace and pride.

The intensity with which he wanted to give this to her shocked him to his core.

Whereas before Virginia Hollis had been something to be observed but not touched in his office, a Mona Lisa behind glass, she was more real to him now than his own heartbeat. She was flesh and bones and blood. She was woman.

His fierce attraction to her, kept tightly on a leash, had spiraled out of control the moment he'd put his lips right over hers, or perhaps the moment she'd called him and Marcos had known, in his gut, he was going to have her.

Fierce and unstoppable, the emotions raged within him now, under his muscles, and the urge to cross the room and sweep her into his arms became acute.

With an effort, he tore his eyes away from Virginia, tried to steady the loud beat of his heart.

A man, notoriously tall, athletic and dark, with a smile that had been known to break a woman's heart or two, caught his attention.

Santos Allende was the only person in the world who would not wear a tie to a black-tie event. As he ambled over, he lifted a sardonic brow at the same time he lifted his wineglass in a mock toast. "Brother."

Marcos nodded in greeting, drained his drink, and introduced Marissa and Santos even though they needed no introductions. They loathed each other.

"How's the hotel business?" Marcos asked him without even a hint of interest.

"Thriving, of course."

Though Santos was irresponsible and wild, Marcos held no antagonism towards his brother, and usually regarded his exploits and antics with amusement. Except tonight he wasn't in the mood for Santos. Or anyone else.

Too smart for his own good sometimes, Santos chuckled at his side.

"So. Is that one yours?" Santos lifted his glass in Virginia's direction, and Marcos gazed at her again. His chest felt heavy and his stomach tight.

"Mine," he confirmed.

"I see." Santos smiled and rammed a hand into his pants pocket. "Mistress or fiancée?"

"Mistress," he snapped.

But his mind screamed in protest at those words.

Would she agree to his proposition to become his mistress? Live with him, be with him? She'd turned his world upside down, inside out, in over a month. He wanted her every second of the day—not only sexually. Her laugh brought on his laughter, her smiles made him smile, too. He was...he didn't know what. Enraptured. Charmed. Taken.

By her.

"That would make her your first mistress, eh, brother?" his brother asked. "No more fiancées after Marissa here."

Marissa whipped her attention back to Marcos. "You mean she's just a fling? Your girlfriend?"

He set the glass down on the nearby table with a harsh thump. "Unless you want me to leave you in prison the next time you're there, don't push it, little brother."

And to Marissa, with a scowl that warned her of all kinds of danger, "I say we've played games long enough, you and I, and I'm not in the mood for them any longer. You have something I want. The shares that belonged to my father—I want a number and I want it now."

She's his submissive, been like this for years...
Old lover demanding she be fired...competition...Allende...
Allende and Galvez...
It was easy at first, to pretend she hadn't caught bits and pieces of the swirling conversation. But after she'd heard it over and over, ignoring the

comments popping up wherever she went became impossible.

It hurt to smile, and to pretend she wasn't hearing all this. But then, he'd taught her to pretend just fine, hadn't he? And she was doing quite well. Had been commending herself all evening for remembering people's names and keeping up with their conversations. And smiling her same smile.

But when the whispers were too much, she pried herself away from a group of women and strolled around the tables with her mind on escaping, finding Mrs. Fuller, Lindsay, a friendly face, but even they seemed engaged in the latest gossip.

She stopped in her tracks and frowned when a young man approached. He was over six feet tall, lean but muscled. He moved with slow, lazy charm, his smile oozing charisma. Rumpled ebony hair was slicked back behind his ears, his hard-boned face and striking features prominent. Laser-blue eyes sparkled with amusement as he halted before her and performed a mock bow.

"Allende. Santos Allende."

He spoke it the way Agent 007 would say,

"Bond, James Bond," and it made her smile. So he was the elusive Santos.

"Virginia Hollis."

Drawing up next to her, he signaled with a cock of his head, a glass of red wine idle in his hand. "The bastard looking at you is my brother."

"Yes, I'm his assistant. You and I have spoken on the phone."

Santos had the looks of a centerfold, the kind that modeled underwear or very expensive suits like Hugo Boss, while Marcos had the very appearance of sin.

As if reading her mind, his lips quirked, and he added, "He didn't mention that."

"He mentioned me?"

Her eyes jerked back to Marcos; it seemed they couldn't help themselves. She always caught herself staring at him.

He was weaving toward the hallway with Marissa. When Marcos ducked his head toward her, Virginia's stomach clenched with envy and a sudden, unexpected fury.

He glanced back over his shoulder and when their gazes collided, a strange wildness surged through her. His face was inscrutable and his tuxedo was perfectly in place; only an odd gleam in his eyes spoke of his inner tumult. And in her mind, Virginia was positively screaming at him. *Everybody knows! Everybody knows I'm your stupid...silly...*

No. It was her fault, not his.

She'd wanted him, and she'd gambled for the first time in her existence. She knew his scent, the feel of his hair, the sounds he made when he was in ecstasy with her.

She knew his mouth, his whispers, knew he slept little but that he would remain in bed beside her, watching her.

She knew he liked to put his head between her breasts, knew he made a sound of encouragement when she stroked his hair.

But she did not know how to make this man love her.

This man with all these secrets, all of the locks and bolts around his heart.

He wanted Allende. To destroy it. He wanted her. To play with.

She was just his toy. Something to fool around with. Once, she might have jumped with glee. But now she wanted so much more from him, thought there could be no greater treasure in this world than to be loved by him.

"So did the affair come before he hired you or after?"

Santos phrased his question so casually and with such a playful gleam in his eyes that Virginia could only blink.

He grinned and shrugged his shoulders. "I'm sorry, I'm just terribly curious. I have to know."

Cheeks burning with embarrassment, Virginia ducked her head and tried to get away. "Excuse me."

With one quick, fluid move, Santos stepped into her path and caught her elbow. "Marissa wants him, you do realize this?"

She stepped back, freeing her arm from his, hating that it was so obvious, so transparent on her face. "I can't see why you think I'd care."

But his curling lips invited her to mischief. "She offers something my brother wants very badly. What do you offer?"

She frowned. "I wasn't aware this was a competition—"

"It's not." He tipped her chin up, those electric-blue eyes dancing with mirth. "Because I think you've already got him."

When she hesitated, he bent to whisper in her

ear, sweetening the offer with words she found she could not resist.

"My brother is very loyal, and if you managed to steal his heart…no ten businesses would top it."

But Virginia knew that one business, one woman did—when she heard the news announced later in the evening that Fintech would be taking over Allende.

Twelve

They rode to the penthouse in dead, flat silence. Marcos seemed engrossed in his thoughts, and Virginia was deeply engrossed in hers.

It took her ten minutes, while he made phone calls to Jack and his lawyers, to pack the meager belongings she'd once, mistakenly or not, left in his apartment.

She was calmer. Immobile on a tiny corner of the bed, actually, and staring at the doorway, nervously expecting him to come in any minute. But calmer.

Though she didn't know whether the nausea inside of her was due to the pregnancy or to the fact that she would not be sleeping with Marcos for the first night in over a month.

She just couldn't do this any longer. Every little word she'd heard tonight had felt like whip-lashes on her back; she could not believe her col-leagues would speak this way about her. And then Marcos...offering her a necklace, but not his love. Him telling his brother she was his... his...

No.

She refused to believe he would refer to her as something tacky. But the truth, no matter how painful, was the truth. Virginia was his assis-tant—one of *three*—and she was sleeping with her boss. It didn't matter if she'd spent the most beautiful moments of her life with him. It didn't matter that every kiss, every touch, she had given with all her might and soul. It didn't matter that she'd loved him before and loved him now.

She was sleeping with her boss, and she'd never be respected if she continued. She'd never respect *herself.*

If only she were able to tuck her determination aside for a moment and enjoy one last night with him. The last night of a month she would not ever forget. The last night with the man she had fallen in love with, the father of her unborn child.

Drawing in a fortifying breath, she left the bedroom and went searching for him.

She'd heard him in his office, barking orders to Jack over the phone, laughing with him, even— he was not concealing his delight over his deal.

The door of the study was slightly ajar, and she slipped inside in silence.

He sat behind his desk at the far end. He looked eerie behind his computer, concentrated, the light doing haunting things to his face. Her stomach clenched with yearning. "Marcos, may I talk to you?"

He stiffened, and his head came up. Her breath caught at the devastating beauty of his liquid black eyes, and her heart leapt with a joy that quickly became dread when he remained silent. There was lust in those orbs, desire, and she seized on to that with all her might before he jerked his gaze back to the computer. "I'm very busy, Virginia."

She tugged at the hem of her dress, uneasy of how to proceed. She tried to sound casual. "Marcos, I thought we could discuss…something.

I may not spend the night and I really feel it's important—"

"Jesus, do we have to do this now?" His hands paused on the keyboard, then he dropped his face and rubbed his eyes with the heel of his palms. "I'm sorry. Right. Okay. What is it, Virginia?"

Her eyes widened at his condescending tone. The thought that he'd always put Allende and his business before her made her stomach twist so tight she thought she would vomit. She'd forgotten she was his plaything. If she produced money maybe he'd give her five minutes now?

"We were going to discuss...us." Her voice trembled with urgency. "At the dinner, you mentioned wanting to say something."

He leaned back, his expression betraying no flicker of emotion, no hint of what was going through his mind. "Can't us wait a day? Hmm?"

"No, Marcos, it can't."

He sat up straighter, linked his hands together, and kept silent for what felt like forever. His calm alarmed her. He was too still, too composed, while his eyes looked...indulgent. "What is it you want to say to me?" he at last asked.

Suddenly she felt like young Oliver Twist, begging, "Please, sir, I want some more." And she hated him for making her feel like that.

Her voice broke and she swallowed in an attempt to recover it. "Look, I realize what kind of arrangement we have," she began. "A-and maybe it was good for a time. But things change, don't they?"

He nodded, his entire face, his smile, indulgent.

She dragged in a breath, trying not to lose her temper. "Marissa, Marcos."

"What about Marissa?" His eyes were so black, so intense, she felt as though they would burn holes through her.

Are the rumors true? she wondered. *Did she force you into a marriage bargain only so you could once again own Allende?* "You loved Marissa. Do you love her still?"

A frustrated sound exited his throat as he flung his hands over his head. "I'm not discussing Marissa now, of all times, for God's sake!" he exploded.

But Virginia plunged on. "I think it very tacky to jump around from bed to bed, don't you?"

His eyebrows drew low across his eyes, and he nodded. "Extremely."

To her horror, her throat began closing as she

pulled her fears out of her little box and showed them to him. "She hurt you, and maybe you wanted to use me to hurt her back—" Why else would he want Virginia? She was not that smart, not that special, not that beautiful, either!

She tried to muffle a sob with her hand and couldn't, and then the tears began to stream down her cheeks in rivers. With a muffled curse, he rose and came around the desk, walking toward her. His face and body became a blur as he reached her, and though she tried to avoid his embrace, her back hit the wall as she tried escaping.

He bent over her, wiped her tears with his thumb. "Don't cry. Why are you crying?"

The genuine concern in his voice, the soul-wrenching tenderness with which he cradled her face, only made the sobs tear out of her with more vigor. "Oh, God," she sobbed, wiping furiously at the tears as they streamed down her face.

When he spoke, he sounded even more tortured than she was. "Don't cry, please don't cry, *amor.*" He kissed her cheek. Her eyelashes. Her forehead. Her nose. When his lips glided across hers, she sucked in a breath of surprise. He opened his lips over hers, probed her lightly with his tongue, and said, in a tone that warned of danger, "Please give me ten minutes and I'm all yours. Please just let me…"

When he impulsively covered her mouth, she opened for the wet thrust of his tongue, offering everything he didn't ask for and more. His kiss was hot and avid, and it produced in her an amazing violence, a feeling that made her feel fierce and powerful and at the same time so vulnerable to him.

The possibility that he was feeling some kind of pity for her made her regain some semblance of control. She pushed at his wrist with one hand and wiped her tears with the other. "I'm all right."

"You're jealous." He took her lips with his warm ones, nibbling the plump flesh between words. "It's all right. Tell me that you are."

She shook her head, not trusting herself to speak.

"I was when you danced with Santos," he rasped, "jealous out of my mind. Out. Of. My. Mind." His teeth were tugging at her ear, and he was making low noises of pleasure as his hands roamed up her sides, following her form, feeling her.

She dragged her mouth across his hair, softly said, "I can't do this anymore, Marcos."

He froze for a shocked moment.

In one blindingly quick move, he lifted her up and pressed her back against the wall, pinioning her by the shoulders. "Is this your idea of getting my attention?"

Her heart thundered in her ears. "I can't do this any longer. I want more." *A father for our child. A man who'll always stand by me. Someone who cares.*

A nearly imperceptible quiver at the corner of his right eye drew her attention. That was all that seemed to move. That and his chest. Her own heaving breasts. They were panting hard, the wild flutter of a pulse at the base of his throat a match to her own frantic heartbeat. "What more do you want?" His voice was hoarse, more a plea than a command.

She grasped the back of his strong neck and made a sound that was more frustrated than seductive. "More! Just more, damn you, and if you can't figure out it's not your money then I'm not going to spell it out for you."

He stared at her as though what she'd just said was the worst kind of catastrophe. Then he cursed in Spanish and stalked away, plunging his hands into his hair. "You picked the wrong moment to share your wish list with me, *amor*."

"It's not a long list," she said glumly. She felt bereft of his kisses, his eyes, his warmth, and wrapped her arms tightly around herself. "We said we'd talk, and I think it's time we did."

"After midnight? When I'm in the midst of closing the deal of my life?"

"I'm sorry about the timing," she admitted.

She swallowed hard for some reason, waiting for him to tell her something. He didn't. His back was stiff as he halted by the window. His breaths were a frightening sound in the room—shallow, so ragged she thought he could be an animal.

But no, he wasn't an animal.

He was a man.

A man who had ruthlessly, methodically isolated his emotions from the world. She did not know how to reach this man, but every atom and cell inside of her screamed for her to try.

But then he spoke.

"Virginia." There was a warning in that word; it vibrated with underlying threat. It made her hold her breath as he turned. There was frustration in his eyes, and determination, and his face was black with lust. "Give me ten minutes. That's all I ask. Ten minutes so I can finish here and then you'll get your nightly tumble."

His words jerked through her, one in particular filling her with outrage. *Tumble!*

She began to quake. A chilling frost seemed to seep into her bones.

Stalking around her, he fell back into his chair, was sucked back into his computer, and began writing.

"Tumble," she said.

He set down the pen and met her gaze. The man was mute as wallpaper.

She signaled with trembling fingers. "For your information." She wanted to fling her shoe at his face, to shred every single paper on the pile she'd neatly organized atop his desk, but she clenched her eyes shut for a brief moment. "I do not want a tumble!"

Several times, Virginia had imagined how their parting would be.

Not even in her nightmares had she imagined this.

She couldn't bear to be in the same room with him, didn't dare glance up to make note of his expression.

Stricken by his lack of apology, she choked

back words that wanted to come out, hurtful things she knew she would regret saying, words about being sorry she'd met him, sorry she loved him, sorry she was pregnant by him, but staring at the top of his silky black hair, she couldn't. Instead she said, "Goodbye, Marcos."

And Marcos…said nothing.

Not *goodbye*. Not *chiquita*. Not *amor*.

But as she waited by the elevator, clutching her suitcase handle as though it was all that kept her from falling apart, a roar unlike any other exploded in his study. It was followed by an ear-splitting crash.

The clock read 1:33 p.m.

He had what he wanted, Marcos told himself for the hundredth time. Didn't he? And yet the satisfaction, the victory, wasn't within reach. Perhaps because what he really wanted was something else. Someone else.

The pressure was off his chest—the lawyers were currently sealing the deal. Allende for a couple of million. Marcos now owned every single share of stock in the company, had recovered every inch and centimeter and brick and truck of what Marissa had taken from him.

It had not taken much at all to bend her to his will; the woman had nothing to bargain with. Marissa had to sell or she'd go bankrupt. She'd held no more attraction for him, as she'd thought, no temptation. After a few harsh words from him and a few tears from her, there had finally been a bit of forgiveness between them.

And with that, everything had changed. By her admittance to defeat, she'd unwittingly granted Marcos the opportunity to color his past another shade that wasn't black.

He felt…lighter, in that respect. But heavy in the chest. So damned heavy and tortured with a sense of foreboding he couldn't quite place.

"You needed me, Mr. Allende?"

His heart kicked into his rib cage when Virginia strolled into his office five minutes after he'd issued the request by phone.

Yes, I need you. I do. And I'm not even ashamed to admit it anymore.

Dressed in slimming black, she held a manila file in her hand, and a few seconds after she closed the doors behind her, Marcos spoke. "You left before the ten minutes were over."

Silently she sat and fiddled with her pearls, her eyes shooting daggers at him when she spared him a glance. "I realized you wanted your space, so I indulged you."

Those last words came barbed, as though he'd once spoken them in sarcasm and she were flinging them back at him. She looked tired, his Miss Hollis, he noted. As though she'd slept less than an hour and tossed around for all the rest. Like he had.

He didn't understand her anger very well. But they'd had plans to speak afterward, had been sleeping together so delightedly he hadn't expected the loss of her last night to affect him like it had. Were ten minutes too much to ask?

"Ten minutes, Miss Hollis. You can't even grant me that?"

"You were being—" As though offended by her own thoughts, she bolted upright in the chair, spine straight. "Something of a jerk."

He choked. "Jerk! This spoken by an opinionated little brat I've spoiled rotten?"

The blow registered in her face first, crumpling her tight expression. Marcos raked his fingers through his hair and shot up to pace his office.

He felt like celebrating with her, like marking this momentous day in his career with something even equally outstanding for him personally. But somehow he sensed he had to make amends with her first.

Virginia had wanted him last night. First, he'd been occupied with Marissa. Who'd deceived and lied to him. And who had become so insignificant in his life, he'd forgiven her. After he got what he wanted from her.

All this, thanks to Virginia.

Suddenly, Marcos felt a grieving need to explain, to placate her, to restore the sparkle in her pretty green eyes. Staring around his office, at the papers scattered across the desk, he quietly admitted, "Virginia, I want to make you a proposition."

Her slow and deep intake of breath was followed by a dignified silence. This was not the way he'd intended to ask her and yet suddenly he had to. Here. Now. Had to know she would belong to him, only him.

They were fighting, the air between them felt electric, charged with anger and lust and something else he couldn't quite place. Something fuzzy and warm that made him feel close to her even when she annoyed him.

He strode over to her chair and bent, put his

palm on her bare knee, and said, with fervor, "Would you be my mistress, Virginia?"

The way she automatically breathed the word *no,* he'd have thought he'd slapped her. Her eyes shone with hurt and her mouth parted as though she wanted to say something else but couldn't. "No," she said again, on another breath, this one made of steel.

"I don't think you understand what I'm saying," he said gently, stroking her knee and moving his hand up to clasp hers where it rested on her lap.

"Don't!" She said it in such a fierce voice that he halted. Even his heart stopped beating. She shook her curls side to side, her face stricken. "Don't touch me."

What was this? What was this?

He caught her face in one hand, his heartbeat a loud, deafening roar in his ears. "Darling, I realize you might have misinterpreted my interests in speaking to Marissa, which I assure you were only business. It's you I want, only you. And I'm very prepared to give you—"

"What? What will you give me?" She stood up, her eyes shooting daggers at him. "Do you even realize that the only thing I've been pretending all this time is that I don't love you?"

His heart vaulted, but his voice sounded dead as he stepped back. The confession felt like a bomb dropped into his stomach. "Love."

She chose to look out the window. And at last handed him the file. "Here's my resignation."

She set it atop his stacks and started for the door, and Marcos tore across the room like a man being chased by the devil. He caught her and squeezed her arms as his paralyzed brain made sense of her words.

"If you're telling me you love me," he said through gritted teeth, "look at me when you say it!"

She wrenched free. "Let go of me."

He caught her elbow and spun her around, and she screamed, *I said don't touch me!"*

Worried the entire floor may have heard that, he let go of her. His chest heaved with the cyclone of feelings inside of him. He curled his fingers into his hands and his fingers dug into his palms, his knuckles jutting out.

"You want me," he growled.

"No." She backed away, glaring at him.

"You tremble for me, Virginia."

"Stop it."

"You want me so much you sob from the pleasure when I'm inside you."

"Because I'm *pretending* to enjoy your disgusting *tumbles!*" she shot. She was flushed and trembling against the wall, her nipples balled into little pearls that begged for his mouth. But in her voice there was nothing but pain.

"Pretend? When the hell have we pretended?" He crushed her against him, squeezed her tight even as she squirmed. "We're fire, Virginia. You and I. Combustion. Don't you understand English? I'm asking you to stay. With me. And be my mistress," he ground out.

Did she even realize he'd never in his life said this to a woman before? When her lashes rose and her gaze met his, the damaged look in her eyes knocked the air out of him. He didn't expect the slicing agony lashing through him at her next words.

"I'm not interested in being your mistress."

When she disengaged from him and pulled the doors open, he cursed under his breath, raked a hand through his hair. All noise across the floor silenced, and he immediately grabbed his jacket, shoved his arms into it as he followed her to the elevator.

He pushed inside before the doors closed, and she turned her face toward the mirror when he demanded, "Do I get two weeks to convince you to stay? I want you here. And I want you in my bed."

"You want. You need." Her voice quivered with anger, and its tentacles curled around him so hard he could've sworn it would kill him. "Is that what you wanted to speak to me about? Becoming your...*mistress?*"

His heart had never galloped this way. His plans had never veered off so unexpectedly, so decidedly. Their gazes met. Hers furious. His... his burned like flames. He grabbed her shoulders. The need inside him was so consuming he saw red. "Say yes. Christ, say yes now."

But the way she looked at him wasn't the same way she always did. "Do you think that's what I want?" she asked, so softly he barely heard through the background elevator music. "Did I ever give you the impression I would...settle for...such an offer?"

Stunned that she would look at him like he was a monster, he took a step away from her, and another. His body burned with the want to show her he meant not to punish but to love her with every graze of his lips and every lick of his tongue.

And he said, out of desperation, impulse, the exact second the elevator halted at the lobby floor, "I love you."

And the words, magic words, ones he'd never, ever said before, didn't have the effect he'd predicted.

Her laugh was cynical. "See, you're so good at pretending, I don't believe you."

And she spun around and walked away, out of the elevator, away from him, away from it all.

Stunned, he braced a hand on the mirror, shut his eyes as he fought to make sense of the rampaging turmoil inside him.

What in the hell?

Thirteen

Alone in his Fintech offices, motionless in his chair, Marcos stared out the window.

The nineteenth floor was empty. It was 3 a.m. But there was no power on this earth, no way in hell, that he'd go back alone to his apartment. His penthouse had never felt so cold now that Virginia Hollis was gone. The sheets smelled of her. He'd found a lipstick under the bathroom sink and he'd never, ever felt such misery. The sweeping loneliness that had accompanied that unexpected find was staggering.

He'd stormed out of his home and now here he was, inside his sanctuary. The place where he evaluated his losses and plotted his comebacks.

Where he'd conquered the unconquerable and ruthlessly pursued new targets. Where, for the last month, he'd spent countless hours staring off into space with the single thought of a raven-haired temptress with pale, jade-green eyes.

And now he stared out the window, blinded to the city below, and he told himself he did not care.

He told himself that a month from now, he would forget Virginia Hollis.

He told himself this was an obsession and nothing more. He told himself the gut-wrenching, staggering throb inside him was nothing. And for the hundredth time, until the words rang true and his insides didn't wince in protest every time he thought them, he told himself he did not love her.

But it was a bluff. A farce. A lie.

Virginia had her money. Their arrangement had culminated at the Fintech party and had left him with an overwhelming sense of loss he couldn't quite shake. She'd left him wanting. Wanting more.

Marcos, I love you.

She hadn't said it in exactly those words—but in his mind, she did. And he'd never heard sweeter words. More devastating words. Because suddenly, and with all his might, he wanted to be a man who could love her like she deserved.

The pain in her eyes—he'd been the one to put it there. Touch of gold? He scoffed at the thought, thinking he destroyed anything he touched that had life. He'd put that misery in Virginia's eyes and he loathed himself for it.

His proposal, what he'd offered her, not even half of what he'd truly wanted from her, sickened him.

All along, he'd wanted her. He was a man accustomed to following his gut, and he did it without a conscience. He knew when he saw land and wanted it. He knew what he looked for when he bought stocks. He knew, had known from the start, he wanted Virginia in his bed, under his starved, burning body. But now, clear as the glass before him, he knew what else he wanted from her.

He wanted it all.

He wanted a million dances and double that amount of her smiles.

He wanted her in his bed, to see her when he woke up, to find her snuggled against him.

He wanted to pay her credit card bills and he

wanted her with a baby in her arms. His baby. His woman. His *wife*.

Mia. Mia. Mia.

He'd been alone his entire lifetime, pursuing meaningless affairs, convincing himself that was enough. It had all changed. Slowly, almost imperceptibly, but surely, ever since the day he'd hired Virginia Hollis.

Now he had broken her heart before she'd truly admitted to having lost it to him. He should've treasured it. Tucked it into his own and never let it go.

Sighing, he pushed his chair around and stared across his office. A dozen plasma TV screens hung on the wall to the right. They usually enlivened the place with noise and light, but were currently off. They lent a gloom to the area that Marcos found quite the match to his mood.

In fact, a morgue was quite the match to his mood.

He stalked outside, and made his way to a sleek wooden desk. Her items were still on it. He scanned the surface—polished to a gleam, all orderly, all her, and he groaned and let his weight drop into her chair.

Her rejection felt excruciatingly painful. Not

even the day Marissa Galvez had stared up at him from his father's bed had he felt such helplessness.

What in the devil did she want from him?

As he stroked a hand along the wood, he knew. Deep in the closed, festering pit of his emotions, he knew what she wanted. Damn her, she'd been playing him for it! Seducing him, delighting and enchanting him, making him love and need and cherish her.

And now he couldn't even remember why he had thought she didn't deserve everything she wanted. Because she was a woman, like Marissa? Why had he thought his bed would be enough for everything she would lack? Had he grown so heartless that he would rob her of a family?

He began opening and closing the desk drawers, looking for some sign of her. Something—anything—she might have left behind.

For the first time in his life, someone else's needs seemed more important than his, and he loathed the overwhelming sense of loss sweeping through him like an avalanche.

If he had an ounce of decency in him, if he was not the unfeeling monster she thought him to be at this moment, Marcos would let her go.

And just when he was certain it was the right thing to do, just when he was determined to forget about her and all the days they'd pretended and all the ways they'd been both wrong and right for each other, he spotted the boxes crowded into the back of her bottom drawer.

And the three test strips. All of them had the same result.

"Nurse, is my father out in the hall?"

Virginia had been transferred to a small private room in the west hospital wing, where she'd slept for the night hooked up to an IV drip, and this morning the one person she longed to see hadn't yet made an appearance. She wanted to go home already—she felt tired, cranky, lonely—and still the nurse kept delaying her departure.

The balmy-voiced nurse fidgeted around the bare room, organizing the trays. "I believe he's outside. I'm sure he'll come in shortly."

Virginia sighed, the sensation of having been run over by an elephant especially painful in her abdomen and breast area. She cupped her stomach. Amazing, that the baby already had its heartbeat. Amazing that just as she left its father, the baby had tried to leave her body, too.

"Virginia?"

She went completely immobile when she heard that.

There, wearing a severe black turtleneck and slacks, stood Marcos Allende in the doorway. Her heart dropped to her toes. She felt the urge to snatch the sleek red carnation her father had set on the side table and hide her pale, teary face behind it, but she was too mesmerized to pull her eyes away. Large, hard, beautiful—Marcos's presence seemed to empower the entire room, and she suspected—no, knew—everyone in this hospital must be feeling his presence.

He stood with his feet braced apart, his arms at his sides, his fingers curled into his palms. And something hummed. Inside her. In her blood, coursing through her veins.

"An acquaintance, miss?"

The nurse's tone gave a hint of her preoccupation. Did she feel the charge in the air? Was the world twirling faster? The floor falling?

Virginia nodded, still shocked and overwhelmed by this visit, but as she stared at the sleek-faced, long-nosed young woman, she hated her mind's eye for gifting her with another, more riveting image of Marcos's dark, cacao gaze. His silken mass of sable hair. Long, tanned fingers. Accent. Oh, God, the accent, that thick baritone, softly saying *Miss Hollis...*

"I'll leave you two for a moment, then."

Oddly close to being devastated, Virginia watched the nurse's careful departure, and then she could find no excuse to stare at the plain white walls, no spot to stare at but Marcos.

If she had just been torpedoed, the impact would have been less than what she felt when he leveled his hot coal eyes on her. He stood as still as a statue.

Why didn't he move? Was he just going to stand there? Why didn't he hold her? Why was he here? He was angry she quit? Angry she hadn't collected her items? Did he miss her just a little bit?

She sucked in a breath when he spoke.

"I'm afraid this won't do."

The deep, quiet, accented voice washed over her like a waterfall. Cleansing. Clear. Beautiful.

Oh, God. Would she ever not love this man?

She pushed up on her hands, glad her vitals were no longer on display or else Marcos would know exactly how hard her heart was beating. "Marcos, what are you doing here—"

He looked directly at her as he advanced, over-powering the room. "I had to see you."

She sucked in breath after breath, watching him move with that catlike grace, his expression somber. Her body quaked from head to toe. The unfairness of it all; he was so gorgeous, so elegant, so tempting. So unreachable. And she! She was so…so beat-up, tired, drained. Hospitalized. Oh, God.

Her lips trembled. As if she weighed next to nothing, he bent and gently scooped her up against him, and Virginia liquefied.

I almost lost our baby, she thought as she wound her arms around him and buried her face in his neck.

He inhaled deeply, as though scenting her. Then, into her ear, his voice ringing so low and true it tolled inside of her, "Are you all right?"

Only Marcos could render such impact with such softly spoken words. Her entire being, down to her bones, trembled at his concern. And then came more. It was just a breath, whispered in her ear, and he whispered it with fervor.

"I love you."

Her muscles clenched in protest, and her head swiveled to her father's when she spotted him at the open doorway. The weathered man's face was inscrutable and his suit was perfectly in place; only the ravaged look in his eyes spoke of what he'd done.

He'd told Marcos about the baby?

"You lied to me, you left me, and yet I love you," Marcos continued, his voice so thick and gruff, as though he were choking.

After the fear, the cramps and the possibility of losing her baby, Virginia had no energy. She just wanted him to speak. The sturdiness of his hard chest against hers gave her the most dizzying sensation on this earth. She'd thought she'd never feel his arms again and to feel them around her, holding her so tight, was bliss.

She didn't realize she was almost nuzzling his neck, breathing in his musky, familiar scent, until her lungs felt ready to explode.

"Do you think we could pretend," he whispered into the top of her bent head, "the past two days never happened, and we can start again?"

More pretending? God, no! No more pretending.

But she refused to wake up from this little fantasy, this one last moment, refused to lift her face, so instead she rubbed her nose against the side of his corded neck. A strange sensation flitted through her, like the soaring she felt when she played on the swings as a child.

His voice was terse but tender as he wiped her brow with one hand and smoothed her hair back. "And our baby?"

Shock didn't come close to what she experienced. Her nerves twisted like wires. "P-pardon?"

"You lost our child?"

For the first time since Marcos had come through that door, Virginia noticed the red rimming his eyes, the strain in his expression. Even his voice seemed to throb in a way she'd never heard before.

She moved not an inch, breathed no breath, as her mind raced to make sense of his question. Then she glanced out the small window, not at what lay beyond, just at a spot where Marcos's face would not distract her. "What makes you say that?" she asked quietly, her fingers tugging on themselves as she scanned the room for the possible culprit behind this misunderstanding. Her father.

"Look at me." Marcos's massive shoulders blocked her view as he leaned over the bed rails. His breath stirred the top of her head as he scraped his jaw against her hair with absolutely no restraint, and then he spoke so passionately her middle tingled. "Look at me. We'll have another baby. I've always wanted one—and I want one with you." He seized her shoulders in a stronghold, his face pained and tortured as he drew away and forced her to meet his gaze. "Marry me. Today. Tomorrow. Marry me."

"I— What do you mean *another* baby?" After many moments, she pinned Hank Hollis with her stare. "Father?"

Wide-eyed, her father hovered by the opposite wall, shifting his feet like an uncertain little boy. He opened his mouth, then snapped it shut, then opened it again, as if he were holding on to great words. "I told him you'd lost the baby."

She gasped. What a horrible thing to say! "W-why? Father! Why would you do that?"

The man rubbed the back of his neck, pacing the little room. "So he'd leave. You said you didn't want any visitors."

While the honest words registered in her foggy mind—the first protective thing her father had done for her in ages—Virginia stared at the aging man. Her heart unwound like an old, twisted shred of paper.

For years, she had been so angry at this man. Maybe if she hadn't changed, become pregnant, fallen in love, she'd still be. But now—she didn't want resentment or anger. She wanted a family, and she'd take even one that had been broken.

Virginia leveled her eyes on the beautiful, thick-lashed cocoa ones she'd been seeing in her dreams and straightened up on the bed, clinging to that fine, strong hand. "Marcos, I'm not sure what he told you, but I'd like to assure you I'm all right. And so is the baby."

When she pictured telling Marcos about a child, she hadn't expected an audience, nor having to do it in a hospital room.

Still. She would never, in her life, forget this moment.

Marcos's expression changed, metamorphosed, into one of disbelief, then joy. Joy so utter and pure it lit his eyes up like shooting stars.

"So we're expecting, then?"

The term *we* coming from his beautiful mouth made her giddy with excitement.

He smiled, and it was brilliant, that smile, that moment.

Did this please him? Yes! She'd bet her life on it.

She nodded, her heart fluttering madly, a

winged thing about to fly out of orbit. "I'd like to go home now," she admitted, and although her father stepped forward to offer assistance, the words weren't meant for him.

She gazed up at Marcos—quiet and mesmerizing—as she eased out of the hospital bed with as much dignity as she could muster.

His attention was no longer hard to bear. She wanted it; she wanted him.

Virginia Hollis knew this man. Inside and out, she knew him. How true he was to his word. How dedicated. How loyal. And how proud. She didn't need any more proof than his presence here, his touch, the look in his eyes and the promise there.

Rising to her full height, she linked her fingers through his and squeezed, feeling flutters in her stomach when he smiled encouragingly down at her. "Yes, Marcos Allende. I'll marry you."

Epilogue

The day arrived three months before the baby did.

Walking up to the altar, with the music shuddering through the church walls, Virginia had eyes only for the dark, mesmerizing man at the far end of the aisle. Tall and smiling, Marcos stood with his hands clasped before him, his broad shoulders and solid arms and steely, stubborn jaw offering love and comfort and protection.

Virginia was certain that nobody who watched him would be blind to the way he stared at her. Least of all she.

They shared a smile. Then her father was letting go of her arm.

Soon Marcos was lifting the flimsy veil to gaze

upon her face and into her eyes, eyes which she used to fervently tell him, *I love you!*

Their palms met, their fingers linked, and the moment they did he gave her a squeeze. She felt it down to her tummy.

I, Virginia, take thee, Marcos, to be my lawfully wedded husband...

When he spoke his vows, the simplest vows, to love and cherish, her eyes began to sting. By the time the priest declared them man and wife, she was ready—more than ready—to be swept into his arms and kissed.

And kiss her he did. The priest cleared his throat. The attendants cheered and clapped. And still he kissed her.

Virginia let herself take her first relaxed breath once they were in the back of the limo. Gravitating toward each other, they embraced, and tiny tremors of desire spread along her torso and limbs. She'd had this fool idea of waiting to be together again until they married—and she was dying for him to touch her.

As they kissed, Virginia found her husband already dispensing with her veil. "There we go," he said contentedly. "Enjoy the dress because I assure you, it is coming off soon."

Actually relieved to be without the veil and anxiously looking forward to Marcos dispensing with the dress, she leaned back on the seat and cuddled against him. "I never knew these things were so heavy," she said. The skirt ballooned at her feet but thankfully there was no volume on top to keep her away from the man she most definitely intended to jump at the first opportunity.

"Come here, wife." He drew her close as the limo pulled into the street and the city landscape slowly rolled past them. Staring absently outside, Virginia sighed. His arms felt so good around her, being against him so right. Being his wife.

Both protectively and possessively, Marcos pressed her face to his chest and with his free hand, reached out to rub her swelling stomach. She'd noticed the more it grew, the more he did that. "How is my little girl today?" he asked against her hair.

Her eyebrows drew into a scowl. "We're having a boy," Virginia countered. "A handsome, dashing boy like his daddy. No girl would kick like this little guy does, trust me."

"Your daughter would, you saucy wench," he said with a rolling chuckle. "And my instincts tell me we are having a plucky, curly-haired, rosy-cheeked daughter. She'll run my empire with me."

Virginia smiled against his chest and slid a hand up his shirt to find the familiar cross lying at his throat and play with it. "Father keeps asking how many grandchildren we plan to have, he's obsessed with wanting it to be at least three."

Marcos laughed, and that laugh alone warmed her up another notch.

"Ahh, darling," he said. "He can rest assured we'll be working on that night and day." The praise in his words and the suggestive pat on her rear filled her with anticipation of tonight and future nights with her complex, breathtakingly beautiful, thoroughly giving and enchanting husband.

"He's so changed now, Marcos," she admitted, feeling so relaxed, *so* happy.

"His work in Allende has been impressive, Virginia. Even Jack is amazed."

"And you?"

He snorted. "I got to say to the moron 'I told you so.'"

She laughed. Then she snuggled closer and said, "Thank you. For believing that people can change. And for forgiving that little fib he told you at the hospital."

He nuzzled the top of her head. "He was trying to protect you—he didn't know me yet, and I respect that. Your father deserved a second chance, Virginia. We all do."

She sighed. "I'm just glad he's put all his efforts into making the best of it. And I'm proud of you, dear sir, for being wise enough to put the past behind you and keep Allende."

And for being most decidedly, most convincingly, most deliciously in love with her.

The band played throughout the evening, and the guests at the reception laughed and danced and drank. Hardly anyone would notice the groom had kidnapped the bride, and if they did, Marcos sure as hell didn't care.

He still could not understand why Virginia had gotten it into her head to play hard-to-get leading up to the wedding, and even less could he comprehend why he had obediently complied.

But now in the cloaked shadows of the closet, he had Virginia right where he'd always wanted her. In his arms. His mouth feasted on her exposed throat while his hands busily searched her dress for access—any access—to the smooth, creamy skin beneath.

"Careful!" Virginia screeched when he yanked on the delicate zipper at the back and an invisible button popped free.

He laughed darkly and maneuvered through the opening. "You're not wearing it again, *reina*. I could tear it apart and dispense with all this silliness." The guests had been crowding them for hours when all Marcos wanted was to be with his bride. Now his hands stole in through the opening at the small of her back, where he instantly seized her cushy rear and drew her up against him. "Come here. You've been teasing me all night."

"How kind of you to notice."

"Hmm. I noticed." He kissed the top of her breasts, all evening looking lush and squeezable thanks to Christian Dior, and then used his hands to gather the volume of her skirts and yank most of them back.

She automatically wrapped her stockinged legs around him when he pressed her against the wall. "You're incorrigible," she said chidingly, but he could hear the smile in her voice and the little tremble that said how very much his wife wanted to be ravaged by him.

He brought his hands up front and lowered them. "I'm open to being domesticated."

"Luckily I'm open to attempting that daunting task. In fact—no, not the panties!" A tear sounded, Virginia gasped, and his fingers found what they were looking for.

"Bingo," he purred.

"Oh, Marcos." Slipping her hands under his jacket and around his shoulders, she placed fervent little kisses along his jaw. "Please."

With a rumbling chuckle, he found her center and grazed it with his fingers. "Please what, *chiquita?*"

Against his lips, she mumbled, "You know what, you evil man."

"Please this?"

"Yes, yes, that." She left a moist path up his jaw and temple, and in his ear whispered, "I was aching to be with you all day."

"Shame on me." He turned his head and seized her earlobe with his teeth, tugging. "For keeping you waiting."

"I adore what you do to me."

He groaned at the husky quality of her voice.

"No more than I, darling." Unable to wait, he freed himself from his trousers and, grasping her hips, began making love to her.

A whimper tore out of her, and she clutched his back with her hands.

"Chiquita." He wound his arms around her and was in turn embraced and enveloped by her silken warmth, completely owned and taken by the woman who had single-handedly stolen his heart.

No matter how quiet they tried to be, they were groaning, moving together. Marcos closed his eyes, savoring her, his wife and partner and mate and woman. When she exploded in his arms with a gasp, crying out his name into his mouth, he let go. Gripping her hips tighter, he muttered a choked, emotional *te amo* then let out a satisfying, "Hmm."

"Hmm," she echoed.

Inconspicuous minutes later, the bride and groom exited the closet. The ballroom brimmed with music and laughter, most of the guests who remained being the people closest to them.

With an appreciative eye, Marcos noticed the bride looked deliciously rumpled. Her cheeks glowed bright, and the fancy hairdo she claimed had taken endless hours to achieve had become magnificently undone.

As if reading his thoughts, she shot him a little black scowl. "I'm sure that everyone who sees me now will know—" she rose up to whisper into his ear "—that you just tumbled me in the closet. Really. Is that how your wife should expect to be treated, *Señor* Allende?"

Smiling into her eyes, he lifted her knuckles to his lips. "My wife can expect to be treated with respect and admiration and devotion."

With a dazzling smile, she let him drag her to the dance floor when a compellingly slow song began. "I believe this dance is mine," he said, and meaningfully added, "So is the one afterward."

She stepped into the circle of his arms, finding her spot under his chin to tuck her head in and sliding her arms around him. "You are a greedy fellow, aren't you?"

His lips quirked, and his eyes strayed toward the arched doorway, where his little brother stood, barely visible through the throng surrounding him. "With Santos around, I don't plan to let you out of my sight."

Virginia laughed. "He's already told me everything. Even about the time you broke his nose and chin. I swear that man loves to make you out as the ogre." She glanced past her shoulder and wrinkled her little nose. "Besides, he seems pretty busy with the two he brought tonight... and the dozen others he's trying to fend off."

Grateful that for the moment the guests were oblivious to them as they danced amidst so many familiar faces, Marcos ran a hand down her back and glanced at the firm swell between their bodies. "How do you feel?" he asked, somber.

She smiled as she canted her head back to meet his gaze. "I feel...perfect." She kissed his lips and gazed up at him with those same green eyes that had haunted him. Their sparkle surpassed the blinding one of the ring on her finger, and her smile took his breath away—like it did every day. "You?" she asked.

His lips curled into a smile, and he bent his head, fully intending to take that mouth of hers. "A hundred thousand dollars shorter," he baited. He touched her lips, and his smile widened. "And I've never felt so lucky."

* * * * *

THE GRASS WIDOW
AND HER COW

THE GRASS WIDOW
AND HER COW

An Enchanting Account
of Country Life
in Wartime Britain

BARBARA PAYNTER

Robson Books

First published in Great Britain in 1997 by Robson Books Ltd, Bolsover House, 5-6 Clipstone Street, London W1P 8LE

British Library Cataloguing in Publication Data
A catalogue record for this title is available from the British Library

ISBN 1 86105 090 9

Set in Plantin by Pitfold Design, Hindhead, Surrey.
Printed in Great Britain by St Edmundsbury Press, Bury St Edmunds, Suffolk.

Contents

I

The Seed is Sown

– I –

'Get a farm going, darling.'

These were Peter's parting words to me on Paddington Station in August 1939. The storm clouds which had been marshalling themselves into a formidable mass were about to burst. Peter, my Royal Air Force husband, had been recalled to his post in the Middle East.

'Get a farm going, darling?' I repeated the words incredulously under my breath. Did he really say that? What a nerve! And he had said it in a matter-of-fact sort of pass-me-the-jam tone.

If I had not been so upset by the parting, I should have felt like starting a domestic argument. It was so typical of the male species. There was Peter, bound for the sunshine and glamour of the East, with all manner of adventures in store for him. It was not enough that I should remain buried in a remote little village in – well, in one of the Home Counties. Terribly safe, with a babe holding me back by each of my apron strings. Nor was it enough that I should have the galling experience of watching my friends leap into smart uniforms and dash about the countryside with the greatest of ease and mobility.

No – Peter's idea while he was abroad was to render me

The express.

completely immobile. With my two begumbooted legs feet deep in manure. And the subtlety with which he produced his argument!

Well, I suppose he was right. Food production would prove to be of great national importance if war came. In any case, there was no one now with whom to argue the point. Peter's tiny handkerchief was fluttering in the distance . . . smaller . . . smaller . . . just a speck . . . gone.

As I turned on my heel, I shook a tiny pearl of moisture on to my gloveless hand. Good gracious! I was crying. What nonsense!

– II –

Food! Food! Food! That would be the battle-cry of the Home Front. And the irony of it all was that I had always hated the sight of it.

I belong to that small band of people, who, unlike the continentals – so keen on their stomachs and what they cram into them – look to some future research in chemistry. A pill packed with vitamins. Why – the very thought of it brings fresh vitality. No more drudgery in the kitchen, shrivelling up into old age like a piece of bacon on a hot range. 'Madam, your pill is served!' With what a thrill of anticipation one would hasten into the dining room!

My sainted aunt! What *is* that disgusting-looking object on the plate? A pig's trotter . . . ?

Well – perhaps food in its 'walking-about' state would be more attractive.

I retraced my steps through the barrier and, with as

business-like an air as I could muster for the occasion, walked up to the bookstall and asked for *Poultry World*.

– III –

It was not until I was journeying homeward in the train that I unrolled my twopenny journal, and began to study the aggressive-looking rooster on the cover. What was there about that bird that gave him the right to advertise himself so brazenly? I suspected something indecent.

Underneath was written in small print – and no wonder – *Pure Bred RIR*. I was afraid to try and translate it for fear of revealing something to outrage my, as yet, unsullied feelings.

I turned over a page or two and scanned the advertisement columns. I read:

Ready to Mate – How did they know? *Brown Leghorns. RIR Cockerels – Fifteen Shillings each. Healthy Birds on Free Range . . . Certified Free BWD . . .* Quite frankly, I did not like that BWD business at all. What could it mean? It was evidently something so horrible that it could not be printed in full.

I continued to read: *Mixed Sexes – RIR x WW.LS.* And then finally the last straw: *Sex-Linked Pullets.* This was too much. It all sounded too grotesque for words. It ought not to be allowed.

I decided that fond as I was of animals, 'getting a farm going' was not my line of country. And just as I was about to divert my eyes to the soothing scenery of the English countryside, I caught sight of the words *Rhode Island Red*.

Why, that surely was the harmless translation of 'RIR', to which my by now not-so-pure mind had attached some sinister meaning!

After that I became quite adept at deciphering. Let me see, LS? Could that be 'Light Sussex'? *Certified BWD?* No, that one was beyond me.

I was just beginning to understand some of the poultry hieroglyphics when the speed of the train slackened as the brakes were applied.

The name of my home town came ringing through the open window of my carriage. And for the first time, it took on a more significant meaning. Here was an agricultural town, if ever there was one! In the heart of a farming county.

My thoughts flew over the house-tops into the surrounding country, where low muslin-like lengths of mist measure themselves over the fields at this time of year. Then gradually there emerged from the vapour weird shapes . . . ridiculous shapes . . . . Why, could they be . . . ? Were they . . . ? Yes – of course – they were sheep.

And the fields . . . that belt of elms with the kink in it. Yes, and there was the house . . . our house. Funny, I never knew we had sheep nearby.

I came back to earth, and found myself sitting quietly in the car. I pushed in the gear, and moved off on the last lap of eleven miles.

It was market day, and still only the forenoon. The car was soon brought to a standstill in the thickly populated streets. But I was not in any hurry. I wanted to enjoy the busy scene. For although I had lived in the district for years, it was all quite new to me today.

The streets were crowded with worthy country folk who had found their way into the town from the outlying villages. Bobbing baskets, laden with the fruits of the soil, bounced their way down the streets, ricocheting from various anatomical points of the good-natured crowd.

Motor cars, with trailers attached, eased their way into every available space in the Market Square.

Rowdy lads with sticks herded frightened bullocks, mid shouts of 'Hey yip, there!'

The little pubs – and they are numerous in my home town, some of them dating back hundreds of years – rang out with jovial laughter, as the farmers met to complete their deals over a pint of ale.

And this is England! It always has been. And, please God, it always will be: the land we love, the land we have fought for in the past, and, if need be, will fight for again. Not even the disturbing events of the past few weeks could upset the spontaneous good humour of this little country town.

– V –

As I moved off in the direction of my village, all manner of memories came crowding through my mind.

The day Peter and I first travelled along this road in search of a nest for our young – Rosemary and John.

I shall never forget that day. That first sight of our future home. It was early spring, before the elm trees had burst their leaf buds. And the ancient willows that stood round about, even they were not yet feathered with green.

The quiet flat fields spoke to us in a language so new

At the window, above the wild hemlock.

that we could scarcely understand. We had been accustomed to the discordant clang of military bands; they whistled and blew, and had screeched past the married quarters in which we had lived for the last few years on a Royal Air Force Station.

This new-found stillness left us awestruck and bewildered. And though ideas and thoughts came tumbling over each other in our minds as we gazed up from the gate, it seemed as though we were afraid to speak.

Might we not perhaps disturb the spirits of the ancient yeoman family who had lived there in this house hundreds of years ago? The old house whispered to us of them.

Peter came back to earth first. Peter generally does – he is the breadwinner!

'Come on, we can't stay gazing at ruins all day long.'

'Ruins?' I protested. 'I don't see any ruins. I see an adorable house with endless possibilities.' And then, with a dramatic aside, I whispered gently in his ear, 'Our house, in fact.'

'It would not surprise me if the death-watch beetle ate it up in front of our very eyes.'

This remark struck horror to my heart. I pictured millions of black beetles branded with the skull and crossbones on their shiny backs 'tucking in' to huge chunks of roof! 'Ugh!' I shuddered.

And then, as if by some miracle, a lead-light window blew gently ajar.

Peter was the first to scramble through. I followed closely on his heels.

At this point, we are in danger of losing the narrative, because we are in danger of being lost ourselves. I cannot

The Swift acts as moving van as we move in.

say what happened to us inside those enchanted walls. It is not for me, a worldly narrator, to break the spell of such a romantic interlude. I can only tell you that Peter, with a masterly flourish of the quill, signed on the dotted line.

Suffice it to say that we came into possession of the yeoman's inheritance.

From that day forward, we began to swell with the pride of landed gentry. We strutted about our fields, counting our acres. There were fifteen of them.

From indoors came the discordant hammering of the British workmen. They swarmed up and down ladders with serpent-like pipes writhing in their hands. Thus was the plumbing completed.

'Get a farm going, darling.' Why, of course, I had forgotten.

II

'Mr' Todd

– I –

A week later Great Britain declared war on Germany. The suspense was ended, and the gates of Hell were once again flung wide. Already Poland had begun to feel the tongues of flame about her.

Somewhere a telephone bell was ringing. But it was no business of mine, and in any case, I was too far away. It would cease ringing before I should have time to reach it.

'Will you answer it, or shall I, ma'am?' gasped Mrs Noble, our dear old cook-housekeeper, as she came panting out of breath into the room.

I was gazing out of the window not two yards away from the telephone. I shook myself out of my reverie.

'I will, thank you,' I replied, as I felt the colour rising to my cheeks.

She must have thought I was crazy. Perhaps I am? And what could be more fitting than a crazy world peopled by crazy folk?

I lifted the receiver. 'Yes, hullo! Oh, yes . . . Mr Todd? . . . Poultry adviser for the district? . . . Oh, yes, you got my letter? . . . Quite quick . . . You could come out this afternoon? . . . Good. Certainly . . . Quite convenient . . . Goodbye.'

Bother!

I had forgotten to ask about payment. I wondered, would Mr Todd be the sort of 'Fee' man? By this, I mean, the man who just casually mentions the sum required while making some joke, while you, sick with anticipation, sit listening at *his* desk, ready to sign the cheque with *his* pen. This procedure always seems to me so unfair. For surely, if it had been *your* desk, and *your* pen, nothing on earth would have induced you to put your signature to such an infamous slip of paper.

I *did* hope Mr Todd would not be a 'Fee' man.

On the other hand, could you just reach for your handbag and say, as you delved optimistically into its usually empty depths, 'How much is that, please?'

I felt it was all very awkward. I should have to rely on my instincts. If they should fail me now, then at least I should be certain of one thing: that I was no longer a lady – and nothing would suit me better at this juncture of my career.

This farm business would bring me in contact with all manner of new friends. I did not doubt that very soon I should be hobnobbing with the local farmers, and smacking the 'behinds' of 'beefy bullocks' with the best of them.

At the moment I could hardly tell one end of a bullock from the other. With cows it was easier. I had made that small discovery when I was a child.

– II –

Mr Todd arrived after tea, and together we discussed chickens.

We walked about the fields and I told him my plans for the garden. I had no intention of digging up the lawn.

Mapping out the kitchen garden.

Nor of planting cabbages all round my front door. It might sound unpatriotic. but I could not see the point of it, when I had a perfectly good paddock, just through the stable yard, that was screaming to yield up its virginity and produce exhibition Brussels sprouts like young coconut trees.

'You have everything you need for a smallholding – plenty of land, and excellent buildings.' Mr Todd was most encouraging, and though we had never mentioned cattle, as that was not his department, I already began to visualize nice, friendly faces peering over the stable doors at me.

'A "Fold Unit" is what I should advise for your hens – commonly known round here as a "Folder".'

'A folder?' I queried. 'What in the name of fortune is that?'

'It is an excellent house for a small number of pullets,' he replied, drawing it out on the grass with his stick. 'A long, narrow-shaped wooden erection with a pointed roof. It is usually made from elm wood to withstand the weather. Part of it is open and covered with wire netting. This forms the run. One end is enclosed—'

'A sort of bedroom?' I chipped in.

'Yes – that's the idea. About twenty to twenty-five pullets may roost together with ease.'

I thought he said 'a small number'. It sounded highly improper to me. And most unhygienic. But, after all, he was the expert. I did not even know what stage of adolescence a pullet reached. And as I pondered on these things, I recalled to mind the rooster on the cover of that twopenny magazine.

Well, I decided. It was no use worrying my head about him. What had he got to do with it, anyhow? Yes, that was just the question. What had he . . . ?

For the present, that problem – pressing though it may seem – will have to remain unanswered. I did not doubt that I should soon find out all I wanted to know, and a great deal more besides. I could not very well have a man-to-man talk with Mr Todd on the subject. Perhaps when I had acquired those corduroys I had ordered and the ploughboy appearance, the mental outlook would follow as a matter of course.

We made our way back into the house, where I could find paper and pencil with which to make a few notes. 'Fold Units' from Messrs So and So . . . Pullets, etc.

Very soon now we shall be able to deal with actual facts. And who knows? Perhaps scatter a few hints gained at the expense of my own incredible follies.

'Another glass of sherry, Mr Todd?'

And to think that I had contemplated paying the man!

– III –

I discovered afterwards that not only *had* I paid Mr Todd for his visit to see me, but that I had been paying him generously for years for not coming anywhere near me! Well, at least one disgruntled taxpayer was getting something for her money.

And now that we know, there will be no need in the future to press that second glass of sherry!

Rosemary, Butler and John in high summer.

III

Butler

– I –

And now, quickly, before the animals arrive, and before I have time to appropriate for myself the credit of achievements – as yet, only in the imagination – we must go out of doors and find Butler.

He will doubtless be digging in the new Victory garden with as much sober determination as he handled his firearms in the last war.

He had been 'seriously wounded' and invalided out of the army with a disability pension. But he was not a man to sit back, and eke out an existence in idleness. He had gradually regained a measure of his former health, and sought once again the medium in which he had been moulded from boyhood – the soil.

Now – believe it or not – Butler is a gentleman. I do not mean in the sense you mean. He lacks education, which, ridiculous though it may seem, entitles him to what is known as 'top-drawer' accommodation (not that Butler, with his open-air instincts, would ever wish to be placed in anything so stuffy as a drawer, whether top, middle, or bottom!).

Butler has a wealth of knowledge, about which even those out of the top drawer of a tallboy would know nothing. He could teach them the philosophy of life, if only they would listen, or better still, watch, as words do

The wartime vegetable garden.

not come very easily to Butler. But they are too stupid to learn about the things that matter.

Higher finance and the science of getting rich are the essence of their superficial existence. And the joke of it all is that Butler has the formula up his sleeve! Incidentally, one of Peter's old sleeves. There was almost a domestic crisis over that jersey. It happened to be one of the favourites! But that is another story . . . .

And we have not yet found Butler. But when we do, well, one has only to catch the twinkle in his eye to know that he is fooling us all!

But I dream, and there is no time for dreaming. One day perhaps, the Butlers of this world will call us out into the fields, and educate us. Show us the poetry of a scythe and the gentle rhythm of its swing.

Just now, it is swords not ploughshares. And until this war is won, we cannot escape from our 'blacked-out' existence. Work alone can free us and bring us peace. And – just in case I am becoming a little too melodramatic – shall we add 'for a thousand years'!

Is that not faintly reminiscent of a gangster?

– II –

But here is Butler.

'Why – what is that colossal thing on the grass beyond you, Butler?'

'Only the folder, ma'am.'

'But how did it get here, and surely it folds up?'

'I know it don't, ma'am. Leastways, not the ones I see before.'

'But, Butler, if it does not fold or take to pieces, why is it called a folder?'

'Couldn't say, ma'am. They things haven't never folded since I knowed 'em.'

Baffled, I let the subject drop. So here was my first piece of farm furniture. A folder which did not fold.

I went up to it and examined it closely. It was well made, about ten feet long, solid and extremely heavy.

Butler demonstrated how to move it. He took up a stout pole which had been delivered with it. There was an iron projection at each end of the 'nonfolder'. (I refuse to call it a 'folder' any longer.) Butler thrust the stick under these in turn, shuffling first one end, and then the other.

'Little by little does it, ma'am.'

Does what? I thought. It did not appear to be moving at all. The strain of its weight brought up the veins over his temples.

'So this is how it came from Messrs—?' I forget the name just now. 'A distance of over five miles? What . . . ' I said jokingly, as I lent him a hand.

Butler was straining every muscle. It was not to be wondered at that he failed to see the humour of my remark. Quite unnecessarily, since it was only too obvious and he himself was short of breath, he repeated, 'Little by little, does it, ma'am.'

The colossus had only been moved a few feet. However, I could see that it had advantages. Each day it could, with an effort, be moved in this manner on to fresh ground. One of the secrets of successful poultry rearing – see page two, column four, in *Poultry World*.

I lifted the lid of the bedroom-end of it. There were

three neat little 'built-in' nest boxes, so modern and convenient.

I immediately set about stuffing them with hay, to make them look really inviting. I was quite certain, in my own mind, that the pullets on seeing them, mid scenes of mass hysteria, would make a wild rush to occupy them, with but one idea in their heads: eggs.

– III –

It was not very long before I discovered that that sort of hysterical make-up does not apply to hens – at least not to *my* hens. I soon learnt that the more alluring the soft hay and cosy nest box, the more disdain on the pullet's face as she struts past it mumbling with her nose in the air, 'Open to the vulgar gaze of all and sundry, certainly not!'

I now firmly believe that eggs are laid more by accident than a genuine desire to do anybody a good turn. Never be deceived by that purposeful 'Win-the-War' look on a pullet's face. It never means what you think it does.

Just you ask her. And as she wanders off in the opposite direction, you will hear her muttering to herself, 'An egg? Nothing is further from my thoughts. The very idea! An egg, indeed!'

– IV –

Where were we? Oh, yes – the folder. We may, however, assume that by now the stage is set, and that we are ready for the animals to walk on and play their natural and primitive parts, with an ease and instinct that only animals possess . . . thank God!

IV

The Egg Is Laid

John, Rosemary and friend in front of the house.

– I –

A few days later, on October the third, the whole household was gathered about the folder.

The pullets were due at any moment. Rosemary, our little girl aged ten, who had just won a prize at school for stuffing an elephant made from American cloth, was busily engaged in packing more hay into the nest boxes. They were now so full that there would be no room for a pullet, should one, in a rash moment, have wished to walk in and deposit an egg.

John, our small eight-year-old, was flooding the run with water from a can in his eagerness to fill up a small zinc trough.

Even Mrs Noble had made one of her rare 'sorties' from the kitchen region over which she reigned supreme. She was engaged in trying out first in one box, then in another, a rather pallid-looking egg, with an unnaturally high gloss.

No self-respecting pullet would be taken in by *that* egg, even supposing it could see it, which would be next to impossible in view of the tangle of hay which obscured it. However, nobody liked telling Mrs Noble that she was wasting her time, so this little pantomime was in full swing when suddenly our hearts stood still. The long expected van was coming down the lane.

The children shrieked. The dog barked. There was pandemonium! The pullets had arrived!

Twenty beautiful white birds, with a few black spots

about their necks and tails. They were a First Cross – Light Sussex with Rhode Island Red, which in the book would be set down as LSxRIR, and is known as one of the heavier breeds.

I think the inference here is much the same as it is with tanks and battleships. There are light and heavy tanks, and light and heavy cruisers, so why not light and heavy chickens? But I have never dared to show my ignorance by asking anybody if it makes any difference to the size and weight of an egg. But being one of those people who believe in getting their money's worth, I plumped for a heavy breed, hoping to get phenomenal eggs so tightly packed with whatever there is in an egg – and I have never quite got to the bottom of this – that they might weigh as heavy as dumb-bells.

'Catch 'em by the legs, missie,' enjoined Butler, as he pulled a pullet out of the box upside down.

'Oh, Butler! How crool you are,' cried the children in unison.

'It be the right way, m'dears. It don't hurt 'em any.'

Meanwhile Rosemary's bird had already flapped its way free from her gently enfolding arms, and had made off to the other end of the paddock. Both she and John pursued at the gallop, and together with Musket, our little beady-eyed black Scottie, were closing in on the poor frightened creature.

She was soon caught, and put into the folder with the others who, even during this short spell of absence, had almost forgotten her and were ready to eye the late-comer with suspicion.

This is one of the curious facts about hens. They have

First came the hens on 3 October.

no memory for faces. I can appreciate their difficulty, as they all look alike to me. Once a bird has departed from their midst, even if she is a blood relation and comes from the same clutch (see – how already I begin to learn!) she at once becomes an outsider. And woe be to her if ever she ventures to stage a 'come-back'. She is promptly set upon by an angry mob, mid shouts of, 'What the . . . ! Who the . . . . ! Get out of here! You . . . ! You . . . !'

And when the feathers have subsided, you will see a dejected and quite indecently naked little pullet slinking around the run, with scarcely a rag to its back. I mean, of course, feather to its 'behind'.

We took it in turns, about once every three hours, to rush out and search for eggs.

For days we lifted the lid in a frenzy of excitement. But
each time only the cold unnatural glaze of Mrs Noble's pot
egg mocked us through the hay.

Then, one day, I reached the end of my tether. I could
stand it no longer. The cold calculating perfidy of that
false egg. There was something sinister about it. It was
bewitched, and casting an evil spell over my beautiful
birds.

Shaking from head to foot, I seized hold of it in a fit of
temper, and hurled it over the nearest hedge.

And in the same mood I walked back into the house with
an abnormally noisy step, and got into touch with Mrs
Wild over the telephone.

'Those pullets you sold me . . . I am afraid they are no
good . . . No, no sign of an egg *yet* and you assured me
they were just coming on to lay . . . Red? Yes, blood red!
Oh, you mean their combs? I don't know – why should
they be? Yes, now I come to think of it, I have noticed one
or two with quite red combs and gills – or whatever those
side bits are called. A good sign . . . ? Do they talk . . . ?
Oh, yes, quite chatty in their own way I should say . . . It's
too early yet? Oh, it's six months, is it? And these pullets
are only five and a half months old. Oh, I see . . . And the
heavier breeds take longer? Is that so . . . ? I
misunderstood. I am so sorry I worried you, but I was
beginning to despair of ever seeing an egg in my lifetime.
Perhaps, the children one day . . . You are sure? Oh, well,
that's all right then . . . No need to worry any more . . . I
am relieved . . . And how are you keeping, Mrs Wild?
And your little girl? Splendid . . . I *am* glad. Well,
goodbye then, and I won't worry any more. You think I

really will get an egg one day, ha! ha! . . . Oh, yes, they get good feeding . . . just as you directed. Dry mash all the time, grain midday, and wet mash at tea-time – also a drop of milk if we have any to spare . . . Yes, everything of the best, with a few scraps thrown in . . . Yes, I am *sure* they will, ha! ha! . . . Goodbye.'

After this enlightening conversation, I hung up the receiver, and went and told everybody that there would be no point in looking for eggs any more at present. The pullets were not quite old enough to lay any.

The silence which followed this depressing statement was broken only by a snort from John.

'Well, what rotten hens!'

– II –

A whole fortnight elapsed before we began once again to look for eggs. From this time onwards my letters to Peter started off something like this :

October 21st Darling, there has not been an egg yet, but I think there will be very soon, as there is every sign. I wonder if that ass Mussolini will get himself mixed up in this war? . . .

October 23rd Sweetheart – still no egg, but the pullets' combs are very red, and they say that is one of the signs, so it won't be long now. John is in bed with a cold . . .

October 27th No eggs yet, dear. But Rosemary thought she saw a hen hovering near one of the nest boxes today, so perhaps tomorrow I shall have something exciting to tell you. The news is very uneventful – perhaps it is just as well . . .

October 30th   No eggs yet, which begins to be a little irksome, but I suppose one must possess oneself in patience . . .

November 2nd   Still no eggs.   We are losing interest.   Only Butler looks now when he feeds . . .

November 5th   Those wretched pullets.   I wish I had never set eyes on them.   It is quite obvious that they intend to go down to their graves 'egg-bound' or something equally revolting . . .

And then – one day not long after this outburst – I was able to start my letter in a different strain.

November 8th   At last!   An egg!   And, sweetheart, it is the most perfect little oval egg that has ever been laid!

I must tell you how it all happened . . .

I was ironing up in the childrens' room, when I suddenly heard a shriek from the garden.   My heart started to gallop, and I felt quite sick as I tore down the back stairs, with all the speed that I could gather.   'Oh! Mummy! Mummy! Quick!   Come here!'   I was in a frenzy of anxiety, thinking something dreadful had happened to one of the children. My fears were soon allayed when I caught sight of their beaming faces.   I guessed at once what had happened, and ran to join them at the folder.

And there, in all its glory, lay our first adorable little egg. It was a poem!

We stood and gazed upon it with deep reverence, It was indeed a miracle.   We had never seen such an egg before. No egg had ever looked so smooth, so radiant, so absolutely indescribable.   We were enraptured, entranced.

And none of us dared to defile it with our hands. Even the children had caught some of the dignity of the moment. And would not have touched it for worlds.

We looked lovingly on the pullets and tried to pick out the one who had so abundantly justified her existence, but we could not find a single expression which seemed to indicate 'Alone I did it.'

Yes, by gad – she had! No rooster had had anything to do with that egg! The realization of which fact set me thinking quite a lot.

John carried the egg back to the house. Then it was Rosemary's privilege to place it reverently in Mrs Noble's outstretched hands. She had heard the shrieks of delight, and was there to greet us at the back door.

'My! What a beauty!' she exclaimed, as she fondled it with her rough old hands. 'It's been worth waiting for, ma'am.' To which rejoinder I heartily agreed.

– III –

Nobody could have believed that such gentle beauty, such simple innocence, could create a situation – a crisis, in fact – as did this egg at breakfast time on the following morning.

'Well, anyhow, I saw it first,' said John, as he grabbed the egg from the kitchen table, and held it behind his back.

'That isn't any reason why you should eat it, you horrid, greedy little boy,' argued Rosemary with some heat.

Mrs Noble held up a peremptory finger before their scowling faces.

'Now, now, you two. Stop quarrelling, or I won't cook it

for either of you,' she interrupted wisely.

At this moment the situation was eased by the timely arrival of Butler with another egg.

But it is an ironic fact that once the first rapture of an enchanted moment – such as the sight of the first primrose, or the first sight of your first child – has spent itself, you can never again recapture the subtle poignancy of that thrill which once caused the pulses to beat so quickly.

It was like that with us when we saw the second egg. It was just too commonplace for words. Why, it could not even be expected to taste so good.

Now for the moment we are going to leave the poultry. But I warn you, we shall often return. The spectre of the rooster on the famous magazine cover still haunts us. He struts up and down in the background. We cannot escape him.

Listen! I hear him now . . . Cock-a-doodle-doo!

V

Three Little Pigs

The pigs arrived in November.

– I –

After having talked 'chickens' for a chapter or two, you may think we are going to talk 'Pigs', and so we are. But not until we have first talked 'Trousers'.

You will ask: 'But what have trousers got to do with pigs?' And all I can say is, that nothing would induce me to go near a pig, with its long cold snout, in anything but trousers.

I ordered a pair of thick corduroys from my local tailor. At the time I had not given a thought to the difficulties that might arise. Although I had often been fitted by this man for various costumes in the past, I had never been fitted for trousers. And when there is only a top-heavy screen between you and the male world, you do become faintly aware of your delicate position.

Skirts are easy. They go over the head. And one need not let go of the old one before the new one is in position.

With trousers it is quite another matter. Things do not work out so well. It is easy enough for men, who may even dispose of the screen altogether. But, for women, that screen is of life and death importance.

'Just slip them on, ma'am. I will come back when you are ready,' says the fitter, as he discreetly retires.

Immediately you begin to panic. There is no time to lose. You wonder just how long he will give you. You rip out important tacking stitches in your flurry to scramble into them. Break out into a cold sweat. And then, when you are finally ready with apparently hours to spare, you wonder just what to do. Whether to emerge from behind the screen, and go sheepishly in search of the fitter, or whether to remain hidden, and shout 'cuckoo' over the top. Although the whole business is one long game of hide and seek, this last practice is not to be recommended for fear of being misunderstood.

If my trousers had not turned out to be the success they were, I should certainly have decided that they were not worth the strain on the nervous system.

But my trousers were a success of the first order. From the moment I stepped into them in the sanctuary of my own bedroom, I felt master of the situation.

I went out into the stable yard to look for Butler. He was busy chopping wood for the house.

'Butler,' I said, with a confidence which had hitherto been lacking. 'Those pigs we were talking about, I have telephoned the County Agricultural Adviser and he has told me of a farm not far from here, where I can get some. I am fetching them this afternoon. Will you get the sty ready, please?'

'Very good, ma'am.'

Was it imagination on my part or did I catch sight of a little nod of approval from Butler as he eyed my new and extremely business-like attire?

– II –

That afternoon I set off in my car Now, my car is a 1933 Ford Eight with a special body. 'Very special!' I can hear the children proclaim in unison, after many uncomfortable rides in the back seat.

I do not deny that it is draughty. The side curtains no longer fit as new, which is not to be wondered at, considering the age of the car. The hood leaks too, if it rains very heavily. And some very weird and wonderful smells exude from beneath the bonnet. Smells which always afford a clue for John's inevitable little joke about his gas mask.

Yes, there certainly have been some very rude remarks from various members of the family. Not least among these come from my mother, who, in the person of 'Gran', will make her debut in a later chapter.

But I must just recall one incident when she and I were caught in a cloud-burst whilst out in the car together one day.

Huge drops of rain were pouring through starlike holes in the hood, when suddenly Gran – never at a loss — hoisted her gamp above her head muttering something about not having her best hat spoilt for 'anybody'!

It mattered little, that I, the long-suffering driver, should be receiving the full force of a young Niagara Falls down the back of my neck from one of the spokes of this wretched contraption.

By the time we finally reached home, we had something resembling a canvas bath on top of the car. You know, the sort of thing you see displayed in the camp equipment section of a big London store.

Gran stepped out of the car and if looks could kill . . . .

But old cars have definite advantages on a farm like this, where, for the present, there is no trailer. It is surprising what a number of farm animals are able to pack into the back seat.

On paper, I should say the seating capacity of my car would be: two adults in front, and one adult or two children behind. There is no mention of pigs. And it is just as well, for I should not like to count how many pigs, four-legged ones I mean, have laid claim to the leather cushions of my back seat.

Just for a start – we are on our way now to collect three little 'weaners'. Yes – that is the name, I have just looked it up!

I had always been in the habit of calling them 'piglets' before. But that apparently is reserved exclusively for Mr A. A. Milne and would not be understood by a real farmer.

– III –

I arrived at the farm, the buildings of which, like most English farms at this time of year, appear to be countersunk in a quagmire. There were cows standing half-way up their legs in it, staring aimlessly at closed gates.

In a distant corner of the large yard, I watched an old sow wallowing for minerals with her snout deep in the mud. Not far away, and scampering in all directions with their tails spinning like Catherine Wheels, were over a dozen little pigs. Every so often they would return to the 'milk bar' under mama for a drop of refreshment before running off for another game.

A motley collection of chickens, a dog straining on the chain of his kennel, made from an old barrel, and a man on top of a muck heap with a 'Four-tine' fork in his hand, completed this everyday scene of English farm life. And in spite of the mud, I found myself fast falling in love with it all. I suspected the corduroys had something to do with my new-found attitude. But in my heart of hearts I knew it went deeper than that. It went back through the years – I shall not say how many, although I know you are burning with curiosity to know – when I lived with my parents in a remote little village in the heart of the country. In those days, whether I leapt over stiles or crawled through holes in hedges at the bidding of my tomboy instincts, it would always be Mr So-and-So's field in which I found myself. And the lambs, they, too, belonged to him.

But today it was different. I am that awe-inspiring Mr So-and-So of my youth. I own the fields. I am the farmer. I no longer wanted to call 'weaners' 'piglets', or 'sows' 'lady pigs'. No, nor even 'boars' 'gentlemen pigs'.

On the contrary, I wanted to shout 'Boars!' at the top of my voice from the house-tops, to proclaim to the world I was no longer an amateur at this farm business. And that I knew what I was talking about. But did I? That was the question.

I picked my way through the mud to one of the barns where I could hear machinery in motion. A man was holding a bag beneath the grinder, into which fresh ground meal was pouring mid a cloud of white dust.

I went up to him unnoticed and shouted— But for some reason or other it was not 'Boars' nor anything like it. I must have lost my nerve at the last moment.

'Are you Mr Yates?'

'Yes, ma'am.' He stopped the tractor which enabled me to lower my voice.

'Have you any weaners to sell me?'

'Why, yes, ma'am, plenty.'

'What age are they?'

'Any age you like, ma'am. I have 'em all ages. Eight weeks? Nine weeks? Ten weeks?'

'Well, I was advised to get them about nine weeks old, if possible.'

'Come this way, ma'am, and I'll show you what I have.' Then he looked at my shoes and added, 'There be a terrible lot of mud about.'

'Never mind,' I reassured him, 'I cannot get my shoes much worse than they are already.'

Mr Yates was doubtless one of the farmers who had been 'let down' after the last war. The Government at that time had promised him a great future. He had sweated and toiled, and when peace had finally come after four long years, he had been cheated of the fruits of his labour.

It was one of the scandals of the post-war period. It must not be allowed to recur after this war. The British lion must no longer be encouraged to lie down with the Canterbury lamb. Such audacity on the lamb's part should lead him to fresh fields and other companionships. And, anyhow, at the moment, we do not want to talk of British lions lying down at all. We want them to rise up on their two hind legs, rampant, and ready for the final assault on the disillusioned vultures of the Third Reich.

But I have wandered away from the point, not to mention the farm. I must go back, or Mr Yates, and possibly you, will get impatient.

Mr Yates, Bill and I waded single file through a sea of liquid manure until we reached an old barn that seemed to me to have been partly devoured by rats. One draughty end of it was partitioned off with old gnarled planks.

There were loud squeals and grunts as we peered over the side and saw eight . . . ten . . . no, there were twelve of them! Little pink pigs, silent now, striking attitudes, motionless, as in some tableau. Some were squinting at us out of their eye corners. And all of them were mesmerized with fright.

Mr Yates and the man went in amongst them.

'How many do you want, ma'am?'

'I think I could take three.'

'You will have a gilt among 'em?'

'Oh, yes, certainly,' I said, not having the remotest idea what a gilt was.

There was much squealing and scuffling as the terrified little weaners scampered about endeavouring to avoid capture.

Bill made a lunge at one of them.

''Old 'er, Bill!' shouted the farmer, with a note of triumph in his voice. 'She be a gilt.'

And with this remark he seized the wretched little animal by the two hind legs and held it upside down in front of me.

'Count 'em, ma'am,' he said. 'She should have at least seven a side to make a good sow.'

So *that* was it. It dawned on me, this gilt business. It was a matter of buttons!

Did Mr Yates really expect me to run up and down the scale with my index finger, counting aloud, in front of him and his man? Luckily I could see at a glance there were enough . . . buttons (I have not yet looked up the correct term here. I doubt if I should use it in any case?) to rear a fair-sized family.

'She will do,' I announced, as I started to walk away to hide my confusion .

Two more little pigs were eventually caught, and bundled into the back of the car.

After handing over my cheque to Mr Yates, I bade him and his man 'good-day' and escaped, driving at top speed to the accompaniment of high-pitched squeals – not to mention whiffs!

Perhaps, after all, there *was* something in John's gas-mask idea. But somehow I could not bring myself to put mine on.

There was something too much like a snout about it for my liking.

Our pigs' taxi.

VI

Betsy

Our resident housekeeper, Mrs Noble.

The sound of the horn as I reached home brought everybody running. The children emitted their usual 'noises off'. Musket barked, and not many minutes were lost before the familiar figure of Mrs Noble was framed in the back doorway. The excitement was too much for her. She hurried out wiping her hands on her fresh white apron.

Only Butler remained unperturbed as he opened the door of the stable – there were no proper pigsties as yet – that he had made ready for the new inmates.

Nothing ever rattles Butler. There is far too much rhythm and music in the man.

As was only to be expected, Rosemary, unable to wait to see the little pigs, had flung open the car door with the inevitable result. After the ensuing chase that the children seemed to regard as the preliminary initiation for membership to our farm, the three bewildered little weaners were eventually driven into their stable home.

They lost little time in seeking out the fresh sweet straw in one corner, and endeavoured to perform the 'ostrich trick' before the interested gaze of a row of faces above the stable door.

'They are sweet, Mummy. Which one can I have for mine?' pleaded Rosemary.

'I want the one with the curly tail,' piped John. 'Is it a boy or a girl, Mummy?'

'That one be a gilt, my son,' interrupted Butler before I could answer.

'A gilt? What is a gilt, Mummy?' asked John.

'Oh! Just a young girl pig,' I replied.

'Then I shall call mine Betsy. What will you call yours, Rosemary?'

'George, if it is a boy.'

'Aye, m'duck. There only be one gilt among they lot,' chipped in Butler.

We were wavering on the brink of the precipice. Any moment we might be over; we were, with John's next remark.

'How can you tell the difference between a girl pig and a boy pig, Mummy?'

This was one of John's own brand, usually reserved for a packed railway carriage or a crowded restaurant. As Butler was still within hearing, I felt it was time to change the subject. Luckily Mrs Noble came to my rescue.

'Your tea will be ready in five minutes, ma'am.'

'Come on then, darlings,' I said breezily, as I lifted John down off the door. 'We must all go in and tidy.'

But at that moment Butler approached with a bucket. I was curious to know what one gave pigs to eat.

'What have you got there, Butler?'

'Just a bucket of water with a measure or two of "toppings" mixed in with it, ma'am.'

He poured the contents out into a shining new zinc trough.

The little pigs, obviously accustomed to trough feeding,

tumbled over each other in their eagerness to get bodily submerged. Their little snouts were very soon lost in the liquid. And all that could be heard as we left them were long-drawn-out sucking noises. Like the last dregs of water being sucked down a sink.

So much for pig-keeping. It was the simplest thing on earth!

Really, this farming racket! There was nothing in it at all. I was saying this under my breath to myself, when I caught sight of that little gilt, squinting at me out of an eye corner. There was meaning in that look. I did not like it at all. It spelt trouble ahead. But it was no use worrying about things at this point.

And now at last – for the light is beginning to fade – we had better go in to tea.

That night, after the children were safely tucked up in bed, I settled down to write to Peter and informed him of his ever-increasing responsibilities at home.

Betsy has a visitor.

VII

Enter The Nuisance Value

Julia, the next to arrive.

– I –

And so the players of this little farmyard drama are fast taking up their positions on the stage.

Soon, very soon now, it will be time for the star performer to make her bow. But to ensure that everybody is keyed up to a fever of expectancy, she must remain a little longer in the wings, while we put the finishing touches to the set; which, by the way, is an author's romantic way of telling you that Julia, the cow, is still over on the island of Jersey, and there is a hell of a lot of scene shifting still to be done, before the curtain can go up!

Before I go any further, I must tell you that Julia was a legacy from the children's great-grandmother. An aged old lady of one hundred years. We venerated her name, bless her, by calling the cow after her. Unfortunately, some of the other members of the family did not altogether appreciate this gesture!

However, very soon the little heifer – don't tell me you don't know what a heifer is? – did leave the island, which turned out to be the cleverest move of her life, in view of the Nazi occupation a few months later.

She eventually came to one of our big towns. And it was here, in the company of Mr Cripps, the County

Agricultural Adviser, that I first made her acquaintance.

– II –

We arrived late at the sale room, and the auctioneer's hammer had already knocked down quite a few head of cattle by the time we reached the ringside.

There were all manner of people seated round on benches. Gentlemen farmers in highly polished boots and rough tweeds. Ladies with fur rugs drawn over their knees to keep out the draught, and an assortment of farming folk from every walk of life.

We watched several heifers fall under the hammer before a particularly pretty little cow, with a distinctly retroussé nose, was led into the ring followed by a calf.

The miniature reproduction seemed to be giving a bit of trouble, and two stalwart men were pushing it from behind so lustily that it seemed in danger of being telescoped at any moment.

Mr Cripps turned up the heifer in the catalogue for Tuberculin Tested Pedigree Jersey Cattle. It read: No. 2864. Draconian Empress. Broken colour. Born July 26th 1939 etc., etc.

It all seemed very complicated to me – but I did my best to look intelligent.

He pointed to the number and said: 'She is the one for you.'

I thought I detected a note of excitement in his voice. 'Is she?' I said. 'Then what do we do about it?'

And before I knew what was happening, he had challenged the ring with a loud, 'Thirty guineas.'

Things were beginning to move now. I felt extremely agitated. I shuffled my 'seat' up and down on the bench which could not have been very good for my corduroys.

'Thirty-one,' called out someone from the other side of the ring.

So the battle was joined. I took an instant dislike to our rival. I wondered what he looked like. I could only see the top of a green felt hat. I pictured a sulky face with heavy-lidded eyes beneath it – a man bent on doing us down.

'Thirty-one, I'm bid . . . Thirty-one . . . Thirty-one . . .' was the parrot-like gibberish of the auctioneer.

'Just look at that milk vein!' whispered Mr Cripps in a perfect ventriloquism before calling out again, 'Thirty-two.'

'Thirty-three,' came from quite a new quarter.

'Thirty-four.'

It was agony, this bidding business, and oh, so confusing. Who said thirty-four? I had already forgotten.

Was the cow ours at the moment? Or had the man beneath the felt hat snatched her away from us with a flick of one of those ponderous lids?

'Thirty-five.'

'Thirty-six.'

'Thirty-six, I'm bid, thirty-six . . . thirty-six . . . thirty-six . . . going . . .'

That was our bid, anyway.

'Thirty-seven.'

Bother that wretched man! He was doing it on purpose. He knew we meant to have that heifer, and he was determined we should pay a top price.

'Thirty-eight,' shouted Mr Cripps, quite undismayed – after all it was not *his* money.

'Thirty-eight, I'm bid . . . thirty-eight . . . thirty-eight.'

Was our sinister opponent silenced at last?

'Thirty-eight . . . going . . . going . . .'

I held my breath. This was the most exciting moment of my life.

'Gone,' thumped the man on the dais with his little wooden mallet.

The tension of the moment had passed – Julia was mine, mine, mine.

I actually owned a cow. I had never done such a thing in my life before. Well, nobody could say I was not a farmer now. I felt like throwing my hat in the air, and flinging my arms round Mr Cripps. And as for that 'poppet' the auctioneer, I could have hugged him. Luckily for him, he was already engaged in selling Julia's little calf.

I followed Mr Cripps out behind the scenes to look at our cow. She was just passing out of the ring in front of us. I ran my hand along her beautiful straight back. It was like silk to the touch.

She was very soon tied up amongst a line of other cows and heifers in a huge covered-in enclosure. She was very bothered about her calf, and kept turning her head and looking underneath her tummy to see if it was there.

No, it was not the calf. What was it then that kept knocking against her legs? Something heavy and uncomfortable that was making her feel hot and restless?

There were two or three men milking the various cows. Mr Cripps called one over, and placing a shilling in his hand, asked him to milk our cow.

'Cruel, I calls it, keeping a bag at bursting point,' the man snorted.

'Yes, I am afraid that wretched little calf has not had its rations today,' was Mr Cripps' retort,

'It's enough to give 'em milk fever,' muttered the man as he started to draw off some of the milk.

I gathered all this was one of the tricks of the trade. A rotten trick, I thought.

What should I have done without Mr Cripps? He was so efficient. He made arrangements for the heifer to travel with another cow that was going in my direction. He took me off to the office, where I wrote out the cheque thus clinching the deal.

Then together we walked off to the buffet where we toasted Julia in tea!

On the way home we collected dairy equipment: seamless milk pails, and white overalls for Butler.

And after I had telephoned the news through to the house and sent a cable to Peter in Cairo, we made off for home as fast as we could go. I wanted to arrive back before the newcomer. I wanted, above all, to be there as stage managing director in general, to bring up the curtain on our beautiful new glamour girl.

– III –

I heard afterwards that my cable had caused a misapprehension amongst Peter's comrades of the sunbaked desert. He had handed it to a friend, one Dickie Herring, who after reading it, blushed and stammered out 'Congrats, old man,' to which Peter, after momentary surprise, had been obliged to reply, 'Oh, no, not that. Julia is my wife's first cow!'

VIII

Bitter Butter

Posing, I'm afraid!

– I –

If the excitement had been great on the arrival of previous animals to our farm, it was nothing to the thrill we experienced as the lorry carrying Julia swung into the stable yard.

It was late in the evening, quite late. That was the sort of girl Julia was! She always believed in choosing her moment. More often than not, she did this with mischievous aptitude. She had no real vice or malice in her. No, it was not that. But there was just some little impishness about her – call it caprice, if you like – which prompted her to cause upsets and annoyances. And just once in a while she revelled in a good commotion.

So it was not to be wondered at that she chose late evening to make her début. Fetching Butler away from his nice warm hearth at night on a winter's evening was the sort of thing that appealed to Julia.

Yes, she played Butler one or two rather scurvy tricks in her time. It was always Sundays, Whit Mondays and Bank holidays that she wanted to 'go places' and 'do things', and once it was Christmas Day, but if that story comes to be written, it will take a chapter to itself.

I never had the courage to question Butler much about Julia's jaunts, but I gathered there was always some fellow involved!

Julia timed her moments to perfection. And she was quite good on atmosphere too. Tonight it was mystery.

She would keep her public guessing. That was the secret of success.

She came to us 'out of the night' wrapped in a 'cloak of darkness'. It was all very tantalizing for the small group of onlookers gathered round the lorry.

On account of the late hour, the children were in bed. They never forgave Julia for this. But I cannot see her submitting to the usual inauguration ceremony of once round the paddock!

The company, however, was not greatly diminished on their account. An interested Mrs Butler had walked down with her husband from their cottage nearby. She joined Mrs Noble and myself. Everybody was in a high state of eagerness to see the newcomer. There was much chatting and torch flashing.

As soon as the ramp was lowered we focused our flashlights on to the lorry. We peered down the shafts of light that they made.

But the result was disappointing. The odd shapes of Julia's broken white patches played pranks with our eyes, and we found it impossible to pick out her form. We could hardly tell one end of the cow from another – in spite of what I said in a previous chapter.

It was maddening! She came down the ramp and glided silently like some wraith, into the loose-box that Butler had made ready for her

I put out my hand to touch her as she passed; the steadily increasing warmth of her breath warned me of her approaching proximity, and I stepped back a few paces just in time to save my toes. (That would have been a triumph for her!)

For a second, somebody held her lovely head in the beam of their torch. We saw the beautiful symmetry of her horns and the typical Jersey ring of light colour round the nose. And oh! That retroussé nose! It was superb!

After a few alluring little 'mooing' noises, which we interpreted as 'how-do-you-dos' but which might well have been, 'What the hell have you done with my calf?' we dispersed, feeling perhaps a little cheated, but none the less impatient for the morning. Which, after all, was exactly what Julia meant us to feel.

– II –

The following day several farmer friends arrived to see the 'lit'le 'eifer'.

'They do say she came from Jersey.'

'Aye, an' I bet she fetched some money, too.'

'What do they want wiv Jerseys is what I'd like to know.'

'There be no money in Jerseys – not much milk neither.'

'Maybe it's the cream they be arter.'

'They won't get nothing for they calves. They be no good for beef – they be 'alf the size of ours.'

'By! She be good to look on though!'

These were some of the asides passed by the interested gathering of onlookers who had filtered through into our yard.

And, of course, they were right! Julia did not turn out to be a great milker. She was no thousand-gallon-a-year cow. In fact, she proved to have a comparatively low milking average. Two and a half to three gallons a day was her moderate contribution, but it was more than enough for the household.

John on his pony.

She provided vitamins for Rosemary and John and skimmed milk for the porkers. Milk, cream, butter and cheese, not, as a dear old lady once thought, ready on tap from the four respective quarters of her udder. No, there was more to it than that.

Indeed, there was quite a lot of sweated labour behind it.

– III –

How often had I seen Mrs Noble, with sleeves rolled up, and beads of perspiration gathering on her brow as she laboured over the glass churn on the kitchen table? But we altered all that. We had brainstorm after brainstorm about butter making, and in the end – in spite of all the kindly advice we received on the subject – we drew up our own formula, which was gained at the expense of much physical and mental effort.

I well recall the day when I 'took over' and relieved Mrs Noble at the churn. She had been turning the handle for over an hour and there was still no sign of any butter. After continuing for some time longer, she finally gave up and sank, beaten and exhausted, into a chair.

I went to the rescue, fresh to the task, and started to turn, uttering facetious remarks.

'It won't be long now. It is really only knack. Just wants a little patience, you know. Not much trouble, really.'

After another half-hour of turning, first with the right hand, then with the left, a little more forced conversation was tossed over my shoulder to Mrs Noble.

But Mrs Noble had discreetly retired. She sensed the growing tension of the situation which was not in any way relieved after I discovered I was talking to myself.

Minutes which seemed like hours passed, and another half-hour later found me turning the handle of the churn so vigorously that it was jumping about the table – like a thing possessed.

Silently now, and in a white heat, I continued to turn. Soon my teeth would be ground down to the gums. But I could not help it, suddenly, there was a rush of blood to my head and something inside me snapped. It was my self-control.

I seized the churn, lifting it by the handle, and rammed it between my two feet on the floor. I held it in a vice-like grip.

'Now it can't jump about any more,' I snarled with sinister satisfaction. 'I'll die rather than be defeated by this beastly butter. Gosh! How I hate it!'

I was muttering to myself in this manner and turning the handle so furiously when Mrs Noble reappeared that, for a moment, she thought I had taken leave of my senses. Luckily Mrs Noble had the good sense not to voice her sentiments, as I think at that moment I might have been dangerous.

Anyhow, it did the trick, but not before my pale and interesting face had turned a vivid puce, and I myself had been very near to throwing an apoplectic fit. All of which, it will be realized, is not worth the wear and tear.

Here then, are a few hints, gained from 'bitter' butter experiences. They are set down to help those who wish to make a little butter in a glass churn, and to retain their youth and good looks - not to mention pleasant disposition.

1. Heat the churn with warm water.
2. Never fill the churn more than half-full of cream.
3. Fix the churn. This is the most important hint of all. A wooden frame, clamped to the table, does very well for this purpose.

And now that we have mastered the butter and our passions, we may go on to something else; and that something, as you will read – always supposing you have mastered your passionate desire to hurl this book into the fire or deliver it up to the Girl Guides for waste paper – is just 'nothing in particular'.

The fruit cages – a friend suggested we were depriving the country of valuable battleship iron!

By the wall border.

IX

A Pleasant Potter

– I –

Iwant to potter. I wish Peter was here because he would accompany me. He loves a good potter. But as he is not, then I must fall back on you – so I hope you like pottering too.

It is a mild November day, and for two pins, one could bluff oneself into believing that Summer himself had come back for one last look round. The low winter sun, peeping not much above the hedgerows, is lighting up the fields with a pale pink glow.

Just the day for a mooch! I had not seen the autumn planting of spring cabbages that Butler had just finished putting in. They should have been planted in September, but we had not been ready for them.

Ah! There they are, and they are just beginning to perk up and acquire that healthy 'blue' look about them, that in plant life suggests a good start.

In the distance I can see the temporary lad from the neighbouring village, who had been helping Butler to turn over the earth. He had proved a good boy and I was sorry not to be in a position to keep him on. But wages were going up every few months, and, in any case, he would soon be called up.

The thought of this sends a shudder down my back. He was so young – only eighteen – and had the face of a child.

The idea of him learning to handle lethal weapons to kill his man, before he himself was killed, was altogether quite horrible.

But the hungry war machine has to be fed, and it likes them like that, young and of a tender age.

He touches his cap to me as I pass, and I thank God he can not read my thoughts.

– II –

A peep at the porkers was the next potter on the programme. They all seemed to have filled out since I last saw them, though Butler had been very particular not to over-feed them at this early stage. He impressed upon me that it was injurious to fatten before a certain amount of normal growth had taken place.

I had provided buckets for several cottages in the village, the inhabitants of which were kind enough to save their scraps for the 'porkers down there'.

Betsy, the gilt, was growing into a lovely girl, and Butler had said that it was time 'she was sorted out from they pigs' and given her own quarters. It was only the boys that we wanted to fatten at this stage. Betsy would come to it, sooner or later . . . We hoped.

Next – the field and the new fence! And, oh! There he is. I knew Musket could not be far away.

Musket loved this field. It was full of gorgeous 'doggie' smells. And in one corner of it there were rabbit holes, hundreds of them. And what could be better fun in life than poking your nose down one of these and sneezing down it to your heart's desire. Nothing, thought Musket.

Circus dog, Musket!

Unless, perhaps, it was finding something really 'fruity' to roll in! Something to hallmark you as a real farmyard dog.

We reached the fence. It had been put up to make a four-acre field for Julia. That, I was told, was the correct quota for grazing a cow. It seemed a vast stretch of grass for one cow to eat her way over. But Julia managed it with the greatest of ease during the summer months, and a complete stack of hay to herself during the winter months that followed.

I never could understand how Julia could eat so much grass. I used to see her lying down and chewing it by the hour. Perhaps when my back was turned she spat some of it out. But I must confess, I never saw her doing anything so indelicate.

The fence was a great success. Those iron standards, bought second-hand, had been a bargain. I only hoped they would not want them for battleships later on. It would be difficult to refuse.

The iron gate, leading through into the big field, had been well placed in the centre of the fence. Altogether I had every reason to be well satisfied with the work.

– IV –

And lastly we retrace our steps and come to the two new chicken runs that we had had erected to the east of the kitchen garden. Out of view from the house, as stipulated by Peter.

I had been very lucky to procure that six-foot wire netting. The new house in the middle of the two runs with its sliding trap doors was so conveniently placed as to enable one run to be in use at a time, while the other was growing its fresh crop of grass.

Butler and I had decided on these new quarters, as we should be increasing the poultry stock in the spring, and should consequently require more runs and housing space.

Besides, I wished to change the pullets over. There had been a certain amount of high jinks – 'feather pulling' and 'egg eating' – which, I learnt, does sometimes occur among birds in closely confined quarters. It had reached the pitch when it had to be checked. I had no doubt more space would soon effect a cure.

The 'folder' would be useful later on for fattening

cockerels for the table. And this puts me in mind of our rooster, who has been side-stepping in the wings all this time, waiting for his cue. But being temperamental he refuses to appear unless he can have the set to himself. So here goes . . . Enter 'Cockie'.

The chicken coop – all my own work!

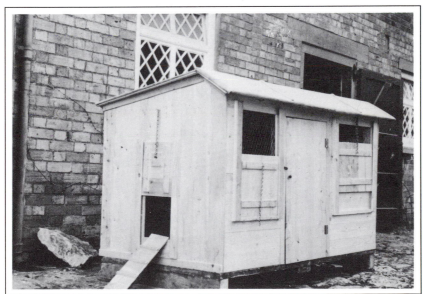

The land girl.

X

'Cockie'

Musket tolerates.

– I –

By the fanfare that has preceded 'Cockie', I have no doubt you are expecting a very magnificent rooster with enormous vermilion comb held erect, and beautiful sweeping tail feathers?

I had rather expected something of the sort myself when a friend offered to present me with a pure-bred Light Sussex stock bird. He was quite young – about the same age as the pullets – so he would be useful for breeding next spring.

I had been warned not to set the eggs this season. Pullets' eggs were no good for breeding. That was the way to produce weaklings, and nobody wanted to do that.

But the rooster . . .

He arrived in a basket. It did not feel very heavy. We carried it to the run before lifting the lid. All the pullets were standing round wondering what all the excitement was about.

Then suddenly, a rather emaciated-looking little cockerel stepped out into their midst. His white feathers were decidedly scruffy and he looked skinny and under-nourished. There was precious little comb on his top-knot, and what bit there was, was of an insipid and rather sickly shade of pink which was more suggestive of the female than the male.

I must confess I was disappointed. But the ladies! They

were not only disappointed, they were downright disgusted, and they were not long in letting him know it, either.

Infuriated, they set upon him. They went for his pink comb and tweaked it at every turn. They pulled out what few feathers he had in his tail, strewing them all over the run. They took running jumps at him, and leapt on to his back, and finally, they closed in on him, and sat upon his head! And when they had knocked all the stuffing out of him, they took it in turns to hurl obscene abuse.

It was all very degrading, and we were obliged to rescue him from their midst, for fear of him being lynched altogether.

We wondered whether he might have stood a better chance with them had he been surreptitiously brought into their midst under cover of darkness. It is a well-known fact that once chickens have retired to roost for the night, they sink into a coma and become inanely stupid.

We knew it would have been better to introduce a hen in this way, but with a cockerel! Well, we never questioned his popularity. We thought they would fall for him at once – perhaps they would have done if only he had had a bit more . . . well, let's call it 'personality', about him.

– II –

There was nothing left for us to do with him but to fatten him up for the table! We shut him up in the folder alone and started intensive feeding.

Mr Todd paid me a visit one day, just to see how I was 'getting on' with the poultry, and I took him to see Cockie.

'No, he'll never make a stock bird! Don't waste your time over him. Why – he has got no "go" about him.' (Funny what a lot of names it gets called by!) 'Boil him, that's my advice to you.'

Poor Cockie – I hoped he was not listening.

We fed him up for a fortnight, during which time he greatly improved. By the end of a month he was a different bird. We could scarcely believe he was the same creature.

His hitherto anaemic comb had spread itself fan-wise across an erect and very proud head. It was no longer pink, but a flaming red. He was sleek and well set up, and from his rear swept magnificent greenish-black feathers tempered with bronze.

It seemed a pity to eat such a bird. He was so ornamental, and added such tone to the farm. We wondered if Mr Todd could have been wrong about him?

We decided to give him another chance.

We unlocked the harem, and pushed him inside.

It was an anxious moment. After a few minutes the danger had passed! The ladies were transfixed. A murmur went up throughout the run, 'What a man!' They were mesmerized by his beauty and spellbound by that comb. They had never seen anything to equal it in their lives before.

Soon they began to mince and sidle up to him, and before very long they were fighting each other for first place next to him.

He was in his element. It was plain to see they were all mad about him. He had only to crow and they came running.

My! What fun he would have when he knew them well

enough to call them by their Christian names!

He was a 'treat 'em rough he-man' if ever there was one.

– III –

A month or two later, Mr Todd called again.

I took him down to the hen run.

'What do you think of *this* stock bird, Mr Todd?' I asked with my tongue in my cheek.

'Ah! Now there you have something . . . very different from that first wretched little bird you had!'

I smiled to myself as I realized that even the experts make mistakes, sometimes.

XI

A Wedding At Christmas

– I –

You would think that Christmas Day was quite a big enough festival in itself for most people. But not so for Julia. She elected for it to be her wedding day as well!

I felt extremely annoyed with her when I was greeted by this piece of news after coming in from church.

I had just lighted the candles on the Christmas tree, and the children were beside themselves with excitement.

All the parcels were in heaps on chairs round the room, and I had even gone to the trouble of wrapping up a small bag of cow-cake for Julia, and hanging it on the tree together with a bone for Musket.

No, it was too bad, but it was typical of Julia. I might have known she would be up to some 'monkey trick' on a day like this. She had been very secretive about the whole thing, as I had already seen her earlier in the day.

I had crept out of the house before breakfast and tied an alluring little bow of scarlet ribbon on each of her horns. I wanted her to look festive for the occasion. And Butler and I had arranged a small side-show for the benefit of the children.

At a signal from me, Butler would lead Julia up to the front door to receive her present off the tree. This little entertainment would have added extra joy and happiness to the festivities. But alas! It was not to be.

Julia was in no mood for tomfoolery.

Oh dear, I sighed to myself. How troublesome it all was, and what a number of people's Christmases seemed in danger of being upset by this thoughtlessness on Julia's part.

'Thoughtlessness!' did I say? Why, it was nothing of the sort! Julia had done this on purpose. She had worked it all out with malicious accuracy down to the minutest detail . . . and this time, she had timed it to the split second.

I crept away unheeded to the telephone in an adjoining room. I rang up Mr Phillips first. He carted coal, and kept the Inn in the neighbouring village. He owned a cattle truck in which he took beasts to market for the local farmers.

Yes, he would do the job . . . no, he did not mind. He would be round with his lorry at 'two sharp'.

He was splendid about it.

I wondered what Mrs Phillips would have to say about all this. She would not like her husband going out on Christmas Day, giving up his spare time, so hard-earned, and leaving her and 'the kids'.

Then there was the owner of the bull.

'Yes . . . It could be arranged . . . Rather an awkward day . . .' but he would speak to his cowman about it.

And, finally, there was Butler.

He would go, of course, and would be ready to start after dinner.

I thought I detected a note of eagerness in his voice. Curious man, Butler.

Meanwhile, the children, mid shrieks of delight, were riding their new bicycles round the dining room.

John and his friend, Mr Fred Young.

Everywhere there was brown paper and string still knotted, which had been flung on to the floor by impatient little fingers.

The room was a shambles. And out in the stables Julia was bellowing. She had succeeded in getting a commotion going, and she meant to see it through . . .

Moo . . . !

– II –

Mr Phillips kept his word and arrived punctually on time.

Butler followed the lorry on foot down from his house. He seemed a little jovial, I thought. He had obviously been celebrating. After all, was it not Christmas Day? A day of merriment and good cheer? One could not blame him. Besides, one was not supposed to notice.

Julia was duly tied up in the back part of the lorry. She still wore the two little bows of ribbon with which to regale her bridegroom.

Butler clambered up with a certain amount of difficulty, I thought, and seated himself beside Mr Phillips.

They set off. It was a curious company that swung out of our stable yard on that bitterly cold Christmas afternoon of 1939.

I watched them swaying round the bend in the lane. By this time, Butler was leaning perhaps just a little too hard up against the publican. But no matter.

I returned indoors full of misgivings. But it was no use worrying. It was Christmas Day. A day for festivity, and besides, the children were waiting to be entertained.

– III –

That afternoon we went for a bicycle ride. I shall never forget that ride. The wind whistled through us and chilled us to the marrow. It was agony. But the children, on their shining new bicycles, enjoyed every minute of it.

'Isn't it *lovely*, Mummy?' shouted John, with beaming face and running nose as he fought against the gale.

'Lovely, darling,' I called back. 'May God forgive me,' I whispered under my breath.

'Bicycling is my favourite pastime,' chimed in Rosemary, her little face screwed up in ecstasy.

Whether it was the wind, I do not know, but I scarcely heard what the children were saying – I rather think it was because my mind was elsewhere. My thoughts were following a motor lorry along a winding road. It was swaying this way and that. I could have borne the mental torture more easily if there had not been a publican aboard. He would be only too well-acquainted with all the ports of call along the route.

The children and I arrived home in time for tea.

Was it perhaps a little too early to expect the lorry to have returned?

I talked without knowing what I was saying, and ate without knowing what I was eating.

After another hour had elapsed, I was beside myself with anxiety. My imagination played havoc with my senses, and I pictured a lorry upside down in a ditch, with the corpses of two men and a cow pinned underneath.

There was a dull patch on the polished table where my hot fingers had been beating a nervous tattoo.

'Where is Julia, Mummy?' demanded Rosemary.

To which question, in all honesty, I was obliged to reply : 'I do not quite know.'

'Well, where has she been? You surely know that?' she continued persistently.

'You can never be sure of anything in wartime,' I snapped irrelevantly.

Rosemary gave me a curious look, but refrained from asking any further questions.

– IV –

We had just finished pulling the crackers and blowing the whistles that came out of them, when I heard the sound of a lorry. I left the table hurriedly, and rushed out into the stable yard.

Yes! Oh, joy! It was Julia. Bless her! Back safe and sound. How glad I was to see her sweet face again.

But Butler – what had happened to him? He walked unsteadily down the ramp with his arm round Julia's neck. His cap was tilted at a jaunty angle on one side of his head. He was apparently oblivious to the fact that he was in the presence of his employer who might take a bad view of all this.

He was humming quietly to himself, and every now and then his voice broke out into snatches of song. 'Daisy, Daisy, give me . . . your answer . . . do.'

I retired indoors. After all, it was Christmas Day and Julia was safe – but was she? She still had to be milked, and there was no electric lighting in the stable. The naked flame of a candle was unsafe at the best of times. I shuddered as I thought of all the straw in Julia's loose-box! One lurch would be enough to set the whole place ablaze.

Later, I crept out into the cold evening air, and peeped unnoticed into the flickering shadows of Julia's stable. She was standing with her eyes closed in ecstatic bliss, being gently lulled to sleep by Butler as he milked her. 'Daisy . . . Daisy . . .'

– V –

One would not have minded so much if anything (meaning, of course, a calf) had come of this midwinter madness. But nothing ever did.

Julia eventually broke off the engagement with her swain and fell for a fellow of her own choice, over the hedge in an adjoining field. A big red chap with a couple of knobs for horns.

XII

Death In the New Year

The greenhouse in the snow.

– I –

Suddenly, without any warning, I went mad. I blame the sun for the whole business. He tricked me into it.

If he had not been sending out his gentle warm rays on that snowy morning in January, I should never have conceived such a crazy idea.

Everywhere there was crisp white snow which crackled under one's feet. It was like walking on a sheet of scintillating diamonds. In the shade it was cold, still freezing in spite of the sun. But it was glorious, exhilarating. I felt happy, elated, and exceedingly well.

I was sure at this moment, I was capable of achieving something great. Something spectacular.

I opened the door of our small, unheated greenhouse and stepped inside. It seemed warm to my wool-encased body.

I was in such a mood, and so warmed by the sun, that the embryo of my first experiment came to life. But alas! Like most first experiments, it was doomed to failure.

I decided to rear day-old chicks in the greenhouse. I would build a nursery brooder out of an old wooden box, line it with flannel like the pictures I had seen in catalogues, and place a lamp inside it. This would be lighted at night. And in the daytime the sun would keep the chicks warm.

Theoretically the scheme was perfect.

I would write to the newspapers about it. There would be headlines . . .

HOW TO MAKE DOUBLE USE OF THE COLD GREEENHOUSE!

REAR YOUNG PLANTS AND CHICKS TOGETHER!

KILL TWO BIRDS WITH ONE STONE!

Unfortunately, I killed rather more than that number. It worked out round about fifty, before the whole tragic story was brought to an end with the last little life.

I sent for fifty sex-linked chicks from a well-known poultry breeder – this is no time to be shocked, we have done with all that long ago. Besides, sex-linked chicks, as I have since learnt, only meant the offspring of a first cross RIR cockerel with an LS hen. (Don't say you have forgotten the code!)

For some curious reason which I am unable to explain, and so far have failed to find anyone who can, the pullets from such a union come out yellow from the egg, while the cockerels retain the purity of their mama. It is, of course, very advantageous to know from the first day which are which. The pullets may then be fed for egg laying while the cockerels may be fattened for *petits poussins.*

After the first cross, however, the miracle of sex-linked chicks loses its magic power, and anything may happen. Why, you may get a black chick with yellow spots, and when you have fed it up for the table, it might one day decide to lay an egg! With me it invariably works the other way round!

The chicks arrived in two neat little cardboard boxes with perforations in the lid for air. They were very tightly packed together in hay, and radiated a warmth which felt hot to the hand as I lifted them out one by one.

There was a ring of cardboard like a clergyman's collar inside the box. This was to prevent the chicks from snuggling up into a corner. A favourite habit. And a very dangerous one. Many a chick has been found smothered in this manner.

For the first forty-eight hours of a chick's life, he does not need anything to eat. He may be given a little crushed-up hard-boiled egg, shell as well, but it is not vital to his welfare. He pecks and kicks his way out into the world well-nourished. This explains why day-old chicks travel so much better than older ones.

After crushed-up egg – which always seems to me such an odd diet for a chick of all creatures – he may go on to the well-known chick feeds Nos. I and II.

These last few hints have a touch of the professional about them. But make no mistake, they are not mine. I have taken them out of the Book.

– II –

We were all delighted with the chicks. They were like little golden powder puffs bobbing about my home-made brooder. And they could not have selected a better day to arrive. It was sunny and hot. Just the day for chick rearing in the greenhouse!

But in winter, the sun soon sinks beyond distant hills and drops out of view behind the trees. And once he has gone, though the day is still moderately young, he seldom comes back. The earth shudders as a chilly mist falls like a shroud to envelop it in night . . . But I see I have lapsed into an author's privilege of padding, and there is no time for that sort of thing just now. We must go back to the chicks and enjoy them while we may, for alas! They will not be with us very long. (After such a lugubrious warning I feel even the strongest-minded chick would have difficulty in remaining in our midst.)

At about four in the afternoon, the temperature dropped considerably, even inside the greenhouse, and I noticed that the little yellow powder-puffs were beginning to cluster together to form one big one (the sort one always kept in the bathroom – I never know quite what it's for!).

It was time to light the lamp, though I must confess I had not anticipated lighting it so early. However, it burnt very little oil, so it would not matter very much. I pushed the lamp through the flannel curtains and into the flannel-padded chamber.

This part of the brooder had roofing boards nailed across it, and underneath was attached a dustbin lid. This ingenious contraption would prevent the lamp from scorching the wood and would also act as a heat reflector. It was my own patent, and I was very proud of it. In fact, when I showed off my home-made brooder to Butler, the dustbin lid was the *pièce de résistance*. It was an excellent idea, I thought. But unfortunately I had overlooked the problem of 'fumes'.

A bought brooder has a chimney through the centre of it. But, then, I argued to myself, a bought brooder must be kept heated by a lamp burning at high pressure all the time. It cannot rely on glass-reflected heat, such as a greenhouse would provide, so in spite of Butler's sceptical remarks: 'It won't never work out, ma'am', I was not to be put off, and in fact, became quite fanatical in the praise of my own efforts.

The effect of lighting the lamp was amazing. The big film star powder-puff broke up into fifty little ones. It was like watching an Eddie Cantor scenario, so popular at one time, photographed in colour from overhead. I was fascinated and could have stayed there watching them for hours, if it had not been for the tea bell. I decided to look in again later.

It was about ten o'clock when I crept out again to have a final peep. It was some way to the greenhouse, through the stable yard, and then half-way down the new kitchen-garden path.

It was freezing harder than ever and very slippery. I found it difficult to remain upright. But it was not necessary to carry a torch. Everything stood out as clear as day: the open gate leading out from the stabling; the farm buildings and broad ambitious layout of the Victory garden; the bonfire, which was still smouldering and from which exuded delightful smoky smells of burnt wood ash.

It was a beautiful night, but the cold was intense. I hurried up to the greenhouse, opened the glass door, and shut myself inside.

Holy Moses! It was cold! I shivered. The place was like an icebox. Was it possible that it was colder inside than out?

I stepped hurriedly up to the brooder at the far end. I lifted the flannel curtains expecting to find that the lamp had gone out. But no, it was still alight. The chicks were huddled together round it. It seemed almost as though they would push it over in their eagerness to get the last ray of heat out of it.

It was quite obvious they were not warm enough. Something had to be done, and done quickly. I retraced my steps to the house and filled two stone hot-water bottles. After covering them with flannel I took them out to the greenhouse.

A free fight ensued for positions on top of the bottles. It was an enchanting sight, seeing them gently dropping off in an ecstatic sleep in a temperature well over 80° Fahrenheit. (Even this does not correspond with the books. They demand even higher temperatures still.)

But in spite of having temporarily solved the difficulty, I was still worried. The night was young and it would grow a great deal colder in the small hours. What then? The hot water bottles would not retain their heat all night. In less than four hours, they would be as cold as the stone from which they were made.

If I wanted to keep the chicks alive until the morning, I should have to continue refilling the bottles every few hours. It was a grim thought, but it was the only course of action left.

After settling the chicks once again I returned to the house and laid my plans for the night. Mrs Noble had retired, so I had the kitchen to myself.

I stoked up the fire, placing a big, black kettle on the hob. At least there would be a constant brewing of tea to stimulate my senses and keep me awake.

Next I brought mending, writing paper, a pack of cards and finally a cushion for the kitchen armchair. One might as well be comfortable even if one did have to prepare for a night of sitting up and keeping watch, a night of hearing the grandfather clock in the hall strike every hour . . .

Eleven . . . twelve . . . and into the small hours.

It would be tedious, but there it was. It had to be faced.

If I succeeded in keeping the chicks alive through the first dread night, I should be able to think out a more practical scheme in the morning.

Just after midnight, I made my way down to the greenhouse again. The moon was up. The ice crackled more than ever under the pressure of my snow boots.

Rows of Brussels sprouts, covered in crisp frozen snow, stood out like a miniature army of alpine troops.

I hastened inside the glasshouse and shut the door. The cold air inside nearly nipped off my nose. The chicks had abandoned their hot-water bottles, which, even in this short time, were scarcely more than lukewarm, and they were once again playing the famous Eton College wall-game with the lamp.

Again I refilled the bottles, and I continued to do so with monotonous repetition all through the night.

It would be a miracle, I thought, if the chicks survived these varying temperatures.

– III –

When morning did eventually come – it had seemed to me that it never would – the chicks were all alive and well. Only I felt dead with fatigue! What a night! Never again! If the chicks could survive another such night, I definitely could not! Nor did I intend to. My complexion would not stand it!

I hunted out another lamp, a big black upright one. One which would heat the whole greenhouse, that would swallow oil at the rate of half a gallon a day. This would be lit at six in the evening and kept going all night.

Another dustbin lid was brought into play and draped with sacks to form a black-out for the new lamp.

For a week or so everything went well and there were no hitches. I used to talk to the farmers' wives, who had been rearing chicks for years in bought brooders, about my patent greenhouse brooder.

They never seemed very enthusiastic, but I interpreted their attitude as perhaps being tainted with a touch of sour grapes. After all, I thought, not everybody has got a greenhouse – perhaps I had been tactless?

And then, one day, I understood the reason for their scepticism. It was the day the big lamp, for no apparent reason, went out. Several chicks were found dead the following morning.

Another time the lamp smoked so badly that, besides being blackened beyond recognition, many were gassed by the fumes beyond recovery.

It is a pitiful story. Every few days the number decreased. We tried bringing some indoors. We placed them in flannel-lined baskets on the rack of the kitchen range.

Mrs Noble was always so helpful over anything like this.

Sometimes they recovered, and when they did, it was nothing short of a miracle. I remember bringing one almost lifeless little creature into the kitchen. It was in the last stages, but it recovered – temporarily, at any rate – even though we did have to practically cook it. It survived several days. Until one day the children forgot to close the greenhouse door.

That unfortunate act accounted for the remainder. It was a bleak day. The sun had remained hidden behind grey clouds. An easterly wind sprang up and started blowing the tree-tops about. It blew out both the lamps in the greenhouse. And not long after, the last little life flickered out as well.

– IV –

It is a dismal story. It seemed sad that so many little lives should have to be sacrificed in order to teach me a lesson in chick rearing.

Temperature! That is the thing that matters most. It must be kept constant throughout the whole process.

The Book says:

1st week . . . . 90° Fahrenheit
2nd week . . . . 80°   ‥
3rd week . . . . 70°   ‥

After such a melancholy experience, it is not to be wondered at that I personally have discarded the idea of brooders altogether, and all the paraphernalia that goes with them. Yes! Even the famous dustbin lid.

I now greatly prefer the natural rearing by a mother hen. No 'ersatz' heat in the chick rearing, in my opinion, is quite as satisfactory as Mummy's tummy!

– V –

When I told Butler that there would be no further need to

fill up the lamp with oil, he quite understood.

'Very good, ma'am.'

If he had not been the gentleman I said he was in an earlier chapter, he might have been tempted to say, 'I told you so!'

XIII

The New Poultry Maid

The house.

– I –

In the spring 'Gran', of whom you have already caught a glimpse in an earlier chapter, came to stay indefinitely.

The children had gone to boarding schools, and there was no point in my living by myself. She would come and 'take over' the poultry.

It seemed an excellent idea and I was delighted. She had never had anything to do with chickens before, but she was fond of animals in general, and was sure that she would soon make friends with the hens.

She arrived one morning, and in the afternoon of the same day, we went over the hen runs together. I showed her the bins where we kept the mash and the corn, and in what quantities we disposed of it.

There had been much talk in the papers about a scarcity of animal feeding stuff, but up to the present, I had been able to procure all I wanted. We fed the hens together for the first two or three feeds.

By the end of a week Gran had completely mastered the poultry situation. She had pet names for most of the hens, and knew them all individually, together with their respective characteristics.

It was a commendable achievement.

She would call them out by name, and feed 'this little

hen' or 'that little hen' with special titbits because they had such a bad time with the others!

She wore rubber shoes – she did not like those 'ungainly gumboots' as they were 'such a job to take off' – a brown leather golfing jacket, and a green woollen 'Grumpy' cap which she had knitted herself completed her 'land-girl' outfit. And very well it suited her too, with her little grey ringlets curling up in the nape of her neck.

Gran was getting on in years as grannies invariably are, but she had twice the energy of the average woman of thirty. She had – I must reluctantly confess – four times the energy that I could display.

I used to meet her, pacing down the garden path to the runs, with a bucket slung over each arm. She had to pass the greenhouse with its cruel secret, but only I saw the ghosts of fifty little chicks looking reproachfully at me through its transparent panes.

I had not dared tell her of the tragedy. The story of that episode was closed. It was too painful to reopen.

Gran succeeded in inciting me to increase the poultry stock. I bought new hen houses and put up more runs. The fields seemed infested with chickens.

Then one evening I found Gran deep in a poultry book.

'It would be nice to rear some baby chicks, wouldn't it?'

'Oh yes,' and I added hastily, 'with hens.' The greenhouse disaster was still fresh in my memory.

'Those older hens,' she continued, 'loose in the field—'

'Free-range,' I corrected, pleased over my superior knowledge.

Gran took no notice of my remark but continued : ' — lay nice big eggs. I noticed when I collected them this afternoon. What about sitting some of them . . . ?'

'But they have not had a cockerel with them,' I said incredulously.

'Is that necessary?' came the incorrigible reply. 'It does not seem to stop them laying.'

'Why, of *course* it's necessary!' I remonstrated.

One would think from the note of precision in my voice that the evolution of the egg was my own particular subject and one to which I had given a lifetime of study. In actual fact, any knowledge gained had been extracted from Butler at the expense of much embarrassment only a day or two ago.

I continued to propound on the subject. 'No egg is fertile unless a cockerel has had something to do with it.'

'Really? How extraordinary,' Gran replied, with a certain amount of Edwardian aplomb. 'Well, what do you propose to do about it, then?' she demanded meaningly, as if she, for her part, intended to wash her hands of the whole business and palm all the dirty work off on to me. 'You always said you could not sit pullets' eggs.'

'Well, before either of *us*,' I emphasized that little word, after all, she was the self-appointed poultry maid '. . . can do anything about it, we must be certain of two essentials,' I affirmed with apparent knowledge.

I could not help thinking that these utterances came well from me, after my disastrous experiences and attempts at chick rearing.

'First,' I said rather pompously, 'we must put a cockerel in with the hens to fertilize the eggs, and secondly, we must have a broody hen who will sit on them for twenty-one days and hatch them out.'

We decided that afternoon to remove Cockie and put him in with the older hens.

The pullets were heartbroken and desolate at losing their Pasha. They came up to the wire in a very forlorn state, and called out farewells to him through the mesh. It was a pathetic sight.

But Cockie was a philanderer by nature, and no honest pullet should have wasted her time over him. He was not worth it.

As soon as he saw the new batch of ladies, he had the nerve to ask their first names. Cockie always started his affairs with this mode of finesse.

He was a bad lad. I should not like to count how many hearts he was responsible for breaking.

– II –

The following day Gran came to me with obvious excitement. Her face, framed in the little green 'Grumpy' bonnet, was beaming all over.

She was bursting with the news. She had a broody hen already. She had found 'the dear little thing' sitting with such patience on a couple of eggs that were laid that morning. She removed the eggs, but the hen had continued to sit. Bless her! Why not put a sitting underneath her! There were plenty of eggs in the larder.

It was rather attractive, this child-like innocence. But was it only the modern generation that had thrashed out the problems and acquainted themselves – however distasteful – with the facts of life. Judging by the size of the Edwardian families, they did rather appear to have

Feeding the chicks.

something of that easy-going *laissez-faire* attitude about it.

I was obliged to explain in delicate English that the cockerel had only been with the hens one day. But in spite of his audacity he should be given at least a fortnight's start (did I not say I would be scattering hints?) before one could begin to expect a fertile egg – not to mention thirteen of them!

We decided to cure the broody hen.

Now, if there really is anything extraordinary about chickens, I think 'broodiness' heads the list.

Imagine the patient sacrifice of a little hen sitting for weeks on end – and they have been known to sit till they die, God rest their little souls – in a comparatively cramped space. She practically gives up eating and drinking altogether. She gives up exercise. What can she be thinking about all through the day? What great thoughts are being turned over in that funny little head? She gives no clue. Only the upward blink of an eyelid to let you know she is still alive, and knows what she is about . . .

But, does she really know? If she did, would she be, could she be big enough, fine enough, to mother so many other people's children with such gentleness and loving care?

Cockie may never have even noticed her. Yet she is content and even happy to cherish and bring up his young.

Surely the feathered spirit world must be peopled with scores of little foster hens with illuminated combs transformed into haloes.

Gran had her own ways of curing broody hens. She did not agree with the ruthless methods as laid down in the Book. Draughty coops, etc., were enough to give the hens arthritis. (Anyone else would call it rheumatism!) She used to shut the hens up in the yard. Cobblestones were not conducive to broodiness, in spite of their egg-like form.

We were always lucky over broody hens. There always seemed to be any number to choose from.

I only remember one failure. It happened during the holidays when one of the children disturbed a sitting hen. With a malicious look on her face, she rose up on the nest and proceeded to do a war-dance upon her eggs. She then decided to have a dust-bath amongst them, and kicked them out from under her in all directions. She swallowed the contents of the remaining two with obvious relish and delight, and then settled down to sit indefinitely upon an empty nest!

Gran made excellent nests in one of the empty stables; grass turfs patted down into cosy beds and lined with hay. There is nothing like earth for retaining the heat. And the warmth of a hen's breast, amazing though it may seem, touches 104° Fahrenheit.

When hatching was in full swing it became beyond a joke. There would be a hen sitting in every corner. Nowhere was safe from them. Gran would come chasing out after one: 'Be quiet in there. I have a sitting hen.'

Even the garage offered no sanctuary from sitting hens. As one came to back out the car the upward blink of that bottom eyelid would catch one's own eye from behind the door.

In every nook and cranny the mystery of birth was being promulgated. Everywhere self-sacrificing little hens were hatching out other hens' chicks.

Perhaps just one of the thirteen children will be truly

their own. But how are they to know which one? Is a mother able to keep track of her own egg? Has she some secret way of initialling it at the offset, and when it has yielded up its precious contents, will she know it by the colour of its eyes, and the turn of its dinky little beak? And what can a hen think when she hatches a little creature with a flat yellow beak and webbed feet, as she so often finds she has done?

That must make her want to check up on herself!

These are problems we amateurs may never be able to solve; meanwhile, we must refrain from trying to 'wheedle' state secrets from Nature's bosom, and go on with the business of rearing chicks, young ducklings, goslings and perhaps later, who knows?

We might even attempt to bring up a New World.

– III –

Gran was most successful with her chick rearing, and she attributes her success to three main rules:

1. Never disturb the hens when they are sitting. If they will not leave the nest to feed, lift them off once a day.
2. The day the chicks hatch out, remove shells with as little fuss as possible. Do not disturb the hen again that day.
3. Do not transfer the hen and her chicks into a coop until the second or third day. If there is no sun, place the coop in a sheltered corner of an outhouse if possible. Give food and water in shallow containers.

XIV

Another Wedding In
The Family

– I –

For the next few weeks, nothing of much importance occurred. The various animals performed their normal functions; the hens produced eggs, and Julia kept us in milk.

Then, one day, just as I was looking forward to another 'potter' round the farm to take stock of our position, as it was six months since we'd started, Butler met me at the front door and asked me whether I had remembered that it was Betsy, the young gilt's Wedding Day.

'What! Another wedding in the family so soon?' I exclaimed.

In actual fact, there had never been any mention of any such fixture. But it was Butler's neat way of letting me know!

I felt rather at a loss with no trailer. I wondered how I should manage to transport Betsy over to the next village where the local police constable kept a handsome boar.

I wondered whether she would perhaps sit in the back of the car?

Butler shook his head, muttering his familiar, 'It won't never work out, ma'am,' when I made the suggestion to him.

Last time he had uttered those ominous words, disaster had followed them.

But this was not a parallel case. No lives were at stake – at least, we hoped not! There was really nothing to go wrong in this experiment. Betsy either *would* sit in the back of the car, or she would not. Everything would be decided within fifteen minutes of the try-out.

Betsy was just over eight months old. She had grown into a big girl lately, and in all probability weighed round about ten score. But the car offered plenty of room when the hood was down, and it was only a very short distance, not more than five or six miles. So unless she was in a very opposing mood (which could never be ruled out on our farm) she might be prevailed upon to oblige us just this once.

Butler, reconciled to my amateurish methods, called in a friend to help, and together the three of us coaxed Betsy near to where the car was drawn up in the yard. But she did not like the look of it at all. She viewed it with suspicion, and squinted at it out of her eye corners. It was, in fact, a 'monster' and she would have none of it.

We had great difficulty in persuading her that the car was quite harmless, that it was hers to command, and that it only wanted to convey her to her betrothed.

We tried lifting her legs in one by one, and gently pushing from behind.

At one time it seemed quite hopeless. She shifted her weight about like a sand-bag half filled with sand. No sooner would we succeed in lifting her forelegs into the car than we would find she had shuffled her ten score on to her seat. All the time she was emitting frantic squeals, which brought everybody from their respective jobs to see what all the commotion was about.

Gran took one Edwardian look and fled indoors, clapping her hands over her ears.

After about twenty minutes of desperate struggling which was enough to give us all blood pressure, we succeeded in heaving the remainder of her into the car.

'Quick with the net!' I cried agitatedly, as she planted a trotter through the plastic window of the hood in its folded position.

The men soon had her netted. But she was very angry, and snorted obscenely with her snout pushed defiantly up through the rope mesh.

I tried to pacify her. 'Come, come, Betsy! This is no mood for a nuptial tryst.'

We sallied forth. I was at the wheel with Butler beside me. And in a sitting posture – looking like a thousand thunderclouds – sat Betsy, with the scowl of a fractious child on her benetted brow. If sows have brows.

We arrived at the village to the accompaniment of low snorts and grunts from the back of the car. And then, as we came round a bend in the road, to my horror and dismay we ran into what seemed to be the whole of the British Army on manoeuvres.

Was it imagination? Or did I hear a chuckle from the back seat?

There were streams of tanks and endless lines of armoured vehicles with tin-hatted men sticking out of the top of them. Several tanks were drawn up stationary on either side of the very gate I was making for.

What a predicament! What was I to do? I was about to

become the laughing-stock of the British Army. By this time Betsy was positively 'guffawing' with the humour of the situation.

I pondered to myself.

Should I cut my losses? Crash in the gear, and sweep past the gate with my mission unaccomplished but my self-respect intact?

But alas! It was too late. The police constable had already caught sight of the car as it rounded the bend, and was even now opening the gate and beckoning us to drive in.

And the boar! Good gracious me! He was there too, looking like Hannibal at his worst!

There was no escape. Not even a hood above me, to act as camouflage and hide my confusion from the khaki boys, so obviously enjoying the indelicacy of my position.

I swung the car between the open gateposts, with as nonchalant a countenance as I could put on for the occasion. But the air rang out with quips and gags of which only the British Tommy is capable.

At that moment I felt I would rather have run into a whole division of Nazi storm-troopers than a handful of British soldiers with their amiable titterings.

As soon as the car came to a standstill, I leapt from the driving seat, and made for the cottage. I dived into the first doorway I could see mid shouts of 'Hurrah!' from the troops.

Five minutes after this galling experience, I was enjoying a hot cup of tea with the constable's wife to restore my shattered nerves.

– II –

When I returned home Gran met me with the words: 'How could you go on such an errand with Butler – a man! Have you no sense of decency?'

'One man, indeed? My dear Mama,' I expostulated. 'Why, the whole of the British Army was there!'

XV

July

A summer picnic.

– I –

We have now arrived at my favourite month: July. Ever since I was a child I have looked forward to this month.

It was on a day in July that, fresh as morning dew, so they tell me (and I always rather like that bit about myself), I first made my appearance on this dusty old Earth. Somewhere round about the beginning of the century.

As a babe, every consecutive July was a landmark. I did something progressive. The first I walked. The second I talked. The early Julys meant new rattles, and later teddy bears.

I grew. July replenished the toy cupboard. Old dolls with fixed eyeballs were replaced by bigger and better dolls. Dolls with real hair and eyes that closed with a 'click'. Dolls with long black curly eyelashes that would have been the envy of any screen star.

Then came those glorious Julys that brought with them the 'summer hols'. Trips to the seaside with buckets and spades complete. Donkey rides, sand castles and, best of all by far, ice-cream on the beach.

And later again, the Julys of adolescence. Lying in a hammock slung between two apple trees in the orchard, engrossed in my first story of romance. Would David tell

Myrtle he loved her in the next chapter? Would there be a stolen kiss between them?

After, came my own young men; the bliss, the heartaches, and in short, all the misery that they bring before the final joy. It was the same story. The same theme. And the same ending to a cavalcade of Julys.

After marriage, there were lazy Julys – made for idleness and repose. Julys spent in deck-chairs in the garden, basking in the sunshine and viewing the world detachedly through the pages of a newspaper. 'What is all this about, raising the standard of living, better conditions for workers, better health services? You know, Peter, there is absolutely nothing of interest in the papers nowadays. I don't know why we continue to take them,' I would murmur, and not far away would come the happy laughter of the children floating on the still, warm air.

All through the spring one had prepared for this month. Seeds of favourite flowers had been sown to fulfil themselves in resplendent maturity in July and proclaim the advent of a birthday in a blaze of riotous colour.

But on a farm, July is not like that. Especially a wartime July. There is no time to worship the sun. No time for ease and carefree abandonment. No time to dream with one's head pillowed in a billowy cushion. And as for birthdays, they are so numerous that they become monotonous. Practically every day something new is born. Today it is lambs, tomorrow, calves. And the day after, who can tell? Perhaps it will be the re-birth of a nation.

The farming folk of England, who have so often and so rightly been called the backbone of the country, must toil and sweat and strain every nerve to keep the nation alive and sufficiently nourished to meet the ordeal that it may one day be called upon to withstand.

It had been a bad start to the year. France had fallen, and our enemies were over the Channel. Any moment the Nazi hordes might be flung across that narrow strip of water.

Our Expeditionary Force had been saved by a miracle! Dunkirk was the name on everybody's lips.

– II –

A kind neighbouring farmer had mown Julia's four-acre field. Within two days, during which time the whole household and anyone else we could call in from outside, had been out turning and tossing it, it was ready to carry.

It was a gruelling day, and there had been no rain for several weeks. Everything was scorched, but it was good quick weather for haymaking.

Once again we had to resort to amateurish methods. We carried every wisp of Julia's two-ton rick in a small pig trailer attached behind the Ford.

'Pig trailer?' did I hear you say? Well, I had bought it second-hand almost immediately after the embarrassing episode with Betsy.

There was grim resolve in our haymaking that first July. Every man, woman and child gave their every ounce of energy to the common effort.

Julia looked on with approval from an adjacent field, and smiled to herself between cud chewings as she thought with a rick such as hers, she could withstand any siege.

Let Hitler invade. She had food enough for the winter and more to spare.

If people were unfortunate enough to call on us at this time, they found nobody at home to welcome them. No one to answer their urgent knocking and bell ringing. They were left standing on the doorstep until the sound of a car engine, humming in the distance, fell on their ears, and brought them out into the hayfield, where all the activity was in progress.

They would approach with a smile, thinking no doubt that it was all rather a joke this haymaking business. Picnic teas, fun and laughter!

One look at me, perspiring on the top of a trailer, loaded with hay, in a sweaty shirt and pair of khaki shorts soon disillusioned any romantic ideas of pretty maids in smocks and sunbonnets!

And when they were told to 'catch hold of this' and found a hay fork thrust in their reluctant grip, they began to wish they had never visited.

And then one day, some very old and very dear friends wrote suggesting a quiet leave with us in the country. 'So lovely to see you again, my dear, and laze in your lovely garden!'

I had not seen them since the war started. No doubt they were recalling memories sweet in peace-time. Peter had been at home and we had disported ourselves on rugs and cushions about the garden, scantily clad and glorying in the sun. Tea had been served daily beneath the shade of an old walnut tree, and together we had sunk with satisfied sighs into deck-chairs round the table.

What happy days! What incredibly lazy days! *Could* they

Haymaking in full swing.

have been good for us? Today, I am inclined to doubt it. I begin to think that this war, in spite of all its carnage, has taught us perhaps one lesson: the lesson of self-denial.

But, good gracious me! This is no time for analysis of this sort. The hay lies on the ground, and if we delay for a moment, our cause will be lost. Thunder-clouds will gather, and the rain will descend in torrents and soak it till it is sodden and then we shall have to turn it all over again. Besides, Julia is scowling at us over the fence. She is thinking of Hitler (no wonder she scowls) and his invasion, and she is urging us to greater efforts on her behalf.

I scribbled 'delighted' in answer to the letter, and hurried off back to the hay.

A good load!

– III –

When the Smiths arrived so unsuspectingly one sunny afternoon, they had scarcely been in the house five minutes before they were relentlessly attacked.

Their coats were torn from off their backs, and before they had time to realize what was happening, they were ruthlessly pushed out into the fields and given a drag-rake apiece.

When nightfall came and it was so dark that they could no longer see to work, they came in exhausted and dead-beat, dragging their tired limbs as best they could.

Meals that had required the minimum preparation were placed before them. Mrs Noble's services were required out of doors. There was no time to serve up dainty dishes. Their only pleasure was a tankard of beer, and even this was a subtle ruse on our part, to keep up their physical strength, which was to our advantage. There was no respite until the last load was carried, and that was the evening before their 'leave' expired.

After a week here they left in a state of exhaustion and collapse. As I saw them off in their car, Bill muttered something about 'Happy visit in spite of Nazi Labour Camp conditions. Nothing like manual labour to get the figure down.'

As a matter of fact, I had done the Army a good turn. I had achieved in a week what the Army had failed to do in a year: reduce Bill's portly 'tumpkin', to borrow an expression from Lady Fortescue.

I must ask the Smiths again next year. I should not mind betting that it will be sometime in July. And what are the odds that they will not come? But then, I had forgotten. You do not know the Smiths.

Rosemary on her pony.

XVI

Milking Made More Difficult

– I –

And now once again it is Julia's turn to figure in these pages. She would like to appear in every chapter, but of course this would not be fair to the others. Besides, there is seldom anything very good to tell about Julia.

I had been apprenticed under Butler to learn how to milk. It had become necessary for me to lend a hand in this during the summer months, especially while hay-making was in full swing.

There had even been talk of a second cow, but of course this had never been breathed above a whisper in front of Julia.

It had taken me over a fortnight to learn to milk. Julia had been quite reasonable about it, and had stood quietly through the ordeal. Occasionally she would turn her head to see what was going on, and more than once I heard her muttering something unconstructive like, 'Really, she hasn't any idea!' But I took no notice and persevered with my task.

At first my fingers ached, and indeed then my whole body ached in every limb with the exertion. And at one time I felt so whacked after every attempt, I thought I should have to give it up altogether.

After straining every nerve and every muscle to extract the liquid, all I would have to show for my pains was a couple of saturated shoes, while the bottom of the pail would be scarcely covered.

It was heartbreaking! What would the Milk Marketing Board say if they could see these little white streamlets running away to waste?

It seemed to me that in learning to milk aim was of paramount importance. One needed a good eye for the job.

I wondered what effect a squint would have on a would-be milker. Disastrous! A spray of crossfire, with never a drop in the bucket!

For the first fortnight of my milking career, Butler always 'finished off' Julia. He did this chiefly because after the first twenty minutes I was invariably in a state of collapse and incapable of carrying on, and secondly because as anybody who knows anything about cows knows, it is essential to the health of the animal and necessary to the maintenance of the milk flow to drain the udder at every milking.

It was not until he failed to squeeze a single drop of milk out of Julia's bag that Butler gave me my 'Passing Out' certificate.

From that time onwards I took over the afternoon milking. Even when I was moderately proficient, I still used to take twice as long as Butler took over the job. But I consoled myself with the thought that whereas Butler had been milking for a lifetime, I had been milking for a few weeks. How could one hope to compete?

– II –

One day, when I went out into the field in order to bring

her in to be milked, Julia was nowhere to be seen.

It had just started to rain. It was one of those rains that, for some hours past, had been trying to make up its mind what to do. 'Shall I? Shan't I? Shall I?'

At the beginning, only a few big drops had fallen, one at a time, and if Julia had been waiting at the gate as was her usual custom at this time in the afternoon, all would have been well, except from the author's point of view, who would have been deprived of a theme for a chapter! But Julia was not at the gate. She was, in fact, nowhere to be found.

By this time the rain was coming down in buckets. I put on an old mackintosh, hoisted an umbrella and went out in search of Butler.

'Butler! Butler!' I called, as I paddled across the stable yard splashing water up to my knees.

There were rivers running over the stones and parts of the yard were rapidly becoming flooded. Water gushed out of the pipes which drain the stable roofs. It was something bordering on a cloud-burst.

'Yes, ma'am,' he answered, his voice coming from the woodshed.

Butler always took refuge in the woodshed when there was heavy rain, but it took more than an ordinary downpour to drive him under cover.

'Julia is nowhere to be seen,' I whined plaintively, unable to conceal my irritation, 'and it is long past her milking time.'

'Very good, ma'am. I'll go and look for her. You stop in the dry.'

But I knew I should have to go with him. He would

never catch her alone, especially if she was in one of her skylarking moods. We should no doubt have to carry out the famous pincer movement on her and we knew that that would take at least two people. We might even have to be reinforced by Gran and the children who were home for the 'hols', but I did not want any more members of the family risking pneumonia by getting soaked through to the skin.

Butler disappeared only to reappear a moment later in an old mackintosh, which he kept on the premises for just such an occasion as this. The water was dripping off the peak of his cap, and at the back of his head it was running down his neck in a constant flow.

We set off in the downpour and made for the elms at the bottom of Julia's field.

I was thinking about all the dreadful things I would do to Julia when I caught her. To make matters worse and aggravate the situation, one of my gumboots sprang a leak. There was a sickening squelch with every step I took.

I began to hum gently to myself to soothe my ragged nerves. I was sure Julia was hiding behind one of those elm trees. It was not difficult to conjure up the picture. She would peer round one side of the trunk, showing just an eye and a horn, and perhaps just the tip of that ridiculous nose. Then as soon as she caught sight of us looking in her direction, she would quickly withdraw everything with one jerk of her head. And then, waiting until we came up within a few yards, without any warning, she would spring out shouting 'Peek-a-boo', or being a cow it might sound more like 'Peek-a-moo'. Anyhow, whatever it was, it would be very maddening.

A drop of rain!

Butler and I reached the elms, but there was no sign of Julia!

It was not until we had scoured the countryside with our eyes that I picked her out at the furthermost end of our big field. It was a ten-acre field, and it was let to a neighbouring farmer.

Yes, that was Julia without a doubt, in company with eight or nine young calves. She was obviously 'holding forth', and judging by the intense interest on the calves' faces, it was evident that she was telling them something that would not have passed their mothers' strict censorship!

Not until we came almost within hearing ourselves did she become restive and start to skip about and throw her . . . 'seat', shall we call it for want of a better word, in the air, and then just as I expected, with a final shake of the head, she capered off to the other end of the field, with all the calves in happy pursuit.

I was in a state bordering on hysteria which had to be concealed at all costs. I turned to Butler and said with my most charming smile – full of good nature, good humour and all that sort of thing – 'I'm afraid, Butler, it looks as though we shall have to have more helpers.'

'Maybe next time we'll head her off, in yon corner, ma'am.'

And unbelievable as it may seem, this is exactly what happened.

Butler produced the halter from behind his back, and with the rope end of it, swung it softly over her neck before she had time to be off on another frolic.

She was led away in disgrace.

I scolded her all the way home, but she only giggled.

The calves formed themselves into a guard of honour and would have followed her into her stall, if a gate had not prevented them.

They were doubtless eager to hear more of her 'naughty nineties'.

The elements can be very provocative, and no sooner had I tied Julia up in the loose-box, than the rain stopped. The sun began to filter through the clouds, and it looked like turning into a lovely evening.

I fetched the zinc milking stool, placed it in position and settled down to milk Julia more than an hour late.

Sometimes out of sheer devilment Julia would withhold her milk for the first two or three minutes. She was doing that now on this already irksome occasion.

'Come on, Juliana, let it down,' I said in my best 'ploughboy' language, but she took no notice.

I went on coaxing, and still nothing happened We shall be here all night, I thought. In sheer desperation I called Butler.

'Butler, Julia refuses to let her milk down. What shall I do?'

'I'll come, ma'am,' he answered, as he reached for his white overall off the peg in the dairy.

Very soon he was sitting on the stool with his head dug into Julia's flank. It all looks easy with Butler. I listened for the steady flow, but none came.

'Why, ma'am; there be no milk there to come.'

'Butler!' I exclaimed with alarm. 'What do you mean?' I was afraid the chase had upset Julia.

'It be they calves she were with, ma'am. They be gone and milked 'er dry.'

I stood aghast.

For some moments I could not speak. I was thinking of my wasted afternoon – my pneumonia risk, and a lot of other things that would not look pretty in print.

'Really, Butler, I can take a joke, but this is too much.' And with these words, I pivoted on my heel and, tense with rage, walked indoors.

I did not want to have anything more to do with cows that evening. I had a shrewd suspicion it would not be in the farm's interest, and would almost certainly be detrimental to my health.

Instead, I shut myself up in the house and wrote a tirade to Peter on cows, and what cads they really are at heart.

XVII

A Week's Leave

– I –

Autumn was upon us before there was time to look round, and the Battle of Britain had been fought and won by a handful of boys in the Royal Air Force.

Their fortitude, inspiration and great gallantry had won for us the day. It was an epic battle which will go down in the annals of history in letters of gold. May we as a nation ever prove ourselves worthy of their great sacrifices.

Down on the farm, the hens were beginning to look most unattractive, with naked tail-pieces and undercarriage. And during the moult, they gave up paying their rent all together.

It was a barren period on the farm. And if it had not been for Betsy who, by this time, amply justified the name of her breed 'Large White', the year looked like settling down into sterile old age.

I was beginning to feel a little *passée* myself, and wondered whether, at this low ebb of the farm's life, I dare take a day or two off, and visit a friend who had been urging me for weeks past to go and stay with her . . .

'For goodness' sake, dig yourself out of that frightful farmyard rut. Those ghastly trousers . . . How could you . . . ? I shall not take "No" for an answer.'

Hitherto, I had been under the mistaken delusion that I was indispensable to the welfare of the farm. If I went away for a single day, or even turned my back for a second, a whole series of tragedies would befall.

Julia would close the 'milk bar' and refuse to re-open until my return; and the hens were almost certain to go on hunger strike, which would doubtless lead to incurable diseases in view of their low state of health at this time.

As for Betsy, there is no knowing what she might be tempted to do in my absence: lock herself up in her stye and refuse to reappear until she heard my silvery voice once again about the place.

However, in spite of all these dreads and anxieties, I decided to leave Gran in charge with full power of attorney for a whole week.

I felt an urgent need to clamber out of the rut while there was still time, before I found myself so deeply embedded that I could no longer see over the top.

I pictured Peter coming home from the war, and looking for me in vain. No, one must keep one's head above ground at all costs. One runs such a risk of being swallowed up altogether, and of never being heard of ever again!

– II –

I discarded my trousers – Kay would never have stood for them – and flaunted my femininity in skirts and high heels. As for the farm, I remembered it no more. I had long since shaken the manure from off the soles of my shoes, and never gave it another thought.

I spent a heavenly week.

– III –

I returned. None of the dreaded happenings had come to pass in my absence, but there were changes. Quite drastic ones, I thought.

The ducks, who up until now had been happy and contented down on the pond, had been enticed up to the house. They had even abandoned their little duck house that I had made for them with my own fair hands. (Excuse a smile! You should see them now!) They had come up to live in the woodshed. They spent most of their time at the back door, and sometimes even ventured into Mrs Noble's 'Holy of Holies', and demanded bread with loud quacks. She told me on the quiet that she did not really like them there. It made so much extra work. She took rather a pride in the red linoleum tiles of the kitchen floor.

But that was not all.

In a little cardboard box tucked under the kitchen table there was a baby pigeon which had to be laboriously fed by hand every few hours. It had been pushed out of the pigeon-cote by heartless parents and had spent two nights shivering on the roof.

'It could not be left to die, poor little thing,' pleaded Gran. 'But it was rather a job getting food down it, as it would not open its beak,' she added, as she forced it apart with a grain of rice.

And then, suddenly, as I gazed with despair out of the kitchen window, wondering how I should ever manage to cope with all these extra responsibilities, I caught sight of a hen followed by three large goslings.

'Good gracious!' I exclaimed. 'There's a hen out on my

border.'

I made a plunge for the back door, only to be checked by an explanation from Gran.

'Oh, that is only "Mama". She does not do any harm. She hated being shut up with all those old maids; it was an insult to her station. After all, she is a mother, and has three strapping great children to show for the privilege.'

Words failed me.

So this is what happens when my back is turned for a moment. There are ducks in my house, and chickens – not to mention geese – in my garden! A pretty state of affairs, I reflected, simmering inwardly, and who knows what I might not yet find upstairs? Perhaps it would be Julia curled up on my bed, and Betsy lying full-length in my bath.

I was very angry. Everything was clear to me now. For the first time I saw through the ingenuity of Gran's plot: 'You are tired and need a change. Do take a week off from the farm, dear.'

I never have liked the subtlety of this sort of remark. It is merely another way of telling you that you are irritable and bad-tempered.

Any good that my week's holiday had done to my 'humour' was undone in the first few moments of my return. In fact, I think I only just averted having a stroke!

Well, there was nothing to be done now. The ducks looked upon the back doorstep as their legitimate billet, and a convenient place to drop cards on Mrs Noble.

And in the flower garden – walking about as though she owned the place – was 'Mama', stalking the shoots of next year's growth up and down the herbaceous border. Her

'Budge up – I want to come in too!'

children trailed along behind her with snapping beaks that ran over the flora like three pairs of shears trimming a privet hedge.

The result was catastrophic! What was not eaten by the geese was scratched out by 'Mama' and everywhere was a network of paths flattened out by webbed feet.

Gran and I had 'words'.

She argued, 'You ought not to bother with flowers when there is a war on . . . If pansies are good for geese, then they ought to be allowed, and even encouraged, to eat whole beds of them. And what is more, you should plant more beds of pansies for future pansy-loving geese.'

It was no use arguing. Gran insisted that 'Mama' must have her freedom. So the process of mowing and rolling by the birds went on unmolested in a dreadful display of misdirected energy.

Every evening 'Mama' retired with her young – who, by the way, towered above her in size (a mother's chief aim in life) – into one of the stables. The geese slept on straw in a corner while 'Mama' kept watch from a manger above . . .

And, oh, joy! One day I found, among other things, a beautiful big brown egg.

For weeks there was always an egg in that manger.

So what could I do, but forgive 'Mama' everything. I took back all the unkind things I had said about her in the past, and withdrew the vindictive 'boiling in oil' resolves.

Next year, I shall doubtless plough up the lawn and plant a dozen or more herbaceous borders with an edging of pansies for pansy-loving geese.

XVIII

A Crime Is Committed

Betsy with the children.

– I –

I should like to omit this chapter altogether; it is sordid to a degree. But if I am to chronicle the true sequence of events that took place on the farm during the first year of its existence, then the story of Betsy, the sow, must be told, however much it hurts in the process.

After I had returned from my short holiday, and had gradually accustomed myself to stepping over the feathered creatures that beset me at every turn, everything went well for a week or two.

Betsy's family was due at any time and we were all agog with anticipation.

Up until the very last fortnight, Betsy had been tethered to take her daily exercise on a piece of land known, due to the nature of the transaction which gave us the right of possession, as 'Naboth's Vineyard', after the Bible story.

Each day the expectant mother required her harness 'letting out' another hole or two in the girth (excuse these indelicate details), and then one day the last hole of all was reached. We decided the time had come for Betsy to discard her trappings, and remain indoors to await her ordeal.

Butler had spent a morning whitewashing one of the

loose-boxes for her. I have already mentioned in a previous chapter that there were no proper pigsties. The stable would serve the purpose equally well, with its well-drained concrete floor; but, of course, it lacked the farrowing rails. This worried Butler considerably, and I was terribly afraid that at any moment he might come out with his – by now, quite historic – 'It won't never work out, ma'am', which had always brought us such bad luck in the past.

Whether it was my stubborn attitude in persisting with amateurish methods that had gradually worn the man down, I do not know. But as far as I know, he never did say the dread words that had hitherto cast such a spell of failure over my efforts, and so there can be no accounting for the sequence of tragic events.

It was true I used to hear Butler muttering to himself as he made up the bed of short chopped straw in one corner of the sty: 'I don't know how we shall go on without they rails . . . pigs be clumsy animals.' But I never attached much importance to these apprehensions borne out on a puff of smoke from his pipe.

Like ladies in the best society, Betsy had her bed remade daily. It was usually scattered all over the floor when Butler called her in the morning. I suspect this was done during 'before breakfast' breathing exercises. A deep intake and an outward paaahh!

– II –

Zero hour arrived about eight o'clock one evening in October. Everybody spoke in hushed whispers and walked about on tiptoe.

Butler came to the house and asked for a torch. He would not disturb her, but there might be complications. After all, it was her first litter, and it was always rather a risk when there were no farrowing rails. (Bother those rails!) He would be 'about'. He did not want any of they 'lit'le 'uns' to get between her and the wall – a favourite trick when there are no farrowing rails. (I shall scream if he mentions them again.)

At about nine o'clock I crept out of doors to enquire how the confinement was progressing.

Butler had peeped surreptitiously and he was not 'over pleased' with what he had seen. 'It was no comfortable affair.' (I could have told him that.)

Five little pigs had been born up to date, and they lay huddled together in the straw. Betsy did not know in the least what to make of them, and their heart-rending squeals were nearly driving her crazy. Poor Betsy, I could picture it all. What was the matter with the wretched little blighters? And who did they belong to, anyhow? *She* had never seen them before.

I retired indoors. The suspense was agony.

Butler brought the torch back about ten o'clock, and reported that another four or five little pigs had arrived, thus making nine or ten to date. 'There'll be a dozen before she be done, but she don't like 'em yet awhile.'

When he left them, they were huddled in twos and threes, abandoned about the place, and she was inclined to be 'rough with 'em when they squealed'. He did not intend to go in and disturb 'yon gilt' tonight. 'She might turn nasty with they 'lit'le 'uns. Better wait till morning, maybe she'll suckle 'em then.'

I only hoped he might be right, and that perhaps by the light of day Betsy would have come to her senses and realized that she was the proud mother of two or three sets of quadruplets, and would have settled down to do something about it.

– III –

When morning came, we were full of fresh hope. We were certain Betsy would by now have taken over both the joys and responsibilities of happy motherhood.

We were waiting for Butler to come and tell us the joyful news, 'A dozen little beauties, and all doing well', or something of that sort.

But he never came. Instead he went down to the furthermost point in one of the fields, as far away from the house as he could get.

It was too far away for me to see what he was doing, but I suspected he was violently digging out ditches. This was Butler's way of giving vent to his feelings of anger mingled with disappointment. He always turned to the spade when things went wrong.

Mrs Noble and I hurried out to the sty. We sensed drama of a sinister kind, and since Butler had not seen fit to tell us, we must investigate for ourselves.

The sight which met our eyes when we looked into the sty was not very reassuring. Betsy lay in the middle of the floor, looking wild-eyed and ferocious. There were bits of straw sticking out of her mouth, and she was emitting angry snorts and snarls.

We searched anxiously for the little ones. They were

nowhere to be seen.

'Why, Mrs Noble, they must be somewhere under the straw, hiding from their unnatural mama . . . Pass me that stick, will you?' I said, pointing to a bamboo cane leaning up against the wall. 'I am going in to find them.'

'Do take care, ma'am. She looks so fierce – fit to eat you up,' warned Mrs Noble, in an agony of mind.

I sidled in along one of the walls, keeping an ever watchful eye on Betsy. Any moment she might attack me. She was mad enough for anything just now.

I gently probed about in the straw, but there was nothing to be seen or felt. The dreadful truth gradually dawned on us both. Betsy had savaged the lot and done away with them in the dead of night. She had indulged in an orgy of her own flesh and blood.

We both withdrew with horror and disgust. Her sty was polluted with the worst form of crime. We left her without a backward glance, to work out her own salvation, which could only be achieved by a true fit of remorse.

No wonder Butler had avoided me. What an anti-climax after last night's grandiose announcement: 'There'll be a dozen before she be done.'

'Well, Butler, how many pigs has she got today?'

'Not a single one, ma'am.'

No, it would not have done. I can quite see his point of view.

– IV –

Butler put it all down to lack of farrowing rails . . . I knew he would. And reluctant though I was to agree with him, there was no other course left open to me.

If the little pigs had been able to get out of her reach when she was stampeding about the sty like a wounded rhinoceros, she would not have trodden on them and made them squeal. It was their squeals that had been their undoing. Betsy, driven mad by the noise, had silenced them in the only way she knew how.

Contrary to all advice, we reprieved Betsy and decided to give her one more chance. Farrowing rails were duly fitted to one of the stables, so there could be no excuse next time.

– V –

Betsy produced another family in due course, and managed to rear four members of it, which was quite an achievement for her.

We never knew the size of this second litter, as like the first, it had been produced overnight. We can only deduce that it was just four pigs over the capacity of Betsy's digestive system, judging by the evidence of grotesque bits and pieces swept up in the morning by Butler. She had, as before, enjoyed no small picnic.

No, Betsy would never make a mother. She had absolutely no maternal instinct whatsoever. She would lie for hours on her waistcoat buttons, denying her young with a sort of 'keep away, they are all mine' look on her face. She used to remind me of the lions at the base of Nelson's monument in Trafalgar Square.

The little pigs cried pitifully for sustenance, but she heeded them not. I can only conjecture that they used to steal up overnight and take a pull, when mama was asleep.

The pigs were weaned at eight weeks, and later sold as store pigs at round about seven score.

As for Betsy, well, if you do not mind, I would rather not say what became of her. It was all very distasteful – the story, I mean, not the ham. It was positively delicious.

Oh, dear! What a vile woman I am! I believe, in an earlier chapter, I said something about hating the sight of food, which only goes to prove that besides being vile, I am a liar as well.

Betsy's babies.

Digging for victory!

XIX

Julia Makes Her Farewell Curtsy

Julia has a calf at last.

And now Julia senses that as the year draws to its close, so also will the chronicle of events recorded in the pages of this little book.

A moment ago she could have sworn she heard a grunt from Betsy, but she knows that Betsy passed away some weeks ago, in which case the grunt must have come from Betsy's ghost.

Anyhow, ghost or no ghost, Julia was determined to have the last word. She would not allow any sow to lord it over her, especially when that sow had turned out to be a murderess. (The news had quickly gone round the farm.)

She must stage one more appearance, and when the time comes for the curtain to swing up and down, as is the custom after the grand finale of any play, Julia alone must be on the set to make her farewell curtsy to the public.

It was getting dangerously near Christmas. It was already December 16th. And one look at Julia told us there was something in the air.

And then all of a sudden, it came to me. It was an anniversary. It was exactly a year ago today that Julia had joined us on the farm – or perhaps it would be more accurate to say Julia had brought the farm to us. Because to all intents and purposes, Julia *is* the farm – the whole farm. Without Julia, now Betsy has gone, we should have to rely on the rooster, and just between you and me, I would not trust him an inch.

Just as without a calf, there can be no milk (did you know that?) so, in my opinion, though there are hundreds who would not agree with me, without a cow, there can be no farm. Julia knew all this. She knew she held the secret of the farm's success. Our hope for the future was centred in her and the gift she carried for us. And hang me! If it did not turn out to be a wretched little bull!

But Julia was not concerned with that now, thank goodness. I really could not stand another birth in the family so soon after the last melancholy affair. Julia had plenty of time to turn that over in her mind, and anywhere else she thought fit. At the moment she is preoccupied with some sort of trump card that she has been secreting in the cleft of her hoof for some days.

Would she play it today! If so, she would have to hurry up about it. It was already late. Or would she hold it back and put it down with a triumphant flourish on Christmas Day?

There was no telling with Julia.

She had not decided on anything by eleven o'clock that night.

We retired to bed, and thought no more about her. The house was full. There were visitors for Christmas, and the children were home for the holidays.

Personally, I prefer the house when it is full. The more people I am able to pack into it, the better I like it. I am one of those people who like putting up camp beds all over the place, and stuffing cushions into pillow slips to make the bedding go round.

I am unlike an uncle of mine in this respect, who, quite rightly, is a bachelor. He says he prefers his house to himself at night, and then if there is any noise, he does not wonder who it is. He *knows* it is a burglar!

However, in spite of my full house, I never had the slightest doubt who was making all the noise that night. I *knew* it was Julia.

The children must have left the gate open. She was bellowing at the top of her voice, and careering up and down the lawn.

I was livid.

Angela and John were awakened, and after recovering from a first momentary fear which is prevalent with most people, whether young or old, when they have been awakened by some unaccustomed noise, they were quick to realize that there was some form of chase afoot which they had every intention of joining. They dressed hurriedly, putting everything on over their pyjamas, even woolly socks.

By this time, the whole household was aroused and walking about on the landing in various types of dressing gown.

'What was the matter . . . and whose wretched cow was it? It wanted shooting . . . roaming about the place and kicking up such a commotion at this time of night.'

It was no use wasting words. Action was needed. I grabbed my corduroys. One always feels at such a disadvantage in one's night attire. Flimsy nightshirts trailing beneath silk dressing gowns (pardon the author's licence, my dressing gown is nothing like that!) are hardly suitable for cattle driving.

I wanted, if possible, to intercept Julia before she broke out of the garden. She was not in a fit state to wander about the roads. She might slip and break a leg. The lanes were covered in ice. Or she might so easily be bumped into by a lorry doing night work for the Government, and there would go her precious little gift to the farm.

Remember! I do not know, yet, it is a horrid little bull calf! Perhaps I should not have shown such anxiety had I known.

Several people were appearing from different bedroom doorways clothed in a various assortment of jerseys over pyjama legs. And some looked quite business-like in overcoats.

We sallied forth, a motley troupe, into the garden. Luckily, the moon was up, so we could see our way about. Everything seemed singularly quiet. I fetched a halter.

Where had Julia got to? And then, in the distance, my question was answered by Julia herself: 'Moo - o - o.'

She was up in the village somewhere. 'Blow this cow! She will be the death of me,' I muttered as I broke into the double. It was enough to give us all pneumonia, going out in something like 3 degrees of frost straight from warm beds.

We lost her. We did not know where to look for her. Had she gone beyond the pond and up the village? Or had she turned left before she reached the pond and gone down wind? It was a north-easterly, by the way!

Everyone was speechless with cold and frustration, but it availed us nothing. Julia no longer bellowed. She had far too much intelligence for that. There was absolutely no trace of her. She had vanished into the night . . .

And then, for one moment, my imagination ran away with me. Perhaps we were searching for something that did not exist. A beautiful wraith, as such she had appeared on that night a year ago. She had come to us wrapped in mystery to play fast and loose with me and my farm. Tonight she had been reclaimed by the animal spirit world (I could see Betsy beckoning as hard as she could go!).

I pinched myself. What incredible nonsense!

In desperation, I called up Butler, shouting up to his bedroom window. My sense of decency had long since gone with the north-easter. I woke rows of peaceful inmates tucked up in cosy beds in beam-roofed cottages. Every dog in the vicinity was awake and howling. And soon the whole village was at its bedroom windows.

The cottagers wondered what all the commotion was about. Some threw open their doors, poked tense faces out into the crisp night air and anxiously enquired, 'What's agoing on hereabouts?' There were even rumours of parachutists and invasion.

Just as we were giving up all hope of ever seeing Julia again, we caught sight of her outside the village pub.

So, that was it! We had caught her red-hoofed. No wonder she had ceased bellowing. She did not want anyone to know her wicked secret.

By this time we had run into a small group of Home Guard returning from some night exercise.

Sensing our rising anger, Julia slipped noiselessly into their ranks and processed home in triumph, protected by a bodyguard from the angry villagers who she had robbed of well-earned rest.

We stood aghast at her incorrigible behaviour. And as

we stared, unable to believe our eyes, was it imagination or reality? That flag, fluttering in the icy wind, being borne ahead of that curious little cortège.

Why, the devil take me! If it was not Julia's own personal standard: the ace of trumps!

Home on leave – Peter's introduction to Julia.

Epilogue

Thus I must bring the story of the farm's first year to an end. For did I not say we had reached December?

But that was all more than two years ago. Two more Decembers have since flashed past the farm at a sickening pace.

We are left breathless as we look back, and in spite of the wind made by the wings of time, we find ourselves still standing firm and erect with our feet embedded ever deeper in the soil of our forefathers.

You may say it is a miracle. But then we live in an age of miracles.

Peter is due back home at any moment.

My hand shakes, so you will forgive me if I put away my pen. I am unable to hold it steady any longer. It is nearly three years since we waved goodbye to each other on Paddington Station in August 1939. So much has happened in between.

Like a falling star, a whole world has plunged into the abyss, and no one can tell the shape of its future, or the day of its emancipation.

But above the roar of thunder and lightning we can hear

'the still small voice' ever borne above the storm to comfort us in our darkest hour.

I have gathered much happiness from my farming career, but like all happiness, it cannot be fully enjoyed unless it is shared by others. True, my beloved is coming home. There goes one half of my share already. And oh! How willingly given.

But if any of my patient readers have caught a measure of that happiness from this little diary, or seen a spark of humour scattered over the pages, then my cup of happiness will still be full.

Meanwhile, Peter is coming home . . . I can think of nothing else. Do you wonder I have lost the thread of the narrative, though I suspect Julia of having swallowed that long ago!

There will be so much to say, so much to do, and one of the very first things will be to synchronize our minds.

At first Peter's mind may run over desert stretches, lost then conquered again (thank God!) while my thoughts will be enclosed by the green hedges of spring . . . A tiny piece of England, and oh! How we will cherish it together to hand it over in good shape some day to Rosemary and John.

Already it is bepeopled by healthy farm animals, for now Julia is no longer the whole farm. The cow stalls are full and land girls are rattling milk cans in the yard. In the fields – there are sheep and bulling heifers.

The farm flourishes. But it has not been without a struggle.

But we are farmers . . . well, 'we can take it' with the rest of our people, even though we are a race apart.